Elastic and Inelastic Stress Analysis

Irving H. Shames
Francis A. Cozzarelli
State University of New York at Buffalo

Prentice Hall
Englewood Cliffs, New Jersey   07632

Library of Congress Cataloging-in-Publication Data

Shames, Irving Herman
    Elastic and inelastic stress analysis / I. H. Shames and F. A.
  Cozzarelli.
      p.   cm.
    Includes bibliographical references and index.
    ISBN 0-13-245465-3
    1. Elasticity. 2. Plasticity. 3. Viscoelasticity.
I. Cozzarelli, F. A. (Francis A.) II. Title.
TA418.S48 1991
620.1′1232—dc20   90-45041
                                          CIP

Acquisitions editor: Doug Humphrey
Editorial/production supervision: Wordcrafters Editorial Services, Inc.
Cover design: Joe DiDomenico
Pre-press buyer: Linda Behrens
Manufacturing buyer: David Dickey

© 1992 by Prentice-Hall, Inc.
A Simon & Schuster Company
Englewood Cliffs, NJ 07632

Printed in the United States of America
10 9 8 7 6 5 4 3 2 1

ISBN 0-13-245465-3

Prentice-Hall International (UK) Limited, *London*
Prentice-Hall of Australia Pty. Limited, *Sydney*
Prentice-Hall Canada Inc., *Toronto*
Prentice-Hall Hispanoamericana, S.A., *Mexico*
Prentice-Hall of India Private Limited, *New Delhi*
Prentice-Hall of Japan, Inc., *Tokyo*
Simon & Schuster Asia Pte. Ltd., *Singapore*
Editora Prentice-Hall do Brasil, Ltda., *Rio de Janeiro*

Contents

Chapter 3
Strain   70

Part II
USEFUL CONSTITUTIVE LAWS   99

Chapter 4
Behavior of Engineering Materials   99

PART A
One-Dimensional Macroscopic Behavior   100

PART B
One-Dimensional Idealized Material Behavior   113

Chapter 5
Linear Elastic Behavior   131

Contents   **v**

Chapter 8
Plasticity   248

Chapter 9
Boundary Value Problems   331

Chapter 11
Torsion of Shafts   460

Chapter 12
Plane Strain   523

Chapter 13
Plane Stress   573

APPENDIXES   641

Appendix I
Sufficiency Conditions for Compatibility   641

Appendix II
Discontinuity Functions   647

Contents

Preface

We started to work on this book some five years ago. Previously, we had collaborated on a text, *Mechanics of Deformable Solids*, published in 1964 by Prentice-Hall and still in print via Krieger Publishers, Melbourne, Florida. Having enjoyed this collaboration, we decided to develop another, more advanced text in some selected areas of solid mechanics. This book is the result.

We strongly believe that our senior and graduate students should have more instruction in inelastic solid mechanics. The belief stems from the increase in interest by engineers in recent times in materials that are more likely to behave inelastically than the traditional metallic materials. Such materials consist of plastics, synthetic rubber, composites, metals at elevated temperatures, rock in the presence of geothermal heating, glacial ice, biomaterials, and others. Also, because modern technology is putting structural components into more hostile environments, including high temperature, irradiation, temperature gradients, large loads, and rapidly changing loads, there is a greater need to undertake the macroscopic study of inelastic effects. This in turn calls for a greater understanding of the microscopic aspects of material behavior. Consequently, we decided that as a primary goal for this new book we would endeavor to present efficiently and clearly certain key aspects of inelastic solid mechanics centered around viscoelasticity, creep, viscoplasticity, and plasticity suitable for competent seniors and graduate students.

In addition to this main thesis, two other factors decisively shaped the development of this book. The first factor had to do with a course taught in recent years by one of the coauthors, incorporating variational methods, energy methods, and finite elements. This culminated in the text *Energy and Finite Element Methods in Structural Mechanics*, published by Hemisphere Publishing Corp. (March 1985). The favorable reception of both the course and the book impressed on the authors that the particular content and arrangement of instructional material of the course and book could be of significance in identifying the role our new book could play in a curriculum. This will be made more clear after we discuss the second factor that shaped our thinking.

This factor came from the outside. About four years ago, three long-time, well-established books on elasticity went out of print within weeks of each other. Why did this occur? Our belief is that because of the effectiveness and the growing use of finite elements and the desirability of teaching it in conjunction with energy methods, some instructors were ceasing to give a full traditional course in elasticity as had been the time-honored custom. The feeling, we believe, is that in addition to deleting energy methods, it is no longer advisable in a crowded program to study highly specialized techniques such as complex variable methods in elasticity. Nor may it be advisable to take much time in presenting many complicated, closed-form solutions to highly idealized problems that are applicable only to linear elastic behavior. But we believe that it is still vital that our students be exposed to a sound treatment of the *fundamentals* of elasticity.

The latter two factors, both having to do with the teaching of elasticity, along with our original main goal having to do with the growing importance of inelastic solid mechanics, underpinned the shaping of the final format of our book and also suggested the roles of this book in a curriculum. Briefly stated, we decided to present the fundamentals of elasticity (leaving energy methods, approximation methods, and finite elements for a separate course of the kind described earlier) and then to proceed with similar treatments of linear and nonlinear viscoelasticity and plasticity. The book would be suitable for senior–graduate or strictly graduate-level courses, and would be presented in a manner that provides flexibility in possible use so that the instructor could develop a course most suitable for his/her students and for his/her own interests. The conjunction of elastic and inelastic solid mechanics would be made very efficient, in that use would be made of the correspondence principles linking linear viscoelasticity with elasticity as well as emphasizing analogy laws linking different areas of elastic and inelastic solid mechanics. Finally, there would be extended treatment of basic problems in static structural mechanics, including elastic and inelastic effects. One role that we believe our book would play would be to change the traditional elasticity course to a form more attuned to present-day needs and present-day teaching proclivities. This book would then complement in coverage the material in the energy–finite element book described earlier, and thus would be a companion volume for that book. The associated courses for our new book would, by the same token, complement the kind of finite element course we alluded to earlier that is finding its way into many curricula.

We pointed out earlier the importance of materials science at the microscopic level in the appreciation and understanding of inelastic solid mechanics. For this reason, we have included in Appendix VII a treatment of this topic that will serve as a review and a focus for students who have already studied materials science. Others may find this material valuable and cogent collateral reading.

The text is divided into three parts, from which the instructor can fashion the course:

- PART I: Fundamentals

- PART II: Useful Constitutive Laws
- PART III: Applications to Simple Structural Members

Part I consists of three chapters, covering tensors, stress, and strain. To limit the complexity of our treatment, only Cartesian tensors are considered, and stress and strain are developed within the framework of small deformation theory. We have endeavored to maintain a degree of rigor that would make clear the limitations of the theory while permitting ready application of the theory to solving engineering problems. In Part II we study constitutive laws, first in one dimension and then in three dimensions, covering classical theories of linear elasticity, linear viscoelasticity, nonlinear viscoelasticity, and plasticity. In Part III we go to static structural theories and applications involving elastic and inelastic behavior for beams, torsion, plane strain, and plane stress.

Obviously, there is more material here than can be covered in a single course. As already pointed out, we have been fully aware of this and as a consequence have labored toward achieving flexibility in the use of this text. Indeed, we have had to do this for our own purposes. One of us has taught a course of selected topics in elastic and inelastic behavior to a class of seniors and graduate students. Graduate students in this course were introduced to additional topics in viscoelasticity and plasticity by means of independent study assignments. The primary goal of the course is the development of a broad overview of elastic and inelastic behavior, as a foundation for a follow-up course in finite element methods. The other author has used this book as the text for a two-course sequence for graduate students only. The first graduate course in the sequence covers the basics of Cartesian tensors, stress and strain, elastic constitutive relations, and the formulation and solution of basic elastic boundary value problems. Most of the students from this first graduate course in elasticity go on to a follow-up course of topics in linear viscoelastic, nonlinear viscoelastic, and plastic constitutive relations, with applications to inelastic boundary value problems. The essential goal of this two-course graduate-level sequence is the preparation of graduate students for research in solid mechanics. The book was found to contain more than enough material for the three courses described above, especially when supplemented by assigned readings from the many references cited in the footnotes. Thus, in each of these courses there were certain different portions of the text formally covered in class and there were certain different portions of the text deleted. Because of our own varied use and the possible varied use to be expected in the field, we have made great efforts to achieve clarity and physical feel in our writing so that a student would be able on his/her own initiative to effectively read portions of the book not covered in class.

We have made very modest demands concerning the mathematical background of the student. Specifically, we expect the student to have a reasonably good grasp of the first two years of mathematics instruction as given in engineering programs. For the mathematics required beyond this level, we present the necessary instruction either directly in the text proper or in the appendixes. Thus we present the necessary instruction for the discontinuity functions and the Laplace transform in Appendixes II and III, respectively, while Cartesian tensors are developed in the text in Chapter 1 and subsequently at various strategic places. Also, the various direct and indirect methods employed for solving partial differential equations are fully explained throughout the text as the need arises.

The authors wish to thank our students in mechanical, civil, and aerospace engineering, who labored with various forms of the notes and were instrumental in the development of the final form of the manuscript. Special thanks go to Dr. E. Graesser, who as a graduate student offered valuable criticisms on the chapter on plasticity and who also obtained solutions to the problems of Part I. Special thanks also go to Ph.D. student Shenyao Yang, who ably performed the monumental task of solving the many difficult problems in Parts II and III. The fruits of their efforts is a Solutions Manual which is available to instructors. Finally, we wish to offer our gratitude to the various typists who had a hand in preparing the manuscript: specifically Mrs. Kathryn Ward, Mrs. Martha Fye, and Mrs. Debra Kinda.

An Acknowledgment

The intellectual seeds for this book were nurtured for years by the dedication and scholarly efforts of my graduate students. The book finally came to fruition through my collaboration with my dear friend and colleague, Irv Shames, who brought to bear his knowledge and consummate writing skills. Finally, the encouragement of my lovely and loving wife, Kathy, was essential to the completion of this book.

Francis A. Cozzarelli
Buffalo, New York

Part I

Fundamentals

Chapter 1

Introduction to Cartesian Tensors

1.1 INTRODUCTION

In this chapter we introduce the concept of the tensor for *rectangular Cartesian coordinates* together with a notation called index or Cartesian tensor notation.*
This introduction will serve most of our needs in this book. Some additional considerations of Cartesian tensors will be introduced later as needed in close proximity to where direct, specific applications occur.

1.2 THE FREE INDEX

You will recall from mechanics that a vector in three-dimensional space has three orthogonal components. Accordingly, the vector **V** may be expressed in the following manner:

$$\mathbf{V} = V_x \hat{\mathbf{i}} + V_y \hat{\mathbf{j}} + V_z \hat{\mathbf{k}} \tag{1.1}$$

Alternatively, we may express the components of **V** as a column matrix and use the notation V_i to represent this column matrix in the following manner:

$$V_i = \begin{Bmatrix} V_x \\ V_y \\ V_z \end{Bmatrix} \tag{1.2}$$

---

* In this book we shall not employ general tensor notation for curvilinear coordinate systems. A thorough, yet concise treatment of this complicated subject is given in L. E. Malvern, *Introduction to the Mechanics of a Continuous Medium* (Englewood Cliffs, NJ: Prentice-Hall, Inc., 1969), Apps. I and II.

The index i may be thought to represent any one element of the column matrix or it may, depending on the context of the discussion, represent the entire matrix as implied by Eq. (1.2). Such an index is called a *free* index since it is "free" to take on three values in three-dimensional space: namely, x, y, and z. In this book any *English* (i.e., *Latin*) letter with the exception of the letters x, y, and z may be used as a free index in place of i above for *three-dimensional spaces*. Furthermore, any *Greek* letter with the exception of μ and ν may be used as a free index above for *two-dimensional* spaces.

We shall also deal with expressions with more than one index. Those indices (other than x, y, z, ν, and μ) that are mutually *different* in an expression are then the free indices of that expression. And the number of these free indices indicates the *order* of the expression. Thus V_j is first-order while $V_j P_{ji} C_k$ is second-order with free indices i and k. Such quantities include all possible expressions, as the free indices take on the different values x, y, and z. As an example of a second-order array, recall from your course in strength of materials that such quantities as stress and strain have nine components representable as a 3×3 matrix. We can represent any element of such a matrix or, indeed, of the entire matrix by using two different free indices. Thus for stress we can say that

$$\tau_{ij} \equiv \begin{bmatrix} \tau_{xx} & \tau_{xy} & \tau_{xz} \\ \tau_{yx} & \tau_{yy} & \tau_{yz} \\ \tau_{zx} & \tau_{zy} & \tau_{zz} \end{bmatrix} \tag{1.3}$$

Extrapolating, we can in this way represent yet higher-order arrays of components by using more mutually different free indices. Thus A_{ijk} represents for three-dimensional space the entire system of 27 components or alternatively, any one of these components. Parenthetically, we note that we cannot represent this system as a square matrix but could arrange the terms along axes of a three-dimensional grid. Such a grid is not convenient, and accordingly is rarely used. Of course, such geometrical constructions lose meaning for fourth- and higher-order arrays.

Also, in this book we shall occasionally write a second-order array using a boldface, block-letter symbol. For the stress matrix we shall employ a boldface symbol underscored with a bar, i.e., $\underline{\boldsymbol{\tau}}$. This notation we call *symbolic* notation, whereas the notation τ_{ij} used earlier we call *index* notation.

As for the forbidden free index English letters x, y, and z, you will recall from earlier studies in mechanics that using x, y, and z as ordinary subscripts implied certain directional connotations. This will similarly be true in this book when the forbidden free index subscripts ν and μ are used as ordinary subscripts. Specifically, ν will indicate in conjunction with an area element a direction *normal* to the area element, while μ will indicate a direction *tangent* to the area element.

1.3 THE DUMMY INDEX

If two indices excluding x, y, z, ν, and μ are repeated in an expression, we will adopt the rule that these indices take on successively the values x, y, and z and that the resulting expressions are added.* Consider the expression T_{ii}. According to our rule, this becomes

$$T_{ii} = T_{xx} + T_{yy} + T_{zz}$$

Using the indices jj or any other pair of admissible indices for T gives the identical result on the right side of the equation above. Because the identity of the repeated indices is inconsequential to the final result, we call the pair used as prescribed above *dummy* indices.

Consider next the expression $V_i W_i$, which is termed the *inner* product of vectors V_i and W_j.† Using the rule for dummy indices, we have

$$V_i W_i = V_x W_x + V_y W_y + V_z W_z$$

Thus the inner product $V_i W_i$ is a scalar quantity identical to the dot product $\mathbf{V} \cdot \mathbf{W}$.

Now consider the expression $V_i T_{ij}$. There is one free index, j, and one set of dummy indices i. We may then write this expression in the following ways:

$$V_i T_{ij} = V_x T_{xj} + V_y T_{yj} + V_z T_{zj}$$

$$\equiv \begin{Bmatrix} (V_x T_{xx} + V_y T_{yx} + V_z T_{zx}) \\ (V_x T_{xy} + V_y T_{yy} + V_z T_{zy}) \\ (V_x T_{xz} + V_y T_{yz} + V_z T_{zz}) \end{Bmatrix}$$

The last expression is a column matrix with three components associated with the free index j.

There may be more than one set of dummy indices in an expression. However, different letters must be used for the various pairs of dummy indices. As an example, consider the expression $T_{ij} U_{ij}$ having two pairs of dummy indices. To carry out the expansion of this expression, we must sum over both i and j. We can do this by first setting $i = x$ and then sum the terms with j going from x to y to z. That is, first get

$$T_{xx} U_{xx} + T_{xy} U_{xy} + T_{xz} U_{xz}$$

Add to this the terms formed by letting i become y and then, as before, sum over j to get

$$T_{yx} U_{yx} + T_{yy} U_{yy} + T_{yz} U_{yz}$$

Finally, let $i = z$ and sum over j yet a third time to get one more expression

$$T_{zx} U_{zx} + T_{zy} U_{zy} + T_{zz} U_{zz}$$

---

* If the subscripts are Greek letters other than ν and μ, a dummy pair requires summation only over two coordinates. We shall use this convention in Chapters 12 and 13 on plane strain and plane stress.

† A more general discussion of the inner product and other types of multiplication will be given in Section 1.6.

which when added to the previous two sums yields for $T_{ij} U_{ij}$

$$T_{ij} U_{ij} = T_{xx} U_{xx} + T_{xy} U_{xy} + T_{xz} U_{xz} +$$
$$T_{yx} U_{yx} + T_{yy} U_{yy} + T_{yz} U_{yz} +$$
$$T_{zx} U_{zx} + T_{zy} U_{zy} + T_{zz} U_{zz}$$

Instead of using x, y, z as coordinates as we have been doing in our formulations thus far, we may instead use x_1, x_2, and x_3 as coordinates, respectively, for x, y, z. In addition, we may use the numerical subscripts 1, 2, and 3 to identify x, y, and z components, respectively. Thus we can say for $V_i W_i$ that for axes $x_1 x_2 x_3$,

$$V_i W_i = V_1 W_1 + V_2 W_2 + V_3 W_3$$

It should then be clear that $V_i W_i$ is identical to

$$\sum_{i=1}^{3} V_i W_i$$

but with the summation instructions embodied in $\sum_{i=1}^{3}$ understood to apply without having to show it explicitly. Also, $T_{ij} U_{ij}$ is identical to

$$\sum_{i=1}^{3} \sum_{j=1}^{3} T_{ij} U_{ij}$$

with the double summation understood to apply without the two sigmas appearing explicitly. Accordingly, the rule of dummy indices discussed above is called the *summation convention*.

1.4 VECTORS AND TENSORS

Consider a vector **V** or, with index notation, V_i. This vector is shown as a directed line segment in Fig. 1.1 along with its orthogonal components. The vector $\hat{\mathbf{s}}$ is a unit vector having an arbitrary direction in space. Let a_{sx} be the direction cosine of the direction defined by $\hat{\mathbf{s}}$ relative to the x axis. Then a_{sy} and a_{sz} are the other two direction cosines for the direction of $\hat{\mathbf{s}}$. We can express the component of **V** in the

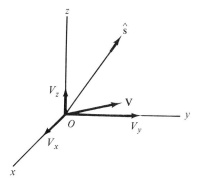

Figure 1.1 Vector **V** and its rectangular components.

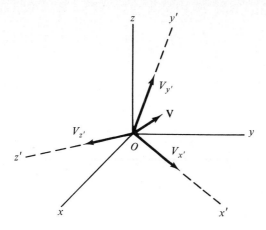

Figure 1.2 Primed components of vector **V**.

direction of $\hat{s}$ by projecting the *components* of **V** in the direction of $\hat{s}$ and then simply adding these components algebraically. Thus we have

$$V_s = a_{sx} V_x + a_{sy} V_y + a_{sz} V_z \tag{1.4}$$

Now we may consider s to be a free index in the equation above for a set of primed axes $x'y'z'$ rotated arbitrarily relative to xyz. Thus Eq. (1.4), with s becoming x', y', and z' successively, yields the rectangular components of the vector **V** along the primed set of axes. This is shown in Fig. 1.2. We can express Eq. (1.4) in the following compact manner:

$$V_{j'} = a_{j'i} V_i \tag{1.5}$$

This equation gives the new set of components of **V** for $x'y'z'$ axes in terms of the components for xyz. The terms $a_{j'i}$ are called the transformation matrix and are direction cosines between primed axes and unprimed axes.* Thus we have in expanded form the following so-called *transformation* equations:

$$V_{x'} = a_{x'x} V_x + a_{x'y} V_y + a_{x'z} V_z$$
$$V_{y'} = a_{y'x} V_x + a_{y'y} V_y + a_{y'z} V_z \tag{1.6}$$
$$V_{z'} = a_{z'x} V_x + a_{z'y} V_y + a_{z'z} V_z$$

where $a_{x'x}$ is the direction cosine between the x' axis and the x axis, and so on. These *transformation equations tell us how the rectangular components of a vector change when computed for a primed reference rotated relative to an unprimed reference.* Since, in forming these equations, we have used both the directed-line-segment concept and the familiar parallelogram law, we can now redefine vectors by saying that *vector components must transform according to Eq. (1.5) when we rotate the axes.* Thus we here define a quantity by the way its components change when we rotate the reference axes.

---

*Since $a_{j'i}$ may also be expressed as a square matrix, we shall on occasion represent it by the boldface, block letter symbol **A**. This square matrix will in general *not* be symmetric; that is, $a_{j'i} \neq a_{i'j}$ or $\mathbf{A} \neq \mathbf{A}^T$, where $\mathbf{A}^T$ is the transpose of **A**. However, since $\cos(x_j', x_i) \equiv \cos(x_i, x_j')$, some authors occasionally rewrite $a_{j'i}$ as $a_{ij'}$. To avoid confusion, in this book we *always* place the primed index in the *first* position.

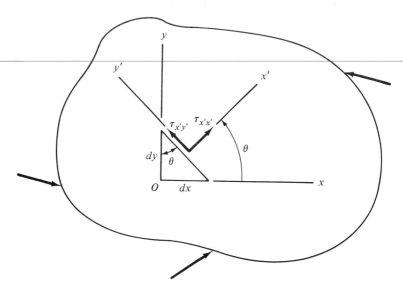

Figure 1.3 Plane stress with infinitesimal element.

When you studied plane stress in your strength-of-materials course, you computed stresses (see Fig. 1.3) on an inclined face of a triangular element using the following familiar formulas for normal and shear stresses:†

$$\tau_{x'x'} = \frac{\tau_{xx} + \tau_{yy}}{2} + \frac{\tau_{xx} - \tau_{yy}}{2} \cos 2\theta + \tau_{xy} \sin 2\theta \qquad \text{(a)}$$

$$\tau_{x'y'} = \frac{\tau_{yy} - \tau_{xx}}{2} \sin 2\theta + \tau_{xy} \cos 2\theta \qquad \text{(b)}$$

(1.7)

We can get the normal stress $\tau_{y'y'}$ by replacing θ in Eq. (1.7a) by $(\pi/2 + \theta)$. Because the element is infinitesimal, the axes $x'y'$ can be considered to have the same origin as xy and are rotated about this origin by an angle θ measured from x toward y. Hence Eqs. (1.7) represent for plane stress the transformation equations generating stresses for a set of axes $x'y'$ at a point in terms of the stresses for reference xy. In Fig. 1.4(a) we have shown stress components for axes xy at O and in Fig. 1.4(b) we have shown stress components again at O but for axes $x'y'$. This is analogous to Figs. 1.1 and 1.2, where we have components of a vector corresponding to two sets of axes at a point. And most important, just as transformation equations (1.6) define what we call a vector, so do the transformation equations (1.7) define a certain quantity.

What is that quantity? To answer this, we shall now allude to three-dimensional stress where instead of the four nonzero components of plane stress, namely, τ_{xx}, τ_{yy}, τ_{xy}, and τ_{yx}, we have nine stress components that may be nonzero. As noted previously, these components may be expressed as a square matrix. Thus

†You may have used the notation σ_x for τ_{xx} and σ_y for τ_{yy}. We will have more to say about notation in Chapter 2.

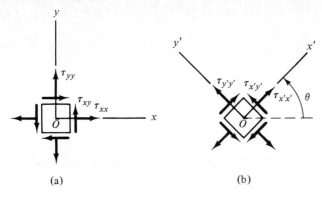

(a)

(b)

Figure 1.4 Plane stress at O for axes xy and $x'y'$.

$$\tau_{ij} \equiv \begin{bmatrix} \tau_{xx} & \tau_{xy} & \tau_{xz} \\ \tau_{yx} & \tau_{yy} & \tau_{yz} \\ \tau_{zx} & \tau_{zy} & \tau_{zz} \end{bmatrix} \tag{1.8}$$

When we rotate the axes at a point in a body from the unprimed reference [see Fig. 1.5(a)] to the primed reference [see Fig. 1.5(b)], we will have a new set of components that can be computed in terms of the original set of components. Thus, using i' and j' as free indices for reference $x'y'z'$, we will show in Chapter 2 that the stresses $\tau_{i'j'}$ can be found using the following transformation equation:

$$\tau_{i'j'} = a_{i'k} a_{j'l} \tau_{kl} \tag{1.9}$$

where $a_{i'k}$ is the direction cosine between the primed axis represented by i' and the unprimed axis represented by k. For example, for stress $\tau_{x'y'}$ we let free index i' be x' and free index j' be y' in the formulation above, and we expand the right-hand side of Eq. (1.9) by summing over dummy indices k and l for reference xyz. We get

$$\tau_{x'y'} = a_{x'x} a_{y'x} \tau_{xx} + a_{x'x} a_{y'y} \tau_{xy} + a_{x'x} a_{y'z} \tau_{xz} +$$
$$a_{x'y} a_{y'x} \tau_{yx} + a_{x'y} a_{y'y} \tau_{yy} + a_{x'y} a_{y'z} \tau_{yz} +$$
$$a_{x'z} a_{y'x} \tau_{zx} + a_{x'z} a_{y'y} \tau_{zy} + a_{x'z} a_{y'z} \tau_{zz}$$

Equation (1.9) is the transformation equation dictating how stress components change when we rotate axes at a point. Thus, just as transformation equation (1.6)

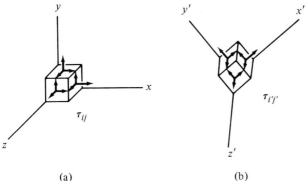

(a)

(b)

Figure 1.5 Unprimed and primed axes at a point.

defines vectors, transformation equation (1.9) defines the *stress tensor*. In general, consider a square matrix T_{ij} having nine components associated with an orthogonal Cartesian reference xyz. If these components transform under a rotation of axes via the formula

$$T_{i'j'} = a_{i'k} a_{j'l} T_{kl}$$
(1.10)

then T_{ij} is a *second-order Cartesian tensor*. You should note that the transformation matrix $a_{i'k}$ is *not* a second-order tensor.* We will be much concerned with Cartesian tensors in this book. They have certain vital properties that will be of much use to us. The plane stress discussed earlier is a *two-dimensional simplification* of the stress tensor and Eqs. (1.7) are special cases of Eq. (1.9).

Furthermore, we can now point out that vectors are called first-order tensors and scalars are called zeroth-order tensors. We note that a first-order tensor has a transformation equation with one direction cosine matrix, while a second-order tensor has a transformation equation with two direction cosine matrices. We can continue to develop yet higher-order tensors. Thus a tensor of order N has N direction cosine matrices in the transformation equation. As an example, a third-order tensor is defined as having 27 components that transform according to the following transformation equation:

$$T_{i'j'k'} = a_{i'l} a_{j'm} a_{k'n} T_{lmn}$$
(1.11)

A fourth-order tensor has 81 terms and is defined by the following transformation formula:

$$T_{i'j'k'l'} = a_{i'm} a_{j'n} a_{k'p} a_{l'q} T_{mnpq}$$
(1.12)

You should have no trouble going further. We shall be using a fourth-order tensor later in the book.

In the next section, we shall see that the rotation of axes considered above is a special case of a more general transformation called an *orthogonal* transformation. Orthogonal transformations may include a combination of *rotation* of axes and *inversion* of axes. The latter involves a reversal of direction of one or more axes. The rotation transformation is sometimes termed a *proper* orthogonal transformation. Strictly speaking, any tensor quantity must obey the transformation laws given in this section under the *general orthogonal transformation* for Cartesian coordinates. We shall frequently encounter quantities that obey these laws only under a proper orthogonal transformation (i.e., only under a rotation of axes). Such quantities are sometimes referred to as *pseudotensors*. Unless specifically noted otherwise in the book, orthogonal transformations are assumed to be proper, in which case the distinction between tensors and pseudotensors disappears.

---

* Various notations for the transformation matrix exist in the literature, [e.g., $\cos(x_{i'}, x_k) = C_{ki} = a_i^k = \alpha_{ik}$]. For such notations one must remember which index is associated with the transformed coordinate system, and this is a source of some ambiguity. Thus we have adopted the unambiguous notation $\cos(x_{i'}, x_k) = a_{i'k}$. We also point out that in an indicial equation such as Eq. (1.10), the free indices are i and j (*without* the primes). Thus if, for example, i is chosen as 1, then $i' = 1'$.

1.5 THE TRANSFORMATION MATRIX; ORTHOGONAL MATRICES

Now consider as a particular vector the position vector $\mathbf{r} = x\hat{\mathbf{i}} + y\hat{\mathbf{j}} + z\hat{\mathbf{k}}$ shown in Fig. 1.6, wherein $\hat{\mathbf{i}}, \hat{\mathbf{j}}$, and $\hat{\mathbf{k}}$ are unit vectors associated with axes x, y, z. We subject this coordinate system to an orthogonal transformation. Under an orthogonal transformation, axes may not change length and are required to remain mutually perpendicular. Thus such a transformation is in general some combination of rigid-body rotation and inversion. (Note that inversions can result in a left-handed system of axes.) Using primes for the new axes, the transformation $xyz \rightarrow x'y'z'$ maps $\mathbf{r}$ into $\mathbf{r}' = x'\hat{\mathbf{i}}' + y'\hat{\mathbf{j}}' + z'\hat{\mathbf{k}}'$, wherein it is clear for the orthogonal transformation that the magnitude of the position vector is invariant (i.e., $\mathbf{r}\cdot\mathbf{r} = \mathbf{r}'\cdot\mathbf{r}'$). The position vector $\mathbf{r}$ can be written as x_i in index notation and the position vector $\mathbf{r}'$ can be given as $x_{i'}$. If we project the components of $\mathbf{r}$ that lie along xyz onto the direction corresponding to $x_{i'}$, we get the *same* result obtained previously when only rotation was considered [i.e., Eq. (1.5)]. Accordingly,

$$x_{i'} = a_{i'j}x_j \tag{1.13}$$

where, as discussed previously, $a_{i'j} \equiv \cos(x_{i'}, x_j)$ is the so-called transformation matrix. Similarly, projecting components of $\mathbf{r}'$ that lie along $x'y'z'$ onto the direction corresponding to x_i, we will get

$$x_i = a_{j'i}x_{j'} \tag{1.14}$$

From the preceding two equations, we can now learn something about the transformation matrix $a_{i'j}$. For this purpose, multiply Eq. (1.13) by $a_{i'k}$ to get

$$a_{i'k}x_{i'} = a_{i'k}a_{i'j}x_j \tag{1.15}$$

Noting Eq. (1.14), we see that the expression on the left side of Eq. (1.15) is x_k, so that the equation can be written as

$$x_k = a_{i'k}a_{i'j}x_j \tag{1.16}$$

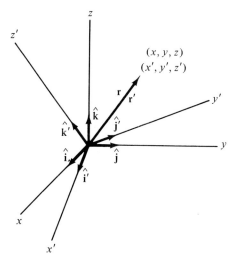

Figure 1.6 Orthogonal transformation of rectangular Cartesian coordinates.

For this equation to be satisfied, the expression $a_{i'k}a_{i'j}$ should equal unity when $j = k$ and be zero otherwise. We define the *Kronecker delta*, δ_{kj}, to have these properties, namely that

$$\delta_{kj} = \begin{cases} 1 & \text{when } j = k \\ 0 & \text{when } j \neq k \end{cases} \tag{1.17}$$

Hence we can say that for an orthogonal transformation,

$$a_{i'k}a_{i'j} = \delta_{kj} \tag{1.18}$$

This is called an *inner product* of the transformation matrices because of the presence of repeated index i' (as in $V_i W_i$ of Section 1.3). Because of the symmetry of Eq. (1.18), this equation yields six conditions. Similarly, we can show that

$$a_{j'i}a_{k'i} = \delta_{j'k'} \tag{1.19}$$

which is still another inner product yielding six more conditions.* Equations (1.18) and (1.19) are important properties, and we say that matrices satisfying these 12 conditions are *orthogonal* matrices.

By expressing the equations above in matrix form, we may obtain some additional properties of the orthogonal matrix. For convenience we shall now use symbolic notation. You will recall from matrix algebra that the elements d_{ij} of a 3×3 square matrix **D**, obtained by multiplying 3×3 square matrices **B** and **C** in the order **BC**, are given by†

$$d_{ij} = b_{ik}c_{kj} \tag{1.20}$$

where b_{ik} and c_{kj} are the elements of **B** and **C**. Furthermore, from the rules of matrix algebra $b_{ki}c_{kj} \equiv \mathbf{B}^T\mathbf{C}$, where $\mathbf{B}^T$ is the transpose of **B** obtained by replacing elements b_{ik} by elements b_{ki} (i.e., by interchanging rows and columns of **B**). Now let us designate the direction cosine matrix $a_{i'k}$ as **A**. Also, the matrix with elements δ_{ij} has nonzero elements only along the main diagonal, and is denoted as the *unit* matrix or as the *identity* matrix with the symbolic designation **I**. It then follows from the matrix product definition given by Eq. (1.20) that Eq. (1.18) may be written as

$$\mathbf{A}^T\mathbf{A} = \mathbf{I} \tag{1.21}$$

Similarly, Eq. (1.19) becomes

$$\mathbf{A}\mathbf{A}^T = \mathbf{I} \tag{1.22}$$

Let us now look at the matrix **A**, which we spell out in detail:

$$\mathbf{A} \equiv \begin{bmatrix} a_{x'x} & a_{x'y} & a_{x'z} \\ a_{y'x} & a_{y'y} & a_{y'z} \\ a_{z'x} & a_{z'y} & a_{z'z} \end{bmatrix}$$

---

*We remind you that the free indices in this equation are j and k (without the primes). Once values have been selected for j and k, the primes are added in the appropriate places. If an index appears with a prime in *every* term in an equation, it is also permissible to refer to the primed subscript as the free index. Thus, in Eq.(1.18) we may consider *either* i or i' to be the dummy index, and in Eq. (1.13) either i or i' is the free index, with i taking on values $1, 2, 3$ and i' taking on values $1', 2', 3'$.

†Note that the dummy indices k between the matrices are adjacent to each other. That is, we take the inner products between rows and columns.

You will note in considering Fig. 1.7 that each row of **A** given above constitutes the components along *xyz* axes of one of the unit vectors $\hat{\mathbf{i}}'$, $\hat{\mathbf{j}}'$, and $\hat{\mathbf{k}}'$. Therefore, if you take the inner product of one row with itself, you are taking the dot product of a unit vector with itself with the resulting value of unity. And because of the orthogonality of the primed unit vectors, the inner product of two *different* rows yields a null value. Equation (1.22) [which is equivalent to Eq. (1.19)] also illustrates this. Thus for the diagonal elements of **I** where the value is unity, consideration of Eq. (1.19) will indicate that for $j' = k'$ you are taking the inner product of one of the primed unit vectors with itself. For the zero off-diagonal terms of **I**, where $j' \neq k'$, you are taking the inner product of two different primed unit vectors. What we have said about rows of the matrix $a_{i'j}$ also applies to columns, as may be seen from an examination of Eq. (1.21) or its equivalent, Eq. (1.18).

We next introduce the *inverse* of a matrix **B** denoted as $\mathbf{B}^{-1}$ with the property that

$$\mathbf{B}\mathbf{B}^{-1} = \mathbf{B}^{-1}\mathbf{B} = \mathbf{I} \tag{1.23}$$

Returning to Eqs. (1.21) and (1.22), we can now conclude that for orthogonal matrix **A**,

$$\mathbf{A}^T = \mathbf{A}^{-1} \tag{1.24}$$

Also, it is well known for a matrix product $\mathbf{D} = \mathbf{B}\mathbf{C}$ that the determinant, denoted as det, may be expressed as follows:

$$\det \mathbf{D} = \det(\mathbf{B}\mathbf{C}) = (\det \mathbf{B})(\det \mathbf{C}) \tag{1.25}$$

Using this property along with Eq. (1.21) or Eq. (1.22), it follows that

$$(\det \mathbf{A}^T)(\det \mathbf{A}) = \det(\mathbf{A}^T\mathbf{A}) = \det \mathbf{I} = 1$$

But det $\mathbf{A}^T$ equals det **A** since interchanging the rows and columns of a square matrix does not change the determinant of the matrix. Hence we conclude from the equation above that

$$(\det \mathbf{A}^T)(\det \mathbf{A}) = (\det \mathbf{A})^2 = 1 \tag{1.26}$$

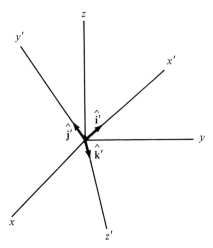

Figure 1.7 Axes $x'y'z'$ rotated relative to *xyz*.

Accordingly, the determinant of orthogonal matrix **A** is ±1. We shall see in the following examples that the +1 value of det **A** corresponds to a rotation of axes while the −1 of det **A** corresponds to an inversion of one or all three axes.

Example 1.1

Consider an orthogonal transformation consisting of a 60° rotation of axes xyz about the x axis (see Fig. 1.8).
(a) Determine the matrix of direction cosines **A** with elements $a_{i'k}$. It follows directly from Fig. 1.8 that

$$\mathbf{A} = \begin{bmatrix} \cos(x',x) & \cos(x',y) & \cos(x',z) \\ \cos(y',x) & \cos(y',y) & \cos(y',z) \\ \cos(z',x) & \cos(z',y) & \cos(z',z) \end{bmatrix} = \begin{bmatrix} 1 & 0 & 0 \\ 0 & \dfrac{1}{2} & \dfrac{\sqrt{3}}{2} \\ 0 & -\dfrac{\sqrt{3}}{2} & \dfrac{1}{2} \end{bmatrix}$$

(b) Check orthogonality of columns and rows.
For columns, we employ Eq. (1.18) and obtain for the first column (i.e., $j = k = 1$)

$$(1)^2 + (0)^2 + (0)^2 = 1$$

Similarly, for the first and second columns (i.e., $j = 1, k = 2$)

$$(1)(0) + (0)\left(\frac{1}{2}\right) + (0)\left(-\frac{\sqrt{3}}{2}\right) = 0$$

For rows, we employ Eq. (1.19) and obtain for the second row ($j' = k' = 2$)

$$(0)^2 + \left(\frac{1}{2}\right)^2 + \left(\frac{\sqrt{3}}{2}\right)^2 = 1$$

It is thus an easy matter to verify that all 12 conditions given by Eqs. (1.18) and (1.19) are verified.
(c) Verify that det **A** = ±1.
In this case we have

$$\det \mathbf{A} = 1\left[\left(\frac{1}{2}\right)\left(\frac{1}{2}\right) - \left(\frac{\sqrt{3}}{2}\right)\left(-\frac{\sqrt{3}}{2}\right)\right] = 1$$

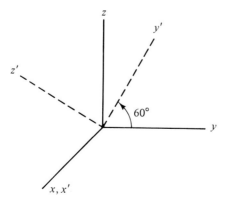

Figure 1.8 Rotation of axes.

and thus for this rotation we get det $\mathbf{A} = +1$. One can readily show that det $\mathbf{A} = +1$ for *any* rotation.

Example 1.2

Repeat Example 1.1 for an inversion of z through the origin, as shown in Fig. 1.9. Note that $x'y'z'$ is a left-handed system.
(a) From Fig. 1.9 we immediately obtain

$$\mathbf{A} = \begin{bmatrix} 1 & 0 & 0 \\ 0 & 1 & 0 \\ 0 & 0 & -1 \end{bmatrix}$$

(b) The orthogonality property of columns and rows is obviously valid.
(c) In this case

$$\det \mathbf{A} = (1)(1)(-1) = -1$$

It should be clear that inverting one axis (as in this example) or all three axes yields det $\mathbf{A} = -1$, whereas inverting two axes yields det $\mathbf{A} = +1$. The latter result is not surprising, since inversion of two axes is equivalent to a 180° rotation about the third axis.

1.6 SIMPLE OPERATIONS ON TENSORS

The rules of tensor algebra and differentiation are incorporated into the indicial notation. In this section we set forth rules for addition (and subtraction), multiplication, and differentiation of tensors as well as some other useful operations. Note that division is not defined in tensor algebra.

1. *Addition.* The addition of two tensors of the *same order* is performed by simply adding the corresponding terms of the matrix array or the higher-order array of the two tensors. The form of the array of course depends on the order of the tensors. You can easily show from the transformation equations that a new tensor is thus formed having the same order (i.e., it must have the *same free indices*) as the original tensors. Thus we have

$$u_i + v_i = w_i$$

$$S_{ij} + K_{ij} = P_{ij} \tag{1.27}$$

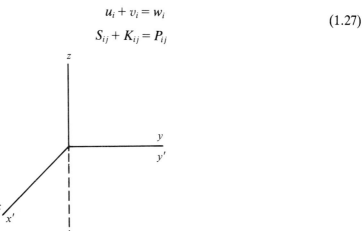

Figure 1.9 Inversion.

Note that *every term* in an indicial equation must have the *same* free indices. Subtraction should be clear from our discussion of addition.

2. *Multiplication.* Consider now the tensors $B_{mno\ldots}$ and $C_{stu\ldots}$ having, respectively, M free indices and N free indices. We define the *outer product* of these tensors as a new tensor having $(M + N)$ free indices. The components of this new tensor consist of *all* possible products between individual components of the B tensor with individual components of the C tensor. This means that the outer product of $B_{mno\ldots}$ and $C_{stu\ldots}$ will have for three-dimensional space 3^{M+N} components. We may denote the outer product between the aforementioned tensors as follows:

$$B_{mno\ldots} C_{stu\ldots} = D_{mno\ldots stu\ldots} \qquad (1.28)$$

wherein $mno\ldots$ and $stu\ldots$ are all free indices.

As a simple case, consider the outer product of B_i and C_{jk}. To find all the members of the tensor $B_i C_{jk}$, multiply separately B_1, B_2, and B_3 with each and every member of C_{jk}. Clearly, we will have 27 members (or components) in the resulting tensor.

A second useful multiplication is the *inner product,* of which we have already seen some examples. Again consider two tensors $B_{mno\ldots}$ and $C_{stu\ldots}$. An inner product is formed by making *any* index in B identical to *any* index in C to form an acceptable pair of dummy indices. For example, set $t = m$ in Eq. (1.28). If we write the left side of this equation,

$$B_{mno\ldots} C_{smu\ldots} \qquad (1.29)$$

we have one of the many possible inner products between the B-tensor and the C-tensor. The resulting tensor has free indices $no\ldots su\ldots$ and is thus a tensor of order $(M + N - 2)$. There are thus $3^{(M+N-2)}$ members of the new tensor from this inner product. The members of the new tensor consist of all possible products between components of B and C tensors involving the remaining $(M + N - 2)$ free indices, wherein each member is a *sum* over the dummy index m. Thus, consider B_{ij} and C_{lm}. If we set $j = k$ and $l = k$, we have the following inner product:

$$B_{ik} C_{km} = D_{im} \qquad (1.30)$$

Each member of the new tensor D_{im} would be of the form

$$D_{im} = (B_{i1} C_{1m} + B_{i2} C_{2m} + B_{i3} C_{3m})$$

The following is another inner product involving *two* pairs of dummy indices:

$$B_{mnop\ldots} C_{mour\ldots} = D_{np\ldots ur\ldots} \qquad (1.31)$$

Note that a dummy index pair may *not* appear more than once in any one expression.*

If B_i and C_j represent components of vectors **B** and **C**, as pointed out earlier

---

* Note that an expression such as $a_{i'j} a_{i'k} u_i$ is *not* permitted, since primes are considered to have been added to an index. Thus the dummy index i appears three times in this expression.

the inner product $B_k C_k$ is clearly the ordinary dot product of vector analysis. Also, the inner product of B_i with itself is simply the square of the magnitude of **B**. Finally, you should note that any two tensors each of any order may have a product yielding a tensor with an order equaling the number of resulting free indices. This is in direct contrast with addition and subtraction of tensors, which is defined only for tensors of the same order.

3. *Contraction.* Consider a tensor having M free indices $B_{mnop...}$. By making any two indices the same to form an acceptable pair of dummy indices, we are undergoing an operation called *contraction*. The order of the resulting tensor has been reduced by 2 and the number of members of the tensor is 3^{M-2}. Each member is a summation over the chosen dummy indices. Thus the contraction of $B_{mnop...}$ over the indices n and o is given as follows:

$$B_{mnnpq...} = D_{mpq...} \tag{1.32}$$

We could perform a contraction operation over two or more sets of indices. As an example, we may contract the tensor $B_{mnopq...}$ over mp and no to get

$$B_{mnnmq...} = D_{q...} \tag{1.33}$$

It is readily seen that a contraction over any pair of indices may be accomplished via the inner product in these indices with the Kronecker delta. Thus for the above we may write

$$\delta_{no} B_{mnopq...} = B_{mnnpq...}$$

$$\delta_{mp} \delta_{no} B_{mnopq...} = B_{mnnmq...}$$

We shall discuss this property of the Kronecker delta further in Section 1.8.

4. *Differentiation.* We wish first to point out notation that is in common use to denote differentiation of Cartesian tensors. This notation makes use of a comma between indices. Specifically, we may write

$$\frac{\partial V_i}{\partial x_j} \equiv V_{i,j}$$

$$\frac{\partial^2 V_i}{\partial x_k \partial x_l} \equiv V_{i,kl} \tag{1.34}$$

One can prove that taking a partial spatial derivative of an Nth-order tensor we get thereby an $(N+1)$th-order tensor. (See Problem 1.19 at the end of the chapter.)

We now illustrate some of the operations discussed here in the following example.

Example 1.3

Given the following tensors:

$$A_i = \begin{Bmatrix} 2 \\ 1 \\ 3 \end{Bmatrix}, \qquad B_{jk} = \begin{bmatrix} 2 & 1 & 0 \\ -1 & 3 & 2 \\ 1 & 4 & -1 \end{bmatrix}$$

(a) What are the terms C_{112} and C_{213} of the outer product between A_i and B_{jk}?

The outer product of the tensors above may be given as

$$A_i B_{jk} = C_{ijk}$$

Here for C_{112} we have $A_1 B_{12} = (2)(1) = 2$ and for C_{213} we have $A_2 B_{13} = (1)(0) = 0$.

(b) What is the tensor representing the inner product over indices i and j?

We have for this computation

$$A_i B_{ik} = A_1 B_{1k} + A_2 B_{2k} + A_3 B_{3k}$$

The tensor is then given as follows:

$$A_i B_{ik} = \begin{Bmatrix} [A_1 B_{11} + A_2 B_{21} + A_3 B_{31}] \\ [A_1 B_{12} + A_2 B_{22} + A_3 B_{32}] \\ [A_1 B_{13} + A_2 B_{23} + A_3 B_{33}] \end{Bmatrix}$$

Inserting numbers, we have for the tensor

$$A_i B_{ik} = \begin{Bmatrix} [(2)(2) + (1)(-1) + (3)(1)] \\ [(2)(1) + (1)(3) + (3)(4)] \\ [(2)(0) + (1)(2) + (3)(-1)] \end{Bmatrix} = \begin{Bmatrix} 6 \\ 17 \\ -1 \end{Bmatrix}$$

(c) What are B_{22} and B_{jj}?

B_{22} is simply one term of the tensor B_{jk}, namely, 3. On the other hand, B_{jj} represents a contraction. Thus

$$B_{jj} = B_{11} + B_{22} + B_{33} = 2 + 3 - 1 = 4$$

1.7 SYMMETRY AND SKEW SYMMETRY

A tensor is said to be symmetric in two free indices if on interchanging these indices, the tensor obtained is equal to the original tensor. Thus the tensor S_{ijklm} is symmetric in indices i and l if

$$S_{ijklm} = S_{ljkim} \tag{1.35}$$

For a second-order tensor to be symmetric, we require that

$$T_{ij} = T_{ji}$$

Here the off-diagonal terms must form mirror images about the main diagonal as follows:

$$\begin{bmatrix} T_{11} & T_{12} & T_{13} \\ T_{12} & T_{22} & T_{23} \\ T_{13} & T_{23} & T_{33} \end{bmatrix}$$

A tensor is said to be *skew-symmetric* or *antisymmetric* in two free indices if, when these free indices are interchanged, the tensor obtained is equal to the *negative* of the original tensor. Thus S_{ijkl} is skew-symmetric in jk if

$$S_{ijkl} = -S_{ikjl} \tag{1.36}$$

Any element of S_{ijkl} for which $j = k$ must equal *zero*. (Why?) For a second-order tensor, skew symmetry means that

$$U_{ij} = -U_{ji}$$

For such a case, you should understand that the main diagonal terms must all be zero. Hence for skew-symmetric matrix U_{ij}, we have for the matrix representation:

$$\begin{bmatrix} 0 & U_{12} & U_{13} \\ -U_{12} & 0 & U_{23} \\ -U_{13} & -U_{23} & 0 \end{bmatrix} \tag{1.37}$$

Suppose next that tensor T_{ijkl} is symmetric in ij while tensor U_{prst} is skew symmetric in pr. Then the inner product between these tensors over indices i and p and over j and r must yield a tensor all of whose members are zero. Thus

$$T_{ijkl} U_{ijst} = 0$$

To show this most simply, expand the left-hand side to form the following arrangement of terms:

$$(T_{11kl} U_{11st} + T_{12kl} U_{12st} + T_{13kl}U_{13st} +$$

$$T_{21kl} U_{21st} + T_{22kl} U_{22st} + T_{23kl}U_{23st} +$$

$$T_{31kl} U_{31st} + T_{32kl} U_{32st} + T_{33kl} U_{33st})$$

Because of the skew symmetry of U_{ijst} for indices ij, the terms U_{11st}, U_{22st}, and U_{33st} along the "diagonal" of the above sum must be zero. Furthermore, because of the skew symmetry of U_{ijst} and the symmetry of T_{ijkl} in both cases for indices ij, then clearly at "image" positions about this main diagonal the expressions in the sum above must be negatives of each other. The sum of all the terms for all free indices *klst* must then be zero, thus justifying our assertion.*

1.8 VECTOR ALGEBRA IN INDEX NOTATION

We have already defined the Kronecker delta δ_{ij}. We wish now to illustrate an important use for this tensor. Accordingly, consider the expression $B_{ij}\delta_{jk}$. During the summation process over the dummy index j, it is only when $j = k$ that we get other than a zero contribution. When $j = k$ we get a unitary value for the Kronecker delta. Hence we can say that

$$B_{ij}\delta_{jk} = B_{ik}$$

Notice particularly that the integrity of the free indices is maintained. We pointed out in Section 1.6 that a contraction over any two indices (say, m and n) of tensor $B_{mno\ldots}$ may be accomplished by a multiplication with the Kronecker delta δ_{mn}. That is,

$$B_{mnop\ldots}\delta_{mn} = B_{mmop\ldots}$$

---

* We can also show that if U_{ijkl} is skew-symmetric in kl and the product $U_{ijkl} T_{kl} = 0$, we can conclude that T_{kl} must be *symmetric* in kl.

which clearly follows from the aforestated property of the Kronecker delta. In the special case of a tensor that is the outer product of two vectors V_m and W_n, we may form a scalar inner product as follows:

$$V_m W_n \delta_{mn} = V_m W_m$$

We thus get the *dot product* $\mathbf{V} \cdot \mathbf{W}$.

Next, we consider the very useful *alternating* tensor. In this regard we consider an operation that is used extensively, namely the *cross product,*

$$\mathbf{A} \times \mathbf{B} = \mathbf{C}$$

where

$$C_1 = A_2 B_3 - A_3 B_2 \qquad \text{(a)}$$
$$C_2 = A_3 B_1 - A_1 B_3 \qquad \text{(b)} \qquad\qquad (1.38)$$
$$C_3 = A_1 B_2 - A_2 B_1 \qquad \text{(c)}$$

or, equivalently, in determinant form:

$$\mathbf{A} \times \mathbf{B} = \mathbf{C} = \begin{vmatrix} \hat{\mathbf{i}} & \hat{\mathbf{j}} & \hat{\mathbf{k}} \\ A_1 & A_2 & A_3 \\ B_1 & B_2 & B_3 \end{vmatrix} \qquad\qquad (1.39)$$

To get this result via index notation, we introduce the *alternating tensor, e_{ijk},* defined as follows:

$e_{ijk} = 1$ for those elements of the alternating tensor having indices that form the sequence $1, 2, 3$ or that can be arranged by an *even* number of permutations to form this sequence. (Such indices are said to be *cyclic.*)

$e_{ijk} = -1$ for those elements of the alternating tensor requiring an *odd* number of permutations to reach the sequence $1, 2, 3$. (Such indices are said to be *anticyclic.*)

$e_{ijk} = 0$ for those elements of the alternating tensor for which the indices do not form some permutation of $1, 2, 3$. (Such indices are said to be *acyclic* and always involve repeated indices.)

Thus we have

$$e_{123} = e_{312} = e_{231} = 1$$
$$e_{321} = e_{132} = e_{213} = -1 \qquad\qquad (1.40)$$
$$e_{113} = e_{122} = e_{111} = \cdots = 0$$

We see from above that $e_{ijk} = e_{kij} = e_{jki}$, $e_{jik} = -e_{ijk}$, and so on. It can be shown that e_{ijk} is a *skew-symmetric* tensor of the *third order* in that it transforms properly for a *rotation* of axes. However, when there is an *inversion* of axes, e_{ijk} does not quite transform properly for a third-order tensor because of sign discrepancies, and for this reason it is sometimes called a *pseudotensor.* You will be asked to prove these statements in Problem 1.29 at the end of the chapter.

Now if we go back to Eq. (1.38), we can readily demonstrate that the following formulation yields the component C_i of the cross product of **A** and **B**

$$\boxed{C_i = e_{ijk} A_j B_k}$$ (1.41)

Thus, carrying out the double summation over dummy indices j and k, we get for $i = 1$:

$$C_1 = e_{1jk} A_j B_k = e_{111} A_1 B_1 + e_{121} A_2 B_1 + e_{131} A_3 B_1 +$$
$$e_{112} A_1 B_2 + e_{122} A_2 B_2 + e_{132} A_3 B_2 +$$
$$e_{113} A_1 B_3 + e_{123} A_2 B_3 + e_{133} A_3 B_3$$

Now employing the definition of the alternating tensor we find that

$$C_1 = A_2 B_3 - A_3 B_2$$

as you may verify. We thus arrive at Eq. (1.38a). Similarly, letting $i = 2$ and $i = 3$, we may arrive at Eqs. (1.38b) and (1.38c). Eq. (1.41), accordingly, is equivalent to the cross product and will be of much use to us.

We pointed out earlier that e_{ijk} was termed a pseudotensor. It should come as no surprise now to find out that the cross product of two vectors is also a pseudotensor, which being of first order is called a *pseudovector*.

An important identity called the e–δ *identity* is given as

$$\boxed{e_{ijk} e_{ilm} = \delta_{jl} \delta_{km} - \delta_{jm} \delta_{kl}}$$ (1.42)

Another more general form of Eq. (1.42) is given, with free indices only, as follows:

$$e_{ijk} e_{lmn} = \begin{vmatrix} \delta_{il} & \delta_{jl} & \delta_{kl} \\ \delta_{im} & \delta_{jm} & \delta_{km} \\ \delta_{in} & \delta_{jn} & \delta_{kn} \end{vmatrix}$$ (1.43)

Equations (1.42) and (1.43) are examined further in Problem 1.24. We now consider a series of examples.

Example 1.4

Derive Eq. (1.14) from (1.13) by using orthogonality conditions (1.18) and using the Kronecker delta.

First multiply (1.13) by $a_{i'k}$ to get

$$a_{i'k} x_{i'} = a_{i'k} a_{i'j} x_j$$ (a)

But $a_{i'k} a_{i'j} = \delta_{kj}$ via Eq. (1.18), and thus

$$a_{i'k} x_{i'} = \delta_{kj} x_j$$ (b)

Finally, since $\delta_{kj} x_j = x_k$ we obtain

$$x_k = a_{i'k} x_{i'}$$ (c)

which is the desired inversion.

Example 1.5

Invert the tensor transformation law (1.10), which we rewrite here:

$$T_{i'j'} = a_{i'k} a_{j'l} T_{kl} \tag{a}$$

In this case, we multiply by $a_{i'm} a_{j'n}$ to get

$$a_{i'm} a_{j'n} T_{i'j'} = a_{i'k} a_{i'm} a_{j'l} a_{j'n} T_{kl} \tag{b}$$

But $a_{i'k} a_{i'm} = \delta_{km}$ and $a_{j'l} a_{j'n} = \delta_{ln}$ and thus

$$a_{i'm} a_{j'n} T_{i'j'} = \delta_{km} \delta_{ln} T_{kl} \tag{c}$$

Then we note that $\delta_{ln} T_{kl} = T_{kn}$ and $\delta_{km} T_{kn} = T_{mn}$, which gives the final result

$$T_{mn} = a_{i'm} a_{j'n} T_{i'j'} \tag{d}$$

You should note that we have in effect *solved* nine simultaneous linear algebraic equations. Inversions of still higher-order tensor transformation laws may be performed in the same straightforward manner.

Example 1.6

Illustrate the use of the identity (1.42) by verifying for the familiar triple vector product that

$$\mathbf{A} \times (\mathbf{B} \times \mathbf{C}) = (\mathbf{A} \cdot \mathbf{C})\mathbf{B} - (\mathbf{A} \cdot \mathbf{B})\mathbf{C} \tag{a}$$

The left side of equation (a) is expressed in index notation and then rearranged as follows:

$$
\begin{aligned}
e_{ijk} A_j (e_{klm} B_l C_m) &= e_{ijk} e_{klm} A_j B_l C_m \\
&= e_{kij} e_{klm} A_j B_l C_m
\end{aligned} \tag{b}
$$

Now employ Eq. (1.42), noting that k is the dummy index in Eq. (b):

$$
\begin{aligned}
e_{kij} e_{klm} A_j B_l C_m &= (\delta_{il} \delta_{jm} - \delta_{im} \delta_{jl}) A_j B_l C_m \\
&= (A_m C_m) B_i - (A_l B_l) C_i \\
&\sim (\mathbf{A} \cdot \mathbf{C})\mathbf{B} - (\mathbf{A} \cdot \mathbf{B})\mathbf{C}
\end{aligned}
$$

where the notation $\sim$ is used to indicate equivalence between indicial and vector notation. Therefore,

$$\mathbf{A} \times (\mathbf{B} \times \mathbf{C}) = (\mathbf{A} \cdot \mathbf{C})\mathbf{B} - (\mathbf{A} \cdot \mathbf{B})\mathbf{C} \tag{c}$$

We now consider certain differential operators.

1.9 DIFFERENTIAL OPERATORS FOR CARTESIAN TENSORS IN INDEX NOTATION

First we have the *gradient* operator, which acting on a *scalar function* ϕ is given as

$$\text{grad } \phi = \nabla \phi = \frac{\partial \phi}{\partial x} \hat{\mathbf{i}} + \frac{\partial \phi}{\partial y} \hat{\mathbf{j}} + \frac{\partial \phi}{\partial z} \hat{\mathbf{k}} \tag{1.44}$$

To write $\nabla\phi$ in index notation, we can express the Cartesian unit vectors as follows:

$$\hat{\mathbf{i}} = \hat{\mathbf{i}}_1$$

$$\hat{\mathbf{j}} = \hat{\mathbf{i}}_2$$

$$\hat{\mathbf{k}} = \hat{\mathbf{i}}_3$$

Accordingly, we can say that

$$\text{grad }\phi = \nabla\phi = \sum_{i=1}^{3} \phi_{,i}\,\hat{\mathbf{i}}_i \sim \phi_{,i} = \frac{\partial\phi}{\partial x_i} \tag{1.45}$$

where, as above, the notation $\sim$ indicates that the expression $\phi_{,i}$, with i as a free index, is the indicial counterpart of $\nabla\phi$.

The *divergence* of a vector, you will recall, is given as follows in Cartesian coordinates:

$$\text{div }\mathbf{V} = \nabla\cdot\mathbf{V} = \frac{\partial V_x}{\partial x} + \frac{\partial V_y}{\partial y} + \frac{\partial V_z}{\partial z} \tag{1.46}$$

Using index notation, we get

$$\text{div }\mathbf{V} = \frac{\partial V_i}{\partial x_i} = V_{i,i} \tag{1.47}$$

Next, we consider the *curl* operator. Again from vector analysis, we have for rectangular Cartesian coordinates:

$$\text{curl }\mathbf{V} = \nabla\times\mathbf{V} = \begin{vmatrix} \hat{\mathbf{i}} & \hat{\mathbf{j}} & \hat{\mathbf{k}} \\ \dfrac{\partial}{\partial x} & \dfrac{\partial}{\partial y} & \dfrac{\partial}{\partial z} \\ V_x & V_y & V_z \end{vmatrix}$$

$$= \begin{vmatrix} \hat{\mathbf{i}}_1 & \hat{\mathbf{i}}_2 & \hat{\mathbf{i}}_3 \\ \dfrac{\partial}{\partial x_1} & \dfrac{\partial}{\partial x_2} & \dfrac{\partial}{\partial x_3} \\ V_1 & V_2 & V_3 \end{vmatrix}$$

You may then readily verify that

$$\text{curl }\mathbf{V} = \nabla\times\mathbf{V} \sim e_{ijk}\frac{\partial V_k}{\partial x_j} = e_{ijk}V_{k,j} \tag{1.48}$$

where the notation $\sim$ again indicates a correspondence between vector and indicial notation.

Finally, we consider the *Laplacian* (harmonic) operator ∇^2. From vector analysis we have

$$\nabla^2 = \frac{\partial^2}{\partial x_1^2} + \frac{\partial^2}{\partial x_2^2} + \frac{\partial^2}{\partial x_3^2} \tag{1.49}$$

Hence, using index notation, we get

$$\nabla^2 \equiv {}_{,ii} \tag{1.50}$$

so

$$\nabla^2 \phi \equiv \phi_{,ii} \tag{1.51}$$

It also follows that

$$\nabla^2(\nabla^2 \phi) = \nabla^4 \phi \equiv \phi_{,iijj} \tag{1.52}$$

where ∇^4 is the so-called *biharmonic* operator.

We now consider two illustrative examples.

Example 1.7

Prove that div(curl **A**) = 0.

In index notation this becomes

$$\frac{\partial}{\partial x_k} e_{kij} A_{j,i} \tag{a}$$

But since e_{kij} is a constant tensor we may move it to the left of the gradient operator to obtain

$$e_{kij} A_{j,ik} \tag{b}$$

First we note that e_{kij} is skew-symmetric in i and k (i.e., $e_{kij} = -e_{ikj}$). Then we note that if $A_{j,ik}$ and $A_{j,ki}$ are continuous in coordinates x_k, then $A_{j,ik}$ is symmetric in i and k (i.e., $A_{j,ik} = A_{j,ki}$). For example, the mixed derivative $A_{j,12}$ is equal to $A_{j,21}$. We thus have the product of tensors, which are, respectively, skew-symmetric and symmetric in indices i and k, and as proven at the end of Section 1.7, this product must be zero.

Example 1.8

Verify the identity

$$\text{curl}(\phi\mathbf{A}) = \phi \, \text{curl} \, \mathbf{A} + \text{grad} \, \phi \times \mathbf{A} \tag{a}$$

In Cartesian coordinates, the left-hand side becomes with index notation

$$e_{ijk} \frac{\partial}{\partial x_j} (\phi A_k) \tag{b}$$

which may be expanded out to give

$$e_{ijk} \phi_{,j} A_k + e_{ijk} \phi A_{k,j} \tag{c}$$

The first term in Eq. (c) is clearly grad $\phi \times \mathbf{A}$ in vector notation and the second is ϕ curl **A**, which verifies the identity.

1.10 ADDITIONAL PROPERTIES OF SECOND-ORDER TENSORS

We shall now briefly consider some additional properties of second-order tensors. In doing so, we shall write a tensor T_{ij} as a boldface, block letter such as **T**. The *trace* of the tensor **T** is the sum of the main diagonal terms and can be denoted T_{ii} or as tr **T**. As indicated earlier, the *determinant* of the tensor **T** is denoted as det **T**. We start by expressing a determinant in the following familiar way using vector and indicial notation:

$$\begin{vmatrix} u_1 & v_1 & w_1 \\ u_2 & v_2 & w_2 \\ u_3 & v_3 & w_3 \end{vmatrix} = \mathbf{u} \cdot (\mathbf{v} \times \mathbf{w}) \sim e_{lmn} u_l v_m w_n \qquad (1.53)$$

If we identify the elements in the determinant above as T_{ij} and also invoke the invariance properties* of determinants when columns are interchanged, we may obtain the following result:

$$e_{ijk} \det \mathbf{T} = e_{lmn} T_{li} T_{mj} T_{nk} \qquad (1.54)$$

You may check this result for $i, j, k = 1, 2, 3$, by making a simple comparison with Eq. (1.53). Upon multiplying by e_{ijk} and setting $e_{ijk} e_{ijk} = 6$ [a result you may also readily verify with the use of Eq. (1.42)], we may express $\det \mathbf{T}$ as

$$\det \mathbf{T} = \tfrac{1}{6} e_{lmn} e_{ijk} T_{li} T_{mj} T_{nk} \qquad (1.55)$$

which with the use of Eq. (1.43) may also be written as

$$\det \mathbf{T} = \tfrac{1}{6} (2 T_{ij} T_{jk} T_{ki} - 3 T_{ij} T_{ji} T_{kk} + T_{ii} T_{jj} T_{kk}) \qquad (1.56)$$

This is a very useful expression. We next present yet another useful formulation involving tensors and determinants.

For this purpose, go to Eq. (1.53) and replace the vector $\mathbf{u}$ by the unit vector $\hat{\mathbf{i}}$. We then obtain

$$\hat{\mathbf{i}} \cdot (\mathbf{v} \times \mathbf{w}) = \begin{vmatrix} 1 & v_1 & w_1 \\ 0 & v_2 & w_2 \\ 0 & v_3 & w_3 \end{vmatrix} = \begin{vmatrix} v_2 & w_2 \\ v_3 & w_3 \end{vmatrix} \qquad (1.57)$$

The last expression you may recognize as the *minor* of element u_1. Proceeding to relabel element u_1 as T_{11}, and so on, as discussed in the preceding paragraph, we denote this minor as $M(T_{11})$. Using this notation and then going back to Eq. (1.54), we can say, upon setting $i = 1$,

$$e_{1jk} \begin{vmatrix} 1 & T_{12} & T_{13} \\ 0 & T_{22} & T_{23} \\ 0 & T_{32} & T_{33} \end{vmatrix} = e_{1jk} M(T_{11}) = e_{lmn} T_{l1} T_{mj} T_{nk}$$

But here $\{T_{l1}\} = \begin{Bmatrix} 1 \\ 0 \\ 0 \end{Bmatrix}$, so we can conclude from the above on noting that $e_{lmn} T_{l1} = e_{1mn}$

$$e_{1jk} M(T_{11}) = e_{1mn} T_{mj} T_{nk}$$

Rewriting the relation above, we have

$$e_{1lm} M(T_{11}) = e_{1jk} T_{jl} T_{km} \qquad (1.58)$$

---

*You will recall that if columns in $\mathbf{T}$ are interchanged an even number of times, $\det \mathbf{T}$ is unchanged, whereas $\det \mathbf{T}$ changes sign if columns are interchanged an odd number of times. The same statement applies to rows.

Next premultiply Eq. (1.58) by e_{1lm} to get

$$e_{1lm} e_{1lm} M(T_{11}) = (e_{123} e_{123} + e_{132} e_{132}) M(T_{11}) = 2M(T_{11}) = e_{1lm} e_{1jk} T_{jl} T_{km}$$

By replacing the pair of ones on the right side of the equation above by dummy indices i, it should be apparent that the *sum* of the principal minors can be written as

$$M(T_{11}) + M(T_{22}) + M(T_{33}) = \tfrac{1}{2} e_{ijk} e_{ilm} T_{jl} T_{km} \tag{1.59}$$

Finally, we may rewrite the right-hand side of the preceding equation by means of Eq. (1.42), so that Eq. (1.59) becomes

$$M(T_{11}) + M(T_{22}) + M(T_{33}) = \tfrac{1}{2}(T_{ii} T_{jj} - T_{ij} T_{ji}) \tag{1.60}$$

Equation (1.60) and those preceding it in this section will be valuable to us when we examine second-order tensor invariants in index notation. [In Problems 1.30 and 1.31 you will be asked, respectively, to extend Eq. (1.58) and to verify Eqs. (1.56) and (1.60).]

The elements of the *square* of a tensor denoted as $\mathbf{T}^2$ are obtained by the matrix multiplication $T_{ij} T_{jk}$ to form a second-order tensor. Thus

$$\mathbf{T}^2 \sim T_{ij} T_{jk} \tag{1.61}$$

where the $\sim$ sign here indicates an equivalence between the symbolic notation on the left and the index notation on the right. The *cube* of a tensor, denoted as $\mathbf{T}^3$, is defined as

$$\mathbf{T}^3 \sim T_{ij} T_{jk} T_{kl} \tag{1.62}$$

The higher powers of $\mathbf{T}$ follow directly.* It should be clear that powers of *symmetric, second-order tensors remain symmetric,* second-order tensors. Finally, note that the nth power of a second-order tensor for principal axes with diagonal elements T_1, T_2, T_3 is given as

$$\mathbf{T}^n = \begin{bmatrix} T_1^n & 0 & 0 \\ 0 & T_2^n & 0 \\ 0 & 0 & T_3^n \end{bmatrix} \tag{1.63}$$

This indicates that the principal axes of $\mathbf{T}$ and $\mathbf{T}^n$ coincide. We shall discuss principal axes and powers of tensors more fully in Chapter 2 on the stress tensor and again in Chapter 7.

---

*Note that in symbolic notation, using the notation tr $\mathbf{T}$ to represent $(T_{11} + T_{22} + T_{33})$ — the so-called *trace* of the tensor, Eq. (1.60) becomes

$$M(T_{11}) + M(T_{22}) + M(T_{33}) = \tfrac{1}{2}[(\text{tr } \mathbf{T})^2 - \text{tr}(\mathbf{T}^2)]$$

whereas Eq. (1.56) becomes

$$\det \mathbf{T} = \tfrac{1}{6}[2 \text{ tr}(\mathbf{T}^3) - 3 \text{ tr}(\mathbf{T}^2) \text{ tr } \mathbf{T} - (\text{tr } \mathbf{T})^3]$$

1.11 INTEGRAL THEOREMS

We shall first derive *Gauss'* theorem and from it the *divergence* theorem as well as other useful results. Assume that we have an nth-order tensor $T_{jk...}$ defined at each point in space (i.e., it is an nth-order tensor field). Consider a domain D in space bounded by a closed surface S of such a shape that lines parallel to the x_1 axis can pierce the boundary only twice (see Fig. 1.10). Imagine now that this volume is composed of infinitesimal prisms having sides dx_2 and dx_3, as has been shown in the diagram. Consider one prism and compute the following integral over the volume δV of this prism.

$$\int_{\delta V} \frac{\partial}{\partial x_1} (T_{jk...})\, dx_1\, dx_2\, dx_3$$

Carrying out the integration with respect to x_1, we get

$$\int_{\delta V} \frac{\partial}{\partial x_1} (T_{jk...})\, dx_1\, dx_2\, dx_3 = (T_{jk...}\, dx_2\, dx_3)_R - (T_{jk...}\, dx_2\, dx_3)_L$$

where the first expression on the right side of the equation above is evaluated at the right end of the prism, while the second expression is evaluated at the left end of the prism. Using $\hat{\nu}$ to represent the unit vector normal to the boundary surface of D, and considering ν_1, ν_2, and $\nu_3{}^*$ to be direction cosine components of $\hat{\nu}$, we can

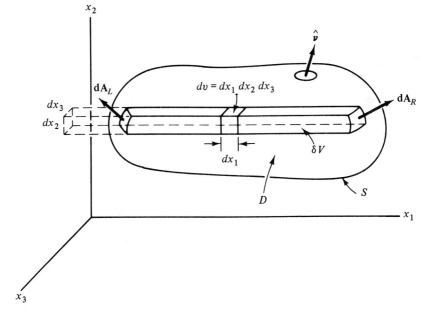

Figure 1.10 Body with prismatic element in x_1 direction.

*Using the *a* form for direction cosines, we would use $a_{\nu x}$, $a_{\nu y}$, and $a_{\nu z}$ for ν_1, ν_2, and ν_3, respectively.

replace $dx_2\,dx_3$ at the right end of the prism by $(+\nu_1\,dA\,)_R$ and by $(-\nu_1\,dA\,)_L$ on the left end of the prism.† We thus have

$$\int_{\delta V} \frac{\partial}{\partial x_1}(T_{jk\ldots})\,dx_1\,dx_2\,dx_3 = (T_{jk\ldots}\,\nu_1\,dA\,)_R + (T_{jk\ldots}\,\nu_1\,dA\,)_L$$

Now integrating over *all the prisms* comprising the domain of the volume D, we get*

$$\iiint_D \frac{\partial}{\partial x_1}(T_{jk\ldots})\,dx_1\,dx_2\,dx_3 = \iint_R (T_{jk\ldots})\nu_1\,dA + \iint_L (T_{jk\ldots})\nu_1\,dA$$

The right side of the equation above clearly covers the entire surface of domain D and is accordingly replaceable by a closed-surface integral. We then have the following statement:

$$\iiint_D \frac{\partial}{\partial x_1}(T_{jk\ldots})\,dx_1\,dx_2\,dx_3 = \oint_S (T_{jk\ldots})\nu_1\,dA \qquad (1.64)$$

We developed Eq. (1.64) for the x_1 direction. We could have proceeded in a similar manner in any direction x_i. Accordingly, the generalization of the above statement is given as follows:

$$\boxed{\iiint_D \frac{\partial T_{jk\ldots}}{\partial x_i}\,dv = \oint_S (T_{jk\ldots})\nu_i\,dA} \qquad (1.65)$$

where i is a free index and $dv = dx_1\,dx_2\,dx_3$ is an element of volume. This is *Gauss'* theorem in a generalized form. Using the notation presented for a spatial partial derivative, we can also give this equation as follows:

$$\boxed{\iiint_D (T_{jk\ldots})_{,i}\,dv = \oint_S (T_{jk\ldots})\nu_i\,dA} \qquad (1.66)$$

The theorem can now be extended by simple summation to bodies whose shape is such that lines parallel to the $x_1, x_2,$ and x_3 axes cut the boundary surface more than twice, provided that such a body can be decomposed into contiguous composite bodies each of which does have the property specified for a boundary surface in this development.

---

† The appearance of the minus sign here is a result of the use of the outward-normal convention for area vectors. Thus ν_1 on the left side of the prism is clearly negative for the kind of domain we have chosen to work with, and a minus sign must be included so that the product $(-\nu_1\,dA\,)$ be the positive number needed to replace $dx_2\,dx_3$ for that side.

* We are assuming tacitly here, in order to be able to carry out the integration, that the surface of the domain D can be split up into a finite number of parts such that there is a continuously varying tangent plane on each piece. That is, the surface should be *piecewise smooth*.

Suppose that $T_{jk\ldots}$ is the zeroth-order tensor ϕ (i.e., a scalar). We then have

$$\iiint_D \phi_{,i}\, dv = \oiint_S \phi \nu_i\, dA \tag{1.67}$$

If we wish to revert to vector notation, this form of Gauss' theorem becomes

$$\iiint_D \boldsymbol{\nabla}\phi\, dv = \oiint_S \phi\, \mathbf{dA} \tag{1.68}$$

where $\mathbf{dA} = \hat{\boldsymbol{\nu}}\, dA$. Suppose next that $T_{jk\ldots}$ is a first-order tensor (i.e., a vector) V_j. We then get

$$\iiint_D V_{j,i}\, dv = \oiint_S V_j \nu_i\, dA \tag{1.69}$$

Next, perform a contraction operation on the free indices i and j in Eq. (1.69). We get

$$\iiint_D V_{j,j}\, dv = \oiint_S V_j \nu_j\, dA \tag{1.70}$$

You should have no difficulty in writing this equation in terms of vectors to arrive at

$$\boxed{\iiint_D \operatorname{div} \mathbf{V}\, dv = \oiint_S \mathbf{V}\cdot\mathbf{dA}} \tag{1.71}$$

We will have much use of this form of Gauss' theorem. In this form it is called the *divergence* theorem.

Next, let us consider the case where the tensor $T_{jkl\ldots}$ is $e_{kij} V_j$. Going back to Eq. (1.66), we then have for this case

$$\iiint_D e_{kij} V_{j,i}\, dv = \oiint_S e_{kij} V_j (\nu_i\, dA) = \oiint_S e_{kij} V_j\, dA_i \tag{1.72}$$

Using Eq. (1.48) for the left side of Eq. (1.72), and noting the index formulation for the cross product for the integrand of the expression on the extreme right side, we can express Eq. (1.72) in vector notation. Thus

$$\boxed{\iiint_D \operatorname{curl} \mathbf{V}\, dv = -\oiint_S \mathbf{V} \times \mathbf{dA}} \tag{1.73}$$

Finally, we wish to present *Stokes'* theorem. Although it can be derived from a two-dimensional form of Gauss' theorem,* it will be more meaningful physically to derive it independently.

* See *Introduction to Mechanics of Continua* by W. Prager (Boston: Ginn & Company, 1961), pp. 30–32.

1.12 STOKES' THEOREM

Consider a vector field $\mathbf{V}(x, y, z, t)$, and designate the z component of its curl as $(\text{curl}\,\mathbf{V})_z$. An infinitesimal rectangular element of area δA is shown in the xy plane in Fig. 1.11. We leave it for you to show (see Problem 1.35) that for this element

$$\oint \mathbf{V} \cdot d\mathbf{s} = \iint_{\delta A} (\text{curl}\,\mathbf{V})_z \, dx \, dy \tag{1.74}$$

where the direction of the line integral is such that the enclosed area is always on the *left*, as has been shown in the diagram. Next, consider an arbitrary surface S (see Fig. 1.12) where a closed curve Γ is an edge and where it is clear that in general an area element δA will not lie in a coordinate plane. We note in Eq. (1.74) that the component of the curl needed in this equation is normal to the area $dx\, dy$. We will now extrapolate this result to apply to the area δA on the arbitrary open-ended surface S. We can then say that for this area element,

$$\oint \mathbf{V} \cdot d\mathbf{s} = \iint_{\delta A} (\text{curl}\,\mathbf{V})_\nu \, dA = \iint_{\delta A} \text{curl}\,\mathbf{V} \cdot d\mathbf{A} \tag{1.75}$$

where $\hat{\boldsymbol{\nu}}$ is the unit vector normal to the area element and $d\mathbf{A} = dA\,\hat{\boldsymbol{\nu}}$. Now sum Eq. (1.75) to include all area elements on the open-ended surface S which we call the capping surface. In doing so, we must remember to integrate always in the same sense (i.e., with the enclosed area on the left) for each and every element. In so doing, it is clear that integrations on all inside boundaries cancel since edges of each internal segment are integrated in *opposite* directions to cause cancellations. Only on the outer edge Γ do we avoid such cancellation. The result above then becomes

$$\boxed{\iint_S \text{curl}\,\mathbf{V} \cdot d\mathbf{A} = \oint_\Gamma \mathbf{V} \cdot d\mathbf{s}} \tag{1.76}$$

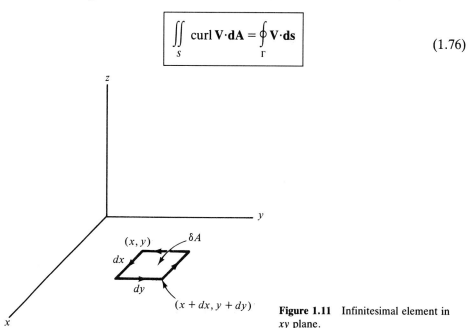

Figure 1.11 Infinitesimal element in xy plane.

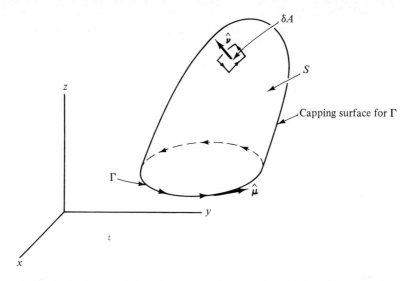

Figure 1.12 Open-ended surface with only one edge Γ. The edge Γ may be considered as "capped" closed curve.

Here $\mathbf{ds} = ds\,\hat{\boldsymbol{\mu}}$, where $\hat{\boldsymbol{\mu}}$ is the unit vector tangent to curve Γ (see Fig. 1.12). This is the well-known Stokes' theorem.

Let us now consider an important restriction on the use of Stokes' theorem (1.76). In Fig. 1.12 we have tacitly assumed that there is only *one* closed curve Γ for a capping surface *S* on which **V** is defined. In a *simply connected* domain each and every closed curve Γ can be taken as the only edge of all possible capping surfaces that reside in the entirety of the domain for which **V** is defined.* Thus in Fig. 1.13 we have shown a simply connected domain. This domain consists of the region of material outside of the internal cavity and inside the outside boundary *B*. For *any closed curve* Γ in this domain we have capping surfaces *S* having only Γ as an edge for which Eq. (1.76) is valid. This validity extends to the entire domain of the simply connected region.

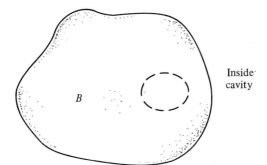

Inside cavity

Figure 1.13 Body which constitutes a simply connected domain.

* An alternative test of connectivity entails displacing and deforming every possible curve Γ in the domain such that each curve approaches a point. If this can be accomplished through sequences of curves that lie entirely in the domain, this domain is *simply connected*.

In Fig. 1.14 we have shown a *multiply connected* domain in the form of a torus (or donut). This region is multiply connected since for curves such as Γ_1 no capping surface S can be formed entirely inside the torus with Γ_1 as the only edge. To form a simply connected domain for the torus, we cut out a very thin slice of the torus, as shown in Fig. 1.15. The region remaining for the torus is now a simply connected domain as you may mentally verify. Hence we can use Eq. (1.76) for any closed curve consisting of part of Γ_1, plus lines along the slice, and finally, plus the curve γ_1 along the inside surface of the torus (see Fig. 1.16). We choose points A and C and points B and D such that they respectively coalesce in the limit as the thickness of the slice vanishes. Thus for the closed curve in Fig. 1.16, we can say that*

$$\iint_S \operatorname{curl} \mathbf{V} \cdot \mathbf{dA} = \int_A^C \mathbf{V} \cdot \mathbf{ds} + \int_C^D \mathbf{V} \cdot \mathbf{ds} + \int_D^B \mathbf{V} \cdot \mathbf{ds} + \int_B^A \mathbf{V} \cdot \mathbf{ds}$$

Now we take the limit of the integrals above as the thickness of the slice vanishes. In the limit the first line integral forms a closed integral *counterclockwise*, while the third line integral becomes a closed integral *clockwise*. The line integrals along the cut will traverse over the same lines but in opposite directions so that the other two line integrals above vanish. We then get in the limit

$$\iint_S \operatorname{curl} \mathbf{V} \cdot \mathbf{dA} = \oint_{\Gamma_1} \mathbf{V} \cdot \mathbf{ds} + \oint_{\gamma_1} \mathbf{V} \cdot \mathbf{ds} \tag{1.77}$$

where the arrows on the line integrals indicate the directions of integration. Reversing the direction of integration for the last line integral, and deleting the arrows since by convention counterclockwise is positive, we then get

$$\iint_S \operatorname{curl} \mathbf{V} \cdot \mathbf{dA} = \oint_{\Gamma_1} \mathbf{V} \cdot \mathbf{ds} - \oint_{\gamma_1} \mathbf{V} \cdot \mathbf{ds} \tag{1.78}$$

Note that Γ_1 could lie next to the outermost boundary of the torus.

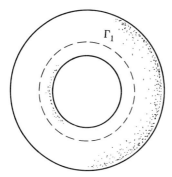

Figure 1.14 Multiply connected domain.

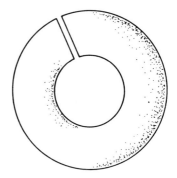

Figure 1.15 Forming a simply connected region from the torus.

* The surface S is any capping surface inside the torus having the dashed line of Fig. 1.16 as an edge.

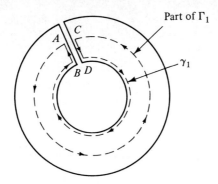

Part of Γ_1

Figure 1.16 $\Gamma_1 + CD + \gamma_1 + BA$ forms a closed curved in a simply connected domain.

If the torus is now replaced by a fat pretzel, such as is shown in Fig. 1.17, we can extend the formulation above to the following for n inside openings:

$$\iint_S \text{curl } \mathbf{V} \cdot \mathbf{dA} = \oint_\Gamma \mathbf{V} \cdot \mathbf{ds} - \sum_{\alpha=1}^n \oint_{\gamma_\alpha} \mathbf{V} \cdot \mathbf{ds} \tag{1.79}$$

Here γ_α are closed curves around each of the n inside cavities of the pretzel and Γ could be the curve along the outermost boundary. This equation is Stokes' theorem for *multiply connected* domains.

We wish to point out that Stokes' theorem in two dimensions for a simply connected domain can be expressed by letting S and Γ coincide with the xy plane and accordingly setting

$$\mathbf{V} = V_x \hat{\mathbf{i}} + V_y \hat{\mathbf{j}} = P(x,y)\hat{\mathbf{i}} + Q(x,y)\hat{\mathbf{j}}$$

$$\mathbf{dA} = dx\,dy\,\hat{\mathbf{k}}$$

$$\mathbf{ds} = dx\,\hat{\mathbf{i}} + dy\,\hat{\mathbf{j}}$$

in Eq. (1.76). This results in the following form of this equation, which is called *Green's lemma*:

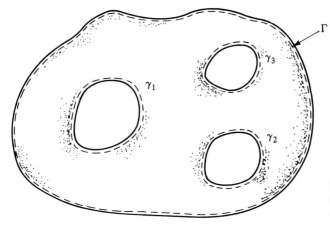

Γ

γ_3

γ_1

γ_2

Figure 1.17 Multiply connected domain showing paths of integration Γ, γ_1, γ_2, and γ_3.

$$\iint\limits_{S} \left(\frac{\partial Q}{\partial x} - \frac{\partial P}{\partial y} \right) dx\, dy = \oint\limits_{\Gamma} (P\, dx + Q\, dy) \tag{1.80}$$

where P and Q need not necessarily be associated with the components of a vector field. It is easily seen that if S is an infinitesimal rectangular element, then Eq. (1.80) is equivalent to our initial equation [i.e., Eq. (1.74)].

We have represented Stokes' theorem above for a vector field, but one can easily extend it to a tensor field. First let us rewrite Eq. (1.76) for a simply connected domain in index notation:

$$\iint\limits_{S} e_{ijk} V_{k,j}\, \nu_i\, dA = \oint\limits_{\Gamma} V_k \mu_k\, ds \tag{1.81}$$

The extension of this equation to a tensor field $T_{klm\ldots}$ is given as

$$\iint\limits_{S} e_{ijk} T_{klm\ldots,j}\, \nu_i\, dA = \oint\limits_{\Gamma} T_{klm\ldots}\, \mu_k\, ds \tag{1.82}$$

The derivation of Eq. (1.82) parallels the derivation of Eq.(1.81), and we see that for each chosen set of values of the free indices $l, m, \ldots$, Eq. (1.82) does indeed reduce back to Eq. (1.81). Finally, note that for multiply connected domains Eq. (1.82) generalizes to

$$\iint\limits_{S} e_{ijk} T_{klm\ldots,j}\, \nu_i\, dA = \oint\limits_{\Gamma} T_{klm\ldots}\, \mu_k\, ds - \sum_{\alpha=1}^{n} \oint\limits_{\gamma_\alpha} T_{klm\ldots}\, \mu_k\, ds \tag{1.83}$$

1.13 CLOSURE

In this chapter we presented Cartesian tensor (or index) notation. This notation will be used in much of this book. We also defined tensors as quantities whose components change or transform in a certain way when the axes are rotated and/or inverted at a point. Why is the tensor concept important? It is important because many vital properties of these quantities are traced back to the nature of these transformation equations. In your earlier studies in mechanics you will recall that mass moments of inertia, stress, and strain all exhibited the property of principal values and principal axes, Mohr's circle, and certain invariants with respect to rotation of axes. All these properties are attributable to the transformation equations that are identical for these three quantities even though physically moments of inertia, stress, and strain are quite different. Thus, showing that some quantity is a second-order tensor means immediately that certain vital properties of this quantity are known without further study. In the following chapter we study the stress tensor, and having done this, we will already have a handle on strain of Chapter 3 as far as certain key properties.

We finished this chapter by considering certain vital integral theorems. We now have set forth much of the mathematical background needed for this book. Other mathematical considerations will be presented later in the book when and where needed, and in the appendices as well.

PROBLEMS

1.1. Given the vector components

$$A_x = 5, \qquad B_x = 4, \qquad C_x = 10$$
$$A_y = -3, \qquad B_y = 6, \qquad C_y = 6$$
$$A_z = 10, \qquad B_z = -2, \qquad C_z = 0$$

evaluate the following by listing all components of any free indices.
(a) $A_i C_i B_x$
(b) $A_i A_2 B_i$
(c) $A_i B_i C_j$
(d) $A_i B_i C_j A_k$

1.2. Using Eq. (1.9), form an equation for $\tau_{y'z'}$ in terms of components τ_{ij} and direction cosines where $x'y'z'$ axes are rotated relative to axes xyz.

1.3. Given the tensor

$$\tau_{ij} = \begin{bmatrix} 1000 & 500 & 6000 \\ 500 & 2000 & 3000 \\ 6000 & 3000 & -3000 \end{bmatrix} \quad \text{psi}$$

and the Kronecker delta δ_{ij}, evaluate:
(a) $\tau_{ij} \delta_{ij}$
(b) $\tau_{3j} \delta_{j3}$
(c) δ_{ii}
(d) $\delta_{ij} \delta_{ij}$
(e) $\delta_{ij} \delta_{jk} \delta_{ki}$

1.4. (a) If B_{ij} is a second-order tensor and λ is a scalar, prove that λB_{ij} is a second-order tensor.
(b) If B_{ij} and C_{ij} are second-order tensors, show that their sum is a second-order tensor.

1.5. Consider the special case of plane stress (see Fig. 1.4). Verify that in this case the general stress transformation law, Eq. (1.9), simplifies to Eqs. (1.7).

1.6. Derive Eq. (1.14) by projecting components of $\mathbf{r}'$ that lie along $x'y'z'$ onto directions corresponding to x, y, and z. Also derive Eq. (1.19) using an approach similar to that used for Eq. (1.18).

1.7. Consider the following matrices:

$$\mathbf{B} = \begin{bmatrix} 1 & 2 & 3 \\ 0 & -1 & 4 \\ -2 & 1 & 3 \end{bmatrix}, \qquad \mathbf{C} = \begin{bmatrix} 2 & 0 & -2 \\ 1 & 1 & 3 \\ 5 & 0 & 1 \end{bmatrix}$$

Verify that

$$\det(\mathbf{BC}) = (\det \mathbf{B})(\det \mathbf{C})$$

and

$$\det \mathbf{B} = \det \mathbf{B}^T$$

1.8. Verify by actually carrying out the matrix multiplications that

$$\mathbf{A}^T \mathbf{A} = \mathbf{I} = \mathbf{A} \mathbf{A}^T$$

where $\mathbf{A}$ is the square transformation matrix $a_{i'k}$, $\mathbf{A}^T$ is the transpose of $\mathbf{A}$, and $\mathbf{I}$ is the unitary matrix.

1.9. Verify by use of the rules for matrix multiplication that in matrix form Eq. (1.10) becomes

$$\mathbf{T}' = \mathbf{ATA}^T$$

where $\mathbf{A}$ is the matrix of direction cosines, $\mathbf{T}$ is a second-order tensor for axes x, y, z, and $\mathbf{T}'$ is this tensor for rotated axes x', y', z'. Similarly, prove that the inverted form of Eq. (1.10) (see Example 1.5 in Section 1.8) becomes in matrix notation

$$\mathbf{T} = \mathbf{A}^T \mathbf{T}' \mathbf{A}$$

1.10. Consider an orthogonal transformation consisting of a 30° rotation of axes xyz about the z axes as shown in Fig. P1.10.

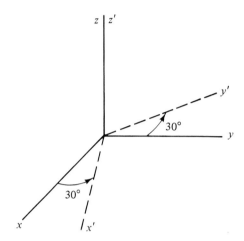

Figure P1.10

(a) Determine the matrix of direction cosines $\mathbf{A}$.
(b) Verify orthogonality of rows.
(c) Verify orthogonality of columns.
(d) Verify $\det \mathbf{A} = \pm 1$. Discuss the sign.
(e) Evaluate the trace of $\mathbf{A}$ (i.e., $a_{i'i}$ in index notation).

1.11. (a) Do Problem 1.10 for an inversion of the *three* axes x, y, z through the origin.
(b) Repeat the process for an inversion of the *two* axes x, y.

1.12. Given the tensors

$$C_{ij} = \begin{bmatrix} 3 & 0 & 2 \\ 0 & -2 & 3 \\ 2 & 3 & 5 \end{bmatrix}, \qquad D_{lm} = \begin{bmatrix} 5 & 3 & 2 \\ 3 & 6 & -5 \\ 2 & -5 & 7 \end{bmatrix}$$

(a) What are the components of an inner product over indices i and m?
(b) For the outer product of C_{ij} and D_{lm}, what are all the components involving component C_{22}?

1.13. Given the following equation relating vector v_j to vector u_i:

$$u_i = T_{ij} v_j$$

prove that T_{ij} is a tensor of second order, given that u_i and v_j are tensors of first order (i.e., vectors). This theorem is called the *quotient rule*, and the equation above is called a *linear transformation* of the vector v_j.

1.14. Suppose that A_i represents an arbitrary vector and that the inner product of A_i and a set of terms C_{irs} forms a second-order tensor B_{rs}. Show that C_{irs} must then be a third-order tensor. (*Hint:* First show that

$$B_{r's'} = a_{r'm} a_{s'l} C_{iml} A_i$$

Then replace $B_{r's'}$ in terms of A_k' and $C_{k'r's'}$ and A_i in terms of primed components. Finally, use the fact that A_i is arbitrary to show that C_{irs} is a third-order tensor.)

1.15. Given the tensor equation

$$\tau_{ij} = C_{ijkl} \varepsilon_{kl}$$

if τ_{ij} and ϵ_{kl} are known to be second-order tensors, prove that C_{ijkl} is a fourth-order tensor. This result will prove useful in Chapter 5.

1.16. Compute the vector:

$$(x_1^2 + 2x_1 x_2^2 + 3x_2^2 x_3)_{,i}$$

1.17. If $\mathbf{V} = 3x\hat{\mathbf{i}} + 2y^2 x\hat{\mathbf{j}} + 3xz^2 \hat{\mathbf{k}}$, compute:
(a) $V_{i,i}$
(b) $V_{i,i2}$
(c) $V_{j,3j}$

1.18. If $\phi = x^2 + 5 \sin y + xyz^3$, compute:
(a) $\phi_{,i}$
(b) $\phi_{,ii}$
(c) $\phi_{,iijj}$
(d) $\phi_{,2ii}$

1.19. If $T_{pr...}$ is an Nth-order tensor, show that $T_{pr...,i}$ is an $(N+1)$th-order tensor. First express $T_{p'r'...}$ in terms of components for an unprimed set of axes. Then differentiate both sides of the resulting equation with respect to $x_{i'}$. Next replace $\partial/\partial x_{i'}$ by

$$\frac{\partial}{\partial x_l} \frac{\partial x_l}{\partial x_{i'}} = a_{i'l} \frac{\partial}{\partial x_l}$$

on the right side of the equation. Use the definition of an $(N+1)$th-order tensor.

1.20. (a) Evaluate $e_{112}, e_{132}, e_{231}, e_{131}, e_{111}$.
(b) The elements of e_{ijk} can be displayed in a three-dimensional cubical matrix array consisting of three rows, three columns, and three aisles, with 27 lattice points. In Fig. P1.20 we have shown 15 lattice points that lie in two of the six faces of such an array. Label the values of e_{ijk} at these 15 lattice points.

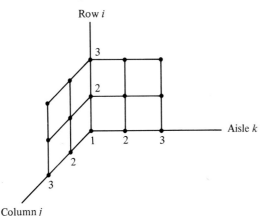

Figure P1.20

1.21. Show that

$$e_{ijk}e_{ijp} = 2\delta_{kp}$$

Hence show that

$$e_{ijk}e_{ijk} = 6$$

Finally, show that

$$\delta_{ik}e_{ikm} = 0$$

1.22. Write indicially:
  (a) $[(\mathbf{A} \times \mathbf{B})\cdot\mathbf{C}]\mathbf{D}$
  (b) $[(\mathbf{A} \times \mathbf{D})\cdot(\mathbf{E} \times \mathbf{F})](\mathbf{E}\cdot\mathbf{F})$
  (c) $\mathbf{A} \times \mathbf{B} + (\mathbf{C}\cdot\mathbf{D})\mathbf{E}$

1.23. Consider a skew-symmetric tensor U_{ij}, which is related to vector V_k via

$$V_k = e_{kji}U_{ij}$$

Use the e–δ identity, Eq. (1.42), to invert this result to

$$U_{ij} = \tfrac{1}{2}e_{kji}V_k$$

1.24. **(a)** Consider the e–δ identity given by Eq. (1.42). The values of two of the four free indices clearly must be equal. Show that if $j = k$ or $l = m$, both sides vanish identically. Also show that even with $j \neq k$ and $l \neq m$, both sides again vanish when $j = l$ *unless* $k = m$ also. Finally, verify the identity for the one case $j = l = 1$ and $k = m = 2$.
  (b) Verify that if we set $l = i$ in identity (1.43), it simplifies to the e–δ identity (1.42).

1.25. Prove the following indicially:
  (a) $\mathbf{A}\cdot(\mathbf{B} \times \mathbf{C}) = \mathbf{B}\cdot(\mathbf{C} \times \mathbf{A})$
  (b) $(\mathbf{A} \times \mathbf{B})\cdot(\mathbf{C} \times \mathbf{D}) = (\mathbf{A}\cdot\mathbf{C})(\mathbf{B}\cdot\mathbf{D}) - (\mathbf{A}\cdot\mathbf{D})(\mathbf{B}\cdot\mathbf{C})$
  (c) $(\mathbf{A} \times \mathbf{B}) \times (\mathbf{C} \times \mathbf{D}) = \mathbf{B}[\mathbf{A}\cdot(\mathbf{C} \times \mathbf{D})] - \mathbf{A}[\mathbf{B}\cdot(\mathbf{C} \times \mathbf{D})]$
  (d) $\mathrm{curl}(\mathrm{grad}\,\phi) = \mathbf{0}$
  (e) $\mathrm{div}(\mathbf{F} \times \mathbf{G}) = \mathbf{G}\cdot\mathrm{curl}\,\mathbf{F} - \mathbf{F}\cdot\mathrm{curl}\,\mathbf{G}$

1.26. Write indicially:
  (a) $(\nabla^2\phi)\,\mathbf{A} \times \mathbf{B}$
  (b) $(\nabla^4\phi)\,\mathbf{A}\cdot\mathbf{B}$
  (c) $(\nabla^4\phi)\,\mathbf{A} + \mathbf{B} = \mathbf{C}$
  (d) $(\nabla^2\phi)(\nabla^4\phi) = K$

1.27. Prove that:
  (a) $\mathrm{curl}\,(\mathrm{curl}\,\mathbf{F}) = \mathrm{grad}\,(\mathrm{div}\,\mathbf{F}) - \nabla^2\mathbf{F}$
  (b) $\mathrm{curl}(\mathbf{F} \times \mathbf{G}) = \mathbf{F}\,\mathrm{div}\,\mathbf{G} - \mathbf{G}\,\mathrm{div}\,\mathbf{F} + (\mathbf{G}\cdot\nabla)\mathbf{F} - (\mathbf{F}\cdot\nabla)\mathbf{G}$

1.28. If $\mathbf{r}$ is a position vector, prove that:
  (a) $\mathrm{div}\,\mathbf{r} = 3$
  (b) $\mathrm{curl}\,\mathbf{r} = \mathbf{0}$
  (c) $(\mathbf{u}\cdot\mathrm{grad})\mathbf{r} = \mathbf{u}$

where $\mathbf{u}$ is an arbitrary vector.

1.29. Prove that for a rotation of axes the alternating tensor e_{ijk} does obey the transformation law for tensors of the third order. Note that e_{ijk} must have the same form for *any* orientation of axes. [*Hint*: Use the expression for the determinant given by Eq. (1.54) along with property (1.26) for the matrix of direction cosines.] Also prove that for an inversion of one or three axes the transformation law is *not* satisfied (i.e., e_{ijk} in a pseudotensor).

1.30. Show as a generalization from Eq. (1.58) that

$$M(T_{pq}) = \tfrac{1}{2} e_{pjl} e_{qkm} T_{jk} T_{lm}$$

Here the minor $M(T_{pq})$ is the determinant of the matrix formed by striking out the pth row and the qth column.

1.31. Verify Eq. (1.60) using Eq. (1.42). Also verify Eq. (1.56) using Eq. (1.43).

1.32. Given the tensor field T_{ij},

$$T_{ij} = \begin{bmatrix} x^2 & x^2 + 2yz & 0 \\ x^2 + 2yz & 0 & 0 \\ 0 & 0 & 0 \end{bmatrix}$$

Evaluate the left side and the right side of Gauss' theorem for T_{12} for the domain shown in Fig. P1.32. Carry out this calculation for $\partial/\partial z$ in Gauss' theorem. Verify that you get unity for each side of the equation and that you thus verify the theorem.

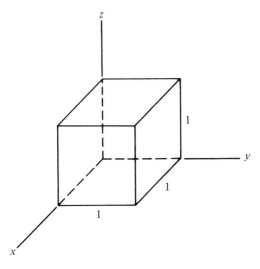

Figure P1.32

1.33. Apply Gauss' theorem to the volume integral

$$\iiint_D \left[\frac{\partial}{\partial x_i} \left(\phi \frac{\partial \psi}{\partial x_i} \right) \right] dv$$

where ϕ and ψ are scalars, and thereby derive *Green's identity*

$$\iiint_D \phi \nabla^2 \psi \, dv = \oiint \phi \frac{\partial \psi}{\partial \nu} dA - \iiint_D \operatorname{grad} \phi \cdot \operatorname{grad} \psi \, dv$$

Note that the directional derivative $\partial \psi / \partial \nu$ is equal to $\nabla \psi \cdot \hat{\nu}$.

1.34. Using the domain of Problem 1.32, demonstrate the divergence theorem for vector field **V**,

$$\mathbf{V} = x^2 y \,\hat{\mathbf{i}} + 3xz \,\hat{\mathbf{j}}$$

1.35. Verify Eq. (1.74). (*Hint:* First write out this equation for the given infinitesimal rectangular element, and carry out *one* of the two integrations for each term on the right-hand side of the equation.)

1.36. Derive Eq. (1.82), which is Stokes' theorem for a tensor field $T_{klm...}$. Use the approach that was employed in the text to obtain Stokes' theorem for a vector field. Also, explain how Eq. (1.82) generalizes to Eq. (1.83) for the case of multiply connected domains.

Chapter 2
Stress

2.1 FORCE DISTRIBUTIONS

In the study of continuous media, we are concerned with the manner in which forces are transmitted through the medium. At this time we set forth two classes of forces that will concern us. The first is the *body-force* distribution distinguished by the fact that it acts directly on the distribution of matter in the domain of specification. Accordingly, it is represented as a function of position and time and will be denoted as $\mathbf{B}(x, y, z, t)$ or as $B_i(x_1, x_2, x_3, t)$. The body-force distribution is an *intensity* function and is generally evaluated per unit mass or per unit volume of the material. We shall use the latter definition and thus the force $\mathbf{df}$ acting on a volume element dv is given as

$$\mathbf{df} = \mathbf{B}\, dv \qquad \text{or} \qquad df_i = B_i\, dv \tag{2.1}$$

As is commonly done, we assume that there are no distributed body couples.

In discussing a continuum, there may be some apparent physical boundary that encloses the domain of interest such as, for example, the outer surface of a beam. On the other hand, we may elect to specify a domain of interest and thereby generate a "mathematical" boundary. In either case we will be concerned with the force distribution that is applied to such boundaries directly from material outside the domain of interest. We call such force distributions *surface tractions* and denote them as $\mathbf{T}(x, y, z, t)$ or $T_i(x_1, x_2, x_3, t)$ with $\mathbf{T}$ or T_i denoted as the *traction* vector. The traction vector is again an intensity given per unit area. Thus we can say for $\mathbf{dF}$ on an area element

$$\mathbf{dF} = \mathbf{T}\, dA \qquad \text{or} \qquad dF_i = T_i\, dA \tag{2.2}$$

As is the usual practice, we assume that no couple traction vectors act on the area element dA, so we exclude traction couple distributions.

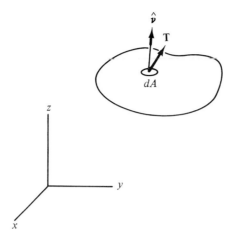

Figure 2.1 Traction force vector.

Note that **T** need not be normal to the area element, so this vector and the unit outward normal vector $\hat{\boldsymbol{\nu}}$ may have any orientation whatever relative to each other (see Fig. 2.1). We have not brought the unit normal $\hat{\boldsymbol{\nu}}$ into consideration thus far, but we will find it useful, as we proceed, to build into the notation for surface traction a superscript referring to the *direction of the area element at the point of application* of the surface traction. Thus we will give the traction vector as

$$\mathbf{T}^{(\nu)}(x, y, z, t) \qquad \text{or} \qquad T_i^{(\nu)}(x_1, x_2, x_3, t) \qquad (2.3)$$

where (ν) is not to be considered as a power. If the area element has the unit normal in the x direction, we would express the traction vector as $T_i^{(x)}$ or $T_i^{(1)}$ in index notation and as $\mathbf{T}^{(x)}$ or $\mathbf{T}^{(1)}$ in vector notation. In the following section we show how we can use the superscript to good advantage.

2.2 STRESS

Consider now a vanishingly small rectangular parallelepiped taken at some time t from a continuum. Choose a reference x, y, z so as to be parallel to the edges of this rectangular parallelepiped, as has been shown in Fig. 2.2. We have shown surface tractions on three rectangular boundary surfaces of the body. Note that we have employed the superscript to identify the surfaces. The Cartesian components of the traction vector $\mathbf{T}^{(x)}$ (or $T_i^{(x)}$) on an interface having a normal in the x direction are denoted as τ_{xx}, τ_{xy}, and τ_{xz}. This is shown in Fig. 2.3. The reader will immediately realize from the diagram that the orthogonal components of the traction vector on a face are the familiar *stresses* on that face. Thus we can say for each of the three faces shown in Fig. 2.3:

$$\mathbf{T}^{(x)} = \tau_{xx}\,\hat{\mathbf{i}} + \tau_{xy}\,\hat{\mathbf{j}} + \tau_{xx}\,\hat{\mathbf{k}}$$
$$\mathbf{T}^{(y)} = \tau_{yx}\,\hat{\mathbf{i}} + \tau_{yy}\,\hat{\mathbf{j}} + \tau_{yz}\,\hat{\mathbf{k}} \qquad (2.4)$$
$$\mathbf{T}^{(z)} = \tau_{zx}\,\hat{\mathbf{i}} + \tau_{zy}\,\hat{\mathbf{j}} + \tau_{zz}\,\hat{\mathbf{k}}$$

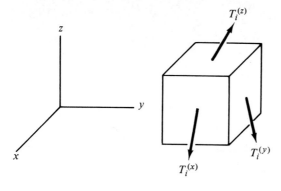

Figure 2.2 Traction vectors.

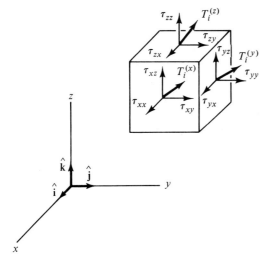

Figure 2.3 Traction vectors and their stress components.

The use of two subscripts for the stresses will now be explained. The first subscript identifies the coordinate which is normal to the area on which the stress acts. The second subscript identifies the coordinate direction of the stress itself. Thus τ_{yz} acts on an interface whose normal is in the plus or minus y direction, while the stress itself acts in the plus or minus z direction. It should be clear that stresses with two different indices, such as τ_{yz}, are shear stresses, while those with repeated indices such as τ_{xx} are normal stresses.

As for the sign convention, we say that stresses having the area normal and the stress direction *both* in either positive coordinate directions or negative coordinate directions are *positive* stresses. The coordinate directions need not be the same—only the signs must be the same. Thus, in Fig. 2.3 the stress τ_{xz} has an area normal in the positive x direction, while the stress is in the positive z direction and is, according to our sign convention, positive. If the directions for the area normal for τ_{xz} were in the negative x direction and the stress itself in the negative z direction, the stress τ_{xz} would still be positive. As for normal stresses, it clearly follows that tensile stresses are positive whereas compressive stresses are negative.

We can now go back to Eq. (2.3) and rewrite it in the following way:

$$\lim_{\delta A \to 0} \frac{\delta \mathbf{F}}{\delta A} = \mathbf{T}^{(\nu)} \tag{2.5}$$

Using rectangular components of $\mathbf{F}$ and choosing the area element to have a normal in the x direction, we may say that

$$\lim_{\delta A_x \to 0} \frac{\delta F_x}{\delta A_x} = [T^{(x)}]_x = \tau_{xx}$$

$$\lim_{\delta A_x \to 0} \frac{\delta F_y}{\delta A_x} = [T^{(x)}]_y = \tau_{xy} \tag{2.6}$$

$$\lim_{\delta A_x \to 0} \frac{\delta F_z}{\delta A_x} = [T^{(x)}]_z = \tau_{xz}$$

Using faces δA_y and δA_z at the same point as δA_x, we can generate the other six stresses for three orthogonal interfaces at a point. We shall soon show that nine stresses on a set of orthogonal interfaces at a point determine three orthogonal stresses for *any* interface at the point. In Chapter 1 we have expressed the nine stresses shown in Fig. 2.3 as the following matrix array:

$$\begin{bmatrix} \tau_{xx} & \tau_{xy} & \tau_{xz} \\ \tau_{yx} & \tau_{yy} & \tau_{yz} \\ \tau_{zx} & \tau_{zy} & \tau_{zz} \end{bmatrix} \equiv \begin{bmatrix} \tau_{11} & \tau_{12} & \tau_{13} \\ \tau_{21} & \tau_{22} & \tau_{23} \\ \tau_{31} & \tau_{32} & \tau_{33} \end{bmatrix} \equiv \tau_{ij} \tag{2.7}$$

where the first subscript gives the row and the second subscript gives the column. Note that the normal stresses form the main diagonal of the matrix. The nine stresses mentioned in Eq. (2.4) can now be expressed as τ_{ij} and the definitive equations (2.6) can be written as follows:

$$\tau_{ij} = \lim_{\delta A_i \to 0} \frac{\delta F_j}{\delta A_i} \tag{2.8}$$

It is now clear why the sign of τ_{ij} is given by the ratio of the signs of δF_j and δA_i. Furthermore, we see that the stresses and traction vector components are related by

$$\tau_{ij} = [T^{(i)}]_j \tag{2.9}$$

It must be emphasized that the concept of stress is not restricted to solids. Our conclusions here and indeed throughout the entire chapter are valid for any continuous medium, as long as these conclusions are applied to the *current deformed state*. In the special case of *small deformation* of a solid, the force δF_j and the area δA_i may correspond to the *original undeformed state* when defining stress without appreciably affecting the accuracy of the results. (The concept of small deformation will be discussed further in the next chapter.) However, for a fluid or for a solid undergoing large (finite) deformation, we must interpret the results in this chapter as being valid only for the current deformed state. If one wishes in such cases to employ for convenience the original undeformed state or some mix of original and deformed states, then clearly the stress along with associated equations must take on other interpretations and forms. Finally, we point out that the limiting processes involved in computing the intensity functions B_i and T_i may be performed with more general volume and area elements than the simple rectangular parallelepipeds and rectangles used in this chapter. For such considerations, the reader is referred to books on continuum mechanics.[*]

In the next section we shall see that knowing nine stresses on three orthogonal interfaces at a point, we can find stresses on *any* interface at the point by using certain simple transformation equations. Therefore, specifying stress distributions for interfaces parallel to a set of Cartesian coordinates is tantamount to specifying all stresses throughout a body.

2.3 TRANSFORMATION EQUATIONS FOR STRESS

Let us consider a small tetrahedron of a continuous medium as shown in Fig. 2.4. The orthogonal edges of the tetrahedron are of length Δx, Δy, and Δz, respectively. Positive shear and normal stresses have been shown on the faces parallel to the reference planes. On the inclined surface whose unit normal vector has been indicated as $\hat{\nu}$, we have shown the normal stress $\tau_{\nu\nu}$ and the total shear stress $\tau_{\nu\mu}$. It is convenient to denote the direction cosines of $\hat{\nu}$ with respect to the x, y, and z axes as $a_{\nu x}$, $a_{\nu y}$, and $a_{\nu z}$, respectively. Clearly, in this double-subscript notation, the first letter identifies the axis whose direction is being denoted and the second subscript gives the particular coordinate axis for the direction cosine desired. With this

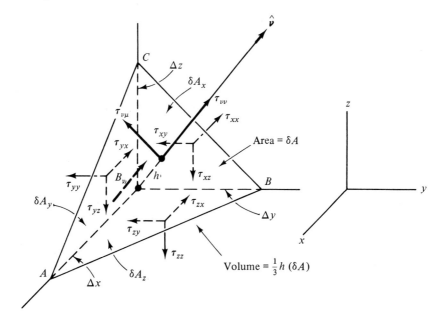

Figure 2.4 Stresses on a tetrahedron.

[*]For example, see L. E. Malvern, *Introduction to the Mechanics of a Continuous Medium* (Englewood Cliffs, NJ: Prentice Hall, Inc., 1969), pp. 70 and 220.

notation, we now express the areas of the coordinate faces (negative) of the tetra-hedron in terms of the area of the inclined face (positive) ABC, whose area we denote as δA, in the following manner:

$$\delta A_x = -\delta A\, a_{\nu x}$$

$$\delta A_y = -\delta A\, a_{\nu y} \tag{2.10}$$

$$\delta A_z = -\delta A\, a_{\nu z}$$

Next, we write Newton's law in the direction of $\hat{\nu}$. Thus

$$\tau_{\nu\nu}\,\delta A \; - \tau_{xx}|\delta A_x|a_{\nu x} - \tau_{xy}|\delta A_x|a_{\nu y} - \tau_{xz}|\delta A_x|a_{\nu z}$$
$$- \tau_{yx}|\delta A_y|a_{\nu x} - \tau_{yy}|\delta A_y|a_{\nu y} - \tau_{yz}|\delta A_y|a_{\nu z} \tag{2.11}$$
$$- \tau_{zx}|\delta A_z|a_{\nu x} - \tau_{zy}|\delta A_z|a_{\nu y} - \tau_{zz}|\delta A_z|a_{\nu z}$$
$$+ B_\nu \tfrac{1}{3}h(\delta A) = \rho \tfrac{1}{3}h(\delta A)\alpha_\nu$$

where B_ν is the body-force intensity in the $\hat{\nu}$ direction and α_ν is the acceleration of the center of mass in the $\hat{\nu}$ direction. Furthermore, h is the altitude of the tetra-hedron as shown in Fig. 2.4. Note that we have arranged the stresses in Eq. (2.11) in a form resembling a matrix array for ease in remembering the equation. Now replace $|\delta A_x|$, $|\delta A_y|$, and $|\delta A_z|$ using Eqs. (2.10) and then divide through by δA; finally, take the limit as the tetrahedron shrinks to zero size, while $\hat{\nu}$ maintains a fixed direction. Noting that $h \to 0$, thus eliminating the last two expressions, we have

$$\tau_{\nu\nu} = \tau_{xx}a_{\nu x}^2 \quad + \tau_{xy}a_{\nu x}a_{\nu y} + \tau_{xz}a_{\nu x}a_{\nu z} +$$
$$\tau_{yx}a_{\nu y}a_{\nu x} + \tau_{yy}a_{\nu y}^2 \quad + \tau_{yz}a_{\nu y}a_{\nu z} + \tag{2.12}$$
$$\tau_{zx}a_{\nu z}a_{\nu x} + \tau_{zy}a_{\nu z}a_{\nu y} + \tau_{zz}a_{\nu z}^2$$

Again, we point out that the sum of terms on the right side of the equation above has been arranged to form a simple array resembling a matrix array. We see that the normal stress on any plane at a point depends only on the stresses on an orthogonal set of planes at the point and the direction cosines associated with the desired nor-mal stress, where these direction cosines are measured relative to coordinate axes parallel to the aforementioned set of orthogonal planes.

We now proceed to compute shear stress on the inclined surface ABC of the tetrahedron by a similar computation as was performed for the normal stress. Accordingly, in Fig. 2.5 we have shown the tetrahedron with shear stress $\tau_{\nu\mu}$ on the inclined face. The direction cosines for $\hat{\mu}$ are $a_{\mu x}$, $a_{\mu y}$, and $a_{\mu z}$. Since $\tau_{\nu\nu}$ and $\tau_{\nu\mu}$ are at right angles to each other, the following equation must be satisfied by the two sets of direction cosines:

$$a_{\mu x}a_{\nu x} + a_{\mu y}a_{\nu y} + a_{\mu z}a_{\nu z} = 0 \tag{2.13}$$

If we now write Newton's law in the direction $\hat{\mu}$ of the shear stress, we may proceed in a manner paralleling the development of Eq. (2.12) to form the following equa-tion:

$$\tau_{\nu\mu} = \tau_{xx}\, a_{\nu x}\, a_{\mu x} + \tau_{xy}\, a_{\nu x}\, a_{\mu y} + \tau_{xz}\, a_{\nu x}\, a_{\mu z} +$$

$$\tau_{yx}\, a_{\nu y}\, a_{\mu x} + \tau_{yy}\, a_{\nu y}\, a_{\mu y} + \tau_{yz}\, a_{\nu y}\, a_{\mu z} + \qquad (2.14)$$

$$\tau_{zx}\, a_{\nu z}\, a_{\mu x} + \tau_{zy}\, a_{\nu z}\, a_{\mu y} + \tau_{zz}\, a_{\nu z}\, a_{\mu z}$$

Transformation equations (2.12) and (2.14) thus permit us to compute all stresses at a point provided that we know the nine stresses on a set of orthogonal faces at the point. You will recall that a vector quantity requires the specification of only three components at a point. The concept of stress, obviously, is more complicated.

We use subscripts ν and μ to represent normal and tangential directions, respectively, to an area interface as has been indicated in Fig. 2.5 for the corresponding unit vectors $\hat{\boldsymbol{\nu}}$ and $\hat{\boldsymbol{\mu}}$. Nevertheless, for Eqs. (2.12) and (2.14) one may consider ν and μ to represent coordinate axes $x_{1'}, x_{2'}, x_{3'}$ rotated relative to x_1, x_2, x_3 as if ν and μ were free indices of these axes. By considering all possible combinations of such primed axes, we may generate three equations from Eq. (2.12) and six equations from Eq. (2.14). We shall use primed free indices i', j' to represent ν and μ in this regard in accordance with the rules we have set forth in Chapter 1 for notation of indices. Accordingly, we can replace Eqs. (2.12) and (2.14) by the single equation

$$\tau_{i'j'} = a_{i'l}\, a_{j'n}\, \tau_{ln} \qquad (2.15)$$

We can now state as a result of Eq. (2.15) that stress is a second-order tensor. In addition to the stress tensor, we shall also find in Chapter 3 that strain is a tensor. And in the study of rigid-body dynamics, one deals with the inertia tensor. Because these quantities change in a certain way when we transform coordinates at a point, they have certain distinct characteristics that set them apart from other quantities. We shall shortly investigate some of these properties for stress.

In the next section we shall again consider a tetrahedron—this time the tetrahedron will be at the boundary of a body.

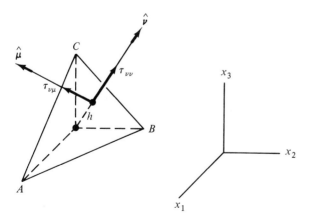

Figure 2.5 Tetrahedron with stresses $\tau_{\nu\nu}$ and $\tau_{\nu\mu}$.

2.4 CAUCHY'S FORMULA

We have used the notation $a_{\nu x}, a_{\nu y}, a_{\nu z}$ for direction cosines in preceding sections. In this section we use the components of the unit vector $\hat{\boldsymbol{\nu}}$ (i.e., ν_x, ν_y, and ν_z or ν_1, ν_2, and ν_3) as direction cosines (clearly, $a_{\nu x} \equiv \nu_x$, $a_{\nu y} \equiv \nu_y$, and $a_{\nu z} \equiv \nu_z$).

Let us again consider a tetrahedron of small size where now the inclined face ABC is at the boundary of a body (see Fig. 2.6). Note that we have shown the traction vector $T_i^{(\nu)}$ and its orthogonal components on face ABC. The other orthogonal faces of the tetrahedron are inside the boundary of the body proper. On these inside faces, nine stress components have been shown. We now express Newton's law in the x_1 direction,

$$T_1^{(\nu)} \, \delta A - \tau_{11} |\delta A_1| - \tau_{21} |\delta A_2| - \tau_{31} |\delta A_3| + B_1 \frac{h}{3} \, \delta A = \frac{\rho h}{3} \, \delta A \, \alpha_1 \qquad (2.16)$$

where B_1 and α_1 are, respectively, the components of body force and acceleration in the x_1 direction. Now using Eqs. (2.10) to replace the area components δA_1, δA_2, and δA_3, and shrinking the volume element to zero size, we note that the last two terms vanish in the limit. We now have for the equation above, on canceling δA,

$$T_1^{(\nu)} = \tau_{11} \, \nu_1 + \tau_{21} \, \nu_2 + \tau_{31} \, \nu_3 \qquad (2.17)$$

For any coordinate direction i, rather than coordinate direction x_1, we can say

$$T_i^{(\nu)} = \tau_{1i} \, \nu_1 + \tau_{2i} \, \nu_2 + \tau_{3i} \, \nu_3 \qquad (2.18)$$

Finally, using a set of dummy indices, we can express Eq.(2.18) as

$$\boxed{T_i^{(\nu)} = \tau_{ji} \, \nu_j} \qquad (2.19)$$

This is the *Cauchy formula*. It may be considered a boundary condition. We shall shortly show that the stress tensor is symmetric, so with $\tau_{ij} = \tau_{ji}$, Cauchy's formula can then be given as

$$\boxed{T_i^{(\nu)} = \tau_{ij} \, \nu_j} \qquad (2.20)$$

As you will soon see, this formula plays an important role in solid mechanics.*

2.5 EQUATIONS OF MOTION

Consider an element of the body of mass dm occupying volume dv at any point P. A velocity field $\mathbf{V}$ describes the instantaneous velocity of all elements in the body.

---

*Although we used the traction force on the *surface* of a body, the resulting equation (2.20) can be used equally as well to give the traction force on *any interface* at a point in terms of the orthogonal stresses at this point. Furthermore, since $T_i^{(\nu)}$ and ν_j are vectors, the application of the quotient rule (see Problem 1.13) to Eq. (2.20) confirms our previous observation that τ_{ij} is a second-order tensor.

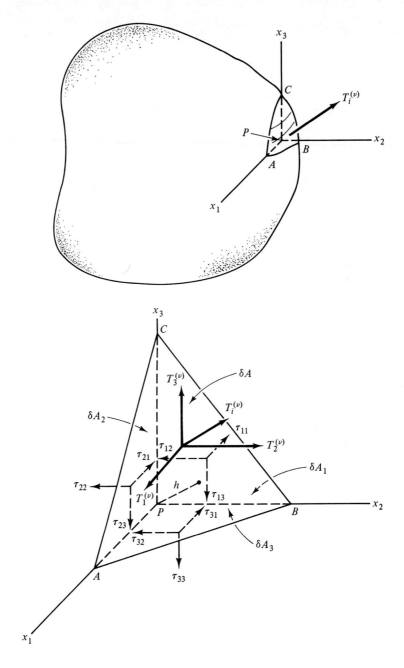

Figure 2.6 Tetrahedron at the boundary.

As you learned in fluid mechanics,[*] we can give Newton's law in the deformed state as

$$\mathbf{dF}_t + \mathbf{dF}_b = dm\,\frac{D\mathbf{V}}{Dt} \equiv dm\left[\frac{\partial \mathbf{V}}{\partial t} + \left(V_x\,\frac{\partial \mathbf{V}}{\partial x} + V_y\,\frac{\partial \mathbf{V}}{\partial y} + V_z\,\frac{\partial \mathbf{V}}{\partial z}\right)\right] \qquad (2.21)$$

where $\mathbf{dF}_t$ is the total traction force on the element and $\mathbf{dF}_b$ is the total body force on the element. You will recall that $D\mathbf{V}/Dt$ is the so-called *substantial* derivative or the *material* derivative. For small deformation, the particle of mass dm will not move substantially, so the expression $V_x\,\partial\mathbf{V}/\partial x + V_y\,\partial\mathbf{V}/\partial y + V_z\,\partial\mathbf{V}/\partial z$, called the *acceleration of transport,* will be small compared to $\partial\mathbf{V}/\partial t$, which is the *local* acceleration. For such cases we will retain only $\partial\mathbf{V}/\partial t$ and denote it simply as $\dot{\mathbf{V}}$. Integrating the equation above over some arbitrary spatial domain having a volume D and a boundary surface S (see Fig. 2.7), we note as a result of Newton's third law that tractions $T_i^{(\nu)}$ cancel out everywhere except on the boundary surface S, and thus we have, using indicial notation,

$$\oint_S T_i^{(\nu)}\,dA + \iiint_D B_i\,dv = \iiint_D \frac{DV_i}{Dt}\,\rho\,dv \qquad (2.22)$$

where ρ is the mass density and B_i is the body force per unit volume. This equation is often called the "global" form of Newton's law, or Newton's law "in the large." Now employ Cauchy's formula [Eq. (2.19)] to relate the traction vector $T_i^{(\nu)}$ to the stresses. Thus

$$\oint_S \tau_{ji}\nu_j\,dA + \iiint_D B_i\,dv = \iiint_D \frac{DV_i}{Dt}\,\rho\,dv$$

Next, employ Gauss' theorem [see Eq. (1.66)] for the first integral and collect terms under one integral sign. We get

$$\iiint_D \left(\tau_{ji,j} + B_i - \frac{DV_i}{Dt}\,\rho\right)dv = 0$$

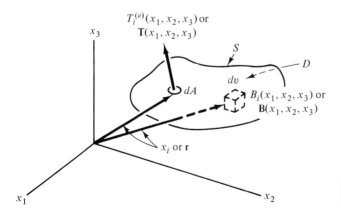

Figure 2.7 Traction and body force distributions.

[*] See I. H. Shames, *Mechanics of Fluids,* 2nd ed. (New York: McGraw-Hill Book Company, 1982), Sec. 4.3.

Stress   Chap. 2

Since the domain D is arbitrary,[†] we conclude from the above that at any point the following must hold:

$$\tau_{ji,j} + B_i = \rho \frac{DV_i}{Dt} \qquad (2.23)$$

These are equations of motion valid for any continua such as fluids and solids. They are often called the "local" form of the equations of motion, or the equations of motion "in the small." As previously indicated, all quantities refer to current deformed geometry. Thus τ_{ij} is computed using components of force (and area) in the current deformed geometry projected along coordinate axes for the current deformed geometry. Such coordinates are called *Eulerian* coordinates, and hence τ_{ij} here is called the *Eulerian stress tensor*. Also, $\tau_{ji,j}$ indicates differentiation with respect to these Eulerian coordinates.

Finally, we restrict ourselves to *small deformation* of a solid. As indicated earlier, we may replace DV_i/Dt for this case by $\partial V_i/\partial t$, the local acceleration, and use the undeformed geometry. And since we shall soon show that τ_{ij} is symmetric, we can also replace $\tau_{ji,j}$ by $\tau_{ij,j}$. We then have for the simplification of the previous equation using $\dot{V_i}$ to represent $\partial V_i/\partial t$:

$$\tau_{ij,j} + B_i = \rho \dot{V_i} \qquad (2.24)$$

We now have the desired equations of motion, which for $\dot{V_i} = 0$ are called the *equations of equilibrium*.

Suppose next that we consider the *moment of momentum* equation derivable from Newton's law. You will recall that for a particle of mass dm, this equation has the form

$$d\mathbf{M}_t + d\mathbf{M}_b = \mathbf{r} \times dm \frac{D\mathbf{V}}{Dt} \qquad (2.25)$$

where $d\mathbf{M}_t$ and $d\mathbf{M}_b$ are the total moments due to tractions and body forces, respectively, about a stationary point in inertial space. As in the preceding case, D/Dt is the material derivative. Integrating over the entire domain and using $\mathbf{T}^{(\nu)}$ and $\mathbf{B}$ (see Fig. 2.7), we have for the equation above in vector notation,

$$\oint_S \mathbf{r} \times \mathbf{T}^{(\nu)} \, dA + \iiint_D \mathbf{r} \times \mathbf{B} \, dv = \iiint_D \mathbf{r} \times \frac{D\mathbf{V}}{Dt} \rho \, dv \qquad (2.26)$$

where here the position vector $\mathbf{r}$ is directed from the fixed origin of axes x_1, x_2, x_3. Note that, as before, we assume that there are no body couple or traction couple distributions. If we restrict ourselves to *small deformation* of solids, the material derivative $D\mathbf{V}/Dt$ can be replaced by $\partial \mathbf{V}/\partial t \, (= \dot{\mathbf{V}})$. However, we shall not have to make

---

[†] By this we mean that this equation is valid not only for any domain D, but also for any subdomain of D.

this restriction in this discussion. Using Cartesian tensor notation, we shall now rewrite the preceding equation in the following manner:

$$\oint_S e_{ijk} x_j T_k^{(\nu)} dA + \iiint_D e_{ijk} x_j B_k dv = \iiint_D e_{ijk} x_j \frac{DV_k}{Dt} \rho \, dv \qquad (2.27)$$

Now replace $T_k^{(\nu)}$ by $\tau_{lk} \nu_l$ according to Cauchy's formula and then employ Gauss' theorem. The equation above may then be written as

$$\iiint_D e_{ijk} \left[(x_j \tau_{lk})_{,l} + x_j B_k - \rho x_j \frac{DV_k}{Dt} \right] dv = 0 \qquad (2.28)$$

Since the formulation above is true for any domain D, we can set the integrand equal to zero. Carrying out differentiation of the first expression in the bracket and collecting terms, we then get

$$e_{ijk} x_j \left[\tau_{lk,l} + B_k - \rho \frac{DV_k}{Dt} \right] + e_{ijk} x_{j,l} \tau_{lk} = 0$$

Because of Newton's law [Eq. (2.23)], we can set the first expression equal to zero, so we get

$$e_{ijk} x_{j,l} \tau_{lk} = 0 \qquad (2.29)$$

Noting that $x_{j,l} = \delta_{jl}$, we have

$$e_{ijk} \delta_{jl} \tau_{lk} = e_{ijk} \tau_{jk} = 0 \qquad (2.30)$$

Since e_{ijk} is *skew-symmetric* in jk and since the inner product over j and k of e_{ijk} and τ_{jk} is always equal to zero, then, as has been noted in Sec. 1.7, we can conclude that τ_{jk} must be *symmetric*. Thus we justify now the earlier assertion that

$$\boxed{\tau_{ij} = \tau_{ji}} \qquad (2.31)$$

This is the well-known *complementary property* of shear.

2.6 PRINCIPAL STRESSES

We have shown that given a system of stresses for an orthogonal set of interfaces at a point, we can associate a traction vector for interfaces having any direction in space according to Cauchy's formula,

$$T_i^{(\nu)} = \tau_{ij} \nu_j \qquad (2.32)$$

We now ask this question. Is there a direction $\hat{\nu}$ such that the traction vector is collinear with $\hat{\nu}$? That is, is there an interface having a normal such that there is only one nonzero stress—the normal stress? We shall call such a stress, if it exists, a principal stress and we shall denote it as τ (see Fig. 2.8). Thus we can express the equation above for this case as follows:

$$\tau \nu_i = \tau_{ij} \nu_j \qquad (2.33)$$

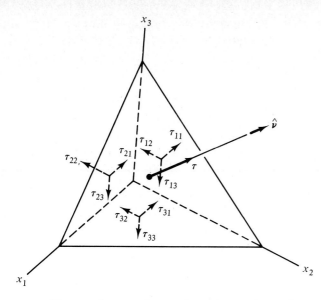

Figure 2.8 Tetrahedron showing principal stress.

Now replace $\tau \nu_i$ by $\tau \nu_j \delta_{ij}$ and rearrange the equation above to form the relation

$$(\tau_{ij} - \tau \delta_{ij}) \nu_j = 0 \qquad (2.34)$$

We have here three simultaneous equations stemming from Newton's law for the three unknowns ν_1, ν_2, and ν_3, but as we shall soon see only two are linearly independent. However, we also have another equation to be satisfied from geometry involving these direction cosines, namely the relation

$$\nu_i \nu_i = 1 \qquad (2.35)$$

We may satisfy Eq. (2.34) by setting ν_1, ν_2, and ν_3 equal to zero, but then we would violate Eq. (2.35). A nontrivial solution (i.e., the ν's are not *all* zero) to the set of equations (2.34) requires that

$$|\tau_{ij} - \tau \delta_{ij}| = 0 \qquad (2.36)$$

Expanded out, we get, since $\tau_{ij} = \tau_{ji}$,

$$\begin{vmatrix} \tau_{11} - \tau & \tau_{12} & \tau_{13} \\ \tau_{12} & \tau_{22} - \tau & \tau_{23} \\ \tau_{13} & \tau_{23} & \tau_{33} - \tau \end{vmatrix} = 0 \qquad (2.37)$$

Hence we have the cubic equation

$$\tau^3 - (\tau_{11} + \tau_{22} + \tau_{33}) \tau^2 + (\tau_{11} \tau_{22} + \tau_{22} \tau_{33} + \tau_{33} \tau_{11} - \tau_{12}^2$$
$$- \tau_{23}^2 - \tau_{13}^2) \tau - (\tau_{11} \tau_{22} \tau_{33} - \tau_{11} \tau_{23}^2 - \tau_{22} \tau_{13}^2 - \tau_{33} \tau_{12}^2 \qquad (2.38)$$
$$+ 2 \tau_{12} \tau_{23} \tau_{13}) = 0$$

We have three roots to this equation, which are the sought-for principal stresses and which we denote as τ_1, τ_2, and τ_3. One can prove that since τ_{ij} is symmetric and real, the principal stresses are all real. It is the usual practice to order the principal stresses such that algebraically $\tau_1 \geq \tau_2 \geq \tau_3$. We can associate for any root τ_j three direction cosines corresponding to the normal direction of the interface on which τ_j acts. We denote these direction cosines as $\overset{j}{\nu_1}$, $\overset{j}{\nu_2}$, and $\overset{j}{\nu_3}$. To determine these direction cosines, substitute the value τ_j into Eq. (2.34). In attempting to solve for the ν's from these equations, you will find that only two (any two) of these three equations are independent. This is a direct consequence of the fact that the determinant of the coefficient matrix is zero [see Eq. (2.36)]. A third independent equation that must be used is Eq. (2.35). We may generate three sets of direction cosines where each set is associated with a principal stress τ_j. We thus have

$$
\begin{aligned}
\tau_1 &\rightarrow \overset{1}{\nu_1},\ \overset{1}{\nu_2},\ \overset{1}{\nu_3}, \\
\tau_2 &\rightarrow \overset{2}{\nu_1},\ \overset{2}{\nu_2},\ \overset{2}{\nu_3}, \\
\tau_3 &\rightarrow \overset{3}{\nu_1},\ \overset{3}{\nu_2},\ \overset{3}{\nu_3},
\end{aligned}
\tag{2.39}
$$

where it can be shown that these three sets of direction cosines yield directions which are mutually orthogonal. It can also be shown that τ_1, τ_2, τ_3 are *extreme* values at a point, that is, τ_1 is the algebraically maximum normal stress, τ_3 is the algebraically minimum normal stress, and τ_2 is intermediate between these two extremes.[*]

We have found three orthogonal planes having only normal stress (i.e., on these planes there is zero shear stress). These planes are called *principal planes* and the normals to these planes are called *principal axes*. It is clear that the stresses on any plane are uniquely determined by the transformation equations (2.15) for *any* set of stresses τ_{ij} at the point under consideration. Thus had we used another set of stresses $\tau_{i'j'}$ for axes $x_{1'}, x_{2'}, x_{3'}$ rotated arbitrarily relative to x_1, x_2, x_3, we would arrive at the same principal stresses and the same principal axes as would be the case using reference x_1, x_2, x_3. This can occur only if the cubic equation (2.38) has unique values for the coefficients of τ^2, τ and for the remaining constant. That is, these values are invariant with respect to a rotation of axes at a point. These values, which we denote as I_τ, II_τ, and III_τ, are, respectively, called the *first*, *second*, and *third tensor invariants*. They are given as follows:

$$
\begin{aligned}
I_\tau &\equiv \tau_{11} + \tau_{22} + \tau_{33} \\
II_\tau &\equiv \tau_{11}\tau_{22} + \tau_{22}\tau_{33} + \tau_{33}\tau_{11} - \tau_{12}^2 - \tau_{23}^2 - \tau_{13}^2 \\
III_\tau &\equiv \tau_{11}\tau_{22}\tau_{33} - \tau_{11}\tau_{23}^2 - \tau_{22}\tau_{13}^2 - \tau_{33}\tau_{12}^2 + 2\tau_{12}\tau_{23}\tau_{13}
\end{aligned}
\tag{2.40}
$$

We may, of course, also compute these invariants for principal axes, in which case they are given simply as

$$
\begin{aligned}
I_\tau &= \tau_1 + \tau_2 + \tau_3 \\
II_\tau &= \tau_1\tau_2 + \tau_2\tau_3 + \tau_3\tau_1 \\
III_\tau &= \tau_1\tau_2\tau_3
\end{aligned}
\tag{2.41}
$$

[*]For proofs that the principal stresses are *real extrema* and that the principal directions are *orthogonal*, see I. H. Shames and C. L. Dym, *Energy and Finite Element Methods in Structural Mechanics* (New York: Hemisphere Publishing Corp., 1985), Sec. 1.6. These properties will also be demonstrated here in the next two sections on stress quadric surfaces and three-dimensional Mohr's circles.

The first tensor invariant is simply the sum of the elements along the left-to-right diagonal from τ_{11} to τ_{33}–the so-called principal diagonal. This sum is called the *trace* of the tensor and can be given in Cartesian tensor notation as

$$I_\tau = \tau_{ii} \tag{2.42}$$

The quantity $\tau_{ii}/3$ is called the *bulk stress*, $\bar{\tau}$. For the case of simple hydrostatic pressure, $\tau_{ij} = -p\delta_{ij}$ and $\bar{\tau}$ then reduces to $-p$. Thus the bulk stress is an extension of the concept of pressure applicable to the case of a general state of stress.* The second tensor invariant is the sum of three subdeterminants formed from the matrix representation of the stress tensor. These subdeterminants are the minors of the elements along the principal diagonal, so II_τ is the *sum of the principal minors*. Thus we have, since $\tau_{ij} = \tau_{ji}$,

$$II_\tau = \begin{vmatrix} \tau_{22} & \tau_{23} \\ \tau_{23} & \tau_{33} \end{vmatrix} + \begin{vmatrix} \tau_{11} & \tau_{13} \\ \tau_{13} & \tau_{33} \end{vmatrix} + \begin{vmatrix} \tau_{11} & \tau_{12} \\ \tau_{12} & \tau_{22} \end{vmatrix} \tag{2.43}$$

Finally, the third tensor invariant can be seen to be simply the *determinant* of the tensor itself. Thus

$$III_\tau = \begin{vmatrix} \tau_{11} & \tau_{12} & \tau_{13} \\ \tau_{12} & \tau_{22} & \tau_{23} \\ \tau_{13} & \tau_{23} & \tau_{33} \end{vmatrix} \tag{2.44}$$

In index notation, the second and third tensor invariants may be written as follows as a result of our work in Section 1.10:

$$II_\tau = \tfrac{1}{2} e_{imn} e_{ijk} \tau_{mj} \tau_{nk} = \tfrac{1}{2}(\tau_{ii}\tau_{jj} - \tau_{ij}\tau_{ji}) \qquad \text{(a)}$$

$$III_\tau = \tfrac{1}{6} e_{lmn} e_{ijk} \tau_{li} \tau_{mj} \tau_{nk} \tag{2.45}$$

$$= \tfrac{1}{6}(2\tau_{ij}\tau_{jk}\tau_{ki} - 3\tau_{ij}\tau_{ji}\tau_{kk} + \tau_{ii}\tau_{jj}\tau_{kk}) \qquad \text{(b)}$$

These tensor invariants to a great extent characterize a tensor just as the invariant length $V_i V_i$ of a vector characterizes a vector.

Example 2.1

Given the following state of stress, find the principal stresses and the principal axes:

$$\tau_{ij} = \begin{bmatrix} 200 & 100 & 300 \\ 100 & 0 & 0 \\ 300 & 0 & 0 \end{bmatrix} \quad \text{psi}$$

Using Eqs. (2.40), we first evaluate the three tensor invariants. Thus

$$I_\tau = 200 \text{ psi} \tag{a}$$

$$II_\tau = -100,000 \text{ (psi)}^2 \tag{b}$$

$$III_\tau = 0 \text{ (psi)}^3 \tag{c}$$

---

* Because natural phenomena proceed without the benefits of man-made reference axes, invariants such as these tensor invariants quite often mimic certain aspects of natural phenomena, as is the case here with pressure. Invariants as a consequence can be of singular importance, as we shall later see in abundance.

The cubic equation (2.38) then becomes

$$\tau^3 - 200\tau^2 - 100{,}000\tau = 0 \tag{d}$$

With the use of the quadratic formula, this may be expressed in terms of factors as

$$\tau(\tau - 432)(\tau + 232) = 0$$

The principal stresses arranged in algebraically descending order are thus

$$\tau_1 = 432 \text{ psi} \tag{e}$$

$$\tau_2 = 0 \text{ psi} \tag{f}$$

$$\tau_3 = -232 \text{ psi} \tag{g}$$

By substituting these stresses into Eqs. (2.41), we obtain values for I_τ, II_τ, III_τ, which check with Eqs. (a), (b), and (c).

To find the direction of the principal axis corresponding to τ_1, we go to Eq. (2.34) and substitute $\tau = 432$. Accordingly, we get

$$(200 - 432)\nu_1 + 100\nu_2 + 300\nu_3 = 0 \tag{h}$$

$$100\nu_1 + (0 - 432)\nu_2 + 0 = 0 \tag{i}$$

$$300\nu_1 + 0 + (0 - 432)\nu_3 = 0 \tag{j}$$

These equations, as pointed out earlier, are not independent. We may use any two of these equations plus Eq. (2.35) to form a complete set for determining the ν's. Thus, using the last two of the equations above and the equation

$$\nu_1^2 + \nu_2^2 + \nu_3^2 = 1 \tag{k}$$

we may solve for the direction cosines. That is, we use Eqs. (i) and (j) to find ν_2/ν_1 and ν_3/ν_1, and then substitute these ratios into Eq. (k) to determine ν_1. Accordingly, we get

$$\overset{1}{\nu}_1 = 0.806 \tag{ℓ}$$

$$\overset{1}{\nu}_2 = 0.187 \tag{m}$$

$$\overset{1}{\nu}_3 = 0.560 \tag{n}$$

Note that $\overset{1}{\nu}_1 = -0.806$, $\overset{1}{\nu}_2 = -0.187$, and $\overset{1}{\nu}_3 = -0.560$ is also a valid solution. We may similarly determine the direction cosines for $\tau_2 = 0$ and $\tau_3 = -232$. We leave this task and the demonstration that the three principal axes are mutually orthogonal to the reader. The signs for the direction cosines may be chosen to give a variety of acceptable combinations, with the condition that the chosen combination yield a *right-handed* set of principal axes.

Returning to Eq. (2.38) and using invariants I_τ, II_τ, and III_τ, we have

$$\tau^3 - I_\tau\tau^2 + II_\tau\tau - III_\tau = 0 \tag{2.46}$$

which can be thought of as three equations in τ_1, τ_2, and τ_3, respectively. We now introduce a boldface symbol underscored with a bar, $\underline{\boldsymbol{\tau}}$, as the symbolic notation for the stress tensor. Noting that

$$\underline{\boldsymbol{\tau}} = \begin{bmatrix} \tau_1 & 0 & 0 \\ 0 & \tau_2 & 0 \\ 0 & 0 & \tau_3 \end{bmatrix}$$

we may use this symbolic notation to express the three equations represented by Eq. (2.46) as a single *tensor equation* by virtue of Eq. (1.63). Denoting the unitary matrix (which you will recall is the symbolic equivalent of δ_{ij}) as **I**, we have

$$\boldsymbol{\tau}^3 - I_\tau \boldsymbol{\tau}^2 + II_\tau \boldsymbol{\tau} - III_\tau \mathbf{I} = 0 \qquad (2.47)$$

This important result is called the *Cayley–Hamilton* theorem. It enables us to express $\boldsymbol{\tau}^3$ in terms of $\boldsymbol{\tau}^2$, $\boldsymbol{\tau}$, and **I**. Furthermore, it is readily shown that it is valid also for $\boldsymbol{\tau}$ computed for nonprincipal axes. This theorem also permits us to express $\boldsymbol{\tau}^4$ in terms of $\boldsymbol{\tau}^2$, $\boldsymbol{\tau}$, and **I**. To do this, multiply Eq. (2.47) by $\boldsymbol{\tau}$ and eliminate $\boldsymbol{\tau}^3$ using Eq. (2.47). Rearranging the terms, we may obtain the desired formulation for $\boldsymbol{\tau}^4$ in terms of $\boldsymbol{\tau}^2$, $\boldsymbol{\tau}$, and the stress invariants. Thus

$$\boldsymbol{\tau}^4 = (I_\tau^2 - II_\tau)\boldsymbol{\tau}^2 - (I_\tau II_\tau - III_\tau)\boldsymbol{\tau} + I_\tau III_\tau \mathbf{I} \qquad (2.48)$$

Continuing this process, we can express $\boldsymbol{\tau}^n$ for $n \geq 3$ as a linear combination of $\boldsymbol{\tau}^2$, $\boldsymbol{\tau}$, and **I** with the coefficients being polynomials in I_τ, II_τ, and III_τ. These results are of singular importance for the development of three-dimensional, nonlinear constitutive laws.

We now conclude this section by introducing the symmetric, *deviator* tensor defined for stress as

$$\boxed{s_{ij} = \tau_{ij} - \tfrac{1}{3}\tau_{kk}\,\delta_{ij}} \qquad (2.49)$$

The stress deviator tensor has important physical significance, especially when considering plastic and viscoelastic material. The tensor invariants for s_{ij} now simplify considerably.* We get, using the notation I_s, II_s, and III_s for these invariants,

$$I_s = \operatorname{tr}\mathbf{S} = s_{ii} = 0 \qquad \text{(a)}$$

$$II_s = -\tfrac{1}{2}\operatorname{tr}(\mathbf{S}^2) = -\tfrac{1}{2}s_{ij}s_{ji} \qquad \text{(b)} \qquad (2.50)$$

$$III_s = \tfrac{1}{3}\operatorname{tr}(\mathbf{S}^3) = \tfrac{1}{3}s_{ij}s_{jk}s_{ki} \qquad \text{(c)}$$

where the boldface block letter **S** is the symbolic notation for the stress deviator tensor, and tr indicates the trace. Accordingly, Eq. (2.48) and the equations for higher powers will have much simpler polynomial coefficients when dealing with the deviatoric stress tensor s_{ij}. We shall be able to take advantage of this kind of simplification when we get to our study of nonlinear constitutive laws.

2.7 THE STRESS QUADRIC SURFACES

Now consider the variations of the normal stress $\tau_{\nu\nu}$ as the direction $\hat{\boldsymbol{\nu}}$ is varied at a point to cover all directions (Fig. 2.9). Using Cauchy's formula, we have

$$T_i^{(\nu)}\nu_i = \tau_{\nu\nu} = \tau_{ij}\,\nu_i\,\nu_j \qquad (2.51)$$

---

*Note that even though we worked with stress in developing the tensor invariants, these results apply to any symmetric, second-order tensor.

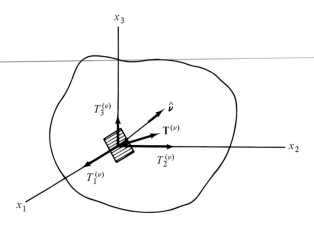

Figure 2.9 Arbitrary interface.

For convenience we lay off, using a second reference with dimensionless coordinates ξ_1, ξ_2, ξ_3, a distance $\overline{OA}$ along the same direction $\hat{\nu}$ (see Fig. 2.10) such that

$$(\overline{OA})^2 = \frac{\pm d^2}{\tau_{\nu\nu}} \tag{2.52}$$

where d^2 is an arbitrary constant with the dimensions of stress. The plus sign obviously must be used if $\tau_{\nu\nu}$ is positive (i.e., tensile stress) and the negative sign is used when $\tau_{\nu\nu}$ is negative (compression). We can then give the direction cosines ν_i as

$$\nu_i = \frac{\xi_i}{\overline{OA}} = \frac{\xi_i}{\sqrt{\pm d^2/\tau_{\nu\nu}}} \tag{2.53}$$

where ξ_i is a dimensionless position vector of magnitude $\overline{OA}$ along the direction ν_i. Hence Eq. (2.51) can be given as

$$\tau_{\nu\nu} = \tau_{ij} \frac{\xi_i \xi_j}{\pm d^2/\tau_{\nu\nu}} \tag{2.54}$$

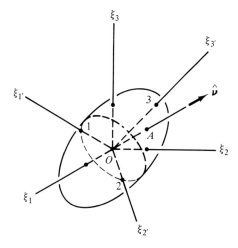

$$\overline{O3} > \overline{O2} > \overline{O1}$$

Figure 2.10 Stress ellipsoid.

Stress   Chap. 2

Canceling $\tau_{\nu\nu}$, we get the following result on rearranging terms in Eq. (2.54):

$$\xi_i \xi_j \tau_{ij} = \tau_{11} \xi_1^2 + \tau_{22} \xi_2^2 + \tau_{33} \xi_3^2 + 2\tau_{12} \xi_1 \xi_2 + 2\tau_{23} \xi_2 \xi_3 + 2\tau_{31} \xi_3 \xi_1 = \pm d^2. \quad (2.55)$$

For a particular choice of sign of $\pm d^2$, the above represents a real second-order surface in a particular region of ξ_1, ξ_2, ξ_3. We call this surface the *stress quadric*. The distance from the origin to this surface in some direction $\hat{\boldsymbol{v}}$ is inversely proportional to the square root of the normal stress $\tau_{\nu\nu}$ [see Eq. (2.52)] for the same direction $\hat{\boldsymbol{v}}$ in physical space reference x_1, x_2, x_3.

The nature of the stress quadric surface depends on the signs of the principal stresses τ_1, τ_2, τ_3. For instance, with τ_1, τ_2, and τ_3 all positive, $+d^2$ in Eq. (2.55) gives the only real surface–that of an ellipsoid as has been shown in Fig. 2.10. It is apparent that for the three symmetrical semiaxes $(\xi_{1'}, \xi_{2'}, \xi_{3'})$ the distances from origin to surface are local extrema. These directions correspond to the principal axes, since for these axes the product terms $2\tau_{1'2'} \xi_{1'} \xi_{2'}$, $2\tau_{2'3'} \xi_{2'} \xi_{3'}$, and $2\tau_{3'1'} \xi_{3'} \xi_{1'}$ in Eq. (2.55) must vanish. Since one of these distances $(\overline{O3})$ is a maximum for the ellipsoid, the corresponding principal stress must be the minimum normal stress, τ_3, at the point in the body; and since the distance $(\overline{O1})$ is a minimum for the ellipsoid, the corresponding normal stress must be the maximum normal stress, τ_1, at the point in the body. The third principal stress, τ_2, corresponding to direction $(\overline{O2})$ must then have some intermediate value such that the sum of the principal stresses gives the proper first tensor invariant at the point in the body. For τ_1, τ_2, τ_3 all negative we must choose the minus sign with d^2, and the stress quadric is again an ellipsoid.

Other kinds of second-order surfaces are possible if the signs of τ_1, τ_2, τ_3 are not all positive or all negative. Thus for the particular case where $\tau_1 \geq \tau_2 > 0, \tau_3 < 0$ we get the hyperboloidal surfaces shown in Fig. 2.11 where $+d^2$ is needed in Eq.

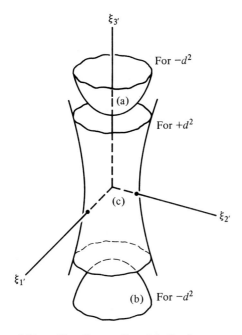

Figure 2.11 Quadric Surfaces.

(2.55) to generate surface (c) as a real surface and where $-d^2$ is needed in Eq. (2.55) to generate (a) and (b) as real surfaces. The stress for any direction is found by measuring $\overline{OA}$ for that direction, and employing Eq. (2.52) using the same sign with d^2 as is associated with that part of the surface intercepted by $\overline{OA}$. Thus the proper sign of $\tau_{\nu\nu}$ is then determined in Eq. (2.52) for that direction. The earlier conclusion that the largest (algebraically) normal stress and the smallest (algebraically) normal stress at a point are principal stresses still holds.

We will not formally use the so-called stress quadric. However, it does serve as a graphical representation of stress (or any other second-order symmetric tensor) just as an arrow is a graphical representation of a vector.

It should be clearly understood that the main ingredient in arriving at the conclusions in the preceding two sections was the fact that stress transforms according to the formula

$$\tau_{i'j'} = a_{i'l} a_{j'm} \tau_{lm} \tag{2.56}$$

and the fact that $\tau_{ij} = \tau_{ji}$. Thus all the conclusions made concerning principal stresses, tensor invariants, and so on, apply to any second-order symmetric tensor. We shall make ample use of these results in studies to follow.

2.8 THREE-DIMENSIONAL MOHR'S CIRCLES

You have all studied Mohr's circle for plane stress, plane strain, and moments and products of area in your earlier courses.* We now present the three-dimensional Mohr's circles.

Consider a tetrahedron in a body (see Fig. 2.12) whose orthogonal faces correspond to principal stresses τ_1, τ_2, and τ_3, where $\tau_1 \geq \tau_2 \geq \tau_3$. On face ABC, whose unit normal vector is $\hat{\nu}$ we have shown the traction vector $T_i^{(\nu)}$, the normal stress $\tau_{\nu\nu}$, and the resultant shear stress $\tau_{\nu\mu}$. From the *Pythagorean* theorem and *Cauchy's* formula, we can respectively write

$$T_i^{(\nu)} T_i^{(\nu)} = \tau_{\nu\nu}^2 + \tau_{\nu\mu}^2 = (\tau_{ij}\nu_j)(\tau_{ik}\nu_k) = \tau_1^2 \nu_x^2 + \tau_2^2 \nu_y^2 + \tau_3^2 \nu_z^2$$

and

$$\tau_{\nu\nu}^2 + \tau_{\nu\mu}^2 = \tau_1^2 \nu_x^2 + \tau_2^2 \nu_y^2 + \tau_3^2 \nu_z^2 \tag{2.57}$$

We have the first of three equations that we will present involving stresses $\tau_{\nu\nu}, \tau_{\nu\mu}$ on face ABC with unit normal vector $\hat{\nu}$ for a state of stress with principal stresses τ_1, τ_2, and τ_3. The second equation comes from *geometry*, for which we say that

$$\nu_x^2 + \nu_y^2 + \nu_z^2 = 1 \tag{2.58}$$

Finally, from the general *transformation* equations for stress at a point, we have

$$\tau_{\nu\nu} = \tau_{ij}\nu_i\nu_j = \tau_1 \nu_x^2 + \tau_2 \nu_y^2 + \tau_3 \nu_z^2 \tag{2.59}$$

---

* See I. H. Shames, *Introduction to Solid Mechanics*, 2nd ed. (Englewood Cliffs, NJ: Prentice-Hall, Inc., 1989), Chaps. 7 and 8. Also, in Problem 2.23 you are asked to discuss the special case of plane stress (i.e., $\tau_3 = 0$).

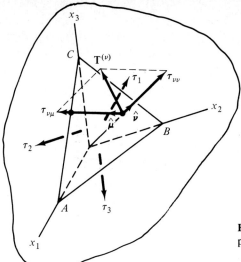

Figure 2.12 Principal stress space at a point.

We may consider Eqs. (2.57), (2.58), and (2.59) to be three simultaneous equations in ν_x^2, ν_y^2, and ν_z^2. Accordingly, we may combine them to yield three equations, where each contains only ν_x^2, or ν_y^2, or ν_z^2.

Let us first eliminate from Eq. (2.59) the variable ν_z^2 using Eq. (2.58). We get as a result

$$(\tau_3 - \tau_1)\nu_x^2 + (\tau_3 - \tau_2)\nu_y^2 = \tau_3 - \tau_{\nu\nu} \qquad (2.60)$$

Eliminating again ν_z^2 from Eq. (2.59) but now by using Eq. (2.57), we have

$$\tau_1(\tau_3 - \tau_1)\nu_x^2 + \tau_2(\tau_3 - \tau_2)\nu_y^2 = \tau_{\nu\nu}(\tau_3 - \tau_{\nu\nu}) - \tau_{\nu\mu}^2 \qquad (2.61)$$

From the preceding two equations, eliminate ν_y^2 to reach the following equation:

$$\tau_{\nu\mu}^2 + [\tau_{\nu\nu} - \tfrac{1}{2}(\tau_2 + \tau_3)]^2 = R_1^2 \qquad (a)$$

where

$$R_1^2 = \tfrac{1}{4}(\tau_2 - \tau_3)^2 + (\tau_1 - \tau_2)(\tau_1 - \tau_3)\nu_x^2 \qquad (b) \qquad (2.62)$$

If we plot $\tau_{\nu\mu}$ versus $\tau_{\nu\nu}$ for a given ν_x^2 on a stress plane (see Fig. 2.13) with $\tau_{\nu\nu}$ as abscissa and $\tau_{\nu\mu}$ as ordinate, Eq. (2.62a) yields a circle of radius R_1 with the center of the circle at point $[\tfrac{1}{2}(\tau_3 + \tau_2), 0]$. Similarly, starting again with Eqs. (2.57), (2.58), and (2.59), we may form two more circles in the $(\tau_{\nu\nu}, \tau_{\nu\mu})$ plane having the following equations:

$$\tau_{\nu\mu}^2 + [\tau_{\nu\nu} - \tfrac{1}{2}(\tau_3 + \tau_1)]^2 = R_2^2 \qquad (a)$$

where

$$R_2^2 = \tfrac{1}{4}(\tau_3 - \tau_1)^2 + (\tau_2 - \tau_3)(\tau_2 - \tau_1)\nu_y^2 \qquad (b) \qquad (2.63)$$

and

$$\tau_{\nu\mu}^2 + [\tau_{\nu\nu} - \tfrac{1}{2}(\tau_1 + \tau_2)]^2 = R_3^2 \qquad (a)$$

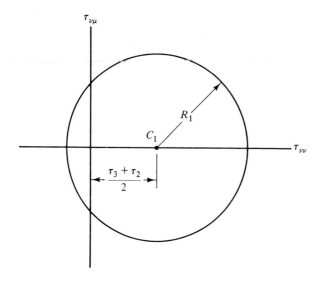

Figure 2.13 Circle for constant v_x^2.

where

$$R_3^2 = \tfrac{1}{4}(\tau_1 - \tau_2)^2 + (\tau_3 - \tau_1)(\tau_3 - \tau_2)v_z^2 \qquad \text{(b)} \qquad (2.64)$$

Each circle for a given set of principal stresses represents all possible stresses $\tau_{\nu\nu}$ and $\tau_{\nu\mu}$ for a given value of a direction cosine. Hence for a given direction cosine vector $\hat{\boldsymbol{\nu}}$ in principal stress space (see Fig. 2.14) and for a given set of principal stresses, there will then be three circles in the $(\tau_{\nu\nu}, \tau_{\nu\mu})$ plane. The point of common intersection of these circles yields the proper stresses $(\tau_{\nu\nu}, \tau_{\nu\mu})$ on an interface having the afore-stated $\hat{\boldsymbol{\nu}}$ as the unit normal. In Fig. 2.14 we have shown portions of the intersecting circles; *any two* of these circles are sufficient for locating the point of intersection.

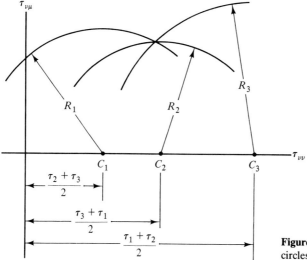

Figure 2.14 Common intersection for circles associated with a direction $\hat{\boldsymbol{\nu}}$.

Because the square of a direction cosine varies from 0 to 1, the values of radii R_1, R_2, and R_3 in Eqs. (2.62) to (2.64) have certain bounds. Since $\tau_1 \geq \tau_2 \geq \tau_3$, we see from Eq. (2.62b) that for R_1 the minimum value $(R_1)_{min}$ corresponds to $\nu_x = 0$, whereas the maximum value $(R_1)_{max}$ corresponds to $\nu_x = 1$. Similarly, from Eq. (2.64b) we have $(R_3)_{min}$ given by $\nu_z = 0$ and $(R_3)_{max}$ by $\nu_z = 1$. Conversely, Eq. (2.63b) gives $(R_2)_{max}$ for $\nu_y = 0$ and $(R_2)_{min}$ for $\nu_y = 1$. Hence we find for the possible ranges of values of the respective radii

$$[\tfrac{1}{2}(\tau_2 - \tau_3)] \leq R_1 \leq |\tau_1 - \tfrac{1}{2}(\tau_2 + \tau_3)| \qquad \text{(a)}$$

$$|\tau_2 - \tfrac{1}{2}(\tau_3 + \tau_1)| \leq R_2 \leq [\tfrac{1}{2}(\tau_1 - \tau_3)] \qquad \text{(b)} \qquad\qquad (2.65)$$

$$[\tfrac{1}{2}(\tau_1 - \tau_2)] \leq R_3 \leq |\tau_3 - \tfrac{1}{2}(\tau_1 + \tau_2)| \qquad \text{(c)}$$

where the magnitude signs are necessary since all radii are positive. Thus R_1 would have two limiting values (see Fig. 2.15) inside of which the possible values of $\tau_{\nu\nu}$ and $\tau_{\nu\mu}$ are permitted. Furthermore, if we are only interested in the magnitude of $\tau_{\nu\mu}$, the region for possible $\tau_{\nu\nu}$ and $|\tau_{\nu\mu}|$ is the crosshatched region shown in Fig. 2.15 above the abscissa. What are the allowed stresses $\tau_{\nu\nu}$ and $|\tau_{\nu\mu}|$ in the general case for a given $\hat{\nu}$ and given principal stresses? To establish this region, we plot the circles corresponding to *minimum* R_1 and R_3 and the circle corresponding to a *maximum* R_2. These circles are the celebrated *Mohr's* circles in three dimensions and are shown in Fig. 2.16. You should note that they intersect the abscissa at τ_1, τ_2, and τ_3.

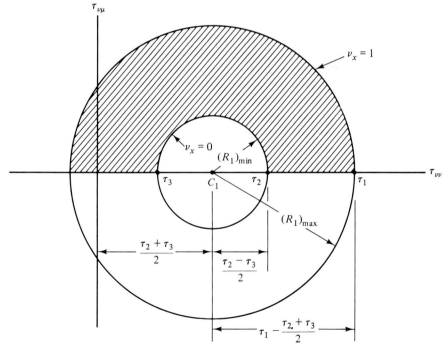

Figure 2.15 For full range of ν_x, crosshatched region gives all possible values of $\tau_{\nu\nu}$ and $|\tau_{\mu\nu}|$ for given set of principal stresses.

It follows that the allowed values of $\tau_{\nu\nu}$ and $|\tau_{\nu\mu}|$ must be restricted to the cross-hatched region between the above three circles.*

Certain results are immediately obvious from the Mohr circle construction in Fig. 2.16. First, that the maximum shear stress occurs at point A and equals the maximum radius $(R_2)_{max}$ (which corresponds to $\nu_y = 0$), so from Eq. (2.65b) we get

$$|\tau_{\nu\mu}|_{max} = \tfrac{1}{2}(\tau_1 - \tau_3) \tag{2.66}$$

We see that the maximum shear stress is one-half the difference between the maximum principal stress and the minimum principal stress. Also, the normal stress $(\tau_{\nu\nu})_A$ on the interface having $|\tau_{\nu\mu}|_{max}$ must have a value corresponding to the abscissa of point A in Fig. 2.16. That is,

$$(\tau_{\nu\nu})_A = \tfrac{1}{2}(\tau_3 + \tau_1) \tag{2.67}$$

If we substitute these stresses into Eq. (2.62), we may solve for ν_x^2, and since we know that $\nu_y^2 = 0$, we may then obtain ν_z^2 from Eq. (2.58). Accordingly, we get

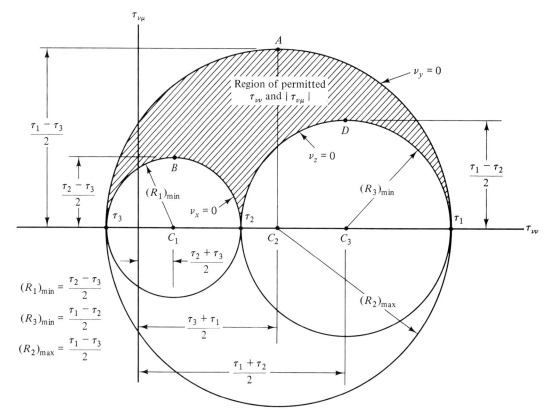

Figure 2.16 Three-dimensional Mohr's circles.

*For a detailed proof of this assertion, see Problem 2.24.

$$\nu_x^2 = \tfrac{1}{2}$$

$$\nu_y^2 = 0 \qquad (2.68)$$

$$\nu_z^2 = \tfrac{1}{2}$$

This means that $\hat{\boldsymbol{\nu}}$ of this interface is perpendicular to the x_2 axis (see Fig. 2.17) and forms an angle of 45° relative to the x_1 and x_3 axes. Recall that x_1, x_2, x_3 are principal axes, and thus the planes normal to these axes have only the principal stresses τ_1, τ_2, τ_3 acting on them, respectively. In other words, the plane of extreme shear stress bisects the dihedral angle between the planes of maximum normal stress and minimum normal stress.

The shear stress at A (see Fig. 2.16) is called a *principal shear stress* and we denote it as τ_{S2}. We may define two other principal shear stresses corresponding to points B and D on Mohr's smaller circles. We shall denote these shear stresses as τ_{S1} and τ_{S3}, respectively. We already have determined the value of τ_{S2} to be $\tfrac{1}{2}(\tau_1 - \tau_3)$. The values of τ_{S1} and τ_{S3} are seen from the diagram to equal $(R_1)_{min}$ and $(R_3)_{min}$, respectively. Accordingly, we can say that

$$\tau_{S1} = \frac{\tau_2 - \tau_3}{2}$$

$$\tau_{S2} = \frac{\tau_1 - \tau_3}{2} \qquad (2.69)$$

$$\tau_{S3} = \frac{\tau_1 - \tau_2}{2}$$

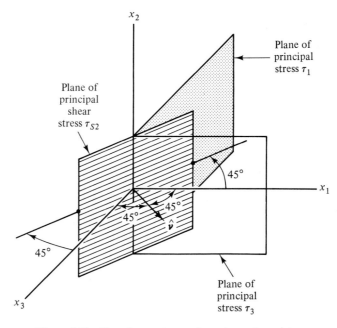

Figure 2.17 Plane for maximum shear stress at a point.

Just as the interface for τ_{S2} bisects the angle between principal planes of τ_1 and τ_3, the interface of τ_{S1} bisects the angle between principal planes of τ_2 and τ_3 while the interface of τ_{S3} bisects the principal planes of τ_1 and τ_2.

As mentioned earlier, to find the coordinates of $(\tau_{\nu\nu}, \tau_{\nu\mu})$ for a given problem, we may proceed as follows. Compute the radii R_1, R_2, R_3 for the given direction $\hat{\nu}$ and given principal stresses τ_1, τ_2, τ_3, using the second parts of Eqs. (2.62) to (2.64). Draw two circles using these radii and the proper centers. The intersection of these circles in the positive ordinate region of the graph gives the proper desired stresses. Now to check the work draw the third circle. It must intersect the other two drawn circles at one common point.

2.9 CLOSURE

With the aid of Cartesian tensor notation we have presented the concept of stress in this chapter. We first demonstrated that stress is a second-order tensor. We then formulated from Newton's law two key equations which we now again give:

1. Cauchy's formula $T_i^{(\nu)} = \tau_{ij} \nu_j$
2. Equations of equilibrium $\tau_{ij,j} + B_i = 0$

where these forms assume that τ_{ij} is symmetric. Using the moment of momentum equation, we proved that the stress tensor is in fact symmetric, that is,

3. $\tau_{ij} = \tau_{ji}$

These three equations will be cornerstones of much of the work to follow.

We then explored certain important characteristics of the stress tensor. It is vital to understand that these characteristics are *common* to all *second-order, symmetric tensors*. We list these next:

1. Principal axes and values and their formulations
2. First, second, and third tensor invariants
3. Quadric surfaces
4. Mohr's circles

This knowledge will be exploited in Chapter 3.

PROBLEMS

2.1. The following is the state of stress at a point D in a body:

$$\tau_{ij} = \begin{bmatrix} 3000 & 4000 & -8000 \\ 4000 & -2000 & 6000 \\ -8000 & 6000 & 5000 \end{bmatrix} \text{ psi}$$

What are the tractions $T_i^{(x)}$, $T_i^{(y)}$, and $T_i^{(z)}$ at point D?

2.2. Derive Eq. (2.14) in a manner paralleling the development of Eq. (2.12).

2.3. The stress components on orthogonal interfaces normal to axes xyz at a point are known to be

$$\tau_{xx} = 1000 \text{ psi}, \qquad \tau_{xy} = 200 \text{ psi}$$
$$\tau_{yy} = -600 \text{ psi}, \qquad \tau_{xz} = 0$$
$$\tau_{zz} = 0, \qquad \tau_{yz} = -400 \text{ psi}$$

Assuming that shear stresses with interchanged indices are equal, determine the normal stress in the direction $\hat{v}$ for

$$\hat{v} = 0.11\,\hat{\mathbf{i}} + 0.35\,\hat{\mathbf{j}} + 0.93\,\hat{\mathbf{k}}$$

2.4. Consider a line forming *equal angles* with axes xyz. Using the stress components given in Problem 2.3, determine the normal stress in the direction of this line.

2.5. Imagine a stress distribution where the stresses τ_{xx}, τ_{yy}, τ_{zz}, τ_{xy}, τ_{xz}, and τ_{yz} are uniform throughout a body. What does this imply for parallel stresses on parallel interfaces at different points? Suppose that for such a distribution we have

$$\tau_{xx} = 1000 \text{ psi}, \qquad \tau_{xy} = 0$$
$$\tau_{yy} = -1000 \text{ psi}, \qquad \tau_{xz} = 500 \text{ psi}$$
$$\tau_{zz} = 1000 \text{ psi}, \qquad \tau_{yz} = -500 \text{ psi}$$

What is the normal stress on plane $ABCD$ of the parallelepiped in the body shown in Fig. P2.5?

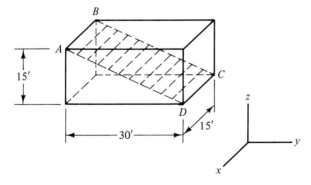

Figure P2.5

2.6. What is the shear stress on plane $ABCD$ in Problem 2.5 in the direction of the x axis?

2.7. In Problem 2.1, what is the traction vector on an interface at D having the normal direction $\hat{v}$?

$$\hat{v} = 0.520\,\hat{\mathbf{i}} + 0.330\,\hat{\mathbf{j}} + 0.788\,\hat{\mathbf{k}}$$

2.8. Using the state of stress given in Problem 2.1, what are the stresses $\tau_{x'y'}$ and $\tau_{y'z'}$ for a set of primed axes formed by rotating xyz $20°$ about the y axis clockwise as you look in along the positive y axis toward the origin?

2.9. Axes xyz are transformed into axes $x'y'z'$ by means of a $30°$ rotation about a line OA forming equal angles α with axes xyz (see Fig. P2.9). Using the stresses given in Problem 2.1, determine the stress tensor $\tau_{i'j'}$. (*Hint:* Consider a coordinate system $x''y''z''$, where z'' lies along OA and x'' lies in the xy plane. Now rotate axes xyz $30°$

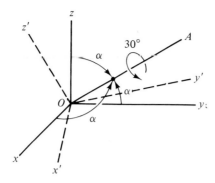

Figure P2.9

about z'' to obtain axes $x'y'z'$. Linear algebra then gives the desired transformation matrix **A** for $x'y'z'$ relative to xyz as

$$\mathbf{A} = \mathbf{C}^T \mathbf{B} \mathbf{C}$$

where **C** and **B** are the matrices for $x''y''z''$ relative to xyz and $x'y'z'$ relative to $x''y''z''$, respectively.)

2.10. Prove that the stress tensor τ_{ij} transforms properly under an *inversion* of an axis (e.g., x_1). (*Hint:* Compare the result found from the sign convention of stress with the result found from the transformation law.)

2.11. We have used a Cartesian reference to generate a set of orthogonal interfaces at a point. Actually, using other orthogonal *curvilinear* coordinates, we can similarly generate a set of orthogonal interfaces at a point. For instance, using cylindrical coordinates at a point, we may generate the following set of stresses on orthogonal interfaces:

$$\begin{bmatrix} \tau_{rr} & \tau_{r\theta} & \tau_{rz} \\ \tau_{\theta r} & \tau_{\theta\theta} & \tau_{\theta z} \\ \tau_{zr} & \tau_{z\theta} & \tau_{zz} \end{bmatrix} \qquad (1)$$

These stresses are shown in Fig. P2.11, and as shown, they are positive in accordance with the sign convention of stress. Suppose that you have a set of stresses for (1) given as

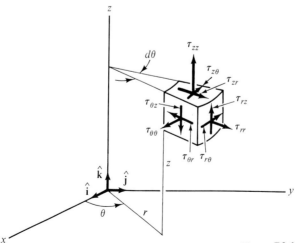

Figure P2.11

$$\begin{bmatrix} 5000 & 0 & -3000 \\ 0 & 2000 & 1000 \\ -3000 & 1000 & 0 \end{bmatrix} \text{psi}$$

representing stresses at $r = 6$, $\theta = 30°, z = 10$ in a body. What is the stress τ_{xx} at this point?

2.12. For the following stress tensor field,

$$\tau_{ij} = \begin{bmatrix} 6x^2 + y & 3z^2 + y & 5y^2 + x \\ 3z^2 + y & 10x^3 & -6x^2 z \\ 5y^2 + x & -6x^2 z & 3y + z \end{bmatrix} \times 10^3 \quad \text{psi}$$

what body-force distribution is needed to maintain equilibrium? Here, x, y, and z are in feet.

2.13. A continuum is known to have the following motion:

$$\mathbf{V} = 0.002xyt^2\,\hat{\mathbf{i}} + 0.001y^2\,t\hat{\mathbf{j}} + (0.003t^2 + 0.005z)\hat{\mathbf{k}} \quad \text{ft/sec}$$

The stress distribution is known to be

$$\tau_{ij} = \begin{bmatrix} 5x^2 + t^2 & 10yt & -6z^2 yt^2 \\ 10yt & 4y + z & 5x^2 + y \\ -6z^2 yt^2 & 5x^2 + y & 6x^2 + t^3 \end{bmatrix} \times 1000 \quad \text{lb/ft}^2$$

What is the body-force distribution? In the above, x, y, z are current (Eulerian) coordinates in feet, and $\rho = 10$ slug/ft^3. Also, do *not* assume small deformation.

2.14. Derive the equations of equilibrium by considering an infinitesimal rectangular parallelepiped as a free body, on which stresses on the front faces are expressed as two-term Taylor series expansions of the stresses on the back faces (see Fig. P2.14).

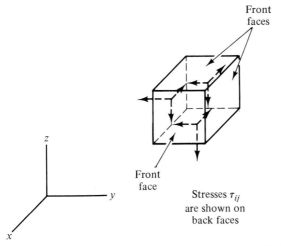

Front
faces

Front
face

Stresses τ_{ij}
are shown on
back faces

Figure P2.14

2.15. By methods analogous to those of Problem 2.14, develop the following equations of equilibrium for *plane stress* using polar coordinates:

$$\frac{\partial \tau_{rr}}{\partial r} + \frac{1}{r}\frac{\partial \tau_{r\theta}}{\partial \theta} + \frac{\tau_{rr} - \tau_{\theta\theta}}{r} = 0$$

$$\frac{1}{r}\frac{\partial \tau_{\theta\theta}}{\partial \theta} + \frac{\partial \tau_{r\theta}}{\partial r} + \frac{2\tau_{r\theta}}{r} = 0$$

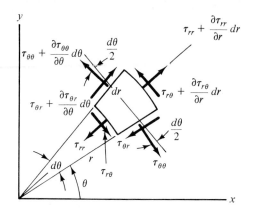

Figure P2.15

Employ Fig. P2.15 as an aid. Assume no body forces. (*Hint:* Approximate the sine and cosine of a small angle.)

2.16. For the state of stress given in Problem 2.1, determine the first, second, and third tensor invariants.

2.17. Verify Eqs. (2.45) using the results of the work in Section 1.10; that is, prove that Eqs. (2.43) and (2.44) are identical with Eqs. (2.45a) and (2.45b), respectively.

2.18. Given the following state of stress at a point

$$\tau_{ij} = \begin{bmatrix} 0 & -800 & 0 \\ -800 & 300 & -500 \\ 0 & -500 & 0 \end{bmatrix} \text{ psi}$$

what are the principal stresses and their directions?

2.19. Given the following state of stress at a point

$$\tau_{ij} = \begin{bmatrix} 8000 & 3000 & -4000 \\ 3000 & -2500 & 1300 \\ -4000 & 1300 & 6000 \end{bmatrix} \text{ psi}$$

determine the principal stresses with the aid of a computer. Find the direction of the maximum normal stress.

2.20. Determine the stress *deviator* tensor s_{ij} for the state of stress given in Problem 2.18. Evaluate the tensor invariants for this tensor. Prove that the principal axes of s_{ij} coincide with the principal axes of τ_{ij}. Explain why this is so.

2.21. **(a)** Describe the state of stress corresponding to a quadric surface that is a sphere about the origin of ξ_1, ξ_2, ξ_3.
   (b) Use Eq. (2.55) to verify that for $\tau_1 \geq \tau_2 > 0$ and $\tau_3 < 0$, the stress quadratic surfaces are as shown in Fig. 2.11.
   (c) What is the nature of the quadric surface for the state of stress at a point where the only nonzero stress for axes *xyz* is τ_{xy}?

2.22. Sketch the three Mohr's circles for the following principal stress state:

$$\tau_1 = 6 \text{ kpsi} \qquad \tau_2 = 3 \text{ kpsi} \qquad \tau_3 = 1 \text{ kpsi}$$

What is the maximum shear stress, and what is the normal stress on the plane of maximum shear stress?

2.23. For each of the following *special* stress states, sketch the three-dimensional Mohr's circle diagram. Discuss each case.

(a) Uniaxial tension: $\tau_1, \tau_2 = 0, \tau_3 = 0$

(b) Plane stress: $\tau_1, \tau_2, \tau_3 = 0$

(c) Hydrostatic compression: $\tau_1 = \tau_2 = \tau_3 = -p$

2.24. To prove that the admissible values of $\tau_{\nu\nu}$ and $|\tau_{\nu\mu}|$ lie in the crosshatched region of the Mohr's circles diagram of Fig. 2.16, proceed as follows:

(a) Solve Eqs. (2.62), (2.63), and (2.64) for ν_x^2, ν_y^2, and ν_z^2, respectively. Accordingly, obtain the expression

$$\nu_x^2 = \frac{\tau_{\nu\mu}^2 + (\tau_{\nu\nu} - \tau_2)(\tau_{\nu\nu} - \tau_3)}{(\tau_1 - \tau_2)(\tau_1 - \tau_3)}$$

plus two similar expressions for ν_y^2 and ν_z^2.

(b) In these expressions use the conditions $\tau_1 \geq \tau_2 \geq \tau_3$ and $\nu_x^2 \geq 0, \nu_y^2 \geq 0, \nu_z^2 \geq 0$ to obtain the inequalities

$$\tau_{\nu\mu}^2 + (\tau_{\nu\nu} - \tau_2)(\tau_{\nu\nu} - \tau_3) \geq 0$$

$$\tau_{\nu\mu}^2 + (\tau_{\nu\nu} - \tau_3)(\tau_{\nu\nu} - \tau_1) \leq 0$$

$$\tau_{\nu\mu}^2 + (\tau_{\nu\nu} - \tau_1)(\tau_{\nu\nu} - \tau_2) \geq 0$$

Explain how it follows that the locus of points satisfying these inequalities lies in the crosshatched region of Fig. 2.16.

Chapter 3
Strain

3.1 INTRODUCTION

In this chapter we consider the *deformation* of a body due to the application of loads. We use the term "deformation" to signify the *entire geometric change* by which the points in a body in the initial state with all loads absent go to another configuration as a result of the action of loads. The aforementioned initial state we shall call the *undeformed* state, and the subsequent state occurring in the presence of loads we call the *deformed state*. The deformation, so defined, will be seen to include the following contributions for each element of a body:

1. *Rigid-body translation* and *rotation*
2. A *dilatation* contribution from changes in geometry associated with the *volume change* of the element
3. A *distortion* contribution from the remaining changes in geometry of the element, which includes as an important contribution the change in *angularity* between line segments in the element

In later chapters we want to relate parts 2 and 3 of the deformation with the stresses in the body. In this regard you may remember from your physics courses that it was the *relative* movement between two atoms that gave rise to a variation in the bonding force between the atoms. Following a similar line of reasoning in this chapter, in anticipation of our desire to relate parts 2 and 3 above with stress, we shall be concerned with the relative movement between any two "adjacent" points (i.e., points *infinitesimally close* to each other in the undeformed geometry). This study will also permit us to separate out and describe mathematically part 1 of the deformation.

70

3.2 THE DISPLACEMENT GRADIENT MATRIX

We start by considering an arbitrary continuum in the initial undeformed geometry as shown in Fig. 3.1. A stationary reference $X_1 X_2 X_3$ has been shown. Position vector **r** locates any point P in the initial undeformed geometry having coordinates (X_1, X_2, X_3). The current deformed state of the body at time t is shown dashed. As a result of some externally applied force field, each point P in the initial undeformed state of the body moves to point P' in the current deformed state of the body. This movement of points can be described by a *displacement field* $\mathbf{u}(X_1, X_2, X_3, t)$ as has been shown in the diagram. In introducing Cartesian tensor notation here, it will as usual be desirable to express the unit vectors $\hat{\mathbf{i}}$, $\hat{\mathbf{j}}$, and $\hat{\mathbf{k}}$, respectively, as $\hat{\mathbf{i}}_1$, $\hat{\mathbf{i}}_2$, and $\hat{\mathbf{i}}_3$. We can then express the displacement field vectorially as

$$\mathbf{u} = \sum_{i=1}^{3} u_i \hat{\mathbf{i}}_i \qquad (3.1)$$

and thus u_i is the indicial counterpart of **u**.

It will be helpful in describing the current deformed state to employ a second stationary reference $x_1 x_2 x_3$ coinciding with $X_1 X_2 X_3$ as has been shown in Fig. 3.2. Furthermore, we shall denote the position vector to point P as X_i and the position vector to point P' as x_i. We can then relate the current deformed geometry with the initial undeformed geometry point by point as follows (see Fig. 3.2):

$$x_i = X_i + u_i(X_1, X_2, X_3, t) \qquad (3.2)$$

The displacement field determines the movement of *each point* in the initial undeformed geometry. However, it is the *relative* movement of adjacent points that will be important to us when we come to relating stress to deformation as suggested in the preceding section. Furthermore, for our purposes it will be sufficient to investigate only infinitesimally close points. Such points, we have already noted, will be called adjacent points. Accordingly, we now consider two adjacent points

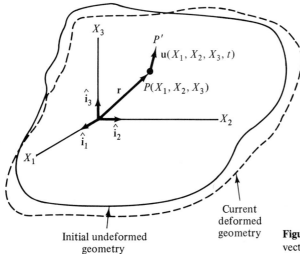

Initial undeformed geometry

Current deformed geometry

Figure 3.1 Body showing a position vector and a displacement vector.

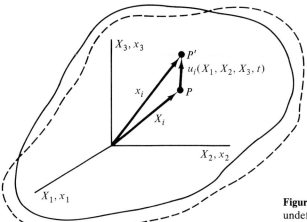

Figure 3.2 Reference $X_1X_2X_3$ used for undeformed state and $x_1x_2x_3$ used for current deformed state.

denoted as P and Q in the undeformed state as shown in Fig. 3.3. By being infinitesimally close to each other, points P and Q are said to be in a *small domain*. The infinitesimal position vector between these points we denote as dX_i. As the body deforms, P goes to P' and Q goes to Q'. The infinitesimal position vector in the current deformed geometry between P' and Q' is dx_i. Note in Fig. 3.3 that the unit vector collinear with dX_i is shown as ϵ_i. Now the relative movement of points P and Q during deformation is embodied in the change of vector dX_i to dx_i as a result of deformation. To relate these vectors, note from Fig. 3.3 that we can go from point P to point Q' via two sets of displacements. Thus we can say that

$$(u_i)_P + dx_i = dX_i + (u_i)_Q \tag{3.3}$$

Rearranging the terms, we get from Eq. (3.3)

$$(dx_i - dX_i) = (u_i)_Q - (u_i)_P \tag{3.4}$$

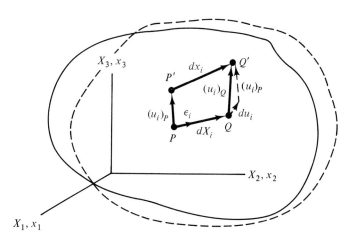

Figure 3.3 Adjacent points shown in the initial undeformed and current deformed states.

where the right-hand side of the equation is the relative displacement between adjacent points Q and P at the instant of time t. Denoting the left-hand side of this equation as $\delta(dX_i)$ (i.e., as the change of the original vector dX_i), we have

$$\delta(dX_i) = (u_i)_Q - (u_i)_P \tag{3.5}$$

Because of the small domain restriction we have imposed by dealing with adjacent points P and Q, the relative displacement must also be differential. That is,

$$(u_i)_Q - (u_i)_P = du_i \tag{3.6}$$

as shown in Fig. 3.3. Furthermore, since at instant t displacement u_i is a function of coordinates X_i [see Eq. (3.2)], we may expand du_i via the chain rule for a differential. Equation (3.6) may then be given as

$$(u_i)_Q - (u_i)_P = \frac{\partial u_i}{\partial X_j} dX_j \tag{3.7}$$

Substituting the right-hand side of Eq. (3.7) for the right-hand side of Eq. (3.5), we get the important result

$$\boxed{\delta(dX_i) = \frac{\partial u_i(X_1, X_2, X_3, t)}{\partial X_j} dX_j} \tag{3.8}$$

The expression $\partial u_i/\partial X_j$ is called the *displacement gradient matrix*.

You will recall from Chapter 1 that differentiating a vector u_i with respect to a spatial coordinate X_k results in a second-order tensor (e.g., see Problem 1.19). Thus by this rule the displacement gradient matrix, $\partial u_i/\partial X_k$, is a second-order tensor. It will nevertheless be informative to show here formally that the displacement gradient matrix is in fact a second-order tensor. Since u_i is a vector, we can say that under an orthogonal transformation of coordinates to primed coordinates $X_{1'}, X_{2'}, X_{3'}$,

$$u_{i'} = a_{i'j} u_j \tag{3.9}$$

The partial derivative operator $\partial/\partial X_{k'}$ is then applied to both sides of the equation. But on the right side of the equation, we will express this partial derivative using the chain rule as follows:

$$\frac{\partial}{\partial X_{k'}} = \frac{\partial}{\partial X_l} \frac{\partial X_l}{\partial X_{k'}} \tag{3.10}$$

Now since the position vector X_l transforms in accordance with the equation

$$X_l = a_{p'l} X_{p'} \tag{3.11}$$

we obtain for $\partial X_l/\partial X_{k'}$ in Eq. (3.10), the result

$$\frac{\partial X_l}{\partial X_{k'}} = a_{p'l} \frac{\partial X_{p'}}{\partial X_{k'}} = a_{p'l} \delta_{p'k'} = a_{k'l} \tag{3.12}$$

We then have for Eq. (3.9), after applying the operator $\partial/\partial X_{k'}$ on the left side, and Eq. (3.10) along with Eq. (3.12) on the right side,

$$\frac{\partial u_{i'}}{\partial X_{k'}} = a_{i'j} a_{k'l} \frac{\partial u_j}{\partial X_l} \tag{3.13}$$

Clearly, $\partial u_i/\partial X_j$ satisfies the transformation equation for second-order tensors and henceforth we shall refer to it as the *displacement gradient tensor*.

If we divide Eq. (3.8) by the original length of the line segment, which we designate as $dS\ (= \sqrt{dX_i\,dX_i})$, we have

$$\frac{\delta(dX_i)}{dS} = \frac{\partial u_i}{\partial X_j}\left(\frac{dX_j}{dS}\right) \equiv \frac{\partial u_i}{\partial X_j}\,\epsilon_j \tag{3.14}$$

where in the last step we have used the definition $dX_j = dS\epsilon_j$ (see Fig. 3.3). Note that the components of the unit vector $\hat{\boldsymbol{\epsilon}}$, namely ϵ_1, ϵ_2, and ϵ_3, are of course not necessarily unity in value. They are simply the direction cosines of $\hat{\boldsymbol{\epsilon}}$. We may also say, by using Eqs. (3.4) through (3.6) in Eq. (3.14), that

$$\frac{dx_i - dX_i}{dS} = \frac{du_i}{dS} \equiv \frac{\partial u_i}{\partial X_j}\,\epsilon_j \tag{3.15}$$

where du_i/dS is called the *unit relative displacement* vector. Note that although the relative displacement is infinitesimal, the unit relative displacement in general is finite.

We shall now illustrate the use of the displacement gradient tensor and the relative displacement vector.

Example 3.1

Given the displacement field

$$\mathbf{u} = [Y^2\hat{\mathbf{i}} + 3YZ\hat{\mathbf{j}} + (4Z + 6X^2)\hat{\mathbf{k}}] \times 10^{-1} \text{ ft} \tag{a}$$

find the change of the length in the Y direction of an infinitesimal line segment at $(1, 1, 2)$ originally along the Z axis, per unit original length. This clearly is the Y component of the unit relative displacement vector, du_i/dS, for line segment dZ.

For this purpose we shall first find the displacement gradient tensor field. Thus, for the term $\partial u_1/\partial X_1$ we get from Eq. (a) the result $[\partial(Y^2)/\partial X] \times 10^{-1}$, which clearly is zero. For $\partial u_1/\partial X_2$ we get $[\partial(Y^2)/\partial Y] \times 10^{-1}$, which is $0.2Y$, and so on. We thus form the following matrix:

$$\frac{\partial u_i}{\partial X_j} = \begin{bmatrix} 0 & 2Y & 0 \\ 0 & 3Z & 3Y \\ 12X & 0 & 4 \end{bmatrix} \times 10^{-1} \tag{b}$$

At position $(1, 1, 2)$ we have

$$\frac{\partial u_i}{\partial X_j}(1, 1, 2) = \begin{bmatrix} 0 & 2 & 0 \\ 0 & 6 & 3 \\ 12 & 0 & 4 \end{bmatrix} \times 10^{-1} \tag{c}$$

Now going to Eq. (3.8), we have

$$\delta(dX_i) = \frac{\partial u_i}{\partial X_j}\,dX_j \tag{d}$$

Noting that $dX_1 = dX_2 = 0$ leaving only dX_3 as nonzero and using $i = 2$ to get the Y component of the change in length, we have on using Eq. (c) in Eq. (d),

$$[\delta(dX_i)]_{i=2} = \left(\frac{\partial u_2}{\partial X_3}\right) dX_3 = (3 \times 10^{-1}) dX_3 \text{ ft} \tag{e}$$

Hence we have the desired result:

$$\frac{du_2}{dS} = \frac{du_2}{dX_3} = \frac{\delta(dX_2)}{dX_3} = 3 \times 10^{-1}$$

As an exercise we suggest that you evaluate the other two components of the unit relative displacement vector for this example.

Note in this section that we have limited ourselves to adjacent (infinitesimally close) points and thus to a small domain.* However, there is no limit yet on the *amount* of the unit relative movement between adjacent points. Thus the results at this stage are valid for what we shall call *finite* deformation. In the next section and indeed throughout the remainder of this book, we will limit ourselves to small deformation.

3.3 SUPERPOSITION; SMALL DEFORMATION

In this section we consider two successive deformations, as illustrated in Fig. 3.4. For the first deformation, point P displaces to point P', and we can state, using Eq. (3.8) with the superscript (1) to indicate displacement to the first deformed state,

$$\delta(dX_i) = \left(\frac{\partial u_i^{(1)}}{\partial X_j}\right)_P dX_j \tag{3.16}$$

Noting from Eqs. (3.4) and (3.5) that

$$\delta(dX_i) = dx_i - dX_i \tag{3.17}$$

we can write Eq. (3.16) as

$$dx_i = dX_i + \left(\frac{\partial u_i^{(1)}}{\partial X_j}\right)_P dX_j \tag{3.18}$$

Next, consider the deformation from deformed state (1) (see Fig. 3.4), for which we use reference $x_1 x_2 x_3$, to deformed state (2), for which we use the reference $x_1' x_2' x_3'$. During this deformation point P' displaces to point P'', and the equation for the second change of deformed state is given in a manner paralleling the preceding development as

$$dx_i' = dx_i + \left(\frac{\partial u_i^{(2)}}{\partial x_j}\right)_{P'} dx_j \tag{3.19}$$

---

*Equation (3.8) is thus valid only for points separated by an *infinitesimal* distance. The relative displacement for points separated by a *finite* distance may be determined by evaluating the displacements at these points from the displacement field [see Eq. (3.2)].

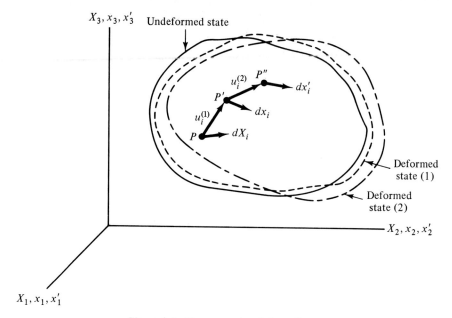

X_2, x_2, x'_2

X_1, x_1, x'_1

Figure 3.4 Two successive deformations.

Next replace dx_i and dx_j in Eq. (3.19) using Eq. (3.18). We get

$$dx'_i = dX_i + \left(\frac{\partial u_i^{(1)}}{\partial X_j}\right)_P dX_j + \left(\frac{\partial u_i^{(2)}}{\partial x_j}\right)_{P'}\left[dX_j + \left(\frac{\partial u_j^{(1)}}{\partial X_k}\right)_P dX_k\right]$$

Combining terms, we have

$$dx'_i = dX_i + \left[\left(\frac{\partial u_i^{(1)}}{\partial X_j}\right)_P + \left(\frac{\partial u_i^{(2)}}{\partial x_j}\right)_{P'}\right]dX_j + \left(\frac{\partial u_i^{(2)}}{\partial x_j}\right)_{P'}\left(\frac{\partial u_j^{(1)}}{\partial X_k}\right)_P dX_k \qquad (3.20)$$

Let us pause now to define what we mean by the principle of *superposition*. Suppose that on a given body we apply a set of loads *I* and thereby develop a deformation. We may then say on utilizing Eq. (3.18) for this case

$$(dx_i)_\mathrm{I} = dX_i + \left(\frac{\partial u_i^\mathrm{I}}{\partial X_j}\right)_P dX_j \qquad (3.21)$$

Now take loads I *off* and put on a second different loading, II.* For the same *point* P as above and the *same* dX_i, we may say that for this deformation,

$$(dx_i)_\mathrm{II} = dX_i + \left(\frac{\partial u_i^\mathrm{II}}{\partial X_j}\right)_P dX_j \qquad (3.22)$$

---

*The term "load" should be interpreted in the general sense of an "input" to the governing equations. For linear materials the input is equal to the applied force, but for nonlinear materials it may be a *function* of the applied force. The concept of superposition is of limited value for nonlinear materials, since one is usually interested in superposing forces, which is *not* equivalent to superposing the inputs.

Note in Eqs. (3.21) and (3.22) that we are using the *same original undeformed geometry*. We now state that we can "superpose" the deformations for loads I and II if for the combined load I plus II we simply add the terms $(\partial u_i^{\text{I}}/\partial X_j)_P\, dX_j$ and $(\partial u_i^{\text{II}}/\partial X_j)_P\, dX_j$ from Eqs. (3.21) and (3.22) to the original vector dX_i to get the total deformed vector, $(dx_i)_{\text{total}}$, as follows:

$$(dx_i)_{\text{total}} = dX_i + \left[\left(\frac{\partial u_i^{\text{I}}}{\partial X_j}\right) + \left(\frac{\partial u_i^{\text{II}}}{\partial X_j}\right)\right]_P dX_j$$

Therefore,

$$(dx_i)_{\text{total}} = dX_i + \left[\frac{\partial}{\partial X_j}(u_i^{\text{I}} + u_i^{\text{II}})\right]_P dX_j \tag{3.23}$$

Clearly, for this procedure, which pinpoints the key aspects of the principle of superposition, the *order of loading is not significant*.

Now compare Eq. (3.23) with Eq. (3.20) to see what the restrictions are in order that the principle of superposition of deformations as given above be approximately valid. We require that loads I equal the loads that resulted in the displacement to deformed state (1), and loads II be the same as the additional loads that generated the displacement from state (1) to state (2). Two primary conditions are then seen to be required. They are:

1. $(\partial/\partial X_j)_P \approx (\partial/\partial x_j)_{P'}$: This means that the *displacement field for each loading must be small so that points P and P' are very close.*

2. $(\partial u_i^{(2)}/\partial x_j)_{P'} \cdot (\partial u_j^{(1)}/\partial X_k)_P \approx 0$: This means that the *displacement gradients must be small.*

The conditions on deformation above identify the kind of deformation that in this book we call *small deformation*. For small deformation wherein we use the initial undeformed geometry for all loadings and stresses, there is no need to use the two references xyz and XYZ. We shall then often use a single reference, which in this book will be xyz.

In the past two sections, we considered the relative displacement between infinitesimally close (adjacent) points and studied the change of the infinitesimal line segment dX_i connecting these points. We have thereby formulated the displacement gradient tensor and the conditions for superposition (i.e., the small deformation concept). We can learn more about deformation by considering *four* infinitesimally close (adjacent) points in a body, one at the origin of a reference XYZ and the others along the coordinate axes. We do this in the next section.

3.4 STRAIN AND ROTATION TENSORS FOR SMALL DEFORMATION

We now consider four adjacent points in the undeformed geometry as shown in Fig. 3.5. The relative displacement of these points can be related to the deformation (which includes what we shall define as rigid-body rotation) of the rectangular

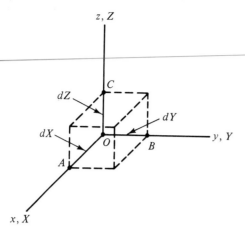

Figure 3.5 Adjacent points.

parallelepiped shown dashed in the diagram. The relative displacement between points A and O can be expressed via Eq. (3.7) as

$$(u_i)_A - (u_i)_O = \left(\frac{\partial u_i}{\partial X_j}\right)_O dX_j \tag{3.24}$$

With no loss in generality, we can take $(u_i)_O$ as zero—that is, take point O as fixed so that the *actual* displacement of point A to point A' is the same as the relative displacement between A and O. In Fig. 3.6 we have shown this displacement for point A for which dX_j has components $dX, 0, 0$; the displacements of points B and C are similarly shown. Using this setup, we now examine in detail the relative displacements between points A, B, C, and O.

Looking at OA, we can first consider the change in distance between O and A when the body is deformed and A is displaced to A'. We shall define the normal strain ε_{xx} as a measure of this action. For *small deformation* we define the normal strain ε_{xx} as follows:

$$\varepsilon_{xx} \equiv \frac{\begin{array}{c}\text{change in length of an infinitesimal line segment}\\ \text{originally in the } X \text{ direction}\end{array}}{\text{original length of this line segment}} \tag{3.25}$$

Another way of stating definition (3.25) is

$$\varepsilon_{xx} = \lim_{\Delta X \to 0} \frac{\widetilde{\Delta X} - \Delta X}{\Delta X} \tag{3.26}$$

where in Fig. 3.6 ΔX corresponds in the limit to the distance from O to A while $\widetilde{\Delta X}$ is the distance from O to A'. Note carefully: The line segment from O to A' is *not* along the X direction. What contributes to the change in length of OA? Clearly, from Fig. 3.6 we see that for the infinitesimal rectangular parallelepiped it is from all three displacement components at A. But for *small deformation*, it can be understood from the diagram that the change in length of OA due to $(\partial u_z/\partial X) dX$ and due to $(\partial u_y/\partial X) dX$ will be *very small* compared to the change in length of OA

78

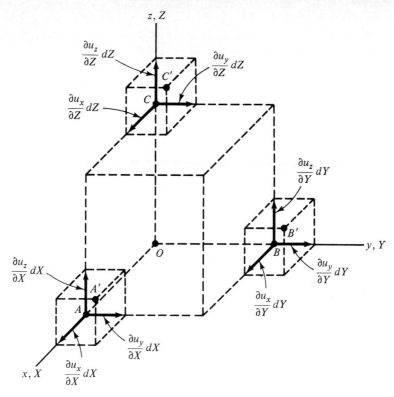

Figure 3.6 Relative displacement of adjacent orthogonal points.

arising from a comparable value of $(\partial u_x/\partial X)\,dX$. Hence we can replace the numerator of Eq. (3.26) with $(\partial u_x/\partial X)\,\Delta X$ to yield in the limit

$$\varepsilon_{xx} = \frac{\partial u_x}{\partial X}$$

Since we are limited to small deformation here, we can also replace X by x as noted at the end of the preceding section, so that we have

$$\varepsilon_{xx} = \frac{\partial u_x}{\partial x} \tag{3.27}$$

The term ε_{xx} is called the *normal strain*. Similarly, for the other two axes, y and z, we have two other normal strains:

$$\varepsilon_{yy} = \frac{\partial u_y}{\partial y}, \qquad \varepsilon_{zz} = \frac{\partial u_z}{\partial z} \tag{3.28}$$

In general, we can say that

$$\varepsilon_{ij} \equiv \lim_{\Delta X_j \to 0} \frac{\widetilde{\Delta X}_i - \Delta X_i}{\Delta X_j} \approx \frac{\partial u_i}{\partial x_j} \qquad i = j \tag{3.29}$$

where $\widetilde{\Delta X}_i$ and ΔX_j represent, respectively, final and original lengths of the line segment originally along the jth coordinate, and where the approximate equality sign signifies that the final result is valid only if we assume small deformation. Note that *positive* normal strain indicates *extension* of a line segment, whereas *negative* normal strain indicates *contraction*.

It is of interest to compare the expression $\delta(dX_1)/dX_1$ stemming from Eq. (3.8) with the normal strain $\varepsilon_{11} = \partial u_1/\partial x_1$. We note that:

1. The expression $\partial u_1/\partial x_1$ corresponds to small deformation, whereas the other expression does not.
2. The original line segment for ε_{11} is in the X_1 direction, whereas for $\delta(dX_1)/dX_1$ the line segment is the X_1 *component* of a line segment having *any* original direction.

Note that $\delta(dX_2)/dX_1 \neq 0$ even if $dX_2 = 0$ originally.

Thus we have found that the normal strains are a measure of the change of length of the sides of the rectangular parallelepiped. But it is also obvious that the sides of the rectangular parallelepiped upon deformation will in general cease to be at right angles to each other. Consider line segments OA and OB of Fig. 3.7. We define the *engineering shear strain* γ_{xy} as follows for these line segments undergoing *small deformation*:

$\gamma_{xy} \equiv$ change in angle in radians between two infinitesimal line segments originally in the X and Y directions

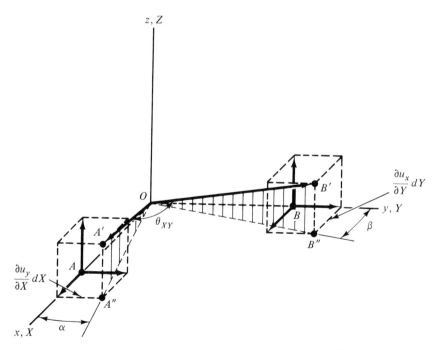

Figure 3.7 Projections of line segments OA and OB onto XY plane after deformation.

Consider for a moment that the rectangular parallelepiped is finite, and that OA'' and OB'' shown in Fig. 3.7 are *projections* onto the XY plane of line segments OA' and OB', respectively, in the deformed geometry. The angle formed by line segments OA' and OB' in the deformed geometry is denoted as θ_{XY}. Hence we can say that

$$\gamma_{xy} = \lim_{\substack{\Delta X \to 0 \\ \Delta Y \to 0}} \left(\frac{\pi}{2} - \theta_{XY}\right) \tag{3.30}$$

Because we are considering small deformation, the angle $(\pi/2 - \theta_{XY})$ above may be taken equal to the angle $(\alpha + \beta)$ formed by OA'' and OB'' in the XY plane (see Fig. 3.7). Thus we can say, using the approximation sign here to indicate the small-deformation assumption, that

$$\gamma_{xy} \approx \lim_{\substack{\Delta X \to 0 \\ \Delta Y \to 0}} (\alpha + \beta) \tag{3.31}$$

Now in the limit and for small deformation we can write for α and β

$$\begin{aligned}
\lim_{\Delta X \to 0} \alpha &\approx \frac{\partial u_y}{\partial X}\, dX \Big/ dX = \frac{\partial u_y}{\partial X} \approx \frac{\partial u_y}{\partial x} \\
\lim_{\Delta Y \to 0} \beta &\approx \frac{\partial u_x}{\partial Y}\, dY \Big/ dY = \frac{\partial u_x}{\partial Y} \approx \frac{\partial u_x}{\partial y}
\end{aligned} \tag{3.32}$$

where we have used the approximate equalities $\alpha \approx \tan \alpha$ and $\beta \approx \tan \beta$. Accordingly, reverting to equality signs now that the small deformation restriction is fully understood, we have

$$\gamma_{xy} = \gamma_{yx} = \frac{\partial u_x}{\partial y} + \frac{\partial u_y}{\partial x} \tag{3.33}$$

In the general case, we can thus say that for small deformation

$$\gamma_{ij} \equiv \lim_{\substack{\Delta X_i \to 0 \\ \Delta X_j \to 0}} \left(\frac{\pi}{2} - \theta_{X_i X_j}\right) \approx \left(\frac{\partial u_i}{\partial X_j} + \frac{\partial u_j}{\partial X_i}\right) \approx \left(\frac{\partial u_i}{\partial x_j} + \frac{\partial u_j}{\partial x_i}\right) \qquad i \neq j$$

or

$$\gamma_{ij} \approx (u_{i,j} + u_{j,i}) \qquad i \neq j \tag{3.34}$$

where $\theta_{X_i X_j}$ is the angle in the deformed geometry of elements originally in the X_i and X_j directions, and where yet once more the approximate equality indicates use of the small deformation assumption. Hence we can add to Eq. (3.33) the following engineering strains:

$$\begin{aligned}
\gamma_{xz} &= \gamma_{zx} = \frac{\partial u_z}{\partial x} + \frac{\partial u_x}{\partial z} \\
\gamma_{yz} &= \gamma_{zy} = \frac{\partial u_z}{\partial y} + \frac{\partial u_y}{\partial z}
\end{aligned} \tag{3.35}$$

Note that a *positive* shear angle indicates a *reduction* in the original 90° angle, whereas a *negative* shear angle denotes an *increase* in this angle.

We now define the *shear strain* ε_{ij} as $\frac{1}{2}\gamma_{ij}$ for $i \neq j$. The *strain matrix* is then composed of three normal strains and six shear strains and is given as

$$\varepsilon_{ij} = \begin{bmatrix} \varepsilon_{xx} & \varepsilon_{xy} & \varepsilon_{xz} \\ \varepsilon_{yx} & \varepsilon_{yy} & \varepsilon_{yz} \\ \varepsilon_{zx} & \varepsilon_{zy} & \varepsilon_{zz} \end{bmatrix} \tag{3.36}$$

In terms of the displacement field we can now combine Eq. (3.29), presented for normal strain, and (3.34), with γ_{ij} replaced by $2\varepsilon_{ij}$, into a single formulation with the previous equality and inequality restrictions on the free indices ij deleted.

$$\boxed{\varepsilon_{ij} = \varepsilon_{ji} = \frac{1}{2}\left(\frac{\partial u_i}{\partial x_j} + \frac{\partial u_j}{\partial x_i}\right) = \tfrac{1}{2}(u_{i,j} + u_{j,i})} \tag{3.37}$$

This formulation clearly holds for all normal strains and shear strains. We have already proven that the displacement gradient matrix $\partial u_i/\partial X_j$, which for small deformations equals $\partial u_i/\partial x_j$, is a tensor of second order. Clearly, the transpose of this matrix $\partial u_j/\partial x_i$ is also a tensor of second order. Thus we can conclude that ε_{ij}, as given by Eq. (3.37), must be a symmetric tensor of second order, and will henceforth be called the *strain tensor*. Note that the introduction of the factor $\frac{1}{2}$ in the definition of shear strains was an essential step in the process of arriving at the single formulation (3.37) for ε_{ij}, therefore facilitating the development of the strain tensor.

The relative displacements we have described thus far give the deformation of the rectangular parallelepiped and it is this set of terms that relates directly to stress through what we shall call a constitutive law. Also, the definition for strain we have used in this discussion is based on the original geometry and is thus called the *Lagrangian* definition of strain. One may use other definitions of strain which are based on the current geometry. However, it should be clear that the distinction between these various definitions disappears when we deal with small deformation.

What other relative displacements do we have to account for? Because we have fully accounted for normal and shear strains of the vanishingly small elements, there can only be rigid-body movements consisting (as we know from Chasles' theorem) of translation and rotation.* Clearly, there can be no relative displacement from translation. As for rigid-body rotation, we go back to Fig. 3.7. Looking at line segment OA we can say for *small deformation* that in the limit as OA shrinks to zero size the rotation of this line segment about the z axis is given as

$$\lim_{\Delta X \to 0} \omega_z|_{OA} \approx \frac{\partial u_y}{\partial X}\, dX \Big/ dX = \frac{\partial u_y}{\partial X} \approx \frac{\partial u_y}{\partial x} \tag{3.38}$$

---

* Chasles' theorem states that the general motion of a rigid body can be represented by the sum of a translation of an arbitrary reference point plus a rigid-body rotation about this reference point. All points in the body translate an amount equal to the displacement at the reference point, and this displacement clearly depends on selection of the reference point. On the other hand, the angular rotation is independent of the choice of the reference point.

where you will note that $\omega_z|_{OA}$ is computed from the projection of OA' onto the XY plane. Similarly, looking at the line segment OB, we have

$$\lim_{\Delta Y \to 0} \omega_z|_{OB} \approx -\frac{\partial u_x}{\partial Y} \, dY \Big/ dY = -\frac{\partial u_x}{\partial Y} \approx -\frac{\partial u_x}{\partial y} \tag{3.39}$$

where the minus sign is a consequence of the usual right-hand rule for the sign of rotation.

We now define "rigid-body" rotation at a point about an axis in a body subject to small deformation as the *average rotation of two infinitesimal line segments, which are at right angles to each other and at right angles to the axis of rotation.* We shall employ infinitesimal line segments along the coordinate axes.[*] Hence, getting the average of the rotation from Eqs. (3.38) and (3.39) yields the rigid-body rotation about the z axis. We can accordingly say that the z component of the rotation vector is

$$\omega_z = \Omega_{yx} = \frac{1}{2}\left(\frac{\partial u_y}{\partial x} - \frac{\partial u_x}{\partial y}\right) \tag{3.40}$$

where we have also denoted ω_z as Ω_{yx}. Similarly, we have for the other components of the rotation vector

$$\omega_x = \Omega_{zy} = \frac{1}{2}\left(\frac{\partial u_z}{\partial y} - \frac{\partial u_y}{\partial z}\right) \tag{3.41}$$

$$\omega_y = \Omega_{xz} = \frac{1}{2}\left(\frac{\partial u_x}{\partial z} - \frac{\partial u_z}{\partial x}\right) \tag{3.42}$$

We note that $\Omega_{yx} = -\Omega_{xy}$, $\Omega_{zy} = -\Omega_{yz}$, and $\Omega_{xz} = -\Omega_{zx}$. Hence taking $\Omega_{xx} = \Omega_{yy} = \Omega_{zz} = 0$, we may form the following skew-symmetric matrix:

$$\Omega_{ij} = \begin{bmatrix} 0 & \Omega_{xy} & \Omega_{xz} \\ -\Omega_{xy} & 0 & \Omega_{yz} \\ -\Omega_{xz} & -\Omega_{yz} & 0 \end{bmatrix} = \begin{bmatrix} 0 & -\omega_z & \omega_y \\ \omega_z & 0 & -\omega_x \\ -\omega_y & \omega_x & 0 \end{bmatrix} \tag{3.43}$$

where

$$\Omega_{ij} = -\Omega_{ji} = \frac{1}{2}\left(\frac{\partial u_i}{\partial x_j} - \frac{\partial u_j}{\partial x_i}\right) = \tfrac{1}{2}(u_{i,j} - u_{j,i}) \tag{3.44}$$

Using the same arguments that we employed previously for ε_{ij}, it readily follows that Ω_{ij} is a skew-symmetric, second-order tensor. We shall call Ω_{ij} the *rotation tensor*.

From Eq.(3.43), we see that the rotation vector $\boldsymbol{\omega}$ is related to the rotation tensor in the following way:

$$\boldsymbol{\omega} = \omega_x \hat{\mathbf{i}} + \omega_y \hat{\mathbf{j}} + \omega_z \hat{\mathbf{k}} = \Omega_{zy} \hat{\mathbf{i}} + \Omega_{xz} \hat{\mathbf{j}} + \Omega_{yx} \hat{\mathbf{k}} \tag{3.45}$$

[*] One can show that for small deformation in a vanishingly small element, the average rotation of *any two* line segments that are at right angles and normal to the axis of rotation will yield the same rigid-body rotation. Furthermore, this is also equal to the average rotation of *all* line segments normal to the axis in the vanishingly small element.

We leave it for you to show that Eq. (3.45), in conjunction with Eq. (3.44), may easily be expressed in vector notation as*

$$\boldsymbol{\omega} = \tfrac{1}{2}\operatorname{curl}\mathbf{u} = \tfrac{1}{2}\nabla\times\mathbf{u} \tag{3.46}$$

which in index notation becomes

$$\omega_i = \tfrac{1}{2}e_{ijk}\frac{\partial u_k}{\partial x_j} \tag{3.47}$$

Before going on to the next section, we shall relate the displacement gradient tensor with the strain and rotation tensors. You may readily verify by combining terms that the following statement is identically valid:

$$\frac{\partial u_i}{\partial x_j} \equiv \frac{1}{2}\left(\frac{\partial u_i}{\partial x_j}+\frac{\partial u_j}{\partial x_i}\right)+\frac{1}{2}\left(\frac{\partial u_i}{\partial x_j}-\frac{\partial u_j}{\partial x_i}\right) \tag{3.48}$$

On noting Eqs. (3.37) and (3.44), we write Eq. (3.48) as follows:

$$\boxed{\frac{\partial u_i}{\partial x_j} = \varepsilon_{ij} + \Omega_{ij}} \tag{3.49}$$

Substituting the result above into Eq. (3.47), we obtain

$$\omega_i = \tfrac{1}{2}e_{ijk}(\varepsilon_{kj}+\Omega_{kj}) \tag{3.50}$$

which reduces to

$$\omega_i = \tfrac{1}{2}e_{ijk}\Omega_{kj} = -\tfrac{1}{2}e_{ijk}\Omega_{jk} \tag{3.51}$$

Note that $e_{ijk}\varepsilon_{kj}$ vanishes as a result of the fact that it is the inner product over indices jk of a skew-symmetric tensor e_{ijk} in jk and a symmetric tensor ε_{jk}. Finally, if we multiply both sides of Eq. (3.51) by e_{ilm} and use the $e - \delta$ identity [see Eq. (1.42) and Problem 1.23], we reach the following useful inverted form of Eq.(3.51):

$$\Omega_{lm} = -e_{ilm}\omega_i \tag{3.52}$$

The following examples will illustrate the use of the concepts of this section.

Example 3.2

A body has deformed so as to have the following small displacement field:

$$u_1 = 0.003x_1 + 0.002x_2 \text{ ft}$$

$$u_2 = -0.001x_1 + 0.0005x_3 \text{ ft} \tag{a}$$

$$u_3 = 0.0006x_1 + 0.003x_2 - 0.003x_3 \text{ ft}$$

What are the strain and rotation tensors?

---

*In your fluids courses you studied *irrotational* flow where the rigid-body angular velocity of particles comprising the flow was zero. The so-called vorticity vector at a point was then defined for rotational flow as twice the angular velocity of a particle at the point. The vorticity vector was then shown to equal curl **V**.

The tensor $\partial u_i / \partial x_j$ is easily determined by inspection from Eq. (a) as

$$\frac{\partial u_i}{\partial x_j} = \begin{bmatrix} 0.003 & 0.002 & 0 \\ -0.001 & 0 & 0.0005 \\ 0.0006 & 0.003 & -0.003 \end{bmatrix} \tag{b}$$

Hence Eq. (3.44) gives

$$\Omega_{11} = 0$$

$$\Omega_{12} = \tfrac{1}{2}(0.002 + 0.001) = 0.0015$$

$$\Omega_{13} = \tfrac{1}{2}(0 - 0.0006) = -0.0003$$

$$\Omega_{21} = \tfrac{1}{2}(-0.001 - 0.002) = -0.0015$$

$$\Omega_{22} = 0$$

$$\Omega_{23} = \tfrac{1}{2}(0.0005 - 0.003) = -0.00125$$

$$\Omega_{31} = \tfrac{1}{2}(0.0006 - 0) = 0.0003$$

$$\Omega_{32} = \tfrac{1}{2}(0.003 - 0.0005) = 0.00125$$

$$\Omega_{33} = 0$$

Thus we have for the rotation tensor

$$\Omega_{ij} = \begin{bmatrix} 0 & 0.0015 & -0.0003 \\ -0.0015 & 0 & -0.00125 \\ 0.0003 & 0.00125 & 0 \end{bmatrix}$$

The components of the rotation vector $\boldsymbol{\omega}$ are given by Eq.(3.45). Thus

$$\omega_1 = \Omega_{32} = 0.00125 \text{ rad}$$

$$\omega_2 = \Omega_{13} = -0.0003 \text{ rad} \tag{c}$$

$$\omega_3 = \Omega_{21} = -0.0015 \text{ rad}$$

Finally, in accordance with Eq. (3.37), the strain tensor for displacement gradient tensor (b) becomes

$$\varepsilon_{11} = 0.003$$

$$\varepsilon_{12} = \tfrac{1}{2}(0.002 - 0.001) = 0.0005$$

$$\varepsilon_{13} = \tfrac{1}{2}(0 + 0.0006) = 0.0003$$

$$\varepsilon_{21} = \tfrac{1}{2}(-0.001 + 0.002) = 0.0005$$

$$\varepsilon_{22} = 0$$

$$\varepsilon_{23} = \tfrac{1}{2}(0.0005 + 0.003) = 0.00175$$

$$\varepsilon_{31} = \tfrac{1}{2}(0.0006 + 0) = 0.0003$$

$$\varepsilon_{32} = \tfrac{1}{2}(0.003 + 0.0005) = 0.00175$$

$$\varepsilon_{33} = -0.003$$

Accordingly,

$$\varepsilon_{ij} = \begin{bmatrix} 0.003 & 0.0005 & 0.0003 \\ 0.0005 & 0 & 0.00175 \\ 0.0003 & 0.00175 & -0.003 \end{bmatrix}$$

Example 3.2 is a case of an *affine* deformation wherein the strain tensor and the rotation tensor are composed of constants. This means that each small element of the body has the same rigid-body rotation and the same strain as every other element. Such deformation also is called *homogeneous* deformation.

Example 3.3

Given the following small displacement field:

$$u_x = (3x^2 y + 6) \times 10^{-3} \text{ ft}$$

$$u_y = (y^2 + 6xz) \times 10^{-3} \text{ ft}$$

$$u_z = (6z^2 + 2yz + 10) \times 10^{-3} \text{ ft}$$

What is the rotation of an element at position $x = 1, y = 0, z = 2$?

We must first ascertain the displacement gradient tensor $\partial u_i / \partial x_j$ for this displacement field. Thus

$$\frac{\partial u_x}{\partial x} = 0.006xy, \qquad \frac{\partial u_x}{\partial y} = 0.003x^2, \qquad \frac{\partial u_x}{\partial z} = 0$$

$$\frac{\partial u_y}{\partial x} = 0.006z, \qquad \frac{\partial u_y}{\partial y} = 0.002y, \qquad \frac{\partial u_y}{\partial z} = 0.006x$$

$$\frac{\partial u_z}{\partial x} = 0, \qquad \frac{\partial u_z}{\partial y} = 0.002z, \qquad \frac{\partial u_z}{\partial z} = (0.012z + 0.002y)$$

Hence

$$\frac{\partial u_i}{\partial x_j} = \begin{bmatrix} 0.006xy & 0.003x^2 & 0 \\ 0.006z & 0.002y & 0.006x \\ 0 & 0.002z & 0.012z + 0.002y \end{bmatrix} \tag{a}$$

We next get the rotation tensor Ω_{ij} from this field. By inspection we get

$$\Omega_{ij} = \begin{bmatrix} 0 & \frac{1}{2}(3x^2 - 6z) & 0 \\ -\frac{1}{2}(3x^2 - 6z) & 0 & \frac{1}{2}(6x - 2z) \\ 0 & -\frac{1}{2}(6x - 2z) & 0 \end{bmatrix} \times 10^{-3} \tag{b}$$

For the point of interest $(1, 0, 2)$ we have

$$\Omega_{ij} = \begin{bmatrix} 0 & -0.0045 & 0 \\ 0.0045 & 0 & 0.001 \\ 0 & -0.001 & 0 \end{bmatrix} \tag{c}$$

Hence we have, for the rotation components,

$$\omega_1 = \Omega_{32} = -0.001 \text{ rad}$$

$$\omega_2 = \Omega_{13} = 0 \text{ rad}$$

$$\omega_3 = \Omega_{21} = 0.0045 \text{ rad}$$

Note that the magnitude of the total rotation is $[(0.001)^2 + (0.0045)^2]^{1/2} = 0.0046$ rad.

You will recall that as used here, "deformation" refers to the entire process by which points in a body map into a deformed configuration, and the "small deformation" hypothesis requires that both the displacement gradients and the displacements be small. Clearly, then, the assumption of small deformation has an important affect on the representation for *both* the strain and the rotation, and we have seen this in this section.* In the next section we show that the strain tensor may be decomposed into a dilational component having to do with changes in volume, and a distortional component associated partly with the changes in angles between line segments.

3.5 CUBICAL DILATATION AND DISTORTION

Again we will consider the relative movement of four adjacent points for which an infinitesimal rectangular parallelepiped can be formed as shown in Fig. 3.8. The deformed volume element is denoted in dashed lines. The infinitesimal line segments along the coordinate axes in the undeformed geometry for the element are denoted as the lengths dX_1, dX_2, and dX_3. These line segments map into deformed lengths $d\widetilde{X}_1$, $d\widetilde{X}_2$, and $d\widetilde{X}_3$, respectively, in the deformed geometry. In Fig. 3.8 we have shown the three differential vectors $\delta x_i, \Delta x_j, dx_k$ forming the three edges of the element in the *deformed* state. The deformed lengths $d\widetilde{X}_1, d\widetilde{X}_2, d\widetilde{X}_3$ are the respective *magnitudes* of these vectors. We now define cubical dilatation for the indicated element as follows: *The cubical dilatation is the change in volume of an infinitesimal, rectangular parallelepiped, with sides originally in the coordinate directions, divided*

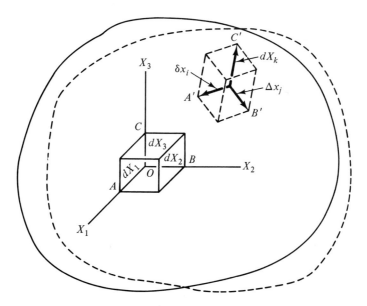

Figure 3.8 Deformation of an infinitesimal rectangular parallelepiped.

* You should be warned that the term "deformation" is often associated only with the changes in the *square* of the lengths of differential line segments. In that context "small deformation" is synonymous with "small strain" and is thus unrelated to rotation. For a presentation of the theory of finite deformation from this approach, see L. E. Malvern, *Introduction to the Mechanics of a Continuous Medium* (Englewood Cliffs, NJ: Prentice Hall, Inc., 1969), Sec. 4.5.

by the original volume. This is the so-called *Lagrangian* definition of cubical dilatation in conformity with our previous definition of strain.

You will recall that the triple scalar product of vectors, namely $(\mathbf{A} \times \mathbf{B}) \cdot \mathbf{C}$, gives the volume of a general parallelepiped having edges defined by vectors $\mathbf{A}$, $\mathbf{B}$, and $\mathbf{C}$. In index notation this volume is

$$v = e_{ijk} A_i B_j C_k \qquad (3.53)$$

As noted above, in deformed geometry (see Fig. 3.8) the edges of the deformed volume element are defined by differential vectors δx_i, Δx_j, and dx_k. We may thus calculate the volume $\widetilde{dv}$ of a general parallelepiped with δx_i, Δx_j, and dx_k as edges as follows:

$$\widetilde{dv} = e_{ijk} \delta x_i \Delta x_j dx_k \qquad (3.54)$$

This result, it is to be noted, is valid for finite deformation.

For *small deformation* we can approximate $\widetilde{dv}$ as given by Eq. (3.54) by

$$\widetilde{dv} \approx \widetilde{dX}_1 \widetilde{dX}_2 \widetilde{dX}_3 \qquad (3.55)$$

where as noted previously, $\widetilde{dX}_1$, $\widetilde{dX}_2$, $\widetilde{dX}_3$ are the lengths of the edges of the deformed volume element.* We can now give the change in volume of the element in Fig. 3.8 approximately as

$$\widetilde{dv} - dv = \widetilde{dX}_1 \widetilde{dX}_2 \widetilde{dX}_3 - dX_1 dX_2 dX_3 \qquad (3.56)$$

Note next that in accordance with Eq. (3.29) the strain ε_{11} at point O in the undeformed geometry is given by

$$\varepsilon_{11} = \lim_{\Delta X_1 \to 0} \frac{\widetilde{\Delta X}_1 - \Delta X_1}{\Delta X_1} = \frac{\widetilde{dX}_1 - dX_1}{dX_1} \qquad (3.57)$$

From this equation we can solve for $\widetilde{dX}_1$ to get

$$\widetilde{dX}_1 = dX_1(1 + \varepsilon_{11}) \qquad \text{(a)}$$

Similarly,

$$\widetilde{dX}_2 = dX_2(1 + \varepsilon_{22}) \qquad \text{(b)} \qquad (3.58)$$

$$\widetilde{dX}_3 = dX_3(1 + \varepsilon_{33}) \qquad \text{(c)}$$

Returning to Eq. (3.56) and inserting the results of Eqs. (3.58), we get

$$\widetilde{dv} - dv = dX_1 dX_2 dX_3(1 + \varepsilon_{11})(1 + \varepsilon_{22})(1 + \varepsilon_{33}) - dX_1 dX_2 dX_3$$

$$\approx dX_1 dX_2 dX_3(\varepsilon_{11} + \varepsilon_{22} + \varepsilon_{33}) = dX_1 dX_2 dX_3 \varepsilon_{kk}$$

where we have deleted the products of strains as negligible for small deformation. We then get for small deformation

$$\frac{\widetilde{dv} - dv}{dv} \equiv \Delta = 3\bar{\varepsilon} = \varepsilon_{kk} \qquad (3.59)$$

---

* The small deformation assumption permits us to neglect the effect of shear deformation on the volume change, and to treat the deformed element as a rectangular parallelepiped.

where Δ is the previously defined *cubical dilatation* and $\bar{\varepsilon}$ is the *average* normal strain. Note that Δ equals the first tensor invariant of ε_{ij}. This is now the second instance whereby an invariant has been shown to have physical significance. (Recall that the bulk stress $\bar{\tau}$ is an extension of the concept of pressure.) We shall later find physical significance for the other tensor invariants.*

Finally, as in the case of stress we define the *strain deviator* tensor e_{ij} as

$$e_{ij} = \varepsilon_{ij} - \tfrac{1}{3} \varepsilon_{kk} \, \delta_{ij} \qquad (3.60)$$

This tensor will be of much use to us in later chapters. Physically, it represents the deviation of a general state of strain from one-third of a state of pure cubical dilatation. We refer to e_{ij} as the *distortional* component of strain since its off-diagonal elements equal the shear strains, and are thus directly related to the changes in *angles* between line segments. The diagonal elements of e_{ij} give the *deviations* of the normal strain from the average normal strain. Note that as with any deviator tensor, $e_{kk} = \text{tr} \ (e) \equiv 0$.

3.6 STRAIN AS A SECOND-ORDER TENSOR

We have already shown that since $\partial u_i / \partial x_j$ is a second-order tensor, then ε_{ij} is a second-order tensor. Hence we can say that

$$\varepsilon_{i'j'} = a_{i'p} \, a_{j'q} \, \varepsilon_{pq} \qquad (3.61)$$

for an orthogonal transformation of coordinates.

Since strain is a symmetric, second-order tensor, we can apply all the conclusions reached in Chapter 2 for the stress tensor directly to the strain tensor. That is:

1. We can associate a second-order surface called a strain quadric with each state of strain.

2. There are three orthogonal directions where, for two of these directions, the normal strains take on the extreme values for the particular state of strain. Also, the shear strains are zero for these axes. These are the principal axes of strain.

3. The three tensor invariants for strain become

$$\varepsilon_{kk} = \varepsilon_{11} + \varepsilon_{22} + \varepsilon_{33} = \text{I}_\varepsilon \qquad \text{(a)}$$

$$\tfrac{1}{2}(\varepsilon_{ii}\,\varepsilon_{jj} - \varepsilon_{ij}\,\varepsilon_{ji}) = \begin{vmatrix} \varepsilon_{22} & \varepsilon_{23} \\ \varepsilon_{23} & \varepsilon_{33} \end{vmatrix} + \begin{vmatrix} \varepsilon_{11} & \varepsilon_{13} \\ \varepsilon_{13} & \varepsilon_{33} \end{vmatrix} + \begin{vmatrix} \varepsilon_{11} & \varepsilon_{12} \\ \varepsilon_{12} & \varepsilon_{22} \end{vmatrix} = \text{II}_\varepsilon \qquad \text{(b)} \qquad (3.62)$$

$$\tfrac{1}{6}(2\varepsilon_{ij}\,\varepsilon_{jk}\,\varepsilon_{ki} - 3\varepsilon_{ij}\,\varepsilon_{ji}\,\varepsilon_{kk} + \varepsilon_{ii}\,\varepsilon_{jj}\,\varepsilon_{kk}) = \begin{vmatrix} \varepsilon_{11} & \varepsilon_{12} & \varepsilon_{13} \\ \varepsilon_{12} & \varepsilon_{22} & \varepsilon_{23} \\ \varepsilon_{13} & \varepsilon_{23} & \varepsilon_{33} \end{vmatrix} = \text{III}_\varepsilon \qquad \text{(c)}$$

* We again state that since natural phenomena proceed without the benefit of man-made coordinates, it should come as no surprise that invariant quantities with respect to rotation of axes often mimic certain physical manifestations.

4. We can solve for the principal strains by employing the same cubic equation that was used for stress [i.e., Eq. (2.38)]. Thus

$$\varepsilon^3 - I_\varepsilon \varepsilon^2 + II_\varepsilon \varepsilon - III_\varepsilon = 0 \tag{3.63}$$

where I_ε, II_ε, and III_ε are the three tensor invariants previously given.

Furthermore, you will recall from Chapter 2 that for three-dimensional stress states we have the three-dimensional Mohr's circles construction, which includes the familiar Mohr's circle of plane stress as a special case. Similarly, for three-dimensional and for plane strain states we have useful Mohr's circle constructions. Note that the tensor component ε_{xy} and not the shear angle γ_{xy} must be used in a Mohr's circle of plane strain.

All the preceding results apply to any symmetric, second-order tensor. We now come to a vital consideration concerning strain variation with position.

3.7 EQUATIONS OF COMPATIBILITY

In Chapter 2 we found that the stress tensor had restrictions as to how it could vary over a finite domain. These restrictions comprise Newton's law [see Eq. (2.24)]. We have already placed certain restrictions on strain at a point in this chapter. For instance, we indicated that for small deformation we could give ε_{ij} via the displacement field u_i in the following manner:

$$\varepsilon_{ij} = \frac{1}{2}\left(\frac{\partial u_i}{\partial x_j} + \frac{\partial u_j}{\partial x_i}\right) = \tfrac{1}{2}(u_{i,j} + u_{j,i}) \tag{3.64}$$

We shall now place additional restrictions on how strain may vary in a body. These restrictions, called *compatibility* equations, play a vital role in solid mechanics. If the displacement field is given, we can readily compute the strain tensor field by substituting u_i into the equations above. The inverse problem of finding the displacement field from a strain field is not so simple. Here the displacement field, composed of three functions u_i, must be determined by integration of the six partial differential equations given by Eq. (3.64). To ensure single-valued, continuous solutions u_i, we must impose certain restrictions on the ε_{ij} which constitute three independent conditions. That is, we cannot set forth an arbitrary strain field ε_{ij} and expect it automatically to be associated with a single-valued continuous displacement field. But actual deformations *must* have single-valued displacement fields. Furthermore, the deformations of interest to us will be those having continuous displacement fields. Hence the restrictions we will reach in rendering u_i single-valued and continuous apply to our formulations. The resulting equations are the above-mentioned compatibility equations.

We shall set forth only necessary conditions on ε_{ij} for single-valuedness and continuity of u_i.* The use of Eq. (3.64) to give ε_{ij} requires that u_i have the afore-stated properties. Accordingly, we shall ensure these properties for u_i by working

---

* A more rigorous derivation involving the sufficiency of these conditions is given in Appendix I.

directly with these equations. We now form the following derivatives from these equations:

$$\varepsilon_{ij,\,kl} = \tfrac{1}{2}(u_{i,\,jkl} + u_{j,\,ikl})$$

$$\varepsilon_{kl,\,ij} = \tfrac{1}{2}(u_{k,\,lij} + u_{l,\,kij})$$

$$\varepsilon_{lj,\,ki} = \tfrac{1}{2}(u_{l,\,jki} + u_{j,\,lki}) = \tfrac{1}{2}(u_{l,\,kij} + u_{j,\,ikl})$$

$$\varepsilon_{ki,\,lj} = \tfrac{1}{2}(u_{k,\,ilj} + u_{i,\,klj}) = \tfrac{1}{2}(u_{k,\,lij} + u_{i,\,jkl})$$

where the rearrangement of the order of differentiation in the last two equations is valid because of the continuity of u_i. By adding the first two equations and then subtracting the last two equations, we may eliminate the u_i components and thus arrive at a set of relations involving only strains. That is,

$$\boxed{\varepsilon_{ij,\,kl} + \varepsilon_{kl,\,ij} - \varepsilon_{lj,\,ki} - \varepsilon_{ki,\,lj} = 0} \tag{3.65}$$

These form a set of 81 equations known as the compatibility equations that a strain field must satisfy if it is to be related to u_i via Eq. (3.64), which in turn means that u_i is single-valued and continuous. These equations are thus *necessary* requirements.

We now demonstrate that the 81 equations (3.65) are in fact only six different equations. First, without loss in generality, we may set $i = j$, yielding*

$$\varepsilon_{ii,\,kl} + \varepsilon_{kl,\,ii} - \varepsilon_{li,\,ki} - \varepsilon_{ki,\,li} = 0 \qquad \text{(no sum on } i) \tag{3.66}$$

This is permissible since i, j, k, and l can only range from 1 to 3, which means that we will always have two of the indices with the same value. Setting any pair other than i and j equal yields the same equation as above. Furthermore, if either or both of the remaining two indices also have this same value, we get a trivial equation $0 = 0$. We will see shortly that there are only six different nontrivial equations contained in Eq. (3.66) and hence in Eq. (3.65). Furthermore, in doing this we shall also obtain an alternative representation of these six compatibility equations which is more convenient than either Eq. (3.65) or Eq. (3.66). To this end, we select specific values of i, k, and l in Eq. (3.66) and label each equation with the notation S_{pq} as indicated below:

$$i = 1, k = l = 2: \qquad S_{33} = \frac{\partial^2 \varepsilon_{xx}}{\partial y^2} + \frac{\partial^2 \varepsilon_{yy}}{\partial x^2} - 2\frac{\partial^2 \varepsilon_{xy}}{\partial x\,\partial y} = 0 \tag{a}$$

$$i = 2, k = l = 3: \qquad S_{11} = \frac{\partial^2 \varepsilon_{yy}}{\partial z^2} + \frac{\partial^2 \varepsilon_{zz}}{\partial y^2} - 2\frac{\partial^2 \varepsilon_{yz}}{\partial y\,\partial z} = 0 \tag{b}$$

$$i = 3, k = l = 1: \qquad S_{22} = \frac{\partial^2 \varepsilon_{zz}}{\partial x^2} + \frac{\partial^2 \varepsilon_{xx}}{\partial z^2} - 2\frac{\partial^2 \varepsilon_{zx}}{\partial z\,\partial x} = 0 \tag{c}$$

$$\tag{3.67}$$

---

* This is *not* a contraction here. In order to indicate that a repeated pair of indices are *free* indices, one may enclose these indices in parentheses. Equation (3.66) would then be written as

$$\varepsilon_{(i)(i),\,kl} + \varepsilon_{kl,\,(i)(i)} - \varepsilon_{l(i),\,k(i)} - \varepsilon_{k(i),\,l(i)} = 0$$

$$i = 1, k = 2, l = 3: \quad S_{23} = -\frac{\partial^2 \varepsilon_{xx}}{\partial y \, \partial z} + \frac{\partial}{\partial x}\left(-\frac{\partial \varepsilon_{yz}}{\partial x} + \frac{\partial \varepsilon_{zx}}{\partial y} + \frac{\partial \varepsilon_{xy}}{\partial z}\right) = 0 \qquad \text{(d)}$$

$$i = 2, k = 3, l = 1: \quad S_{31} = -\frac{\partial^2 \varepsilon_{yy}}{\partial z \, \partial x} + \frac{\partial}{\partial y}\left(-\frac{\partial \varepsilon_{zx}}{\partial y} + \frac{\partial \varepsilon_{xy}}{\partial z} + \frac{\partial \varepsilon_{yz}}{\partial x}\right) = 0 \qquad \text{(e)}$$

$$i = 3, k = 1, l = 2: \quad S_{12} = -\frac{\partial^2 \varepsilon_{zz}}{\partial x \, \partial y} + \frac{\partial}{\partial z}\left(-\frac{\partial \varepsilon_{xy}}{\partial z} + \frac{\partial \varepsilon_{yz}}{\partial x} + \frac{\partial \varepsilon_{zx}}{\partial y}\right) = 0 \qquad \text{(f)}$$

Several things must be noted for the set of equations above. First, when $k = l$ (i.e., the first three equations), the p and q indices for S_{pq} both equal the number different than i and $l = k$. Also, for these cases we take the S_{pq} directly from substituting i, k, and l values into Eq. (3.66). When $k \neq l$ (i.e., the last three equations above) we take the p and q indices for S_{pq} to be $p = k$ and $q = l$. Furthermore, for $k \neq l$ we multiply Eq. (3.66) by -1 to get the proper S_{pq} formulations. Note further that for Eqs. (a), (b), (c), indices $i, k = l$ and $p = q$ are cyclic. Also, in Eqs. (d), (e), (f) indices $i, k = p$ and $l = q$ are cyclic. Additionally, you may readily show from Eq. (3.66) that $S_{pq} = S_{qp}$. Most important, we point out that *no additional different equations can be formed by using other combinations of i, k, and l values.* You may verify this yourself by attempting to form new equations from Eq. (3.66). For instance, we now have for $i = 1$ the case for $k = l = 2$ [Eq. (a)] and also the case for $k = 2, l = 3$ [Eq. (d)]. We might also propose for $i = 1$ the case $k = l = 3$. On examining such a possibility we see by considering Eq. (3.66) for this case that we already have this equation [i.e., Eq. (c)].

In index notation we have for the set of six equations above the following simple alternative form of compatibility:

$$S_{pq} = e_{pkm}\, e_{qln}\, \frac{\partial^2 \varepsilon_{kl}}{\partial x_m \, \partial x_n} = e_{pkm}\, e_{qln}\, \varepsilon_{kl,\, mn} = 0 \qquad (3.68)$$

You may readily verify the formulation above. It can also easily be shown that

$$\frac{\partial S_{pq}}{\partial x_q} = 0 \qquad (3.69)$$

which are three conditions called the *Bianchi conditions*. This result follows directly from the symmetry of the mixed derivative $\partial^2/\partial x_q \, \partial x_n$ and the skew symmetry of e_{qln}. This in turn means that the six different compatibility equations represent only three independent* conditions, and thus with these conditions the six strain displacement equations are now integrable for the three displacement components.

If we are given a continuous, single-valued displacement field and the strain field stems from this field via Eq. (3.64), we need not employ the compatibility equations since they will be identically satisfied. However, if a strain field is given not having been explicitly formed as described above, we must employ the compati-

---

*More precisely, compatibility equations (3.68) are six *linearly* independent conditions but because of Eq. (3.69) they yield only three *functionally* independent conditions. Equations (3.68) are derived in a more direct way in Appendix I.

bility equations as a necessary condition that the associated displacement field (which has not been explicitly stated) must be single-valued and continuous. In general, there are six compatibility equations as we have shown, but for the special case of plane strain ($\varepsilon_{zx} = \varepsilon_{zy} = \varepsilon_{zz} = 0$) there is only one nontrivial compatibility equation.

We now state without proof that the satisfaction of the compatibility equations comprises for a body with one point fixed, both the necessary and sufficient conditions for a single-valued, continuous displacement field, when the body is *simply connected*. We will only remark here that the simply connected condition follows directly from the presence of that condition in Stokes' theorem, as discussed in Chapter 1. If the body is *multiply connected*, the compatibility equations are only *necessary* conditions for a single-valued, continuous displacement field. *Other* conditions, which we shall not discuss in detail here, must be imposed for the *sufficiency* requirement (see Appendix I). We shall merely say here that these additional conditions are line integral conditions around the cavities of the multiply connected domain, and we call these the Cesàro integral conditions.

3.8 CLOSURE

In this chapter we have carefully developed the concept of the displacement gradient tensor, and from this and the definition of superposition the conditions for small deformation:

1. Small displacement field
2. Small displacement gradients

By considering the relative displacements of adjacent points (small domain) along coordinate axes, we were then able to formulate the concept of the Lagrangian strain tensor $\varepsilon_{ij} = \frac{1}{2}(u_{i,j} + u_{j,i})$ and the rotation tensor $\Omega_{ij} = \frac{1}{2}(u_{i,j} - u_{j,i})$, both for small deformation. Once having shown that strain is a second-order symmetric tensor, we were then able to draw from our studies in Chapter 2 many vital conclusions without further study, thus rewarding the efforts put forth in studying Cartesian tensors in Chapters 1 and 2.

We finished the chapter by presenting the six compatibility equations, which are necessary requirements to ensure that the displacement field associated with a given strain field is single-valued and continuous. We wish to point out that in the in-depth study of the energy methods of solid mechanics,* one finds that the compatibility equations play a vital role comparable and symmetric to the equations of equilibrium.

With the stress and strain tensors thus developed, our next efforts will be to present constitutive laws for elastic and inelastic behavior in Part II.

---

*See Chapter 3 of *Energy and Finite Element Methods in Structural Mechanics* by I. H. Shames and C. L. Dym (New York: Hemisphere Publishing Corp., 1985).

PROBLEMS

3.1. Given the displacement field

$$\mathbf{u} = [20X^2 Y\hat{\mathbf{i}} + 10(Y^2 + Z^2)\hat{\mathbf{j}} + (X + 3Z^3)\hat{\mathbf{k}}] \times 10^{-2} \text{ ft}$$

what is the position vector x_i in the deformed geometry of point P at $(1, 2, -3)$ in the undeformed geometry?

3.2. A displacement field is given as

$$\mathbf{u} = (0.16X^2 + \sin Y)\hat{\mathbf{i}} + \left(0.1Z + \frac{X}{Y^3}\right)\hat{\mathbf{j}} + 0.4\hat{\mathbf{k}} \text{ ft}$$

As a result of deformation, what is the increase in distance between two points, which in the undeformed geometry have position vectors

$$\mathbf{r}_1 = 10\hat{\mathbf{i}} + 3\hat{\mathbf{j}} \text{ ft}$$

$$\mathbf{r}_2 = 3\hat{\mathbf{j}} + 4\hat{\mathbf{k}} \text{ ft}$$

3.3. A displacement field given as

$$u_i = \lambda_{ij} X_j$$

where λ_{ij} form a set of constants, is called an *affine deformation*. If

$$\lambda_{ij} = \begin{bmatrix} 0.2 & -0.05 & -0.1 \\ 0.03 & 0.1 & -0.02 \\ 0.003 & -0.2 & 0.03 \end{bmatrix}$$

what is the displacement of a point whose position vector from the fixed point in the undeformed geometry is

$$\mathbf{r} = \hat{\mathbf{i}} - \hat{\mathbf{j}} + 3\hat{\mathbf{k}}$$

3.4. Show that for affine deformations (see Problem 3.3):
(a) Plane sections remain plane during deformation.
(b) Straight lines remain straight lines during deformation.

3.5. In Problem 3.3, what is the equation of the surface that was the XY plane in the undeformed geometry? [*Hint*: A simple procedure is to consider two position vectors in the XY plane such as $X_a\hat{\mathbf{i}}$ and $Y_b\hat{\mathbf{j}}$. Find the normal $\hat{\mathbf{n}}$ to these vectors in the deformed geometry. Now the plane desired must have in it position vectors

$$\mathbf{r} = (x\hat{\mathbf{i}} + y\hat{\mathbf{j}} + z\hat{\mathbf{k}})$$

such that $\hat{\mathbf{n}}\cdot\mathbf{r} = 0$. This will lead to a relation between coordinates x, y, and z.]

3.6. Find the displacement gradient matrix for the displacement field of Problem 3.1. What is $\partial u_y/\partial Z$ at $(2, 0, 3)$ in the undeformed geometry?

3.7. In Problem 3.1, what is the displacement component at position $(2, 0, 1)$ in the direction

$$\hat{\boldsymbol{\epsilon}} = 0.6\hat{\mathbf{i}} + 0.8\hat{\mathbf{j}}$$

3.8. In Example 3.1 of Section 3.2, find the displacement gradient tensor components for a primed set of axes $X'Y'Z'$ formed by rotating axes XYZ 30° about the X axis in a clockwise direction, as one looks along the positive X axis toward the origin.

3.9. In Example 3.1 of Section 3.2, find the other two components of the unit relative displacement vector.

3.10. Using the displacement field of Problem 3.1, find the unit relative displacement vector at $(3, 1, 1)$ for a line segment originally along axis X_3.

3.11. Using the displacement field of Example 3.1 of Section 3.2, find the unit relative displacement vector at $(1, 2, 0)$ for a line segment having the direction given by the unit vector

$$\hat{\epsilon} = 0.2\,\hat{i} + 0.8\,\hat{j} + 0.566\,\hat{k}$$

3.12. Suppose that we have two successive small deformations represented by the displacement gradient tensors at point P:

$$\left(\frac{\partial u_i^{(1)}}{\partial x_j}\right)_P = \begin{bmatrix} 0.02 & 0.01 & 0 \\ 0 & 0.01 & -0.02 \\ 0 & 0 & -0.02 \end{bmatrix}$$

and

$$\left(\frac{\partial u_i^{(2)}}{\partial x_j}\right)_P = \begin{bmatrix} 0.01 & 0.015 & -0.02 \\ 0 & 0 & -0.01 \\ 0 & -0.03 & 0.04 \end{bmatrix}$$

What is the total change at point P of a vector Δs given by

$$\Delta s = (6\,\hat{i} + 10\,\hat{j} + 2\,\hat{k}) \times 10^{-3}$$

3.13. For the following small displacement field

$$\mathbf{u} = [(3x^2 + y)\hat{i} + (3y + z^2)\hat{j} + 2z^2\,\hat{k}] \times 10^{-3} \text{ ft}$$

what are strains ε_{xz} and ε_{zz} at $(2, 1, 3)$? What is the rotation at this point about the y axis?

3.14. A body element undergoes a small rotation $\boldsymbol{\omega}$ given as follows:

$$\boldsymbol{\omega} = 0.0002\,\hat{i} + 0.0005\,\hat{j} - 0.0002\,\hat{k} \text{ rad}$$

What is the rotation tensor Ω_{ij} at this point?

3.15. Given the small displacement field

$$\mathbf{u} = [(6y + 5z)\hat{i} + (-6x + 3z)\hat{j} + (-5x - 3y)\hat{k}] \times 10^{-3}$$

show that this field is that of pure rigid-body rotation. What is the rotation vector $\boldsymbol{\omega}$ for the body?

3.16. An element at P is subject to a small deformation given by the displacement gradient tensor

$$\left(\frac{\partial u_i}{\partial x_j}\right)_P = \begin{bmatrix} 0.01 & 0 & 0 \\ -0.02 & 0.03 & 0 \\ 0 & -0.02 & -0.01 \end{bmatrix}$$

What are the rotation tensor, the strain tensor, and the angle of rotation for this element?

3.17. Given the small displacement field

$$\mathbf{u} = [(x^3 + 10)\hat{i} + 3yz\hat{j} + (z^2 - yx)\hat{k}] \times 10^{-3} \text{ ft}$$

what is the rigid-body translation of the body, with the origin chosen as the reference point? What is the rotation of an element at position $(2, 1, 0)$?

3.18. Given the small displacement field

$$u_x = 0.06x + 0.05y - 0.01z \text{ ft}$$

$$u_y = 0.01y - 0.03z \text{ ft}$$

$$u_z = -0.02x + 0.01z \text{ ft}$$

what is the normal strain ε_{xx} at all points of the body? If there is a line segment 10 ft long parallel to the x axis in the undeformed geometry, what will be the new length of this line segment?

3.19. The following state of strain exists at a point in a body

$$\varepsilon_{ij} = \begin{bmatrix} 0.01 & -0.02 & 0 \\ -0.02 & 0.03 & -0.01 \\ 0 & -0.01 & 0 \end{bmatrix}$$

In a direction $\hat{\mathbf{p}}$ having the direction cosines $l = 0.6$, $m = 0$, $n = 0.8$, what is ε_{pp}?

3.20. In Problem 3.19, a set of axes $x'y'z'$ is chosen as is shown in Fig. P3.20. What is the strain tensor at the point of interest for this new reference?

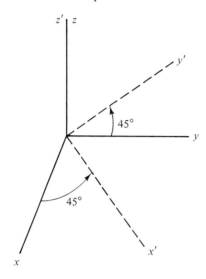

Figure P3.20

3.21. Prove that the strain tensor for small deformations

$$\varepsilon_{ij} = \tfrac{1}{2}(u_{i,j} + u_{j,i})$$

transforms properly under an *inversion* of the x_1 axis. (*Hint:* Compare the result found by using the sign conventions for the u_i and $\partial/\partial x_j$ vectors with the result from the tensor transformation law.)

3.22. The principal strains at a point in a body are $\varepsilon_{xx} = 0.002$, $\varepsilon_{yy} = 0.001$, and $\varepsilon_{zz} = 0$. What is the shear angle $\gamma_{x'y'}$ using Fig. P3.20 to get the direction of the coordinate axes?

3.23. In Problem 3.19, what are the three strain tensor invariants at the point of interest?

3.24. Using Fig. P3.24, show for plane strain that

$$\varepsilon_{x'x'} = \frac{\varepsilon_{xx} + \varepsilon_{yy}}{2} + \frac{\varepsilon_{xx} - \varepsilon_{yy}}{2} \cos 2\theta + \frac{\gamma_{xy}}{2} \sin 2\theta$$

and

$$\gamma_{x'y'} = \gamma_{xy} \cos 2\theta - (\varepsilon_{xx} - \varepsilon_{yy}) \sin 2\theta.$$

3.25. Given the following state of strain at a point,

$$\varepsilon_{ij} = \begin{bmatrix} 0 & 0.002 & 0 \\ 0.002 & -0.001 & -0.003 \\ 0 & -0.003 & 0 \end{bmatrix}$$

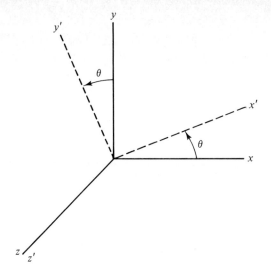

Figure P3.24

what are the maximum and minimum normal strains? What are the corresponding directions?

3.26. Given the following state of strain at a point,

$$\varepsilon_{ij} = \begin{bmatrix} 0.003 & 0 & -0.003 \\ 0 & 0.004 & 0 \\ -0.003 & 0 & 0.002 \end{bmatrix}$$

what are the magnitude and direction of the algebraically maximum normal strain?

3.27. Express the compatibility equations for the case of *plane strain*. Show that there is only one nontrivial compatibility equation for this case if we assume that the nonzero in-plane strains are independent of the coordinate normal to this plane. (In Chapter 13 we shall learn that for *plane stress* the full set of compatability equations must in general be considered, since the in-plane stresses will *not* in general be independent of the normal coordinate.)

3.28. Given the plane-strain distribution

$$\varepsilon_{xx} = 3x^2 y$$

$$\varepsilon_{yy} = 4y^2 x + 10^{-2}$$

$$\varepsilon_{xy} = yz + x^3$$

are the compatibility equations satisfied?

3.29. Verify the following in reference to compatibility equations (3.65) and (3.66).
  (a) Setting $k = l$ in Eq. (3.65) again yields Eq. (3.66), which was obtained by setting $i = j$.
  (b) Setting $i = k$ in Eq. (3.66) yields the trivial result $0 = 0$.
  (c) Setting $i = 3$ and $k = l = 2$ in Eq. (3.66) is equivalent to setting $i = 2$ and $k = l = 3$ [i.e., it yields Eq. (3.67b), which is S_{11}].
  (d) Setting $i = 3$, $k = 2$, and $l = 1$ in Eq. (3.66) is equivalent to setting $i = 3$, $k = 1$, and $l = 2$ (i.e., $S_{21} = S_{12}$).

Useful Constitutive Laws

Behavior of
Engineering Materials

4.1 INTRODUCTION

Most of the working knowledge on material properties we now possess stems from macroscopic testing of materials, and it is the results of such tests as well as the macroscopic theories stemming from such tests that concern us in this chapter. In Part A of the chapter we focus most of our attention on the tensile test and discuss certain basic aspects of the resulting one-dimensional stress-strain laws. The creep test will also be discussed in some detail. We then develop these considerations further by giving in Part B various one-dimensional idealized stress-strain diagrams. This is followed by a presentation of some useful elastic, viscoelastic, and plastic phenomenological material models. The emphasis throughout the chapter is on simple, one-dimensional tests, since multidimensional laws may usually be obtained via appropriate extension of the results from such tests.

For some time, however, solid-state physicists and engineers have been intensively studying the microscopic bases for mechanical properties (i.e., actions at the atomic and molecular level). Modern technology is putting our structures into more complex environments and under more complex conditions for which macroscopic laboratory tests, such as the ones we describe in this chapter, are becoming inadequate. Needed for a better understanding of how a material is to behave under a combination of conditions, such as high temperature, dynamic loads, radiation, temperature gradients, vibration, and so on, is a comprehension of how mechanical action relates to atomic and molecular structure. For this reason we have included certain introductory discussions concerning the microscopic level in Appendix VII.

PART A
ONE-DIMENSIONAL MACROSCOPIC BEHAVIOR

4.2 THE TENSILE TEST

The most basic test in the study of stress-strain relations is the simple tensile test wherein a cylindrical specimen of the type shown in Fig. 4.1 is subjected by a tensile test machine to a force F along the centerline of the specimen. The distance L between two points on the specimen is measured at all times by extensometer gauge (1) as seen in the diagram. Another extensometer gauge (2) meanwhile measures the diameter D of the cylinder. As the force F is varied, we measure L and D for each setting of F. Hence, at any setting, we have the following information.

1. *Eulerean* or *actual stress* $(\tau_{zz})_{act}$: computed as F/A_{act}, where A_{act} is the cross-sectional area of the cylinder found by employing the actual diameter D given by gauge 2

2. *Lagrangian or engineering stress* $(\tau_{zz})_{eng}$: computed as F/A_0, where A_0 is the initial unstrained cross-sectional area of the cylinder

3. *Lagrangian strain*, ε_{zz}: computed by the ratio $\Delta L/L_0$, where ΔL is found using gauge 1 and L_0 is the unstrained length

It should be pointed out that the rate of loading of the specimen should be slow enough to avoid dynamic effects, and the temperature should not be so high as to bring into play long-time effects, such as creep, an action that we shall describe in

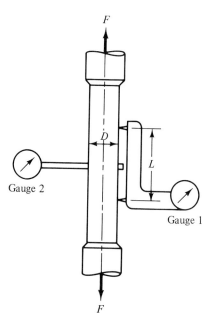

Figure 4.1 Test specimen with extensometer gauges.

more detail later. Also, we mention that various other definitions of strain are also possible,* but we shall not consider these here.

It is customary to plot the engineering stress, $(\tau_{zz})_{\text{eng}}$, versus the strain ε_{zz} for such a test. Because the volume of the specimen will change only slightly, there will normally take place a contraction of the cross-sectional area A as the tensile load is increased so that the engineering stress will be less than the actual stress at all times. This is the Poisson effect, which we shall discuss later. For small loads, A will not be appreciably smaller than A_0, so that little difficulty is encountered by using the simpler engineering stress. However, for large loads there will be a significant difference between A and A_0 with the result that the curve $(\tau_{zz})_{\text{eng}}$ versus ε_{zz} will appear to be "unnatural." Nevertheless, because $(\tau_{zz})_{\text{eng}}$ is related simply by a direct proportionality to F through the constant $1/A_0$, and because the lateral contractions are not easily measured accurately, engineers are often motivated to use the engineering stress, $(\tau_{zz})_{\text{eng}}$, rather than the actual stress, $(\tau_{zz})_{\text{act}}$.

We have shown a stress-strain diagram from a simple tensile test in Fig. 4.2. This is a typical curve for a low-carbon-steel specimen. Although stress-strain curves may be quite different for other materials, we shall consider this particular curve in some detail so as to set forth most easily certain general definitions. The compression test is very similar to the tensile test. The mechanical properties that we shall discuss appear in compression tests in the same way for many materials as they do in tensile tests. Notice that the curve in Fig. 4.2 is a straight line at the early stages of the loading. That is, the stress is proportional to strain and we may then state that

$$\tau_{zz} = E\varepsilon_{zz} \tag{4.1}$$

where the proportionality constant E is called *Young's modulus* of elasticity having

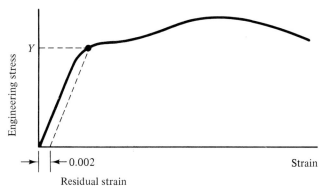

Figure 4.2 Typical stress-strain curve for low-carbon steel.

* For *large* deformation, frequent use is made of the *natural strain increment* defined as

$$d\varepsilon_{zz} = \frac{dL}{L}$$

where L is the *current* length. An integration of this equation then yields a *logarithmic* definition of strain. For details, see p. 150 of L. E. Malvern, *Introduction to the Mechanics of a Continuous Medium* (Englewood Cliffs, NJ: Prentice Hall, Inc., 1969).

dimensions $(F)/(L)^2$, as you may easily verify yourself. Essentially, this result was reached about 300 years ago by Robert Hooke,* who as a result of his experiments with metallic rods under axially applied tensile loads, concluded that *ut tensio sic vis* or roughly "the extension is proportional to the force," a relation known by every high school student as *Hooke's law*. The stress at which the linear relationship between stress and strain ceases is called the *proportional limit*. Its value, however, is not easily measured.

Not all materials have a finite straight-line portion at the outset of the stress-strain diagram. For instance, rubber is a material that generally does not, and a stress-strain curve for a particular specimen of this material is shown in Fig. 4.3. Despite the apparent difference in appearance between the curves for steel and rubber in Figs. 4.2 and 4.3, there is an important similarity to be pointed out. That is, if that particular rubber specimen is unloaded to zero load, it will return to its original geometry along the loading curve as will the steel specimen, provided that the load on the latter develops a stress τ_{zz} below the proportional limit. Thus both materials may act in a *perfectly elastic* manner.

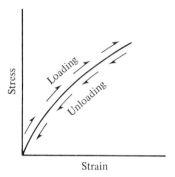

Strain   **Figure 4.3**   Nonlinear elastic behavior.

For the steel specimen, there is a stress level greater than the proportional limit such that when the specimen is unloaded from a stress level above the aforementioned level, the original geometry is no longer recovered. We call this stress level, which gives the limit of elastic behavior and the onset of inelastic behavior, the *elastic limit*. For steels, the elastic limit is very close to the proportional limit, so close that one usually does not make a distinction between these two stresses. A material having a proportional limit close to the elastic limit, such as steel, is termed a *linear elastic material*. Materials that have a proportional limit far below the elastic limit and which have loading and unloading curves that coincide, such as case of the particular rubber specimen discussed, are called *nonlinear elastic materials*.

If the specimen returns to the original geometry but along an unloading curve different than the loading curve (see Fig. 4.4), the material is called *anelastic*. Since the work put into the material is proportional to the area under the stress-strain curve, it is clear that a net amount of work is done on the material during a loading

---

*For details, see A. E. Love, *A Treatise on the Mathematical Theory of Elasticity* (New York: Dover Publications, 1944), p. 2.

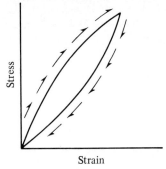

Stress

Strain　　　　　　　　**Figure 4.4**　Anelastic behavior.

cycle. This work goes into the material as thermal energy and is eventually dissipated to the surroundings. Some rubber materials having stress-strain diagrams such as is shown in Fig. 4.4, are very useful for damping vibrations and are used to support motors and other rotating machinery.

Returning to the stress-strain diagram for steel, it is to be pointed out that the elastic limit like the proportional limit is difficult to measure accurately. Hence engineers employ as a more useful definition of the beginning of inelastic behavior the *yield stress* or the *yield point*, which is the value of stress resulting in a small specified residual strain (usually, 0.002) upon unloading. The point Y on the stress-strain diagram in Fig. 4.2 corresponds to the yield point.

Our discussion of the stress-strain diagram has taken us thus far only to the yield point. In the domain up to the yield point, the actual cross-sectional area and the original area of the specimen differ by a very small amount, so it matters little which area one uses for computations. We have been using A_0 for reasons set forth earlier. However, as pointed out earlier, at all times during the tensile test, a continual decrease in the cross-sectional area of the specimen takes place as the load is applied. (In the case of a compression test, there is clearly a corresponding increase in the cross-sectional area as the load is applied.) This lateral strain effect is called the *Poisson effect*. After the yield point there may be a rapid increase in the strain ε_{zz}, and simultaneously, there will then be a rapid change in the cross-sectional area owing to the Poisson effect. This will cause the values of engineering stress and actual stress to diverge appreciably from each other. To illustrate this, Fig. 4.5 shows simple stress-strain curves using both the actual stress and the engineering stress for a tensile test. (Also shown dashed is the corresponding compression test using engineering stress.) We also point out that the actual tensile stress continually increases until the specimen breaks (i.e., *fracture* occurs).

As pointed out earlier, the engineering stress is proportional to the force F, so the maximum load capability of the specimen is developed at the highest point of the engineering tensile stress-strain curve. The engineering stress at this point, denoted as U in Fig. 4.5, is termed the *ultimate stress*. We may express the approach to the ultimate stress condition mathematically by considering the relation

$$F = A_0(\tau_{zz})_{\text{eng}} = A\,(\tau_{zz})_{\text{act}} \tag{4.2}$$

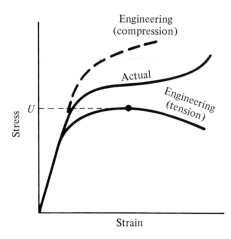

Figure 4.5 Different diagrams for one material.

Using the symbol δ for the elongation ΔL, we can then say on differentiating the preceding equation with respect to δ:

$$\frac{A_0 \, d(\tau_{zz})_{\text{eng}}}{d\delta} = A \frac{d(\tau_{zz})_{\text{act}}}{d\delta} + (\tau_{zz})_{\text{act}} \frac{dA}{d\delta} \qquad (4.3)$$

For small values of force (i.e., for conditions below the yield point), the quantity $(\tau_{zz})_{\text{act}} \, dA/d\delta$, which clearly is always negative for a tensile test, is extremely small in magnitude compared to the term $A \, d(\tau_{zz})_{\text{act}}/d\delta$, which is always positive for a tensile test. However, increasing $(\tau_{zz})_{\text{eng}}$ beyond the yield point results in a significant rate of increase in the magnitude of the negative quantity $(\tau_{zz})_{\text{act}}(dA/d\delta)$ until, at the ultimate stress condition, the right side of Eq. (4.3) becomes zero. What happens after this point has been reached? Our engineering stress-strain curve tells us that the load-carrying capacity of the specimen then falls off as the strain increases further. Actually, when the ultimate stress has just been passed in a test, the specimen cannot maintain the applied load and the test proceeds precipitously to fracture of the specimen. So quickly does this happen that it is difficult to record data for the portion of the engineering stress-strain curve beyond the ultimate-stress point.

The loss in load-carrying capacity beyond the ultimate stress point just described does not occur as a result of rapid area decrease of the entire specimen. Rather, it occurs as a result of a rapid area decrease at some localized portion of the specimen. We call this action "necking" of the specimen. The portion in the specimen where necking takes place depends primarily on local imperfections of the material. We have shown a diagram of a specimen loaded to fracture in Fig. 4.6. The necking action can easily be seen by observing the broken portion of the specimen. When there is large inelastic deformation occurring rapidly in a small domain, as in the necked region of the tensile specimen, we say there is *plastic flow* in this domain. The fact that plastic flow can occur locally in a structure is the underlying basis for the development of the field of *limit analysis*.* This affords a means of making simple structural computations beyond the elastic limit of the material involved.

* Limit analysis is discussed briefly in Chapter 10.

Figure 4.6 Fractured specimen.

This brings us through the tensile test of a low-carbon (mild) steel specimen. We thus have examined one of the most important of structural materials. What about other structural materials? We have already considered some rubber materials in this section, and we see that there can be great departures from the case exemplified by mild steel. However, we can use mild steel as a basis of comparison in our discussion of other material so as to make our communication more meaningful. Furthermore, the definitions that we set up while discussing the mild steel case hold for general discussions. Figure 4.7 shows typical tensile stress-strain diagrams for iron, aluminum, and some of their alloys. In Table 4.1 we have listed representative values for some of the parameters we have been discussing in this section for certain important structural materials. For other types of materials (e.g., other metals, plastics, rock, ice, etc.), similar behavior is often observed. However, features of behavior which are characteristic of each particular material may also occur, and the mechanical properties may change significantly with slight changes in heat treatment, alloying, temperature, and so on. For more precise, detailed information of this type you are urged to consult structural or materials handbooks.

In this section we have focused our attention on the one-dimensional tensile test. As we consider more general loadings and geometries in later chapters, it will become necessary to consider other simple tests. Consequently, we briefly discuss two such *simple* tests here. One of these is the *pure shear test*. In this test a torsion

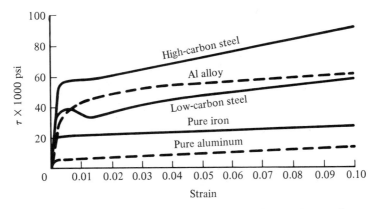

Figure 4.7 Stress-strain diagrams for iron and aluminum and some alloys.

TABLE 4.1 Some Mechanical Properties of Common Engineering Materials

Material	Young's Modulus of Elasticity, E ($\times 10^6$ psi)	Ultimate Stress, U ($\times 10^3$ psi)	Yield Stress at 0.002, Y ($\times 10^3$ psi)	Shear Modulus, G ($\times 10^6$ psi)
Aluminum alloy				
(heat treated)	10	60	45	4
Brass (cast)	13	45	20	5
Copper (hard drawn)	17	55	40	6
Cast iron	14[a]	20	—	5.6
Magnesium	6.5	35	23	2.4
Structural steel	29	60	35	12
Stainless steel	28	120	80	10

[a] The modulus of elasticity is about the same in tension and compression for all materials listed except cast iron, where only the tensile modulus has been given.

apparatus applies a carefully controlled twist on a cylindrical specimen. Within the linear elastic range of the material the shear stress τ_{xy} is related to the engineering shear strain γ_{xy} by the linear relation

$$\tau_{xy} = G\gamma_{xy} \tag{4.4}$$

where G is called the *shear modulus* of elasticity. Values of G are also tabulated in Table 4.1. The other simple test is the *pressure* test, in which a material is subjected to carefully controlled *hydrostatic* pressure $p = -\tau_{kk}/3$ while the volume dilatation $\Delta = \varepsilon_{kk}$ is measured. For the linear elastic range of the material, we again obtain a linear relation

$$p - -K\Delta \tag{4.5}$$

where K is called the *bulk modulus* of elasticity.

4.3 STRAIN HARDENING

In many materials, such as mild steel, aluminum, and copper, it is observed that ever-increasing actual stress is required for continued deformation beyond the yield point. This is the case for the stress-strain diagrams shown in Fig. 4.7. We call this effect *strain hardening*. Strain hardening can be explained qualitatively for metals by the use of *dislocation* theory, and we present such an explanation in Section VII.10 of Appendix VII.

There is another important phenomenon in the plastic range that is associated with strain hardening. It has to do with the unloading of a specimen, having a linear elastic range, from the plastic range. You will recall that in the preceding section we discussed the unloading of a linear elastic material when the load was in the elastic range, as well as the unloading of a nonlinear elastic material. In those cases, complete removal of load results in a recovery of the original geometry (i.e., there is no permanent set). Furthermore, the unloading path must retrace the loading path in the stress-strain diagram. In unloading a material with a linear elastic range from a load in the plastic range, we do not retrace the loading path but instead move along a new path that is essentially parallel to the linear elastic portion of the original loading path. This has been shown in Fig. 4.8, where the initial loading has been stopped at *A* and the first unloading is shown to take place along a straight line to point *B* on the abscissa. Thus we have introduced a permanent set given by *OB* on the abscissa. The elastic recovery, on the other hand, clearly is *BE*. Now on a second loading, we move along path *BA*. A second unloading from a stress below that corresponding to point *A* will essentially move along path *BA* back to *B*, so we have for practical purposes a linear elastic range from *B* to *A*. An inspection of the diagram will indicate that the yield point has been raised for the second loading as a result of the first loading into the plastic range. The raising of the yield point by this action is another manifestation of strain hardening. Beyond the new yield point, the second loading proceeds along *AC*, which you will notice is essentially along the stress curve that would be followed by an uninterrupted first loading. At *C*, a second unloading is shown and the same process is repeated.

It is to be pointed out that unloading and reloading curves do not exactly overlap. Instead, they form a small hysteresis loop as shown in Fig. 4.9 in an exaggerated manner. There is an energy loss during a cycle represented by the area of

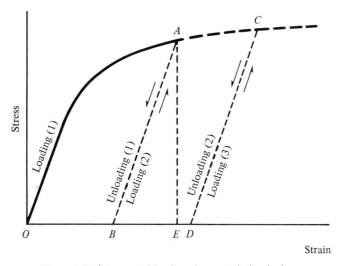

Figure 4.8 Interrupted loading shows strain hardening.

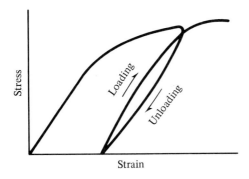

Figure 4.9 Interrupted loading with hysteresis.

the hysteresis loop. This energy, however, usually is very small. Finally, it should be pointed out that the change in yield point by strain hardening is observable only in the direction of initial loading. That is, there is no increase in yield stress in the material at right angles to the direction of the initial loading.

4.4 OTHER PROPERTIES PERTAINING TO THE TENSILE TEST

On the basis of the simple tensile test described earlier and the simple compression test, which is essentially the same except for direction, we can make additional useful classifications that are meaningful in describing mechanical behavior of materials.

First we can form classes of materials on the basis of the behavior of a specimen in a tensile test carried out to the point where the specimen fractures. Materials exhibiting little or no plastic deformation up to fracture, such as cast iron and glass, are called *brittle* materials. Materials exhibiting substantial plastic deformation up to the point of fracture, such as low-carbon steel, are called *ductile* materials. There is a wide range of behavior between the brittle and ductile designations (e.g., high-carbon steel is less ductile than low-carbon steel). For a brittle material, a stress-strain curve carried out in a tensile test will generally differ from the corresponding curve carried out as a compression test. Furthermore, brittle materials usually exhibit a considerable scatter in the breaking points found by a series of many tests. Ductile materials, on the other hand, give essentially the same stress-strain curve for tensile or compression test and have yield points, breaking points, and so on, which are more reproducible in a series of tests. We next consider another important property.

It was pointed out earlier that a tensile load on the specimen causes a lateral contraction which we called the Poisson effect. By the same mechanism a compression test induces a lateral expansion. In the linear elastic range, we find from these tests that the lateral strain is proportional to the longitudinal strain and may be expressed as follows:

$$\varepsilon_{lat} = -\nu\varepsilon_{long} \tag{4.6}$$

where the constant of proportionality ν is called *Poisson's ratio* and usually ranges for engineering materials from 0.2 to 0.5. In Chapter 5 we shall see that Poisson's ratio can be considered as one of the fundamental constants characterizing the general mechanical behavior of linear elastic, homogeneous, isotropic materials. (Poisson's ratio is also discussed in Section VII.6 of Appendix VII from the microscopic point of view.) In a *homogeneous* medium material properties are independent of *position*, while in an *isotropic* medium material properties are independent of *direction* at a point.* Thus we see that for such materials, the simple tensile test

---

*Thus far we have introduced the four linear elastic material constants E, G, K, and ν. In Chapter 5 we shall learn that only *two* of the elastic constants are independent if the material is isotropic. Furthermore, whereas E, G, and K must be nonnegative, Poisson's ratio must lie in the interval $-1 \leq \nu \leq \frac{1}{2}$ and thus in theory *may* be negative. This point will be of great importance when we discuss uniqueness theorems in Chapter 9.

permits the evaluation of the Poisson ratio. One may also introduce a plastic Poisson's ratio ν_p to describe lateral contraction in the plastic range of a tensile test. Plastic deformation is almost incompressible, and it immediately follows that the plastic Poisson's ratio is close to 0.5. To show this consider a tensile test with longitudinal strain $\varepsilon_{zz} > 0$ and lateral strains $\varepsilon_{xx} = \varepsilon_{yy} = -\nu_p \varepsilon_{zz}$. Since $\Delta \equiv \varepsilon_{xx} + \varepsilon_{yy} + \varepsilon_{zz}$ vanishes for incompressible behavior, we clearly have $\nu_p = 0.5$ for this case.

In the tensile tests discussed up to this time, we have assumed that the temperature of the specimen was uniform and low enough to avoid long-time creep effects. Also we pointed out that tests were conducted slowly enough to avoid short-time dynamic effects; such tests are said to be *quasi-static*. Knowledge of the behavior of materials under conditions where temperature is elevated and where short- or long-time effects become significant is becoming increasingly more essential in our progressing technology. We therefore shall now discuss these effects briefly.

Time Effects

A rapid rate of loading will result in a different stress-strain curve than a slow rate of loading. This will particularly be so for a soft material or for structural materials at elevated temperatures. These materials are termed *rate-sensitive* materials. In such cases, information as to the rate of loading must be included as pertinent information for the stress-strain curve. Essentially there will be a raising of the stress-strain curve as the rate of loading is increased. Rate sensitivity can be associated with *viscoelastic* or *viscoplastic* effects, and we shall consider these phenomena in subsequent sections. Also, if the stress is repeatedly cycled in time, we find that the stress required for rupture is reduced. This important phenomenon is called *fatigue* failure. Fatigue is a highly specialized and important area of current research, but this topic is beyond the scope of the present book. Those interested in this subject are referred to the extensive literature in machine design, fracture mechanics, and damage theory.

Temperature–Time Effects

At the other extreme, we now examine long-time effects wherein temperature plays an important role. We shall consider the case of a tensile specimen on which a constant stress is maintained over a long period of time. In any material at an elevated temperature there will take place a continued increase in strain with time. As a rule of thumb, the temperature (on the absolute scale) is considered to be "elevated" when it exceeds about one-third of the melting temperature (also in degrees absolute) of the particular material. This phenomenon is called *creep* and is another manifestation of viscoelastic or viscoplastic behavior. In structures such as boilers, reactor shells, and gas turbines, this effect can be of great significance. If the load is maintained over a long enough time, the specimen will eventually fail even though the stress is initially considerably lower than the ultimate stress. For testing purposes, *creep strain* is defined as the *time-dependent* strain developed *after* the specimen has been brought up to the desired constant stress. The characteristics of the creep strain curve are discussed in some detail in the next section. We will only mention here that creep testing is made difficult by large scatter of the data.

Other Temperature Effects

We have already pointed out how elevated temperatures give rise to the phenomenon of creep. We can also state that decreasing the temperature results in an increase in the slope of the linear-elastic portion of a stress-strain diagram. This, of course, means that the modulus of elasticity increases with decreasing temperature. And for increasing temperature, the slope of the linear part of the stress-strain diagram decreases, indicating a decreasing modulus of elasticity with increasing temperature. In Section VII.6 of Appendix VII this phenomenon is explained, for a crystalline material, from the microscopic point of view.

Another important thermal effect results from the fact that most materials expand as a result of an increase in temperature. If the temperature field is nonuniform there will result a stress field that is called the *thermal stress*. We shall have more to say about thermal expansion in Chapter 5, where we shall see that a temperature change ΔT produces an axial strain for an unconfined element having the value $\alpha \, \Delta T$, where α is called the *linear coefficient of thermal expansion*.

4.5 CREEP

As noted in the preceding section, creep strain is the time-dependent strain observed during a constant stress test at an elevated temperature. Creep curves for a particular level of temperature are usually plotted as strain versus time with stress as a parameter. Figure 4.10 shows a typical family of such curves for metals. Note that, as expected, the greater the stress, the greater the creep strain at a given time, but also note that the creep strain is *not* linearly proportional to the stress. Thus,

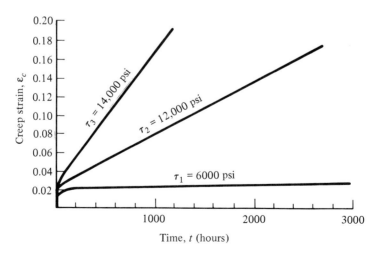

Figure 4.10 Creep strain versus time.

notice that if the stress is doubled from 6000 psi to 12,000 psi, the creep strain is much more than doubled. We note in Appendix VII that this is characteristic of *polycrystalline* materials (e.g., metals, rock, ice), whereas *amorphous* materials (e.g., polymers) tend to have strains which at time t are linearly related to the stress. Creep strain will, of course, also increase if the test temperature is increased and the rate of increase is dramatic. We also point out in Section VII.11 of Appendix VII that this is a consequence of an exponential dependence of material viscosity on temperature.

The solid curve in Fig. 4.11 is a more detailed depiction of a typical creep curve, and the following characteristic regions are observed:

1. *Initial elastic and plastic response.* Immediately upon loading at the test temperature, an elastic strain ε_e, occurs. If the applied stress exceeds the yield stress at the test temperature, a plastic strain, ε_p, also follows. The elastic strain occurs in a very short time interval. Although the plastic strain occurs over a greater time interval than the elastic strain, the plastic strain time interval is still short when compared with the time scale of a creep test. Thus, for practical purposes, *both* ε_e and ε_p can be considered instantaneous responses.

2. *Primary creep region.* This is an interval of the creep curve in which the strain rate, $\dot{\varepsilon}$, decreases continuously. If one is concerned mainly with creep over very long periods of time at constant stress, the strain accumulated during the primary creep region may be small compared with the strain accumulated in the subsequent intervals. However, primary creep is important if the load duration is short. Furthermore, if the stress is not constant in time, the mechanisms active during the primary creep interval of a constant stress test will be active during the entire load history.

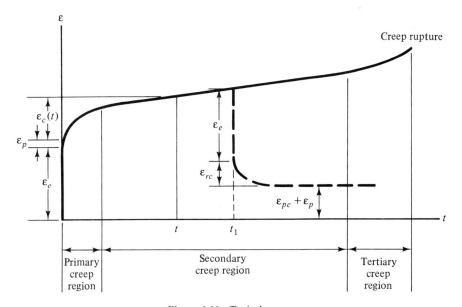

Figure 4.11 Typical creep curve.

3. *Secondary creep region.* The *creep rate* is essentially constant in this region. In many instances it is actually decreasing slowly during this interval, but the data are frequently approximated nicely by a straight line. The secondary creep region is usually the dominant interval of a creep curve. However, for some materials under high levels of stress or temperature, this interval can almost disappear (i.e., primary creep will transform directly into the final period of creep, to be discussed next).

4. *Tertiary creep region.* In this region $\dot{\varepsilon}$ increases until *creep rupture* finally occurs. Creep tests are frequently conducted at constant load rather than at constant stress, since it is not an easy matter to adjust the load continually in proportion to the change in cross-sectional area due to the creep Poisson effect. However, the tertiary creep region is greatly exaggerated during a constant load test, since the actual stress is in fact increasing. Accordingly, data obtained under constant load must be used with great care.

It is clear from the remarks above that the total strain at any time t is given by

$$\varepsilon(t) = \varepsilon_e + \varepsilon_p + \varepsilon_c(t) \tag{4.7}$$

where $\varepsilon_c(t)$ is the total amount of creep strain at time t. If the load is removed at time $t = t_1$, all of the elastic strain is recovered instantaneously plus some of the creep strain over an interval of time (see the dashed curve in Fig. 4.11). Hence it is clear that the creep strain at time t_1 may be divided into recoverable and nonrecoverable types, and we may write

$$\varepsilon_c(t_1) = \varepsilon_{rc} + \varepsilon_{pc} \tag{4.8}$$

where ε_{rc} designates recoverable creep, and ε_{pc} designates permanent nonrecoverable creep. In the case of metals ε_{rc} is usually small, and in particular it is usually smaller than the strain accumulated during primary creep. All of the strain components contained in Eqs. (4.7) and (4.8) have been shown in Fig. 4.11. We also point out that other simple creep tests, such as the shear creep test, result in creep curves with similar characteristics.

In this section we have focused our attention on creep due to elevated temperatures, that is, absolute temperatures in excess of about one-third of the melting-point absolute temperature of the material. This phenomenon is called *thermally induced* creep. As we have noted earlier, this kind of creep tends to be nonlinear in stress for polycrystalline materials such as metals, whereas it is essentially linear in stress for amorphous materials. We would like to point to another kind of creep, other than thermally induced creep. In this regard we note that high levels of neutron flux (such as occurs in the fuel rods of a nuclear reactor) can also cause creep. This phenomenon is called *irradiation-induced* creep. The creep curves for this kind of creep are plotted versus time for various levels of neutron flux rather than stress. These curves nevertheless have the same characteristic regions described above for thermally induced creep. However, there is one important difference between the two kinds of creep, and that is this: If for a given neutron flux level different constant stresses are maintained on the material, we find that at time t the irradiation-induced creep is essentially *linear* in the stress for all materials—even for metals.

The creep curve is of vital importance in the understanding of thermal and irradiation-induced time-dependent strain. Accordingly, we return to it again in Appendix VII on microscopic considerations, and in Chapters 6 and 7 on linear and nonlinear viscoelastic constitutive laws.

PART B
ONE-DIMENSIONAL IDEALIZED MATERIAL BEHAVIOR

4.6 IDEALIZED ONE-DIMENSIONAL STRESS-STRAIN DIAGRAMS

It should be apparent by now that stress-strain diagrams in general are complex with the possibility of many ramifications. We have introduced some of these complexities in previous sections. To permit an analytical treatment of material behavior under certain conditions, at times we employ idealizations of stress-strain diagrams. In this section we consider the *quasi-static* tensile test at *moderate temperatures*.

The most simple stress-strain idealization is, of course, the rigid idealization that is shown in Fig. 4.12. We have used such an idealization in rigid-body mechanics courses, and you will recall that we were able to assume rigid behavior in ascertaining supporting forces for structures supported in a statically determinate manner.

In Fig. 4.13 we have shown the stress-strain curve for a *linear elastic* material. This idealization is one we shall often employ. We must not forget that the stress-strain diagram is taken from a simple one-dimensional state of stress. In Chapter 5 we generalize this to a general state of stress, and the resulting formulation is then called the *generalized Hooke's law*. We shall often be able to use these results for the analysis of bodies composed of the usual structural materials, such as steel and aluminum, as well as some nonstructural materials, such as glass, in cases where temperatures are moderate and the stress has not exceeded the yield stress. Parenthetically, in Chapter 8 we also generalize the criterion for yielding to a general state of stress.

There are situations where there may be plastic deformations involved that far exceed the elastic deformations present, and it may be profitable to formulate the

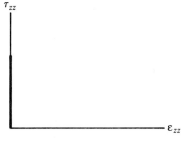

Figure 4.12 Rigid.

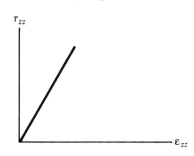

Figure 4.13 Linear elastic.

idealization of a stress-strain diagram shown in Fig. 4.14, which embodies *rigid behavior up to a certain stress and then exhibits perfectly plastic behavior*. If we include strain hardening in the plastic range, our idealizations become more accurate albeit more complex. We have shown in Fig. 4.15 the idealization of *rigid behavior with linear strain hardening* to illustrate this case.

There may be times when the elastic deformations cannot be deleted from considerations and where there is little strain hardening. For such cases, one may be able to employ the idealization shown in Fig. 4.16 called the *linear elastic, perfectly plastic* stress-strain curve. And allowing for linear strain hardening, we get the *bilinear* curve shown in Fig. 4.17, which is reasonably close to certain actual stress-strain diagrams. Finally, the more accurate but more complex case of non-linear hardening is shown in Fig. 4.18.

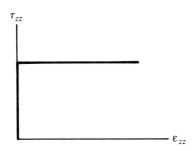

Figure 4.14   Rigid, perfectly plastic.

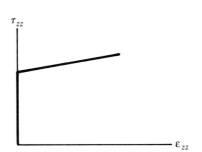

Figure 4.15   Rigid, plastic with linear strain hardening.

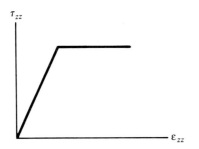

Figure 4.16   Linear elastic, perfectly plastic.

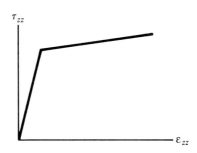

Figure 4.17   Linear elastic, plastic with linear strain hardening.

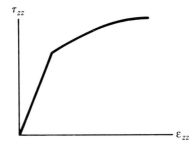

Figure 4.18   Linear elastic, plastic with nonlinear strain hardening.

Now we refer you back to Fig. 4.11, where we have shown a typical plot of creep behavior during a tensile test with a constant stress and at an elevated temperature. We shall make some introductory remarks about such viscoelastic (or viscoplastic) behavior in the following section with the aid of mechanical spring and dashpot models. Plastic and viscoplastic models will also be introduced, by means of which one could obtain idealized stress-strain diagrams such as those given in this section. In Chapters 6, 7, and 8 we will return to these subjects with much more detailed treatments.

4.7 PHENOMENOLOGICAL MODEL CLASSIFICATION OF MATERIALS

In Section 4.6 we demonstrated that a simple one-dimensional quasi-static load test at moderate temperatures is useful in the classification of solid materials according to idealized behaviors. As examples of this, we discussed the *elastic* material and the *plastic* material. This is a phenomenological approach, since it is based on idealizations of macroscopic observations of deformation. In this section we formalize and extend the phenomenological approach still further for more general one-dimensional loading conditions on more complex materials. Although again deformations under simple one-dimensional load only will be considered, *the restrictions of static loading and moderate temperatures will now be dropped*. For simplicity, only tensile load ($\tau_{zz} > 0$) and axial elongation ($\varepsilon_{zz} > 0$) will be discussed in classifying a material, and we shall employ simple mechanical models involving springs, dashpots, and dry-friction elements to portray the relationship between these quantities. However, it should be understood that for any material other deformation characteristics (such as the Poisson effect or behavior under axial compression) are not necessarily portrayed by the same model. For example, concrete exhibits significantly different characteristics under tension and compression.

Consider a material specimen subjected to the application and removal of an arbitrary tensile stress τ_{zz}. As explained in Part A, an *elastic* material is one that upon being unloaded from any stress τ_{zz} returns to its original geometry, with the loading curve corresponding exactly with the unloading curve in the stress-strain diagram. The latter characteristic indicates that the forces acting during the process are *conservative*, so that there is zero dissipation of energy during the loading and unloading process. Mathematically,

$$\varepsilon_{zz} = f(\tau_{zz}) \qquad (4.9)$$

where, in accordance with the previous remarks, f is a single-valued function that does not contain time explicitly. You have concentrated in earlier courses on the special case of the *linear elastic* (Hookean) material, for which $f = \tau_{zz}/E$, where E is Young's modulus. As we learned in Part A, many metals are linear elastic up to a stress called the *proportional limit*. In Fig. 4.19 we have plotted the stress-strain curve for a Hookean material, and we have used a simple spring as the mechanical model mentioned earlier to represent the characteristics of this material. (We shall later see just how we can make good use of such models.) Also shown is a stress-strain curve for a nonlinear elastic material, which is sometimes called a Hencky

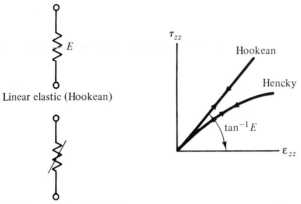

Linear elastic (Hookean)

Nonlinear elastic (Hencky)

Figure 4.19   Elastic models.

material. The model for this material is a nonlinear spring, which has been depicted in the diagram as a spring with a slash through it. In using a spring as an aid, we consider τ_{zz} to be the force in the spring and ε_{zz} to be the elongation of the spring. Accordingly, for the linear elastic case, E may be referred to as the spring constant.

If the test indicates that the *strain rate* rather than the strain is a function of stress, that is,

$$\frac{d\varepsilon_{zz}}{dt} = \dot{\varepsilon}_{zz} = g(\tau_{zz}) \qquad (4.10)$$

the material is termed *viscous* by analogy with the behavior of a fluid. The strain in this case occurs with dissipation and is not in general recovered upon removal of the load, since ε_{zz} is an explicit function of time. Extending the analogy, a linear (ideal) viscous material is called *Newtonian*, and we use a linear dashpot as the mechanical model for this behavior. In this case $\dot{\varepsilon}_{zz} = \tau_{zz}/\eta$, where η is the viscosity coefficient in tension.* In using the dashpot representation, we again consider τ_{zz} to be the force while $\dot{\varepsilon}_{zz}$ is the speed of the piston, and hence η may be referred to as the damping constant of the dashpot. We have illustrated a Newtonian material in Fig. 4.20, and we have also indicated a so-called quasi-viscous or non-Newtonian case. This case is sometimes called a *Stokes* material. Since these models represent viscous flow, they are also called *rheological* models.

Many materials possess a combination of viscous and elastic characteristics (not necessarily linear) and are logically called *viscoelastic* materials. For example, structural metals and even rock at high temperature and plastics at room temperature behave viscoelastically under load. To help in the study of such behavior, we use combinations of springs and dashpots to represent the material. Thus, in Fig. 4.21(a) we have shown the linear *Maxwell model*, which consists of a linear spring and a linear dashpot in series. A series arrangement such as this one is used to indicate that the forces in the elements (and the stresses they represent) are equal, while the deformations (and the strains represented) as well as the deformation rates are

---

* We shall see in Chapter 6 that the viscosity coefficient in tension is not generally equal to the viscosity coefficient in shear.

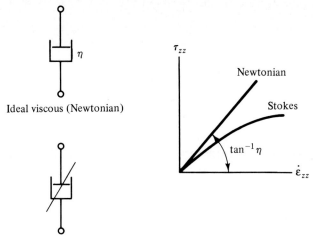

Ideal viscous (Newtonian)

Quasi-viscous (Stokes)

Figure 4.20 Viscous models.

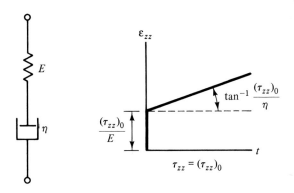

(a) Linear Maxwell model

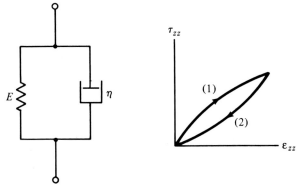

(b) Linear Kelvin model

Figure 4.21 Linear viscoelastic models.

additive. When we apply a stress that is not necessarily constant, we find that the strain rate $\dot{\varepsilon}_{zz}$ is composed of two parts. The spring element in the model responds by contributing a strain rate directly proportional to and in phase with the stress rate $\dot{\tau}_{zz}$. This strain rate contribution is $\dot{\tau}_{zz}/E$. However, the dashpot strain rate responds only to the instantaneous level of stress, so we get a second contribution of strain rate which is τ_{zz}/η. Thus we can say that

$$\dot{\varepsilon}_{zz} = \frac{\dot{\tau}_{zz}}{E} + \frac{\tau_{zz}}{\eta} \tag{4.11}$$

Note that when $E \to \infty$ (i.e., rigid action of the spring) we get viscous flow, and when $\eta \to \infty$ we get elastic behavior. We now consider an example to illustrate the results above.

Example 4.1

Develop the equations for strain in a linear Maxwell model subject to a suddenly applied constant stress $(\tau_{zz})_0$. Then compute τ_{zz} for this same model with a suddenly applied, constant strain $(\varepsilon_{zz})_0$.

(a) First, let us integrate Eq. (4.11) to obtain an expression for strain due to any stress

$$\varepsilon_{zz} = \frac{\tau_{zz}}{E} + \int_0^t \frac{\tau_{zz}(t')}{\eta} \, dt' \tag{a}$$

Then, for a constant stress $(\tau_{zz})_0$ suddenly applied at time $t = 0$, we get from the equation above,

$$\varepsilon_{zz} = (\tau_{zz})_0 \left(\frac{1}{E} + \frac{t}{\eta} \right) \qquad t > 0 \tag{b}$$

This strain function is sketched in Fig. 4.21(a). Note the resemblance of this strain curve to the creep curves in Fig. 4.10, so the Maxwell material has the characteristics of a "creeping" material. However, there *is* an important difference between these curves and that is this. As can be seen from Eq.(b), the plot of Fig. 4.21(a) must be linear in $(\tau_{zz})_0$. And as we have already pointed out, the curves in Fig. 4.10 at time t are nonlinear in the applied stress. Also, the curve in Fig. 4.21(a) does not have a primary creep region.

(b) For a constant strain $(\varepsilon_{zz})_0$ suddenly applied at $t = 0$, we get from Eq. (4.11)

$$0 = \frac{\dot{\tau}_{zz}}{E} + \frac{\tau_{zz}}{\eta} \qquad t > 0 \tag{c}$$

Separating the variables, we have for Eq. (c),

$$\frac{d\tau_{zz}}{\tau_{zz}} = -\frac{E}{\eta} \, dt \qquad t > 0 \tag{d}$$

Now at $t = 0^+$ (i.e., *immediately after* load application) the strain $(\varepsilon_{zz})_0$ produces a sudden displacement of the spring in the model, and accordingly the stress at $t = 0^+$ is given by $E(\varepsilon_{zz})_0$. Thereafter, the stress may be obtained by integrating Eq. (d) from $t = 0^+$ to a variable upper time limit. Thus, using the initial condition $\tau_{zz}(0^+) = E(\varepsilon_{zz})_0$, we get

$$\ln \left[\frac{\tau_{zz}}{E(\varepsilon_{zz})_0} \right] = -\frac{E}{\eta} t \qquad t > 0 \tag{e}$$

which yields the stress

$$\tau_{zz} = (\varepsilon_{zz})_0 \, E e^{-(E/\eta)t} \qquad t > 0 \tag{f}$$

In the previous example, we developed two useful formulas which we shall restate here. First, for a suddenly applied stress $(\tau_{zz})_0$, we have

$$\varepsilon_{zz} = (\tau_{zz})_0 \left(\frac{1}{E} + \frac{t}{\eta} \right) \tag{4.12}$$

and second, for a suddenly applied strain $(\varepsilon_{zz})_0$, we have

$$\tau_{zz} = (\varepsilon_{zz})_0 \, E e^{-(E/\eta)t} \tag{4.13}$$

In Chapter 6 we shall use *discontinuity functions* to derive equations such as these in a more efficient manner. We have already remarked that Eq. (4.12) demonstrates that a Maxwell material exhibits the characteristics of a creeping material. Furthermore, because of the ever-decreasing stress exhibited by Eq. (4.13), the Maxwell material is also called a "relaxing" material for which η/E is a material parameter called the *relaxation time*.* One may employ models such as this to compute how the stress will relax, for example, in a suddenly tightened bolt, when the absolute temperature exceeds about one-third the absolute melting-point temperature.

As a second important model, consider a linear spring and a linear dashpot in parallel [see Fig. 4.21(b)]. This model is called a linear *Kelvin* or *Voigt* model. Note that the dashpot and spring forces (i.e., the stresses) are in *parallel* and thus will *add*. On the other hand, the displacements (strains) of the spring and dashpot elements are *equal*.† The spring represents a stress component given as $E \varepsilon_{zz}$, while the dashpot represents a stress component that is proportional to the strain rate and hence is given as $\eta \dot{\varepsilon}_{zz}$. We can then say that

$$\eta \dot{\varepsilon}_{zz} + E \varepsilon_{zz} = \tau_{zz} \tag{4.14}$$

Note that when $E \to 0$ (i.e., we have a spring of zero stiffness) we get viscous flow, and when $\eta \to 0$ we have elastic behavior. Because of the parallel arrangement of the dashpot and spring, the Kelvin model is characterized by always achieving a complete recovery of geometry when an applied force is removed. However, this recovery, because of the dashpot, is dissipative. As shown in Fig. 4.21(b), the loading and unloading paths in the stress-strain diagram do not coincide, whereupon the designation *anelastic* is applied to such materials as mentioned in Part A of this chapter. We point out that the curvatures of the loading and unloading paths in Fig. 4.21(b) are *not* due to nonlinear elasticity. We explore this point more fully in the next example.

---

*This is the time needed for a stress to reduce to $1/e$ of its original value.

†Note that a suddenly applied stress will induce no instantaneous strain because of the presence of the dashpot in *parallel* to the spring. This is in contrast to the Maxwell model, where we got an instantaneous elastic strain response to a suddenly applied load, wherein the spring in series with the dashpot was free to respond.

Example 4.2

Consider a *linear* Kelvin material subjected to a stress that increases linearly in time from zero at $t = 0$ to τ_0 at $t = t_1$, that is,

$$\tau_{zz}(t) = \frac{\tau_0}{t_1} t \qquad 0 \le t \le t_1 \quad \text{and} \quad \tau_0 > 0 \tag{a}$$

Verify that the loading path in the stress-strain diagram has the type of slope and curvature shown for path (1) in Fig. 4.21(b).

Substituting Eq. (a) into Eq. (4.14), we get for a Kelvin material

$$\dot{\varepsilon}_{zz} + \frac{E}{\eta} \varepsilon_{zz} = \frac{\tau_0}{\eta t_1} t \qquad 0 \le t \le t_1 \tag{b}$$

By introducing an integrating factor, we may rewrite this equation as

$$\frac{d}{dt} \left(\varepsilon_{zz} e^{(E/\eta)t} \right) = \frac{\tau_0}{\eta t_1} t e^{(E/\eta)t} \tag{c}$$

and accordingly,

$$\varepsilon_{zz}(t) = \frac{\tau_0}{\eta t_1} e^{-(E/\eta)t} \int_0^t t' e^{(E/\eta)t'} dt' \tag{d}$$

where we have set $\varepsilon_{zz}(0) = 0$. The integral in Eq. (d) is easily evaluated by means of an integration by parts, and you should verify that

$$\varepsilon_{zz}(t) = \frac{\tau_0}{Et_1} \left[t - \frac{\eta}{E} \left(1 - e^{-(E/\eta)t} \right) \right] \qquad 0 \le t \le t_1 \tag{e}$$

We may now eliminate t from Eq. (e) by means of Eq. (a) to obtain the strain-stress relation

$$\varepsilon_{zz}(t) = \frac{\tau_{zz}(t)}{E} - \frac{\alpha \tau_0}{E} \{1 - \exp\left[-\tau_{zz}(t)/(\alpha \tau_0)\right]\} \qquad 0 \le t \le t_1 \tag{f}$$

where we have a set $\alpha = \eta/(Et_1)$. The slope of the strain-stress curve then follows as

$$\frac{d\varepsilon_{zz}}{d\tau_{zz}} = \frac{1}{E} \{[1 - \exp\left(-\tau_{zz}/(\alpha \tau_0)\right)]\} \qquad 0 \le t \le t_1 \tag{g}$$

and the curvature is given by

$$\frac{d^2 \varepsilon_{zz}}{d\tau_{zz}^2} = \frac{1}{E \alpha \tau_0} \exp\left[-\tau_{zz}/(\alpha \tau_0)\right] \qquad 0 \le t \le t_1 \tag{h}$$

Since E, α, and τ_0 are all positive, it immediately follows that both the slope and curvature of the ε_{zz} versus τ_{zz} curve are nonnegative at all times in the interval $0 \le t \le t_1$, and the indicated character of path (1) in Fig. 4.21(b) is thus verified.

Finally, let us briefly consider *plastic* behavior. We learned in Part A that plastic flow occurs in a metal when $\tau_{zz} \ge Y$, where Y is the yield stress, and that flow ceases upon unloading ($\dot{\tau}_{zz} < 0$), resulting in a retention of all plastic deformation in a permanent set. To simplify our discussion, we shall at first ignore hardening effects and will concentrate on the simple but useful rigid, perfectly plastic idealization (see Fig. 4.14).

For such a material, the stress-strain diagram is as shown in Fig. 4.22(a). A *flow rule* may be written for this case in terms of some function of stress, $f(\tau_{zz})$. That

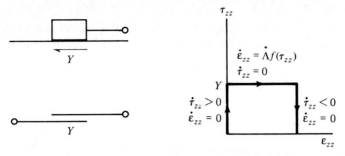

(a) Rigid, perfectly plastic (Saint-Venant)

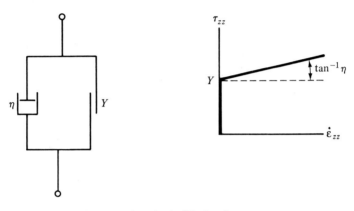

(b) Linear viscoplastic (Bingham)

Figure 4.22 Plastic models.

is, for $\tau_{zz} \geq 0$,

$$\dot{\varepsilon}_{zz} = \begin{cases} 0 & \text{if } \tau_{zz} < Y \quad \text{or if } \tau_{zz} = Y \quad \text{and} \quad \dot{\tau}_{zz} < 0 \quad \text{(a)} \\ \dot{\Lambda} f(\tau_{zz}) & \text{if } \tau_{zz} = Y \quad \text{and} \quad \dot{\tau}_{zz} = 0 \quad \text{(b)} \end{cases}$$ (4.15)

where for perfect plasticity $\dot{\Lambda}$ is a positive but *indeterminate* proportionality factor.* This indeterminacy and the existence of Y distinguish this material from a simple viscous material. We should also mention that although viscous models are usually used to study slow deformation, plastic models are frequently employed for the study of rapid deformation. Schematically, the rigid, perfectly plastic idealization may be represented by a *dry-friction model* consisting of a block on a plane or alternatively by two plates [see Fig. 4.22(a)]. This model is sometimes called the *Saint-Venant* (or the *Coulomb*) model, and you should note that τ_{zz} can never exceed Y in such a model.

---

*It is important to note that $\dot{\Lambda}$ is *not* a material constant. We shall have much more to say about this in Chapter 8.

To eliminate the indeterminacy from Eq. (4.15b), one must introduce hardening into the model. One simple way of doing this is by employing a model consisting of a dry-friction element in parallel with a linear viscous element, as shown in Fig. 4.22(b). This model represents a combination of linear viscous and perfectly plastic behaviors, and is accordingly called a linear *viscoplastic* (or Bingham) model. If $\tau_{zz} < Y$, it is clear that this model is rigid, since the stress in the dry-friction element will be less than Y. If, on the other hand, $\tau_{zz} > Y$, the stress in the dry-friction element equals its maximum permissible value Y, while an *overstress* $(\tau_{zz} - Y)$ is exerted on the parallel viscous element. Accordingly, the *flow rule* for the Bingham model is given for $\tau_{zz} \geq 0$ as

$$\dot{\varepsilon}_{zz} = \begin{cases} 0 & \text{if } \tau_{zz} < Y \quad \text{(a)} \\ \dfrac{\tau_{zz} - Y}{\eta} & \text{if } \tau_{zz} \geq Y \quad \text{(b)} \end{cases} \qquad (4.16)$$

The stress-strain rate diagram for a Bingham material is as shown in Fig. 4.22(b). Note that this diagram is *not* equivalent to the rigid, linear strain-hardening idealization depicted in Fig. 4.15. Keep in mind that the latter relates stress to *strain*, while here we are relating stress to *strain rate*. This point, as well as the rate sensitivity of this model, will be brought out clearly in the following example.

Example 4.3

Consider a linear Bingham material subjected to a stress that equals the yield stress Y at $t = 0^+$, and which then increases at the constant stress rate $\dot{\tau}_0$, that is,

$$\tau_{zz}(t) = Y + \dot{\tau}_0 t \qquad t > 0 \qquad (a)$$

Verify that this linear material under this load experiences *nonlinear* hardening.
Substituting Eq. (a) into Eq. (4.16b), we obtain the strain rate as

$$\dot{\varepsilon}_{zz}(t) = \frac{\dot{\tau}_0}{\eta} t \qquad t > 0 \qquad (b)$$

The strain then follows immediately via integration as

$$\varepsilon_{zz}(t) = \frac{\dot{\tau}_0}{2\eta} t^2 \qquad t > 0 \qquad (c)$$

where we have set $\varepsilon_{zz}(0^+) = 0$. Eliminating time from this result by use of Eq. (a), we obtain the relation

$$\varepsilon_{zz} = \frac{1}{2\eta\dot{\tau}_0} (\tau_{zz} - Y)^2 \qquad \text{or} \qquad \tau_{zz} = Y + \sqrt{2\eta\dot{\tau}_0} \, \varepsilon_{zz}^{1/2} \qquad (d)$$

You will note for $\dot{\tau}_0 > 0$ that Eq. (d) indicates quadratic nonlinear hardening and not linear hardening. Furthermore, if the constant stress rate $\dot{\tau}_0$ is increased, then for a given value of ε_{zz} we see that Eq. (d) yields a greater value of τ_{zz}. In other words, the stress-strain diagram *rises* as the stress rate is increased. Thus a linear Bingham material not only experiences nonlinear hardening when $\dot{\tau}_0 > 0$, but it is also *rate sensitive* in the plastic region. Finally, note that for $\dot{\tau}_0 = 0$, Eq.(d) gives $\tau_{zz} = Y$ while ε_{zz} is indeterminate (i.e., there is *no hardening*). Clearly, the hardening observed above is *not* the strain hardening typically found in a quasi-static tensile test, but rather is due to the rate sensitivity. We shall explore this point fully in our treatment of viscoplasticity in Chapter 8.

4.8 CLOSURE

In this chapter we have considered one-dimensional macroscopic models of materials and have proposed mathematical idealizations of various behaviors. This led to the presentation of spring–dashpot–friction mechanical devices to further help portray these behaviors.

Of course, the linear models we have discussed in this section may be combined in an unlimited number of ways to represent additional effects such as primary creep. We saw that the linear Maxwell, Kelvin, and Bingham models are governed by first-order, ordinary, linear differential equations. If one adds more elements to these models, higher-order linear differential equations are needed to depict the behavior associated with these more complex models. Such complex models are usually required in dynamic problems (e.g., in the study of wave propagation in the Earth's crustal rock). These studies comprise an essential part of a branch of geophysics called *seismology*. Furthermore, nonlinear models are often required for a realistic representation of effects such as nonlinear creep and nonlinear plastic hardening. Of course, the resulting differential (or integral) equations will then be nonlinear. We shall consider such matters in detail in Chapters 6, 7, and 8.

As indicated at the outset of this section and indeed at the outset of this chapter, we have limited our discussion to *macroscopic* considerations. The interested reader will find in Appendix VII a self-contained discussion of interesting topics pertaining to the *microscopic* explanation of the various phenomena presented in this chapter, such as creep and plastic deformation.

In Chapter 5 we focus on linear elastic behavior in three dimensions.

PROBLEMS

4.1. A linear elastic test specimen has a diameter of $\frac{3}{4}$ in. and when loaded by a force of 1500 lb, it undergoes a decrease in diameter of 0.00006 in. Also the longitudinal gauge measuring an initial length L_0 of 2 in. has an increase in length of 0.000660 in. Determine:
  (a) The engineering stress at the 1500-lb load
  (b) The actual stress at the 1500-lb load
  (c) The modulus of elasticity
  (d) The Poisson ratio

4.2. In Fig. P4.2 is shown a hypothetical stress-strain curve. Determine:
  (a) The proportional limit
  (b) The ultimate stress
  (c) The modulus of elasticity for this material
  (d) The 0.002 offset yield stress

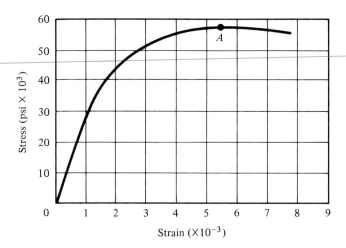

Figure P4.2

4.3. In Problem 4.2, the specimen is unloaded from a stress of 57,000 psi at point A. What is the permanent set? If it is reloaded to a stress of 50,000 psi and then unloaded, what is the strain recovery?

4.4. A light rod at an elevated temperature supports a weight of 12,000 lb as shown in Fig. P4.4. If the material behaves as in Fig. 4.10, how long a time t_1 would you estimate before the elongation is 0.6 ft? If you change the stress by the ratio $14,000/12,000 = 1.167$, do you decrease the time for this elongation by the corresponding fraction $1/1.167 = 0.857$? If not, what fraction of t_1 is required?

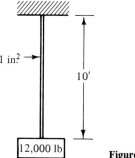

Figure P4.4

4.5. **(a)** Explain the differences between the primary, secondary, and tertiary creep regions in terms of the strain rates for a given stress.

(b) Explain the difference between thermally induced creep in polycrystalline materials and in amorphous materials in terms of the effect of stress.

(c) What is the essential difference between thermally induced creep and irradiation-induced creep in metals?

4.6. **(a)** Shown in Fig. P4.6 are (1) rigid, perfectly plastic, (2) elastic, perfectly plastic, and (3) elastic, plastic with linear strain-hardening stress-strain idealizations. What stress is needed in each case to have a strain of 0.001? What is the stress in each case needed for a strain of 0.004?

(b) What is the permanent set in each case if the specimen is unloaded from a strain of 0.004?

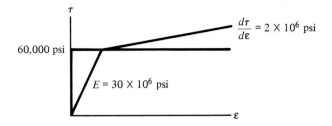

4.7. Three cylinders are welded together and support a weight W (Fig. P4.7). What is the largest weight that can be supported with only elastic deformation in the system? Each cylinder is to be considered to behave in a linear elastic, perfectly plastic manner having the following data:

$$E_1 = 30 \times 10^6 \text{ psi}, \qquad E_2 = 25 \times 10^6 \text{ psi}, \qquad E_3 = 35 \times 10^6 \text{ psi}$$

$$Y_1 = 80,000 \text{ psi}, \qquad Y_2 = 60,000 \text{ psi}, \qquad Y_3 = 50,000 \text{ psi}$$

If the weight W is increased slightly above the maximum value for elastic behavior, what can you say about the elongation of each member?

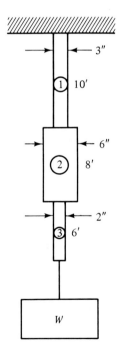

Figure P4.7

4.8. Stress-strain diagrams have been shown in Fig. P4.8 for cylinders A and B. What is the maximum load P for elastic deformation only? What is the downward movement of the end E from this load? What load is needed to *double* this movement? What is the length of each member when the latter load is removed?

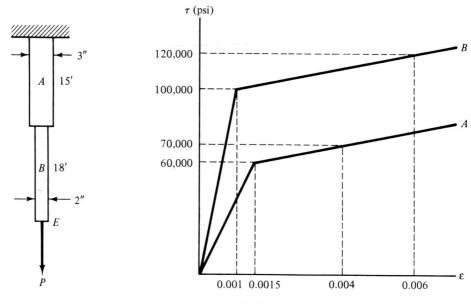

Figure P4.8

4.9. A series of cylindrical rods are welded to a rigid drum of radius 2 ft as shown in Fig. P4.9. When stationary the clearance between a cylinder and the wall of the enclosure is 0.001 in. At what angular speed ω will a rod just start to touch the wall? Neglect the weight effects on the cylinders. The density of the cylinders is 460 lbm/ft³. Assume that the cylinders are linear elastic and take $E = 30 \times 10^6$ psi.

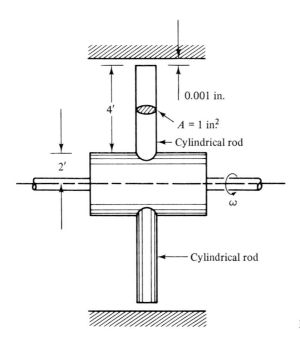

Figure P4.9

4.10. In Problem 4.9, what is the maximum angular speed ω for elastic behavior of the cylinders? If this speed is increased by 40%, what is the maximum stress in a cylinder and the elongation of a cylinder? Use the stress-strain diagram in Fig. P4.10.

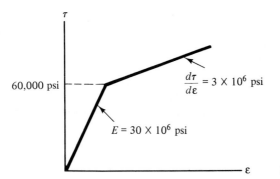

60,000 psi

$$\frac{d\tau}{d\varepsilon} = 3 \times 10^6 \text{ psi}$$

$E = 30 \times 10^6$ psi

Figure P4.10

4.11. A Maxwell material in the form of a cylinder of length L is given a suddenly applied uniform constant stress τ_0 in the direction of its axis at time t_1. This stress is suddenly removed at time t_2. What is the equation for the elongation δ of the cylinder in terms of t, t_1, t_2, L, E, and η? Plot δ versus time. Show clearly and evaluate the value of δ after the stress is removed.

4.12. In Example 4.2 we subjected the Kelvin specimen to a stress linearly proportional to time starting with $\tau = 0$ at $t = 0$. Show for a suddenly applied stress τ_0 at $t = 0$ that the strain is given as

$$\varepsilon(t) = \frac{\tau_0}{E}[1 - e^{-(E/\eta)t}] \qquad t > 0$$

for the case where $\varepsilon(0^-) = 0$.

4.13. Do the same for a Kelvin material as is done for a Maxwell material in Problem 4.11. Show δ after time t_1. Does the specimen finally recover its original length? Is energy conserved in this process? Use the results of Problem 4.12.

4.14. Consider a hypothetical viscoelastic model consisting of a spring connected in series with a Kelvin model, as shown in Fig. P4.14. If a stress τ_0 is suddenly applied to the system, sketch the strain versus time curve. Express ε as a function of time in terms of E_1, E_2, and η_2. Use the results of Problem 4.12. (*Hint*: The strains from the spring and the Kelvin element add while the stress is the same for both models. Why?)

4.15. Recent research has indicated that the skin of a guinea pig behaves viscoelastically. The specimen is quick-frozen on removal from the animal and then quick-thawed for use in a test machine. It is found that a Kelvin model in series with a dashpot (see Fig. P4.15) can reasonably simulate the viscoelastic behavior of the specimen. If a stress is suddenly applied at time t_0 and released at time t_1, draw a graph of the expected strain of the specimen with time. Use two curves that are to be added. What is the formula for strain as a function of time for a suddenly applied constant stress τ_0? Use the results of Problem 4.12. Can you use the hint in Problem 4.14 adjusted for this case?

4.16. By combining a Maxwell model and a Kelvin model in series (see Fig. P4.16) we obtain the very useful *Burgers fluid* model of a material. Plot the expected strain as a function of time if a stress τ_0 is suddenly applied to such a material, kept on for a time t, and then suddenly removed.

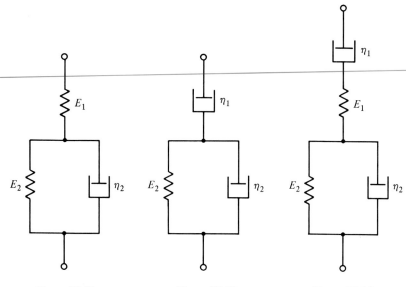

| Figure P4.14 | Figure P4.15 | Figure P4.16 |

4.17. Two rods each of diameter $\frac{1}{2}$ in. support a 10,000-lb block. The rods are viscoelastic Maxwell materials with

$$E_1 = 30 \times 10^6 \text{ psi}, \qquad E_2 = 15 \times 10^6 \text{ psi}$$

$$\eta_1 = 1.5 \times 10^{13} \text{ psi-sec}, \qquad \eta_2 = 1.2 \times 10^{13} \text{ psi-sec}$$

If C and D are at the same level before loading, what angle of inclination with the horizontal will A take just after loading, after 500 hours, and after 5000 hours?

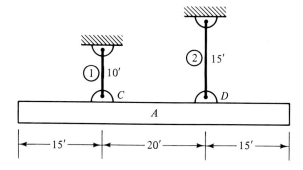

Figure P4.17

4.18. Do Problem 4.17 for 50 and 500 hours for rods that are Kelvin material in behavior. Use the results of Problem 4.12. What is the angle as $t \to \infty$?

4.19. In Problem 4.9, take the cylinders to be a Maxwell material where

$$E = 20 \times 10^6 \text{ psi}$$

$$\eta = 10^{13} \text{ psi-sec}$$

If the system is quickly brought up to a rotational speed of 1000 rpm, what is the elongation of each cylinder after 5000 hours? Disregard the walls of the enclosure.

4.20. Do Problem 4.19 for a Kelvin material, making use of the results of Example 4.12. Take the elapsed time as 50 hours.

4.21. A linear Kelvin material is subjected to a stress $\tau_{zz}(t)$ that increases exponentially such that

$$\tau_{zz}(t) = \kappa e^{\beta t}$$

where κ and β are constants. Derive, in a manner paralleling Example 4.2, the formulation of $\varepsilon_{zz}(t)$.

4.22. A linear elastic rod (1) is welded to a viscoelastic shaft (2) (Fig. P4.22). Both shafts are held firmly at supports A and B. The following data apply:

$$E_1 = 15 \times 10^6 \text{ psi}$$

$$E_2 = 20 \times 10^6 \text{ psi}$$

$$\eta_2 = 10^{10} \text{ psi-sec}$$

Using a Maxwell model for (2), find the supporting forces at A and B as functions of time. Neglect the weight of the rods.

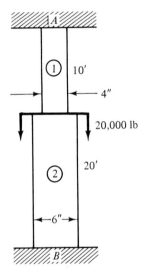

Figure P4.22

4.23. A Bingham material has the following material constants:

$$Y = 80,000 \text{ psi}$$

$$\eta = 10^{12} \text{ psi-sec}$$

If the stress on a rod is varied such that

$$\tau_{zz}(t) = 0.20t + 20,000 \text{ psi} \qquad (t \text{ in seconds})$$

what is the strain at $t = 30$ hours? What is the strain at 150 hours? Sketch the strain history $\varepsilon_{zz}(t)$.

4.24. In Example 4.3 we determined the strain-stress relation for a Bingham material subjected to the linear stress history $\tau_{zz}(t) = Y + \dot{\tau}_0 t$ for $t > 0$. Redo this example for the quadratic stress history $\tau_{zz}(t) = Y + At^2$ for $t > 0$, where Y is the yield point and A is a positive constant. Discuss your result. What happens as the constant A is increased?

4.25. A rod of linear Bingham material is undergoing the axial strain history $\varepsilon_{zz}(t) = \varepsilon_0 + At + Bt^2$, where ε_0, A, and B are nonnegative constants. Determine the axial stress in the rod $\tau_{zz}(t)$, in terms of ε_0, A, B, η, and Y. Discuss the special cases $B = 0$ and $A = B = 0$.

Chapter 5

Linear Elastic Behavior

5.1 INTRODUCTION

In this chapter we consider linear elastic materials. We begin with an examination of isotropic homogeneous materials. Recall that an *isotropic material has properties at a point that are independent of direction*. We point out that the constitutive laws presented in this chapter are easily extended to inhomogeneous materials simply by allowing the various elastic constants to be functions of the spatial coordinates. Later we shall examine certain *anisotropic* materials where the properties at a point are *direction sensitive*. The material considered in most of the chapter will be isothermal. However, at the end of the chapter we briefly consider thermoelasticity wherein we allow for nonisothermal effects. Later chapters such as those on viscoelastic behavior will rely on an understanding of linear elastic behavior, and accordingly, this chapter is a vital one.

5.2 ISOTROPIC HOOKE'S LAW VIA SUPERPOSITION

In this section we assume that the properties of the materials are both constant and independent of the direction. That is, we obtain the same constant E when analyzing one-dimensional test data in the x, y, and z directions. The same G is used for the three orthogonal faces defined by axes x, y, z. Individual crystals of structural materials are actually not isotropic (i.e., they are anisotropic), but because of the usual random orientation of the crystals and their large number, the macroscopic behavior of structural materials is usually considered isotropic. However, as a result of working a metal, such as in a rolling operation, the crystals do attain at times a certain preferential alignment, and we then must take into account anisotropic effects. To formulate a multidimensional, isotropic Hooke's law, we shall consider a vanishingly small rectangular parallelepiped of linear-elastic, isotropic material. We shall apply to the element successively three sets of normal stresses on three sets of opposite faces and three sets of shear stresses on these faces. Next, we evaluate the strain for each stress and then we superpose the result to relate stress and strain for the three-dimensional case at a point. Such superposition is valid since the equations are linear.

Before proceeding as described above, it will be valuable at this time to prove the following statements for an isotropic material:*

1. Normal stresses can only generate normal strains.
2. A shear stress, say τ_{xy}, can only generate the corresponding engineering shear strain γ_{xy}.

Consider statement 1 first. For this purpose we have shown an element in Fig. 5.1(a) under the normal stress τ_{zz}. We will assume that a shear strain γ_{xy} has resulted from the stress τ_{zz} as shown in the diagram. Now rotate the element 180° about the x axis to reach the configuration in Fig. 5.1(b). We now have the same normal stress, producing a shear strain that is different in sign. But for an isotropic material the relation between stress and the resulting strain should be independent of the orientation of an element relative to the axes. The only way to avoid the dilemma we find ourselves in now is to preclude the possibility of shear strain arising relative to a reference from normal stresses for that reference.

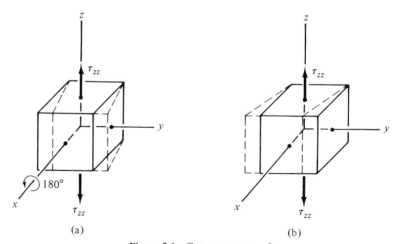

(a) (b)

Figure 5.1 Can τ_{zz} cause γ_{xy}?

As for assertion 2, consider the element of Fig. 5.1 now undergoing a pure shear stress τ_{xy} as shown in Fig. 5.2(a). We assume here that a normal strain ε_{yy} has resulted from τ_{xy}. By rotating the element 180° about an axis in the xy plane at an

---

*Although we are concerned in this chapter with linear elastic materials, the geometric arguments we present in this section apply equally well to nonlinear and inelastic materials. However, superposition is *not* valid for nonlinear materials.

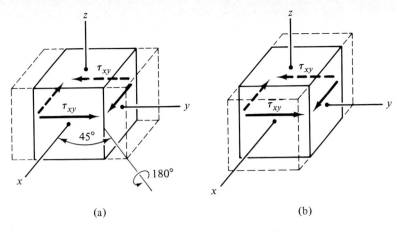

Figure 5.2 Can τ_{xy} cause ε_{yy}?

angle of 45° from the x axis, we arrive at the configuration shown by Fig. 5.2(b). Here we have the same shear stress but a different normal strain. For an isotropic material, there should not be a change in material behavior arising from a change in orientation of the element. To avoid this dilemma we are again in, we must conclude that a shear stress on a face parallel to any pair of orthogonal axes cannot create a normal strain for these axes in an isotropic material. Finally, to complete the substantiation of assertion 2, we assume that the shear stress τ_{xy} in Fig. 5.2(a) causes a shear strain γ_{yz} as shown in Fig. 5.3(a). This time we rotate the element 180° about the z axes to arrive at the configuration in Fig. 5.3(b). For the same stress τ_{xy} we now have a strain γ_{yz} of opposite sign to that of Fig. 5.3(a). This must not be permitted because of isotropy, so we conclude that a shear stress τ_{xy} can only produce the corresponding engineering shear strain γ_{xy}. A similar statement can, of course, be made for shear stresses τ_{yz} and τ_{zx}. We now proceed with the general discussion.

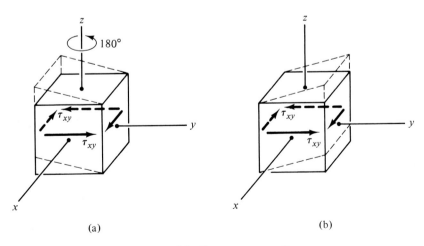

Figure 5.3 Can τ_{xy} cause γ_{yz}?

Sec. 5.2   Isotropic Hooke's Law Via Superposition

In Fig. 5.4 we show an infinitesimal element subject only to a normal stress τ_{xx} which is less than the yield stress Y. Using the results from our study in Chapter 4 of the one-dimensional tensile test, we can say that for linear elastic behavior

$$\varepsilon'_{xx} = \frac{\tau_{xx}}{E} \tag{5.1}$$

where we shall use primes to denote the different strain contributions stemming from different stresses. You will recall from the one-dimensional test that while the element extends in the x direction, it will simultaneously contract in directions normal to the x direction. This is the so-called Poisson effect. The Poisson ratio ν is a measure of this lateral effect and is determined from the one-dimensional test data. Thus we can also say that

$$\varepsilon'_{yy} = -\nu\varepsilon'_{xx} = -\nu\frac{\tau_{xx}}{E}$$

$$\varepsilon'_{zz} = -\nu\varepsilon'_{xx} = -\nu\frac{\tau_{xx}}{E} \tag{5.2}$$

where isotropy requires that ν be the same for the y and z directions. No other strains for reference xyz result from the normal stress τ_{xx} since, as proven above, normal stresses for a reference xyz cannot produce shear strains for this reference. If next we apply a normal stress to the element only in the y direction, the following new normal strains are developed:

$$\varepsilon''_{yy} = \frac{\tau_{yy}}{E}$$

$$\varepsilon''_{xx} = -\nu\varepsilon''_{yy} = -\nu\frac{\tau_{yy}}{E} \tag{5.3}$$

$$\varepsilon''_{zz} = -\nu\varepsilon''_{yy} = -\nu\frac{\tau_{yy}}{E}$$

where again there are no shear strains. Also, because of isotropy, E and ν in Eqs. (5.3) have the same values as in Eqs. (5.2). Finally, a separate stress τ_{zz} yields for our element

$$\varepsilon'''_{zz} = \frac{\tau_{zz}}{E}$$

$$\varepsilon'''_{xx} = -\nu\varepsilon'''_{zz} = -\nu\frac{\tau_{zz}}{E} \tag{5.4}$$

$$\varepsilon'''_{yy} = -\nu\varepsilon'''_{zz} = -\nu\frac{\tau_{zz}}{E}$$

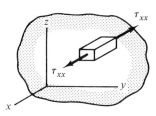

Figure 5.4 Element under normal stress τ_{xx}.

Linear Elastic Behavior Chap. 5

Again, shear strains do not occur, and ν and E have the same values as heretofore because of isotropy. Now apply the three normal stresses τ_{xx}, τ_{yy}, and τ_{zz} simultaneously. The resulting strains are given via superposition as follows:

$$\varepsilon_{xx} = \frac{1}{E}\left[\tau_{xx} - \nu(\tau_{yy} + \tau_{zz})\right] \qquad \gamma_{xy} = 0$$

$$\varepsilon_{yy} = \frac{1}{E}\left[\tau_{yy} - \nu(\tau_{zz} + \tau_{xx})\right] \qquad \gamma_{yz} = 0 \qquad (5.5)$$

$$\varepsilon_{zz} = \frac{1}{E}\left[\tau_{zz} - \nu(\tau_{xx} + \tau_{yy})\right] \qquad \gamma_{zx} = 0$$

We now turn to a consideration of behavior under the action of shear stresses. As mentioned in Chapter 4, to investigate experimentally the relation between shear stress and shear strain, we could use the simple torsion test. Here a hollow circular cylinder (see Fig. 5.5) is twisted at the ends. You will recall from your study of torsion in strength of materials that the element shown at A is subject only to a pure shear stress τ_{xy}. Experiments for linear elastic materials show that the shear stress τ_{xy} is proportional to the engineering shear strain γ_{xy} up to a shear yield stress. In Section VII.7 of Appendix VII, we called this the critical shear stress τ_{crit} and we were able to relate it to the tensile yield stress Y. We shall be able to do this again in more general circumstances when we consider yielding macroscopically in Chapter 8. Thus we can say for shear stress τ_{xy} less than the shear yield stress that

$$\gamma_{xy} = \frac{\tau_{xy}}{G} \qquad (5.6)$$

where you will recall that the proportionality constant G is called the *shear modulus* of elasticity. Furthermore, there are no other shear or normal strains (for axes x, y, z) since, as proven earlier, τ_{xy} can only generate γ_{xy} in an isotropic material. For the three sets of orthogonal faces of a vanishingly small rectangular parallelepiped on which shear stresses τ_{xy}, τ_{yz}, and τ_{zx} are applied simultaneously, it is clear that on superposition we get the following strains:

$$\gamma_{xy} = \frac{\tau_{xy}}{G} \qquad \varepsilon_{xx} = 0$$

$$\gamma_{yz} = \frac{\tau_{yz}}{G} \qquad \varepsilon_{yy} = 0 \qquad (5.7)$$

$$\gamma_{zx} = \frac{\tau_{zx}}{G} \qquad \varepsilon_{zz} = 0$$

where G is the same value for each set of faces because of isotropy.

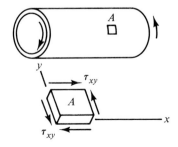

Figure 5.5 Pure shear stress.

Finally, we consider an element subjected to normal stresses τ_{xx}, τ_{yy}, and τ_{zz} as well as to shear stresses τ_{xy}, τ_{yz}, and τ_{zx}. The multidimensional isotropic Hooke's law can now be formulated by superposing Eqs. (5.5) and (5.7), giving

$$
\begin{aligned}
\varepsilon_{xx} &= \frac{1}{E}\left[\tau_{xx} - \nu(\tau_{yy} + \tau_{zz})\right] \\[2mm]
\varepsilon_{yy} &= \frac{1}{E}\left[\tau_{yy} - \nu(\tau_{zz} + \tau_{xx})\right] \\[2mm]
\varepsilon_{zz} &= \frac{1}{E}\left[\tau_{zz} - \nu(\tau_{xx} + \tau_{yy})\right] \\[2mm]
\gamma_{yz} &= 2\varepsilon_{yz} = \frac{1}{G}\,\tau_{yz} \\[2mm]
\gamma_{zx} &= 2\varepsilon_{zx} = \frac{1}{G}\,\tau_{zx} \\[2mm]
\gamma_{xy} &= 2\varepsilon_{xy} = \frac{1}{G}\,\tau_{xy}
\end{aligned}
\tag{5.8}
$$

There are three constants given in the equations above–E, G, and ν. These three constants are sometimes called the engineering elastic constants. Actually for an isotropic material only two of the engineering elastic constants are independent; any two may be taken as the independent pair. In the next section we show the interdependence of these constants. In closing, we point out again that these constants become functions of x, y, z if the material is inhomogeneous.

5.3 INTERDEPENDENCE OF ENGINEERING ELASTIC CONSTANTS FOR ISOTROPIC MATERIALS

Consider a state of plane stress for the square plate of thickness t shown in Fig. 5.6 wherein a uniform tensile stress loading S is applied in the y direction, while a uniform compressive stress loading S is applied in the x direction. At each point in the

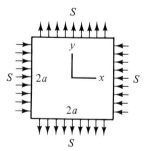

Figure 5.6 Special state of stress.

plate, we can say that

$$\tau_{xx} = -S$$

$$\tau_{yy} = S$$

$$\tau_{xy} = 0$$

In Fig. 5.7 we consider next a portion of the square plate formed by cutting along a diagonal. We may imagine that a line along the cut diagonal is an x' axis, while a line normal to the cut diagonal is a y' axis. This has been shown in the diagram. Consequently, the normal stress and shear stress along the cut section are, respectively, $\tau_{y'y'}$ and $\tau_{y'x'}$. Summing forces in the x' direction, we have, from equilibrium,*

$$(\tau_{y'x'})(2a)(\sqrt{2})t - 2\left[(S)(2a)\left(\frac{1}{\sqrt{2}}\right)t\right] = 0$$

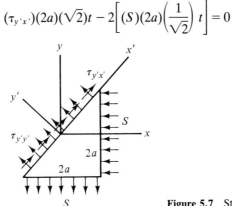

Figure 5.7 Stresses for axes $x'y'$.

Therefore,

$$\tau_{y'x'} = \tau_{x'y'} = S \tag{5.9}$$

We can also easily show that $\tau_{y'y'} = 0$, and thus this *biaxial* loading yields a state of *pure shear*.

Now consider the deformation of the square plate, which is shown by the dashed lines in Fig. 5.8. Again we have shown reference xy as well as reference $x'y'$, the latter along the diagonal of the undeformed plate. We desire shear strain $\varepsilon_{x'y'}$. Observing Fig. 5.8, we can conclude the $\varepsilon_{x'y'}$ equals the angle α between the diagonal in the undeformed geometry and the diagonal in the deformed geometry. Again observing Fig. 5.8, we can say that for small deformations

$$\varepsilon_{x'y'} = \frac{\overline{cb}}{\overline{Ob}} \tag{5.10}$$

Now $\overline{cb}$ is the hypotenuse of a 45°–45°–90° triangle gbc, where leg $\overline{bg}$ is half the change in length of the plate in the x direction, while leg $\overline{gc}$ is half the change in length of the plate in the y direction. The change in length $\overline{bg}$ is a result of two

---

* We could also use the stress and strain transformation equations here to get stresses and strains for the primed axes. We believe it will be beneficial here to work from first principles.

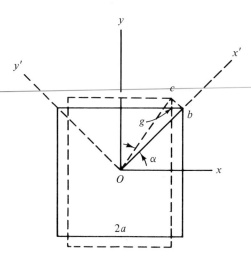

Figure 5.8 Original and deformed geometries.

effects. First there is that due to the compressive stress S in the x direction giving a contribution $(S/E)(a)$. Added to this is a change in length due to the Poisson effect from the strain in the direction coming from the tensile stress S in the y direction. This contribution is then $\nu[(S/E)a]$. Accordingly, for $\overline{gb}$ we can say that

$$\overline{gb} = \frac{S}{E}a + \nu\frac{S}{E}a = \frac{Sa}{E}(1+\nu)$$

We can then conclude for triangle gbc on using the result above that

$$\overline{cb} = \frac{\overline{gb}}{\cos 45°} = \sqrt{2}\,gb = \sqrt{2}\,\frac{Sa}{E}(1+\nu) \tag{5.11}$$

Finally, noting from Fig. 5.8 that

$$\overline{Ob} = \frac{a}{\cos 45°} = \sqrt{2}\,a$$

we have, from Eqs. (5.10) and (5.11),

$$\varepsilon_{x'y'} = \frac{\sqrt{2}\,(Sa/E)(1+\nu)}{\sqrt{2}\,a} = \frac{S}{E}(1+\nu) \tag{5.12}$$

Hooke's law in shear states next that

$$\tau_{x'y'} = G(2\varepsilon_{x'y'}) \tag{5.13}$$

Substituting for $\tau_{x'y'}$ from Eq. (5.9) and for $\varepsilon_{x'y'}$ from Eq. (5.12), for Eq. (5.13) we get*

$$S = G\left[2\frac{S}{E}(1+\nu)\right]$$

---

*The result is *general* for linear-elastic isotropic materials even though we reached it using a special state of stress, since only constants are involved in this result.

Therefore,

$$G = \frac{E}{2(1+\nu)} \tag{5.14}$$

We may now substitute Eq. (5.14) into Eqs. (5.8). Introducing index notation, we can then form a very compact equation for isotropic Hooke's law. Thus

$$\varepsilon_{ij} = \frac{1+\nu}{E}\, \tau_{ij} - \frac{\nu}{E}\, \tau_{kk}\, \delta_{ij} \tag{5.15}$$

It will be useful to invert this equation to get stress in terms of strain, and for this purpose we perform a contraction in Eq. (5.15) to get

$$\varepsilon_{kk} = \frac{1+\nu}{E}\, \tau_{kk} - \frac{\nu}{E}\, \tau_{kk}\,(3) = \frac{1-2\nu}{E}\, \tau_{kk} \tag{5.16}$$

Next, use Eq. (5.16) to replace τ_{kk} in Eq. (5.15). Solving the resulting equation for τ_{ij}, we then obtain the desired equation

$$\tau_{ij} = \frac{E}{1+\nu}\left(\varepsilon_{ij} + \frac{\nu}{1-2\nu}\, \varepsilon_{kk}\, \delta_{ij}\right) \tag{5.17}$$

5.4 GENERALIZED HOOKE'S LAW; ANISOTROPIC BEHAVIOR

In the preceding section for isotropic, linear-elastic materials, we found that the stress tensor and the strain tensor are linearly related in the special way given by Eqs. (5.15) and (5.17). We shall now consider anisotropic, linear elastic behavior wherein each stress component is linearly related, in the general case, to *all* the strains by equations of the form

$$\tau_{ij} = C_{ijkl}\, \varepsilon_{kl} \tag{5.18}$$

where C_{ijkl} is, for homogeneous materials, a set of constants that we call the *elastic constants*. For an inhomogeneous material the C_{ijkl} vary with position but are still called elastic constants. The foregoing law, called the *generalized Hooke's law*, is the most general linear relation between all of the stresses and all of the strains. Because τ_{ij} and ε_{ij} are second-order tensors, one may easily show that C_{ijkl} is a fourth-order tensor with 81 elements.[*] Furthermore, since τ_{ij} and ε_{ij} are not pseudo-tensors, one can also show that C_{ijkl} transforms properly under an inversion of axes (see Problem 5.10).

[*] See Problem 1.15 for a proof of this. We also point out that the form of Eq.(5.18) gives $\tau_{ij} = 0$ when $\varepsilon_{kl} = 0$ (i.e., there is *no initial stress*).

Because τ_{ij} is symmetric, it should be clear from Eq. (5.18) that C_{ijkl} must be symmetric in ij. That is,

$$C_{ijkl} = C_{jikl} \tag{5.19}$$

Since ε_{kl} is symmetric, we can always express the components of C_{ijkl} in a form symmetric in kl without violating Eq. (5.18). That is, we will also stipulate that

$$C_{ijkl} = C_{ijlk} \tag{5.20}$$

Considering Eqs. (5.19) and (5.20), we conclude that the indices $ijkl$ vary only in pairs (ij) and (kl) wherein each pair may take on the six different values: (11), (22), (33), (12) = (21), (13) = (31), and (23) = (32). Thus we can conclude that the 81 constants C_{ijkl} are in fact only at most 36 different constants. Each stress is then related linearly to the six independent strains via six of the independent elastic constants C_{ijkl}. For example, we can say

$$\tau_{xx} = C_{1111}\,\varepsilon_{xx} + C_{1122}\,\varepsilon_{yy} + C_{1133}\,\varepsilon_{zz} + 2C_{1123}\,\varepsilon_{yz} + 2C_{1131}\,\varepsilon_{zx} + 2C_{1112}\,\varepsilon_{xy} \tag{5.21}$$

We can rewrite Eq. (5.21) using as alternative notation the constants C_{11}, C_{12}, and so on, as follows:

$$\tau_{xx} = C_{11}\,\varepsilon_{xx} + C_{12}\,\varepsilon_{yy} + C_{13}\,\varepsilon_{zz} + C_{14}\,\gamma_{yz} + C_{15}\,\gamma_{zx} + C_{16}\,\gamma_{xy} \tag{5.22}$$

By comparing Eq. (5.22) with Eq. (5.21), we see that $C_{1111} = C_{11}$, $C_{1122} = C_{12}$, $C_{1133} = C_{13}$, $C_{1123} = C_{14}$, $C_{1131} = C_{15}$, and $C_{1112} = C_{16}$. In general, we find that when the pairs (ij) and (kl) take on the values (11), (22), (33), (23), (31), and (12), the subscripts p and q in C_{pq} take on the values 1, 2, 3, 4, 5, 6, respectively. We can, accordingly, express generalized Hooke's law in the following alternative form with 36 C_{pq} coefficients, which are now called *elastic moduli*:

$$
\begin{aligned}
\tau_{xx} &= C_{11}\,\varepsilon_{xx} + C_{12}\,\varepsilon_{yy} + C_{13}\,\varepsilon_{zz} + C_{14}\,\gamma_{yz} + C_{15}\,\gamma_{zx} + C_{16}\,\gamma_{xy} & \text{(a)} \\
\tau_{yy} &= C_{21}\,\varepsilon_{xx} + C_{22}\,\varepsilon_{yy} + C_{23}\,\varepsilon_{zz} + C_{24}\,\gamma_{yz} + C_{25}\,\gamma_{zx} + C_{26}\,\gamma_{xy} & \text{(b)} \\
\tau_{zz} &= C_{31}\,\varepsilon_{xx} + C_{32}\,\varepsilon_{yy} + C_{33}\,\varepsilon_{zz} + C_{34}\,\gamma_{yz} + C_{35}\,\gamma_{zx} + C_{36}\,\gamma_{xy} & \text{(c)} \\
\tau_{yz} &= C_{41}\,\varepsilon_{xx} + C_{42}\,\varepsilon_{yy} + C_{43}\,\varepsilon_{zz} + C_{44}\,\gamma_{yz} + C_{45}\,\gamma_{zx} + C_{46}\,\gamma_{xy} & \text{(d)} \\
\tau_{zx} &= C_{51}\,\varepsilon_{xx} + C_{52}\,\varepsilon_{yy} + C_{53}\,\varepsilon_{zz} + C_{54}\,\gamma_{yz} + C_{55}\,\gamma_{zx} + C_{56}\,\gamma_{xy} & \text{(e)} \\
\tau_{xy} &= C_{61}\,\varepsilon_{xx} + C_{62}\,\varepsilon_{yy} + C_{63}\,\varepsilon_{zz} + C_{64}\,\gamma_{yz} + C_{65}\,\gamma_{zx} + C_{66}\,\gamma_{xy} & \text{(f)}
\end{aligned} \tag{5.23}
$$

In matrix form, we have for the above:

$$\{\tau\} = [C]\{\varepsilon\} \tag{5.24}$$

where $\{\tau\}$ and $\{\varepsilon\}$ are 6×1 column matrices and $[C]$ is a 6×6 square matrix. In contrast to τ_{ij}, ε_{ij}, and C_{ijkl}, C_{pq} is *not* a tensor in three-dimensional space. If the elements of C_{pq} of the matrix $[C]$ are symmetric (i.e., $C_{pq} = C_{qp}$), we say that the material is *hyperelastic*. One can prove that a material is hyperelastic if its stress-strain law is derivable from an elastic potential such as the strain-energy density.[*]

We know that for linear-elastic *isotropic* behavior,

$$\tau_{zz} = E \varepsilon_{zz} \tag{5.25}$$

for a simple uniaxial stress in the z direction. Using the z direction, and noting that shear strains are zero in an isotropic material for x, y, z axes, we can then say, from Eq. (5.23c), that for this uniaxial case,

$$\tau_{zz} = C_{31} \varepsilon_{xx} + C_{32} \varepsilon_{yy} + C_{33} \varepsilon_{zz} \tag{5.26}$$

But we have previously shown that ε_{yy} and ε_{xx} are each proportional to ε_{zz} through the Poisson effect for linear-elastic isotropic material. Thus we can say that for an isotropic Poisson effect,

$$\tau_{zz} = C_{31}(-\nu\varepsilon_{zz}) + C_{32}(-\nu\varepsilon_{zz}) + C_{33}\varepsilon_{zz}$$

Hence

$$\tau_{zz} = (-\nu C_{31} - \nu C_{32} + C_{33})\varepsilon_{zz} \tag{5.27}$$

We see that Eq. (5.25) is the same form as Eq. (5.27). We can thus partially justify the generalized formulation by the fact that it properly includes in it the simpler stress-strain relations that we deduced for our tensile tests of linear-elastic, isotropic materials. The primary justification for the use of the linear, generalized, stress-strain law must, of course, be based on experiment. We do find, by using this constitutive law in computations involving linear-elastic materials, that the analytical results we reach are in agreement with experimental results.

If a material has the same composition throughout, we have termed such materials homogeneous. It would then appear that the linear-elastic, homogeneous body has 36 constants or elastic moduli (21 moduli if hyperelastic), which are needed to relate stress and strain below the proportional limit. It would at first seem that we have a frightfully complicated situation on our hands for the handling of problems. However, as we have noted in Section 5.2, many materials that we employ in engineering applications are isotropic and thus have mechanical properties that are not dependent on any particular directions. In this case the generalized Hooke's law for some new reference $x'y'z'$ would retain the same moduli C_{pq} as when the law is expressed for the xyz reference as in Eq. (5.23). Thus the equation for $\tau_{x'x'}$ would be given as

$$\tau_{x'x'} = C_{11} \varepsilon_{x'x'} + C_{12} \varepsilon_{y'y'} + C_{13} \varepsilon_{z'z'} + C_{14} \gamma_{y'z'} + C_{15} \gamma_{z'x'} + C_{16} \gamma_{x'y'} \tag{5.28}$$

where the moduli C_{pq} have the same values as in Eq. (5.23a). We shall now verify that generalized Hooke's law as given by Eq. (5.18), or equivalently by Eq. (5.23), reduces to Eq. (5.17) in the special case of an isotropic material. This will be accomplished by performing a sequence of transformations of axes, requiring each

[*] See Problem 5.25, and for more detail see I. H. Shames and C. L. Dym, *Energy and Finite Element Methods in Structural Mechanics* (New York: Hemisphere Publishing Corp., 1985). We also briefly consider elastic potentials for isotropic elastic materials in Section 5.5.

time that the elastic constants C_{ijkl} or the elastic moduli C_{pq} be invariant for these transformations of axes (i.e., $C_{i'j'k'l'} = C_{ijkl}$ or $C_{p'q'} = C_{pq}$).

Orthotropic Symmetry

We will first consider a material that has three mutually orthogonal planes of elastic symmetry. Such a material is said to have *orthotropic* symmetry and is called an orthotropic material. We will enforce elastic symmetry first about the $x_2 x_3$ plane. This is accomplished by requiring the elastic constants C_{ijkl} to be invariant with respect to an *inversion* of the x_1 axis. This inversion is shown in Fig. 5.9. The matrix of direction cosines for this case, $a_{m'i}$, is given as

$$a_{m'i} = \begin{bmatrix} -1 & 0 & 0 \\ 0 & 1 & 0 \\ 0 & 0 & 1 \end{bmatrix} \tag{5.29}$$

Now C_{ijkl} is a fourth-order tensor that transforms properly under inversion. Hence we may write for this transformation

$$C_{m'n'o'p'} = a_{m'i} a_{n'j} a_{o'k} a_{p'l} C_{ijkl} \tag{5.30}$$

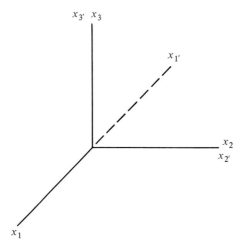

Figure 5.9 Inversion of x_1 axis to $x_{1'}$.

It follows from Eqs. (5.29) and (5.30) that, for example, $C_{1'1'1'2'} = -C_{1112}$ and $C_{1'2'2'3'} = -C_{1223}$. But from the invariance requirement we require in addition that $C_{1'1'1'2'} = C_{1112}$ and $C_{1'2'2'3'} = C_{1223}$. We must as a consequence conclude that these elastic constants are zero in value. By the same reasoning, we would find that any elastic constant with one or three 1's as subscripts vanishes. Furthermore, by considering inversion of the x_2 axis and enforcing invariance, we arrive at the orthotropic material* and find in the process that those elastic constants with an odd number of *any* index must vanish. When done, the following are the only nonzero elastic constants remaining:

---

* We will soon see that having symmetry with respect to two orthogonal planes is sufficient for having complete orthotropic symmetry.

$$C_{1122}, \quad C_{2233}, \quad C_{3311}, \quad C_{2211}, \quad C_{3322}, \quad C_{1133} \qquad \text{(a)}$$

$$C_{2323}, \quad C_{3131}, \quad C_{1212} \qquad\qquad\qquad\qquad\qquad \text{(b)} \qquad (5.31)$$

$$C_{1111}, \quad C_{2222}, \quad C_{3333} \qquad\qquad\qquad\qquad\qquad \text{(c)}$$

where we have formed three distinct groupings of constants.

If we convert our elastic constants C_{ijkl} in (5.31) to elastic moduli C_{pq}, we can give the elastic modulus matrix as follows for orthotropic materials:

$$C_{pq} = \begin{bmatrix} C_{11} & C_{12} & C_{13} & 0 & 0 & 0 \\ C_{21} & C_{22} & C_{23} & 0 & 0 & 0 \\ C_{31} & C_{32} & C_{33} & 0 & 0 & 0 \\ 0 & 0 & 0 & C_{44} & 0 & 0 \\ 0 & 0 & 0 & 0 & C_{55} & 0 \\ 0 & 0 & 0 & 0 & 0 & C_{66} \end{bmatrix} \qquad (5.32)$$

We see that we need 12 elastic moduli for this case.* If the material is also *hyperelastic*, we need only nine elastic moduli, as you can see by setting $C_{pq} = C_{qp}$ in Eq. (5.32). Although a significant number of materials are orthotropic hyperelastic (examples are wood and composite materials), in this book we nevertheless restrict ourselves to completely isotropic behavior.

Before moving on, we wish to point out that when all the elastic constants C_{ijkl} with an odd number of index 1 or 2 are set equal to zero, there will remain no elastic constants with an odd number of index 3. You may readily deduce this yourself. We can accordingly conclude from this that symmetry with respect to two orthogonal planes is sufficient to have complete orthotropic symmetry. Finally, it is worth noting that we could have reached Eq. (5.32) by considering two 180° rotations of axes (one about the x_1 axis and one about the x_2 axis) to enforce elastic symmetry, instead of the two inversions of x_1 and x_2 that we did use (see Problem 5.12).

Cubic Symmetry

We continue now toward developing the isotropic Hooke's law. *In addition* to having orthotropic symmetry, we now require further that properties be the *same* in the *three orthogonal directions* x_1, x_2, and x_3, including the *negative* of these directions. Such a material is said to have *cubic* symmetry. (The FCC and BCC crystals discussed in Appendix VII have such cubic symmetry.) For cubic symmetry the constants must be invariant when we perform the following *permutations* of the axes and the associated indices:

$$123 \rightarrow 231 \rightarrow 312 \rightarrow 213 \rightarrow 321 \rightarrow 132 \qquad (5.33)$$

Note that the last three permutations yield left-handed coordinate systems, which correspond to right-handed coordinate systems in which one of the axes has been replaced by its negative direction. With (5.33) in mind, notice that the constants in Eq. (5.31a) are mutually equal. This is similarly true for the respective sets of

---

*Matrix (5.32) is valid only if the axes are coincident with the orthotropic axes of symmetry. For other orientations of axes, the matrix is more complex and involves more than 12 elastic moduli.

constants in Eqs. (5.31b) and (5.31c). Hence only C_{1122}, C_{2323}, and C_{1111} remain as independent, nonzero constants. Thus a material with cubic symmetry has only *three* independent nonzero elastic components; the assumption of hyperelasticity causes no further reduction in the number of such constants. The elastic modulus matrix for cubic symmetry is thus given as

$$C_{pq} = \begin{bmatrix} C_{11} & C_{12} & C_{12} & 0 & 0 & 0 \\ C_{12} & C_{11} & C_{12} & 0 & 0 & 0 \\ C_{12} & C_{12} & C_{11} & 0 & 0 & 0 \\ 0 & 0 & 0 & C_{44} & 0 & 0 \\ 0 & 0 & 0 & 0 & C_{44} & 0 \\ 0 & 0 & 0 & 0 & 0 & C_{44} \end{bmatrix} \tag{5.34}$$

It is worth noting that Eq. (5.34) could also have been obtained by imposing isotropy for two 90° rotations of axes (e.g., about the x_1 and x_3 axes) (see Problem 5.13).

Isotropic Symmetry

As a final step, we consider the isotropic material for which the elastic constants must be invariant under an *arbitrary* rotation of the coordinate axes about *any* axis. We will consider an arbitrary *differential* rotation $d\theta$ about x_3 as has been shown in Fig. 5.10. We shall soon see that when the elastic constants for a material with cubic symmetry are required, *in addition*, to be invariant under such a rotation, the material will be isotropic. The matrix of direction cosines for this rotation follows as

$$a_{m'i} = \begin{bmatrix} \cos(d\theta) & \sin(d\theta) & 0 \\ -\sin(d\theta) & \cos(d\theta) & 0 \\ 0 & 0 & 1 \end{bmatrix} = \begin{bmatrix} 1 & d\theta & 0 \\ -d\theta & 1 & 0 \\ 0 & 0 & 1 \end{bmatrix} \tag{5.35}$$

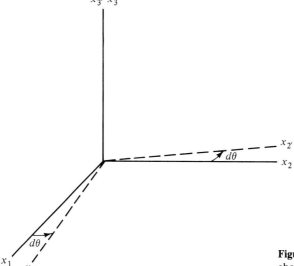

Figure 5.10 Infinitesimal rotation about the x_3 axis.

By using the Kronecker delta and the alternating tensor, we may express the last matrix above in index notation as

$$a_{m'i} = \delta_{mi} + e_{mi3} \, d\theta \qquad (5.36)$$

where m and i are free indices.* Now, in Eq. (5.30) we can use the format above for the four direction cosine matrices stated there. Thus for $a_{n'j}$ we would have

$$a_{n'j} = \delta_{nj} + e_{nj3} \, d\theta$$

Replacing the four direction cosine matrices in this way and carrying out the multiplication, with terms with $(d\theta)^2$ and higher-order products of $d\theta$ deleted, we get

$$C_{m'n'o'p'} = C_{mnop} + (e_{mi3} C_{inop} + e_{nj3} C_{mjop} + e_{ok3} C_{mnkp} + e_{pl3} C_{mnol}) \, d\theta$$

as you may readily verify. Setting $C_{m'n'o'p'} = C_{mnop}$ by virtue of the invariance requirement and dividing through by $d\theta$, we thus get

$$e_{mi3} C_{inop} + e_{nj3} C_{mjop} + e_{ok3} C_{mnkp} + e_{pl3} C_{mnol} = 0 \qquad (5.37)$$

Now, if we set $m = 2$ and $n = o = p = 1$ in Eq. (5.37) and solve for the first term, which gives C_{1111} in terms of the other terms, we get the relation

$$C_{1111} = C_{2211} + C_{2121} + C_{2112} = C_{1122} + 2C_{2323} \qquad (5.38)$$

where we have used on the extreme right the fact from Eqs. (5.33) and (5.31) that $C_{2211} = C_{1122}$ and $C_{2121} = C_{2112} = C_{1212} = C_{2323}$ for a material with cubic symmetry. No additional relations follow from Eq. (5.37) for a material with cubic symmetry. [We shall see in Problem 5.15 that for a material with orthotropic symmetry, Eq. (5.37) yields additional relations which then give us the elastic constants for the so-called *transversely isotropic* material.] If we perform any other rotations of axes (either differential or finite), we get no further simplifications.† We thus see that for isotropic behavior we have only *two* elastic constants. We may summarize the results for matrix (5.34) in the following manner:

$$C_{1122} = C_{12} = \lambda$$

$$C_{2323} = C_{44} = \mu \qquad (5.39)$$

$$C_{1111} = C_{11} = \lambda + 2\mu$$

where λ and μ are called the *Lamé constants*. Accordingly, for an isotropic material

---

* We may obtain the same result by considering a rotation of a *vector* $\mathbf{r}$ by an angle equal to $-d\theta$ about axis x_3. This new vector is given as $\mathbf{r}' = \mathbf{r} + (-d\theta \hat{\mathbf{k}}) \times \mathbf{r}$, which is written indicially as $x_{m'} = (\delta_{mi} + e_{mi3} \, d\theta)x_i$. Thus for the free index m set equal to 1, we get $x_{i'} = (\delta_{1i} + e_{1i3} \, d\theta)x_i = x_1 + d\theta x_2$.

† The results obtained in this section may be obtained by using various coordinate transformations, in conjunction with *either* tensor constitutive relation (5.18) or matrix constitutive relation (5.24). The particular approach followed here is similar to that given in *Introduction to Mechanics of Continua* by W. Prager (Boston: Ginn & Company, 1961), pp. 89–91. Some alternative approaches are illustrated in the problems at the end of this chapter. See also *Mathematical Theory of Elasticity* by I. S. Sokolnikoff (Melbourne, FL: R.E. Krieger Publishing Co., reprint edition, 1987), pp. 62–66.

the generalized Hooke's law [Eq. (5.18)] reduces to

$$
\begin{aligned}
\tau_{xx} &= (\lambda + 2\mu)\varepsilon_{xx} + \lambda(\varepsilon_{yy} + \varepsilon_{zz}) \\
\tau_{yy} &= (\lambda + 2\mu)\varepsilon_{yy} + \lambda(\varepsilon_{zz} + \varepsilon_{xx}) \\
\tau_{zz} &= (\lambda + 2\mu)\varepsilon_{zz} + \lambda(\varepsilon_{xx} + \varepsilon_{yy}) \\
\tau_{yz} &= \mu\gamma_{yz} \\
\tau_{zx} &= \mu\gamma_{zx} \\
\tau_{xy} &= \mu\gamma_{xy}
\end{aligned}
\tag{5.40}
$$

In index notation Eq. (5.40) is given as

$$
\tau_{ij} = \lambda\varepsilon_{kk}\delta_{ij} + 2\mu\varepsilon_{ij}
\tag{5.41}
$$

Since the isotropic elastic modulus matrix is symmetric, this material is also hyper-elastic. Accordingly, Eq. (5.41) [and also Eq. (5.17)] must be derivable from a potential, and we discuss this in the next section.

5.5 ALTERNATIVE FORMS OF ISOTROPIC HOOKE'S LAW; RELATIONS BETWEEN ELASTIC CONSTANTS

We have thus far obtained isotropic Hooke's law in both unabridged form [see Eqs. (5.8) and (5.40)] and in compact form [see Eqs. (5.15), (5.17), and (5.41)] involving in their entirety the elastic constants E, ν, G, λ, and μ. We know from the preceding section that of this set only two constants are independent. On comparing Eqs. (5.8) and (5.40) we see immediately that $\mu = G$, where you will recall that G is the shear modulus. Thus μ and G are not an independent pair of constants. However, any other pair of elastic constants may be chosen as the independent pair. Other relations can be found by comparing Eqs. (5.17) with Eqs. (5.41). Thus we see that

$$
\lambda = \frac{\nu E}{(1 + \nu)(1 - 2\nu)}
\tag{5.42}
$$

and

$$
\mu = G = \frac{E}{2(1 + \nu)}
\tag{5.43}
$$

where the last result is the same as relation (5.14) obtained previously. Thus if we choose ν and E as found from the tensile test to be the independent pair, we can readily find λ, μ, and G.

If, on the other hand, the Lamé constants λ and μ have been given, we may attempt to solve for E and ν from Eqs. (5.42) and (5.43). However, it is more instructive to compare Eqs. (5.8) with the inverted form of Eq. (5.41). Thus, solving for ε_{ij} in Eq. (5.41), we get

$$\varepsilon_{ij} = \frac{1}{2\mu} \left[\tau_{ij} - \lambda \varepsilon_{kk} \delta_{ij} \right] \tag{5.44}$$

In Eq. (5.41) again, set $i = j$ to form a contraction and obtain

$$\tau_{ii} = (3\lambda + 2\mu)\varepsilon_{ii}$$

Therefore,

$$\varepsilon_{kk} = \frac{\tau_{kk}}{3\lambda + 2\mu} \tag{5.45}$$

Now replace ε_{kk} in Eq. (5.44) using Eq. (5.45) to get

$$\boxed{\varepsilon_{ij} = \frac{\tau_{ij}}{2\mu} - \frac{\lambda \tau_{kk} \delta_{ij}}{2\mu(3\lambda + 2\mu)}} \tag{5.46}$$

Let us next consider $i = j = 1$ in Eq. (5.46).

$$\begin{aligned} \varepsilon_{xx} &= \frac{\tau_{xx}}{2\mu} - \frac{\lambda(\tau_{xx} + \tau_{yy} + \tau_{zz})}{2\mu(3\lambda + 2\mu)} \\ &= \left[\frac{1}{2\mu} - \frac{\lambda}{2\mu(3\lambda + 2\mu)} \right] \tau_{xx} - \frac{\lambda}{2\mu(3\lambda + 2\mu)} (\tau_{yy} + \tau_{zz}) \end{aligned} \tag{5.47}$$

Going back to Eqs. (5.8) and comparing the result above with the first equation of this system, we can conclude that

$$\frac{1}{E} = \left[\frac{1}{2\mu} - \frac{\lambda}{2\mu(3\lambda + 2\mu)} \right] = \frac{\lambda + \mu}{\mu(3\lambda + 2\mu)} \qquad \text{(a)}$$

and $\tag{5.48}$

$$\frac{\nu}{E} = \frac{\lambda}{2\mu(3\lambda + 2\mu)} \qquad \text{(b)}$$

We finally form the following useful equations from the preceding two equations:

$$\boxed{E = \frac{\mu(3\lambda + 2\mu)}{\lambda + \mu}} \qquad \text{(a)}$$

$$\tag{5.49}$$

$$\boxed{\nu = \frac{\lambda}{2(\lambda + \mu)}} \qquad \text{(b)}$$

In Chapter 4 we introduced yet another elastic constant, called the bulk modulus, denoted as K. To relate this constant with λ and μ, we go back to Eq. (5.45) and divide both sides by 3. Then, solving for τ_{kk}, we get

$$\frac{\tau_{kk}}{3} = \frac{3\lambda + 2\mu}{3} \varepsilon_{kk} \tag{5.50}$$

The left side of the equation above is the *bulk stress* and the coefficient of the volume dilatation, ε_{kk}, is our bulk modulus K. Hence

$$\boxed{K = \frac{3\lambda + 2\mu}{3}} \tag{5.51}$$

We shall on occasion rewrite Eq. (5.50) as

$$\boxed{\bar{\tau} = (3\lambda + 2\mu)\bar{\varepsilon} = 3K\bar{\varepsilon} = K\Delta} \tag{5.52}$$

Where $\bar{\tau} = \tau_{kk}/3$ is the bulk stress, and $\bar{\varepsilon} = \varepsilon_{kk}/3 = \Delta/3$ is one-third the volume dilatation. Also, we can replace λ and μ using Eqs. (5.42) and (5.43), respectively, so that the equation for K above becomes

$$\boxed{K = \frac{E}{3(1 - 2\nu)}} \tag{5.53}$$

You will note that as $\nu \to \frac{1}{2}$ above, $K \to \infty$. From Eq. (5.52) we conclude that in this case we get zero volume dilatation for any finite value of bulk stress. Hence such a material is said to be *incompressible*.

In Chapters 2 and 3 we introduced the stress and strain deviator tensors, s_{ij} and e_{ij}, respectively. We rewrite these definitions here.

$$s_{ij} = \tau_{ij} - \tfrac{1}{3}\tau_{kk}\delta_{ij} \qquad \text{(a)}$$
$$e_{ij} = \varepsilon_{ij} - \tfrac{1}{3}\varepsilon_{kk}\delta_{ij} \qquad \text{(b)} \tag{5.54}$$

We shall formulate a constitutive equation between s_{ij} and e_{ij} by first multiplying Eq. (5.50) by δ_{ij} and subtracting this equation from Eq. (5.41) to get

$$\left(\tau_{ij} - \frac{\tau_{kk}}{3}\delta_{ij}\right) \equiv s_{ij} = \lambda\varepsilon_{kk}\delta_{ij} + 2\mu\varepsilon_{ij} - (\lambda + \tfrac{2}{3}\mu)\varepsilon_{kk}\delta_{ij}$$

This equation then simplifies to

$$s_{ij} = 2\mu\left(\varepsilon_{ij} - \frac{\varepsilon_{kk}}{3}\delta_{ij}\right) \tag{5.55}$$

Noting that the expression in the parentheses is simply e_{ij} [see Eq. (5.54b)], we have the following desired simple result:

$$s_{ij} = 2\mu e_{ij} = 2Ge_{ij} \qquad (5.56)$$

We will find this equation of considerable use in Chapter 6 when we study linear viscoelasticity. Note that for $i \neq j$, Eq. (5.56) reduces to the results for the simple pure shear tests in the three coordinate planes [i.e., Eqs. (5.7)]. However, for $i = j$ we obtain three additional relations of the same form between the *normal* stress and strain deviators. Since $s_{ii} = e_{ii} \equiv 0$, it is clear that Eq. (5.56) represents only *five* independent conditions.

While developing various alternative forms of isotropic Hooke's law in this chapter, we have introduced and mutually related the elastic constants E, ν, G $(= \mu)$, λ, and K. Only two of these five constants are independent. We can choose any two to be independent; the others must be computable from these two. In Table 5.1 we have chosen such pairs in the left-hand column; the formulations to the right of these pairs, set equal to the corresponding term at the top, give the relations needed to determine any constant in terms of any pair of different constants. Note that for an *incompressible*, linear elastic, isotropic material, $K \to \infty$,

TABLE 5.1 Relations between Elastic Constants for the Isotropic Forms of Hooke's Law

	E	ν	$G\ (=\mu)$	λ	K
E, ν			$\dfrac{E}{2(1+\nu)}$	$\dfrac{\nu E}{(1+\nu)(1-2\nu)}$	$\dfrac{E}{3(1-2\nu)}$
E, G		$\dfrac{E-2G}{2G}$		$\dfrac{(2G-E)G}{E-3G}$	$\dfrac{GE}{3(3G-E)}$
E, λ		$\dfrac{-E-\lambda+R}{4\lambda}$ $R=\sqrt{E^2+2E\lambda+9\lambda^2}$	$\dfrac{E-3\lambda+R}{4}$ $R=\sqrt{E^2+2E\lambda+9\lambda^2}$		$\dfrac{E+3\lambda+R}{6}$ $R=\sqrt{E^2+2E\lambda+9\lambda^2}$
E, K		$\dfrac{3K-E}{6K}$	$\dfrac{3EK}{9K-E}$	$\dfrac{3K(3K-E)}{9K-E}$	
ν, G	$2G(1+\nu)$			$\dfrac{2G\nu}{1-2\nu}$	$\dfrac{2G(1+\nu)}{3(1-2\nu)}$
ν, λ	$\dfrac{\lambda(1+\nu)(1-2\nu)}{\nu}$		$\dfrac{\lambda(1-2\nu)}{2\nu}$		$\dfrac{\lambda(1+\nu)}{3\nu}$
ν, K	$3K(1-2\nu)$		$\dfrac{3K(1-2\nu)}{2(1+\nu)}$	$\dfrac{3K\nu}{1+\nu}$	
G, λ	$\dfrac{G(3\lambda+2G)}{\lambda+G}$	$\dfrac{\lambda}{2(\lambda+G)}$			$\dfrac{3\lambda+2G}{3}$
G, K	$\dfrac{9KG}{3K+G}$	$\dfrac{1}{2}\left(\dfrac{3K-2G}{3K+G}\right)$		$\dfrac{3K-2G}{3}$	
λ, K	$\dfrac{9K(K-\lambda)}{3K-\lambda}$	$\dfrac{\lambda}{3K-\lambda}$	$\dfrac{3(K-\lambda)}{2}$		

$\lambda \to \infty$, and $\nu = \frac{1}{2}$, $E = 3G$. We also point out that a *stable* elastic material is defined as one for which $0 < E < \infty$, $0 < G = \mu < \infty$, $0 < K < \infty$, and $-1 < \nu < \frac{1}{2}$, $-\infty < \lambda < \infty$, which are all consistent with the entries in Table 5.1.

Finally, we note that the property of hyperelasticity ensures that isotropic Hooke's law may also be expressed in terms of a *strain energy density* $\mathcal{U}(\varepsilon_{ij})$ and a *complementary strain energy density* $\mathcal{U}^*(\tau_{ij})$ in accordance with the definitions*

$$\tau_{ij} = \frac{\partial \mathcal{U}(\varepsilon_{ij})}{\partial \varepsilon_{ij}} \qquad \text{(a)}$$

$$\varepsilon_{ij} = \frac{\partial \mathcal{U}^*(\tau_{ij})}{\partial \tau_{ij}} \qquad \text{(b)}$$

(5.57)

Using the chain rule of calculus, we have

$$d\mathcal{U}(\varepsilon_{ij}) = \frac{\partial \mathcal{U}(\varepsilon_{ij})}{\partial \varepsilon_{ij}} d\varepsilon_{ij} = \tau_{ij}\, d\varepsilon_{ij} \tag{5.58}$$

where we have used Eq. (5.57a). Using Eq. (5.41), we then get for the strain energy density,

$$\mathcal{U}(\varepsilon_{ij}) = \int (\lambda\,\varepsilon_{kk}\,\delta_{ij} + 2\mu\,\varepsilon_{ij})\, d\varepsilon_{ij} = \frac{\lambda}{2} \int d(\varepsilon_{ii}\,\varepsilon_{jj}) + \mu \int d\,(\varepsilon_{ij}\,\varepsilon_{ij})$$

Hence

$$\mathcal{U}(\varepsilon_{ij}) = \frac{\lambda}{2}\varepsilon_{ii}\,\varepsilon_{jj} + \mu\,\varepsilon_{ij}\,\varepsilon_{ij} = \frac{1}{2}\varepsilon_{ij}(\lambda\,\varepsilon_{kk}\,\delta_{ij} + 2\mu\,\varepsilon_{ij}) = \frac{1}{2}\tau_{ij}\,\varepsilon_{ij} \tag{5.59}$$

where we have used Eq. (5.41) to reach the last formulation. In a similar manner we may employ Eqs. (5.57b) and (5.15) to obtain the complementary energy density as

$$\mathcal{U}^*(\tau_{ij}) = \frac{1+\nu}{2E}\tau_{ij}\,\tau_{ij} - \frac{\nu}{2E}\tau_{ii}\,\tau_{jj} = \frac{1}{2}\varepsilon_{ij}\,\tau_{ij} \tag{5.60}$$

(See Problem 5.20 in regard to the final formulation above.) On comparing Eqs. (5.59) and (5.60) we see that although $\mathcal{U}$ and $\mathcal{U}^*$ have different functional forms, for linear elastic materials they are equal *numerically*. Although we shall not focus on energy methods in this book, we will on occasion refer to Eqs. (5.59) and (5.60). Up to this time, we have considered isothermal elastic materials. In the next section we briefly consider nonisothermal elasticity.

5.6 INTRODUCTION TO THERMOELASTICITY

Our considerations thus far have been based on the assumption that the body is of uniform temperature throughout (i.e., the so-called isothermal case). The strains induced for such a case result purely from applied external loads. We now relax this

---

* The *strain energy U* is given as $U = \int_D \mathcal{U}\, dv$ while the *complementary strain energy U^** is given as $U^* = \int_D \mathcal{U}^*\, dv$, where D is the domain of the volume.

restriction and consider the case where there may be a nonuniform temperature field in an isotropic elastic body. However, we shall assume that the temperature variation is not great enough to cause the elastic moduli of the material to vary appreciably throughout the body.

We start by noting that an unconstrained, isotropic solid element will expand uniformly in all directions when there is an increase in temperature. Thus a sphere will remain a sphere but will undergo a change in radius; a cubic element remains a cubic element but will undergo a change in length of edge. This means that there will be equal normal strain in all directions but no shear strain for the unconstrained element whose temperature has been changed. If the element is completely confined so that no change in shape is permitted as the temperature is changed, the element will be subject to hydrostatic stress. On the other hand, if only a part of the total expansion of the element is permitted, there can be a general state of strain and a general state of stress in the element dependent on the nature of the constraint. In an isotropic body subject to a nonuniform temperature distribution, the elements attempt to undergo dilatation or shrinkage as a result of the changes in temperature from some initially uniform temperature. However, the elements cannot dilate or shrink in an unrestricted manner. Since the body must remain continuous during the change in temperature, there will be partial constraint as to change in geometry.* We may then introduce in this way a general stress field in the body. This stress field is called *thermal stress*. High-speed aircraft and space vehicles are subject to considerable thermal stress from aerodynamic heating on the outside surfaces and from the heat originating in propulsion systems. The study of these thermally induced stresses is of vital importance in present-day technology. In addition to thermal stress from a nonuniform temperature distribution in a body, there may also be a thermal stress distribution developed when a body changes temperature but is confined in some way by external constraints.

How do we measure the strain developed in a body when it is subject to a temperature field as well as to a system of loads? Most simply, we superpose the strain associated with free dilatation of the element with the strain associated with the total actual state of stress of the element. This stress includes the thermally induced stress as well as stress due to the external loads. Thus we can imagine that an element is first allowed to dilate or shrink freely, giving a strain ε'. The restraints due to nonuniform expansion and external constraints then lead to a thermally induced stress that causes a strain ε''. With no external loads, the net strain from these separate actions is the actual strain. Thus for the completely confined element mentioned earlier, the strain ε' and the strain ε'' from the aforementioned actions give a zero total strain when superposed. If there are external loads, there will be additional strain ε''' which we can superpose in light of our small deformation restriction. Thus we have, for the strain at a point,

$$\varepsilon = \underset{\substack{\text{from free expansion} \\ \text{or shrinkage}}}{\varepsilon'} + \underset{\substack{\text{from thermally} \\ \text{induced stress}}}{\varepsilon''} + \underset{\substack{\text{from stress due} \\ \text{to external loads}}}{\varepsilon'''}$$

* If this is not clear, imagine the body at a uniform initial temperature to be composed of elemental equal cubes. If the temperature is now raised nonuniformly, the cubes expand differently. If no voids are allowed in the material, it should be clear that the cubes will interact with each other.

We shall here compute $(\varepsilon'' + \varepsilon''')$ using the familiar isotropic Hooke's law for linear, elastic materials [Eqs. (5.8)]. The stresses to be used are clearly the total actual stresses. We next direct our attention to the strain ε' from unconfined dilatation or shrinkage of an element. Thus, for small temperature changes $\Delta T(x, y, z)$ the change in length of a vanishingly small line segment δL is

$$\Delta(\delta L) = \alpha \, \delta L \, \Delta T \tag{5.61}$$

where α is the *coefficient of linear thermal expansion*. The normal strain in the direction ν, $\varepsilon'_{\nu\nu}$, from unconfined expansion or shrinkage at a point is then*

$$\varepsilon'_{\nu\nu} = \lim_{\delta L \to 0} \frac{\Delta(\delta L)}{\delta L} = \alpha \, \Delta T \tag{5.62}$$

Combining the strains computed for unconstrained dilatation [Eq. (5.62)] and from the total stress [Eqs. (5.8)], we get the following important set of equations:

$$
\begin{aligned}
\varepsilon_{xx} &= \frac{1}{E} \left[\tau_{xx} - \nu(\tau_{yy} + \tau_{zz}) \right] + \alpha \, \Delta T \\[2mm]
\varepsilon_{yy} &= \frac{1}{E} \left[\tau_{yy} - \nu(\tau_{zz} + \tau_{xx}) \right] + \alpha \, \Delta T \\[2mm]
\varepsilon_{zz} &= \frac{1}{E} \left[\tau_{zz} - \nu(\tau_{xx} + \tau_{yy}) \right] + \alpha \, \Delta T \\[2mm]
\gamma_{yz} &= \frac{1}{G} \tau_{yz} \\[2mm]
\gamma_{zx} &= \frac{1}{G} \tau_{zx} \\[2mm]
\gamma_{xy} &= \frac{1}{G} \tau_{xy}
\end{aligned}
\tag{5.63}
$$

A material having the constitutive law given above is said to be a *linear, isotropic, thermoelastic* material. In index notation we get on replacing G by $E/[2(1 + \nu)]$,

$$\varepsilon_{ij} = \frac{1 + \nu}{E} \tau_{ij} - \frac{\nu}{E} \tau_{kk} \delta_{ij} + \alpha \, \Delta T \, \delta_{ij} \tag{5.64}$$

We may invert this equation to yield stress in terms of strain. Thus we get

$$\tau_{ij} = 2G \varepsilon_{ij} + \lambda \varepsilon_{kk} \delta_{ij} - \beta \, \Delta T \delta_{ij} \tag{5.65}$$

---

*Note that, as explained in Chapter 1, ν is *not* an index and thus there is no sum on ν in Eq. (5.62).

Linear Elastic Behavior   Chap. 5

where

$$\beta = (3\lambda + 2G)\alpha \tag{5.66}$$

We may also obtain from Eq. (5.64) an expression for volume dilatation. This is done by performing a contraction. Thus

$$\varepsilon_{kk} = \Delta = \frac{1-2\nu}{E}\,\tau_{kk} + 3\alpha\,\Delta T \tag{5.67}$$

From this equation we see that the coefficient of *volume* thermal expansion is three times the coefficient of linear thermal expansion.

What happens to the other basic laws for this kind of thermoelastic problem? Newton's law [i.e., Eq. (2.24)] is unchanged, since it is based on purely mechanical considerations. The strain-displacement relations, Eq. (3.37), are also unchanged since they are based on purely geometrical considerations. This is similarly true for the compatibility equations, Eq. (3.68). We can then say that if the temperature distribution is known and if body forces and surface tractions or surface displacements are known, the problem presented herein is essentially little different mathematically except in complexity from those posed earlier for isothermal elasticity.

In our discussion thus far, we have implied that the computation of the temperature field in a solid can be carried out separately from that of the stress distribution. It can be shown* that for most practical problems the effect of stress and strain on temperature is very small and can be neglected. Computation of the temperature field is then a heat transfer problem involving solution of the classical heat conduction equation. Considerably more complex problems arise when we cannot uncouple the heat transfer analysis from the stress-strain analysis or when properties are taken as temperature dependent.

We consider next an elementary problem involving thermal stress.

Example 5.1

A steel pipe with a 5-in. inside diameter D_i and a 6-in. outside diameter D_o is held by two fixed supports as shown in Fig. 5.11. When mounted, the temperature of the pipe

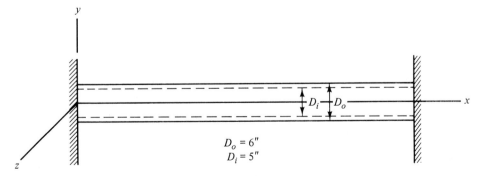

Figure 5.11 Fluid moving through a pipe.

---

*See B. Boley and J. Weiner, *Theory of Thermal Stress* (New York: John Wiley & Sons, Inc., 1960; reprinted 1985 by R.E. Krieger Publishing Co., Inc., Melbourne, FL), Chap. 2.

was 60°F. In use, however, cold fluid moves through the pipe, causing it to cool considerably. If we assume that the pipe has a uniform temperature of 0°F and if we take the coefficient of linear expansion to be $6.5 \times 10^{-6}/°F$ for the temperature range, determine the state of stress and strain in the pipe as a result of this cooling. We shall neglect all body forces and the surface tractions on the lateral surfaces of the pipe.

Away from the end supports, we can assume for the stress due to temperature change a one-dimensional stress distribution in the x direction. Thus we can say that

$$\tau_{yy} = \tau_{zz} = \tau_{xy} = \tau_{yz} = \tau_{zx} = 0 \tag{a}$$

for the reference shown. Only τ_{xx} is nonzero. Clearly, such a stress distribution satisfies both the boundary conditions of this problem and Newton's law. We can get the strain distribution from the stress-strain relation given by using Eq. (5.63). Thus

$$\varepsilon_{xx} = \frac{\tau_{xx}}{E} + \alpha \, \Delta T \qquad \text{(i)}$$

$$\varepsilon_{yy} = -\frac{\nu \tau_{xx}}{E} + \alpha \, \Delta T \qquad \text{(ii)}$$

$$\text{(b)}$$

$$\varepsilon_{zz} = -\frac{\nu \tau_{xx}}{E} + \alpha \, \Delta T \qquad \text{(iii)}$$

$$\gamma_{yz} = \gamma_{zx} = \gamma_{xy} = 0 \qquad \text{(iv)}$$

Because of the constraint in the x direction imposed by the walls and because of the uniformity of temperature and geometry in the x direction, we can say that $\varepsilon_{xx} = 0$ and from Eq. (i) of Eqs. (b) above we get τ_{xx} as

$$\tau_{xx} = -E\alpha \, \Delta T$$

This then permits the evaluation of the remaining strain terms

$$\varepsilon_{yy} = \alpha \, \Delta T (1 + \nu)$$

$$\text{(c)}$$

$$\varepsilon_{zz} = \alpha \, \Delta T (1 + \nu)$$

The strains are thus all constant. Clearly, they will satisfy the compatibility equations. The tensile force P on the supports is now available. Thus

$$P = \tau_{xx} A = -E\alpha A \, \Delta T \tag{d}$$

We may evaluate τ_{xx} and P numerically for this problem. Taking $E = 30 \times 10^6$ psi for steel, we have

$$\tau_{xx} = -(30 \times 10^6)(6.5 \times 10^{-6})(-60) = 11,700 \text{ psi}$$

$$P = (11,700) \frac{(\pi)(6^2 - 5^2)}{4} = 101,100 \text{ lb}$$

We see that considerable forces can be developed by thermal effects.

5.7 CLOSURE

In this chapter we have examined linear elastic behavior. We started by considering the isotropic case wherein we superposed results from the one-dimensional tensile test of Chapter 4 and a simple torsion test to reach a much used constitutive law

[Eqs. (5.8)] that is probably familiar to you from your earlier studies. We then found that of the three constants introduced from the tensile and torsion tests, only two are independent. We next presented a generalized Hooke's law where each stress is linearly related to all the strains. This formulation describes general linear anisotropic behavior. We reached the case of orthotropic linear behavior by requiring invariance of the elastic constants for inversions of the axes. Next, we proceeded to the case of cubical material behavior by imposing additional invariance requirements on permutations of axes. In this progression from complete anisotropy toward complete isotropy, we went from 36 elastic constants to 12 for the orthotropic case and to 3 for the cubically symmetric case. Now requiring invariance for a rotation about any axis reduced the independent constants to two. No further reductions were possible, and we accordingly reached the isotropic case that will concern us most in this book. We also presented a number of forms of the isotropic Hooke's law, and related the various elastic constants arising from these formulations.

Finally, we examined briefly the isotropic constitutive law for thermoelasticity. This was done without including the effect of temperature dependence in the properties, nor did we consider the contribution of temperature change due to loading. If we wish to include such effects, we get involved in a very difficult undertaking. For such cases Newton's law is unchanged, but now the first law of thermodynamics must be carefully considered. This law will include heat transfer, energy of deformations, and so on. It is to be pointed out that the second law of thermodynamics must also now be carefully taken into account.

In the next two chapters we turn to the viscoelastic behavior of materials. This behavior has increasingly become more important to us in structural mechanics problems and in geophysical applications involving ice and the Earth's crust. We shall consider linear viscoelasticity first, and in Chapter 7 we will study nonlinear viscoelasticity.

PROBLEMS

5.1. (a) Prove that a normal stress τ_{zz} cannot cause a shear strain γ_{yz} for isotropic behavior.
   (b) Prove that for isotropic behavior a shear stress τ_{xy} cannot cause a normal strain ε_{xx}.
   (c) Prove that for isotropic behavior a shear stress τ_{zx} cannot cause the shear strain γ_{xy}.

5.2. A strain rosette on the surface of a body permits us to compute principal stresses there. If the z axis is normal to the surface of the body at the position of the rosette, we get the following principal stresses in the xy plane.

$$\tau_1 = 32,000 \text{ psi}$$

$$\tau_2 = 16,000 \text{ psi}$$

If $E = 30 \times 10^6$ psi and $\nu = 0.3$, what is the strain ε_{zz}? Assume that $\tau_{zz} = 0$.

5.3. We have for steel the following data:

$$E = 2 \times 10^{11} \text{ Pa}$$

$$G = 0.8 \times 10^{11} \text{ Pa}$$

For a state of strain at a point in this material given as

$$\begin{bmatrix} 0.002 & 0 & -0.002 \\ 0 & -0.003 & 0.0005 \\ -0.002 & 0.0005 & 0 \end{bmatrix}$$

determine the stress tensor. Assume isotropic behavior.

5.4. A rectangular strain rosette is mounted on the surface of a body (Fig. P5.4). The gauges read

$$\varepsilon_① = 0.002$$

$$\varepsilon_② = 0.003$$

$$\varepsilon_③ = 0.004$$

(a) If $E = 2 \times 10^{11}$ Pa and $\nu = 0.3$, what are the principal stresses? Neglect atmospheric pressure.

(b) What is the normal strain in a direction normal to the surface?

(*Hint*: Make use of two-dimensional transformation equations for strain to find ε_{ij}, but do *not* assume plane strain. Then find τ_{ij} and principal stresses τ_1, τ_2, τ_3.)

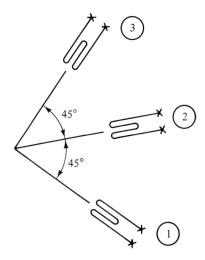

Figure P5.4

5.5. An equiangular strain rosette is mounted on the surface of a body (Fig. P5.5). The strain gauges read

$$\varepsilon_① = -0.003$$

$$\varepsilon_② = 0.002$$

$$\varepsilon_③ = 0.001$$

and $E = 20 \times 10^6$ psi and $\nu = 0.28$. Find the stress tensor at the location of the rosette if only air acts on the surface. Neglect air pressure. (*Hint*: Make use of two-dimensional transformation equations for strain to find ε_{ij}, but do *not* assume plane strain. Then find τ_{ij}.)

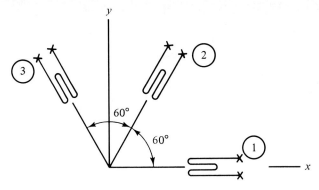

Figure P5.5

5.6. In a thick-walled cylinder subject to an inside pressure only, the following strains exist at point A in Fig. P5.6:

$$\varepsilon_{rr} = \quad 0.002$$

$$\varepsilon_{\theta\theta} = \quad 0.004$$

$$\varepsilon_{zz} = -0.001$$

(a) What are the stresses τ_{rr}, $\tau_{\theta\theta}$, and τ_{zz} for $G = 1.0 \times 10^{11}$ Pa and $\nu = 0.3$?
(b) What is the stress tensor τ_{ij} at A for the Cartesian coordinates shown in the figure?

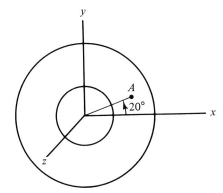

Figure P5.6

5.7. Show that for an isotropic linear elastic material, principal axes for stress and strain coincide at any point.

5.8. Express Hooke's law as given by Eq. (5.15) for *plane stress*, giving strains in terms of stresses. Next, invert these equations and thereby obtain stresses in terms of strains. Finally, express Hooke's law as given by Eq. (5.17) for *plane strain*, with stresses expressed in terms of strains. Compare this result with your result for plane stress.

5.9. Consider an inversion of the x_2 axis. Which of the elastic constants C_{ijkl} can you decide from this inversion must be zero for elastic symmetry?

5.10. Show that C_{ijkl} transforms properly as a fourth-order tensor under an inversion of an axis—say the x_1 axis. You may use the fact that τ_{ij} and ε_{ij} transform properly under inversion (see Problems 2.10 and 3.21).

5.11. Are the principal axes of strain coincident with those of stress for:
(a) An anisotropic material satisfying generalized Hooke's law?

(b) A material with *one* plane of elastic symmetry, say $x_2 x_3$?

(c) An orthotropic material?

5.12. Consider a 180° rotation of axes x_1, x_2, x_3 about the x_1 axis. Prove that for the elastic constants C_{ijkl} to be invariant with respect to this transformation, we must require that any elastic constant, with one or three 1's as subscripts, vanish. Note that this is precisely the result obtained in the text for invariance with respect to an inversion of x_1 (i.e., for this material the $x_2 x_3$ plane is an elastic plane of symmetry).

5.13. Consider two 90° rotations of axes x_1, x_2, x_3—one about x_1 and one about x_3. Prove that for the elastic constants to be invariant with respect to *both* of these transformations, we must set

$$C_{1122} = C_{2233} = C_{3311} = C_{2211} = C_{3322} = C_{1133}$$

$$C_{2323} = C_{3131} = C_{1212}$$

$$C_{1111} = C_{2222} = C_{3333}$$

Note that these are precisely the permutation conditions for cubic symmetry set forth in the text.

5.14. Show that Eq. (5.36) yields the proper direction cosine matrix as given by Eq. (5.35). Then using this matrix, justify Eq. (5.37).

5.15. An orthotropic hyperelastic material that also satisfies Eq. (5.37) is called transversely isotropic. By appropriate choices of the free indices m, n, o, p, show that for such a material

$$C_{11} = C_{22} = C_{12} + 2C_{66}$$

$$C_{23} = C_{13}$$

$$C_{55} = C_{44}$$

Do *not* assume cubic symmetry; that is, work from matrix (5.32).

5.16. Consider a material with cubic symmetry. Require that its elastic constants also be invariant with respect to a 45° rotation of axes x_1, x_2, x_3 about the x_3 axis. Prove that such a material is isotropic; that is, show that in matrix (5.34) the elastic modulus $C_{11} = C_{12} + 2C_{44}$.

5.17. Starting with the constitutive law for deviatoric stress and deviatoric strain [Eq. (5.56)], develop from it and Eq. (5.52) the constitutive law for stress and strain.

5.18. In a linear elastic isotropic body the following data apply:

$$G = 12 \times 10^6 \text{ psi}$$

$$\nu = 0.3$$

Find the values of E, λ, μ, and K.

5.19. Starting with Eq. (5.60), justify Eq. (5.57b). Conversely, integrate Eq. (5.57b) to obtain Eq. (5.60).

5.20. **(a)** Using Eq. (5.15) in Eq. (5.60), justify the final formulation $\frac{1}{2} \varepsilon_{ij} \tau_{ij}$.

(b) Another way to reach the result for $\mathcal{U}$, as given by Eq. (5.59), or for $\mathcal{U}^*$, as given by Eq. (5.60), is to assume stresses and strains are raised in "concert." That is,

$$\tau_{ij} = \alpha (\tau_{ij})_{\text{final}} \qquad \varepsilon_{ij} = \alpha (\varepsilon_{ij})_{\text{final}}$$

which implies linearity between τ_{ij} and ε_{ij}. (Why?) Using this idea with α as a variable running from 0 to 1, derive

$$\mathcal{U} = \mathcal{U}^* = \tfrac{1}{2} \tau_{ij} \varepsilon_{ij}$$

from

$$\mathcal{U} = \int \tau_{ij}\, d\varepsilon_{ij} \quad \text{and} \quad \mathcal{U}^* = \int e_{ij}\, d\tau_{ij}$$

5.21. Given the strain field

$$\varepsilon_{ij} = \begin{bmatrix} x^2 + 2yx & 8zx & z^3 - 6xy \\ 8zx & 5y + zy & x^2 + 2z^3 \\ z^3 - 6xy & x^2 + 2z^3 & -x - yz \end{bmatrix}$$

what is the strain energy density field? What is the complementary energy density field?

5.22. For a plane strain *orthotropic* medium the constitutive law is usually given as

$$\tau_{xx} = C_{11}\,\varepsilon_{xx} + C_{12}\,\varepsilon_{yy}$$

$$\tau_{yy} = C_{21}\,\varepsilon_{xx} + C_{22}\,\varepsilon_{yy}$$

$$\tau_{xy} = G_{12}\,\varepsilon_{xy}$$

Construct an appropriate strain energy density function. Note that for strain energy to exist we must have $C_{12} = C_{21}$. Check your strain energy density function by computing stresses τ_{xx}, τ_{yy}, and τ_{xy}.

5.23. What is the strain energy for the beam shown in Fig. P5.23? Consider only strain energy due to bending. Take $E = 2 \times 10^{11}$ Pa. Use the results of strength of materials.

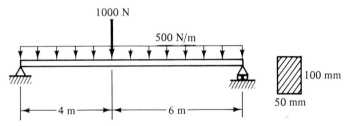

Figure P5.23

5.24. Find the complementary strain energy for the hollow shaft shown under torsion with $G = 1.5 \times 10^{11}$ Pa (Fig. P5.24). Use the results of strength of materials.

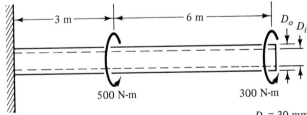

$D_i = 30$ mm
$D_o = 50$ mm

Figure P5.24

5.25. If $\mathcal{U}$ exists for an anisotropic material, it must be given as

$$\mathcal{U} = \tfrac{1}{2} C_{ijkl}\,\varepsilon_{ij}\,\varepsilon_{kl}$$

with the symmetry requirement

$$C_{ijkl} = C_{klij}$$

in order to satisfy Eq. (5.57a). Demonstrate this for the specific case of ε_{13} by showing that

$$\frac{\partial \mathcal{U}}{\partial \varepsilon_{13}} = \tau_{13}$$

5.26. Using only the linearity of the constitutive law, derive the *Betti reciprocal theorem*,

$$\int_D \tau_{ij}^{(1)} \, \varepsilon_{ij}^{(2)} \, dv = \int_D \tau_{ij}^{(2)} \, \varepsilon_{ij}^{(1)} \, dv$$

The superscripts represent different states of loading on the same body with the same constraints. (*Hint:* Make use of the symmetry conditions presented for C_{ijkl} in Problem 5.25.)

5.27. Demonstrate the correctness of the Betti reciprocal theorem for the loads P_1 and P_2 in Fig. P5.27 with $E = 2 \times 10^{11}$ Pa (see Problem 5.26).

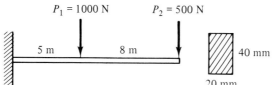

Figure P5.27

5.28. A steel rod A and aluminum sleeve B are held by an immovable wall D at one end and at the other, through a stiff plate E, to a spring having a spring constant K, which in turn is held by immovable wall G (Fig. P5.28). Initially, the spring is unstretched and the temperature is uniform at 60°F. If the temperature of the rod and sleeve goes to 100° throughout, what are the stresses in the rod and sleeve? Assume that τ_{xx} is the only nonzero stress, where x runs along the center of the steel rod.

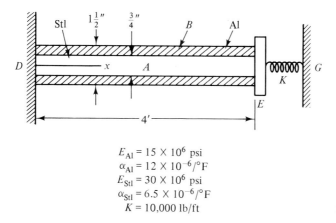

$$E_{Al} = 15 \times 10^6 \text{ psi}$$
$$\alpha_{Al} = 12 \times 10^{-6}/°F$$
$$E_{Stl} = 30 \times 10^6 \text{ psi}$$
$$\alpha_{Stl} = 6.5 \times 10^{-6}/°F$$
$$K = 10,000 \text{ lb/ft}$$

Figure P5.28

5.29. Do Problem 5.28 where the temperature varies linearly, from left to right, from 60°F at D to 100°F at E.

5.30. Do Problem 5.28 for the case where the temperature goes from 60°F to 100°F linearly from left to right for the sleeve, but goes parabolically (i.e., in the form $T = A + Bx^2$) from 60°F to 100°F left to right for the rod.

5.31. Invert Eq.(5.64) and thereby obtain Eq. (5.65).

Chapter 6
Linear Viscoelastic Behavior

6.1 INTRODUCTION

In this chapter we consider linear viscoelastic behavior in detail having merely introduced one-dimensional, linear viscoelastic behavior in Chapter 4. Why is such behavior important? As we have pointed out in Chapter 4, amorphous polymers such as plastics and synthetic rubbers may frequently be considered to behave in a linear viscoelastic manner. In addition, fibrous materials (e.g., silk, rayon, and cellulose), glasses, ceramics, biomaterials (e.g., skin and muscle), and nonmetals in general may frequently be considered as linear viscoelastic materials. Although conventional structural elements were in the past seldom made entirely from the aforementioned materials, there are now two vital reasons for considering linear viscoelastic theory in detail. *First*, we note that modern structural components frequently do contain at least some linear viscoelastic material. One example is the lightweight sandwich structure whose core material may be linear viscoelastic. Another example is the modern composite material, which can be *entirely* viscoelastic. In addition to these examples, we note that stresses in concrete and cement, and irradiation-induced creep in metals, are also topics involving the possible use of linear viscoelasticity theory.*

Thus our first reason for studying linear viscoelasticity is quite specific. The *second* basic reason for this study is perhaps more philosophic but it is just as important as the first. It is simply this. If one seeks a full understanding of a complex nonlinear theory, one should first have a sound grasp of the corresponding linear theory. This is significant since many important materials are nonlinear viscoelastic or viscoplastic. In connection with this point, we note that we may be considering

---

* An interesting use of linear viscoelasticity occurs in geophysical mechanics involving the study of waves in the Earth's crustal rock.

a nonlinear problem for which no closed-form solution exists. To check a numerical solution for such a problem, it is often desirable to reduce the problem to a corresponding linear case for which a closed-form solution does exist. We point out further that perturbation and iteration techniques are widely used in the analysis of nonlinear viscoelastic problems, such as those concerned with the deformations in metals at elevated temperatures. And it is frequently the case in such analyses that the nonlinear problem is linearized.

In Part A of this chapter we consider one-dimensional models both simple and complex. In Part B we go to the classical theory for isotropic, multidimensional behavior. Here, we extrapolate from the one-dimensional case to the multi-dimensional case in a manner that parallels what we did in Chapter 5 for linear elastic behavior. In the development we utilize the discontinuity functions (i.e., the step, delta, and doublet functions) as well as the Laplace transformation. These topics are reviewed in Appendices II and III, respectively.

PART A
ONE-DIMENSIONAL MODELS

6.2 SIMPLE MODELS AND THE STANDARD TEST PROCEDURES

We have already introduced the Maxwell material in Section 4.7 [see Fig. 4.21(a)]. Note that a Hookean element (linear spring) and a Newtonian element (dashpot) are connected in series. Because we have a series arrangement, the associated stresses for this model are equal, while the associated strains are additive. Using S and D subscripts to identify the spring and dashpot elements, respectively, the remarks above lead to the following formulations:

$$\tau = \tau_S = \tau_D \quad \text{(a)}$$
$$\varepsilon = \varepsilon_S + \varepsilon_D \quad \text{(b)}$$
(6.1)

Also, we can say that

$$\varepsilon_S = \frac{\tau_S}{E} \qquad \dot{\varepsilon}_D = \frac{\tau_D}{\eta}$$
$$\dot{\varepsilon}_S = \frac{\dot{\tau}_S}{E}$$
(6.2)

In the above, the τ's and the ε's represent uniaxial stress and strain (e.g., τ_{zz} and ε_{zz}) which may vary with time and possibly one space coordinate. The dot that we have used in general represents the partial time derivative $\partial/\partial t$. For most one-dimensional problems, however, there is no variation with the space coordinate, and the partial time derivative for such cases reduces to the ordinary time derivative d/dt. Also, we will assume at present that the elastic tensile parameter E and the viscous tensile parameter η are constants. Adding the strain rates of Eqs. (6.2), we get with the use of Eqs. (6.1),

$$\dot{\varepsilon} = \dot{\varepsilon}_S + \dot{\varepsilon}_D = \frac{\dot{\tau}}{E} + \frac{\tau}{\eta} \qquad \text{(Maxwell)} \qquad (6.3)$$

You will note that Eq. (6.3) was set forth in Section 4.7 as Eq. (4.11).

Next, we consider in greater detail the *Kelvin* model first discussed in Section 4.7 [see Fig. 4.21(b)]. Here we have a parallel arrangement of Hookean and Newtonian elements. This parallel arrangement leads us to conclude that the strains associated with the elements of this model are equal, whereas the stresses associated with the elements are additive. As a consequence, we can say that

$$\tau = \tau_S + \tau_D \qquad \text{(a)}$$
$$\varepsilon = \varepsilon_S = \varepsilon_D \qquad \text{(b)} \qquad\qquad (6.4)$$

We can also say that

$$\varepsilon_S = \frac{\tau_S}{E} \qquad \dot{\varepsilon}_D = \frac{\tau_D}{\eta} \qquad\qquad (6.5)$$

From these results, we arrive again at Eq. (4.14), which we now rewrite as

$$\tau = \eta\dot{\varepsilon} + E\varepsilon \qquad \text{(Kelvin)} \qquad\qquad (6.6)$$

A physical understanding of the behavior of viscoelastic models can be achieved by subjecting these models to certain standard testing procedures. We now consider, in some detail, two standard tests: the creep test and the relaxation test applied to Maxwell and Kelvin materials:*

The Creep Test

The most widely used standard tensile test procedure is the *creep* test, wherein a stress τ_0 is suddenly applied at time $t = 0$ on the model and then maintained constant thereafter. This stress can be expressed as a function of time with the aid of the unit step function $[u(t)]$.† Thus

$$\tau(t) = \tau_0[u(t)] \qquad\qquad (6.7)$$

Let us first consider the *Maxwell* material under such a test. Substituting the foregoing stress into Eq. (6.3), we get

$$\dot{\varepsilon} = \frac{\tau_0}{E}\frac{d}{dt}[u(t)] + \frac{\tau_0}{\eta}[u(t)]$$

Therefore,

$$\dot{\varepsilon} = \frac{\tau_0}{E}[\delta(t)] + \frac{\tau_0}{\eta}[u(t)] \qquad\qquad (6.8)$$

---

* The Maxwell material was introduced by J. C. Maxwell in 1868, and the Kelvin material by Lord Kelvin (W. Thomson) in 1875. W. Voigt also introduced the Kelvin material in 1889, and thus that material is also referred to as the Kelvin–Voigt material.

† The unit step function and other discontinuity functions are discussed in Appendix II.

where we have used Eq. (II.7) of Appendix II to introduce the delta function $[\delta(t)]$ in Eq. (6.8). Integrating from $t = 0^-$ and setting $\varepsilon(0^-) = 0$, we then get

$$\varepsilon(t) = \tau_0\left(\frac{1}{E} + \frac{t}{\eta}\right)[u(t)] \qquad \text{(Maxwell)} \tag{6.9}$$

We have plotted Eq. (6.9) in Fig. 6.1. From this test we see that the Maxwell material acts like a linear elastic solid with strain equal to τ_0/E at time $t = 0^+$, and then approaches the behavior of a linear viscous fluid as $t \to \infty$. We will adopt the convention that a viscoelastic material is considered a fluid if in a creep test the material tends toward viscous behavior as $t \to \infty$. Accordingly, a Maxwell material will be termed a "fluid." We may also investigate the asymptotic behavior of a Maxwell material by means of a Laplace transform (see Appendix III). Thus, transforming Eq. (6.3) with homogeneous initial conditions at $t = 0^-$, we get

$$s\bar{\varepsilon}(s) = \frac{s\bar{\tau}(s)}{E} + \frac{\bar{\tau}(s)}{\eta} \tag{6.10}$$

In the case of a creep test $\tau(t) = \tau_0[u(t)]$ and thus $\bar{\tau}(s) = \tau_0/s$. Accordingly, Eq. (6.10) simplifies to

$$s\bar{\varepsilon}(s) = \tau_0\left(\frac{1}{E} + \frac{1}{\eta s}\right) \tag{6.11}$$

Using the limit theorems of Section III.6 of Appendix III, we then get

$$\varepsilon(0^+) = \lim_{s \to \infty} s\bar{\varepsilon}(s) = \frac{\tau_0}{E} \qquad \text{(Maxwell)} \qquad \text{(a)}$$

$$\varepsilon(\infty) = \lim_{s \to 0} s\bar{\varepsilon}(s) \to \infty \qquad \text{(Maxwell)} \qquad \text{(b)} \tag{6.12}$$

which are consistent with Fig. 6.1.

Next, consider the creep test procedure applied to a *Kelvin* material. Thus, we apply to this model the stress given by Eq. (6.7). Inserting this stress into Eq. (6.6), we get, on rearranging terms,

$$\dot{\varepsilon} + \frac{E}{\eta}\varepsilon = \frac{\tau_0}{\eta}[u(t)] \tag{6.13}$$

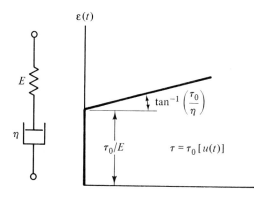

Figure 6.1 Creep test procedure for a Maxwell material.

This equation may be rewritten in the following manner:

$$e^{-(E/\eta)t}\frac{d}{dt}(\varepsilon e^{(E/\eta)t}) = \frac{\tau_0}{\eta}[u(t)]$$

Therefore,

$$d(\varepsilon e^{(E/\eta)t}) = \frac{\tau_0}{\eta}e^{(E/\eta)t}[u(t)]\,dt \qquad (6.14)$$

Now integrating from $t = 0^-$ to a variable upper limit, we have on taking $\varepsilon = 0$ at $t = 0^-$,

$$\varepsilon(t)\,e^{(E/\eta)t} = \frac{\tau_0}{\eta}\int_{0^-}^{t}e^{(E/\eta)t'}[u(t')]\,dt'$$

$$= \frac{\tau_0}{\eta}[u(t)]\frac{\eta}{E}e^{(E/\eta)t'}\Big|_{0^-}^{t}$$

$$= \frac{\tau_0}{E}(e^{(E/\eta)t} - 1)[u(t)]$$

Solving for $\varepsilon(t)$, we then get from the equation above,

$$\varepsilon(t) = \frac{\tau_0}{E}(1 - e^{-(E/\eta)t})[u(t)] \qquad \text{(Kelvin)} \qquad (6.15)$$

We have plotted Eq. (6.15) in Fig. 6.2 and we see that $\varepsilon(0) = 0$. Also note that as $t \to \infty$, the behavior of this material in the test tends toward that of an elastic solid with strain τ_0/E, and it is for this reason the convention is to classify the Kelvin material as a "solid." By taking the Laplace transform of Eq. (6.13) and again using the limit theorems of Appendix III, you should verify that

$$\varepsilon(0^+) = \lim_{s \to \infty}\frac{\tau_0}{\eta s + E} = 0 \qquad \text{(Kelvin)} \qquad (a)$$

$$\varepsilon(\infty) = \lim_{s \to 0}\frac{\tau_0}{\eta s + E} = \frac{\tau_0}{E} \qquad \text{(Kelvin)} \qquad (b)$$

$$(6.16)$$

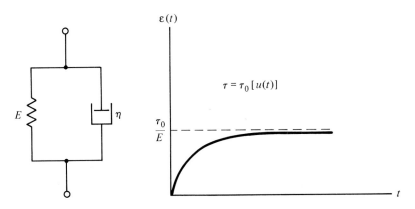

Figure 6.2 Creep test procedure for a Kelvin material.

as expected. The ratio η/E in Eq. (6.15) has the dimension of time and may be considered as a material constant. In conjunction with Eq. (6.15), it is termed the *retardation time* of the limiting strain. We shall on occasion use the notation t_ε to indicate the retardation time of strain.

The Relaxation Test

We now consider a *second* important standard tensile test procedure. For this test procedure, we apply a sudden strain ε_0 on the material at time $t = 0$. This strain is maintained constant thereafter. This standard test procedure is called the *relaxation* test. The applied sudden strain can be given as a function of time as follows:

$$\varepsilon(t) = \varepsilon_0[u(t)] \qquad (6.17)$$

Let us first apply this test to a *Maxwell* material. Thus using Eq. (6.17) in Eq. (6.3) we get

$$\varepsilon_0 \frac{d}{dt}[u(t)] = \frac{\dot{\tau}}{E} + \frac{\tau}{\eta}$$

Noting again that the derivative of the step function is the delta function, we get, on rearranging the equation,

$$\dot{\tau} + \frac{E}{\eta}\tau = \varepsilon_0 E[\delta(t)] \qquad (6.18)$$

Multiplying by the integrating factor $e^{(E/\eta)t}$ leads us to the following form for Eq. (6.18):

$$d(\tau e^{(E/\eta)t}) = \varepsilon_0 E e^{(E/\eta)t}[\delta(t)]\,dt \qquad (6.19)$$

Setting $\tau = 0$ at $t = 0^-$ and integrating from $t = 0^-$ to a variable upper limit, we get the result

$$\tau(t) = \varepsilon_0 E e^{-(E/\eta)t}[u(t)] \qquad \text{(Maxwell)} \qquad (6.20)$$

We have plotted Eq. (6.20) in Fig. 6.3. Note from this diagram that the stress diminishes from the initial value $\varepsilon_0 E$ toward zero as time $t \to \infty$. Here the ratio η/E is called the *relaxation time* associated with the stress $\varepsilon_0 E$. We shall occasionally use the designation t_τ for the relaxation time of stress.

It is again instructive to consider the limit theorems as applied to the relaxation test procedure for a Maxwell material. For this purpose, take the Laplace transform of Eq. (6.18). Recalling that $\mathbf{L}\{\delta(t)\} = 1$ for a lower limit of 0^-, we obtain

$$s\bar{\tau}(s) = \frac{\varepsilon_0 E\eta s}{\eta s + E} \qquad (6.21)$$

Now applying the two limit theorems we get

$$\tau(0^+) = \lim_{s \to \infty} s\bar{\tau}(s) = \varepsilon_0 E$$

$$\tau(\infty) = \lim_{s \to 0} s\bar{\tau}(s) = 0 \qquad (6.22)$$

You will note that these results are in conformity with Fig. 6.3.

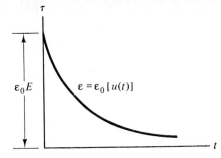

Figure 6.3 Relaxation test procedure for a Maxwell fluid.

Next, we apply the relaxation test procedure on a *Kelvin* solid. For this purpose we go back to Eq. (6.6) and insert $\varepsilon(t)$ as given by Eq. (6.17). We then get

$$\tau = \varepsilon_0 \{\eta[\delta(t)] + E[u(t)]\} \tag{6.23}$$

This equation indicates that a step increase in strain corresponds to a delta input in stress followed by a constant stress. Thus the Kelvin solid exhibits rather peculiar behavior during a relaxation test. This should not cause undue concern. You must realize that the Kelvin model is an idealization representing more complex behavior. To be more realistic we may need more complex models. We discuss this fact in the next section.

We conclude this section by pointing out four other standard tensile (and compressive) test procedures which are frequently conducted. These test procedures are identified by the nature of the applied stress or strain as follows:

$$
\begin{aligned}
\tau &= \dot{\tau}_0 t[u(t)] &&\text{(constant stress rate)} \\
\varepsilon &= \dot{\varepsilon}_0 t[u(t)] &&\text{(constant strain rate)} \\
\tau &= \tau_0 \sin \omega t &&\text{(oscillating stress)} \\
\varepsilon &= \varepsilon_0 \sin \omega t &&\text{(oscillating strain)}
\end{aligned}
\tag{6.24}
$$

The latter two test procedures are particularly important for developing constitutive laws applicable to vibration or wave propagation problems.

6.3 MORE COMPLEX ONE-DIMENSIONAL MODELS

We can readily extend our simple viscoelastic models to more complex models by adding more elements. Accordingly, in Fig. 6.4 we have shown three such models, where the E's and η's are elastic and viscous coefficients in tension. These models are denoted, respectively, as

1. Three-parameter solid
2. Three-parameter fluid
3. Four-parameter fluid

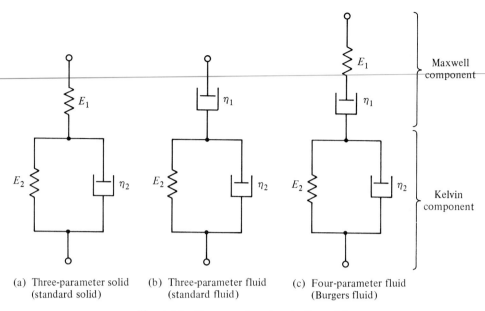

Figure 6.4 More complex viscoelastic models.

(a) Three-parameter solid
(standard solid)

(b) Three-parameter fluid
(standard fluid)

(c) Four-parameter fluid
(Burgers fluid)

You will also note from the diagram that these models are also called the *standard solid*, the *standard fluid*, and the *Burgers fluid*,[*] respectively. Note that the Burgers fluid model consists of a Maxwell component and a Kelvin component in series.

In order to formulate differential equations governing the behavior of materials represented by more complex models such as these models, we shall make use of the operator D for the derivative $\partial/\partial t$. Also, we shall use the formulations for the simple components as developed in Section 6.2 for the purpose of superposing certain results. As an example of the use of the operator D and the superposition approach, consider the *four-parameter fluid* (the Burgers fluid) shown in Fig. 6.4(c). Using the subscripts M and K to denote the Maxwell and Kelvin components of the model, we may write

$$\tau = \tau_M = \tau_K \qquad \text{(a)}$$

$$\varepsilon = \varepsilon_M + \varepsilon_K \qquad \text{(b)}$$

(6.25)

Now go back to Eq. (6.3) for the Maxwell model. Using the operator D, we may express this equation as

$$D\varepsilon_M = \frac{D\tau_M}{E_1} + \frac{\tau_M}{\eta_1}$$

(6.26)

where subscript 1 indicates constants in the Maxwell component. Treating D *formally* here, Eq. (6.26) may be written as

[*] Named after J. M. Burgers, who presented spring–dashpot models in "Mechanical Considerations, Model Systems, Phenomenological Systems," in Academy of Sciences, *First Report on Viscosity and Plasticity* (Amsterdam: North-Holland Publishing Co., 1935).

$$\varepsilon_M = \frac{\tau_M}{E_1} + \frac{\tau_M}{\eta_1 D} \tag{6.27}$$

Doing the same for Eq. (6.6) for the Kelvin model, we get

$$\varepsilon_K = \frac{\tau_K}{E_2 + \eta_2 D} \tag{6.28}$$

where the subscript 2 indicates constants in the Kelvin model. Combining these equations in accordance with Eq. (6.25b), we get, noting Eq. (6.25a):

$$\varepsilon = \frac{\tau}{\eta_1 D} + \frac{\tau}{E_1} + \frac{\tau}{E_2 + \eta_2 D} \tag{6.29}$$

Next find the common denominator for the right side of the equation and multiply ε by this expression.* We get

$$[(\eta_1 D)(E_1)(E_2 + \eta_2 D)]\varepsilon = [(E_1)(E_2 + \eta_2 D)]\tau \tag{6.30}$$
$$+ [(\eta_1 D)(E_2 + \eta_2 D)]\tau + (\eta_1 D)(E_1)\tau$$

Remember that D is a time derivative operator when "multiplying" τ or ε by this expression. Using dots to represent the operator D $(\equiv \partial/\partial t)$, we then get for Eq. (6.30):

$$E_1 \eta_1 \eta_2 \ddot{\varepsilon} + E_1 E_2 \eta_1 \dot{\varepsilon} = \eta_1 \eta_2 \ddot{\tau} + (E_1 \eta_2 + E_2 \eta_1 + E_1 \eta_1)\dot{\tau} + E_1 E_2 \tau \tag{6.31}$$

As an alternative procedure to the use of the D operator followed in the development above, we could instead combine the governing equations in the Laplace transform space. Doing so would result in an equation identical to Eq. (6.30) except for the fact that operator D would be replaced by the transform parameter s. Equation (6.31) would then be obtained by a Laplace transform inversion.

For a Burgers fluid we thus arrived at a linear, second-order differential equation. This equation can be expressed compactly as

$$\boxed{P\tau = Q\varepsilon} \tag{6.32}$$

where P and Q are linear differential operators forming what we shall call an *operator pair*. The other two models in Fig. 6.4, and indeed other models formed in a manner similar to those in Fig. 6.4, in general are governed by linear differential equations that can be expressed in the *standard form* of Eq. (6.32). The operators P and Q forming the operator pair of this standard form may be expressed as follows:

$$P \equiv \sum_{j=0}^{m} p_j \frac{\partial^j}{\partial t^j} = \sum_{j=0}^{m} p_j D^j \quad \text{(a)} \tag{6.33}$$

$$Q \equiv \sum_{j=0}^{n} q_j \frac{\partial^j}{\partial t^j} = \sum_{j=0}^{n} q_j D^j \quad \text{(b)}$$

* Note that we are now undoing the "formal" step taken in forming Eqs. (6.27) and (6.28).

where the p's and q's are to be considered as constants for the present.* It is the practice to set $p_0 = 1$ in Eq. (6.33a); that is, we "normalize" the differential equation by dividing through by the coefficient of the zeroth-order derivative of τ. This procedure is always possible since for spring–dashpot models the coefficient of the zeroth-order derivative of stress is never zero. Thus for the four-parameter fluid (Burgers fluid) we can write Eq. (6.31) as

$$\tau + p_1 \dot{\tau} + p_2 \ddot{\tau} = q_1 \dot{\varepsilon} + q_2 \ddot{\varepsilon} \qquad (6.34)$$

where $q_0 = 0$ and

$$p_1 = \frac{\eta_1}{E_1} + \frac{\eta_2}{E_2} + \frac{\eta_1}{E_2} \qquad q_1 = \eta_1$$

$$p_2 = \frac{\eta_1 \eta_2}{E_1 E_2} \qquad q_2 = \frac{\eta_1 \eta_2}{E_2} \qquad (6.35)$$

Note that the material constants E_1, E_2, η_1, and η_2 are positive and are mutually independent. Because these constants are positive, it follows from Eqs. (6.35) that the coefficients p_1, p_2, q_1, and q_2 must also be positive. However, even though E_1, E_2, η_1, and η_2 are independent, it does *not* follow that the coefficients p_1, p_2, q_1, and q_2 are independent. This is so since E_1, E_2, η_1, and η_2 must all be positive. For example, by solving Eqs. (6.35) for $1/E_2$, we may obtain the condition that

$$\frac{1}{E_2} = \frac{p_1}{q_1} - \frac{q_2}{q_1^2} - \frac{p_2}{q_2} > 0 \qquad (6.36)$$

showing an interdependence of the p's and q's.

Let us now observe Fig. 6.4(a) and (c). Note that each of these models has a spring that is not in parallel with a dashpot. We shall call such springs *free springs*. Consider the situation in which we arrange *any number* of elements in *series*, where each element is either a spring, a dashpot, or a Kelvin element. One may prove (see Problem 6.5) that if a free spring is present in such a viscoelastic spring–dashpot model, the *highest-order* derivatives for operators P and Q are the *same* order. That is, in Eqs. (6.33), $m = n$ for such models. On the other hand, if a free spring is *not* present, then $n = m + 1$. Furthermore, one can show that if a dashpot in such a spring–dashpot viscoelastic model is not in parallel with a spring (such a dashpot is called a *free dashpot*), then in Eq. (6.33b) we have $q_0 = 0$. Such is the case for the models in Fig. 6.4(b) and (c).† If, on the other hand, a free dashpot is not present, then $q_0 \neq 0$. These results are summarized in Table 6.1.

It will be constructive at this juncture to consider the *creep test* procedure of Section 6.2 applied to the *four-parameter fluid*. For this purpose, go to Eq. (6.34) with coefficients (6.35) and insert $\tau_0[u(t)]$ for τ. We then get as the appropriate equation for this test on dividing by q_2:

$$\ddot{\varepsilon} + \frac{q_1}{q_2} \dot{\varepsilon} = \frac{\tau_0}{q_2} \{ [u(t)] + p_1[\delta(t)] + p_2[\eta(t)] \} \qquad (6.37)$$

---

* In Section 6.11 we shall allow these coefficients to vary with the spatial coordinates to take temperature variation into account.

† Note from Eq. (6.34) that $m = n = 2$ and $q_0 = 0$ for the Burgers fluid as stipulated here.

TABLE 6.1 Models with Spring,
Dashpot, or Kelvin
Elements in Series

Free spring present	$m = n$
No free spring	$n = m + 1$
Free dashpot present	$q_0 = 0$
No free dashpot	$q_0 \neq 0$

There is no need here to solve this differential equation formally, since we can accomplish the same result by superposing the creep test results from the Maxwell and Kelvin models. This is possible since the four-parameter fluid model is simply the Kelvin and Maxwell models in series. Thus, noting Eq. (6.25b) first, and then using Eqs. (6.9) and (6.15), we get the desired solution of Eq. (6.37) as

$$\varepsilon(t) = \tau_0 \left[\frac{1}{E_1} + \frac{t}{\eta_1} + \frac{1}{E_2} \left(1 - \exp(-t/t_\varepsilon) \right) \right] [u(t)] \qquad (6.38)$$

where t_ε is the retardation time of strain, which equals η_2/E_2. This equation is plotted in Fig. 6.5. You will note on comparing Fig. 6.5 with Fig. 4.11 that the four-parameter fluid exhibits the primary and secondary creep regions found in typical experimental creep curves. Since the superposition procedure as followed here may not always be convenient, you will be asked in Problems 6.7 and 6.8 to obtain Eq. (6.38) by means of a formal solution to Eq. (6.37) via two different methods.

In this section we have considered some viscoelastic models more complex than the simple Kelvin and Maxwell models. In practice, it is sometimes necessary to employ viscoelastic models of even greater complexity. This is particularly so for dynamic problems. In this regard, if we arrange a discrete number of *Maxwell* components in *parallel*, we get the so-called *generalized Maxwell* model. If we take a discrete number of *Kelvin* components in *series*, we get the so-called *generalized*

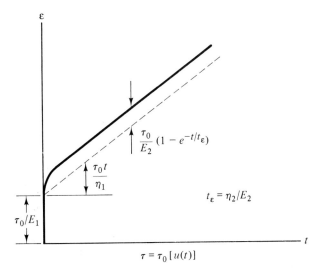

Figure 6.5 Creep curve for a four-parameter fluid.

Kelvin model (one free spring and one free dashpot may also be present). We also point out that we can take the foregoing processes to the limit by considering a *continuous* distribution of components. Apropos of this general discussion of building up of components to form more complex models, it is important to note that model representation is not unique in that various model configurations can yield the same constitutive law. We shall not delve further into developing more complex models since the underlying concepts are not essentially different from what we have expounded thus far. The reader interested in additional details for such models is referred to the literature on linear viscoelasticity.*

6.4 THE CREEP COMPLIANCE AND RELAXATION MODULUS FUNCTIONS

In general, the equation for $\varepsilon(t)$ during a *creep* test may be expressed as

$$\varepsilon(t) = \tau_0 J(t)[u(t)] \tag{6.39}$$

where the material function $J(t)$ is called the *creep compliance function*. Going back to Eqs. (6.9) and (6.15), we see by inspection that the creep compliance functions for a Maxwell fluid and a Kelvin solid are, respectively, given as

$$J(t) = \left(\frac{1}{E} + \frac{t}{\eta} \right) \qquad \text{(Maxwell fluid)} \qquad \text{(a)}$$

$$J(t) = \frac{1}{E} \left(1 - e^{-(E/\eta)t} \right) \qquad \text{(Kelvin solid)} \qquad \text{(b)}$$

$$\tag{6.40}$$

In an analogous manner, we can express $\tau(t)$ for a *relaxation* test in the form

$$\tau(t) = \varepsilon_0 Y(t)[u(t)] \tag{6.41}$$

where $Y(t)$ is called the *relaxation modulus function*. For the Maxwell fluid, we see from Eq. (6.20) that

$$Y(t) = Ee^{-(E/\eta)t} \qquad \text{(Maxwell fluid)} \tag{6.42}$$

Note that in the special case of a linear elastic material the material function $J(t)$ reduces to the elastic compliance $1/E$, while $Y(t)$ reduces to the elastic modulus E.

We will next explain how the functions $J(t)$ and $Y(t)$ can be used to construct solutions to the general viscoelastic equation (6.32). For this purpose, we point out from the theory of linear ordinary differential equations the well-known fact that given the solution of an equation for a unit step input, we can construct the general solution of this differential equation by means of a so-called *hereditary integral*. We shall exhibit such integrals in conjunction with alternative forms of the general viscoelastic equation

$$P\tau = Q\varepsilon \tag{6.43}$$

---

* See W. Flügge, *Viscoelasticity* (Berlin: Springer-Verlag, 1975) and D. R. Bland, *Linear Viscoelasticity* (New York: Pergamon Press, 1960).

and solutions to this equation stemming from our creep and relaxation tests. Using the creep compliance function and the relaxation modulus function as described above, we state again for these two standard tests

$$\varepsilon(t) = \tau_0 J(t)[u(t)] \quad \text{for } \tau = \tau_0[u(t)] \quad \text{(creep test)} \quad \text{(a)}$$

$$\tau(t) = \varepsilon_0 Y(t)[u(t)] \quad \text{for } \varepsilon = \varepsilon_0[u(t)] \quad \text{(relaxation test)} \quad \text{(b)}$$

(6.44)

Now let us consider the case where some given arbitrary stress function $\tau(t)$ is applied to the material as shown in Fig. 6.6(a). We will be able to make good use of the creep compliance function if we consider the applied stress $\tau(t)$ to be a succession of infinitesimal steps $d\tau(t)$ as has been shown in Fig. 6.6(a). Consider one such step at time t', which is indicated as $d\tau(t')$ and is shown crosshatched. The strain increment $d\varepsilon(t)$ that this step in stress induces is shown in Fig. 6.6(b) starting at time t'. This strain increment is obtained by using the creep compliance function with the time $(t - t')$, replacing t in Eq. (6.44a), and thus

$$d\varepsilon(t) = J(t - t') d\tau(t')[u(t - t')] \quad (6.45)$$

where $d\tau(t')$ has replaced τ_0. If we consider the creep compliance function to be zero for negative values of $(t - t')$, we do not need the step function $[u(t - t')]$ in

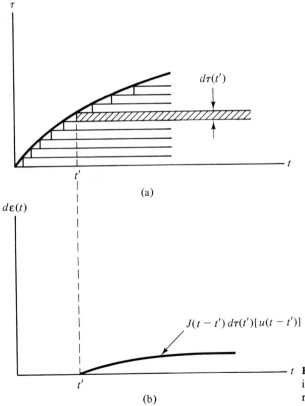

(a)

(b)

Figure 6.6 Strain response from an infinitesimal step in stress using the results of the creep test.

Eq. (6.45). To account for all the infinitesimal stress steps from $t = 0^-$ to time t, we now integrate with respect to t' from $t' = 0^-$ to $t' = t$ in the following manner:

$$\varepsilon(t) = \int_{0^-}^{t} J(t - t') \left[\frac{\partial \tau(t')}{\partial t'} \right] dt' \tag{6.46}$$

Here we replaced $d\tau(t')$ by $\dfrac{\partial \tau(t')}{\partial t'} dt'$ to make t' the integration variable instead of τ. Equation (6.46) yields one of the two desired hereditary integrals. The other one is developed in an analogous manner using the relaxation modulus function $Y(t)$ and Eq. (6.44b). That is, for an arbitrary applied strain, the associated stress field may be given as

$$\tau(t) = \int_{0^-}^{t} Y(t - t') \left[\frac{\partial \varepsilon(t')}{\partial t'} \right] dt' \tag{6.47}$$

Note that Eqs. (6.46) and (6.47) imply *homogeneous* initial conditions at $t = 0^-$ [i.e., $\varepsilon(0^-) = \tau(0^-) = 0$].

The hereditary integrals obtained above are also called *superposition integrals*,* since as we have shown, they may be obtained by superposing the responses due to a sequence of step inputs. It is important to note that the use of $J(t - t')$ in Eq. (6.45) implies that the shape of the creep compliance function is invariant with respect to a shift in the time origin [i.e., $J(t)$ for $t \geq 0$ has the same shape as $J(t - t')$ for $t \geq t'$]. Thus the strain response in a material subjected to some applied stress at $t = t'$ is identical to the response that would have occurred if this same stress had been applied at $t = 0$. A material satisfying this condition is said to be *nonaging*. For aging materials, $J(t - t')$ and $Y(t - t')$ in Eqs. (6.46) and (6.47) would be replaced by the more general material functions $J(t, t')$ and $Y(t, t')$. In Chapter 7 we shall not only encounter superposition integrals for nonlinear viscoelastic behavior but shall also consider aging materials. We shall now illustrate the use of hereditary integrals for nonaging, linear viscoelastic materials.

Example 6.1

What is the strain as a function of time for a Maxwell material subjected to a *constant stress-rate test* (i.e., $\dot{\tau} = \dot{\tau}_0$ for $t > 0$ where $\dot{\tau}_0$ is a constant)?

The stress as a function of time is thus given as

$$\tau(t) = \dot{\tau}_0 t [u(t)] \tag{a}$$

The creep compliance function is given by Eq. (6.40a) as

$$J(t) = \frac{1}{E} + \frac{t}{\eta} \tag{b}$$

---

* They are usually called *Boltzmann* superposition integrals, in recognition of L. Boltzmann, who apparently presented the first three-dimensional theory of isotropic linear viscoelasticity in 1874. In 1909 this was extended to the case of anisotropic materials by V. Volterra.

Now going to Eq. (6.46), we insert Eq. (b) with t replaced by $(t - t')$ and employ the time derivative of Eq. (a). We then get

$$\varepsilon(t) = \int_{0^-}^{t} \left(\frac{1}{E} + \frac{t}{\eta} - \frac{t'}{\eta} \right) \dot{\tau}_0 \{ [u(t')] + t'[\delta(t')] \} \, dt' \tag{c}$$

The delta function times t' or $(t')^2$ contributes nothing to $\varepsilon(t)$.[*] Hence we need only consider $[u(t')]$. We then get on integration

$$\varepsilon(t) = \dot{\tau}_0 \left(\frac{t}{E} + \frac{t^2}{\eta} - \frac{t^2}{2\eta} \right) [u(t)]$$

$$\varepsilon(t) = \dot{\tau}_0 t \left(\frac{1}{E} + \frac{t}{2\eta} \right) [u(t)] \tag{d}$$

We have thus shown that using the creep compliance function for a step stress input in the hereditary integral permits us to get the response of a material to a different stress input.

6.5 USEFUL RESULTS FROM DIFFERENTIAL AND INTEGRAL FORMS OF VISCOELASTIC CONSTITUTIVE LAWS

It should be apparent that the differential equation (6.43) and the integral equations (6.46) and (6.47) are alternative forms of the same viscoelastic constitutive law. We shall explore this fact in this section by making use of the Laplace transform with 0^- chosen as the lower limit of integration (see Appendix III). Thus

$$\mathbf{L}\{f(t)\} = \int_{0^-}^{\infty} f(t) e^{-st} \, dt \equiv \bar{f}(s) \tag{6.48}$$

In the ensuing discussion, we assume that all initial conditions are homogeneous [i.e., $f(t)$ and all its time derivatives in a given problem are zero at $t = 0^-$]. We now take the transform of the differential equation (6.43). Using Eqs. (6.33) for the operators P and Q, we get

$$\int_{0^-}^{\infty} \left(\sum_{j=0}^{m} p_j \frac{\partial^j \tau}{\partial t^j} \right) e^{-st} \, dt = \int_{0^-}^{\infty} \left(\sum_{j=0}^{n} q_j \frac{\partial^j \varepsilon}{\partial t^j} \right) e^{-st} \, dt$$

Using Eq. (III.6) in Appendix III for the Laplace transform of derivatives with homogeneous initial conditions, we have for the equation above the following form:

$$\bar{P}(s) \bar{\tau}(s) = \bar{Q}(s) \bar{\varepsilon}(s) \tag{6.49}$$

---

[*] Recall that $\delta(t') \equiv \delta(t' - 0)$ where the singularity occurs at $t' = 0$, and that

$$\int_{0^-}^{t} f(t')[\delta(t' - a)] \, dt' = f(a)[u(t - a)]$$

In our case, $f(t')$ is either t' or $(t')^2$, and $a = 0$. For t' we then have

$$\int_{0^-}^{t} (t')[\delta(t' - 0)] \, dt' = 0$$

The same result is obtained for $(t')^2$.

where $\bar{P}(s)$ and $\bar{Q}(s)$ are *polynomials* in s which are given by

$$\bar{P}(s) = \sum_{j=0}^{m} p_j s^j \qquad \bar{Q}(s) = \sum_{j=0}^{n} q_j s^j \tag{6.50}$$

Note that the zeroth-order terms p_0 and q_0 in operators P and Q again yield p_0 and q_0 as zeroth-order terms in the polynomials $\bar{P}(s)$ and $\bar{Q}(s)$, *not* p_0/s and q_0/s as in the case of a constant function.

We next apply the *convolution* theorem (see Section III.5 of Appendix III) to the integral equations (6.46) and (6.47). Thus, noting Eqs. (III.16) and (III.19), we get

$$\mathbf{L}\{\varepsilon(t)\} = \mathbf{L}\{J(t)\}\,\mathbf{L}\{\partial\tau(t)/\partial t\} \tag{6.51}$$
$$\mathbf{L}\{\tau(t)\} = \mathbf{L}\{Y(t)\}\,\mathbf{L}\{\partial\varepsilon(t)/\partial t\}$$

In transform notation, we have for the equations above,

$$\bar{\varepsilon}(s) = [\bar{J}(s)][s\,\bar{\tau}(s)] \tag{6.52}$$
$$\bar{\tau}(s) = [\bar{Y}(s)][s\,\bar{\varepsilon}(s)]$$

Going back to Eq. (6.49), we can say that

$$\frac{\bar{\varepsilon}(s)}{\bar{\tau}(s)} = \frac{\bar{P}(s)}{\bar{Q}(s)} \tag{6.53}$$

Using Eq. (6.53) in Eqs. (6.52) to replace $\bar{\varepsilon}(s)/\bar{\tau}(s)$, we then may rewrite (6.52) in the following manner:

$$s\,\bar{J}(s) = \frac{\bar{P}(s)}{\bar{Q}(s)} \tag{6.54}$$
$$\frac{1}{s\,\bar{Y}(s)} = \frac{\bar{P}(s)}{\bar{Q}(s)}$$

From Eqs. (6.54) and (6.53), we can now make the following important conclusions:

$$s\,\bar{J}(s) = \frac{1}{s\,\bar{Y}(s)} = \frac{\bar{P}(s)}{\bar{Q}(s)} = \frac{\bar{\varepsilon}(s)}{\bar{\tau}(s)} \tag{6.55}$$

You will recall that $\bar{P}(s)$ and $\bar{Q}(s)$ are polynomials in s [see Eqs. (6.50)]. We may now conclude that *given the operator pair P, Q, one may compute both the creep compliance function $J(t)$ and the relaxation modulus function $Y(t)$ using the equations above. This computation, of course, requires a Laplace transform inversion, which may be difficult to obtain in closed form. One may also use Eqs. (6.55) to compute $Y(t)$ from $J(t)$, and so on.

We have previously mentioned only briefly the oscillating stress standard test procedure using an oscillation frequency ω [see the third of Eqs. (6.24)]. The strain response to such a stress input yields the so-called *complex compliance function*, which may be designated as $J^*(\omega)$. It is also possible to relate $J^*(\omega)$ to $J(t)$ and $Y(t)$. It should now be clear that in the one-dimensional case, only *one* standard tensile test procedure is needed since the results from other standard tensile tests procedures are related to this one standard test procedure via equations such as Eqs. (6.55).*

We have thus used the differential equation and hereditary integral to make certain useful conclusions stated above. Now, in the following example we illustrate the validity of either using the differential equation [Eq. (6.43)] or the integral equations [Eqs. (6.46) and (6.47)] as constitutive laws.

Example 6.2

Verify the validity of Eqs. (6.55) for the case of a Maxwell material, and then obtain its constitutive laws in the form of hereditary integrals.

From Eq. (6.3) we have

$$P = 1 + \frac{\eta}{E} \frac{\partial}{\partial t} \tag{a}$$

$$Q = \eta \frac{\partial}{\partial t} \tag{b}$$

From Eqs. (6.40a) and (6.42), we have

$$J(t) = \frac{1}{E} + \frac{t}{\eta} \tag{c}$$

$$Y(t) = E e^{-(E/\eta)t} \tag{d}$$

Using Eq. (6.50) and Table III-1 of Appendix III, we obtain the Laplace transforms of P, Q, $J(t)$, and $Y(t)$ as

$$\bar{P}(s) = 1 + \frac{\eta s}{E} \tag{e}$$

$$\bar{Q}(s) = \eta s \tag{f}$$

$$\bar{J}(s) = \frac{1}{Es} + \frac{1}{\eta s^2} \tag{g}$$

$$\bar{Y}(s) = \frac{E\eta}{s\eta + E} \tag{h}$$

As pointed out earlier, the term 1 in the operator given in Eq. (a) does not transform into $1/s$.

Now from Eqs. (6.55), we may form the ratio $\bar{\varepsilon}(s)/\bar{\tau}(s)$ in several ways using Eqs. (e) to (h). Accordingly, we get, using either $s\bar{J}(s)$, or $1/[s\bar{Y}(s)]$, or $\bar{P}(s)/\bar{Q}(s)$:

$$\frac{\bar{\varepsilon}(s)}{\bar{\tau}(s)} = \frac{1}{E} + \frac{1}{\eta s} \tag{i}$$

and thus

$$\bar{\varepsilon}(s) = \left(\frac{1}{E} + \frac{1}{\eta s} \right) \bar{\tau}(s) \tag{j}$$

---

*The interrelation between the various viscoelastic functions for the standard test procedures is presented in a systematic manner in B. Gross, *Mathematical Structures of the Theories of Viscoelasticity* (Paris: Hermann, 1953).

Multiplying through by s and then taking the inverse Laplace transform brings us back to the familiar constitutive law for a Maxwell material [see Eq. (6.3)]:

$$\tau + \frac{\eta}{E}\dot{\tau} = \eta\dot{\varepsilon} \tag{k}$$

In arriving at the correct equation above, we have used both the differential equation (6.43) and certain results from the hereditary integrals (6.46) and (6.47). This in turn demonstrates the validity of using any one of the three formulations involving $\bar{J}(s)$, $\bar{Y}(s)$, $\bar{P}(s)$, and $\bar{Q}(s)$, in Eqs. (6.55). Accordingly, using $J(t)$ and $Y(t)$ from Eqs. (c) and (d) above in Eqs. (6.46) and (6.47), we may form the following two additional forms of the constitutive law for a Maxwell material:

$$\varepsilon(t) = \int_{0^-}^{t} \left(\frac{1}{E} + \frac{t}{\eta} - \frac{t'}{\eta} \right) \frac{\partial\tau}{\partial t'} dt' \tag{ℓ}$$

$$\tau(t) = \int_{0^-}^{t} Ee^{-(E/\eta)(t-t')} \frac{\partial\varepsilon}{\partial t'} dt' \tag{m}$$

Although the three forms of the constitutive law given by Eqs. (6.43), (6.46), and (6.47) are equivalent to each other, they may not be equally convenient for use. For example, if $\varepsilon(t)$ is given as a complicated function of time or in numerical form and one wants to compute $\tau(t)$, the most convenient equation for this purpose of the three equations is Eq. (6.47). On the other hand, if $\tau(t)$ is prescribed as was $\varepsilon(t)$ above, Eq. (6.46) is most convenient for computing the strain function.

We should like to point out in closing this section that although in previous sections we have developed viscoelastic constitutive laws via spring–dashpot models, it is *not necessary* that the operator pair P, Q and the material functions $J(t), Y(t)$ of this section be based on such models. For example, one may give integral equation (6.46) as the defining equation for a linear viscoelastic material, without relating the creep compliance function $J(t)$ to springs and dashpots in some model configuration. However, if one follows this route, it becomes necessary to introduce conditions on $J(t)$ such that the predicted response is consistent with observed behavior.*

PART B
MULTIDIMENSIONAL LINEAR, ISOTROPIC VISCOELASTIC LAWS

6.6 INTRODUCTION

In Part B we shall first consider isothermal, linear, isotropic, multidimensional viscoelastic laws. Later we shall briefly consider nonisothermal forms of these laws. Our general procedure will be to extrapolate the one-dimensional results of Part A to three dimensions, in a manner paralleling the extrapolation that was made in linear elasticity to go from one dimension to three dimensions.

---

*For a presentation of linear viscoelasticity from this more general viewpoint, see R. M. Christensen, *Theory of Viscoelasticity—An Introduction* (New York: Academic Press, 1971).

6.7 POSTULATES FROM SIMPLE TESTS

We proceed by first considering the results of the simple tests: the tensile, torsion, and pressure tests. Thus, for the *tension* or *compression test* we know from linear elastic behavior that for the axial direction x we have $\tau_{xx} = E\varepsilon_{xx}$, while for the transverse direction y we have $\varepsilon_{yy} = -\nu\varepsilon_{xx}$. For viscoelastic materials, on the other hand, we learned in Part A of this chapter that the stress τ_{xx} and the strain ε_{xx} are related through an operator pair [see Eq. (6.43)]. For this reason it is to be expected that the strain ε_{xx} is related to ε_{yy} through another operator pair. Thus we will write for the viscoelastic material:

$$P^E \tau_{xx} = Q^E \varepsilon_{xx} \qquad \text{(a)}$$
$$P^\nu \varepsilon_{yy} = -Q^\nu \varepsilon_{xx} \qquad \text{(b)} \qquad\qquad (6.56)$$

The superscript E in Eq. (6.56a) identifies a *longitudinal* action while the superscript ν in Eq. (6.56b), as you would expect, identifies a *transverse* action. The operators above are defined in a manner analogous to Eqs. (6.33). That is,

$$P^E = \sum_{j=0}^{m^E} p_j^E \frac{\partial^j}{\partial t^j} \qquad Q^E = \sum_{j=0}^{n^E} q_j^E \frac{\partial^j}{\partial t^j}$$
$$P^\nu = \sum_{j=0}^{m^\nu} p_j^\nu \frac{\partial^j}{\partial t^j} \qquad Q^\nu = \sum_{j=0}^{n^\nu} q_j^\nu \frac{\partial^j}{\partial t^j} \qquad\qquad (6.57)$$

The various p's and q's are, for the present, viscoelastic constants and $p_0^E = p_0^\nu = 1$. It is clear from our development that we have established an analogy between the tensile test formulation for the elastic case (see Section 5.2) and the viscoelastic case. We may express this in the following *analogy* relations:

$$\frac{Q^E}{P^E} \sim E \qquad \text{(a)}$$
$$\frac{Q^\nu}{P^\nu} \sim \nu \qquad \text{(b)} \qquad\qquad (6.58)$$

where Q^E/P^E and Q^ν/P^ν are called the tensile *operator ratios* for the axial and transverse directions, respectively.

Now let us turn to the *simple shear test*. In a manner similar to the tensile test, we can say for the viscoelastic case

$$P^G \tau_{xy} = Q^G \varepsilon_{xy} \qquad\qquad (6.59)$$

Here P^G, Q^G is a linear operator pair for shear, leading us by virtue of Eq. (5.6) to the analogy relation

$$\frac{Q^G}{P^G} \sim 2G \qquad\qquad (6.60)$$

where Q^G/P^G is the shear operator ratio and G is the familiar shear modulus of elasticity. The operators P^G and Q^G are given by the same formulations as in Eqs.(6.57) but with superscript G. It is to be pointed out that any of the standard test procedures mentioned in connection with the tensile test, such as the constant stress (creep) procedure, the constant strain (relaxation) procedure, and the constant stress-rate procedure, can also be performed in connection with a simple shear test.

In addition to the simple tensile test and the simple shear test, we consider finally the simple *pressure test*. In this test we apply a bulk stress $\bar{\tau}(t) = \tau_{kk}/3 = -p$, where p is the pressure, and measure $\bar{\epsilon}(t) = \epsilon_{kk}/3$, where $\bar{\epsilon}(t)$ is one-third the cubical dilatation. For a viscoelastic material, we introduce for this case yet another operator pair, namely P^K and Q^K, such that

$$P^K \bar{\tau} = Q^K \bar{\epsilon} \tag{6.61}$$

From Eq. (5.52) we obtain one more analogy relation

$$\frac{Q^K}{P^K} \sim 3K \tag{6.62}$$

where, you will recall, K is the bulk modulus, and where Q^K/P^K is the pressure operator ratio. The forms of Q^K and P^K are again as given in Eq. (6.57) but now with the superscript K. And like the tensile and shear tests, any of the standard test procedures involving creep, relaxation, and so on, can be developed for the simple pressure test.

Furthermore, we can form hereditary integrals for the shear and pressure tests just as we did for the tension test. Considering torsion we note that we can express ϵ_{xy} in terms of τ_{xy} for viscoelastic behavior by first considering a step $(\tau_{xy})_0 [u(t)]$. Thus

$$\epsilon_{xy} = (\tau_{xy})_0 \, J^G(t)[u(t)] \tag{6.63}$$

where $J^G(t)$ is the *shear creep compliance function*. Similarly, by considering a step $(\epsilon_{xy})_0 [u(t)]$ we have

$$\tau_{xy} = (\epsilon_{xy})_0 \, Y^G(t)[u(t)] \tag{6.64}$$

where $Y^G(t)$ is the *shear relaxation modulus function*. Additionally, we can say for the pressure test

$$\begin{aligned}
\bar{\epsilon} &= (\bar{\tau})_0 \, J^K(t)[u(t)] \qquad \text{(a)} \\
\bar{\tau} &= (\bar{\epsilon})_0 \, Y^K(t)[u(t)] \qquad \text{(b)}
\end{aligned} \tag{6.65}$$

where $J^K(t)$ and $Y^K(t)$ are, respectively, the *pressure creep compliance function* and the *pressure relaxation modulus function*. We can next form the following hereditary integrals via the methodologies presented in discussing the tensile test:

$$\epsilon_{xy}(t) = \int_{0^-}^{t} J^G(t - t') \frac{\partial \tau_{xy}}{\partial t'} dt' \qquad \text{(a)}$$

$$\tau_{xy}(t) = \int_{0^-}^{t} Y^G(t - t') \frac{\partial \epsilon_{xy}}{\partial t'} dt' \qquad \text{(b)}$$

$$\bar{\epsilon}(t) = \int_{0^-}^{t} J^K(t - t') \frac{\partial \bar{\tau}}{\partial t'} dt' \qquad \text{(c)} \tag{6.66}$$

$$\bar{\tau}(t) = \int_{0^-}^{t} Y^K(t - t') \frac{\partial \bar{\epsilon}}{\partial t'} dt' \qquad \text{(d)}$$

Constitutive law (6.61) was expressed in the standard form of a differential equation, and we have referred to P^K and Q^K as the *operator pair*. On the other hand, this equation may be *formally* rewritten as

$$\bar{\tau}(t) = \left(\frac{Q^K}{P^K}\right)\bar{\varepsilon}(t) \tag{6.67}$$

where we have referred to (Q^K/P^K) as the *operator ratio*. We can now form a *formal integral* equation corresponding to Eq. (6.66d) by replacing $\bar{\tau}(t)$ on the left side using the right side of Eq. (6.67). Thus

$$\left(\frac{Q^K}{P^K}\right)\bar{\varepsilon}(t) = \int_{0^-}^{t} Y^K(t - t')\frac{\partial\bar{\varepsilon}}{\partial t'}dt' \tag{6.68}$$

We thus see that Eq. (6.67) is the formal equivalent of a hereditary integral over the *history* of $\bar{\varepsilon}(t)$ from 0^- to t. Similarly, express Eq. (6.67) in the following formal manner:

$$\bar{\varepsilon}(t) = \left(\frac{P^K}{Q^K}\right)\bar{\tau}(t) \tag{6.69}$$

Now going to Eq. (6.66c), we can form the following formal hereditary integral statement for the integral over the history of $\bar{\tau}(t)$:

$$\left(\frac{P^K}{Q^K}\right)\bar{\tau}(t) = \int_{0^-}^{t} J^K(t - t')\frac{\partial\bar{\tau}}{\partial t'}dt' \tag{6.70}$$

We can also form other formal hereditary integral statements for shear using $J^G(t)$ and $Y^G(t)$, as well as for the Poisson effect.*

We shall now express the above formulations in a more general and concise manner. Let τ^M and ε^M be quantities having dimensions, respectively, of stress and strain which are associated with an elastic *material* constant M measured in a simple test. For instance, for a simple tensile test in the x direction, M corresponds to the elastic modulus E while τ^M and ε^M correspond to τ_{xx} and ε_{xx}. On the other hand, for a pressure test M corresponds to the bulk modulus K, whereas τ^M and ε^M now correspond to $\bar{\tau}$ and $\bar{\varepsilon}$. With this notation the equivalence between operator ratios and hereditary integrals can be expressed concisely as

$$\left(\frac{P^M}{Q^M}\right)\tau^M(t) = \int_{0^-}^{t} J^M(t - t')\frac{\partial\tau^M(t')}{\partial t'}dt' \tag{6.71}$$

$$\left(\frac{Q^M}{P^M}\right)\varepsilon^M(t) = \int_{0^-}^{t} Y^M(t - t')\frac{\partial\varepsilon^M(t')}{\partial t'}dt' \tag{6.72}$$

Finally, let us return to analogy relations (6.58), (6.60), and (6.62). These relations were obtained with time t as the independent variable, and we may say that they apply in the t-space. An alternative approach is to take the Laplace transform of Eqs. (6.56), (6.59), and (6.61), and then to compare these results with those stemming from the Laplace transforms of the corresponding linear elastic equa-

---

*In Section 6.10 we shall define $J_x^E(t)$ and $J_y^E(t)$, which are *axial* and *lateral* tensile creep compliance functions, respectively.

tions. In so doing, one obtains the following alternative set of analogy relations in the transformed s-space:

$$\frac{\overline{Q}^E(s)}{\overline{P}^E(s)} \sim E \qquad \frac{\overline{Q}^G(s)}{\overline{P}^G(s)} \sim 2G$$

$$\frac{\overline{Q}^\nu(s)}{\overline{P}^\nu(s)} \sim \nu \qquad \frac{\overline{Q}^K(s)}{\overline{P}^K(s)} \sim 3K \qquad \text{in } s\text{-space} \qquad (6.73)$$

Here $\overline{P}^E(s)$, $\overline{Q}^E(s)$, and so on, are *polynomials* in s of the kind given in Eqs. (6.50). Analogy relations (6.73) will be used in Chapter 9 to set forth the important elastic-viscoelastic *correspondence principle*.

6.8 EXTRAPOLATION TO THREE DIMENSIONS: ISOTROPY

We shall now generalize the results from the simple tests of Section 6.7 in a manner paralleling the generalizations that were carried out in our study of elastic behavior. Accordingly, we postulate for anisotropic viscoelastic materials with three-dimensional stress states the following tensor equation:

$$\tau_{ij} = \left[C\left(\frac{Q}{P}\right) \right]_{ijkl} \varepsilon_{kl} \qquad (6.74)$$

where $[C(Q/P)]_{ijkl}$ is a fourth-order tensor with each element expressed as a general operator ratio, such as was presented in the preceding section. The tensors τ_{ij} and ε_{kl} are generally functions of one or more space coordinates and time. The differential operators Q and P are thus in general linear combinations of *partial* time derivatives. Equivalently, referring to analogy relations (6.73) we could postulate in s-space for anisotropic viscoelastic materials with three-dimensional stress states

$$\overline{\tau}_{ij}(s) = \left[C\left(\frac{\overline{Q}(s)}{\overline{P}(s)}\right) \right]_{ijkl} \overline{\varepsilon}_{ij}(s) \qquad (6.75)$$

where now $[C(\overline{Q}(s)/\overline{P}(s))]_{ijkl}$ is a fourth-order tensor with each element expressed as a ratio of polynomials in s.

We thus initially have 81 coefficients in the tensor $[C(Q/P)]_{ijkl}$ in Eq. (6.74). We can now proceed in a manner similar to the considerations of the anisotropic linear elastic material to impose complete isotropy. You wil recall that in Section 5.4 we imposed various symmetry requirements which in the end led to complete isotropic behavior of the linear elastic material. This can also be done here since these aforementioned arguments are valid for any linear continuum. Hence, as a first step we invoke the symmetry of τ_{ij} and ε_{kl} and require that in Eq. (6.74),

$$\left[C\left(\frac{Q}{P}\right) \right]_{ijkl} = \left[C\left(\frac{Q}{P}\right) \right]_{jikl} = \left[C\left(\frac{Q}{P}\right) \right]_{ijlk} \qquad (6.76)$$

The equations above indicate that the indices vary only in pairs (ij) and (kl), with each pair selected from the six combinations (11), (22), (33), (23) = (32), (31) = (13), and (12) = (21). We thus conclude that for anisotropic behavior, there are at most 36 independent coefficients in $[C(Q/P)]_{ijkl}$. We may next reduce the number of independent coefficients further to 12 for the orthotropic material by employing two inversions of axes as we did in Section 5.4. Finally, by further transformations of axes we may arrive at the isotropic, linear viscoelastic material for which only *two* independent coefficients remain. As noted previously, each coefficient is an operator ratio.

Thus, for an isotropic material, we need only carry out *two* types of measurements to obtain two independent operator ratios. For example, one could perform a simple tensile test and from axial and transverse measurements one could obtain operator ratios Q^E/P^E and Q^ν/P^ν. Or one could perform both simple torsion and simple pressure tests to obtain Q^G/P^G and Q^K/P^K, and so on. Recall that any particular simple test may be performed in accordance with a variety of standard procedures (e.g., creep, relaxation, constant stress rate, etc.). And as explained in Part A, the results of such standard procedures are interrelated.

In continuing our analogy with elastic materials we recall (see Section 5.5) that isotropic Hooke's law could be expressed in a variety of forms with each form containing a pair of constants. Each such set of constants could be considered the independent pair for the material. Two such forms are [see Eqs. (5.15) and (5.41)]

$$\varepsilon_{ij} = \frac{1+\nu}{E}\,\tau_{ij} - \frac{\nu}{E}\,\tau_{kk}\,\delta_{ij} \qquad \text{(a)}$$

$$\tau_{ij} = \lambda\,\varepsilon_{kk}\,\delta_{ij} + 2G\,\varepsilon_{ij} \qquad \text{(b)}$$

$$(6.77)$$

We also showed in Section 5.5 that Eq. (6.77b) may be decomposed into the following pair of equations:

$$\tau_{kk} = 3K\,\varepsilon_{kk}, \qquad s_{ij} = 2Ge_{ij} \tag{6.78}$$

where s_{ij} and e_{ij} are deviator tensors, which you will recall are defined as

$$s_{ij} = \tau_{ij} - \tfrac{1}{3}\tau_{kk}\,\delta_{ij} \qquad \text{(a)}$$

$$e_{ij} = \varepsilon_{ij} - \tfrac{1}{3}\varepsilon_{kk}\,\delta_{ij} \qquad \text{(b)}$$

$$(6.79)$$

In this and the next section we use *analogy* relations such as those given in Section 6.7 to convert Eqs. (6.77) and (6.78) to corresponding viscoelastic laws. This procedure is valid since the linear viscoelastic laws in three dimensions may be obtained by *superposing the simple one-dimensional linear viscoelastic laws* in precisely the same manner as in linear elasticity, where we superposed simple test results for the three orthogonal directions (see Section 5.2) to arrive at three-dimensional isotropic Hooke's law. Before proceeding we wish to point out that while Eqs. (6.78) are not widely used in linear elasticity, the analogous forms that we will reach for linear viscoelasticity are by contrast widely used, for reasons that will soon become apparent.

Let us first focus our attention on Eq. (6.77a). To extend this equation to apply to linear viscoelastic materials, we proceed by employing replacements for E and ν by operator ratios as proposed in Eqs. (6.58). We thus get

$$\varepsilon_{ij} = \frac{1 + (Q^\nu/P^\nu)}{Q^E/P^E}\,\tau_{ij} - \frac{Q^\nu/P^\nu}{Q^E/P^E}\,\tau_{kk}\,\delta_{ij} \tag{6.80}$$

By clearing out *all* reciprocal operators, we may rewrite the above as the following differential equation:

$$Q^E P^\nu \, \varepsilon_{ij} = P^E (P^\nu + Q^\nu) \tau_{ij} - P^E Q^\nu \, \tau_{kk} \, \delta_{ij} \qquad (6.81)$$

Note that we may commute an operator product in Eq. (6.81). That is, we may, for example, replace $Q^E P^\nu$ by $P^\nu Q^E$ since the coefficients in the operators are independent of time.

In the following example, we shall find the form of Eq. (6.81) by considering a particular material.

Example 6.3

Determine the form of Eq. (6.81) for an isotropic material, which, when subject to a tensile test in *any* coordinate direction, behaves as a Maxwell material in that direction. Furthermore, this material exhibits an *incompressible* Poisson effect in the direction lateral to that of the loading.

Referring to Eq. (6.3), we express it now for a tensile test of a Maxwell material in the x direction. Also, noting that $\nu = 0.5$ because of incompressibility, we can then say that

$$\frac{1}{E}\frac{\partial \tau_{xx}}{\partial t} + \frac{1}{\eta}\tau_{xx} = \frac{\partial \varepsilon_{xx}}{\partial t} \qquad (a)$$

$$\varepsilon_{yy} = \varepsilon_{zz} = -\tfrac{1}{2}\varepsilon_{xx} \qquad (b)$$

where you will recall that E and η are, respectively, the elastic and viscous coefficients in *tension*. Because of isotropy Eq. (a) also applies to the y and z directions. Also, from Eq. (b) it is clear that $\varepsilon_{kk} = 0$ as required by the incompressibility condition. We shall next rewrite the equations above by introducing the derivative operator $D \equiv \partial/\partial t$ and rearranging the constant coefficients. Thus

$$\left(1 + \frac{\eta D}{E}\right)\tau_{xx} = \eta D \, \varepsilon_{xx} \qquad (c)$$

$$\varepsilon_{yy} = -\tfrac{1}{2}\varepsilon_{xx} \qquad (d)$$

Let us now compare Eqs. (c) and (d) with Eqs. (6.56a) and (6.56b), respectively. The operator pairs in Eqs. (6.56) for our material are then seen to be

$$P^E = \left(1 + \frac{\eta}{E}D\right) \qquad Q^E = \eta D \qquad (e)$$

$$P^\nu = 1 \qquad Q^\nu = \tfrac{1}{2} \qquad (f)$$

Finally, going back to the three-dimensional constitutive law given by Eq. (6.81) and using the results above from the simple tensile test, we then get for this material

$$(\eta D)(1)\varepsilon_{ij} = \left(1 + \frac{\eta}{E}D\right)\left(\frac{3}{2}\right)\tau_{ij} - \left(1 + \frac{\eta}{E}D\right)\left(\frac{1}{2}\right)\tau_{kk}\,\delta_{ij} \qquad (g)$$

Replacing the D operators by $\partial/\partial t$ and collecting terms, we get the desired differential equation

$$\frac{\partial \varepsilon_{ij}}{\partial t} = \frac{3}{2}\left(\frac{1}{E}\frac{\partial \tau_{ij}}{\partial t} + \frac{1}{\eta}\tau_{ij}\right) - \frac{1}{2}\left(\frac{1}{E}\frac{\partial \tau_{kk}}{\partial t} + \frac{1}{\eta}\tau_{kk}\right)\delta_{ij} \qquad (b)$$

Various other viscoelastic formulations may be obtained by replacing G, K, and λ with the analogous operator ratios* in Eqs. (6.77b) and (6.78). Furthermore, the relation between an operator pair and any other two independent operator pairs may be obtained from the formulations developed in Section 5.5 mutually relating the isotropic elastic constants. For example, we have, from Table 5.1,

$$G = \frac{E}{2(1 + \nu)} \qquad K = \frac{E}{3(1 - 2\nu)} \qquad (6.82)$$

Now employing the analogy relations given by (6.58), (6.60), and (6.62), we can say that

$$\frac{Q^G}{P^G} = \frac{Q^E/P^E}{1 + Q^\nu/P^\nu} \qquad \text{(a)}$$

$$\frac{Q^K}{P^K} = \frac{Q^E/P^E}{1 - 2Q^\nu/P^\nu} \qquad \text{(b)} \qquad\qquad (6.83)$$

We thus have each of the operator ratios Q^G/P^G and Q^K/P^K related to the operator ratios Q^E/P^E and Q^ν/P^ν. In a similar way, we may use Table 5.1 to obtain the Q^λ/P^λ operator ratio in terms of the other ratios.

We now illustrate the use of Eqs. (6.83) in the next example.

Example 6.4

What are the operator pairs (P^G, Q^G) and (P^K, Q^K) for the material considered in Example 6.3? Also compare results of this example with those of Example 6.3.

We start by substituting the operators given by Eqs. (e) and (f) of Example 6.3 into the right side of Eq. (6.83a) to get

$$\frac{Q^G}{P^G} = \frac{(\eta D)/[1 + (\eta/E)D]}{1 + (\frac{1}{2})/1} = \frac{\frac{2}{3}(\eta D)}{1 + (\eta/E)D} \qquad \text{(a)}$$

Hence

$$P^G = \left(1 + \frac{\eta}{E}D\right) \qquad \text{(b)}$$

$$Q^G = \frac{2}{3}\eta D \qquad \text{(c)}$$

where you will note that in accordance with convention we have set $p_0^G = 1$. An interesting observation can be made by returning to Eq. (6.59), which we now restate

$$P^G \tau_{xy} = Q^G \varepsilon_{xy} \qquad \text{(d)}$$

Replacing P^G and Q^G using Eqs. (b) and (c), this equation becomes

$$\left(1 + \frac{\eta}{E}D\right)\tau_{xy} = \frac{2}{3}\eta D\,\varepsilon_{xy} \qquad \text{(e)}$$

Now compare Eq. (e) representing *shear* with Eq. (c) of Example 6.3 representing *simple tension* for a Maxwell material. They are of the same form, although the

---

* Although we have not presented in Section 6.7 an analogy relation between λ and an operator ratio, such a correspondence may easily be introduced.

coefficients are not identical, leading us to conclude that the material we are dealing with is *also* of the Maxwell type in pure shear.

Now let $E \to \infty$ in Eq. (e) above and in Eq. (c) of Example 6.3. We get for these equations, respectively,

$$\tau_{xy} = \tfrac{2}{3}\eta D\, \varepsilon_{xy} = \zeta D\, \varepsilon_{xy} \tag{f}$$

$$\tau_{xx} = \eta D\, \varepsilon_{xx} \tag{g}$$

where we have introduced ζ as the *viscosity coefficient in shear*. We conclude that for the incompressible material of this example, the viscosity coefficient in shear, ζ, is two-thirds of the viscosity coefficient in tension, η. Now let $\eta \to \infty$ in Eq. (e) above (thus resulting in elastic behavior) and also in Eq. (c) of Example 6.3. We can conclude from this operation

$$\tau_{xy} = \tfrac{2}{3}E\, \varepsilon_{xy} = 2G\, \varepsilon_{xy} \tag{h}$$

$$\tau_{xx} = E\, \varepsilon_{xx} \tag{i}$$

Accordingly, twice the modulus of elasticity in shear, $2G$, for this incompressible material must be two-thirds of the modulus of elasticity in tension E. (Does this check with the results from Table 5.1 relating G and E for an incompressible material?) We may thus rewrite Eq. (e) as follows:

$$\left(1 + \frac{\zeta}{2G}D\right)\tau_{xy} = \zeta D\, \varepsilon_{xy} \tag{j}$$

Finally, for Eq. (6.83b) we see that the denominator goes to zero when we substitute for Q^ν and P^ν using Eqs. (f) of Example 6.3. This leads us to conclude that $P^K = 0$. Going to Eq. (6.61), we must then also conclude that $\bar\varepsilon = 0$. This verifies that the material as initially postulated is incompressible.

6.9 BULK AND DISTORTIONAL BEHAVIORS

Now we turn to Eqs. (6.78). With the use of analogy relation (6.62), the *first* of Eqs. (6.78), namely,

$$\tau_{kk} = 3K\, \varepsilon_{kk} \tag{6.84}$$

converts to

$$\tau_{kk} = \left(\frac{Q^K}{P^K}\right)\varepsilon_{kk} \tag{6.85}$$

Dividing by 3 and clearing the operator P^K, we then get

$$P^K\left(\frac{\tau_{kk}}{3}\right) = Q^K\left(\frac{\varepsilon_{kk}}{3}\right)$$

Therefore,

$$\boxed{P^K\bar\tau = Q^K\bar\varepsilon} \tag{6.86}$$

This brings us back to Eq. (6.61) for the simple pressure test, although now the bulk stress $\bar\tau$ need *not* in general correspond to a state of hydrostatic pressure p. We shall refer to Eq. (6.86) as representing *bulk behavior*, in order to distinguish it from the special case of behavior under simple pressure where $\bar\tau = -p$.

As for the *second* of Eqs. (6.78), namely,

$$s_{ij} = 2Ge_{ij} \qquad (6.87)$$

we use the analogy relation (6.60) to get

$$s_{ij} = \left(\frac{Q^G}{P^G}\right) e_{ij} \qquad (6.88)$$

Clearing the operator P^G, we then get the following important viscoelastic law:

$$\boxed{P^G s_{ij} = Q^G e_{ij}} \qquad (6.89)$$

Note that this equation is more general than the equations obtained from simple shear tests [e.g., Eq. (6.59)], since it reduces to such equations only when $i \neq j$. For $i = j$, Eq. (6.89) yields three additional relations between the deviators of the *normal* components of stress and strain. For example, for $i = j = 1$, we get

$$P^G s_{xx} = Q^G e_{xx}$$

which with the use of definitions (6.79) is found to be equivalent to

$$P^G(2\tau_{xx} - \tau_{yy} - \tau_{zz}) = Q^G(2\varepsilon_{xx} - \varepsilon_{yy} - \varepsilon_{zz})$$

where we have cleared out the fraction $\frac{1}{3}$. Equations (6.86) and (6.89) are very convenient because of their simple form. To help distinguish Eq. (6.59) from Eq. (6.89), we shall refer to the former as representing behavior under *simple shear* and to the latter as representing behavior under *distortion*.

We can form hereditary integrals for $\bar{\varepsilon}$, $\bar{\tau}$, e_{ij} and ε_{ij} from differential equations (6.86) and (6.89), as we have done in the past. Thus

$$\bar{\varepsilon}(t) = \int_{0^-}^{t} J^K(t - t') \frac{\partial \bar{\tau}}{\partial t'} dt' \qquad (a)$$

$$\bar{\tau}(t) = \int_{0^-}^{t} Y^K(t - t') \frac{\partial \bar{\varepsilon}}{\partial t'} dt' \qquad (b)$$

$$e_{ij}(t) = \int_{0^-}^{t} J^G(t - t') \frac{\partial s_{ij}}{\partial t'} dt' \qquad (c) \qquad (6.90)$$

$$s_{ij}(t) = \int_{0^-}^{t} Y^G(t - t') \frac{\partial e_{ij}}{\partial t'} dt' \qquad (d)$$

A comparison of differential equations (6.86) and (6.89) with integral equations (6.90) immediately gives the following *formal statements* in terms of operator ratios:

$$\left(\frac{P^K}{Q^K}\right) \bar{\tau} = \int_{0^-}^{t} J^K(t - t) \frac{\partial \bar{\tau}}{\partial t'} dt' \qquad (a)$$

$$\left(\frac{Q^K}{P^K}\right) \bar{\varepsilon} = \int_{0^-}^{t} Y^K(t - t) \frac{\partial \bar{\varepsilon}}{\partial t'} dt' \qquad (b)$$

$$\left(\frac{P^G}{Q^G}\right) s_{ij} = \int_{0^-}^{t} J^G(t - t') \frac{\partial s_{ij}}{\partial t'} dt' \qquad (c) \qquad (6.91)$$

$$\left(\frac{Q^G}{P^G}\right) e_{ij} = \int_{0^-}^{t} Y^G(t - t') \frac{\partial e_{ij}}{\partial t'} dt' \qquad (d)$$

Experimental evidence indicates that the operator pair P^G, Q^G and the material functions $J^G(t)$ and $Y^G(t)$ may be rather complex* for a viscoelastic material, but the operator pair P^K, Q^K and functions $J^K(t)$ and $Y^K(t)$ tend to be rather simple. Briefly put, the distortional behavior tends to be complex, whereas the bulk behavior tends to be simple. The reason for this simplicity is that the volumetric deformation of a viscoelastic material is often nearly elastic. As a consequence, for the pair of equations (6.86) and (6.89) most of the complexity is usually concentrated in *one* of the equations [i.e., Eq. (6.89)]. This concentration in complexity in one equation over the other is present also in the corresponding hereditary integral pair of equations (6.90a) and (6.90c) as well as in the pair (6.90b) and (6.90d), where the concentration in complexity occurs in the second equation of each pair. This is the prime reason why these equations are generally preferred over equations such as Eq. (6.81).

We now consider Example 6.5, which is a continuation of Examples 6.3 and 6.4 of the preceding section, to illustrate the above results.

Example 6.5

For the incompressible Maxwell material considered in Examples 6.3 and 6.4 of the preceding section, determine the differential equation relating the tensor deviators s_{ij} and e_{ij}. Then determine the creep compliance function for shear, $J^G(t)$, for use in hereditary integral (6.90c).

For this material we have already obtained the operator pair P^G, Q^G [see Example 6.4, Eqs. (b) and (c)]. Applying these results to Eq. (6.89), we get

$$\frac{2}{3}\eta\frac{\partial e_{ij}}{\partial t} = s_{ij} + \frac{\eta}{E}\frac{\partial s_{ij}}{\partial t} \tag{a}$$

Thus we obtain the desired differential equation immediately.

Now consider a deviator stress input given as the step function $(s_{ij})_0[u(t)]$, where $(s_{ij})_0$ is constant. To find the response of the strain deviator, we substitute $(s_{ij})_0[u(t)]$ into Eq. (a) to get

$$\frac{2}{3}\eta\frac{\partial e_{ij}}{\partial t} = (s_{ij})_0[u(t)] + \frac{\eta}{E}(s_{ij})_0[\delta(t)] \tag{b}$$

Next, integrate this result with respect to time from 0^- to t and solve for e_{ij}. Accordingly, we get

$$e_{ij} = (s_{ij})_0\frac{3}{2}\left(\frac{1}{E} + \frac{t}{\eta}\right)[u(t)] \tag{c}$$

From the definition of $J^G(t)$ we can say that

$$e_{ij} = (s_{ij})_0 J^G(t)[u(t)] \tag{d}$$

and thus by comparing Eqs. (c) and (d), we can conclude that

$$J^G(t) = \frac{3}{2}\left(\frac{1}{E} + \frac{t}{\eta}\right) = \frac{1}{2G} + \frac{t}{\zeta} \tag{e}$$

---

* An alternative approach that sometimes gives simpler material functions is based on the use of *fractional calculus*. In this approach, the material functions are expressed in terms at t^α, where α may be a fraction. We shall see examples of this in Chapter 7.

where the result on the extreme right follows from Eqs. (f) and (h) of Example 6.4. We may now use this result in the hereditary integral given in Eq. (6.90c). In a similar manner we may obtain the relaxation modulus function for shear to be

$$Y^G(t) = \tfrac{2}{3} E e^{-(E/\eta)t} = 2G e^{-(2G/\zeta)t} \tag{f}$$

which may then be used in the hereditary integral (6.90d).

The creep compliance and relaxation modulus functions for a Maxwell material under simple tension were given by Eqs. (6.40a) and (6.42), respectively, as

$$J^E(t) = \frac{1}{E} + \frac{t}{\eta} \tag{g}$$

$$Y^E(t) = E e^{-(E/\eta)t} \tag{h}$$

where we have now introduced the superscript E in accordance with the notations used in Eqs. (6.71) and (6.72). On comparing the first of Eqs. (e) and (f) with Eqs. (g) and (h), we once again notice the factor $\tfrac{2}{3}$ first mentioned in Example 6.4.

6.10 THE VISCOELASTIC POISSON EFFECT

In the preceding sections we considered examples in which the Poisson effect was assumed to correspond to incompressible deformation (i.e., $\varepsilon_{yy} = -\tfrac{1}{2}\varepsilon_{xx}$). However, it is clear from operator equation (6.56b) that the Poisson effect in a viscoelastic material will in general be some complex function of time. This function of time will depend on the viscoelastic model chosen and on the load history. In general, ε_{yy} and ε_{xx} will *not* be in the same proportion for all time. And in some instances the Poisson effect may behave in a manner contrary to intuition, as we shall see in this section.

To explore this point, we again consider the simple *tension test* for which [see Eq. (6.56a)] the viscoelastic constitutive law has been expressed as

$$Q^E \varepsilon_{xx} = P^E \tau_{xx} \tag{6.92}$$

In the creep test procedure, for which $\tau_{xx}(t) = (\tau_{xx})_0 [u(t)]$, we shall express the solution to Eq. (6.92) as

$$\varepsilon_{xx}(t) = (\tau_{xx})_0 J_x^E(t)[u(t)] \tag{6.93}$$

where $J_x^E(t)$ is the *axial* tensile creep compliance function. If we eliminate ε_{xx} between Eqs. (6.56a) and (6.56b), by first operating on Eq. (6.56a) with Q^V and then replacing $Q^V \varepsilon_{xx}$ using Eq. (6.56b), we get

$$Q^E P^V \varepsilon_{yy} = -Q^V P^E \tau_{xx} \tag{6.94}$$

For the same creep test procedure indicated above, we shall now give the solution to Eq. (6.94) in the form

$$\varepsilon_{yy}(t) = -(\tau_{xx})_0 J_y^E(t)[u(t)] \tag{6.95}$$

where $J_y^E(t)$ is the *lateral* tensile creep compliance function. Finally, we define the *creep Poisson function* $\nu_c(t)$ as the *negative* ratio of $\varepsilon_{xx}(t)$ and $\varepsilon_{yy}(t)$ above. That is,

$$\nu_c(t) = \frac{J_y^E(t)}{J_x^E(t)} \tag{6.96}$$

Now consider a material that exhibits *elastic compressibility* for *bulk* behavior and is a *Kelvin-type* material under multidimensional *distortion*. Accordingly, Eqs. (6.86) and (6.89) become

$$\bar{\tau} = 3K\bar{\varepsilon} \qquad (a)$$

$$s_{ij} = (2G + \zeta D)e_{ij} \qquad (b)$$

(6.97)

and hence

$$
\begin{array}{ll}
P^K = 1 & Q^K = 3K \\
P^G = 1 & Q^G = 2G + \zeta D
\end{array}
$$

(6.98)

where K is the elastic bulk modulus, G the elastic shear modulus, and ζ the viscosity coefficient in shear. Note that in Eq. (6.97b), $s_{ij} \rightarrow 2Ge_{ij}$ as $\zeta \rightarrow 0$ and $s_{ij} \rightarrow \zeta \dot{e}_{ij}$ as $G \rightarrow 0$.

In order to find the creep Poisson function for this particular material by means of Eq. (6.96), we must first determine the P^E, Q^E and P^ν, Q^ν operator pairs. Table 5.1 gives us for an isotropic elastic material

$$E = \frac{9KG}{3K + G} \qquad \nu = \frac{3K - 2G}{2(3K + G)}$$

(6.99)

and by the usual procedure of replacing E, K, G, and ν by their analogous operator ratios, we may obtain the following relations for an isotropic viscoelastic material:

$$\frac{Q^E}{P^E} = \frac{3Q^K Q^G}{2P^G Q^K + P^K Q^G} \qquad \frac{Q^\nu}{P^\nu} = \frac{P^G Q^K - P^K Q^G}{2P^G Q^K + P^K Q^G}$$

(6.100)

Substituting operators (6.98) into Eqs. (6.100) and normalizing the operators, we then get for the present material:

$$
\begin{array}{lll}
P^E = 1 + p_1^E D & Q^E = q_0^E + q_1^E D & (a) \\
P^\nu = P^E & Q^\nu = q_0^\nu + q_1^\nu D & (b)
\end{array}
$$

(6.101)

where

$$
p_1^E = \frac{\zeta}{6K + 2G} \qquad q_0^E = \frac{18KG}{6K + 2G} \qquad q_1^E = \frac{9K\zeta}{6K + 2G}
$$

$$
q_0^\nu = \frac{3K - 2G}{6K + 2G} \qquad q_1^\nu = -\frac{\zeta}{6K + 2G} = -p_1^E
$$

(6.102)

Note that q_1^ν is negative. On examining Eq. (6.92) with operators (6.101a) we find that during a tension test this material behaves as a *standard solid* [see Fig. 6.4(a) and compare with Eq. (6.31) with $\eta_1 \rightarrow \infty$].

Equations (6.92) and (6.94) now become

$$
(q_0^E + q_1^E D)\varepsilon_{xx} = (1 + p_1^E D)\tau_{xx} \qquad (a)
$$

$$
(q_0^E + q_1^E D)\varepsilon_{yy} = -(q_0^\nu + q_1^\nu D)\tau_{xx} \qquad (b)
$$

(6.103)

where the relation $P^\nu = P^E$ according to Eqs. (6.101b) has been used to simplify the form of Eq. (6.103b). Solving these equations for the creep test input

$\tau_{xx}(t) = (\tau_{xx})_0 [u(t)]$ then gives us the following creep compliance functions in accordance with Eqs. (6.93) and (6.95):

$$J_x^E(t) = \frac{1}{q_0^E}\left[1 + \left(\frac{p_1^E q_0^E}{q_1^E} - 1\right)\exp\left(-\frac{q_0^E}{q_1^E}t\right)\right] \qquad \text{(a)}$$

$$J_y^E(t) = \frac{q_0^\nu}{q_0^E}\left[1 + \left(\frac{q_0^E q_1^\nu}{q_1^E q_0^\nu} - 1\right)\exp\left(-\frac{q_0^E}{q_1^E}t\right)\right] \qquad \text{(b)}$$

$$(6.104)$$

In conformity with Fig. 6.4(a), this material under creep loading approaches a linear elastic solid both as $t \to 0^+$ and as $t \to \infty$. Finally, inserting the expressions for the p and q coefficients from Eqs. (6.102) into Eqs. (6.104) and then using definition (6.96), we get

$$\nu_c(t) = \frac{3K(1 - e^{-(2G/\zeta)t}) - 2G}{6K(1 - e^{-(2G/\zeta)t}) + 2G} \qquad (6.105)$$

Note that $\nu_c(0) = -1$, $\nu_c(t_1) = 0$, where

$$t_1 = \frac{\zeta}{2G}\ln\left(\frac{3K}{3K - 2G}\right) \qquad (6.106)$$

and $\nu_c(\infty) = (3K - 2G)/(6K + 2G) = \nu$, where ν is the elastic Poisson's ratio of the limiting elastic solid at $t \to \infty$. This rather startling result indicates that such a material experiences lateral *expansion* under axial tension in the time interval $0 \le t \le t_1$, and then undergoes lateral contraction for $t > t_1$. Thus we have shown that a material which behaves as an elastic solid during a pressure test and as a Kelvin-type viscoelastic material under multidimensional distortion will behave as a standard linear solid under tension with a creep Poisson function as described above. Although such behavior may seem anomalous, it is mathematically possible. Some typical values of viscoelastic material constants for polymers* are given below:

$$K = 1.7 \times 10^9 \text{ dyne-cm}^{-2}$$

$$G = 2.9 \times 10^8 \text{ dyne-cm}^{-2} \qquad (6.107)$$

$$\zeta = 2.8 \times 10^9 \text{ dyne-sec-cm}^{-2}$$

The creep Poisson function for these constants as determined from Eq. (6.105) has been plotted in Fig. 6.7. Note that $\nu_c(t)$ changes in a very short time from negative to positive (i.e., at approximately 0.6 sec), and $\nu_c(\infty) = \nu = 0.42$.

We may obtain a more physical interpretation of Eq. (6.105) by associating with *each component* of strain (i.e., instantaneous elastic strain and time dependent strain) a *constant* Poisson coefficient, where these coefficients are not necessarily equal. For the standard solid the axial tensile creep compliance function [see Eq. (6.38) with $\eta_1 \to \infty$] is given as

$$J_x^E = \frac{1}{E_1} + \frac{1}{E_2}\left[1 - \exp\left(-t\frac{E_2}{\eta_2}\right)\right] \qquad (6.108)$$

---

* See L. E. Nielson, *Mechanical Properties of Polymers* (New York: Reinhold Publishing Co., 1962), p. 50. For a similar presentation of the anomalous Poisson effect described here, see W. Flügge, *Viscoelasticity* (Berlin: Springer-Verlag, 1975), p. 169. Also for further information on polymers, see J. D. Ferry, *Viscoelastic Properties of Polymers* (New York: John Wiley & Sons, Inc., 1970).

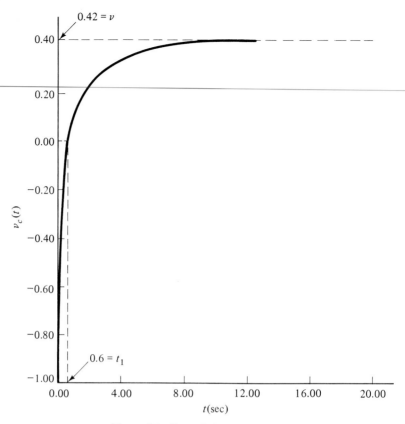

Figure 6.7 Creep Poisson function.

We now introduce *two* Poisson coefficients ν_1 and ν_2 as mentioned above, and accordingly, the lateral tensile creep compliance function follows as

$$J_y^E = \frac{\nu_1}{E_1} + \frac{\nu_2}{E_2}\left[1 - \exp\left(-t\frac{E_2}{\eta_2}\right)\right] \qquad (6.109)$$

Equation (6.96) then gives for the creep Poisson function

$$\nu_c(t) = \frac{\nu_2 E_1\left[1 - \exp\left(-t\dfrac{E_2}{\eta_2}\right)\right] + \nu_1 E_2}{E_1\left[1 - \exp\left(-t\dfrac{E_2}{\eta_2}\right)\right] + E_2} \qquad (6.110)$$

If we now set $\nu_1 = -1$, $E_1 = 9K$, $\nu_2 = \frac{1}{2}$, $E_2 = 3G$, and $\eta_2 = \frac{3}{2}\zeta$, Eq. (6.110) reduces back to Eq. (6.105). (You should verify that these values are in conformity with Table 5.1.) Thus in this model the instantaneous elastic strain produces a negative Poisson effect with $\nu_1 = -1$, whereas the subsequent time-dependent strain is incompressible with $\nu_2 = \frac{1}{2}$. Also, we see that $\nu_c(\infty) = \nu = (0.5E_1 - E_2)/(E_1 + E_2)$.

Linear Viscoelastic Behavior   Chap. 6

6.11 NONISOTHERMAL LINEAR VISCOELASTIC BEHAVIOR

Temperature fields affect viscoelastic behavior by generating a thermal expansion that contributes directly to the volumetric strain. In addition, a *spatially* dependent temperature field $T(x_i) = T(x, y, z)$ introduces a variation in the highly temperature-dependent viscoelastic material parameters. Accordingly, we shall generalize Eqs. (6.86) and (6.89) to the following forms:

$$Q^K \bar{\varepsilon} = P^K \bar{\tau} + \alpha Q^K (T - T_0) \qquad \text{(a)}$$
$$Q^G e_{ij} = P^G s_{ij} \qquad \text{(b)}$$

$$(6.111)$$

Here α is the *coefficient of linear thermal expansion* (assumed constant) and T_0 is a constant reference temperature. Furthermore, the operator pairs given above are expressed as follows:

$$Q^K = \sum_{j=0}^{nK} q_j^K(T) \frac{\partial^j}{\partial t^j} \qquad P^K = \sum_{j=0}^{mK} P_j^K(T) \frac{\partial^j}{\partial t^j} \qquad \text{(a)}$$
$$Q^G = \sum_{j=0}^{nG} q_j^G(T) \frac{\partial^j}{\partial t^j} \qquad P^G = \sum_{j=0}^{mG} p_j^G(T) \frac{\partial^j}{\partial t^j} \qquad \text{(b)}$$

$$(6.112)$$

Note first that when $\bar{\tau} = 0$ and $\varepsilon_{xx} = \varepsilon_{yy} = \varepsilon_{zz}$ so that $\bar{\varepsilon} = \varepsilon_{kk}/3 = \varepsilon_{xx}$, Eq. (6.111a) satisfies the familiar condition involving α, namely,

$$\varepsilon_{xx} = \alpha(T - T_0) = \alpha \, \Delta T$$

Also note in Eqs. (6.112) that the p's and q's are now functions of the spatially dependent temperature field $T(x_i)$. Finally, we remark that since T has been assumed to be independent of the time, the second expression on the right side of Eq. (6.111a) simplifies to $\alpha q_0^K(T)(T - T_0)$. We shall not consider the more complex case where T also varies with the time.*

In general, Eqs. (6.112) cannot be expressed in terms of one independent variable since t appears in the derivatives, and x, y, z appear in the p and q coefficients. However, there is a large class of viscoelastic materials called *thermorheologically simple* materials for which we can replace variables t and x_i by a *single independent variable*. These materials are characterized by having *all* of the coefficients of the jth-order time derivatives in Eqs. (6.112) proportional to the jth power of a single function of temperature, $f(T)$. That is,

$$q_j^K(T) = q_{0j}^K[f(T)]^j$$
$$q_j^G(T) = q_{0j}^G[f(T)]^j$$
$$p_j^K(T) = p_{0j}^K[f(T)]^j$$
$$p_j^G(T) = p_{0j}^G[f(T)]^j$$

$$(6.113)$$

---

*For this more general case, see L. W. Morland and E. H. Lee, "Stress Analysis for Linear Viscoelastic Materials with Temperature Variation," *Trans. Soc. Rheol.*, Vol. 4, p. 233 (1960). Also for more recent applications and extensions of this principle, see G. W. Scherer, *Relaxation in Glass and Composites* (New York: John Wiley & Sons, Inc., 1986).

where q_{0j}^K, q_{0j}^G, p_{0j}^K, and p_{0j}^G are *proportionality constants*. This assumed behavior is supported by experimental evidence for a large class of viscoelastic materials. For spring–dashpot models, this behavior requires all viscosity coefficients to be proportional to $f(T)$, while the elastic coefficients are taken as independent of temperature.* [For example, see Eq. (6.31) for the four-parameter fluid with particular attention to the number of times viscosity appears in each coefficient.] Accordingly, we can determine $f(T)$ by investigating how the viscosity coefficients for a given material vary with temperature.

We shall now show that by an appropriate variable change we will be able to express the constitutive laws for thermorheologically simple materials in terms of a *single independent variable*. This will then enable us to rewrite such laws as hereditary integrals of the type we have previously seen. For this purpose, we introduce the *new* variable $\xi(x_i, t)$ defined as

$$\xi(x_i, t) = \frac{t}{f[T(x_i)]} \tag{6.114}$$

where $\xi(x_i, t)$ is interpreted to be a modified time scale and is hence called the *reduced time*. One can then easily show by repeated use of the chain rule that

$$f(T)^j \frac{\partial^j}{\partial t^j}\bigg|_{x_i} = \frac{\partial^j}{\partial \xi^j}\bigg|_{x_i} \tag{6.115}$$

Using this reduced time, we can reformulate Eqs. (6.112) as follows in terms of the constants of proportionality set forth in Eqs. (6.113):

$$Q^K = \sum_{j=0}^{n^K} q_{0j}^K \frac{\partial^j}{\partial \xi^j} \qquad P^K = \sum_{j=0}^{m^K} p_{0j}^K \frac{\partial^j}{\partial \xi^j}$$

$$Q^G = \sum_{j=0}^{n^G} q_{0j}^G \frac{\partial^j}{\partial \xi^j} \qquad P^G = \sum_{j=0}^{m^G} p_{0j}^G \frac{\partial^j}{\partial \xi^j} \tag{6.116}$$

By a change of variable, we have thus arrived at operator pairs having, once again, *constant coefficients* as in Eqs. (6.33). We may now proceed to find hereditary integrals in the manner indicated by Eqs. (6.90a) and (6.90c). Thus if we "clear" out the Q operators on the left sides of Eqs. (6.111), we arrive at the hereditary integrals

$$\bar{\varepsilon}(\xi) = \int_{0^-}^{\xi} J_0^K(\xi - \xi') \frac{\partial \bar{\tau}(\xi')}{\partial \xi'} d\xi' + \alpha(T - T_0) \qquad \text{(a)}$$

$$e_{ij}(\xi) = \int_{0^-}^{\xi} J_0^G(\xi - \xi') \frac{\partial s_{ij}(\xi')}{\partial \xi'} d\xi' \qquad \text{(b)} \tag{6.117}$$

where $J_0^K(\xi)$ and $J_0^G(\xi)$ are creep compliance functions in ξ only. If we had employed the original operator forms [i.e., Eqs. (6.112)] we would have obtained the more complicated creep compliance functions $J^K(x_i, t)$ and $J^G(x_i, t)$ in both x_i and t. In

---

*We use the convenience of the spring–dashpot model in our development of the properties associated with thermorheologically simple behavior. However, it is not actually necessary for the constitutive relations to be associated with spring–dashpot models. It suffices for us to examine the behavior of creep compliance or relaxation modulus functions when temperature is varied. We discuss this point later in this section.

formulating a boundary value problem with the use of Eqs. (6.117), we remind you that t must be replaced by ξ in *all* governing equations (see Problem 6.32).

One method of determining how closely a given material satisfies the thermo-rheologically simple representation involves performing a number of creep tests on the material at various steady and uniform temperatures but with the same stress. For example, if one performs torsional creep tests with the stress given as $(\tau_{xy})_0 [u(t)]$, a family of curves giving $J^G(t) = \varepsilon_{xy}(t)/(\tau_{xy})_0$ at various temperatures is obtained [see Fig. 6.8(a)]. For thermorheologically simple materials there exists a function of temperature $f(T)$ such that the time axis may be mapped into the ξ reduced time axis according to Eq. (6.114). As noted previously, this $f(T)$ is directly related to the temperature dependence of the viscosity coefficients. Most important, for this new axis the $J^G(t)$ curves of Fig. 6.8(a) coalesce into a *single* curve $J_0^G(\xi)$ when plotted versus ξ as in Fig. 6.8(b). (The relaxation modulus function behaves in a similar manner.) This is the main objective of introducing the transformation from the t abscissa to the ξ abscissa. This simplification then permits the formulation of hereditary integrals such as Eqs. (6.117) using the new ξ axis.

We pointed out in Sections VII.11 and VII.12 of Appendix VII that studies in materials science indicate that the viscosity* of many materials (both crystalline and amorphous) tends to have an exponential dependence on temperature of the form

$$\eta = \eta_0 e^{B/T} \tag{6.118}$$

where η_0 and B are temperature-independent material constants. Thus we may initially choose $f(T) = \eta_0 e^{B/T}$ in computing ξ via Eq. (6.114), and then use this result to see if the process in Fig. 6.8 occurs. It is frequently necessary to refine $f(T)$ further by allowing η_0 to vary with T in order to obtain a satisfactory coalescence of creep curves.

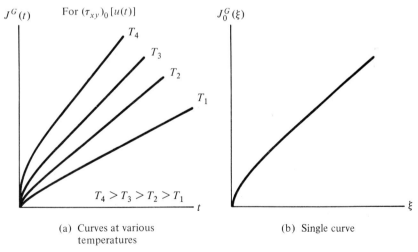

(a) Curves at various temperatures

(b) Single curve

Figure 6.8 Mapping of $J^G(t)$ curves for thermorheologically simple materials.

---

* Actually, in Appendix VII we discussed the *reciprocal* viscosity, which varied with temperature as $e^{-B/T}$.

6.12 CLOSURE

In this chapter we have studied linear viscoelastic material behavior. In essence the strain was related *linearly* to stress by a variety of differential and integral constitutive laws. In the next chapter we study nonlinear viscoelastic materials wherein strain is *nonlinearly* related to stress.

As the temperature is increased virtually all materials exhibit some viscoelastic characteristics.* These characteristics may be linear or nonlinear or possibly some combination of these. For a rough guide we can say that amorphous materials (e.g., plastics, muscle, asphalt, and cement) tend to behave as linear viscoelastic materials, whereas crystalline materials (e.g., metals, rock, and ice) tend to behave as nonlinear viscoelastic materials. We must point out, however, that the reverse behavior can also occur. For example, even though the creep behavior of metals is usually dominated by non-Newtonian (nonlinear) dislocation creep as suggested above, we find that at low stress levels Newtonian (linear) diffusion creep may be the only active mechanism (see Section VII.11 in Appendix VII). Also, by the same token, amorphous materials at high stress levels may behave as nonlinear viscoelastic materials (see Section VII.12 in Appendix VII).

It is thus apparent that as the stress (or pressure) and temperature are varied, a material passes through various patterns of behavior wherein different deformation mechanisms dominate at each stage. Thus we can have elastic, plastic, linear viscoelastic, and nonlinear viscoelastic behavior dominate at any particular stage. In recent years, considerable effort has been directed toward showing these different behavior characteristics as regions in a stress-temperature space with definite boundaries. The resulting diagrams are called *deformation maps*.† Thus these maps will indicate whether at a given temperature and stress a material should be treated as linear or nonlinear viscoelastic. Unfortunately, such maps are not yet available in sufficient detail for many important materials of interest to engineers. In contrast to the above, we have the recent trend toward the development of *unified theories*, whereby the above-mentioned "boundaries" are eliminated. Since such theories are still in the formative stages, in this book we confine ourselves to the "classical" theories of inelastic behavior.

PROBLEMS

6.1. With the use of the D operator, derive the differential equation for the three-parameter solid. What are the p and q constants?

---

* In Chapter 4 we pointed out that neutron flux may also cause linear viscoelastic behavior. For example, see D. R. Olander, *Fundamental Aspects of Nuclear Reactor Fuel Elements*, Energy Research and Development Administration, National Technical Information Service, Springfield, Virginia, 1976. An extension of the thermorheologically simple concept to irradiated materials is given in F. A. Cozzarelli and S. Huang, "On the Analogy Between Thermally and Irradiation Induced Creep," *Nuclear Eng. Design*, Vol. 22, No. 2, pp. 409–421 (1977).

† For a presentation of deformation maps for the Earth's mantle, see "Micromechanisms of Flow and Fracture, and Their Relevance to the Rheology of the Upper Mantle," by M. F. Ashby and R. A. Verrall, *Phil. Trans. R. Soc. Lond.*, Vol. 288, pp. 59–95 (1977).

6.2. Consider a Maxwell model in parallel with the Kelvin model (see Fig. P6.2). Using the D operator, find the differential equation involving τ, ε, and their time derivatives.

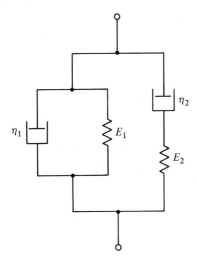

Figure P6.2

6.3. Consider the Burgers fluid model. Using the limit theorems of Laplace transform theory, evaluate the asymptotic behavior for strain at $t = 0$ and $t \to \infty$ for a creep stress input with homogeneous initial conditions at $t = 0^-$. Do your results make sense? Explain. Start with Eq. (6.31).

6.4. Use the Laplace transform limit theorems to determine the behavior of a three-parameter solid as $t \to 0^+$ and as $t \to \infty$ for a creep stress input. Employ the differential equation obtained in Problem 6.1,

$$\tau + \frac{\eta_2}{E_1 + E_2}\dot{\tau} = \frac{E_1 E_2}{E_1 + E_2}\varepsilon + \frac{\eta_2 E_1}{E_1 + E_2}\dot{\varepsilon}$$

6.5. Consider a series arrangement of any number of springs, dashpots, and Kelvin elements. Prove that if the highest-order derivatives for the operators P and Q are of the *same* order, a free spring is present in such a viscoelastic spring–dashpot model. (*Hint*: Set $m = n$ in operators P, Q and then use the Laplace transform limit theorem for $t = 0^+$.)

6.6. Form Eq. (6.31) by working with the Laplace transform rather than the D operator.

6.7. Solve Eq. (6.37) with the use of the Laplace transform. Use homogeneous initial conditions at $t = 0^-$.

6.8. Solve Eq. (6.37) by two successive integrations, where the second integration is accomplished with the use of an integrating factor.

6.9. Solve differential equation (6.34) for a Burgers fluid for the case of a *relaxation test* $\varepsilon(t) = \varepsilon_0 [u(t)]$. *Hint*: Use the Laplace transform, and note that

$$\mathsf{L}\{e^{\beta t} \sinh \alpha t\} = \frac{\alpha}{(s - \beta)^2 - \alpha^2} \quad \text{and} \quad \mathsf{L}\{e^{\beta t} \cosh \alpha t\} = \frac{s - \beta}{(s - \beta)^2 - \alpha^2}$$

6.10. Evaluate the strain as function of time for a stress that varies with time according to the formula

$$\tau(t) = \tau_0 \sin \omega t [u(t)]$$

Do this for a Maxwell material.

6.11. Do Problem 6.10 for the case of a Kelvin material.

6.12. Shown in Fig. P6.12 is a four-parameter solid. If $E_1 = E_2$ and $\eta_1 = \eta_2$ or if $E_1/\eta_1 = E_2/\eta_2$, show that this system yields the same differential equation as obtained from a Kelvin model.

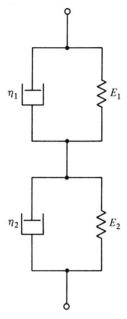

Figure P6.12

6.13. Show that the model given in Fig. P6.13 is equivalent to a simple Kelvin model, for *any* values of E_1, E_2, η_1, η_2. Compare this result with the result obtained for Problem 6.12.

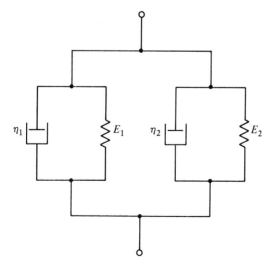

Figure P6.13

6.14. Consider two Maxwell models in parallel as shown in Fig. P6.14. Using the D operator, find the differential equation involving τ, ε, and their time derivatives.

Linear Viscoelastic Behavior   Chap. 6

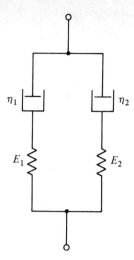

Figure P6.14

6.15. The model shown in Fig. P6.15 is called a *generalized Kelvin fluid*. Note that the zeroth element is a free spring, elements one to $N-1$ are Kelvin elements, and the Nth element is a free dashpot. Derive the stress-strain relation in terms of the D operator, and express it in the form $\varepsilon = f(D)\tau$, where $f(D)$ is a summation of terms involving $D, E_0, E_1, \ldots, E_{N-1}, \eta_1, \eta_2, \ldots, \eta_N$. Show that by considering $\eta_0 = E_N = 0$, the following result can be reached:

$$\varepsilon = \sum_{i=0}^{N} \frac{\tau}{E_i + \eta_i D}$$

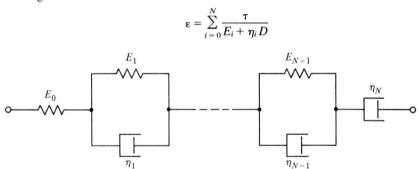

Figure P6.15

6.16. For the generalized Kelvin model of Problem 6.15, determine $\varepsilon(t)$ for a creep test. (*Hint*: Use superposition.)

6.17. The model shown in Fig. P6.17 is called a *generalized Maxwell fluid*. Derive the stress-strain equation in the form $\tau = g(D)\varepsilon$, where $g(D)$ is a summation of terms involving D and the material constants. Note that there are M Maxwell elements arranged in parallel.

6.18. Using the stress-strain laws for elastic, viscous, Maxwell, and Kelvin materials, verify that the models in Fig. P6.18 are equivalent (i.e., they yield the same differential equation). Note that the E's and η's in the various models are different (e.g., η_2 in the first model is *not* equal to η_2 in the second model).

6.19. Consider the Burgers fluid, for which material the strain history for a creep test input has been obtained as Eq. (6.38). What is the creep compliance function $J(t)$? Use this

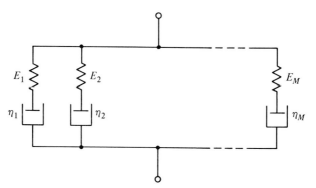

Figure P6.17

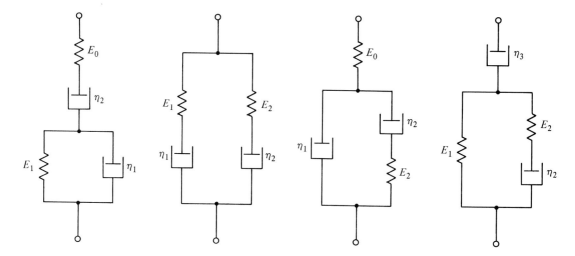

Figure P6.18

$J(t)$ to rewrite differential equation (6.31) as a hereditary integral over arbitrary stress history $\tau(t)$. Verify by a direct substitution into differential equation (6.31) that this hereditary integral is, in fact, the equivalent of this differential equation. (*Hint*: Make use of Leibnitz's rule for the derivative of an integral.)

6.20. Equation (6.55) gives $\bar{J}(s)\bar{Y}(s) = 1/s^2$ in the Laplace transform domain. Use the convolution theorem given in Appendix III to invert this equation back into the time domain. Express your answer as an integral equation, which may be expressed in two equivalent forms.

6.21. Assume that the creep compliance function, $J(t)$, and its transform, $\bar{J}(s)$, are given for the case of a Burgers fluid (see Problem 6.19). Invert the relation $\bar{Y}(s) = 1/[s^2\bar{J}(s)]$ to obtain the relaxation modulus function, $Y(t)$.

6.22. Find the three-dimensional, isotropic, linear, viscoelastic constitutive law for ε_{ij} in terms of τ_{ij}, for a material that is incompressible and behaves like a Kelvin material under tension. Make use of Eq. (6.80).

6.23. Starting with the three-dimensional linear elastic constitutive law

$$\tau_{ij} = \lambda\delta_{ij}\varepsilon_{kk} + 2G\varepsilon_{ij}$$

find the corresponding viscoelastic three-dimensional constitutive law in terms of operators P^E, Q^E, P^V, and Q^V. Verify by a tensor equation inversion that your result is equivalent to Eq. (6.81).

6.24. What is the operator pair (P^G, Q^G) for the incompressible isotropic Kelvin material of Problem 6.22? Write the constitutive law for simple torsion using these P^G and Q^G operators, and compare this equation with that of simple tension. Is this material Kelvin in simple torsion?

6.25. In Example 6.5 of Section 6.9, verify Eq. (f).

6.26. Consider the incompressible Kelvin material of Problem 6.22. Find $J^G(t)$ for this material, using the same approach given in Example 6.5 for an incompressible Maxwell material.

6.27. Verify Eqs. (6.102) and (6.104).

6.28. Show that with operators given by Eqs. (6.101), the material depicted in Section 6.10 behaves as a standard solid during a tension test. Use Eq. (6.31) with $\eta_1 \to \infty$ for this purpose to get the form of a constitutive law for a standard solid. Finally, demonstrate that the values used after Eq. (6.110), namely $\nu_1 = -1$, $E_1 = 9K$, $\nu_2 = \frac{1}{2}$, and $E_2 = 3G$, are consistent with Table 5.1.

6.29. Using the values for K, G, ζ given in Eqs. (6.107), determine the values of the p, q coefficients given by Eqs. (6.102). Use these p, q coefficients in Eq. (6.104b) to determine the lateral tensile creep compliance function $J_y^E(t)$. Plot this function and discuss its characteristics.

6.30. Consider a material that exhibits elastic compressibility and is Maxwell under distortion, that is,

$$\bar{\tau} = 3K\bar{\varepsilon}$$

$$\left(1 + \frac{\zeta D}{2G}\right)s_{ij} = \zeta D e_{ij}$$

Find the creep Poisson function $\nu_c(t)$.

6.31. Assume elastic compressibility in Eq. (6.111a) (i.e., $P^K = 1$ and $Q^K = 3K$), but let P^G, Q^G in Eq. (6.111b) be arbitrary. For this case combine Eqs. (6.111) into a single equation which relates ε_{ij} to τ_{ij}, τ_{kk}, and T.

6.32. For τ_{ij} expressed as a function of coordinates x_i and time t, the equation of equilibrium was obtained in Chapter 2 as

$$\left. \frac{\partial \tau_{ij}(x_i, t)}{\partial x_i} \right|_t = 0$$

If τ_{ij} is expressed as a function of x_i and *reduced* time ξ, this equation will take on a different form. Use the chain rule of differentiation and the definition of ξ to obtain this different form. Use this same chain rule to convert the strain–displacement relation

$$\varepsilon_{ij} = \frac{1}{2}\left[\left.\frac{\partial u_i(x_i, t)}{\partial x_j}\right|_t + \left.\frac{\partial u_j(x_i, t)}{\partial x_i}\right|_t \right]$$

to its proper form for u_i expressed in terms of x_i and ξ.

Introduction to Nonlinear Viscoelastic Behavior: Creep

7.1 INTRODUCTION

Creep strain curves for metals, plastics, rock, ice, and some other materials often exhibit a highly nonlinear dependence on stress. Accordingly, the linear viscoelastic constitutive laws presented previously, where strain was linearly related to stress, are then not applicable for such materials. Furthermore, the Laplace transformation is unfortunately usually not applicable for such cases.

In Part A we first discuss several nonlinear, one-dimensional constitutive laws which are formulated by an analysis of creep data curves obtained at *constant stress* and *temperature*. We then obtain nonlinear viscoelastic model representations for *variable stress* by postulating generalizations in accordance with the so-called "strain-hardening" and "time-hardening" hypotheses. In Part B we introduce some classical *multidimensional*, nonlinear viscoelastic constitutive laws.

We wish to caution the reader that although the nonlinear constitutive laws introduced in this chapter are widely used, various other laws are also to be found in the literature. Furthermore, it should be understood that nonlinear viscoelasticity is still a "developing" discipline, and accordingly, one can expect that some of the concepts to be presented may undergo some modification.*

---

* The formulations in this chapter are usually referred to as "creep" in the engineering literature. However, we shall employ this term *only for constant stress* conditions, so as to be consistent with our definition of a "creep test." For variable stress conditions we shall use the designation "nonlinear viscoelasticity." If plastic deformation is also included, then the designation "viscoplasticity" is more appropriate; we will discuss this topic in Chapter 8.

PART A
NONLINEAR VISCOELASTIC BEHAVIOR IN ONE DIMENSION

7.2 CREEP LAWS FOR CONSTANT STRESS; GENERAL ASPECTS

In previous discussions of creep in Section 4.5 and also in Section VII.11 of Appendix VII, we considered (see Fig. 4.11) the strain arising over time resulting from a constant uniaxial stress τ_0 while the temperature was maintained constant at T_0. The development of strain consisted of an "instantaneous" elastic (and possibly some plastic) response. This was followed by three periods of deformation characterized respectively by decreasing strain rate, constant strain rate, and increasing strain rate. These periods were identified, respectively, as *primary, secondary,* and *tertiary* creep. As is commonly done in engineering practice, we shall assume here that creep strain has *not* been accumulating for a sufficient amount of time to have entered the tertiary period.[*] Additionally, we shall assume that the stress τ_0 is below the yield stress corresponding to the temperature T_0. As a result, we can assume that the initial instantaneous response is entirely elastic. All told, we shall seek a mathematical representation of the idealized creep curve shown in Fig. 7.1.

For this purpose, we shall express the strain due to constant uniaxial stress τ_0 as a superposition of three components. That is,

$$\varepsilon(t) = \varepsilon_e + \varepsilon_s(t) + \varepsilon_t(t), \qquad t > 0 \tag{7.1}$$

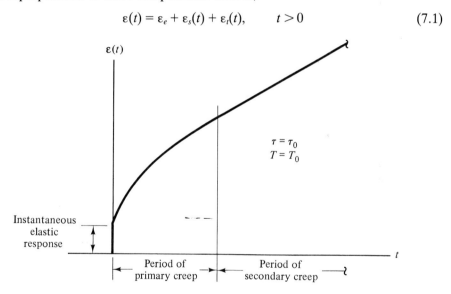

Figure 7.1 Idealized creep curve.

---

[*] Tertiary creep can be studied by introducing a *damage variable* which represents the formation of microscopic voids, but this active field of current research is beyond the scope of this book. For information on this topic, see L. M. Kachanov, *Introduction to Continuum Damage Mechanics,* (Amsterdam: Martinus Nijhoff Publishers, 1986). For recent trends in this and other aspects of creep mechanics, see *Creep of Engineering Materials and Structures,* G. Bernasconi and G. Piatti (eds.) (London: Applied Science Pub. Ltd., 1979), and also *Creep in Structures,* A. Ponter and D. Hayhurst (eds.) (New York: Springer-Verlag, 1981).

where

$$\varepsilon_e \equiv \text{elastic strain component}$$

$$\varepsilon_s(t) \equiv \text{steady creep strain component}$$

$$\varepsilon_t(t) \equiv \text{transient creep strain component}$$

The elastic strain ε_e above is independent of time; the steady creep component $\varepsilon_s(t)$ is *linear* in t, giving a *constant* steady creep strain rate; and finally, the transient component, $\varepsilon_t(t)$, is some function of time which is zero at $t = 0$ and which in the limit as $t \to \infty$ has a *zero time derivative*. Note particularly that $\varepsilon_t(t)$ and $\varepsilon_s(t)$ act over *all* time t, but that $\varepsilon_t(t)$ should dominate during the primary creep period shown in Fig. 7.1, whereas $\varepsilon_s(t)$ should dominate during the secondary creep period shown in the figure. We shall express the aforementioned three strain components in terms of τ_0 and t in the following way:

$$\varepsilon_e = f_e(\tau_0)$$

$$\varepsilon_s = f_s(\tau_0)\, t \tag{7.2}$$

$$\varepsilon_t = f_t(\tau_0)\, g(t)$$

The stress functions $f_e(\tau_0)$, $f_s(\tau_0)$, and $f_t(\tau_0)$ and the time function $g(t)$ above may be expressed in a large variety of monotonically increasing forms for various nonlinear viscoelastic materials. However, as noted above, we require that $g(0) = \dot{g}(\infty) = 0$. In the ensuing discussion, we consider a number of such expressions.

For purposes of comparison, we first reconsider *linear* viscoelastic materials represented by spring–dashpot models. In this case the functions $f_e(\tau_0)$, $f_s(\tau_0)$, and $f_t(\tau_0)$ are linear in τ_0, and $g(t)$ is expressed in terms of exponentials. As an example, consider the linear four-parameter fluid discussed in Section 6.3. From Eq. (6.38) we see that in this case

$$f_e(\tau_0) = \frac{\tau_0}{E_1} \qquad \text{(a)}$$

$$f_s(\tau_0) = \frac{\tau_0}{\eta_1} \qquad \text{(b)}$$

$$\tag{7.3}$$

$$f_t(\tau_0) = \frac{\tau_0}{E_2} \qquad \text{(c)}$$

$$g(t) = 1 - \exp\left(\frac{-t}{t_\varepsilon}\right) \qquad \text{(d)}$$

where in Eq. (7.3d), t_ε is the *retardation time* of strain. Note that as required, $g(0) = \dot{g}(\infty) = 0$.

The instantaneous elastic response is frequently *linear* in τ_0 even for materials exhibiting nonlinear creep. Hence we shall always simply set $f_e(\tau_0) = \tau_0/E$ as in Eq. (7.3a) but will examine in some detail various forms for the other functions in Eqs. (7.2), namely $f_s(\tau_0)$, $f_t(\tau_0)$, and $g(t)$.

7.3 STEADY CREEP; CONSTANT STRESS

We consider first the *steady creep function* $f_s(\tau_0)$. Three expressions have been widely used, each involving two material parameters. These pairs of material parameters generally will vary with the temperature, which for now has been assumed constant. The three expressions are given as follows:

$$f_s(\tau_0) = A\tau_0^n \qquad (a)$$

$$f_s(\tau_0) = B e^{\alpha \tau_0} \qquad (b) \qquad\qquad (7.4)$$

$$f_s(\tau_0) = C \sinh(\beta \tau_0) \qquad (c)$$

Using the first of the expressions above, we have for the steady creep component

$$\varepsilon_s(t) = A \tau_0^n t \qquad\qquad (7.5)$$

where A is a *reciprocal viscosity coefficient* and where n is called the *stress power*. This formulation is called the *stress power* law and is the most widely used equation for the steady creep component. Accordingly, we shall focus most of our attention on this law. We point out first that this law is easily extended to the three-dimensional case, and we shall do this in Part B. Second, we note that with appropriate values of A and n it will generally fit experimental data quite well except at *high stress* levels. At these stresses the plot of $\log f_s(\tau_0)$ versus $\log \tau_0$ may deviate from the straight line required by Eq. (7.4a). For such elevated stress levels, the steady creep function (7.4b) may, with appropriate values of B and α, give a better fit with experimental data. The resulting creep law in that case is called the stress *exponential* law and is given as

$$\varepsilon_s(\tau_0) = B e^{\alpha \tau_0} t \qquad\qquad (7.6)$$

To cover the entire range of τ_0 there is the possibility of a combined exponential law and power law with three material parameters. However, the added complexity attending such a formulation is frequently not justified. The function given by Eq. (7.4c) is closely related to the stress exponential function. The corresponding law called the *hyperbolic sine law*

$$\varepsilon_s(\tau_0) = C \sinh(\beta \tau_0) t \qquad\qquad (7.7)$$

has some physical justification since it may be deduced from microscopic considerations.[*] We note finally that both of the laws given by Eqs. (7.6) and (7.7) are not convenient for extension to multidimensional forms, and in order to limit the complexity of our development these laws will be considered no further here.

Getting back to the stress power law, as given by Eq. (7.5), we note that in

---

[*] Equations (7.5), (7.6), and (7.7) are often referred to, respectively, as the Norton–Bailey, Ludwik, and Prandtl–Nadai steady creep laws. A modified form of the Ludwik law is attributed to Soderberg. These laws have also been attributed to others. For further information, see A. J. Kennedy, *Process of Creep and Fatigue in Metals* (New York: John Wiley & Sons, Inc., 1963), Chap. 4. Also, for a three-parameter law, see F. Garofalo, *Fundamentals of Creep and Creep-Rupture in Metals* (New York: Macmillan Publishing Company, 1965), Chap. 3.

order to get real negative strain for a compressive stress the power n must be restricted to odd, positive integers (i.e., $n = 1, 3, 5, \ldots$). Since n is obtained by curve fitting, it will rarely be precisely an odd positive integer. Consequently, Eq. (7.5) is sometimes rewritten as

$$\varepsilon_s(t) = A |\tau_0|^n (\operatorname{sgn} \tau_0) t \qquad (7.8)$$

where n is now any positive number and $\operatorname{sgn} \tau_0$ is the *signum* function, defined as

$$\operatorname{sgn} \tau_0 = \begin{cases} -1 & \tau_0 < 0 \\ 0 & \tau_0 = 0 \\ +1 & \tau_0 > 0 \end{cases} = 2[u(\tau_0)] - 1 \qquad (7.9)$$

where $[u(\tau_0)]$ is the unit step function in *stress*. Another alternate and possibly more convenient form for the power law (7.5) is given as

$$\varepsilon_s(t) = \left(\frac{\tau_0}{\lambda_c}\right)^n t \qquad (7.10)$$

where now as $n \to 1$ the creep parameter λ_c approaches the linear viscous coefficient in tension.* Again, to allow for n to be any positive number as may result from curve fitting, we can modify Eq. (7.10) just as we modified Eq. (7.5) by once more employing the signum function so as to allow for negative strain. Thus we have, in place of Eq. (7.10),

$$\varepsilon_s(t) = \left(\frac{|\tau_0|}{\lambda_c}\right)^n (\operatorname{sgn} \tau_0) t \qquad (7.11)$$

Note, if $\tau_0 > 0$, Eq. (7.11) reduces to Eq. (7.10).

Now looking back at the four forms of the power law thus far presented, Eqs. (7.5), (7.8), (7.10), and (7.11), you will notice that the dimensions of A in the first two of these equations and the dimensions of λ_c in the last two of these equations are rather inconvenient. This is so because they will involve the power n which varies with the material. To overcome this difficulty, one sees in the literature still another form of the power law:

$$\varepsilon_s(t) = A_r \left(\frac{\tau_0}{\tau_r}\right)^n t \qquad n = 1, 3, 5, \ldots \qquad (7.12)$$

where τ_r is any convenient reference stress (it is *not* a material constant). Now the dimension of A_r is simply $\sec^{-1}$ or more commonly hr^{-1}. Again, Eq. (7.12) may easily be modified for the case of arbitrary positive n to account properly for negative stress.

Of the various forms of stress power law presented in this section, we shall

---

* You may recall that in Chapter 6 the linear viscous coefficient in tension was designated as η, and that in Chapter 5 the symbol λ was used for the linear elastic Lamé constant. We have used the notation λ_c for the creep parameter to avoid confusion with the Lamé constant.

TABLE 7.1 Steady Creep Constants[a]

	Type 316 Stainless Steel		Aluminum Alloy 1100, 500°F
	1300°F	1500°F	
n	3.64	3.50	4.55
λ_c (lb/in.^{2}-hr$^{1/n}$)	19.18×10^4	7.86×10^4	3.64×10^3

[a] Determined from data in F. Garofalo, *Fundamentals of Creep and Creep-Rupture in Metals* (New York: Macmillan Publishing Company, 1965), p. 52. Another good source of creep data for metals is F. K. G. Odqvist, *Mathematical Theory of Creep and Creep Rupture* (Oxford: Clarendon Press, 1974), Chap. 15.

generally use Eq. (7.10) for reasons of physical and mathematical simplicity. However, when negative stresses occur, it may become necessary to use Eq. (7.11). We have presented in Table 7.1 typical values for λ_c and n for a stainless steel at two different temperatures and for an aluminum alloy. You should note from this table that as temperature is increased, n decreases slightly while λ_c^n decreases greatly.

We have plotted Eq. (7.10) in Fig. 7.2, with axes ε_s/t and τ_0/λ_c, for various odd integer values of the stress power n. You will note that all the curves cross at points $(0,0)$ and $(1,1)$ of the plot. The slopes at these points are given as follows:

$$\frac{d(\varepsilon_s/t)}{d(\tau_0/\lambda_c)} = \begin{cases} 1 & \text{at } \dfrac{\tau_0}{\lambda_c} = 0 & \text{for } n = 1 \\ 0 & \text{at } \dfrac{\tau_0}{\lambda_c} = 0 & \text{for } n = 3, 5, 7, \ldots \\ n & \text{at } \dfrac{\tau_0}{\lambda_c} = 1 & \text{for } n = 1, 3, 5, 7, \ldots \end{cases} \qquad (7.13)$$

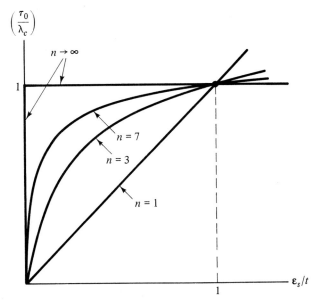

Figure 7.2 Plot of stress power law.

Also, note in Fig. 7.2 that as pointed out previously, the case for $n = 1$ corresponds to linear viscous behavior. In addition, note for the limiting case where $n \to \infty$ that the strain is zero for $\tau_0 < \lambda_c$ [i.e., for $(\tau_0/\lambda_c) < 1$] and has an indeterminate value for $(\tau_0/\lambda_c) = 1$. Clearly this case corresponds to the rigid, perfectly plastic case set forth in Chapter 4. A problem formulated with these two extreme cases (i.e., $n = 1$ and $n = \infty$) often can be solved analytically. The resulting solution curves in many instances will *bracket* the desired solution involving some finite nonunitary value of n for which numerical calculations may be required. This bracketing capability can then give us a valuable check on our numerical calculations.

For the sake of completeness we will now prove rigorously that as $n \to \infty$, the power function does in fact approach the rectangular form shown in Fig. 7.2. First note that from Eq. (7.10) with $n = 1, 3, 5, \ldots$ the strain ε_s will be negative when the stress is negative. Accordingly, the curves shown in Fig. 7.2 extend as odd functions into the negative range of ε_s/t. Now rewrite Eq. (7.10) as

$$\frac{\tau_0}{\lambda_c} = \left(\frac{\varepsilon_s}{t}\right)^{1/n}, \qquad n = 1, 3, 5, \ldots$$

Since $\varepsilon_s = |\varepsilon_s|\,\mathrm{sgn}\,\varepsilon_s$ (see Problem 7.3), this equation becomes

$$\frac{\tau_0}{\lambda_c} = \left(\frac{|\varepsilon_s|}{t}\right)^{1/n}(\mathrm{sgn}\,\varepsilon_s)^{1/n} = \left(\frac{|\varepsilon_s|}{t}\right)^{1/n}\mathrm{sgn}\,\varepsilon_s$$

Now take the limit

$$\lim_{n \to \infty}\frac{\tau_0}{\lambda_c} = \mathrm{sgn}\,\varepsilon_s \lim_{n \to \infty}\left(\frac{|\varepsilon_s|}{t}\right)^{1/n} = \mathrm{sgn}\,\varepsilon_s$$

We have thus obtained the rectangular form shown in Fig. 7.2 for $n \to \infty$, with the appropriate extension as an odd function into the negative range of ε_s.

We shall now perform some simple calculations involving stress power law (7.10), in order to develop some feeling for the numbers involved.

Example 7.1

Answer the following questions for the materials and temperatures indicated in Table 7.1. The melting point T_m for the stainless steel is 2500°F and for the aluminum alloy it is 935°F.

(a) Would you expect creep to be significant in these materials at these temperatures?

To answer this question, we must compute the various T/T_m ratios using the absolute scale. Thus for:

$$\text{Steel at 1300°F:} \quad \frac{T}{T_m} = \frac{1760°R}{2960°R} = 0.595$$

$$\text{Steel at 1500°F:} \quad \frac{T}{T_m} = \frac{1960°R}{2960°R} = 0.662$$

$$\text{Aluminum at 500°F:} \quad \frac{T}{T_m} = \frac{960°R}{1395°R} = 0.688$$

These T/T_m ratios are well in excess of one-third in all three cases, and thus creep should be very significant in each case.

(b) Consider a 10,000-psi tensile stress on the steel. What are the steady creep strain rates at 1300°F and at 1500°F?

Using Eq. (7.10) and Table 7.1, we get after differentiation with respect to time:

$$\text{At } 1300°F: \quad \dot{\varepsilon}_s = \left(\frac{\tau_0}{\lambda_c}\right)^n = \left(\frac{10^4}{19.18 \times 10^4}\right)^{3.64} = 0.000021 \text{ hr}^{-1}$$

$$\text{At } 1500°F: \quad \dot{\varepsilon}_s = \left(\frac{10^4}{7.86 \times 10^4}\right)^{3.50} = 0.000735 \text{ hr}^{-1}$$

Thus an increase of only 11% in the absolute temperature caused the creep rate to increase by *a factor of 34*. Note that at 1300°F it would take 19.8 days for the strain to reach 1%, whereas at 1500°F it would take only 13.6 hours.

(c) Consider the steel at 1500°F. What is the creep strain rate for 20,000 psi? Again using Eq. (7.10) and Table 7.1, we get

$$\text{At } 20,000 \text{ psi}: \quad \dot{\varepsilon}_s = \left(\frac{2 \times 10^4}{7.86 \times 10^4}\right)^{3.50} = 0.00831 \text{ hr}^{-1}$$

Thus, when the stress is doubled, $\dot{\varepsilon}_s$ increases by a *factor of 11.3*. Note that now the strain $\varepsilon_s = 0.01$ requires only 1.20 hours.

(d) Now consider the aluminum alloy. What stress τ_0 would produce the same creep rate as for the steel at 1500°F with a stress τ_0 equal to 10,000 psi?

In this case

$$0.000735 = \left(\frac{\tau_0}{3.64 \times 10^3}\right)^{4.55}$$

and therefore

$$\tau_0 = (0.000735)^{1/4.55}(3.64 \times 10^3) = 745 \text{ psi}$$

Thus, although the T/T_m ratios are fairly close in these two cases (i.e., 0.662 versus 0.688 for a 4% difference) the stress required in the steel is *13.4 times* the stress required in the aluminum alloy for the same creep rate. Clearly, this stainless steel is much more resistant to creep than this aluminum alloy. It has been suggested that a better basis for comparing stresses in different materials is the use of the ratio τ_0/E rather than τ_0 itself. In the present case this would reduce the 13.4 ratio by a factor of approximately 3.

7.4 TRANSIENT AND TOTAL CREEP; CONSTANT STRESS

Let us now consider the *transient* creep component law at constant stress which we now rewrite

$$\varepsilon_t = f_t(\tau_0) g(t) \tag{7.14}$$

As in the case of the steady creep stress function, the transient creep stress function $f_t(\tau_0)$ may also be expressed as a stress power function. That is,

$$f_t(\tau_0) = \left(\frac{\tau_0}{\mu_c}\right)^p \tag{7.15}$$

Here again, if we do not introduce the signum function, p is an odd positive integer that is usually found to lie in the interval $1 \le p \le n$, where n is the power used in the steady creep stress power law. As for the time function $g(t)$ in Eq. (7.14), various expressions have been proposed and we give the following two:[*]

$$g(t) = 1 - \exp\left(\frac{-t}{t_\varepsilon}\right) \qquad \text{(a)}$$

$$g(t) = t^{1/q} \qquad \text{(b)}$$

(7.16)

The first time function in the above is the same time exponential function encountered in linear viscoelasticity [see Eq. (7.3d)], and as noted previously, $g(0) = \dot{g}(\infty) = 0$. This time function thus has the behavior expected of a transient, and in addition it is *bounded* as $t \rightarrow \infty$ since $g(\infty) = 1$. When the time exponential function [Eq. (7.16a)] is joined with the stress power function [Eq. (7.15)], we then have for the transient strain component $\varepsilon_t(t)$

$$\varepsilon_t(t) = \left(\frac{\tau_0}{\mu_c}\right)^p \left[1 - \exp\left(\frac{-t}{t_\varepsilon}\right)\right] \qquad (7.17)$$

From this formulation we see that the asymptotic behavior is given by the nonlinear elastic relation

$$\varepsilon_t(\infty) = \left(\frac{\tau_0}{\mu_c}\right)^p \qquad (7.18)$$

It then follows from Eq. (7.18) that when $p = 1$, the transient creep constant μ_c represents an elastic modulus. It is thus not surprising that both μ_c and p are *relatively insensitive* to temperature. However, since the retardation time (t_ε) is the ratio of a viscosity coefficient to an elastic modulus, t_ε is *very sensitive* to temperature, as was the viscosity coefficient λ_c in the steady creep equation.

Let us next consider the second of our $g(t)$ functions [Eq. (7.16b)]. In conjunction with Eq. (7.15), the transient strain becomes[†]

$$\varepsilon_t(t) = \left(\frac{\tau_0}{\mu_c}\right)^p t^{1/q} \qquad (7.19)$$

This formulation is sometimes used, because of its simplicity, instead of Eq. (7.17), which involves the time exponential expression. Experimental evidence indicates that generally $q > 1$. It then follows from Eq. (7.16b) that $g(0)$ and that $\dot{g}(\infty) = 0$, which is clearly characteristic of transient behavior. However, note that $g(\infty) \rightarrow \infty$ and accordingly, the asymptotic behavior cannot be interpreted as nonlinear elastic as was the case for Eq. (7.17). Since transient creep is usually bounded, the time power function may yield a poor fit with experimental data at large times. By contrast, the exponential time function is applicable over a wide range of time, although it tends to lose some accuracy at very early times.

In using either the exponential time function or the time power function,

---

[*] Equation (7.16a) is usually attributed to McVetty, and Eq. (7.16b) is a generalization of a law first proposed by Andrade. See A. J. Kennedy, *Process of Creep and Fatigue in Metals* (New York: John Wiley & Sons, Inc., 1963), Chapter 4.

[†] The μ_c in Eq. (7.17) will not in general be equal to the μ_c in Eq. (7.19). In fact, they will have different dimensions if time is not rewritten in nondimensional form.

greater accuracy can be achieved by employing a *summation* of transient creep terms. That is,

$$\varepsilon_t(t) = \sum_{i=1}^{N} \varepsilon_{ti}(t) \tag{7.20}$$

Equations (7.17) and (7.19) can in this way be generalized in the following manner:

$$\varepsilon_t(t) = \sum_{i=1}^{N} \left(\frac{\tau_0}{\mu_{ci}}\right)^{p_i} \left[1 - \exp\left(\frac{-t}{t_{\varepsilon i}}\right)\right] \qquad \text{(a)}$$

$$\varepsilon_t(t) = \sum_{i=1}^{N} \left(\frac{\tau_0}{\mu_{ci}}\right)^{p_i} t^{1/q_i} \qquad \text{(b)} \tag{7.21}$$

In the case of Eq. (7.21a), two terms will often give a very nice fit with experimental data over the full range of time.

We may now set forth a useful equation for the *total* creep strain ε_c for constant stress by employing Eqs. (7.10) and (7.17). Thus

$$\varepsilon_c(t) = \varepsilon_s(t) + \varepsilon_t(t) = \left(\frac{\tau_0}{\lambda_c}\right)^n t + \left(\frac{\tau_0}{\mu_c}\right)^p \left[1 - \exp\left(\frac{-t}{t_\varepsilon}\right)\right] \tag{7.22}$$

As pointed out earlier, it is usually the case that $p < n$. However, a considerable simplification occurs if we set $p = n$ in the equation above. This equation can then be written simply as

$$\varepsilon_c(t) = \left(\frac{\tau_0}{\mu_c}\right)^n J(t) \tag{7.23}$$

where $J(t)$ is the nondimensional creep compliance function*

$$J(t) = \gamma t + \left[1 - \exp\left(\frac{-t}{t_\varepsilon}\right)\right] \tag{7.24}$$

with

$$\gamma = \left(\frac{\mu_c}{\lambda_c}\right)^n \tag{7.25}$$

A more accurate albeit more complicated creep law can be obtained by employing Eq. (7.21a) for $\varepsilon_t(t)$ using $N = 2$, $p_1 = p_2 = n$, $\mu_1 = \mu_2 = \mu_c$, $t_{\varepsilon 1} = t_\varepsilon$, and $t_{\varepsilon 2} = t_\varepsilon/10$. We again get Eq. (7.23) except that for $J(t)$ we now have

$$J(t) = \gamma t + 2 - \exp\left(\frac{-t}{t_\varepsilon}\right) - \exp\left(\frac{-10t}{t_\varepsilon}\right) \tag{7.26}$$

This particular formulation is employed in Fig. 7.3 for the plot of ε_c versus t for aluminum alloy D-16T at $T = 150°C$ and at two different stresses.† Note that metric units have been used with the kilogram as the unit of force. Clearly, a good fit with experimental data has been achieved over the entire time span.

---

* We shall discuss $J(t)$ further in the next section. Note that, in contrast with the usual practice for linear viscoelastic materials, $J(t)$ here does *not* include the instantaneous elastic response.

† For the data source, see Y. N. Rabotnov, *Creep Problems in Structural Members* (Amsterdam: North-Holland Publishing Co., 1969), p. 227.

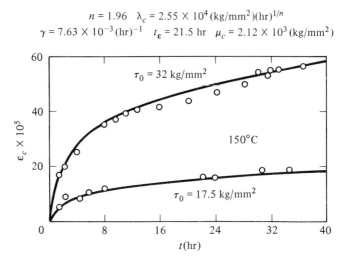

$$n = 1.96 \quad \lambda_c = 2.55 \times 10^4 \, (\text{kg/mm}^2)(\text{hr})^{1/n}$$
$$\gamma = 7.63 \times 10^{-3} \, (\text{hr})^{-1} \quad t_\varepsilon = 21.5 \, \text{hr} \quad \mu_c = 2.12 \times 10^3 \, (\text{kg/mm}^2)$$

Figure 7.3 Aluminum alloy D-16T fit with two transient terms.

For long time periods it may be permissible to approximate the total creep entirely by using only the steady creep component. That is,

$$\varepsilon_c(t) \approx \left(\frac{\tau_0}{\lambda_c}\right)^n t \tag{7.27}$$

On the other hand, for short times it may suffice as an approximation to use for the total creep only the transient component. And if we select the time power law (7.19), we have

$$\varepsilon_c(t) \approx \left(\frac{\tau_0}{\mu_c}\right)^p t^{1/q} \tag{7.28}$$

Note that having used Eq. (7.28) for short times one can get the approximation for long time from this formula by formally setting $p = n$, $\mu_c = \lambda_c$, and $q = 1$. Thus a solution to a problem based on Eq. (7.28) also contains the solution based on Eq. (7.27).

This completes our discussion of one-dimensional, nonlinear, viscoelastic material behavior for constant stress. We now consider one-dimensional nonlinear viscoelastic behavior with variable time-dependent stress.

7.5 NONLINEAR VISCOELASTIC LAWS FOR VARIABLE STRESS; STRAIN-HARDENING HYPOTHESIS

In this section we propose a procedure for generalizing the constant stress case of the previous sections to that of time-dependent stress $\tau(t)$. The most commonly used hypothesis requires that for the case of variable stress we express the instantaneous creep *rate* as some function of the instantaneous creep strain as well as the instantaneous stress. That is,

$$\dot{\varepsilon}(t) = f\left[\varepsilon(t), \tau(t)\right] \tag{7.29}$$

You will note in this formulation that there is no *explicit dependence on time*. Since $\varepsilon(t)$ may also possibly vary with one space coordinate, the dot in general represents the partial derivative $\partial/\partial t$. Nevertheless, in many one-dimensional examples there will be no variation with a space coordinate and $\partial/\partial t$ becomes the ordinary derivative d/dt for such cases. In Eq. (7.29), $\varepsilon(t)$ may refer either *to the total creep strain* $\varepsilon_c(t)$ *or to some component of creep strain* [i.e., $\varepsilon_s(t)$ or $\varepsilon_t(t)$], but in either case the *elastic strain is excluded*. This equation is called the *strain-hardening hypothesis. It implies that if one has manipulated a creep law obtained for a particular stress $\tau_1(t)$ (a constant stress τ_0 could be such a stress) into the form of Eq. (7.29), this form of the creep law is still valid for any stress variation $\tau(t)$.* When Eq. (7.29) is applicable, we also say that the creep deformation is given by a *mechanical equation of state.* [*] This means that the state is uniquely defined by the instantaneous values of ε and τ, with no consideration given to the manner in which the strain has accumulated.

To understand why the strain-hardening designation has been used for Eq. (7.29), consider briefly the transient creep component for constant stress as given for example by Eq. (7.17) of the preceding section. This creep component plays a most prominent role during the *early* period of primary creep, where the strain-time curve is steep (see Fig. 7.1) but which then flattens rapidly as time progresses. This means that the strain rate during the period of primary creep decreases with time. Now with $\tau(t)$ constant in Eq. (7.29), we can conclude that this decrease in strain rate is entirely due to the accumulation of strain—hence the designation "strain hardening." The strain-hardening hypothesis and the associated mechanical equation of state appear to work well for *structurally stable* materials, that is, for those materials which experience relatively minor changes in microscopic structure during creep deformation. We now consider four cases: the use of this hypothesis to generalize to variable stress, (A) the steady creep component, (B) the exponential transient creep component, (C) the total creep, and (D) the power transient creep component.

Case A: Steady Creep Component

We shall illustrate the use of the strain-hardening law [Eq. (7.29)] by first applying it to the *steady creep component power law* for constant stress as given by Eq. (7.10). Differentiating that equation with respect to time, we get

$$\dot{\varepsilon}_s(t) = \left(\frac{\tau_0}{\lambda_c}\right)^n \tag{7.30}$$

We shall consider the law above as a special case of strain hardening with the strain absent, although strictly speaking there is no "hardening" in this case. We may thus

---

[*] For further discussion on the mechanical equation of state, see J. Lubahn and R. Felgar, *Plasticity and Creep of Metals* (John Wiley & Sons, Inc., 1961), Chap. 7.

postulate that this equation is *also valid* in this form for the case of *variable stress*. That is,

$$\dot{\varepsilon}_s(t) = \left(\frac{\tau(t)}{\lambda_c}\right)^n \qquad (7.31)$$

or equivalently,

$$\varepsilon_s(t) = \int_{0^-}^{t} \left(\frac{\tau(t')}{\lambda_c}\right)^n dt' \qquad (7.32)$$

The viscoelastic behavior as given by the two equations above may be represented by a nonlinear viscous (i.e., non-Newtonian) model as shown in Fig. 7.4, where the slash indicates a nonlinear dependence on stress.

We now illustrate the use of Eqs. (7.30) and (7.31) by considering the *stress relaxation* test procedure.

Example 7.2

Consider a material in which the elastic strain component is linear elastic, the steady creep component is nonlinear viscous, and the transient creep component is negligible. Equation (7.1) then becomes, with the use of Eq. (7.32),

$$\varepsilon(t) = \frac{\tau(t)}{E} + \int_{0^-}^{t} \left(\frac{\tau(t')}{\lambda_c}\right)^n dt' \qquad n = 1, 3, 5, \ldots, \quad t \ge 0^- \qquad (a)$$

which may be represented by the nonlinear Maxwell model given in Fig. 7.5. [Note that for a constant stress τ_0 the solution to Eq. (a) gives a creep curve of constant slope, where this slope is proportional to τ_0^n.] Determine for this material the stress history $\tau(t)$ due to the relaxation test procedure $\varepsilon(t) = \varepsilon_0[u(t)]$.

It will be more convenient to use 0^+ rather than 0^- as the origin of time, and thus we require $\tau(0^+)$. Setting $t = 0^+$ in Eq. (a) and noting that the integral then vanishes since the integrand does not contain a singularity function, we get

$$\tau(0^+) = E\varepsilon(0^+) = E\varepsilon_0 \qquad (b)$$

which also follows by inspection of the model in Fig. 7.5. We now differentiate Eq. (a) to obtain the differential equation

$$\dot{\varepsilon}(t) = \frac{\dot{\tau}(t)}{E} + \left(\frac{\tau(t)}{\lambda_c}\right)^n \qquad n = 1, 3, 5, \ldots, \quad t \ge 0^+ \qquad (c)$$

But for $t \ge 0^+$ we have $\varepsilon(t) = \varepsilon_0$ and thus $\dot{\varepsilon}(t) = 0$, and Eq. (c) becomes

$$0 = \frac{\dot{\tau}(t)}{E} + \left(\frac{\tau(t)}{\lambda_c}\right)^n \qquad (d)$$

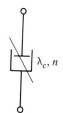

λ_c, n

Figure 7.4 Non-Newtonian viscous model–a representation of the steady creep component.

Figure 7.5 Nonlinear Maxwell model–transient creep component neglected.

which may be expressed in separated form as

$$\frac{d\tau}{\tau^n} = -\frac{E}{\lambda_c^n}\,dt \qquad n = 1, 3, 5, \ldots, \quad t \geq 0^+ \tag{e}$$

We have already shown in Chapter 6 that the solution to Eq. (d) in the linear case $n = 1$ [see Eq. (6.20) with η replaced by λ_c] is given as the exponential

$$\tau(t) = \varepsilon_0\,E\,e^{-(E/\lambda_c)t} \qquad n = 1, \quad t \geq 0^+ \tag{f}$$

For $n = 3, 5, \ldots$ we integrate Eq. (e) from $t' = 0^+$ to t and get with the use of Eq. (b),

$$\int_{E\varepsilon_0}^{\tau(t)} \frac{d\tau}{\tau^n} = -\frac{1}{n-1}\left[\frac{1}{\tau^{n-1}} - \frac{1}{(E\varepsilon_0)^{n-1}}\right] = -\frac{E}{\lambda_c^n}\,t \tag{g}$$

We thus obtain the solution

$$\tau(t) = \left[\frac{1}{(E\varepsilon_0)^{n-1}} + \frac{(n-1)E}{\lambda_c^n}\,t\right]^{-1/(n-1)} \qquad n = 3, 5, 7, \ldots, \quad t \geq 0^+ \tag{h}$$

Note that $\tau(0^+) = E\varepsilon_0$ as required and $\tau(\infty) \to 0$, and also that $d\tau(t)/dt < 0$ for finite t, which indicates monotonic stress relaxation. Also note that Eq. (f) *cannot* be reached by simply setting $n = 1$ in Eq. (h).

Case B: Time Exponential Transient Creep Component

Now consider the more complicated case of a *transient* creep component in the form of a time exponential. We start by restating the transient creep strain component for constant stress as set forth in Eq. (7.17):

$$\varepsilon_t(t) = \left(\frac{\tau_0}{\mu_c}\right)^p\left[1 - \exp\left(\frac{-t}{t_\varepsilon}\right)\right] \tag{7.33}$$

Hence

$$\dot{\varepsilon}_t(t) = \frac{1}{t_\varepsilon}\left(\frac{\tau_0}{\mu_c}\right)^p \exp\left(\frac{-t}{t_\varepsilon}\right) \tag{7.34}$$

We wish to put Eq. (7.34) in a form consistent with the strain-hardening hypothesis. For this purpose, we eliminate $\exp(-t/t_\varepsilon)$ and thus also t from Eq. (7.34) by using Eq. (7.33). Thus, from Eq. (7.33) we have

$$\exp\left(\frac{-t}{t_\varepsilon}\right) = -\left(\frac{\tau_0}{\mu_c}\right)^{-p} \varepsilon_t(t) + 1$$

Substituting the result above into Eq. (7.34), we then obtain

$$\dot{\varepsilon}_t(t) = \frac{1}{t_\varepsilon}\left(\frac{\tau_0}{\mu_c}\right)^p\left[-\left(\frac{\tau_0}{\mu_c}\right)^{-p} \varepsilon_t(t) + 1\right]$$

and therefore

$$\dot{\varepsilon}_t(t) = -\frac{\varepsilon_t(t)}{t_\varepsilon} + \frac{1}{t_\varepsilon}\left(\frac{\tau_0}{\mu_c}\right)^p \tag{7.35}$$

The equation above now has the desired form of Eq. (7.29) and thus we may now replace τ_0 by $\tau(t)$. Rearranging the result, we get

$$\dot{\varepsilon}_t(t) + \frac{1}{t_\varepsilon}\varepsilon_t(t) = \frac{1}{t_\varepsilon}\left[\frac{\tau(t)}{\mu_c}\right]^p \tag{7.36}$$

Equation (7.36) can be expressed more compactly as

$$Q\,\varepsilon_t = Pf_t(\tau) \tag{7.37}$$

where P, Q is a differential operator pair given as

$$Q = 1 + t_\varepsilon\frac{\partial}{\partial t} \qquad \text{(a)}$$
$$P = 1 \qquad \text{(b)} \tag{7.38}$$

and where $f_t(\tau)$ is the power *function of* $\tau(t)$

$$f_t(\tau) = \left(\frac{\tau}{\mu_c}\right)^p \tag{7.39}$$

On comparing Eqs. (7.37) and (7.38) with the linear viscoelastic relation (6.6) of Chapter 6, we see that the operator pair P, Q is in the form of a Kelvin operator pair, where now the P operator acts on a nonlinear function of stress. We can accordingly represent the *transient viscoelastic behavior given by Eq. (7.36) by a nonlinear Kelvin model* as shown in Fig. 7.6. Note, additionally, when we make the following substitutions in Eq. (7.36):

$$p = 1$$
$$t_\varepsilon = \frac{\eta}{E}$$
$$\mu_c = E$$

we get the linear form of the Kelvin equation as given by Eq. (6.6).

As in the linear case $p = 1$, we may rewrite the left side of Eq. (7.36) as

$$\exp\left(\frac{-t}{t_\varepsilon}\right)\frac{\partial}{\partial t}\left[\exp\left(\frac{-t}{t_\varepsilon}\right)\varepsilon(t)\right]$$

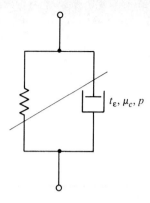

Figure 7.6 Nonlinear Kelvin model–representation of strain-hardened transient creep component.

and thereby obtain the following integral form:

$$\varepsilon_t(t) = \frac{1}{t_\varepsilon} \int_{0^-}^{t} \exp\left(\frac{t'-t}{t_\varepsilon}\right) \left[\frac{\tau(t')}{\mu_c}\right]^p dt' \tag{7.40}$$

We may recast Eq. (7.40) in another useful form by first noting that it may be rewritten as follows:

$$\varepsilon_t(t) = \int_{0^-}^{t} \left[\frac{\partial}{\partial t'} \exp\left(\frac{t'-t}{t_\varepsilon}\right)\right] \left[\frac{\tau(t')}{\mu_c}\right]^p dt'$$

Next, integrate by parts:

$$\varepsilon_t(t) = \left[\frac{\tau(t')}{\mu_c}\right]^p \exp\left(\frac{t'-t}{t_\varepsilon}\right) \Big|_{0^-}^{t} - \int_{0^-}^{t} \exp\left(\frac{t'-t}{t_\varepsilon}\right) \frac{\partial}{\partial t'} \left[\frac{\tau(t')}{\mu_c}\right]^p dt'$$

The first expression on the right side of the equation above is simply $[\tau(t)/\mu_c]^p$ since $\tau(0^-)$ is zero. We may then combine this result with the second expression on the right side of the equation above to form the following equation:

$$\varepsilon_t(t) = \int_{0^-}^{t} \left[1 - \exp\left(\frac{t'-t}{t_\varepsilon}\right)\right] \frac{\partial}{\partial t'} \left[\frac{\tau(t')}{\mu_c}\right]^p dt' \tag{7.41}$$

Equation (7.41) has the proper form for a *hereditary* integral. That is, we can write

$$\varepsilon_t(t) = \int_{0^-}^{t} J(t - t') \frac{\partial}{\partial t'} \left[\frac{\tau(t')}{\mu_c}\right]^p dt' \tag{7.42}$$

where

$$J(t) = 1 - \exp\left(\frac{-t}{t_\varepsilon}\right) \tag{7.43}$$

The material function $J(t)$ given by Eq. (7.43) is a nondimensionalized creep compliance function for a Kelvin material, as can be verified by replacing t_ε by η/E and going back to Eq. (6.40b). This further justifies our representing differential equation (7.36) [or the equivalent integral equations (7.40) and (7.41)] by the nonlinear Kelvin model depicted in Fig. 7.6. We can say that Eq. (7.42) is a *nonlinear hereditary integral* since for the case $p = 1$ we get back to the form of a linear hereditary integral given by Eq. (6.46). The integral in Eq. (7.42) is also called a *modified superposition integral*,* since it may be obtained by superposing step increments of the function $(\tau/\mu_c)^p$ in the same manner that steps in τ were superposed as depicted in Fig. 6.6.

Case C: Total Creep

We wish next to find a nondimensional creep compliance function for the *total* creep ε_c. For this purpose return to Eq. (7.32), which is the integral form of the steady creep component:

$$\varepsilon_s(t) = \int_{0^-}^{t} \left[\frac{\tau(t')}{\lambda_c} \right]^n dt'$$

Now integrate by parts as we did for the transient case. We get as a result

$$\varepsilon_s(t) = \int_{0^-}^{t} (t - t') \frac{\partial}{\partial t'} \left[\frac{\tau(t')}{\lambda_c} \right]^n dt' \qquad (7.44)$$

We now define the total creep $\varepsilon_c(t)$ as the sum of $\varepsilon_t(t)$ as given by Eq. (7.41) and $\varepsilon_s(t)$ as given above. In so doing, we also simplify our result by setting $p = n$ [as we did in Eq. (7.23) for constant stress]. We then get

$$\varepsilon_c(t) = \int_{0^-}^{t} J(t - t') \frac{\partial}{\partial t'} \left[\frac{\tau(t')}{\mu_c} \right]^n dt' \qquad (7.45)$$

where $J(t)$ is the nondimensional creep compliance function defined by Eq. (7.24). Equation (7.45) is a useful nonlinear hereditary integral with a very convenient form. Finally, adding a linear elastic strain component, we get the following formulation for the total strain $\varepsilon(t)$:

$$\varepsilon(t) = \frac{\tau}{E} + \int_{0^-}^{t} J(t - t') \frac{\partial}{\partial t'} \left[\frac{\tau(t')}{\mu_c} \right]^n dt' \qquad (7.46)$$

The behavior expressed by Eq. (7.46) may be represented by the nonlinear Burgers model given in Fig. 7.7.†

In obtaining Eqs. (7.31) and (7.36) we applied the strain-hardening hypothesis to a steady or transient *component* of creep strain, and then Eq. (7.45) for the total creep was obtained by adding the solutions to Eqs. (7.31) and (7.36). For many nonlinear materials (especially metals), one obtains a better fit with experimental data if the procedure is applied to the *total* creep strain at constant stress.‡ For

---

*The modified superposition integral was first introduced by H. Leaderman in *Elastic and Creep Properties of Filamentous Materials and Other High Polymers* (Washington, DC: The Textile Foundation, 1943). It has since been widely used for both metals and nonmetals.

†The model shown in Fig. 7.7 is essentially the one introduced by Marin in 1953. For details, see J. Marin, *Mechanical Behavior of Engineering Materials* (Englewood Cliffs, NJ: Prentice-Hall, Inc., 1962), Chap. 7.

‡Whether the material be linear or nonlinear viscoelastic, this second approach will in general yield a different result. The linear viscoelastic relations presented in Chapter 6 are consistent with the *first* approach.

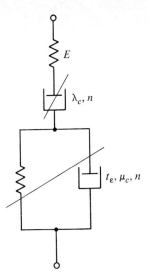

Figure 7.7 Nonlinear Burgers model–representation of total strain.

example, consider the total creep strain at constant stress as given by Eq. (7.23). Inserting Eq. (7.24) for $J(t)$, we have

$$\varepsilon_c(t) = \left(\frac{\tau_0}{\mu_c}\right)^n [\gamma t + 1 - \exp(-t/t_\varepsilon)] \qquad (7.47)$$

You will be asked to show in Problem 7.9 that for variable stress we can say, for Eq. (7.47), upon eliminating the explicit dependence on time in accordance with the strain-hardening hypothesis:

$$\dot{\varepsilon}_c + \frac{\varepsilon_c}{t_\varepsilon} = \left(\gamma + \frac{1}{t_\varepsilon}\right)\left(\frac{\tau}{\mu_c}\right)^n - \gamma\left(\frac{\tau}{\mu_c}\right)^n \ln\left\{\left[\frac{\dot{\varepsilon}_c}{(\tau/\mu_c)^n} - \gamma\right]t_\varepsilon\right\} \qquad (7.48)$$

This formulation is not readily expressible in integral form and is very inconvenient for analytical work.* Fortunately, however, the strain-hardening hypothesis for the total creep ε_c has for some load histories a simple graphical interpretation. We illustrate and discuss this fact in Section 7.7.

Case D: Time Power Transient Creep Component

In Cases A to C of this section we have considered steady and transient creep components, with *stress power* and *exponential time* transient terms. We now finish this section by reconsidering transient creep, again with a *stress power function but*

---

* Equation (7.48) may also be inconvenient for numerical calculations, and it is probably simpler to work directly with strain-hardening hypothesis (7.29). For some information on the use of finite difference and finite element techniques in creep problems, see R. Penny and D. Marriott, *Design for Creep* (New York: McGraw-Hill Book Company, 1971). For more recent information on numerical techniques, see S. Nakazawa, K. Willam, and N. Redelo (eds.), *Advances in Inelastic Analysis* (New York: American Society of Mechanical Engineers, 1987); and also H. Kraus, *Creep Analysis* (New York: John Wiley & Sons, Inc., 1980).

this time multiplied by a time power function. For this purpose we go back to Eq. (7.19):

$$\varepsilon_t(t) = \left(\frac{\tau_0}{\mu_c}\right)^p t^{1/q} \qquad p = 1, 3, 5, \ldots, \quad q > 1 \tag{7.49}$$

We can thus say that

$$\varepsilon_t(t)^q = \left(\frac{\tau_0}{\mu_c}\right)^{pq} t \tag{7.50}$$

and it then follows that

$$\frac{\partial}{\partial t}[\varepsilon_t(t)]^q = \left(\frac{\tau_0}{\mu_c}\right)^{pq} \tag{7.51}$$

which may also be written as

$$\dot{\varepsilon}_t(t) = \frac{1}{q}\left(\frac{\tau_0}{\mu_c}\right)^{pq}[\varepsilon_t(t)]^{-(q-1)} \tag{7.52}$$

From Eq. (7.52) we see that the strain rate decreases as the strain increases, thereby satisfying the strain-hardening hypothesis (7.29). We may thus generalize Eq. (7.51), which is equivalent to Eq. (7.52), by using $\tau(t)$ in place of τ_0 to obtain

$$\boxed{\frac{\partial}{\partial t}[\varepsilon_t(t)]^q = \left[\frac{\tau(t)}{\mu_c}\right]^{pq}} \tag{7.53}$$

The integral forms of Eq. (7.53) follow directly as

$$\varepsilon_t(t) = \left[\int_{0^-}^t \left(\frac{\tau(t')}{\mu_c}\right)^{pq} dt'\right]^{1/q} \tag{7.54}$$

and (on integrating by parts)

$$\varepsilon_t(t) = \left[\int_{0^-}^t (t - t')\frac{\partial}{\partial t'}\left(\frac{\tau(t')}{\mu_c}\right)^{pq} dt'\right]^{1/q} \tag{7.55}$$

Note that as $q \to 1$, Eqs. (7.53), (7.54), and (7.55) take on the same forms as Eqs. (7.31), (7.32), and (7.44), respectively, for the steady creep component, which is in conformity with our remarks at the end of Section 7.4. Equation (7.55) indicates that the *function of strain* ε_t^q is a nonlinear hereditary integral over the history of the *function of stress* $(\tau/\mu_c)^{pq}$ with creep compliance $J(t) = t$. This behavior has no apparent viscoelastic model representation.*

We have seen in this section that applying the strain-hardening hypothesis to the creep components can yield nonlinear hereditary integrals with viscoelastic model interpretations. On the other hand, we have also found that this procedure can in some cases yield nonlinear hereditary integrals with no apparent model representation. Furthermore, if we apply the strain-hardening hypothesis to the total

---

* The equations for case D may be expressed in the formal framework of *fractional calculus*. See K. B. Oldham and J. Spanier, *The Fractional Calculus* (New York: Academic Press, 1974).

creep strain we can get constitutive relations, which are neither expressible in integral form nor representable by viscoelastic models. It should now be apparent that the extension of linear theory to nonlinear theory may be accomplished in many different ways. As yet another example, one can choose to superpose stress (i.e., use *parallel* arrangements of viscoelastic elements) and thereby obtain stress as a nonlinear hereditary integral over the history of a function of strain, with the relaxation modulus function $Y(t)$ in the integrand. A yet completely different approach is to employ a summation of multiple integrals of increasing order, rather than a single integral with a nonlinear integrand. For further details on the many alternative approaches to nonlinear theory, refer to the literature on nonlinear viscoelasticity and nonlinear creep.* In the next section we consider still another variation in the constitutive law, which will be the result of material aging.

7.6 TIME-HARDENING HYPOTHESIS

Some materials experience significant microscopic change during creep. This change may be due to the creep deformation itself or it may be due to some chemical change due to the elevated temperature. In such cases, it may be best to postulate that for variable stress the creep rate at any time t is a function of the instantaneous stress and the time. That is,

$$\dot{\varepsilon}(t) = f[\tau(t), t] \qquad (7.56)$$

This formulation is referred to as the *time-hardening* hypothesis. In the special case of $\tau(t)$ specified as a constant τ_0, we see that Eq. (7.56) indicates that the decrease in strain rate during the primary creep period is entirely due to the passage of time and the associated "aging" of the material—hence the name "time hardening." More generally, the *time-hardening hypothesis implies that if the creep law for an "aging" material for some particular stress function* $\tau_1(t)$ *(usually chosen as the constant stress* τ_0 *) is manipulated into the form of Eq. (7.56), this form of the creep law is also valid for any stress function* $\tau(t)$. A more general approach consists of postulating some combination of strain hardening [Eq. (7.29)] and time hardening [Eq. (7.56)]. Several such generalizations are to be found in the creep mechanics literature (e.g., see Problem 7.16).

It was argued earlier that the *steady* creep strain rate law at constant stress

$$\dot{\varepsilon}_s(t) = \left(\frac{\tau_0}{\lambda_c}\right)^n$$

could be considered a special case of strain hardening with the strain absent and with the required lack of explicit dependence on time. It is *equally true* that the

---

* In particular, see Y. N. Rabotnov, *Creep Problems in Structural Members* (Amsterdam: North-Holland Publishing Co., 1969); F. J. Lockett, *Nonlinear Viscoelastic Solids* (New York: Academic Press, 1972); and W. N. Findley, J. S. Lai, and K. Onaran, *Creep and Relaxation of Nonlinear Viscoelastic Materials* (Amsterdam: North-Holland Publishing Co., 1976).

equation above can be considered a special case of *time hardening* with the explicit dependence on time in this case *missing*. Thus, using the time-hardening hypothesis, we arrive at the same creep law obtained via the strain-hardening hypothesis for variable stress, that is,

$$\dot{\varepsilon}_s(t) = \left(\frac{\tau(t)}{\lambda_c}\right)^n \tag{7.57}$$

This should come as no surprise, since as noted previously, there is in fact no hardening (i.e., no decrease in strain rate) during steady creep at constant stress.

Next we go back to the *exponential form* of the *transient creep strain rate* component given by Eq. (7.34) for the case of constant stress τ_0:

$$\dot{\varepsilon}_t(t) = \frac{1}{t_\varepsilon}\left(\frac{\tau_0}{\mu_c}\right)^p \exp\left(\frac{-t}{t_\varepsilon}\right)$$

We see directly that this equation already contains the explicit dependence on time required by the time-hardening hypothesis. Accordingly, for variable stress, we may replace τ_0 by $\tau(t)$ to obtain the equation

$$\dot{\varepsilon}_t(t) = \frac{1}{t_\varepsilon}\left[\frac{\tau(t)}{\mu_c}\right]^p \exp\left(\frac{-t}{t_\varepsilon}\right) \tag{7.58}$$

This equation may be rewritten as

$$\dot{\varepsilon}_t(t) = \left[\frac{\tau(t)}{\eta(t)}\right]^p \tag{7.59}$$

where

$$\eta(t) = \mu_c t_\varepsilon^{1/p} \exp[t/(pt_\varepsilon)]$$

is a viscosity coefficient which *increases* with time. Hence Eqs. (7.58) and (7.59) may be interpreted as the constitutive law for a nonlinear, viscous, *aging* material. The model representing this behavior is shown in Fig. 7.8, where the letter A in the diagram indicates the aging.

It will again be instructive to obtain integral forms of Eq. (7.58). By direct integration we get

$$\varepsilon_t(t) = \frac{1}{t_\varepsilon}\int_{0^-}^{t} \exp\left(\frac{-t'}{t_\varepsilon}\right)\left[\frac{\tau(t')}{\mu_c}\right]^p dt' \tag{7.60}$$

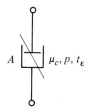

A μ_c, p, t_ε

Figure 7.8 Aging nonlinear viscous material–representation of time-hardening transient creep.

which is equivalent to

$$\varepsilon_t(t) = -\int_{0^-}^{t} \frac{\partial}{\partial t'} \exp\left(\frac{-t'}{t_\varepsilon}\right) \left[\frac{\tau(t')}{\mu_c}\right]^p dt' \tag{7.61}$$

Performing the usual integration by parts we get

$$\varepsilon_t(t) = -\left[\frac{\tau(t')}{\mu_c}\right]^p \exp\left(\frac{-t'}{t_\varepsilon}\right)\Bigg|_{0^-}^{t} + \int_{0^-}^{t} \exp\left(\frac{-t'}{t_\varepsilon}\right) \frac{\partial}{\partial t'}\left[\frac{\tau(t')}{\mu_c}\right]^p dt' \tag{7.62}$$

The first term in the above is simply

$$-\left[\frac{\tau(t)}{\mu_c}\right]^p \exp\left(\frac{-t}{t_\varepsilon}\right)$$

which may be combined with the second to yield the following result for the time-hardening hypothesis:

$$\varepsilon_t(t) = \int_{0^-}^{t} \left[\exp\left(\frac{-t'}{t_\varepsilon}\right) - \exp\left(\frac{-t}{t_\varepsilon}\right)\right] \frac{\partial}{\partial t'}\left[\frac{\tau(t')}{\mu_c}\right]^p dt' \tag{7.63}$$

You will recall that the corresponding equation obtained via the strain-hardening hypothesis [i.e., Eq. (7.41)] could be expressed as [see Eq. (7.42)]

$$\varepsilon_t(t) = \int_{0^-}^{t} J(t - t') \frac{\partial}{\partial t'}\left[\frac{\tau(t')}{\mu_c}\right]^p dt' \qquad \text{strain hardening} \tag{7.64}$$

where

$$J(t) = 1 - \exp\left(\frac{-t}{t_\varepsilon}\right) \tag{7.65}$$

You will also recall that in Chapter 6 we noted that a superposition integral with $J(t - t')$ in its integrand, such as Eq. (7.64), implies that the material is *nonaging*. Now examine Eq. (7.63) obtained by the time-hardening hypothesis, and note that it can be expressed as

$$\varepsilon_t(t) = \int_{0^-}^{t} [J(t) - J(t')] \frac{\partial}{\partial t'}\left[\frac{\tau(t')}{\mu_c}\right]^p dt' \qquad \text{time hardening} \tag{7.66}$$

where $J(t)$ is again given by Eq. (7.65). Clearly, the material represented by this equation is an *aging* material, since $[J(t) - J(t')]$ is a function of (t, t') rather than $(t - t')$. Note that $J(t - t')$ may be obtained from $J(t)$ by shifting it *horizontally* to the right by an amount t', while $J(t) - J(t')$ may be obtained from $J(t)$ by shifting it *vertically* downward by an amount $J(t')$. These horizontal and vertical shifts have important graphical interpretations, which we shall explore further in the next section.

Let us now briefly examine the application of the time-hardening hypothesis to the *time-power* form of the *transient creep* component. Thus at constant stress τ_0 we have

$$\varepsilon_t(t) = \left(\frac{\tau_0}{\mu_c}\right)^p t^{1/q} \qquad p = 1, 3, 5, \dots, \quad q > 1 \tag{7.67}$$

Differentiating with respect to time, we get

$$\dot{\varepsilon}_t(t) = \left(\frac{1}{q}\right)\left(\frac{\tau_0}{\mu_c}\right)^p t^{-[(q-1)/q]} \tag{7.68}$$

This is in the form of time-hardening hypothesis (7.56), and thus we may replace τ_0 by $\tau(t)$ to obtain the more general expression

$$\dot{\varepsilon}_t(t) = \frac{1}{q}\left[\frac{\tau(t)}{\mu_c}\right]^p t^{-[(q-1)/q]} \tag{7.69}$$

In Problem 7.11 you will be asked to obtain integral forms of Eq. (7.69).

The *total creep strain* $\varepsilon_c(t)$ may now be obtained by superposing some of the results obtained above. For example, if we define the total creep as the sum of Eqs. (7.32) [integral form of Eq. (7.57)] and (7.60) with $p = n$, we get in accordance with the time-hardening hypothesis,

$$\varepsilon_c(t) = \int_{0^-}^{t}\left[\gamma + \frac{1}{t_\varepsilon}\exp\left(\frac{-t'}{t_\varepsilon}\right)\right]\left[\frac{\tau(t')}{\mu_c}\right]^n dt' \tag{7.70}$$

where γ was defined in Eq. (7.25) as $(\mu_c/\lambda_c)^n$. Each *component* of strain in Eq. (7.70) obeys the time-hardening hypothesis, but we learned in the preceding section that one will in general not get the same result by applying a hardening hypothesis to the *total* creep at constant stress. To pursue this point, let us turn to the expression for total creep given by Eq. (7.23) with Eq. (7.24). Differentiating this expression with respect to time, we get for $\dot{\varepsilon}_c$,

$$\dot{\varepsilon}_c(t) = \left(\frac{\tau_0}{\mu_c}\right)^n\left[\gamma + \frac{1}{t_\varepsilon}\exp\left(\frac{-t}{t_\varepsilon}\right)\right] \tag{7.71}$$

If we now generalize this expression via the time-hardening hypothesis by replacing τ_0 by $\tau(t)$ and integrate the result, we *again* get Eq. (7.70). We thus find that for the *time-hardening hypothesis* applied to *component* creep strains, we do get the *same* result for the total creep strain as when the time-hardening hypothesis is applied *directly* to the total creep strain. This is in *direct contrast* to our experience with the strain-hardening hypothesis, which when applied as described above yielded *different* results. In the next section we compare results obtained from the various hypotheses.

7.7 COMPARISON OF HYPOTHESES USING A STEP-STRESS TEST

Starting with Eq. (7.23) at constant stress we have obtained *three* possible generalizations to the case of variable stress. Specifically, we got Eq. (7.45) by applying the *strain-hardening* hypothesis to the *creep components*, Eq. (7.48) by applying it to the *total creep strain*, and Eq. (7.70) by applying the *time-hardening hypothesis* to *either* the *components* or to the *total creep*. We shall now make a comparison of the results obtained via these three procedures, for the case of a stress history that is constant at τ_0 in the time interval $0^+ \leq t \leq t_1^-$, and is then stepped up to the constant value $k\tau_0$ (where $k > 1$) in the interval $t \geq t_1^+$ (see Fig. 7.9). Such a prescribed stress

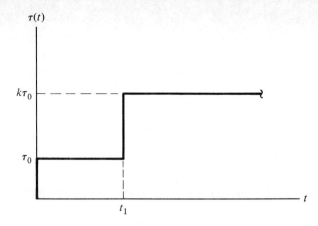

Figure 7.9 Step-stress test procedure.

history is called the *step-stress test procedure*, and with the use of step functions it may be expressed as

$$\tau(t) = \tau_0\{[u(t)] - [u(t - t_1)] + k[u(t - t_1)]\} \qquad (7.72)$$

The integrals in Eqs. (7.45) and (7.70) may be evaluated in closed form without much difficulty with Eq. (7.72) as the input, but Eq. (7.48) would have to be solved numerically for $\varepsilon_c(t)$. Fortunately, we may illustrate the solution in all three cases by means of a simple graphical procedure, which we shall describe below.

In Fig. 7.10 we have shown creep curves for some material at the constant stresses τ_0 and $k\tau_0$ (solid lines), where $\varepsilon(t)$ represents either some form of the *transient creep* component $\varepsilon_t(t)$ or the *total creep strain* $\varepsilon_c(t)$. [Since the steady creep component $\varepsilon_s(t)$ is always simply a straight line at constant stress, it is unnecessary to discuss its graphical representation.] What would the strain response $\varepsilon(t)$ look

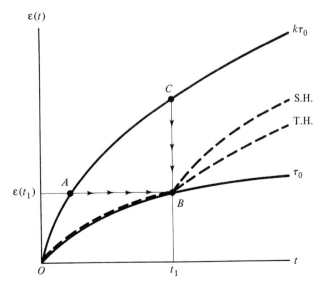

Figure 7.10 Strain response for step-stress input via strain and time-hardening hypotheses.

like for step-stress input (7.72)? Clearly, in the time interval $0 < t < t_1$ it is identical with that portion of the creep curve for stress τ_0 which lies in this interval (shown dashed from O to B). At time t_1, the stress suddenly jumps from τ_0 to $k\tau_0$ (see Fig. 7.9). The *strain-hardening* hypothesis (7.29) then requires that the *strain rate* at $t = t_1$ jump to the value

$$\dot{\varepsilon}(t_1^+) = f[\varepsilon(t_1), k\tau_0] \qquad (7.73)$$

where $\varepsilon(t_1)$ does *not* jump since it is obtained via an integration. But Eq. (7.73) is precisely the slope at point A on the creep curve for stress $k\tau_0$ for which $\varepsilon(t) = \varepsilon(t_1)$. Since the stress is again held constant at $k\tau_0$ for $t > t_1^+$, it is clear that we may obtain the strain response in this interval by *shifting* the portion of the $k\tau_0$ curve beyond point A *horizontally* to the right to point B. The result is shown dashed beyond B in Fig. 7.10 and labeled S.H., for "strain hardening."

If, instead, we use the *time-hardening* hypothesis (7.56), the strain rate at t_1 jumps to the different value

$$\dot{\varepsilon}(t_1^+) = f[k\tau_0, t_1] \qquad (7.74)$$

and again the strain itself does not jump. But this is the slope at point C on the $k\tau_0$ curve corresponding to $t = t_1$, and accordingly, we may obtain $\tau(t)$ for $t > t_1^+$ by *shifting* the portion of the curve beyond point C *vertically* downward to point B. This result is dashed and labeled T.H. in the figure, and always gives less strain than does the strain-hardening procedure for this load history. Note that the shifts described above are consistent with our earlier remarks concerning integrals (7.64) and (7.66).

We illustrate the use of these graphical procedures in the next example.

Example 7.3

Choose for the creep material constants in Eqs. (7.23) to (7.25) the values $\gamma = 1$, $t_\varepsilon = 0.1$, and $n = 3$, and in the step-stress function (7.72) set $t_1 = 0.5$ and $k = 1.5$. Then obtain normalized strain curves $\varepsilon_c/(\tau_0/\mu_c)^3$ versus time for the three possible generalizations for total creep discussed prior to Eq. (7.72): namely, Eqs. (7.45), (7.48), and (7.70).

Figure 7.11 contains all of the curves for this example. The curve labeled τ_0 is a creep curve for *constant stress* τ_0 obtained by plotting

$$\frac{\varepsilon_c}{(\tau_0/\mu_c)^3} = J(t) = t + 1 - e^{-10t} \qquad (a)$$

in accordance with Eqs. (7.23) and (7.24). The $\frac{3}{2}\tau_0$ curve is for $\tau = k\tau_0$ and is simply Eq. (a) multiplied by $(\frac{3}{2})^3 = 3.375$. Solutions for the *step-stress* input are labeled 1, 2, and 3. As indicated at the upper left corner of Fig. 7.11, 1 indicates the use of *strain hardening* on the *components*; 2 indicates *time hardening* applied to *components* or *total creep*; and 3 indicates *strain hardening* applied to *total creep*.

Let us consider first the development of curve 1 in some detail (see Fig. 7.12, in which the τ_0 and $\frac{3}{2}\tau_0$ curves have been reproduced from Fig. 7.11). First we obtain the *steady creep* solution OAB for this step stress input, which is simply a straight line with unit slope in interval $0 \leq t \leq t_1$ followed by another straight line with slope 3.375. Also, the steady creep solution for $\frac{3}{2}\tau_0$ is shown (OF). Next we subtract from the $\frac{3}{2}\tau_0$ curve values corresponding to the *steady creep* solution for the *stress* $\frac{3}{2}\tau_0$ (i.e., we subtract dashed straight line OF from curve $OC'H$ and thereby obtain curve $OD'F$). This curve represents the *transient creep strain* at the *stress* $\frac{3}{2}\tau_0$. Similarly, we subtract straight line OA from the τ_0 curve OC to obtain curve OD, which represents the *transient creep*

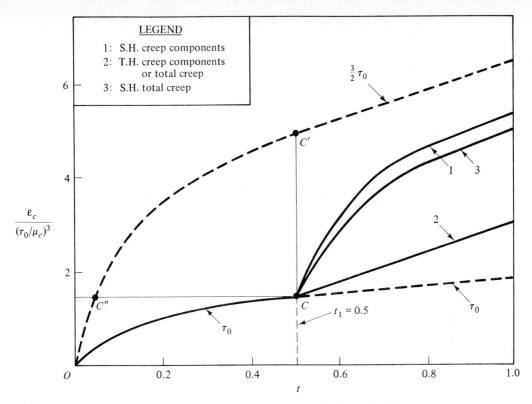

Figure 7.11 Strain responses for Example 7.3.

strain for the *stress* τ_0. We may now *shift* the curve $D'F$ to the right, as discussed earlier for the strain-hardening hypothesis, to obtain the *transient solution DE* in the interval $t \geq t_1$, for the *step stress input*. Finally, we add the *steady creep* solution AB to the *transient creep* solution DE to obtain the desired curve 1. Curve OCG in Fig. 7.12 is then the solution to Eq. (7.45) with input (7.72), which as noted previously, may also be obtained analytically (see Problem 7.12).

Curve 2 (for *time hardening*) on the other hand, is obtained as we discussed earlier simply by *shifting* the $\frac{3}{2}\tau_0$ curve *downward* from C' to C as shown in Fig. 7.11. This curve represents the solution to Eq. (7.70), which may also be determined analytically (see Problem 7.13). Finally, we obtain curve 3 simply by *shifting* the $\frac{3}{2}\tau_0$ curve from C'' in Fig. 7.11 to the right as discussed earlier. This curve gives the solution to Eq. (7.48), which would otherwise have to be determined numerically. All operations involved in obtaining curves 1, 2, and 3 are easily accomplished with the use of a straightedge, a pair of dividers, and French curves.

On examining Fig. 7.11, we see that for this stress input, *strain hardening* applied to *creep components* (curve 1) gives a slightly *greater value* of strain increase than does *strain hardening* applied to *total creep* (curve 3). Clearly, the *time-hardening* approach (curve 2) yields substantially *smaller values*. This is generally true for any input in which the stress is stepped *up*, but is *not true* if stress is stepped *down* (see Problem 7.14).

The question of which hypothesis to use is a difficult one to answer. For *structurally stable* materials, *strain hardening* applied to the *total creep* often works

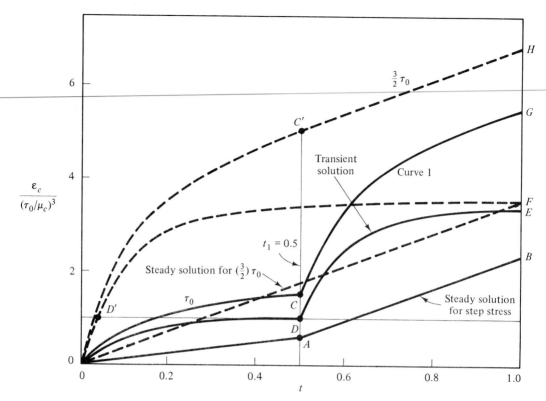

Figure 7.12 Details for development of curve 1.

best. However, it has some analytical disadvantages since one may obtain complicated equations such as Eq. (7.48). If a problem is treated entirely numerically, this disadvantage is minimal. *Strain hardening* applied to *components* gives similar results if loads are *stepped up*. Furthermore, the governing equations are more convenient for computation. However, this approach tends to overestimate the recovery of strain when loads are *stepped down*. Of course, for *structurally unstable* materials it may become necessary to employ *time hardening* or at least some *mixture* of *time* and *strain hardening*. In this category we have concrete that ages due to chemical reaction, and metals held for long periods at elevated temperatures such that metallurgical changes can accumulate. Since *all* of the hypotheses we have discussed involve the generalization of constant stress laws to the case of variable stress, we should in general expect them to work best for *quasi-static* problems. However, they have also been used to study some dynamic problems. For additional comparisons between some of the approaches presented here and other approaches, see the creep mechanics literature.*

---

*For example, see R. K. Penny and D. L. Marriott, *Design for Creep* (New York: McGraw-Hill Book Company, 1971), Chap. 2. A variety of hypotheses are compared in this reference, including the strain-hardening and time-hardening generalizations of the time-power law [i.e., Eqs. (7.53) and (7.69), respectively]. For stress reversals the hardening laws frequently require modification [e.g., see H. Kraus, *Creep Analysis* (New York: John Wiley & Sons, Inc., 1980), p. 25].

Introduction to Nonlinear Viscoelastic Behavior: Creep   Chap. 7

PART B
NONLINEAR VISCOELASTIC BEHAVIOR IN THREE DIMENSIONS

7.8 A COMMENT

In Part B we present some possible generalizations of the one-dimensional laws of Part A to three dimensions. For the sake of brevity we consider only the *power law* form of the stress dependence and focus our attention on the *exponential form* for the time dependence of the transient creep component. Furthermore, we employ the *strain-hardening* hypothesis for generalization to variable stress. In addition, we assume that in three dimensions the creep strain is *incompressible** and that the material is isotropic. At appropriate times we will introduce other simplifications to the forms of the three-dimensional laws. As in Part A, we begin by considering constant stress and then later generalize to the case of variable stress.

7.9 INTRODUCTORY CONSIDERATIONS

In the case of one-dimensional, nonlinear behavior at *constant normal stress* τ_0, we have seen in Part A that the creep strain may be expressed as

$$\varepsilon(t) = A\tau_0^n f(t), \qquad n = 1, 3, 5, \dots \tag{7.75}$$

where $\varepsilon(t)$ could be some component of creep strain as in Eqs. (7.5), (7.17), and (7.19), or $\varepsilon(t)$ could be the total creep strain as in Eq. (7.23). Because of the incompressibility assumption of creep strain and because of isotropy, we stipulate, for a constant normal stress in the x_1 direction, that the normal strain in that direction is given as

$$\varepsilon_1 = A\tau_1^n f(t) \tag{7.76}$$

and the transverse strains are given as

$$\varepsilon_2 = \varepsilon_3 = -\tfrac{1}{2}\varepsilon_1 \tag{7.77}$$

Furthermore, we note that in conformity with the incompressibility assumption the cubical dilatation follows as

$$\varepsilon_{kk} = 3\bar{\varepsilon} = 0 \tag{7.78}$$

Also note that as a consequence of isotropy the shear strains for axes x_1, x_2, x_3 are zero (see Section 5.2) and thus these axes are *principal axes* for *both* stress and strain. Keep in mind that we are assuming *only* that the *creep* strain is incompressible, *not* the *elastic* strain.

---

*In Appendix VII we discuss the fact that creep in metals, rock, and ice is usually dominated by dislocation glide, which is a process of consecutive slip. This process involves only local changes in interatomic distance, and thus the assumption of incompressibility is usually very good for these materials. For information on glacial ice, see W. Paterson, *The Physics of Glaciers* (New York: Pergamon Press, 1981); and for information on lithospheric rock, see D. Turcotte and G. Schubert, *Geodynamics–Application of Continuum Physics to Geological Problems* (New York: John Wiley & Sons, Inc., 1982).

Let us for the moment recall three-dimensional, linear viscoelasticity for variable stress. We had from Eq. (6.86) the following relation between the bulk stress $\bar{\tau}$ and one-third of the volume dilatation $\bar{\varepsilon}$:

$$P^K \bar{\tau} = Q^K \bar{\varepsilon} \tag{7.79}$$

And between the stress and strain deviatoric tensors we had, from Eq. (6.89),

$$P^G s_{ij} = Q^G e_{ij} \tag{7.80}$$

It is our goal in the ensuing discourse to obtain nonlinear multidimensional constitutive laws for variable stress which reduce to Eqs. (7.79) and (7.80) in the linear case, and also to the power law (7.76) in the case of constant uniaxial stress. However, since $\bar{\varepsilon} = 0$ for us here, the generalization of Eq. (7.79) is of no interest. Accordingly, we seek a power law generalization of the deviator law (7.80).

For this purpose we now consider the deviator form of Eq. (7.75). Note first that the strain deviator tensor for the case where $\varepsilon_{kk} = 0$ becomes [see Eq. (6.79b) with the use of Eq. (7.77)]:

$$e_{ij} = \begin{bmatrix} e_1 & 0 & 0 \\ 0 & e_2 & 0 \\ 0 & 0 & e_3 \end{bmatrix} = \begin{bmatrix} \varepsilon_1 & 0 & 0 \\ 0 & \varepsilon_2 & 0 \\ 0 & 0 & \varepsilon_3 \end{bmatrix} \tag{7.81}$$

With τ_1 as the only nonzero stress, the stress tensor is

$$\tau_{ij} = \begin{bmatrix} \tau_1 & 0 & 0 \\ 0 & 0 & 0 \\ 0 & 0 & 0 \end{bmatrix}$$

Hence the deviator stress tensor s_{ij} becomes [see Eq. (6.79a)]

$$s_{ij} = \begin{bmatrix} s_1 & 0 & 0 \\ 0 & s_2 & 0 \\ 0 & 0 & s_3 \end{bmatrix} = \begin{bmatrix} 2\tau_1/3 & 0 & 0 \\ 0 & -\tau_1/3 & 0 \\ 0 & 0 & -\tau_1/3 \end{bmatrix} \tag{7.82}$$

Substituting for τ_1 and ε_1 in Eq. (7.76) in terms of s_1 and e_1 by using the equations above for $i = j = 1$, we get

$$e_1 = A \left(\tfrac{3}{2} s_1 \right)^n f(t) = B s_1^n f(t) \tag{7.83}$$

where

$$B = \left(\tfrac{3}{2} \right)^n A \tag{7.84}$$

It will be our task now to form the three-dimensional form between the stress and strain deviators that degenerates to Eq. (7.83) for the nonlinear, one-dimensional, constant-stress case. For this purpose, we must discuss certain properties pertaining to powers of second-order tensors beyond those first set forth in Sections 1.10 and 2.6.

7.10 POWERS OF TENSORS

You will recall that in Section 1.10 we expressed a symmetric, second-order tensor T_{ij} in symbolic notation as $\mathbf{T}$ and noted that $\mathbf{T}^2 \equiv T_{ij}\,T_{jk}$. Higher powers of symmetric second-order tensors were defined as

$$\mathbf{T}^n = T_{ij}\,T_{jk} \cdots T_{pr}\,T_{rs} \qquad n = 1, 2, 3, 4, \ldots \tag{7.85}$$

wherein there are n matrices on the right side of Eq. (7.85). As for the traces of tensors and of powers of tensors, we have

$$\operatorname{tr}\mathbf{T} = T_{ii} \qquad\qquad\qquad (a)$$

$$\operatorname{tr}\mathbf{T}^2 = T_{ij}\,T_{ji} \qquad\qquad\qquad (b) \qquad (7.86)$$

$$\operatorname{tr}\mathbf{T}^n = T_{ij}\,T_{jk} \cdots T_{pr}\,T_{ri} \qquad (c)$$

Also, for principal axes of T_{ij}, we have

$$T_{ij} = \begin{bmatrix} T_1 & 0 & 0 \\ 0 & T_2 & 0 \\ 0 & 0 & T_3 \end{bmatrix}$$

and from Eq. (7.85), we have

$$\mathbf{T}^n = \begin{bmatrix} T_1^n & 0 & 0 \\ 0 & T_2^n & 0 \\ 0 & 0 & T_3^n \end{bmatrix} \tag{7.87}$$

Thus, as noted in Section 1.10, we see that a second-order, symmetric tensor and the nth power of this tensor have the *same* principal axes.

In Section 2.6 we introduced the *Cayley–Hamilton* theorem applied to stress [see Eq. (2.47)]. In general this equation states that for a tensor T_{ij}, on using $\mathbf{I}$ as the unitary matrix,

$$\mathbf{T}^3 = I_T\mathbf{T}^2 - II_T\mathbf{T} + III_T\mathbf{I} \tag{7.88}$$

where I_T, II_T, and III_T are the tensor invariants. These invariants are

$$I_T = T_{ii} = \operatorname{tr}\mathbf{T} \qquad\qquad (a)$$

$$II_T = \tfrac{1}{2}(T_{ii}\,T_{jj} - T_{ij}\,T_{ji}) = \tfrac{1}{2}[(\operatorname{tr}\mathbf{T})^2 - \operatorname{tr}\mathbf{T}^2] \qquad (b)$$

$$III_T = \tfrac{1}{6}(2T_{ij}\,T_{jk}\,T_{ki} - 3T_{ij}\,T_{ji}\,T_{kk} + T_{ii}\,T_{jj}\,T_{kk}) \qquad (7.89)$$

$$= \tfrac{1}{6}[2\operatorname{tr}\mathbf{T}^3 - 3(\operatorname{tr}\mathbf{T}^2)(\operatorname{tr}\mathbf{T}) + (\operatorname{tr}\mathbf{T})^3] \qquad (c)$$

where we have used Eqs. (7.86) to obtain the second form of each invariant. We can say that the Cayley–Hamilton theorem requires a matrix to satisfy its own characteristic equation.

Let us now consider any second-order, symmetric, *deviator* tensor D_{ij}, which we denote symbolically as $\mathbf{D}$. The Cayley–Hamilton equation for $\mathbf{D}$ then becomes

$$\mathbf{D}^3 = I_D\mathbf{D}^2 - II_D\mathbf{D} + III_D\mathbf{I} \tag{7.90}$$

where the invariants now are simply

$$I_D = \text{tr}\,\mathbf{D} = 0 \tag{a}$$

$$II_D = -\tfrac{1}{2}D_{ij}D_{ji} = -\tfrac{1}{2}\,\text{tr}\,\mathbf{D}^2 \tag{b} \tag{7.91}$$

$$III_D - \tfrac{1}{3}D_{ij}D_{jk}D_{ki} = \tfrac{1}{3}\,\text{tr}\,\mathbf{D}^3 \tag{c}$$

For principal axes, the deviator invariants become

$$I_D = 0 \tag{a}$$

$$II_D = -\tfrac{1}{2}(D_1^2 + D_2^2 + D_3^2) \tag{b} \tag{7.92}$$

$$III_D = \tfrac{1}{3}(D_1^3 + D_2^3 + D_3^3) \tag{c}$$

We see from Eqs. (7.91) and (7.92) that II_D is nonpositive, whereas III_D can be positive or negative. Also, with $I_D = 0$, the Cayley–Hamilton equation (7.90) becomes simply

$$\mathbf{D}^3 = -II_D\,\mathbf{D} + III_D\,\mathbf{I} \tag{7.93}$$

In Section 2.6 we described how the Cayley–Hamilton theorem may be used to express the nth power (for $n \geq 3$) of the stress tensor (i.e., $\underline{\tau}^n$) as a linear combination of $\underline{\tau}^2$, $\underline{\tau}$, and $\mathbf{I}$. We shall now carry out this process in detail for any deviator tensor $\mathbf{D}$, and thereby obtain $\mathbf{D}^n$ in terms of $\mathbf{D}^2$, $\mathbf{D}$, and $\mathbf{I}$. For $n = 3$ the result is given by the theorem itself [i.e., Eq. (7.93)], and the result for $n = 4$ follows directly from a multiplication by $\mathbf{D}$, that is,

$$\mathbf{D}^4 = -II_D\,\mathbf{D}^2 + III_D\,\mathbf{D} \tag{7.94}$$

Now multiply this equation by $\mathbf{D}$ to obtain

$$\mathbf{D}^5 = -II_D\,\mathbf{D}^3 + III_D\,\mathbf{D}^2$$

Replacing $\mathbf{D}^3$ in this result by means of Eq. (7.93), we get

$$\mathbf{D}^5 = -II_D(-II_D\,\mathbf{D} + III_D\,\mathbf{I}) + III_D\,\mathbf{D}^2$$
$$= III_D\,\mathbf{D}^2 + II_D^2\,\mathbf{D} - II_D\,III_D\,\mathbf{I} \tag{7.95}$$

We have thus far accomplished our objectives for $n = 3$, 4, and 5. Clearly, we can continue in this manner and obtain $\mathbf{D}^n$, for $n \geq 3$, in terms of $\mathbf{D}^2$, $\mathbf{D}$, and $\mathbf{I}$. You should verify that for $n = 6, 7, 8, 9$, one obtains

$$\mathbf{D}^6 = II_D^2\,\mathbf{D}^2 - 2II_D\,III_D\,\mathbf{D} + III_D^2\,\mathbf{I} \tag{a}$$

$$\mathbf{D}^7 = -2II_D\,III_D\,\mathbf{D}^2 + (III_D^2 - II_D^3)\,\mathbf{D} + II_D^2\,III_D\,\mathbf{I} \tag{b}$$

$$\mathbf{D}^8 = (III_D^2 - II_D^3)\,\mathbf{D}^2 + 3II_D^2\,III_D\,\mathbf{D} - 2II_D\,III_D^2\,\mathbf{I} \tag{c} \tag{7.96}$$

$$\mathbf{D}^9 = 3II_D^2\,III_D\,\mathbf{D}^2 - II_D(3III_D^2 - II_D^3)\,\mathbf{D} + III_D(III_D^2 - II_D^3)\,\mathbf{I} \tag{d}$$

We can then say for $\mathbf{D}^n$, $n \geq 3$, that

$$\mathbf{D}^n = [\,p_n(II_D, III_D)]\mathbf{D}^2 + [q_n(II_D, III_D)]\mathbf{D} + [r_n(II_D, III_D)]\mathbf{I} \tag{7.97}$$

where p_n, q_n, and r_n are *polynomials* in the invariants II_D and III_D. Note from Eqs. (7.91) that II_D and III_D are quadratic and cubic, respectively, in the components of

D, and also from Eq. (7.96) that p_n, q_n, and r_n are of orders $(n-2)$, $(n-1)$, n, respectively, in these components. In Problem 7.19 you will be asked to obtain recursion formulas for the polynomials p_n, q_n, and r_n in any nth-order power of **D**.

We are now ready to proceed further with the development of the three-dimensional, nonlinear, viscoelastic law, the one-dimensional form of which has been presented in Section 7.9.

7.11 THREE-DIMENSIONAL, NONLINEAR, VISCOELASTIC LAW FOR CONSTANT STRESS

Equation (7.83) expressed the strain deviator in terms of the stress deviator in the one-dimensional, constant-stress case as

$$e_1 = Bs_1^n f(t) \tag{7.98}$$

We will in the ensuing discourse attempt to extrapolate this equation to three dimensions. In this regard, we note first that in three dimensions we may employ symbolic notation to denote s_{ij} as **S** and e_{ij} as **E**. Next we apply Eqs. (7.85) and (7.97) to the deviatoric stress tensor. We thus have

$$\mathbf{S}^n = s_{ij}s_{jk} \cdots s_{pr}s_{rs} \tag{a}$$

$$\mathbf{S}^n = p_n(J_2, J_3)\mathbf{S}^2 + q_n(J_2, J_3)\mathbf{S} + r_n(J_2, J_3)\mathbf{I} \tag{b}$$

$$\tag{7.99}$$

where the tensor invariants of s_{ij} are now expressed as J_2, J_3 in accordance with the following equations formed from Eqs. (7.91), which apply to all deviatoric tensors:

$$\mathbf{I}_s = s_{ii} = 0 \tag{a}$$

$$-\mathbf{II}_s = \tfrac{1}{2}s_{ij}s_{ji} = \tfrac{1}{2}\operatorname{tr}\mathbf{S}^2 = J_2 \tag{b}$$

$$\tag{7.100}$$

$$\mathbf{III}_s = \tfrac{1}{3}s_{ij}s_{jk}s_{ki} = \tfrac{1}{3}\operatorname{tr}\mathbf{S}^3 = J_3 \tag{c}$$

Note that a *minus sign* has been introduced in Eq. (b) so that J_2 is nonnegative. We are now ready to try to extrapolate Eq. (7.98) to three dimensions.

As a first effort we simply insert the deviator tensors **E** and **S** in place of e_1 and s_1. That is, we assume that the following equation applies:

$$\mathbf{E} = B\mathbf{S}^n f(t) \tag{7.101}$$

and by using Eq. (7.99b), we have

$$\mathbf{E} = B[p_n(J_2, J_3)\mathbf{S}^2 + q_n(J_2, J_3)\mathbf{S} + r_n(J_2, J_3)\mathbf{I}]f(t) \tag{7.102}$$

Now take the trace of Eq. (7.102). Noting that the trace of the deviatoric tensor **E** is zero, we get

$$B[p_n(J_2, J_3)\operatorname{tr}\mathbf{S}^2 + q_n(J_2, J_3)\operatorname{tr}\mathbf{S} + r_n(J_2, J_3)\operatorname{tr}\mathbf{I}]f(t) = 0 \tag{7.103}$$

Furthermore, we note that $\operatorname{tr}\mathbf{I} = 3$, $\operatorname{tr}\mathbf{S} = 0$, and from Eq. (7.100b), that $\operatorname{tr}\mathbf{S}^2 = 2J_2$. Equation (7.103) then requires that

$$3r_n(J_2, J_3) = -2J_2 p_n(J_2, J_3) \tag{7.104}$$

Unfortunately, this equality is *not* consistent with our previous results concerning the forms of polynomials p_n and r_n. For example, the use of polynomials p and r associated with Eq. (7.96b) for $n = 7$ in Eq. (7.104), while making use of Eqs. (7.100), results in the following contradiction:

$$3J_2^2 J_3 = -4J_2^2 J_3$$

Accordingly, we must conclude that the assumption (7.101) is *invalid*. That is,

$$\mathbf{E} \neq B\mathbf{S}^n f(t)$$

It is clear from the above that Eq. (7.101) and its equivalent, Eq. (7.102), are not sufficiently general. For this reason we now introduce *three constant multipliers*, α, β, and γ, into Eq. (7.102) in the following way:

$$\mathbf{E} = B[\alpha p_n(J_2, J_3)\mathbf{S}^2 + \beta q_n(J_2, J_3)\mathbf{S} + \gamma r_n(J_2, J_3)\mathbf{I}]f(t) \tag{7.105}$$

Now taking the trace of this equation yields, on noting again that $\operatorname{tr}\mathbf{E} = \operatorname{tr}\mathbf{S} = 0$,

$$B[\alpha p_n(J_2, J_3) \operatorname{tr}\mathbf{S}^2 + 3\gamma r_n(J_2, J_3)]f(t) = 0 \tag{7.106}$$

We can then solve for γ in terms of α from Eq. (7.106) and thereby obtain

$$\gamma = -\frac{\alpha}{3}\frac{p_n(J_2, J_3) \operatorname{tr}\mathbf{S}^2}{r_n(J_2, J_3)} \tag{7.107}$$

Returning to Eq. (7.105) and eliminating γ via Eq. (7.107), we then get

$$\mathbf{E} = B[\alpha p_n(J_2, J_3)\mathbf{S}^2 + \beta q_n(J_2, J_3)\mathbf{S} - \frac{\alpha}{3} p_n(J_2, J_3)(\operatorname{tr}\mathbf{S}^2)\mathbf{I}]f(t)$$

$$= B\{\alpha p_n(J_2, J_3)[\mathbf{S}^2 - \tfrac{1}{3}(\operatorname{tr}\mathbf{S}^2)\mathbf{I}] + \beta q_n(J_2, J_3)\mathbf{S}\}f(t) \tag{7.108}$$

Upon examining Eq. (7.108), we see that polynomial $r_n(J_2, J_3)$ has been eliminated. Furthermore, the expression inside the brackets is the *deviator* of the *square* of the stress deviator tensor, and we shall denote this expression as $\mathbf{R}$. That is,

$$\mathbf{S}^2 - \tfrac{1}{3}(\operatorname{tr}\mathbf{S}^2)\mathbf{I} = \mathbf{R} \tag{7.109}$$

Finally, setting $B\alpha = D$ and $B\beta = C$ in Eq. (7.108), we obtain

$$\boxed{\mathbf{E} = [Cq_n(J_2, J_3)\mathbf{S} + Dp_n(J_2, J_3)\mathbf{R}]f(t)} \tag{7.110}$$

This important equation is the sought-for generalization of Eq. (7.98) to three dimensions. In index notation it is expressed as[*]

$$\boxed{e_{ij} = \varepsilon_{ij} = [Cq_n(J_2, J_3)s_{ij} + Dp_n(J_2, J_3)r_{ij}]f(t)} \tag{7.111}$$

where $e_{ij} = \varepsilon_{ij}$ because of incompressibility.

---

[*] The development of Eq. (7.111) as given in this section essentially follows a treatment given by W. Prager, in "Strain Hardening Under Combined Stresses," *J. Appl. Phys.*, Vol. 16, p. 837 (1945).

We may gain some insight into the implications of the manipulations performed above by presenting an alternative derivation of Eq. (7.111). We start by assuming the existence of a *creep potential function* $\Phi(J_2, J_3)$ such that the constitutive law is given as

$$e_{ij} = \frac{\partial \Phi(J_2, J_3)}{\partial \tau_{ij}} f(t) \tag{7.112}$$

You may immediately see the similarity between $\Phi(J_2, J_3)$ and the complementary energy density function $\mathcal{U}^*(\tau_{ij})$ for an elastic material [see Eq. (5.57b)]. Using the chain rule for differentiation in Eq. (7.112), we get

$$e_{ij} = \left[\frac{\partial \Phi}{\partial J_2} \frac{\partial J_2}{\partial \tau_{ij}} + \frac{\partial \Phi}{\partial J_3} \frac{\partial J_3}{\partial \tau_{ij}} \right] f(t) \tag{7.113}$$

We shall now examine the derivatives of J_2 and J_3 with respect to τ_{ij} that appear on the right side of Eq. (7.113). As a first step, note from Eq. (7.100b) that

$$J_2 = \tfrac{1}{2} S_{pq} S_{pq} \tag{7.114}$$

Hence, on replacing the deviatoric stress tensor by the stress tensor, we have

$$J_2 = \tfrac{1}{2}[\tau_{pq} - \tfrac{1}{3}\tau_{kk}\delta_{pq}][\tau_{pq} - \tfrac{1}{3}\tau_{ll}\delta_{pq}]$$

$$= \tfrac{1}{2}[\tau_{pq}\tau_{pq} - \tfrac{1}{3}\tau_{pp}\tau_{ll} - \tfrac{1}{3}\tau_{kk}\tau_{pp} + \tfrac{1}{3}\tau_{kk}\tau_{ll}]$$

Canceling the last two terms, we now form $\partial J_2 / \partial \tau_{ij}$, to get

$$\frac{\partial J_2}{\partial \tau_{ij}} = \tfrac{1}{2}[2\delta_{pi}\delta_{qj}\tau_{pq} - \tfrac{1}{3}\delta_{pi}\delta_{pj}\tau_{ll} - \tfrac{1}{3}\delta_{li}\delta_{lj}\tau_{pp}]$$

$$= \tau_{ij} - \tfrac{1}{3}\tau_{kk}\delta_{ij} = S_{ij} \tag{7.115}$$

Similarly, we can show that (see Problem 7.20)

$$\frac{\partial J_3}{\partial \tau_{ij}} = r_{ij} \tag{7.116}$$

where r_{ij} are the components of **R** defined in Eq. (7.109). Noting Eqs. (7.85) and (7.86b) in conjunction with Eq. (7.109), we then may write

$$r_{ij} = S_{ik} S_{kj} - \tfrac{1}{3} S_{lk} S_{kl} \delta_{ij} \tag{7.117}$$

Now we go back to Eq. (7.113) and insert the results above for the derivatives of J_2 and J_3 with respect to τ_{ij} to get

$$e_{ij} = \left[\frac{\partial \Phi}{\partial J_2} S_{ij} + \frac{\partial \Phi}{\partial J_3} r_{ij} \right] f(t) \tag{7.118}$$

If we denote $\partial \Phi / \partial J_2$ as $Cq_n(J_2, J_3)$ and $\partial \Phi / \partial J_3$ as $Dp_n(J_2, J_3)$, we get back to the constitutive law (7.111) presented earlier, namely,

$$e_{ij} = \varepsilon_{ij} = [Cq_n(J_2, J_3)S_{ij} + Dp_n(J_2, J_3)r_{ij}]f(t) \tag{7.119}$$

Thus we have shown that the procedure whereby we introduced constant coefficients α, β, γ into Eq. (7.105) and then solved for γ [i.e., Eq. (7.107)], was *equivalent* to assuming the existence of a *creep potential* which is a function of J_2 and J_3 [i.e., Eq. (7.112)]. Equation (7.112) is readily extendable to include the effects of compressibility and anisotropy. For compressible materials, the creep potential Φ is a function of I_τ in addition to J_2 and J_3, where I_τ is the first invariant of stress (i.e., the bulk stress). For anisotropic materials, Φ must also depend on the orientation of the coordinate axes. Such generalizations are seldom employed because they introduce still more complexity to an already complex formulation. In the next section we reduce this complexity by assuming that dependence on the third invariant J_3 may be ignored.

7.12 NEGLECTING THE EFFECT OF THE THIRD INVARIANT

The use of Eq. (7.119) not only leads to difficult boundary value problems, but in addition the various material parameters contained therein are difficult to determine experimentally. Accordingly, it is highly desirable to obtain a simplified version of this equation. Thus let us again examine the forms of the polynomial coefficients p_n and q_n that entered our deliberations in Eq. (7.99b). You will recall that in the absence of a signum function in the one-dimensional law, the stress power n must be restricted to odd positive integers. We have assembled in Table 7.2 polynomial coefficients of odd orders of $\mathbf{D}^n$, using Eqs. (7.93), (7.95), and (7.96) with $\mathrm{II}_D = -J_2$ and $\mathrm{III}_D = J_3$.

Note first that for $n = 1, 3$ we have $p_n = 0$, while $q_n = 1$ for $n = 1$ and $q_n = J_2$ for $n = 3$. Thus in these two cases Eq. (7.119) simplifies considerably to

$$e_{ij} = \begin{cases} C s_{ij} f(t) & n = 1 \\ C J_2 s_{ij} f(t) & n = 3 \end{cases} \tag{7.120}$$

A stress power n of 3 is very common, but it is not uncommon for n to be greater than 3 (e.g., see Table 7.1 in Section 7.3). If we ignore the effect of J_3 for *all* values of n, then Table 7.2, with $J_3 \equiv 0$, indicates that we again get $p_n = 0$, and in addition

$$q_n = J_2^m \qquad m = \frac{n-1}{2} - 0, 1, 2, 3, \ldots \tag{7.121}$$

where m is a nonnegative integer. With this simplification, Eq. (7.119) becomes

$$\boxed{e_{ij} = \varepsilon_{ij} = C J_2^m s_{ij} f(t)} \tag{7.122}$$

TABLE 7.2 Polynomial Coefficients

n	$p_n(J_2, J_3)$	$q_n(J_2, J_3)$	$m = \dfrac{n-1}{2}$
1	0	1	0
3	0	J_2	1
5	J_3	J_2^2	2
7	$2J_2 J_3$	$J_3^2 + J_2^3$	3
9	$3J_2^2 J_3$	$3J_2 J_3^3 + J_2^4$	4

Fortunately, experimental evidence indicates that ignoring the effect of J_3 is usually justified, and thus Eq. (7.122) is widely used. Since J_2 is nonnegative, it is clear that the restriction that m be an *integer* in Eq. (7.122) may now be removed. To show this, go back to Eq. (7.98) and replace s_1^n by $|s_1|^{n-1}s_1$ where $|s_1| = s_1(\text{sgn } s_1)$, thereby removing the restriction that n be an odd positive integer. In generalizing this form of Eq. (7.98) from one to multidimensions, we replace Bs_1 by Cs_{ij} and $|s_1|^{n-1}$ by $J_2^{(n-1)/2} = J_2^m$. We thus again arrive at Eq. (7.122), but now the *only* restriction on m is that it be *nonnegative*. Parenthetically, an alternative way of obtaining Eq. (7.122) is to postulate that the creep potential in Eq. (7.118) is simply*

$$\Phi = \frac{C}{m+1} J_2^{m+1} \tag{7.123}$$

which result you may easily verify by using Eqs. (7.113) and (7.115).

The constitutive law given by Eq. (7.122) has the following restrictions that have been directly or indirectly alluded to in the development:

1. Incompressibility of creep strain so that $\varepsilon_{ij} = e_{ij}$
2. Isotropic material behavior
3. Existence of the creep potential
4. Negligible effect of J_3

In addition, we have assumed that τ_{ij}, and thus s_{ij}, are independent of time. We shall remove the latter restriction in Section 7.14, but first we shall introduce some one-dimensional considerations and present some examples of three-dimensional constant stress laws.

7.13 EXPERIMENTAL INPUT FROM TENSILE TEST; SOME THREE-DIMENSIONAL CONSTANT STRESS LAWS

We shall now demonstrate that the creep parameter C and the stress power m in Eq. (7.122) may be determined from the one-dimensional tensile test with the stress *independent* of time. For this purpose, consider the one-dimensional form of Eq. (7.122), that is,

$$e_1 = C J_2^m s_1 f(t) \tag{7.124}$$

where e_1 and s_1 have previously been displayed in tensors (7.81) and (7.82). Note that $e_1 = \varepsilon_1$ and $s_1 = 2\tau_1/3$. Also noting that $s_2 = s_3 = -\tau_1/3$, we obtain for J_2,

$$J_2 = \tfrac{1}{2}s_{ij}s_{ij} = \tfrac{1}{2}(s_1^2 + s_2^2 + s_3^2) = \tfrac{1}{2}[\tfrac{4}{9}\tau_1^2 + \tfrac{1}{9}\tau_1^2 + \tfrac{1}{9}\tau_1^2] = \tfrac{1}{3}\tau_1^2 \tag{7.125}$$

---

* The existence of creep potential (7.123) forms the basis of an important analogy between creep law (7.122) and the plastic flow law based on the Mises yield criterion. (We shall discuss these topics in Chapters 8 and 9.) Accordingly, creep law (7.122) is often referred to as the Mises J_2 creep flow rule. In 1934, F. Odqvist used the *effective stress* concept of plasticity (see Section 8.14) to develop the steady creep form of Eq. (7.122). For details, see F. K. G. Odqvist, *Mathematical Theory of Creep and Creep Rupture* (Oxford: Clarendon Press, 1974), Chap. 5.

Substituting these values in Eq. (7.124) then yields

$$\varepsilon_1 = C(\tfrac{1}{3}\tau_1^2)^m(\tfrac{2}{3}\tau_1)f(t)$$

and therefore

$$\varepsilon_1 = \left(\frac{2C}{3^{m+1}}\right)\tau_1^{2m+1}f(t) \tag{7.126}$$

Let us next compare this one-dimensional form of the *three-dimensional*, nonlinear, viscoelastic constitutive law with the *one-dimensional*, nonlinear viscoelastic constitutive law first presented in this section [see Eq. (7.76)]. We rewrite the latter equation:

$$\varepsilon_1 = A\tau_1^n f(t) \tag{7.127}$$

To bring Eqs. (7.126) and (7.127) to the same form, we see immediately that the powers of τ_1 must be identical in both cases. This leads us to the requirement

$$n = 2m + 1 \qquad \text{or} \qquad m = \frac{n-1}{2} \tag{7.128}$$

in conformity with the condition in Eq. (7.121). Also, considering the coefficients, we have

$$A = \frac{2C}{3^{m+1}}$$

Hence

$$C = \frac{3^{m+1}A}{2} = \frac{3^{(n+1)/2}A}{2} \tag{7.129}$$

We can determine (via curve fitting) constants A and n from a one-dimensional creep tensile test. Using Eqs. (7.128) and (7.129), we can then get m and C, respectively. Thus the three-dimensional constitutive law [Eq. (7.122)] does *not* require a three-dimensional test to evaluate the appropriate constants.

As in the one-dimensional case [see Eq. (7.1)] we shall express the total strain tensor as the sum of elastic, steady creep, and transient creep components, that is,

$$\varepsilon_{ij} = \varepsilon_{ij}^e + \varepsilon_{ij}^s + \varepsilon_{ij}^t \tag{7.130}$$

Consider first the case in which *transient creep is negligible*. The elastic component is compressible and governed by Eq. (5.15), while the steady creep component is incompressible and governed by Eq. (7.122) with $f(t) = t$. Thus we have

$$\varepsilon_{ij} = \frac{1+\nu}{E}\tau_{ij} - \frac{\nu}{E}\tau_{kk}\delta_{ij} + CJ_2^m s_{ij}t \tag{7.131}$$

You should verify that for the one-dimensional stress state, $\tau_{xx} = \tau_1$, Eq. (7.131) yields, with the use of Eqs. (7.128) and (7.129),

$$\varepsilon_1 = \frac{\tau_1}{E} + A\tau_1^n t \qquad \text{(a)}$$

$$\varepsilon_2 = \varepsilon_3 = -\frac{\nu\tau_1}{E} - \frac{A}{2}\tau_1^n t \qquad \text{(b)} \tag{7.132}$$

Note that, as expected, ν is the elastic Poisson coefficient, whereas $\frac{1}{2}$ is the creep Poisson coefficient. We previously encountered different Poisson coefficients in our study of linear viscoelastic materials (see Section 6.10).

For *transient creep* we use a different function for $f(t)$ in Eq. (7.122). Furthermore, if the transient and steady creep stress powers are the same, these two $f(t)$ functions may be combined into a single $f(t)$ function for the *total creep*. Thus, assuming that the stress power m is the same in the steady and transient creep components and using the same time function as in Eq. (7.23) for the $f(t)$ of the total creep, Eq. (7.131) becomes

$$\varepsilon_{ij} = \frac{1+\nu}{E} \tau_{ij} - \frac{\nu}{E} \tau_{kk} \delta_{ij} + C_t J_2^m s_{ij} \left[\gamma t + 1 - \exp\left(\frac{-t}{t_\varepsilon}\right) \right] \tag{7.133}$$

In this equation the coefficient of the steady creep component is written as $C_t \gamma$, where C_t is the coefficient of the transient creep component. Another form of Eq. (7.133) may be formulated by having the power m different for the steady and transient creep components. Using the subscript s for steady creep and again using subscript t for transient creep, we have as an alternative, more general formulation:

$$\varepsilon_{ij} = \left(\frac{1+\nu}{E} \tau_{ij} - \frac{\nu}{E} \tau_{kk} \delta_{ij} \right) + C_s J_2^{m_s} s_{ij} t + C_t J_2^{m_t} s_{ij} [1 - \exp(-t/t_\varepsilon)] \tag{7.134}$$

We may of course also use other functions for the $f(t)$ of the transient creep component, such as the time power function $t^{1/q}$ discussed in Part A of this chapter.

The formulations reached in this section are valid for *constant* stress. In the next section we consider three-dimensional creep under variable stress.

7.14 THREE-DIMENSIONAL, NONLINEAR VISCOELASTIC LAWS FOR VARIABLE STRESS

We shall generalize Eq. (7.134) to *variable* time-dependent stress by applying the *strain-hardening* technique to the creep components of the strain tensor, that is,

$$\dot{\varepsilon}_{ij}(t) = f[\varepsilon_{ij}(t), \tau_{ij}(t)] \tag{7.135}$$

where ε_{ij} is a component of *steady* or *transient creep*. We first rewrite Eq. (7.134) in component form [i.e., as in Eq. (7.130)] with components

$$\varepsilon_{ij}^e = \frac{1+\nu}{E} \tau_{ij} - \frac{\nu}{E} \tau_{kk} \delta_{ij} \tag{a}$$

$$\varepsilon_{ij}^s = C_s (J_2)_0^{m_s} (s_{ij})_0 t \tag{b} \tag{7.136}$$

$$\varepsilon_{ij}^t = C_t (J_2)_0^{m_t} (s_{ij})_0 [1 - \exp(-t/t_\varepsilon)] \tag{c}$$

where the $(s_{ij})_0$ and $(J_2)_0$ in Eqs. (b) and (c) indicate that these two equations are valid only for constant stress.

In accordance with Eq. (7.135), the *steady creep component* given by Eq. (7.136b) above generalizes to the case of $s_{ij}(t)$ as

$$\dot{\varepsilon}_{ij}^s = C_s J_2^{m_s} s_{ij}(t) \tag{7.137}$$

which may be rewritten in integral form as

$$\varepsilon_{ij}^s = C_s \int_{0^-}^{t} J_2^{m_s} s_{ij}(t')\, dt' \qquad (7.138)$$

Proceeding as in the one-dimensional case [see Eqs. (7.33) to (7.36)], Eq. (7.136c) for the *transient creep component* generalizes to

$$\dot{\varepsilon}_{ij}^t + \frac{1}{t_\varepsilon}\,\varepsilon_{ij}^t = \frac{C_t}{t_\varepsilon}\, J_2^{m_t} s_{ij}(t) \qquad (7.139)$$

Using the integrating factor $\exp(t/t_\varepsilon)$ we can integrate Eq. (7.139) to get ε_{ij}^t in integral form as

$$\varepsilon_{ij}^t = \frac{C_t}{t_\varepsilon}\exp(-t/t_\varepsilon)\int_{0^-}^{t} J_2^{m_t} s_{ij}\exp(t'/t_\varepsilon)\, dt' \qquad (7.140)$$

Finally, substituting Eqs. (7.136a), (7.138), and (7.140) into Eq. (7.130), we obtain the following equation for variable stress:

$$\begin{aligned}
\varepsilon_{ij} = \frac{1+\nu}{E}\,\tau_{ij} - \frac{\nu}{E}\,\tau_{kk}\,\delta_{ij} + C_s \int_{0^-}^{t} J_2^{m_s} s_{ij}\, dt' \\
+ \frac{C_t}{t_\varepsilon}\exp(t'/t_\varepsilon)\int_{0^-}^{t} J_2^{m_t} s_{ij}\exp(t'/t_\varepsilon)\, dt'
\end{aligned} \qquad (7.141)$$

The model interpretation of Eq. (7.141) will become clear after we separate it into its bulk and deviatoric parts. Proceeding in the usual manner [e.g., see Eqs. (5.52) and (5.56) for elastic materials], we get

$$\boxed{\begin{aligned}
\bar{\varepsilon} &= \frac{\bar{\tau}}{3K} & \text{(a)} \\[2ex]
e_{ij} &= \frac{s_{ij}}{2G} + C_s \int_{0^-}^{t} J_2^{m_s} s_{ij}\, dt' + \frac{C_t}{t_\varepsilon}\exp(-t/t_\varepsilon)\int_{0^-}^{t} J_2^{m_t} s_{ij}\exp(t'/t_\varepsilon)\, dt' & \text{(b)}
\end{aligned}} \qquad (7.142)$$

where K and G are the bulk modulus and shear modulus, respectively (also see Table 5.1). Equation (7.142a) clearly indicates linear elastic behavior under pressure, while Eq. (7.142b) may be represented by a nonlinear Burgers model for distortion, similar to the model encountered in one dimension (see Fig. 7.7). The two models for multidimensional equations (7.142) have been depicted in Fig. 7.13. As in one dimension, we may rewrite Eq. (7.142b) in terms of hereditary integrals with the use of integrations by parts. Also, one may obtain different generalizations to variable stress through the use of alternate generalization techniques.* Since such considerations would parallel our previous one-dimensional development, we shall not pursue them further here.

---

* As pointed out in Part A, for metals it is frequently better to generalize the total creep, rather than the components of creep, to the case of variable stress. In the former case it is usually not fruitful to carry out the generalization in analytical form, but instead it is preferable to proceed directly to numerical finite-difference "time-marching" techniques. For example, see H. Kraus, *Creep Analysis* (New York: John Wiley & Sons, Inc., 1980), Chap. 8.

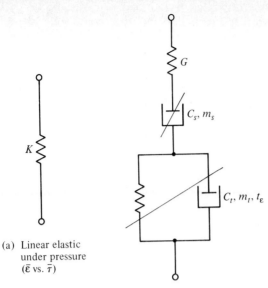

(a) Linear elastic
under pressure
($\bar{\varepsilon}$ vs. $\bar{\tau}$)

(b) Nonlinear Burgers
model for distortion
(e_{ij} vs. s_{ij})

Figure 7.13 Model representation for three-dimensional nonlinear viscoelastic law.

It is often convenient to have an expression for stress in terms of strain or strain rate, as for example when computing bending moments in beams and plates. Unfortunately, the inversion of Eq. (7.141) can only be accomplished numerically. However, if we ignore the elastic and transient creep components of strain, an *inversion* of the remaining *steady creep* component may be accomplished in *closed form*. In this special case Eq. (7.141) simplifies upon differentiation to the widely used *nonlinear viscous* relation

$$\dot{\varepsilon}_{ij} = \dot{e}_{ij} = C J_2^m s_{ij} \qquad (7.143)$$

where $\dot{\varepsilon}_{ij} = \dot{e}_{ij}$ because of the incompressibility, and where for convenience we have dropped the s subscript. Solving Eq. (7.143) for s_{ij}, we immediately obtain

$$s_{ij} = \frac{\dot{e}_{ij}}{C J_2^m} \qquad (7.144)$$

The inversion is not complete until we express J_2 on the right side of Eq. (7.144) in terms of a function of the creep strain rate. Thus we use this equation to form the following expression for J_2:

$$J_2 = \tfrac{1}{2} s_{ij} s_{ij} = \frac{\dot{e}_{ij} \dot{e}_{ij}}{2 C^2 J_2^{2m}} \qquad (7.145)$$

We now define K_2 to be

$$K_2 = \tfrac{1}{2} \dot{e}_{ij} \dot{e}_{ij} \qquad (7.146)$$

which will be recognized [see Eq. (7.91b)] as the negative of the second invariant of the strain-rate deviator tensor. Now going back to Eq. (7.145) and introducing K_2 as given above, we obtain after solving for J_2:

$$J_2 = C^{-2/(2m+1)} K_2^{1/(2m+1)} \tag{7.147}$$

Finally, eliminating J_2 from Eq. (7.144) by means of Eq. (7.147) and setting $\dot{e}_{ij} = \dot{\varepsilon}_{ij}$, we obtain, after simplification,

$$\boxed{s_{ij} = C^{-1/(2m+1)} K_2^{-m/(2m+1)} \dot{\varepsilon}_{ij}} \tag{7.148}$$

We have thus obtained a useful inverted form of the three-dimensional steady creep equation.

7.15 CLOSURE

In this chapter we have introduced some equations in one-dimensional and multi-dimensional nonlinear viscoelasticity. These laws can be expected to work best in *quasi-static* problems, but they are applicable to some dynamic problems. And we have cautioned the reader on numerous occasions that a variety of alternative approaches may be found in the literature on nonlinear creep and nonlinear visco-elasticity. In the next chapter we go on to still another facet of inelastic behavior (i.e., plastic deformation in solids), which we introduced very briefly in Chapter 4 from the macroscopic point of view and in Appendix VII from the microscopic viewpoint. We have already noted that as the creep stress power approaches infinity, the power law for creep approaches the form of rigid, perfectly plastic behavior. We shall also learn in Chapter 9 that a close analogy exists between the plastic yield surface with the associated plastic flow laws and the concept of a creep potential presented in Sections 7.11 and 7.12. Also, we shall briefly consider multidimensional *viscoplasticity*, which is closely related to viscoelasticity.

PROBLEMS

7.1. An aluminum alloy is subjected to a constant stress of $\tau_0 = 15$ kg/mm^2 and the *steady* creep strain *rate* is measured as $\dot{\varepsilon}_s = 0.63 \times 10^{-5}$ hr^{-1}. For a stress of 25 kg/mm^2, the steady creep strain rate increases to 1.95×10^{-5} hr^{-1}. Using Eq. (7.10), determine n and λ_c for this material. Express λ_c both in (kg/mm^2)(hr)$^{1/n}$ units and in (lb/in.^{2})(hr)$^{1/n}$ units.

7.2. For Problem 7.1 use Eq. (7.5) and determine the constant A. Also, use Eq. (7.12) with the reference stress $\tau_r = 20$ kg/mm^2 and determine the constant A_r.

7.3. Verify the following properties of the signum function for a function of time $F(t)$.
   (a) $F(t) = |F(t)| \, \text{sgn} \, F(t)$
   (b) $|F(t)| = F(t) \, \text{sgn} \, F(t)$
   (c) $\text{sgn}^2 F(t) = 1$ if $F(t) \neq 0$

(d) $\dfrac{d}{dt}[F(t)\,\mathrm{sgn}\,F(t)] = \dfrac{dF}{dt}\,\mathrm{sgn}\,F(t) \qquad \text{if } F(t) \neq 0$

Use Eq. (a) above to rewrite Eq. (7.8) in a form that does *not* contain the signum function.

7.4. For the aluminum alloy of Problem 7.1, the *total* creep strain at 50 hr is measured as $\varepsilon_c = 0.000544$ for $\tau_0 = 15\ \mathrm{kg/mm^2}$ and as $\varepsilon_c = 0.001733$ for $\tau_0 = 25\ \mathrm{kg/mm^2}$. Assume that $\varepsilon_c = \varepsilon_s + \varepsilon_t$, where ε_s is given by Eq. (7.10) and ε_t is given by Eq. (7.17), and also assume that at 50 hr the transient creep has reached its asymptotic value $\varepsilon_t(\infty)$. Use the steady creep strain rates given in Problem 7.1 to determine $\varepsilon_t(\infty)$ for these two stresses. Then evaluate p and μ_c.

7.5. Consider integral equation (7.32) for the steady creep component $\varepsilon_s(t)$. Let $\tau(t)$ be the slowly varying sinusoidal input $\tau(t) = \tau_0 \sin \omega t$. Carry out the integration for $n = 1$ and for $n = 3$. Redo the problem for the ramp input $\tau(t) = \dot{\tau}_0 t$, where $\dot{\tau}_0$ is the constant stress rate. Redo the problem once more for a creep stress applied at time t_1 (i.e., $\tau(t) = \tau_0[u(t - t_1)]$).

7.6. For variable stress $\tau(t)$ the steady creep stress–exponential law (7.6) generalizes to

$$\dot{\varepsilon}_s(t) = B e^{\alpha \tau(t)}$$

Consider a material governed by the equation

$$\dot{\varepsilon}(t) = \frac{\dot{\tau}(t)}{E} + B e^{\alpha \tau(t)}$$

Determine $\tau(t)$ for the *relaxation test* $\varepsilon(t) = \varepsilon_0[u(t)]$. (Note: The stress-exponential law is invalid at *low* stress levels, and thus the associated relaxation curve is meaningful only for *early* times.)

7.7. Consider a material for which the elastic strain component is linear, and the only creep component is a transient creep component in the form of Eq. (7.53). Thus $\varepsilon(t) = \tau(t)/E + \varepsilon_t(t)$ and

$$\frac{d}{dt}\left[\varepsilon(t) - \frac{\tau(t)}{E}\right]^q = \frac{d}{dt}[\varepsilon_t(t)]^q = \left[\frac{\tau(t)}{\mu_c}\right]^{pq}$$

For this material determine $\tau(t)$ for a relaxation test $\varepsilon(t) = \varepsilon_0[u(t)]$. Verify that for $q = 1$, $p = n$, and $\mu_c = \lambda_c$, your result reduces to the solution given in Example 7.2.

7.8. Consider integral equation (7.45) with compliance $J(t)$ given by Eq. (7.24). Differentiate this integral equation once and then twice with respect to t, using homogeneous initial conditions at $t = 0^-$. Use these results to convert the integral equation to a differential equation. Show that for $n = 1$ you obtain the differential equation for a standard linear fluid [see Fig. 6.4(b) and Eq. (6.29) with $E_1 \to \infty$].

7.9. Verify that Eq. (7.48) is the generalization of Eq. (7.47) to variable stress via the strain-hardening hypothesis. Explain why Eq. (7.48) is not readily expressed in integral form.

7.10. Assume a nondimensional creep compliance function

$$J(t) = 1 - e^{-10t}$$

Plot $J(t)$, $J(t - 0.5)$ and $J(t) - J(0.5)$ on the interval $0 \leq t \leq 1$. Use a pair of dividers to verify that $J(t - 0.5)$ is given by $J(t)$ shifted to the right by the amount 0.5, and $J(t) - J(0.5)$ is given by shifting it downward by the amount $J(0.5)$.

7.11. By applying the time-hardening hypothesis to the time-power form of the transient creep component, we obtained the result

$$\dot{\varepsilon}_t(t) = \frac{1}{q}\left[\frac{\tau(t)}{\mu_c}\right]^p t^{-[(q-1)/q]}$$

Obtain an integral form of this equation by direct integration. Rewrite this integral form as a hereditary integral by carrying out an integration by parts. Identify the creep compliance function $J(t)$, and show that it appears in the integrand in the form characteristic of an aging material.

7.12. Show that Eq. (7.45), which was obtained by applying the strain-hardening hypothesis to the creep components, is equivalent to

$$\varepsilon_c(t) = \int_{0^-}^{t}\left[\gamma + \frac{1}{t_\varepsilon}\exp\frac{(t'-t)}{t_\varepsilon}\right]\left[\frac{\tau(t')}{\mu_c}\right]^n dt'$$

where $\gamma = (\mu_c/\lambda_c)^n$. Evaluate this integral in closed form with $\tau(t)$ given by the step stress input (7.72). Note that

$$\tau(t)^n = \tau_0^n\{[u(t)] - [u(t-t_1)] + k^n[u(t-t_1)]\}$$

7.13. By applying the time-hardening hypothesis to the creep components (or to the total creep) we obtained

$$\varepsilon_c(t) = \int_{0^-}^{t}\left[\gamma + \frac{1}{t_\varepsilon}\exp\left(\frac{-t'}{t_\varepsilon}\right)\right]\left[\frac{\tau(t')}{\mu_c}\right]^n dt'$$

Evaluate this integral for the step stress input (7.72). (See the note in Problem 7.12.)

7.14. In Example 7.3 the stress was stepped *up* with k set equal to $\frac{3}{2}$. Now consider the case of stress stepped *down* with k equal to $\frac{2}{3}$, but let the values of γ, t_ε, n, and t_1 be the same as in the example. Redo this example for cases 2 (time hardening applied to total creep) and 3 (strain hardening applied to total creep). Obtain your results by using the graphical shifting techniques explained in Section 7.7. Compare and discuss your results. On your plot define the normalized strain as $\varepsilon_c/(2\tau_0/3\mu_c)^3$.

7.15. In Example 7.3 the stress was stepped up at the time $t_1 = 0.5$. Redo cases 2 and 3 (see Fig. 7.11) in this example for a stress stepped up at the earlier time $t_1 = 0.05$, using the same values of γ, t_ε, n, and k given in the example. Employ the graphical shifting techniques developed in Section 7.7, and compare your results with those given in the text for $t_1 = 0.5$. On your plot use the normalized strain $\varepsilon_c/(\tau_0/\mu_c)^3$.

7.16. In generalizing constant stress data to the case of variable stress, we may employ some combination of strain hardening and time hardening. For example, we may generalize Eq. (7.33) by a linear combination of Eqs. (7.40) and (7.60):

$$\varepsilon_t(t) = \frac{1}{t_\varepsilon}\left\{a\exp\left(\frac{-t'}{t_\varepsilon}\right)\int_{0^-}^{t}\exp\left(\frac{t'}{t_\varepsilon}\right)\left[\frac{\tau(t')}{\mu_c}\right]^p dt' + (1-a)\int_{0^-}^{t}\exp\left(\frac{-t'}{t_\varepsilon}\right)\left[\frac{\tau(t')}{\mu_c}\right]^p dt'\right\}$$

where a is a hardening parameter, which equals 1 for complete strain hardening and zero for complete time hardening.[*] Solve this equation for the case of a constant stress τ_0 suddenly applied at $t = 0$ and then suddenly removed at $t = t_1$ (see Fig. P7.16). Plot $\varepsilon_t/(\tau_0/\mu_c)^p$ versus t for $a = 0$, 0.5, and 1; set $t_\varepsilon = 1$ and $t_1 = 1$.

7.17. Integral creep law (7.45), that is,

$$\varepsilon_c(t) = \int_{0^-}^{t} J(t-t')\frac{\partial}{\partial t'}\left[\frac{\tau(t')}{\mu_c}\right]^n dt'$$

---

[*] For details, see F. A. Cozzarelli and R. P. Shaw, "A Combined Strain and Time Hardening Nonlinear Creep Law," *Int. J. Non-Linear Mechanics*, Vol. 7, No. 2, pp. 221–234 (1972).

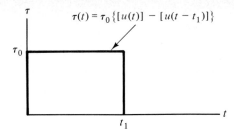

$$\tau(t) = \tau_0 \{[u(t)] - [u(t - t_1)]\}$$

Figure P7.16

where $J(t) = \gamma t + 1 - \exp(-t/t_\varepsilon)$, gives the strain $\varepsilon_c(t)$ as a *linear* hereditary integral over the *function* of stress $[\tau(t)/\mu_c]^n$. Use the convolution theorem of Laplace transform theory to *invert* this equation [i.e., express $\tau(t)$ in terms of a hereditary integral over the history of creep strain $\varepsilon_c(t)$].

7.18. A nonlinear generalized Maxwell model, composed of N nonlinear Maxwell components arranged in parallel, is shown in Fig. P7.18. Note that each Maxwell component consists of a *nonlinear* elastic element in series with a nonlinear viscous element. The constitutive laws for the ith elastic and ith viscous elements are given, respectively, by

$$\varepsilon_{ei} = \left(\frac{\tau_i}{\xi_i}\right)^n \qquad \dot{\varepsilon}_{vi} = \left(\frac{\tau_i}{\lambda_{ci}}\right)^n$$

Show that the strain in the ith Maxwell component may be expressed as

$$\varepsilon_i(t) = \int_{0^-}^{t} (\beta_i + t - t') \frac{\partial}{\partial t'} \left[\frac{\tau_i(t')}{\lambda_{ci}}\right]^n dt'$$

where $\beta_i = (\lambda_{ci}/\xi_i)^n$. Obtain the constitutive equation for the *entire* nonlinear generalized Maxwell model. (*Note*: As discussed in Problem 7.17, you may use the convolution theorem to solve the equation above for the stress, τ_i, in the ith Maxwell component.)

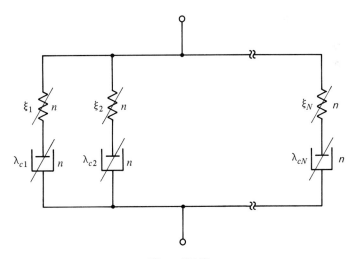

Figure P7.18

7.19. Verify Eqs. (7.96) for $n = 6, 7, 8, 9$. Then use these equations to verify that the polynomials p_n, q_n, r_n in Eq. (7.97) satisfy the following recursion formulas:

$$p_n = q_{n-1}$$

$$q_n = -\mathrm{II}_D p_{n-1} + r_{n-1}$$

$$r_n = \mathrm{III}_D p_{n-1}$$

Finally, use these recursion formulas to determine p_{10}, q_{10}, and r_{10}.

7.20. Consider the first invariant of stress, $I_\tau = \tau_{pp}$. Prove that

$$\frac{\partial I_\tau}{\partial \tau_{ij}} = \delta_{ij}$$

Now consider the third invariant of the stress deviator, $J_3 = \frac{1}{3} s_{pq} s_{qr} s_{rp}$. Verify Eq. (7.116); that is,

$$\frac{\partial J_3}{\partial \tau_{ij}} = r_{ij}$$

where r_{ij} is defined by Eq. (7.117).

7.21. For compressible creep strain the creep potential Φ will in general depend not only on the invariants J_2 and J_3 but also on the first invariant of stress, I_τ. Explain why in this case Eq. (7.118) generalizes to

$$\varepsilon_{ij} = \left[\frac{\partial \Phi}{\partial I_\tau} \delta_{ij} + \frac{\partial \Phi}{\partial J_2} s_{ij} + \frac{\partial \Phi}{\partial J_3} r_{ij} \right] f(t)$$

A possible choice for Φ is to replace Eq. (7.123) by

$$\Phi(I_\tau, J_2) = \frac{C}{m+1} \left[J_2 + \frac{1-2\nu}{6(1+\nu)} I_\tau^2 \right]^{m+1}$$

where ν is the creep Poisson coefficient.* Prove that we then obtain the compressible constitutive law

$$\varepsilon_{ij} = C \left[J_2 + \frac{1-2\nu}{6(1+\nu)} I_\tau^2 \right]^{m} \left(\tau_{ij} - \frac{\nu}{1+\nu} I_\tau \delta_{ij} \right) f(t)$$

Show that in the special cases $\nu = \frac{1}{2}$ (incompressible) and $m = 0$ (linear) we obtain equations given in the text. Also show that for a one-dimensional test, $\varepsilon_{22} = -\nu \varepsilon_{11}$.

7.22. If we set $f(t) = t$ (steady creep) in the result obtained in Problem 7.21 and generalize to the case of variable stress, we obtain

$$\dot{\varepsilon}_{ij} = C \left[J_2 + \frac{1-2\nu}{6(1+\nu)} I_\tau^2 \right]^{m} \left(\tau_{ij} - \frac{\nu}{1+\nu} I_\tau \delta_{ij} \right)$$

Prove that this equation inverts to

$$\tau_{ij} = C^{-1(2m+1)} \left[K_2 + \frac{1+\nu}{6(1-2\nu)} I_{\dot{\varepsilon}}^2 \right]^{-m(2m+1)} \left(\dot{\varepsilon}_{ij} - \frac{\nu}{1-2\nu} I_{\dot{\varepsilon}} \delta_{ij} \right)$$

where $I_{\dot{\varepsilon}} = \dot{\varepsilon}_{pp}$ and $K_2 = \frac{1}{2} \dot{e}_{ij} \dot{e}_{ij}$. (*Hint:* First express I_τ and J_2 in terms of $I_{\dot{\varepsilon}}$ and K_2.)

7.23. A steel bar under constant uniaxial tensile stress $\tau_0 = 5000$ psi experiences a steady creep rate of $\dot{\varepsilon}_s = 0.5 \times 10^{-5}$ hr^{-1}. If the stress is increased by a factor of 2, the creep rate increases by a factor of 8. Use Eq. (7.5) to determine the values of the one-

---

*For a development of this equation from energy principles, see S. A. Patel, F. A. Cozzarelli, and B. Venkatraman, "Creep of Compressible Circular Plates," *Int. J. Mech. Sci.*, Vol. 5, pp. 77–85 (1963).

dimensional material parameters A and n. Now use Eqs. (7.128) and (7.129) to determine the material parameters C and m, which appear in multidimensional creep law (7.122) with $f(t) = t$ in this case.

7.24. Verify that the bulk and deviatoric parts of Eq. (7.141) are in fact given by Eqs. (7.142). Use integrations by parts to rewrite Eq. (7.142b) in terms of nonlinear hereditary integrals.

7.25. Equation (7.141) was obtained by applying the strain-hardening generalization to the transient and steady creep *components* in Eq. (7.134). Repeat the procedure, but now apply the time-hardening generalization to the creep components or to the total creep.

7.26. Let the total creep strain at *constant stress* be given by the power time function

$$\varepsilon_{ij} = e_{ij} = C(J_2)_0^m (s_{ij})_0 \, t^{1/q}$$

where the subscript $(\cdot)_0$ indicates evaluation at constant stress. Generalize this equation to the state of variable stress by using the time-hardening procedure. Then generalize it by using the strain-hardening procedure; express your result in terms of the invariant

$$I_2 = \tfrac{1}{2} e_{ij} e_{ij}$$

and examine the special case of $q = 1$. [*Note*: Since q is not necessarily an integer, $(e_{ij})^q$ is not defined in a simple manner, and thus it is not apparent how one may solve for t from the creep law above. However, we may avoid this dilemma by first forming the *scalar* invariant I_2 and then solving for t.]

Chapter 8
Plasticity

8.1 INTRODUCTION

In this chapter we study the stress and deformation in materials loaded beyond the elastic limit such that plastic yielding occurs. When the stress-strain law is independent of the rate of deformation but is dependent on the history of deformation, this area of study is called rate-independent plasticity, classical plasticity, or simply *plasticity*. Although constitutive laws for plasticity are not fully developed, we shall nevertheless present relations that are useful under certain conditions. We have already introduced the one-dimensional elastic, perfectly plastic model and the rigid, perfectly plastic model in Chapter 4. The concept of strain hardening was discussed in Section 4.3; we also call this phenomenon *work hardening*. Recall that on unloading from a point B (see Fig. 8.1) in the nonlinear zone, we find linear elastic behavior with a modulus of elasticity equal to that experienced on initial loading of the specimen. On reloading as shown in the diagram, we find that the yield point has been raised. Such complex behavior is indicative of a basic difference between elasticity and plasticity. In the latter it is clear that the strain is a *history-dependent* function of the stress. This greatly increases the difficulty encountered in the application of plasticity theory.

There are many practical situations where materials have plastic properties as described above, and in addition certain of these materials experience significant deformation-rate dependency once the plastic state has been reached. That is, the rate of plastic flow is now an important factor, such as we have seen in earlier chapters on viscoelastic behavior. We say then that such materials display both *plastic* and *viscous* properties. The study of such materials is called rate-sensitive plasticity or simply *viscoplasticity*. Such studies involve dependency on the path of loading (the plasticity aspect) plus dependency on the rate of loading (the viscous aspect). These studies are quite complex and still in a formative stage.

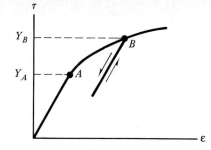

Figure 8.1 One-dimensional stress-strain curve showing work hardening.

In Part A of the chapter we consider some one-dimensional theories of rate-independent plasticity and viscoplasticity. Then in Part B we shall consider in some detail classical, three-dimensional, nonhardening plasticity theories. Finally, in Part C, we consider three-dimensional work hardening, including an introductory treatment of three-dimensional viscoplasticity.

PART A
ONE-DIMENSIONAL PLASTICITY AND VISCOPLASTICITY

8.2 RATE-INDEPENDENT PLASTICITY MODELS

In Figure 8.2 we show a one-dimensional stress-strain diagram wherein you will note that the *loading* in tension and compression of identical specimens gives curves which are identical reflections about the origin O. In particular, the same yield stress is reached (i.e., $Y_A = |Y_{A'}|$). For some materials (e.g., brittle materials) we find that $Y_A \neq |Y_{A'}|$ when loaded separately in tension and compression. We shall

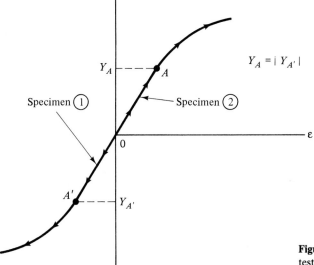

Figure 8.2 Tensile and compressive tests of two identical specimens.

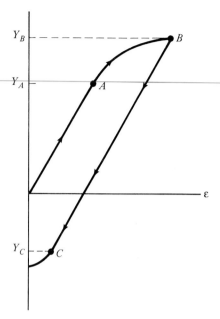

Figure 8.3 Specimen showing Bauschinger effect.

not consider such materials here. In Fig. 8.3 we show an *unloading* of one of the specimens *from* the *tensile* zone *into* the *compression zone*. Note that now a *new* yield stress Y_C is reached whose magnitude is smaller than the yield stress initially reached at A or which will subsequently be attained at B. This is called the *Bauschinger* effect. It is to be pointed out that it is possible (but unlikely) for the yield point on unloading to occur while the specimen is still in tension. In addition to the exclusion of materials exhibiting stress-strain curves that are nonsymmetric about origin O from the *separate* tension and compression loading tests, we shall also disregard the Bauschinger effect in our undertakings in this section. However, we shall return to the Bauschinger effect briefly in Part C.*

In this section we consider some one-dimensional rate-independent models taking us into the plastic zone beyond the yield point. Let us first consider the *linear elastic, perfectly plastic model*. We have already considered this model briefly in Chapter 4 and we show it again in Fig. 8.4. The total strain ε once point A has been passed consists of elastic strain ε_e and plastic strain ε_p. We can then say that

$$\varepsilon_e = \frac{\tau}{E} \tag{8.1a}$$

$$\dot{\varepsilon} = \dot{\varepsilon}_p + \dot{\varepsilon}_e = \dot{\varepsilon}_p + \frac{\dot{\tau}}{E} \tag{8.1b}$$

where for Eq. (8.1b)

$$\dot{\varepsilon}_p = 0 \begin{cases} \text{if } |\tau| < Y & \text{(8.1c)} \\ \text{or if } |\tau| = Y \text{ and } \tau\dot{\tau} < 0 & \text{(8.1d)} \end{cases}$$

---

* In Part C we introduce the *kinematic hardening* model, which would require that distance $\overline{AA}'$ in Fig. 8.2 equal distance $\overline{BC}$ in Fig. 8.3.

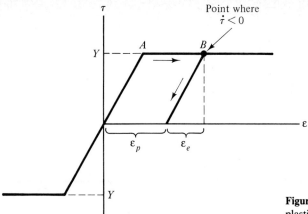

Figure 8.4 Linear elastic, perfectly plastic model with identical tensile and compressive behavior.

In the above we have introduced the magnitude operation so as to allow for the possibility of negative stress, and as noted previously, we have assumed identical tensile and compressive loading behaviors. Condition (8.1d) corresponds to *unloading* (e.g., point B in Fig. 8.4), and you should note that here τ and $\dot{\tau}$ are of *opposite* sign. Also note that ε_p is indeterminate in the model above.

We next consider the *linear elastic, plastic model with power-law strain hardening*. For this model we generalize from the preceding case to include power-law hardening beyond the yield stress Y. This constitutive law can be stated for $\tau \geq 0$ and $\dot{\tau} \geq 0$ as

$$\varepsilon = \frac{\tau}{E} \qquad \text{if } \tau < Y \tag{8.2a}$$

and for $\tau \geq Y$ we employ

$$\varepsilon = \frac{\tau}{E} + \left(\frac{\tau - Y}{\mu_p}\right)^n, \qquad n \geq 1 \tag{8.2b}$$

where μ_p and n are plastic material constants. Immediately at the onset of plastic deformation (i.e., at $\tau = Y$) the total accumulated strain is Y/E, and this strain is entirely elastic. This is evident from Eq. (8.2b). Now, upon continued loading from the yield point the elastic portion of the strain in Eq. (8.2b) is τ/E, which exceeds the initial elastic strain by the amount $(\tau - Y)/E$. (If unloading occurs at $\tau = \tau_1$, the elastic strain τ_1/E is fully recovered, thus leaving the plastic strain $[(\tau_1 - Y)/\mu_p)]^n$ as the permanent set.) Finally, we mention that if we let $Y \to 0$ in Eqs. (8.2), we obtain a frequently used form due to Ramberg and Osgood.[*]

Differentiating Eq. (8.2b) with respect to τ, we get for the slope of the strain-stress curve

$$\frac{d\varepsilon}{d\tau} = \frac{1}{E} + n\left(\frac{\tau - Y}{\mu_p}\right)^{n-1}\frac{1}{\mu_p} \tag{8.3}$$

[*] See A. Mendelson, *Plasticity: Theory and Application* (Melbourne, FL: R.E. Krieger Publishing Co., 1988), p. 20. We should also mention that a power law was proposed by P. Ludwik in 1909.

At $\tau = Y$ and for $n \neq 1$, we thus obtain

$$\frac{d\varepsilon}{d\tau} = \frac{1}{E}, \qquad \tau = Y \qquad (n \neq 1) \tag{8.4}$$

For the case of linear hardening where $n = 1$, we get on differentiating Eq. (8.2b) after setting $n = 1$,

$$\frac{d\varepsilon}{d\tau} = \frac{1}{E} + \frac{1}{\mu_p}, \qquad \tau \geq Y \qquad (n = 1) \tag{8.5}$$

We see from this result that when $n = 1$ the constant μ_p is a *plastic modulus*. Since $d\varepsilon/d\tau = 1/E$ at $\tau = Y^-$ for *any* n, it follows from Eq. (8.4) that the slope of stress-strain diagram at the point $\tau = Y$ is continuous for $n \neq 1$, whereas it is discontinuous for $n = 1$ [see Eq. (8.5)]. This has been illustrated in Fig. 8.5, where we have labeled the $n = 1$ case as a *bilinear* material.* Unloading has also been illustrated in this figure, and we see that the recovered elastic strain ε_r exceeds the initial elastic strain ε_{ei}, since the former includes *additional* elastic strain accumulated during the period of *plastic deformation*.

To allow for negative stress (i.e., compressive stress), we must modify the forms of Eqs. (8.2) by introducing the magnitude operation and the signum function. Thus for *any* τ, we now write for $\tau\dot{\tau} \geq 0$ (i.e., loading)

$$\varepsilon = \begin{cases} \dfrac{\tau}{E} & \text{if } |\tau| < Y \quad \text{(a)} \\[2mm] \dfrac{\tau}{E} + \left(\dfrac{|\tau| - Y}{\mu_p}\right)^n \operatorname{sgn}\tau & \text{if } |\tau| \geq Y \quad \text{(b)} \end{cases} \tag{8.6}$$

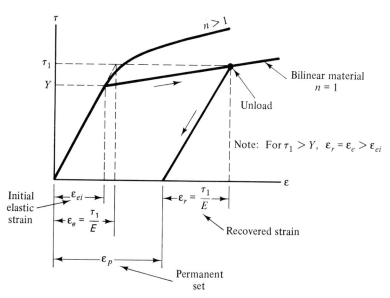

Figure 8.5 Stress-strain model with power-law strain hardening.

* You will recall that this is the case studied in earlier courses and in Chapter 4 as the next more complex model after the elastic, perfectly plastic case.

where we are once more assuming identical tensile and compressive loading behaviors. The presence of the signum function in Eq. (8.6b) ensures that an applied stress generates a plastic strain component of the same sign. We will usually work with the simpler form given in Eqs. (8.2), but the reader is cautioned that if negative stresses are involved, one must use Eqs. (8.6).

Power-law strain hardening is but one of many empirical hardening laws that may be found in the plasticity literature. We shall also employ power-law hardening in the next section (8.3), on rate-sensitive materials. In so doing we shall obtain both strain hardening and strain-rate hardening. In Section 8.4, on generalized rate-sensitive models, we briefly discuss the use of other hardening laws.

8.3 A RATE-SENSITIVE VISCOPLASTIC MECHANICAL MODEL

We now introduce a *rate-sensitive* mechanical model consisting of a nonlinear Kelvin element arranged in parallel with a Saint-Venant (Coulomb) dry-friction element, wherein this arrangement is placed in series with a linear spring (see Fig. 8.6). This is one example of a linear elastic, nonlinear *viscoplastic* model. We shall soon see that this mechanical model gives a reasonable representation of the zone of plastic deformation for various *positive stresses and positive stress rates*. However, this mechanical model and our formulation would require some modification if compression and/or unloading were to be considered. For the sake of simplicity, we shall, at the onset, consider only tensile loads with nonnegative loading rates (i.e., $\tau \geq 0$ and $\dot{\tau} \geq 0$), in our discussion of this particular mechanical model.

Let us first examine each element of this model. Recall that for a linear Kelvin model, on noting that stresses add, we have

$$E\varepsilon + \eta\dot{\varepsilon} = \tau$$

Now dividing by η and introducing the *strain retardation time*, $t_\varepsilon = \eta/E$, we have

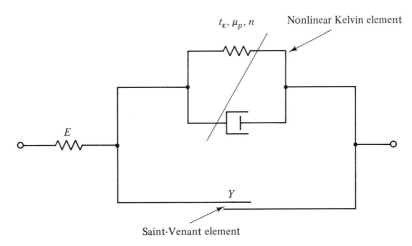

Figure 8.6 Example of a linear elastic, nonlinear viscoplastic mechanical model.

$$\dot{\varepsilon} + \frac{\varepsilon}{t_\varepsilon} = \frac{1}{t_\varepsilon}\left(\frac{\tau}{E}\right) \qquad\qquad (8.7)$$

To make this constitutive equation nonlinear, we use the power-law format [look back at Eq. (7.36)] and generalize it to the following form:

$$\dot{\varepsilon} + \frac{\varepsilon}{t_\varepsilon} = \frac{1}{t_\varepsilon}\left(\frac{\tau}{\mu_p}\right)^n, \qquad n \geq 1 \qquad\qquad (8.8)$$

[We shall soon see that μ_p and n are the same plastic constants employed in rate-independent equation (8.2).] Next we go to the rigid, perfectly plastic *dry friction* (Saint-Venant) element in Fig. 8.6, whose stress-strain rate diagram is shown in Fig. 8.7. We can immediately say that for this element,

$$\dot{\varepsilon} = 0 \qquad \text{if } \tau < Y \qquad \text{(a)}$$
$$\dot{\varepsilon} \geq 0 \qquad \text{if } \tau = Y \qquad \text{(b)} \qquad\qquad (8.9)$$

Note that Eqs. (8.9) may be obtained from Eqs. (8.1) for linear elastic, perfectly plastic behavior, by setting $\varepsilon_e = 0$ in these equations with $\tau \geq 0$ and $\dot{\tau} \geq 0$.

We are now ready to consider the entire linear elastic, nonlinear viscoplastic mechanical model of Fig. 8.6. It is clear that the total strain is given by

$$\varepsilon = \frac{\tau}{E} + \varepsilon_p \qquad\qquad (8.10)$$

where ε_p is the plastic strain stemming from the parallel Kelvin, Saint-Venant viscoplastic system. In determining the equation for ε_p, we shall use the subscripts V and K to denote components in the Saint-Venant and Kelvin elements, respectively. First, due to the parallel arrangement, we note that the applied stress τ and the plastic strain ε_p are expressed in terms of components as

$$\tau = \tau_K + \tau_V \qquad \text{(a)}$$
$$\varepsilon_p = \varepsilon_K = \varepsilon_V \qquad \text{(b)} \qquad\qquad (8.11)$$

If $\tau < Y$, the Saint-Venant element is *rigid* [see Eq. (8.9a)], and any applied stress is carried entirely by this element. Thus

$$\tau_V = \tau, \qquad \tau_K = 0$$
$$\dot{\varepsilon}_V = \dot{\varepsilon}_K = \dot{\varepsilon}_p = 0 \qquad \text{for } \tau < Y \qquad\qquad (8.12)$$

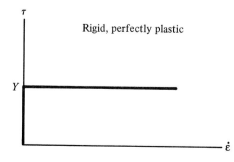

Figure 8.7 Stress-strain rate diagram for Saint-Venant element.

On the other hand, if $\tau \geq Y$, the Saint-Venant element carries a stress equal to Y resulting in a nonnegative strain-rate [see Eq. (8.9b)], that is,

$$\tau_V = Y, \qquad \dot{\varepsilon}_V \geq 0 \qquad \text{for } \tau \geq Y \tag{8.13}$$

Note that $\dot{\varepsilon}_V$ will be zero if the strain rate in the parallel Kelvin element (i.e., $\dot{\varepsilon}_K$) is zero. The stress that is in excess of Y (i.e., the *overstress* $\tau - Y$) is transmitted to the parallel Kelvin element, resulting in the following strain response [see Eq. (8.8)]:

$$\dot{\varepsilon}_K + \frac{\varepsilon_K}{t_\varepsilon} = \frac{1}{t_\varepsilon} \left(\frac{\tau - Y}{\mu_p} \right)^n \qquad \text{for } \tau \geq Y \tag{8.14}$$

Since $\dot{\varepsilon}_p = \dot{\varepsilon}_K = \dot{\varepsilon}_V$, we now see that ε_V and ε_p are *determinate*. For $\tau = Y$ and $\varepsilon_K = 0$ (i.e., no initial strain), Eq. (8.14) gives $\dot{\varepsilon}_K = 0$, and thus $\dot{\varepsilon}_V$ and $\dot{\varepsilon}_p$ also vanish for this condition.

By combining Eqs. (8.10), (8.12), and (8.14), we may express the results above as

$$\dot{\varepsilon} = \frac{\dot{\tau}}{E} + \dot{\varepsilon}_p \tag{8.15a}$$

where

$$\dot{\varepsilon}_p = 0 \qquad \text{for } \tau < Y \tag{8.15b}$$

$$\dot{\varepsilon}_p = \frac{1}{t_\varepsilon} \left(\frac{\tau - Y}{\mu_p} \right)^n - \frac{\varepsilon_p}{t_\varepsilon} \qquad \text{for } \tau \geq Y \tag{8.15c}$$

Furthermore, since $\varepsilon_p = \varepsilon - \tau/E$, we may also express the above as

$$\dot{\varepsilon} = \begin{cases} \dfrac{\dot{\tau}}{E} & \text{for } \tau < Y \quad \text{(a)} \\[2ex] \dfrac{\dot{\tau}}{E} + \dfrac{1}{t_\varepsilon} \left[\left(\dfrac{\tau - Y}{\mu_p} \right)^n - \varepsilon + \dfrac{\tau}{E} \right] & \text{for } \tau \geq Y \quad \text{(b)} \end{cases} \tag{8.16}$$

Note that if we multiply Eq. (8.16b) by t_ε and then set $t_\varepsilon = 0$, we get rate-independent law (8.2).*

Now consider the *static load test* in which case $\dot{\varepsilon} \approx 0$ and $\dot{\tau} \approx 0$ (i.e., the strain and stress rates are *very small*) and $\varepsilon = \varepsilon_s$ and $\tau = \tau_s$. First integrate Eq.(8.16a) for this static case. Then set $\dot{\varepsilon} = \dot{\tau} = 0$ in Eq. (8.16b) and solve for ε, which now becomes ε_s, in terms of τ, which now becomes τ_s. We get for these equations,

$$\varepsilon_s = \begin{cases} \dfrac{\tau_s}{E} & \text{for } \tau_s < Y \quad \text{(a)} \\[2ex] \dfrac{\tau_s}{E} + \left(\dfrac{\tau_s - Y}{\mu_p} \right)^n & \text{for } \tau_s \geq Y \quad \text{(b)} \end{cases} \tag{8.17}$$

which is the rate-independent model with power-law strain hardening presented

---

* You may recall that in Chapter 4 we studied the linear *Bingham* viscoplastic model. If in Eq. (8.16) we let $n = 1$, $E \to \infty$, $t_\varepsilon \to \infty$, $\mu_p \to 0$, and $t_\varepsilon \mu_p \to \eta$, this equation simplifies to Eq. (4.16) for a Bingham material and the model in Fig. 8.6 becomes the Bingham model of Fig. 4.22.

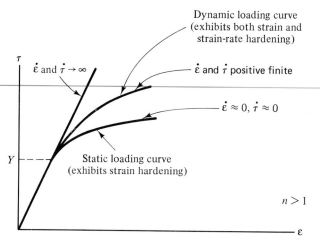

Figure 8.8 Linear elastic, viscoplastic curves for various loading rates.

earlier [see Eqs. (8.2)]. Next let $\dot{\varepsilon}$ and $\dot{\tau} \to \infty$ in Eq. (8.16), which corresponds to *infinitely rapid loading* with stress τ_∞ and strain ε_∞. This results in the simple linear elastic relation

$$\varepsilon_\infty = \frac{\tau_\infty}{E} \qquad \text{for all } \tau_\infty \qquad\qquad (8.18)$$

since in this case the strain and stress rates in Eq. (8.16b) completely dominate the other terms.[*] In Fig. 8.8 we have sketched τ versus ε for these two extreme cases with $n > 1$. The general case of $\dot{\varepsilon}$ and $\dot{\tau}$ positive finite will fall within these limiting cases, and this has also been shown in the figure. Note how the plastic zone "lifts" as the loading rate is increased. Clearly, this model exhibits strain-rate hardening as well as strain hardening.

We remind you that the formulation in this section has been restricted to cases in which $\tau \geq 0$ and $\dot{\tau} \geq 0$ (i.e., tensile stress with no unloading). We may easily extend it to also include the case of compressive stress with no unloading (i.e., $\tau \leq 0$ and $\dot{\tau} \leq 0$). Thus, assuming identical tensile and compressive behaviors, we modify Eq. (8.15) as follows when τ and $\dot{\tau}$ have the *same sign*:

$$\dot{\varepsilon}_p = \begin{cases} 0 & \text{for } |\tau| < Y \\ \dfrac{1}{t_\varepsilon}\left(\dfrac{|\tau| - Y}{\mu_p}\right)^n \operatorname{sgn}\tau - \dfrac{\varepsilon_p}{t_\varepsilon} & \text{for } |\tau| \geq Y, \quad \tau\dot{\tau} \geq 0 \end{cases} \qquad (8.19)$$

The case of unloading (i.e., $\tau \geq 0$ and $\dot{\tau} \leq 0$, or $\tau \leq 0$ and $\dot{\tau} \geq 0$) would in general require a more complex modification. However, it is reasonable to assume that the viscoplastic element in the mechanical model of Fig. 8.6 simply "locks" upon unloading (i.e., $\dot{\varepsilon}_p = 0$ for $\tau\dot{\tau} < 0$).

---

[*] This point will be illustrated in Example 8.1 of the next section and in the problems at the end of the chapter.

8.4 THE CASE OF STRESS HISTORY VARYING LINEARLY WITH TIME

To illustrate how we obtain the *stress-strain* curve for a positive finite $\dot{\tau}$ in the linear elastic, nonlinear viscoplastic model of the preceding section, consider the special case of a stress which increases linearly with time. Thus

$$\tau(t) = \tau_0 + \dot{\tau}_0 t, \qquad \tau_0 < Y, \quad \tau \geq 0^+ \tag{8.20}$$

where τ_0 and $\dot{\tau}_0$ are positive constants equal to the initial stress and the constant stress rate, respectively. It is clear that here $\tau(0^+) = \tau_0$ and $\tau = Y$ at $t = (Y - \tau_0)/\dot{\tau}_0$. We assume that $\tau_0 < Y$ and thus* the plastic strain component is zero at $t = 0^+$. Let us now integrate Eqs. (8.15) for stress history (8.20). Equation (8.15b) immediately gives

$$\varepsilon_p(t) = 0 \qquad \text{for } 0^+ \leq t < \frac{Y - \tau_0}{\dot{\tau}_0} \tag{8.21}$$

where we have used the initial condition $\varepsilon_p(0^+) = 0$. Equation (8.15c) may first be rewritten as

$$\frac{d}{dt}[\varepsilon_p \exp(t/t_\varepsilon)] = \exp(t/t_\varepsilon)\frac{1}{t_\varepsilon}\left(\frac{\tau - Y}{\mu_p}\right)^n \qquad \text{for } t \geq \frac{Y - \tau_0}{\dot{\tau}_0}$$

Since ε_p is not discontinuous, we now have the initial condition $\varepsilon_p = 0$ at $t = (Y - \tau_0)/\dot{\tau}_0$. Integrating then from $t = (Y - \tau_0)/\dot{\tau}_0$ to a variable upper limit t and setting ε_p at time $t = [(Y - \tau_0)/\dot{\tau}_0]$ equal to zero, we get from the above,

$$\varepsilon_p(t) = \frac{1}{t_\varepsilon}\int_{(Y-\tau_0)/\dot{\tau}_0}^t \exp\left(\frac{t'-t}{t_\varepsilon}\right)\left[\frac{\tau(t')-Y}{\mu_p}\right]^n dt' \qquad \text{for } t \geq \frac{Y-\tau_0}{\dot{\tau}_0} \tag{8.22}$$

Finally, we use Eq. (8.20) to eliminate t from Eqs. (8.21) and (8.22) and also from their respective specified ranges of applicability. We thereby obtain the relation

$$\varepsilon_p(\tau) = 0 \qquad \text{for } \tau_0 \leq \tau < Y \tag{a}$$

$$\varepsilon_p(\tau) = \frac{1}{t_\varepsilon \dot{\tau}_0}\int_Y^\tau \exp\left(\frac{\tau'-\tau}{t_\varepsilon \dot{\tau}_0}\right)\left[\frac{\tau'-Y}{\mu_p}\right]^n d\tau' \qquad \text{for } \tau \geq Y \tag{b}$$

$$\tag{8.23}$$

The strain-stress curve is then formed from $\varepsilon = \tau/E + \varepsilon_p(\tau)$. We illustrate this process in the following example.

Example 8.1

Determine the equation of the strain-stress curve for a viscoplastic material governed by Eq. (8.23) with $n = 1$. Investigate the extreme cases $\dot{\tau}_0 \to 0$ and $\dot{\tau}_0 \to \infty$, and also examine the continuity of the slope at $\tau = Y$ for a general $\dot{\tau}_0$.

---

* It would make no mathematical sense to let $\tau_0 > Y$ in Eq. (8.20), since the onset of plastic behavior would then occur in the infinitesimally small time interval $0^- \leq t \leq 0^+$. We could avoid this dilemma by replacing Eq. (8.20) by a more realistic expression such as

$$\tau(t) = \tau_0[1 - \exp(-t/t_0)] + \dot{\tau}_0 t$$

For such a stress input the expression for $\varepsilon_p(t)$ is essentially the same as for the linear input above, but now $\varepsilon_p(\tau)$ is not expressible in explicit form.

Setting $n = 1$ in Eq. (8.23), we have for the plastic strain

$$\varepsilon_p(\tau) = \frac{1}{t_\varepsilon \dot{\tau}_0} \int_Y^\tau \exp\left(\frac{\tau' - \tau}{t_\varepsilon \dot{\tau}_0}\right)\left(\frac{\tau' - Y}{\mu_p}\right) d\tau' \qquad \text{for } \tau \geq Y \qquad \text{(a)}$$

To facilitate the integration of Eq. (a), we introduce the variable change $\sigma' = \tau' - Y$ and thereby obtain

$$\varepsilon_p(\tau) = \frac{1}{t_\varepsilon \dot{\tau}_0 \mu_p} \exp\left[\frac{-(\tau - Y)}{t_\varepsilon \dot{\tau}_0}\right] \int_0^{\tau - Y} \sigma' \exp\left(\frac{\sigma'}{t_\varepsilon \dot{\tau}_0}\right) d\sigma' \qquad \text{for } \tau \geq Y \qquad \text{(b)}$$

Carrying out an integration by parts, we find for the integral above

$$\int_0^{\tau - Y} \sigma' \exp\left(\frac{\sigma'}{t_\varepsilon \dot{\tau}_0}\right) d\sigma' = \sigma' t_\varepsilon \dot{\tau}_0 \exp\left(\frac{\sigma'}{t_\varepsilon \dot{\tau}_0}\right)\Big|_0^{\tau - Y} - \int_0^{\tau - Y} t_\varepsilon \dot{\tau}_0 \exp\left(\frac{\sigma'}{t_\varepsilon \dot{\tau}_0}\right) d\sigma'$$

$$= t_\varepsilon \dot{\tau}_0\left\{(\tau - Y)\exp\left(\frac{(\tau - Y)}{t_\varepsilon \dot{\tau}_0}\right) - t_\varepsilon \dot{\tau}_0\left[\exp\left(\frac{(\tau - Y)}{t_\varepsilon \dot{\tau}_0}\right) - 1\right]\right\}$$

Substituting back into Eq. (b) and adding the elastic term, we finally get

$$\varepsilon(\tau) = \frac{\tau}{E} + \frac{\tau - Y}{\mu_p} - \frac{t_\varepsilon \dot{\tau}_0}{\mu_p}\left[1 - \exp\left(\frac{-(\tau - Y)}{t_\varepsilon \dot{\tau}_0}\right)\right] \qquad \text{for } \tau \geq Y \qquad \text{(c)}$$

Note that as indicated in Eq. (8.22), solution (c) above is valid for the time interval $t \geq (Y - \tau_0)/\dot{\tau}_0$.

In the preceding section we stated that in the *static load case* we let $\dot{\tau} \to 0$ and set $\varepsilon = \varepsilon_s$ and $\tau = \tau_s$. For Eq. (8.20) this implies that $\dot{\tau}_0 \to 0$, but since $\tau_0 < Y$ the possibility of plastic deformation at *finite* time is precluded. However, it will suffice for us to set $\varepsilon = \varepsilon_s$, $\tau = \tau_s$, and $\dot{\tau}_0 = \Delta$, where Δ is *very small*. In this case the last term in Eq. (c) is negligibly small, and this equation is closely approximated by

$$\varepsilon_s(t) \approx \frac{\tau_s}{E} + \frac{\tau_s - Y}{\mu_p} \qquad \text{for } \tau \geq Y \quad \text{and} \quad \dot{\tau}_0 = \Delta \approx 0 \qquad \text{(d)}$$

which checks with Eq. (8.2) for $n = 1$ (i.e., the bilinear case). Equation (d) applies to the time interval $t \geq t_s = (Y - \tau_0)/\Delta$, where t_s is very large since Δ is very small.

Turning now to the case of *infinitely rapid loading* (i.e., $\dot{\tau}_0 \to \infty$, $\varepsilon = \varepsilon_\infty$, and $\tau = \tau_\infty$), we employ l'Hospital's rule to evaluate the last term in Eq. (c). Thus

$$\lim_{\dot{\tau}_0 \to \infty} \frac{t_\varepsilon \dot{\tau}_0}{\mu_p}\left[1 - \exp\left(\frac{-(\tau - Y)}{t_\varepsilon \dot{\tau}_0}\right)\right] = \lim_{x = (1/\dot{\tau}_0) \to 0} \frac{t_\varepsilon}{\mu_p}\left(\frac{1 - \exp[-(\tau - Y)x/t_\varepsilon]}{x}\right)$$

$$= \frac{t_\varepsilon}{\mu_p} \lim_{x \to 0} \frac{[(\tau - Y)/t_\varepsilon]\exp[-(\tau - Y)x/t_\varepsilon]}{1} = \frac{\tau - Y}{\mu_p}$$

Substituting this result into Eq. (c) yields, with $\tau = \tau_\infty$ and $\varepsilon = \varepsilon_\infty$,

$$\varepsilon_\infty(\tau) = \frac{\tau_\infty}{E} \qquad \text{for } \tau_\infty \geq Y \quad \text{and} \quad \dot{\tau}_0 \to \infty \qquad \text{(e)}$$

which again checks with previous results [see Eq. (8.18)]. Since $\varepsilon = \tau/E$ for $\tau < Y$ with any value for $\dot{\tau}_0$, it is clear from Eqs. (d) and (e) that whereas the slope at the point $\tau = Y$ is continuous for $\dot{\tau}_0 \to \infty$, it is discontinuous for $\dot{\tau}_0 = \Delta \approx 0$.

For $\dot{\tau}_0$ *nonzero finite* we return to Eq. (c) and differentiate with respect to τ, giving

$$\frac{d\varepsilon}{d\tau} = \frac{1}{E} + \frac{1}{\mu_p}\left[1 - \exp\left(\frac{-(\tau - Y)}{t_\varepsilon \dot{\tau}_0}\right)\right] \qquad \text{for } \tau \geq Y \qquad \text{(f)}$$

It then follows that

$$\frac{d\varepsilon}{d\tau} = \frac{1}{E} \quad \text{and} \quad \frac{d\tau}{d\varepsilon} = E \qquad \text{at } \tau = Y \qquad \text{(g)}$$

$$\frac{d\varepsilon}{d\tau} \to \frac{1}{E} + \frac{1}{\mu_p} \quad \text{and} \quad \frac{d\tau}{d\varepsilon} \to \frac{E\mu_p}{E + \mu_p} \qquad \text{as } \tau \to \infty \quad \text{and} \quad \varepsilon \to \infty \qquad \text{(h)}$$

From Eq. (f) it is evident that as τ increases the slope of ε versus τ increases. This indicates that as we have shown in Fig. 8.9 for $\dot{\tau}_0$ positive finite, the slope of τ versus ε is monotonically decreasing for $\tau \geq Y$ and is continuous at *all points* (including $\tau = Y$). Furthermore, the slope of the τ–ε curve for a general nonzero finite $\dot{\tau}_0$ approaches the slope of the static case ($\dot{\tau}_0 = \Delta \approx 0$) as both τ and $\varepsilon \to \infty$, as can be seen by considering Eq. (h) and the derivative of Eq. (d). This has also been indicated in Fig. 8.9.

Let us now discuss the time factor for the curves in the plastic region of Fig. 8.9. For the case $\dot{\tau}_0 = \Delta \approx 0$ (i.e., the static load case), each point on the curve represents the strain when the corresponding stress has been applied for very long times which are greater than t_s [see comment after Eq. (d)]. At the other extreme (i.e., as $\dot{\tau}_0 \to \infty$), each point on the curve represents a strain reached *directly after* the corresponding stress has been *suddenly* applied. This is because the time interval required for the onset of yielding [i.e., $(Y - \tau_0)/\dot{\tau}_0$] approaches *zero* as $\dot{\tau}_0$ approaches infinity. Clearly, we have not considered inertial effects for this loading and the other loadings. For $\dot{\tau}_0$ positive finite, as time proceeds from zero onward we move along the indicated curve in Fig. 8.9. Each point corresponds to a time t. What happens if at a certain time we stop increasing the load and keep τ constant? We no longer stay on the indicated intermediate curve, because $\dot{\tau}$ is no longer greater than zero. As time progresses, we would move *horizontally* (to keep τ constant) and after a very long time period we would end up on the *static loading curve*.

In the above example we obtained closed-form expressions for $n = 1$, but we may also obtain such expressions for cases where $n > 1$. For example, for the nonlinear hardening case $n = 3$ one may proceed in the same manner as presented in Example 8.1, except that now three integrations by parts would be required. The calculations are straightforward, although somewhat tedious (see Problem 8.6).

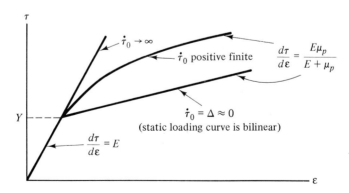

Figure 8.9 Linear elastic, viscoplastic curves for case $n = 1$ with various constant loading rates $\dot{\tau}_0$.

8.5 SOME GENERALIZATIONS FOR RATE-SENSITIVE VISCOPLASTIC MATERIALS

The linear elastic, nonlinear viscoplastic law presented in the preceding sections is just *one example* of the *many* viscoplastic laws that have been proposed. We chose to present this particular law since it was obtainable from a spring–dashpot–dry friction model, and such mechanical models are a useful aid in physical visualization. Although viscoplastic laws are in general not obtainable from such mechanical models, a close examination of Eqs. (8.16) will enable us to present a generalization that includes various other laws. First note that Eq. (8.16b) may be rewritten as

$$\dot{\varepsilon} = \frac{\dot{\tau}}{E} + \frac{1}{t_\varepsilon}[f(\tau) - \varepsilon] \qquad \text{for } \tau \geq Y \text{ and } \dot{\tau} \geq 0 \qquad (a)$$

where

$$f(\tau) = \frac{\tau}{E} + \left(\frac{\tau - Y}{\mu_p}\right)^n \qquad (b)$$

(8.24)

is the power-law representation for the *static* strain-stress curve [see Eq. (8.17)].

We shall now prove that the conditions $\tau \geq Y$ and $\dot{\tau} \geq 0$ in Eq. (8.24a) imply that $\dot{\varepsilon} \geq \dot{\tau}/E$ and $f(\tau) \geq \varepsilon$. Let t_0 be the time at which plastic deformation commences. Thus the elastic solution gives us the initial conditions $\tau(t_0) = Y$, $\varepsilon(t_0) = Y/E$, and $\dot{\varepsilon}(t_0) = \dot{\tau}(t_0)/E$. First we rewrite Eq. (8.24a) in the form

$$\left(\dot{\varepsilon} + \frac{\varepsilon}{t_\varepsilon}\right) - \frac{1}{E}\left(\dot{\tau} + \frac{\tau}{t_\varepsilon}\right) = \frac{1}{t_\varepsilon}\left(\frac{\tau - Y}{\mu_p}\right)^n$$

Differentiating this equation we obtain

$$\left(\ddot{\varepsilon} + \frac{\dot{\varepsilon}}{t_\varepsilon}\right) - \frac{1}{E}\left(\ddot{\tau} + \frac{\dot{\tau}}{t_\varepsilon}\right) = \frac{n}{t_\varepsilon}\left(\frac{\tau - Y}{\mu_p}\right)^{n-1}\frac{\dot{\tau}}{\mu_p} \geq 0$$

where the inequality follows from the conditions $\tau \geq Y$ and $\dot{\tau} \geq 0$. The inequality above may be rewritten more compactly as

$$\exp\left(\frac{-t}{t_\varepsilon}\right)\frac{d}{dt}\left[\exp\left(\frac{t}{t_\varepsilon}\right)\left(\dot{\varepsilon} - \frac{\dot{\tau}}{E}\right)\right] \geq 0$$

After multiplying the above by the positive factor $\exp(t/t_\varepsilon)$, we conclude that the expression in brackets is monotonically increasing, that is,

$$\exp\left(\frac{t}{t_\varepsilon}\right)\left[\dot{\varepsilon}(t) - \frac{\dot{\tau}(t)}{E}\right] \geq \exp\left(\frac{t_0}{t_\varepsilon}\right)\left[\dot{\varepsilon}(t_0) - \frac{\dot{\tau}(t_0)}{E}\right] = 0$$

where the equality on the right follows from the previously stated initial conditions. Multiplying by $\exp(-t/t_\varepsilon)$, we finally have

$$\dot{\varepsilon}(t) \geq \frac{\dot{\tau}(t)}{E}$$

Using this result in Eq. (8.24a) we see that $f(\tau) \geq \varepsilon$, and this enables us to rewrite this equation as

$$\dot{\varepsilon} = \frac{\dot{\tau}}{E} + \frac{1}{t_\varepsilon}\left[f(\tau) - \varepsilon\right], \qquad f(\tau) \geq \varepsilon \tag{8.25}$$

This equation clearly says that the *plastic strain rate is a function of the excess stress above the static yield condition.*

One could write Eq. (8.25) more generally as

$$\dot{\varepsilon} = \frac{\dot{\tau}}{E} + A\left[F(\tau) - \varepsilon\right], \qquad F(\tau) \geq \varepsilon \tag{8.26}$$

where A is a material constant with dimensions $(\sec)^{-1}$, and $F(\tau)$ is *any* (not necessarily power-law) function representing the *static strain-stress curve.* Instead of Eq. (8.26), we could also write

$$\dot{\varepsilon} = \frac{\dot{\tau}}{E} + K\left[\tau - g(\varepsilon)\right], \qquad \tau \geq g(\varepsilon) \tag{8.27}$$

where the constant K has dimensions $(\text{psi})^{-1}(\sec)^{-1}$, and $g(\varepsilon)$ is the *static stress-strain function* obtained by *inverting* the equation $\varepsilon = F(\tau)$ [i.e., $g(\varepsilon) = F^{-1}(\varepsilon)$].*

Further generalizations of Eq. (8.27) can be made and indeed have been made. For example, if we replace the constant K by another function of strain, we get

$$\dot{\varepsilon} = \frac{\dot{\tau}}{E} + G(\varepsilon)\left[\tau - g(\varepsilon)\right], \qquad \tau \geq g(\varepsilon) \tag{8.28a}$$

If in particular we set $G(\varepsilon) = B/g(\varepsilon)$, where B is a material constant with dimensions $(\sec)^{-1}$, we get

$$\dot{\varepsilon} = \frac{\dot{\tau}}{E} + B\left[\frac{\tau}{g(\varepsilon)} - 1\right], \qquad \tau \geq g(\varepsilon) \tag{8.28b}$$

which is a variation of the form given by Eq. (8.27). Note that Eqs. (8.28a) and (8.28b) satisfy the requirements

$$\tau = \begin{cases} g(\varepsilon) & \text{for } \dot{\varepsilon} \approx 0 \quad \text{and} \quad \dot{\tau} \approx 0 \quad \text{(static case)} \\ E\varepsilon & \text{for } \dot{\varepsilon} \to \infty \quad \text{and} \quad \dot{\tau} \to \infty \quad \text{(infinitely rapid loading)} \end{cases}$$

Various viscoplastic laws in the plasticity literature are in the form of Eq. (8.28a). Once again, we point out that viscoplastic laws such as (8.25), (8.26), (8.27), (8.28a), and (8.28b) are often valid only for the case of nonnegative stress and nonnegative stress rates (i.e., $\tau \geq 0$ and $\dot{\tau} \geq 0$). Such laws are usually easily extended to the case $\tau \leq 0$ and $\dot{\tau} \leq 0$ (i.e., $\tau\dot{\tau} \geq 0$), but when considering stress reversals and cyclic stresses

---

*Equation (8.27) was proposed by V. V. Sokolovsky in 1948, and then generalized in 1951 by L. E. Malvern, who replaced the term $K[\tau - g(\varepsilon)]$ by the *function* $\phi[\tau - g(\varepsilon)]$. See L. E. Malvern, "The Propagation of Longitudinal Waves of Plastic Deformation in a Bar of Material Exhibiting a Strain-Rate Effect," *J. Appl. Mech.*, Vol. 18, pp. 203–208 (1951). For further information on early viscoplastic laws, see N. Cristescu, *Dynamic Plasticity* (New York: John Wiley & Sons, Inc., 1967), p. 111. For an application of power law (8.24) to wave propagation, see R. P. Shaw and F. A. Cozzarelli, "Wave-Front Stress Relaxation in a One-Dimensional Nonlinear Inelastic Material with Position and Temperature Dependent Properties," *J. Appl. Mech.*, Vol. 38, pp. 47–50 (1971).

it is best to proceed to more complex modern laws. Much of the recent literature is concerned with rather complex laws, which are able to accurately generate the "hysterisis loop" characteristics of cyclic loading.*

This ends our main discussion of one-dimensional plasticity and viscoplasticity. In Part C we shall come back to a brief discussion of three-dimensional viscoplasticity. Before going on to the next part of this chapter, we should point out that the present trend in this field is directed toward an approach that unifies the constitutive laws of nonlinear viscoelasticity and viscoplasticity. The underlying logic of this "unified approach" is based on the fact that as we have shown in Appendix VII, the primary mechanism in most creep and plasticity processes is the movement of dislocations. This is a field of active research, and the reader is referred to the recent literature.†

PART B
THREE-DIMENSIONAL NONHARDENING PLASTICITY THEORY

8.6 GENERAL YIELD CRITERIA IN THREE DIMENSIONS

We will now extend the criterion for yielding from the one-dimensional concept of a yield stress Y to general three-dimensional states of stress. We will do this while making a series of postulates concerning the onset of yielding. Work hardening and rate-sensitive models will not be considered here, but will be discussed later in Part C.

Postulate 1: General Yield Function Exists

We suppose that initial yielding is dependent only on the state of stress and not on how the stress state is reached. This law will thus define the limit of elasticity and will be referred to as a criterion for yielding. Accordingly, we assume the existence of a *yield function* $f(\tau_{ij})$ such that:

$$\text{Material behavior is elastic}$$

$$\text{if} \quad f(\tau_{ij}) < 0$$

$$\text{or if} \quad f(\tau_{ij}) = 0 \quad \text{and} \quad \dot{f}(\tau_{ij}) < 0 \tag{8.29}$$

where $f(\tau_{ij}) = 0$ defines the *yield surface* in stress space and where $\dot{f}(\tau_{ij}) < 0$ indicates *unloading*.

$$\text{Material behavior is plastic}$$

$$\text{if} \ f(\tau_{ij}) = 0 \quad \text{and} \quad \dot{f}(\tau_{ij}) \geq 0 \tag{8.30}$$

The nonpositive function f, because of the symmetry of the stress tensor, can be

---

*See the review article by E. Krempl, "Models of Viscoplasticity–Some Comments on Equilibrium (Back) Stress and Drag Stress," *Acta Mech.*, Vol. 69, pp. 25–42 (1987).

†For example, see A. K. Miller (ed.), *Unified Constitutive Equations for Creep and Plasticity* (New York: Elsevier Applied Science Publishers Ltd., 1987).

expressed as

$$f = f(\tau_{11}, \tau_{22}, \tau_{33}, \tau_{23}, \tau_{31}, \tau_{12}) \tag{8.31}$$

where we have six independent stress variables. Also, the function f can be expressed as a function of the principal stresses τ_1, τ_2, τ_3 and three angles $\alpha_1, \alpha_2, \alpha_3$ defining the orientation of the principal axes.* That is,

$$f = f(\tau_1, \tau_2, \tau_3, \alpha_1, \alpha_2, \alpha_3) \tag{8.32}$$

Postulate 2: Material Is Isotropic

If the material is isotropic, there can be no preferred directions and the function should have the same form no matter how we orient the axes. This means two things here. First the function f in Eq. (8.32) will not be a function of the angles $\alpha_1, \alpha_2, \alpha_3$ defining the principal axes. Thus we can say that as a result of isotropy,

$$f = f(\tau_1, \tau_2, \tau_3) \tag{8.33}$$

The second conclusion stemming from isotropy is that the function f should not change if the axes are interchanged, so that axis 2 becomes axis 1, and so on. This in turn leads us to conclude that

$$f(\tau_1, \tau_2, \tau_3) = f(\tau_2, \tau_1, \tau_3) = f(\tau_1, \tau_3, \tau_2), \quad \text{etc.} \tag{8.34}$$

We can say that this function is a *symmetric* function of the principal stresses. Furthermore, the principal stresses are completely determined by the three stress tensor invariants $I_\tau, II_\tau, III_\tau$, in accordance with Eq. (2.46). Thus we can also write

$$f = f(I_\tau, II_\tau, III_\tau) \tag{8.35}$$

The latter form *ensures* symmetry in τ_1, τ_2, τ_3, since $I_\tau, II_\tau, III_\tau$ are symmetric in the principal stresses [see Eqs. (2.41)].

Postulate 3: Yielding Is Independent of Hydrostatic Stress

This signifies that the function f depends only on the *deviatoric* principal stresses s_1, s_2, s_3. That is, in place of Eq. (8.33) we have the symmetric function of the deviatoric principal stresses

$$f = f(s_1, s_2, s_3) \tag{8.36}$$

Also, we can use the deviatoric stress invariants $J_1 = I_s, J_2 = -II_s, J_3 = III_s$ [see Eqs. (7.100)] instead of the deviatoric principal stresses above. Noting that by definition $J_1 \equiv 0$, we then have

$$f = f(J_2, J_3) \tag{8.37}$$

---

*A logical choice for $\alpha_1, \alpha_2, \alpha_3$ would be the widely used Euler angles θ, ϕ, ψ of rigid-body dynamics. For details, see I. H. Shames, *Engineering Mechanics—Statics and Dynamics*, 3rd ed. (Englewood Cliffs, NJ: Prentice-Hall, Inc., 1980), p. 810.

Again, we point out that this last function f will as required be symmetric in τ_1, τ_2, τ_3, since J_2 and J_3 are symmetric in s_1, s_2, s_3 and thus in τ_1, τ_2, τ_3.

Postulate 4: Identical Tensile and Compressive Behaviors

We require here that the value of the yield function be unchanged when the signs of *all* stresses are changed. That is,

$$f(\tau_{ij}) = f(-\tau_{ij}) \tag{8.38}$$

Although J_2 is always positive, the third-order invariant J_3 reverses sign if the signs of the stresses are all changed. Condition (8.38) thus requires that in function (8.37) this sign reversal be suppressed, that is, by expressing f as an *even* function of J_3 (e.g., in terms of the *square* of J_3). Equation (8.38) clearly requires that previously untested and identical specimens behave the same way in tension and in compression. Furthermore, if we also require that this condition be obeyed after a specimen has been subjected to an initial plastic deformation, the Baushinger effect is also precluded.

These are then the key postulates for the development of a yield function $f(\tau_{ij})$ in the *classical* theory of plasticity.

8.7 THE GENERAL YIELD SURFACE

The function $f(J_2, J_3) = 0$ defines a surface in a principal stress space having orthogonal axes τ_1, τ_2, τ_3. This surface is called a *yield surface*. Referring back to Eqs. (8.29) and (8.30), we see that if we exclude unloading (i.e., $\dot{f} < 0$), the points inside the yield surface indicate elastic behavior, whereas the points on the yield surface indicate plastic behavior. In this space, the line $\tau_1 = \tau_2 = \tau_3$ is called the *hydrostatic line* and is equally inclined toward the three axes (see Fig. 8.10) with direction cosines $1/\sqrt{3}$. Because of the fact that f is independent of the hydrostatic stress, it should be clear that the yield surface must form an infinite cylinder whose generator is parallel to the hydrostatic line.

In Fig. 8.10 a point P has been shown that lies either inside or on the yield surface, denoting a vector $\boldsymbol{\tau}$ having components τ_1, τ_2, and τ_3.* Also shown as vector components of $\boldsymbol{\tau}$ at P are $\boldsymbol{\tau}_t$, the tangential vector parallel to the hydrostatic line and the yield surface, and the radial vector $\boldsymbol{\tau}_r$, extending from the origin on a plane going through the origin and oriented normal to the hydrostatic line. This plane has been denoted as the *deviator plane* for reasons soon to be seen. We can now write

$$\boldsymbol{\tau}_t = (\boldsymbol{\tau} \cdot \hat{\boldsymbol{\epsilon}}_t)\hat{\boldsymbol{\epsilon}}_t$$

---

* The stress vector $\boldsymbol{\tau}$ (or equivalently, τ_i) is defined here *only* in the *three-dimensional principal* stress space. If one wishes to employ axes which are not necessarily principal axes, we must speak of a *nine-dimensional* space in which the components of the stress vector are τ_{ij}. By invoking the symmetry of τ_{ij}, this nine-dimensional stress space may be replaced by a *six-dimensional* stress space.

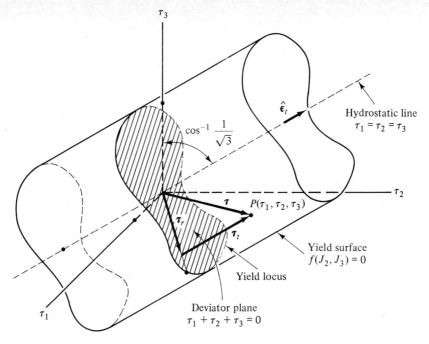

Figure 8.10 Yield surface.

where $\hat{\boldsymbol{\epsilon}}_t$ is the unit vector along the hydrostatic line. Hence

$$\boldsymbol{\tau}_t = \left[(\tau_1 \hat{\mathbf{i}} + \tau_2 \hat{\mathbf{j}} + \tau_3 \hat{\mathbf{k}}) \cdot \frac{1}{\sqrt{3}} (\hat{\mathbf{i}} + \hat{\mathbf{j}} + \hat{\mathbf{k}}) \right] \frac{1}{\sqrt{3}} (\hat{\mathbf{i}} + \hat{\mathbf{j}} + \hat{\mathbf{k}})$$

$$= \tfrac{1}{3}(\tau_1 + \tau_2 + \tau_3)(\hat{\mathbf{i}} + \hat{\mathbf{j}} + \hat{\mathbf{k}}) = \bar{\tau}(\hat{\mathbf{i}} + \hat{\mathbf{j}} + \hat{\mathbf{k}})$$

(8.39)

where $\bar{\tau}$ you will recall is the bulk stress. Also,

$$\boldsymbol{\tau}_r = \boldsymbol{\tau} - \boldsymbol{\tau}_t = (\tau_1 - \bar{\tau})\hat{\mathbf{i}} + (\tau_2 - \bar{\tau})\hat{\mathbf{j}} + (\tau_3 - \bar{\tau})\hat{\mathbf{k}}$$

$$= s_1 \hat{\mathbf{i}} + s_2 \hat{\mathbf{j}} + s_3 \hat{\mathbf{k}}$$

(8.40)

Accordingly, we can now see why we call the crosshatched plane in Fig. 8.10 containing $\boldsymbol{\tau}_r$ the *deviator plane* as indicated above. On this plane we clearly have $\boldsymbol{\tau}_t = \mathbf{0}$. From Eq. (8.39) we can then say that the deviator plane can be given as

$$\tau_1 + \tau_2 + \tau_3 = 0 \qquad \text{deviator plane} \tag{8.41}$$

In Fig. 8.10 the closed curve marking the intersection of the deviator plane with the yield surface has been denoted as the *yield locus*.

It is useful to view the deviator plane along the hydrostatic line (i.e., normal to the deviator plane). The axes are then seen as *projections* onto the deviator plane (see Fig. 8.11).* These axes are accordingly denoted as $(\tau_1)_p$, $(\tau_2)_p$, and $(\tau_3)_p$. We will now show that the elastic region in the deviator plane (crosshatched region) of Fig.

---

* The view of the deviator plane shown in Fig. 8.11 is sometimes called the Π plane.

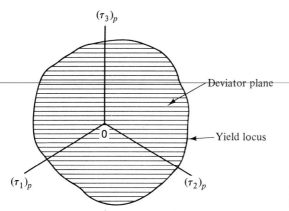

Figure 8.11 View along hydrostatic line showing deviator plane.

8.11 consists of twelve 30° radial segments. We will also find that all 30° radial segments are geometrically identical, except for the fact that adjacent segments are mirror images. First we know that because of isotropy $f(\tau_1, \tau_2, \tau_3)$ must be symmetric in τ_1, τ_2, τ_3. This means that the yield locus (the boundary of the deviator plane) must be symmetric about each of the stress axes, including the extensions in the negative stress directions, which in Fig. 8.12(a) we have designated as $-(\tau_1)_p$, $-(\tau_2)_p$, and $-(\tau_3)_p$. Because of the aforestated symmetry of $f(\tau_1, \tau_2, \tau_3)$ with respect to τ_1, τ_2, and τ_3, clearly 60° radial segment (1) in Fig. 8.12(a) must be the mirror image about $-(\tau_1)_p$ of 60° radial segment (2). Furthermore, 60° segment (2) must be the mirror image about $(\tau_3)_p$ of 60° segment (3), and so on, all around the region enclosed by the yield locus.

In Fig. 8.12(b) we have added bisectors (dashed lines) to the axes of Fig. 8.12(a), thus forming twelve 30° segments from the original six 60° segments. Consider next an observer at O looking outward toward the yield locus curve. This observer looking at bc in a counterclockwise sweep (see dashed arrow ①) will see the same curve looking at arc fh in a counterclockwise sweep (see the dashed arrow ②). This follows from our mirror-image symmetry arguments of the preceding paragraph concerning adjacent 60° segments.* Furthermore, because fh is the mirror image of kg, the observer sees identical views of these curves if he sweeps in opposite senses as illustrated by dashed arrows ② and ③. At this time we invoke the requirements of identical tensile and compressive behaviors. This means that Fig. 8.12(b) must be corrected such that in addition to having Oc equal to Og, we must have Oe equal to Ok. This is so because each point on the yield locus is at the same distance from the origin as the point on the yield locus found by reversing the direction of the radial line through the original point. More generally, we can say that the observer at O sees the same curves kg and ec if he sweeps in the same sense as indicated by dashed arrows ③ and ④. Thus to an observer at O all four curves discussed [and darkened for identification in Fig. 8.12(b)] must be identical if viewed with the directions indicated by the dashed arrows or if viewed with the directions of *all* arrows reversed. Note in particular that curves ec and bc must be

---

* Note that in Fig. 8.12(b) cb is the mirror image of mf about Oe, and mf is also the mirror image of hf about Of. Therefore, bc and fh are identical when viewed from O with the same direction of sweep.

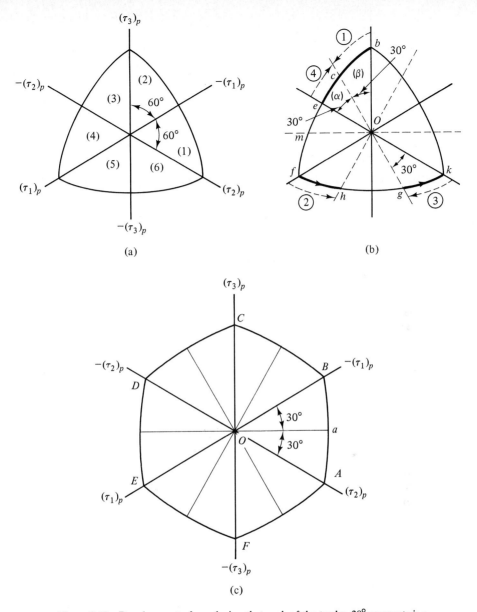

Figure 8.12 Development of conclusion that each of the twelve 30° segments is a mirror image of its adjacent segments.

identical if viewed in opposite sweeps, as indicated by our arrows ④ and ①. This can only mean that contiguous 30° segments (α) and (β) are mirror images of each other. Indeed, we can conclude further, on extending the arguments to other adjacent 30° segments, that they are all mirror images of each other. This is shown in Fig. 8.12(c), in which we have shown *twelve 30° segments, each of which is a mirror image of its contiguous neighbors*. Thus one need only determine the boundary of one of these 30° segments [e.g., curve Aa in Fig. 8.12(c)] to fully establish the entire yield locus and thus the yield surface.

We shall next consider two yield loci that have proven to be very useful.

8.8 TRESCA AND MISES YIELD CRITERIA FOR DUCTILE MATERIALS

Unfortunately, there is no theoretical formulation that precisely gives the state of stress for the condition of yielding in the general three-dimensional case. Experiments with ductile materials do indicate, however, that according to postulate 3 in Section 8.6, the *yield condition at a point tends to be independent of hydrostatic stress at the point*.* We shall present two empirical criteria for the prediction of yielding that satisfy this insensitivity to hydrostatic stress. These two criteria will also satisfy postulates 2 (isotropy) and 4 (identical tensile and compressive behaviors), but we shall defer a detailed determination of the associated yield functions and surfaces to a later section.

The Tresca Yield Criterion

One criterion, called the *Tresca* condition, was first presented by H. Tresca in 1864. This condition states that yielding will begin to occur if one-half the largest difference between the principal stresses reaches a certain critical value k_T, which depends only on the nature of the material. Note that one-half of the largest difference in principal stresses is the *maximum shear stress* at a point [see Eq. (2.66), obtained from three-dimensional Mohr's circles]. Note also that this quantity does not change value when the state of stress is changed hydrostatically. We may now state the Tresca criterion as follows:

$$\text{for onset of yielding} \qquad \tfrac{1}{2}(\tau_{\max} - \tau_{\min}) = k_T \qquad (8.42)$$

where $\tau_{\max}$ and $\tau_{\min}$ signify the *algebraic* maximum and minimum values of the principal stresses, respectively.

We pointed out above that *ideally*, k_T depends only on the material, with the implication that it does *not* depend on the state of stress attending the yield condition. Real materials do not exactly conform to our stated postulates, and thus will also not exactly conform to the Tresca criterion for yielding. Hence, for real materials the value of k_T will be stress-state dependent to some degree in addition to being material dependent. The question then arises as to what constant value we shall assign k_T for general use of the Tresca criterion for real materials. In this regard recall from Chapter 5 (see Section 5.3) that the biaxial stress state, $\tau_{yy} = -\tau_{xx} = S$ and $\tau_{zz} = \tau_{xy} = \tau_{yz} = \tau_{zx} = 0$, corresponds to a state of *pure shear* $\tau_{x'y'} = S$ along axes $x'y'$ oriented 45° from the xy axes. Now, set $\tau_{\max} = S_{(y)}$ and $\tau_{\min} = -S_{(y)}$ in Eq. (8.42),

---

* Hydrostatic stress can be very important when considering yielding in nonmetals such as soils. For further discussion, see R. Hill, *The Mathematical Theory of Plasticity* (London: Oxford University Press, 1950). For more recent work on soil plasticity, see C. S. Desai and H. J. Sirilwardane, *Constitutive Laws for Engineering Materials* (Englewood Cliffs, NJ: Prentice-Hall, Inc., 1984).

where the subscript (y) indicates that we have yielding for this state of stress: namely, pure shear. Just as we have used Y to signify the normal yield stress for pure tension, we shall henceforth use the letter k without subscripts to indicate the *shear yield stress*, so that $(\tau_{x'y'})_{(y)} = S_{(y)} = k$ for *pure shear*. Thus from Eq. (8.42) we see that the Tresca constant k_T equals k, when it is experimentally evaluated by examining pure shear at yield. We restate this important result below:

$$k_T = k \qquad (8.43)$$

This value of k_T could also be found from a simple standard *torsion test* for a thin-walled tube. We may then use this value of k_T for other stress states, to predict yielding with some degree of approximation for real materials.

We can on the other hand use the simple *tensile test* to give us an experimentally determined value of k_T. At yielding the maximum principal stress is now Y and the minimum principal stress is zero. Hence, we can give Eq. (8.42) for this case as follows:

$$\tfrac{1}{2}(Y - 0) = k_T$$

Therefore,

$$k_T = \frac{Y}{2} \qquad (8.44)$$

We may then use *this* value of k_T to predict yielding via Tresca for other states of stress. For instance, consider a state of pure shear again where k represents the shear yield stress. Then using $k_T = Y/2$ as determined experimentally from the tensile test and employing it for a state of pure shear at yield, we see that for ideal Tresca behavior (constant value of k_T) we have

$$(\tau_{xy})_{(y)} = \frac{Y}{2}$$

Therefore,

$$k = \frac{Y}{2} \qquad (8.45)$$

This relates the *yield stresses* for *pure tension*, Y, and *pure shear*, k, for ideal Tresca behavior, using a constant value of k_T as experimentally found from the tensile test. (Note also if we use $k_T = k$ as experimentally obtained from the pure shear test and apply it to a state of pure tension, we get the *same relation* between Y and k as above.) For real materials the yield stress in tension, Y, will *not be exactly* equal to twice the yield stress in pure shear, k. This shows that k_T in real materials is stress-state dependent to some degree. We can use a constant k_T determined experimentally either by the simple tensile test or by the pure shear test, but we shall usually make use of the tensile test result.

Thus, to ascertain with some degree of approximation whether we have yielding at a point for a given state of stress, we can compare the quantity $\tfrac{1}{2}(\tau_{max} - \tau_{min})$ with $Y/2$ resulting from *a one-dimensional tensile test* of the same material at yielding. If

$$\frac{1}{2}(\tau_{\max} - \tau_{\min}) < \frac{Y}{2}$$

we have elastic behavior, and if

$$\frac{1}{2}(\tau_{\max} - \tau_{\min}) \geq \frac{Y}{2}$$

we can expect yielding according to the Tresca criterion. The inequality in the latter expression is possible only if hardening occurs. For the *onset* of yielding we accordingly have

$$\boxed{\frac{1}{2}(\tau_{\max} - \tau_{\min}) = k_T = \frac{Y}{2}} \qquad \text{(Tresca)} \qquad (8.46)$$

The Mises Yield Criterion

We turn next to a yield criterion postulated by *R. von Mises* in 1913. This condition states that yielding occurs when the second invariant of the stress deviator tensor equals the value k_M^2, a value which ideally depends only on the material. Thus at the *onset* of yielding

$$J_2 = \tfrac{1}{2} s_{ij} s_{ij} = k_M^2 \qquad (8.47)$$

In expanded notation the invariant J_2 may be written in the following alternative forms:

$$J_2 = \tfrac{1}{2}(s_{xx}^2 + s_{yy}^2 + s_{zz}^2) + s_{xy}^2 + s_{yz}^2 + s_{zx}^2 \qquad \text{(a)}$$

$$J_2 = \tfrac{1}{6}[(s_{xx} - s_{yy})^2 + (s_{yy} - s_{zz})^2 + (s_{zz} - s_{xx})^2] + s_{xy}^2 + s_{yz}^2 + s_{zx}^2 \qquad \text{(b)} \quad (8.48)$$

$$J_2 = \tfrac{1}{6}[(\tau_{xx} - \tau_{yy})^2 + (\tau_{yy} - \tau_{zz})^2 + (\tau_{zz} - \tau_{xx})^2] + \tau_{xy}^2 + \tau_{yz}^2 + \tau_{zx}^2 \qquad \text{(c)}$$

Equation (8.48a) follows directly from the definition of J_2 given in Eq. (8.47). By subtracting the null quantity $\tfrac{1}{6}(s_{xx} + s_{yy} + s_{zz})^2$, one may obtain Eq. (8.48b), which is clearly equivalent to Eq. (8.48c). Also, for the principal axes of stress (and stress deviator) we have

$$J_2 = \tfrac{1}{2}(s_1^2 + s_2^2 + s_3^2) \qquad \text{(a)}$$

$$J_2 = \tfrac{1}{6}[(s_1 - s_2)^2 + (s_2 - s_3)^2 + (s_3 - s_1)^2] \qquad \text{(b)} \quad (8.49)$$

$$J_2 = \tfrac{1}{6}[(\tau_1 - \tau_2)^2 + (\tau_2 - \tau_3)^2 + (\tau_3 - \tau_1)^2] \qquad \text{(c)}$$

Using the condition of *pure shear* as, for example, found in a torsion test of a thin-walled tube at yield [e.g., $(\tau_{xy})_{(y)} = k$, $\tau_{yz} = \tau_{zx} = \tau_{xx} = \tau_{yy} = \tau_{zz} = 0$], Eqs. (8.47) and (8.48c) give the experimental value

$$k_M = k \qquad (8.50)$$

Thus when the Tresca and Mises criteria are examined experimentally for pure shear at yield to determine k_T and k_M, we get the *same values* for these terms [see

Eq. (8.43)], so we can say for this procedure that

$$k_M = k_T = k \qquad (8.51)$$

A value of k_M can *also* be found experimentally from a *simple tension* test [e.g., $(\tau_{xx})_{(y)} = Y$, $\tau_{yy} = \tau_{zz} = \tau_{xy} = \tau_{yz} = \tau_{zx} = 0$]. In this case Eqs. (8.47) and (8.48c) give

$$k_M = \frac{Y}{\sqrt{3}} \qquad (8.52)$$

We see now on using the k_M from the above stemming from tensile data in Eq. (8.50), which represents yielding for a state of pure shear, that for *ideal* Mises behavior

$$k = \frac{Y}{\sqrt{3}} \qquad (8.53)$$

(Similarly, if we accept $k_M = k$ from the pure shear data and apply it to a state of tension so that at yield $Y/\sqrt{3} = k_M = k$, we get the same relation as above.) A comparison of Eq. (8.53) with Eq. (8.45) indicates that the shear yield stress in pure shear, k, for *ideal Mises behavior* (again constant k_M) is related *differently* to the yield stress in pure tension, Y, than was the case for *ideal Tresca behavior*. Since neither Eq. (8.53) nor (8.45) is satisfied precisely for real materials, it is clear that like k_T, k_M is *stress-state dependent*. Thus for the *onset* of yielding using the *tensile test* result for k_M, the Mises criterion says that

$$\boxed{J_2 = k_M^2 = \frac{Y^2}{3}} \qquad \text{(Mises)} \qquad (8.54)$$

Now, if we set $k_M = k_T = k$ as deduced by using testing in *pure shear,* we can be assured that the Tresca and Mises criteria are identical in predicting yielding for this case, but they *will predict differently for pure tension*. Similarly, if we get k_M and k_T established to predict the same pure tensile yielding stress Y [i.e., $2k_T = \sqrt{3}k_M = Y$ via Eqs. (8.44) and (8.52)], the criteria will now predict differently for yielding in pure shear. As we will see in Section 8.10, if the criteria agree by choosing k_M and k_T properly for yielding in pure shear (i.e., they are equal), they will *disagree* (although not radically) on predicting yielding for *all other states* of stress. And if the two criteria agree by choosing k_T and k_M properly for yielding in pure tension or compression, they will then disagree (again not radically) on yielding for all other states of stress.

We shall next present two possible physical interpretations for the Mises yield criterion*: the maximum distortion strain-energy theory and octahedral stress theory.

---

* The Mises criterion is sometimes referred to as the Hencky–Mises or the Huber–Mises criterion. Also, the Tresca criterion is sometimes called the Coulomb–Tresca or the Saint-Venant–Tresca criterion.

8.9 MAXIMUM DISTORTION STRAIN-ENERGY AND OCTAHEDRAL STRESS THEORIES

We present first the *maximum distortion strain-energy theory*, which is concerned with the *difference* between the *total* elastic strain energy density of deformation at a point, $\mathcal{U}_t$, and that from a *hydrostatic* state of stress, $\mathcal{U}_h$, having normal stresses equal to the bulk stress $\bar{\tau} = \frac{1}{3}[\tau_1 + \tau_2 + \tau_3]$. The corresponding elastic strain-energy densities are given as (see Problem 8.15)

$$\mathcal{U}_t = \frac{1}{2E}\left[(\tau_1^2 + \tau_2^2 + \tau_3^2) - 2\nu(\tau_1\tau_2 + \tau_1\tau_3 + \tau_2\tau_3)\right] \tag{8.55}$$

$$\mathcal{U}_h = \frac{3}{2E}\bar{\tau}^2(1 - 2\nu) = \frac{1}{6E}(\tau_1 + \tau_2 + \tau_3)^2(1 - 2\nu) \tag{8.56}$$

Hence, for the *distortion* strain energy, $\mathcal{U}_d$, we obtain after some algebra

$$\mathcal{U}_d = \mathcal{U}_t - \mathcal{U}_h$$
$$= \frac{1}{6E}(1 + \nu)[(\tau_1 - \tau_2)^2 + (\tau_1 - \tau_3)^2 + (\tau_2 - \tau_3)^2] \tag{8.57}$$

Note that $\mathcal{U}_d$ is unchanged when the state of stress is altered hydrostatically. The theory asserts that when $\mathcal{U}_d$ equals or exceeds a value dependent on the particular material, yielding will occur at the point.* That value can be found from the simple tensile test, where for yielding, $\tau_1 = Y, \tau_2 = 0, \tau_3 = 0$. Thus from Eq. (8.57),

$$\mathcal{U}_d^t = \frac{1}{3E}(1 + \nu)Y^2 \tag{8.58}$$

where the superscript *t* indicates the value obtained from the simple tensile test. The procedure is to compare $\mathcal{U}_d$ as given by Eq. (8.57) for a given state of stress at a point with $\mathcal{U}_d^t$ as given above for the same material under simple tensile yielding. If $\mathcal{U}_d$ is less than $\mathcal{U}_d^t$, the theory predicts no yielding at the point. If, on the other hand, $\mathcal{U}_d$ equals or is greater than $\mathcal{U}_d^t$, the theory predicts yielding at the point. At the *onset* of yielding we have, accordingly,

$$\frac{1}{6E}(1 + \nu)[(\tau_1 - \tau_2)^2 + (\tau_1 - \tau_3)^2 + (\tau_2 - \tau_3)^2] = \frac{1}{3E}(1 + \nu)Y^2$$

and therefore

$$\frac{\sqrt{2}}{2}[(\tau_1 - \tau_2)^2 + (\tau_1 - \tau_3)^2 + (\tau_2 - \tau_3)^2]^{1/2} = Y \tag{8.59}$$

This is clearly *identical to Mises criterion* (8.54) with J_2 given by Eq. (8.49c).

We shall now present the *same theory* in yet a different manner. In this regard,

---

*Recall that a hydrostatic state of stress involves no shear stress at a point, and hence for Hookean materials there is no shear strain. Accordingly, for hydrostatic stress in such materials there takes place only expansion or shrinkage with no angular distortion. It can then be concluded that $\mathcal{U}_d$ is the elastic strain energy resulting from change of shape at a point, as the name "distortion" implies. The theory argues that it is this energy that is significant for determining whether there will be yielding.

consider a point P inside a body (see Fig. 8.13). The principal axes have been shown for the point, and in addition an interface ABC has been drawn infinitesimally close to P with an outward normal oriented so that it is equally inclined to the principal axes. We call this plane at point P the *octahedral* plane. Of interest to us will be the maximum shear stress on this plane. We shall call this shear stress the *octahedral shear stress*, τ_{oc}. To compute the octahedral shear stress we start with Cauchy's formula and from this we get the normal stress on interface ABC equally inclined to the principal axes (again see Fig. 8.13). In the figure $\hat{\boldsymbol{\nu}}$ is the unit vector directed normal to the octahedral plane, and $\hat{\boldsymbol{\mu}}$ is the unit vector lying in the octahedral plane along the direction of the resultant shear stress. First, the traction vector on ABC is by definition

$$T_i^{(\nu)} = \tau_{ij}\,\nu_j \quad \text{or} \quad \mathbf{T}^{(\nu)} = (\tau_1\,\hat{\mathbf{i}} + \tau_2\,\hat{\mathbf{j}} + \tau_3\,\hat{\mathbf{k}})\,\frac{1}{\sqrt{3}}$$

Hence the normal stress becomes

$$\tau_{\nu\nu} = T_i^{(\nu)}\,\nu_i = \tau_{ij}\,\nu_j\,\nu_i = \tfrac{1}{3}\,(\tau_1 + \tau_2 + \tau_3) \tag{8.60}$$

The octahedral shear stress τ_{oc} is $\tau_{\nu\mu}$ in Fig. 8.13, and so using the Pythagorean theorem, we can say employing the result above for $\tau_{\nu\nu}$,

$$\tau_{oc} = [\,|T_i^{(\nu)}|^2 - \tau_{\nu\nu}^2\,]^{1/2} = [\tfrac{1}{3}\,(\tau_1^2 + \tau_2^2 + \tau_3^2) - \tfrac{1}{9}\,(\tau_1 + \tau_2 + \tau_3)^2]^{1/2}$$

Therefore,

$$\tau_{oc} = \tfrac{1}{3}\,[(\tau_1 - \tau_2)^2 + (\tau_1 - \tau_3)^2 + (\tau_2 - \tau_3)^2]^{1/2} \tag{8.61}$$

We can ascertain the value of the octahedral shear for the onset of yielding through the familiar simple tensile test. We denote this value as τ_{oc}'. Hence from the yielding condition for this test, we can say that

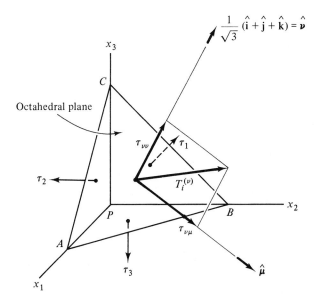

Figure 8.13 Octahedral plane.

$$\tau_{oc}^t = \tfrac{1}{3}[(Y-0)^2 + (Y-0)^2 + (0-0)^2]^{1/2}$$

$$= \frac{\sqrt{2}}{3} Y \tag{8.62}$$

Now if τ_{oc} for a given state of stress at a point as given by Eq. (8.61) is less than $(\sqrt{2}/3)Y$ for the same material, the theory indicates that we do not have yielding at the point. On the other hand, if $\tau_{oc} \geq \tau_{oc}^t$, the theory predicts yielding. For the *onset* of the yielding we have

$$\tfrac{1}{3}[(\tau_1 - \tau_2)^2 + (\tau_1 - \tau_3)^2 + (\tau_2 - \tau_3)^2]^{1/2} = \frac{\sqrt{2}}{3} Y$$

and therefore

$$\frac{\sqrt{2}}{2}[(\tau_1 - \tau_2)^2 + (\tau_1 - \tau_3)^2 + (\tau_2 - \tau_3)^2]^{1/2} = Y \tag{8.63}$$

Comparing Eqs. (8.59) and (8.63), we see that we arrive at the *same Mises yielding criterion* via the octahedral stress concept or by the maximum elastic distortion energy theory.[*]

We have now set forth two yield criteria (Tresca and Mises) which establish those combinations of stresses for which a structure may yield at some point in the structure. When such a condition is reached it does not necessarily mean that the structure will fail. Indeed, other parts of the structure may act as constraints to prevent excessive deformation, so the structure is not necessarily in jeopardy. Finally, we remark that for yielding action we frequently need not be concerned with stress concentrations occurring at small notches, fillets, keyways, and so on. In ductile materials there takes place local yielding encompassing these regions of stress concentration whereby such local yielding actions often do no serious harm. At the same time we remind you that this is *not true* for *fatigue* considerations. Here stress concentrations are always important.

8.10 YIELD SURFACES FOR THE TRESCA AND MISES CRITERIA

In this section we consider the three-dimensional yield functions and yield surfaces for both the Tresca and Mises yield criteria. We shall also develop yield curves for the special case of plane stress for these two criteria. A comparison will also be made between them, to establish a correspondence.

Case A: Tresca in Three Dimensions

We turn first to the *Tresca* condition for yielding [i.e., Eq. (8.46)]. This equation allows for the following six possibilities expressed in terms of the principal stresses:[†]

---

[*] The physical interpretation of the Mises yield criterion via the maximum distortional energy theory was suggested by H. Hencky in 1924. The interpretation based on the octahedral stress concept was proposed by A. Nadai in 1937. Other interpretations have also been proposed. See R. Hill, *The Mathematical Theory of Plasticity* (New York: Oxford University Press, 1950), Chap. 2.

[†] Here we do not necessarily use the convention that algebraically $\tau_1 \geq \tau_2 \geq \tau_3$.

$$\tau_1 - \tau_2 = \pm 2k_T \qquad \text{(a)}$$

or
$$\tau_2 - \tau_3 = \pm 2k_T \qquad \text{(b)} \qquad\qquad (8.64)$$

or
$$\tau_3 - \tau_1 = \pm 2k_T \qquad \text{(c)}$$

The locus of points satisfying these six conditions defines the yield surface. We may introduce the yield function

$$f(\tau_1, \tau_2, \tau_3) = f_1(\tau_1, \tau_2)f_2(\tau_1, \tau_2)f_3(\tau_2, \tau_3)f_4(\tau_2, \tau_3)f_5(\tau_3, \tau_1)f_6(\tau_3, \tau_1)$$

$$= (\tau_1 - \tau_2 - 2k_T)(\tau_1 - \tau_2 + 2k_T)(\tau_2 - \tau_3 - 2k_T) \cdot \qquad (8.65a)$$

$$(\tau_2 - \tau_3 + 2k_T)(\tau_3 - \tau_1 - 2k_T)(\tau_3 - \tau_1 + 2k_T)$$

which may be rewritten compactly as

$$f(\tau_1, \tau_2, \tau_3) = [(\tau_1 - \tau_2)^2 - 4k_T^2][(\tau_2 - \tau_3)^2 - 4k_T^2][(\tau_3 - \tau_1)^2 - 4k_T^2] \quad (8.65b)$$

Clearly, when we set $f = 0$ in the above we arrive back at Eqs. (8.64) (i.e., *at least one* of the six factors f_i must vanish). However, it is also necessary to require that when one of the six factors f_i in Eq. (8.65a) vanishes, *none* of the other five factors is positive. Otherwise, the stress state will fall *outside* the yield surface. Since $(\tau_1 - \tau_2) = (s_1 - s_2)$, and so on, we can also say in place of Eq. (8.65b),

$$f(s_1, s_2, s_3) = [(s_1 - s_2)^2 - 4k_T^2][(s_2 - s_3)^2 - 4k_T^2][(s_3 - s_1)^2 - 4k_T^2] \quad (8.66)$$

Furthermore, Eq. (8.66) can be transformed (see Problem 8.17) to the following form in terms of the stress deviator invariants:

$$f(J_2, J_3) = 4J_2^3 - 27J_3^2 - 36k_T^2 J_2^2 + 96k_T^4 J_2 - 64k_T^6 \qquad (8.67)$$

Although this last form is too complicated to be very useful, its existence guarantees that postulates 2 and 3 in Section 8.6 (isotropy and independence of hydrostatic stress) are satisfied. Furthermore, since J_2 and J_3^2 are always positive, it clearly also satisfies postulate 4 (identical tensile and compressive behaviors).

In developing the plot of Eqs. (8.64) in principal stress space, we note first that each of these six equations defines a plane. Each of these six planes is in turn parallel to the hydrostatic line, since no solution is obtainable when one attempts to solve any one of these six equations simultaneously with the conditions $\tau_1 = \tau_2 = \tau_3$. The yield cylinder is thus an infinite prismatic cylinder composed of six planar faces parallel to the hydrostatic line (as required by postulate 3 of Section 8.6), so it is sufficient to view it in the direction along the hydrostatic line. In this view the principal axes appear as the projections $(\tau_1)_p$, $(\tau_2)_p$, $(\tau_3)_p$, and the aforementioned planes appear as the six straight lines defining the yield locus plotted in Fig. 8.14. To illustrate how these lines are obtained, consider the plane

$$\tau_1 - \tau_2 = 2k_T$$

Clearly, this plane is also parallel to the τ_3 axis (since τ_3 is absent), intersects the τ_1 axis at $2k_T$ (set $\tau_2 = 0$), and intersects the τ_2 axis at $-2k_T$ (set $\tau_1 = 0$). We shall now show that the corresponding intersection with the $(\tau_1)_p$ axis is $(2\sqrt{2}/\sqrt{3})/k_T$, as has been shown in Fig. 8.14. First refer back to Fig. 8.10 and note that the angle be-

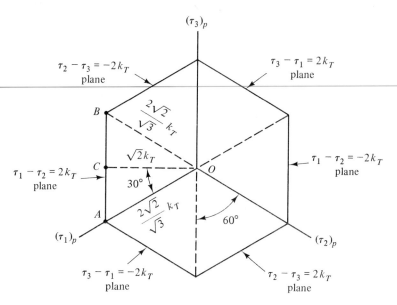

Figure 8.14 Tresca yield locus.

tween the hydrostatic line and any principal axis is $\cos^{-1}(1/\sqrt{3})$, which may also be expressed as $\sin^{-1}(\sqrt{2}/\sqrt{3})$. This is also shown in Fig. 8.15, where the aforementioned plane $\tau_1 - \tau_2 = 2k_T$ is shown intersecting the τ_1 axis at A' such that $\overline{OA'} = 2k_T$, and intersecting the τ_2 axis at B' so that $\overline{OB'} = -2k_T$. In Fig. 8.16 we show the axes τ_1, τ_2, τ_3, the hydrostatic line, the plane normal to the hydrostatic line, and the projection of the τ_1 axis onto the plane normal to the hydrostatic line. This projected axis is $(\tau_1)_p$. The projection of $\overline{OA'}$ onto $(\tau_1)_p$ is shown as $\overline{OA}$ of right triangle OAA'. Clearly,

$$\overline{OA} = \overline{OA'} \cos \alpha = \overline{OA'} \sin \beta = \overline{OA'}\left(\frac{\sqrt{2}}{\sqrt{3}}\right) = 2k_T \frac{\sqrt{2}}{\sqrt{3}}$$

This justifies the lengths of $\overline{OA}$ and $\overline{OB}$ shown in Fig. 8.14. Also, the distance $\overline{OC}$ in Fig. 8.14 follows as $(2k_T\sqrt{2}/\sqrt{3}) \cos 30° = \sqrt{2}k_T$. Clearly, the Tresca yield surface is an infinite cylinder, whose cross-sectional boundary (i.e., yield locus) is a *regular hexagon* as shown in Fig. 8.14. A three-dimensional view of this yield surface is also shown in Fig. 8.17.

Case B: Tresca for Plane Stress

Now consider those special states of stress for which $\tau_3 = 0$ (i.e., *plane stress*). The resulting *yield curve* in the $\tau_1\tau_2$ plane, representing the locus of states for which we can expect the onset of yielding, is given by the intersection of the $\tau_1\tau_2$ plane with the yield surface. For the Tresca criterion this yield curve is prescribed by Eqs.

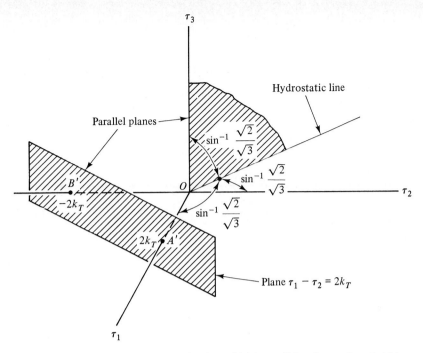

Figure 8.15 Portion of $\tau_1 - \tau_2 = 2k_T$ plane which is parallel to the τ_3 axis and which intersects τ_1 at $\tau_1 = 2k_T$ and τ_2 at $\tau_2 = -2k_T$.

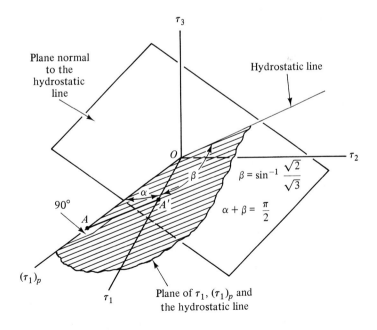

Figure 8.16 Projection of OA' onto $(\tau_1)_p$ axis from τ_1 axis.

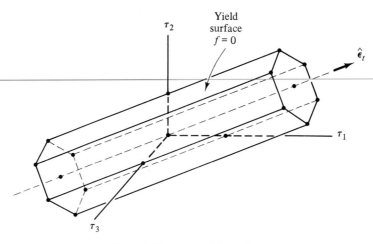

Figure 8.17 Tresca yield surface.

(8.64) with $\tau_3 = 0$, that is,

$$\tau_1 - \tau_2 = \pm 2k_T \qquad \text{(a)}$$

$$\tau_2 = \pm 2k_T \qquad \text{(b)}$$

$$-\tau_1 = \pm 2k_T \qquad \text{(c)}$$

(8.68)

Clearly, the Tresca yield curve for plane stress consists of six straight lines defined by Eqs. (8.68). These lines have been plotted in Fig. 8.18. We see that the yield curve is a polygon that runs along adjacent sides of squares in the first and third quadrants, and along the hypotenuses of isosceles right triangles in the second and fourth quadrants. Distances $\overline{Oa}$ and $\overline{Oc}$ clearly equal $2k_T$ and simple trigonometry gives $\overline{Ob} = 2\sqrt{2}k_T$ and $\overline{Og} = \sqrt{2}k_T$.

Let us reexamine the boundary lines in Fig. 8.18 in terms of our original form of the Tresca criterion, that is,

$$\tau_{\max} - \tau_{\min} = 2k_T \tag{8.69}$$

Along line ab we have $\tau_1 \geq \tau_2 \geq 0$ and $\tau_3 = 0$ and thus $\tau_{\max} = \tau_1$ and $\tau_{\min} = 0$, giving $\tau_1 = 2k_T$, which is the same as the second of Eqs. (8.68c). Going next to line bc, we have $\tau_2 \geq \tau_1 \geq 0$ and $\tau_3 = 0$ or $\tau_{\max} = \tau_2$ and $\tau_{\min} = 0$, whereupon $\tau_2 = 2k_T$, which is identical with the first of Eqs. (8.68b). Now consider line cd, where the algebraic maximum at any point along this line is τ_2 (since it is positive) and the algebraic minimum at this point is τ_1 (since it is negative). Equation (8.69) then gives $\tau_2 - \tau_1 = 2k_T$, which is identical with the second of Eqs. (8.68a). One may proceed in a similar manner to lines de, ef, and fa. Clearly, Eq.(8.69) yields the same plane stress yield curve as given by Eqs. (8.68).

Plasticity   Chap. 8

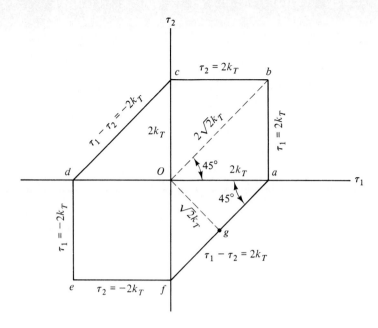

Figure 8.18 Plane stress ($\tau_3 = 0$) yield polygon for Tresca.

Case C: Mises in Three Dimensions

We now go on to the three-dimensional *Mises* condition for yielding [i.e., Eq. (8.54)], which we repeat below:

$$J_2 = k_M^2 \tag{8.70}$$

The yield function corresponding to this condition is simply

$$f(J_2) = J_2 - k_M^2 \tag{8.71}$$

which clearly satisfies postulates 2, 3, and 4 in Section 8.6. For J_2 let us use the form in terms of the principal deviatoric stresses given by Eq. (8.49a), that is,

$$J_2 = \tfrac{1}{2}(s_1^2 + s_2^2 + s_3^2) \tag{8.72}$$

Combining Eqs. (8.72) and (8.70) we obtain for $f = 0$ the result

$$(s_1^2 + s_2^2 + s_3^2)^{1/2} = \sqrt{2J_2} = \sqrt{2}k_M \tag{8.73}$$

Recall that the yield locus is the intersection of the deviator plane with the yield surface (refer back to Fig. 8.10), and thus the distance from the origin to the yield locus is obtained from Eq. (8.40) as

$$|\boldsymbol{\tau}_r| = (s_1^2 + s_2^2 + s_3^2)^{1/2} \tag{8.74}$$

where here the values of s_i correspond to points on the yield surface and thus are the same s_i of the preceding two equations. Hence on comparing Eqs. (8.73) and

(8.74), we see that $|\boldsymbol{\tau}_r|$ is the constant $\sqrt{2}k_M$, and thus the Mises yield locus is a *circle* of radius $\sqrt{2}k_M$ as shown in Fig. 8.19. Furthermore, the corresponding yield surface is a *right circular cylinder* of radius $\sqrt{2}k_M$ with its axis equally inclined to the principal stress axes (see Fig. 8.20).

By comparing the Tresca and Mises yield loci given in Figs. 8.14 and 8.19, respectively, we may establish a correspondence between the two criteria. First note that the relation, as we have pointed out earlier, between k and Y is different for these two criteria [see Eqs. (8.45) and (8.53)]. We reiterate that we may assume that *either k or Y* is the same for Mises and Tresca, but we may not assume that both are the same for the two criteria. As we have pointed out earlier, if k is chosen to be the same, the two yield conditions will coincide only for a simple shear test, whereas if Y is the same, they will coincide only for a simple tension (or compression) test. In the former case ($k_T = k_M = k$) the Mises circle can be shown to be *inscribed* in the Tresca hexagon. In this regard, first note that the radius of the Mises circle

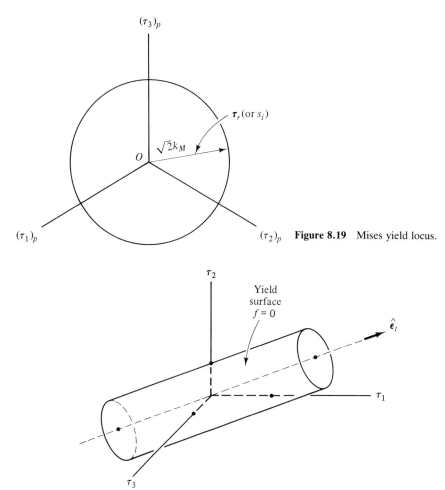

Figure 8.19 Mises yield locus.

Figure 8.20 Mises yield surface.

according to Fig. 8.19 equals $\sqrt{2}k_M = \sqrt{2}k_T$, which coincides with radius Oa in Fig. 8.21. In this figure we have inscribed the Mises circle of radius $\overline{Oa}$ inside a hexagon. The distance $\overline{Og}$ in Fig. 8.21 equals $\overline{Oa}/\cos 30° = \overline{Oa}/(\sqrt{3}/2)$, which becomes $(\sqrt{2}k_T)(2/\sqrt{3}) = (2\sqrt{2}/\sqrt{3})k_T$. But on comparing the hexagon in Fig. 8.21 with the Tresca yield locus given in Fig. 8.14, we see that distances $\overline{Oa} = \overline{OC}$ and $\overline{Og} = \overline{OB}$. Thus $\overline{Oa}$ is the radius of the Mises circle for a pure shear calibration, where this circle is inscribed in the Tresca hexagon. Now in Fig. 8.22 we have shown a Mises circle calibrated with Tresca for pure tension (i.e., Y is the same). For this case $k_M = (2/\sqrt{3})k_T = Y/\sqrt{3}$ [see Eqs. (8.44) and (8.52)], so as in Fig. 8.19, the radius of the Mises circle becomes $(2\sqrt{2}/\sqrt{3})k_T$. But from Fig. 8.14 again we see that this radius equals distance $\overline{OB}$, which is equal to distance $\overline{Og}$ for the very *same Tresca hexagon* in Fig. 8.21. Here, however, it is clear that the Mises circle *circumscribes* the Tresca hexagon. We see that in Fig. 8.21 we got coincidence of the two criteria only at the six cases of pure shear (i.e., points a, b, c, d, e, and f), whereas in Fig. 8.22 we get coincidence only at the six cases of pure tension or compression (i.e., points g, h, i, j, k, and l).

Case D: Mises for Plane Stress

As done previously for Tresca (case B), we shall now also examine Mises for those states of stress where $\tau_3 = 0$ (plane stress). To obtain the yield curve that gives the locus of the states in the $\tau_1 \tau_2$ plane for the onset of yielding, we employ Eq. (8.70) using Eq. (8.49c) with $\tau_3 = 0$ for J_2. Thus we get the following equation in terms of the principal stresses:

$$\tau_1^2 - \tau_1 \tau_2 + \tau_2^2 = 3k_M^2 \qquad (8.75)$$

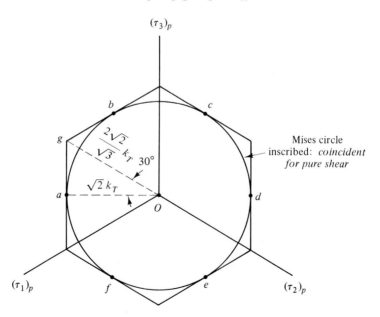

Figure 8.21 Correspondence between Tresca and Mises for pure shear calibration, $k_M = k_T = k$.

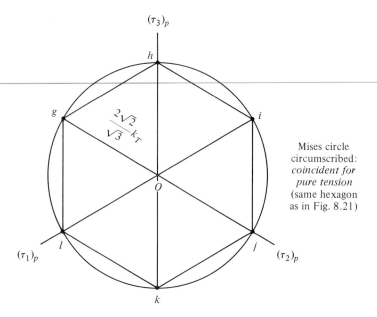

Figure 8.22 Correspondence between Tresca and Mises for pure tension calibration, $k_M = (2/\sqrt{3})\,k_T = Y\sqrt{3}$.

Equation (8.75), upon realizing that k_M is constant for a given material, is a second-order curve in the $\tau_1\tau_2$ plane. Actually, it is an ellipse with its major and minor diameters oriented in directions at 45° to the τ_1 and τ_2 axes (see Fig. 8.23). We can readily show this by expressing the equation of the curve for axes ξ and η rotated 45° from τ_1 and τ_2 (again see Fig. 8.23). The corresponding transformation equations are given as

$$\tau_1 = \xi \cos 45° - \eta \sin 45° = \frac{\xi - \eta}{\sqrt{2}}, \qquad \tau_2 = \xi \sin 45° + \eta \cos 45° = \frac{\xi + \eta}{\sqrt{2}}$$

Substituting the above into Eq. (8.75), we get

$$\frac{\xi^2}{6k_M^2} + \frac{\eta^2}{2k_M^2} = 1$$

The Mises yield curve is now clearly established as an ellipse symmetric about the axes $\xi\eta$ which are rotated 45° relative to $\tau_1\tau_2$. The semimajor and semiminor diameters for the ellipse are then $\sqrt{6}k_M$ and $\sqrt{2}k_M$, respectively, as shown in Fig. 8.23.

   Let us now reconcile Figs. 8.19 (Mises yield locus) and 8.23 (Mises plane stress yield curve). A moment's thought will reveal that line OD in Fig. 8.23 is along the trace between the deviator plane and the $\tau_1\tau_2$ plane. This means that the semiminor diameter of the Mises yield ellipse should equal the radius of the Mises yield cylinder. On comparing Figs. 8.19 and 8.23, we see that it indeed does have the value $\sqrt{2}k_M$, which is the radius of the cylinder. Next note that the angle θ between the normal to the deviator plane (i.e., the hydrostatic line) and the normal to the $\tau_1\tau_2$ plane (i.e., τ_3) has a cosine given as (look back at Fig. 8.10)

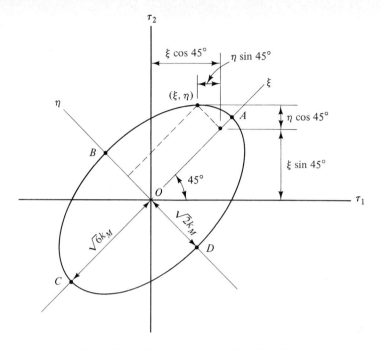

Figure 8.23 Plane stress yield ellipse for Mises.

$$\cos \theta = \frac{1}{\sqrt{3}}$$

Hence the length $\overline{OC}$ in Fig. 8.23, which is the semimajor diameter, must have the value

$$\overline{OC} = \frac{\sqrt{2}k_M}{1/\sqrt{3}} = \sqrt{6}k_M$$

Again this is the case.

Finally, let us compare the plane stress yield curves of Tresca and Mises shown in Figs. 8.18 and 8.23, respectively. Note that if $k_T = k_M$ (the case of pure shear calibration), the semiminor diameter of the Mises ellipse (i.e., $\overline{OD} = \sqrt{2}k_M$ in Fig. 8.23) coincides with distance $\overline{Og} = \sqrt{2}k_T$ of the Tresca polygon in Fig. 8.18. On the other hand, if the tensile test is used for calibration, the semimajor axis of Mises, $\overline{OA} = \sqrt{6}k_M$, coincides with distance $\overline{Ob} = 2\sqrt{2}k_T$ of Tresca since $k_M = (2/\sqrt{3})k_T$ for this case. In the first case (same k) the Mises ellipse is inscribed in the Tresca polygon, whereas in the second case (same Y) it is circumscribed. Note that in this second case we may use Eq. (8.52) to set $k_M = Y/\sqrt{3}$ and thus $\overline{OA} = \sqrt{2}Y$. The above is consistent with the result obtained previously for the three-dimensional yield cylinders (see Figs. 8.21 and 8.22), and both configurations for the case of plane stress are shown in Fig. 8.24. We should point out that the *circumscribed* configuration is the *conventional* one.

We shall say more about yield surfaces following the Drucker hypothesis to be

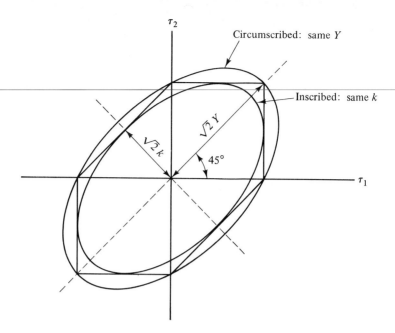

Figure 8.24 Correspondence between Tresca polygon and Mises ellipse.

set forth in the next section. Meanwhile we point out that the Tresca condition (8.42) may have greater physical appeal than the more abstract Mises condition (8.54). However, the normal to the Tresca yield surface has discontinuities in slope, whereas the Mises yield surface is smooth. In fact, the Mises yield surface (in the circumscribed configuration) usually correlates better with experiment than does Tresca. Also note that the Tresca condition gives linear equations, whereas Mises gives quadratic equations. Thus the Tresca condition may be simpler to use in theoretical applications *if* one knows the portions of the yield surface that are applicable. If one does not know which portions of the Tresca yield surface are to be used, a tedious and frequently unjustifiable trial-and-error procedure must be followed.

8.11 DRUCKER'S POSTULATE; NORMALITY PRINCIPLE AND CONVEXITY

There is yet another constraint on the shape of the yield surface that we shall now investigate. In this section the yield surface may change geometry because of hardening according to some model, such as the isotropic hardening model to be presented in Part C.

Drucker's Postulate

We first introduce the following notation:

$$Q_i = \text{generalized stress vector}$$

$\dot{q}_i$ = generalized rate of deformation vector

$\dot{W}$ = power

where Q_i and $\dot{q}_i$ are vectors* in a six-dimensional space (i.e., $\underline{i} = 1, \ldots, 6$). The components of these vectors are defined as

$$Q_{\underline{i}} = \left\{ \begin{matrix} \tau_{11} \\ \tau_{22} \\ \tau_{33} \\ \tau_{23} \\ \tau_{31} \\ \tau_{12} \end{matrix} \right\}, \qquad \dot{q}_{\underline{i}} = \left\{ \begin{matrix} \dot{\varepsilon}_{11} \\ \dot{\varepsilon}_{22} \\ \dot{\varepsilon}_{33} \\ 2\dot{\varepsilon}_{23} \\ 2\dot{\varepsilon}_{31} \\ 2\dot{\varepsilon}_{12} \end{matrix} \right\} \tag{8.76}$$

The power $\dot{W}$ is by definition

$$\dot{W} = \sum_{i,j=1}^{3} \tau_{ij}\dot{\varepsilon}_{ij} = \tau_{ij}\dot{\varepsilon}_{ij} \tag{8.77}$$

which in terms of generalized vectors becomes

$$\dot{W} = \sum_{i=1}^{6} Q_{\underline{i}}\dot{q}_{\underline{i}} = Q_{\underline{i}}\dot{q}_{\underline{i}} \tag{8.78}$$

We may now introduce the following postulate due to Drucker,† for the behavior of a plastic material:

Given a body, in an initial state of equilibrium with stress state Q_i^0, subjected to an *external agency* which slowly applies a set of self-equilibrating forces and then slowly removes them; then the *net work* performed by the *external agency* during the cycle of adding and removing stress is *nonnegative*.

A material satisfying this postulate is said to be a *stable*, work-hardening plastic material.

To see where this postulate leads, consider a yield surface at time $t = 0$ in a six-dimensional generalized stress space with "axes" Q_i, as shown schematically in Fig. 8.25. A point in this space is defined by a vector Q_i directed from the origin O, where all stresses are zero, to the point in question. Furthermore, each point in the space has a rate of deformation vector $\dot{q}_i$ associated with it, and we visualize this vector as being drawn with its "tail" at the point. Consider an *initial* stress vector Q_i^0 to a point anywhere *inside* the yield surface at time $t = 0$. An "external agency" first changes Q_i^0 to $Q_i^{(1)}$ (see dashed curve), which is directed to a point *on* the yield surface at time t_1, at which time plastic deformation begins. Then this agency changes the generalized stress by an amount δQ_i during time increment δt. If *perfectly plastic* behavior is present, the stress vector $Q_i^{(1)} + \delta Q_i$ is directed to an-

---

* We shall use the notation that any index underscored with a bar runs from 1 to 6.

† This requirement was first postulated by D. C. Drucker in 1950, and in essence states that energy put into plastic deformation cannot be recovered. It is related to, but not equivalent to, the second law of thermodynamics. For more discussion, see J. N. Goodier and P. G. Hodge, Jr., *Elasticity and Plasticity* (New York: John Wiley & Sons, Inc., 1958), p. 59, and also R. M. Christensen, *Theory of Viscoelasticity: An Introduction* (New York: Academic Press, 1971), p. 88.

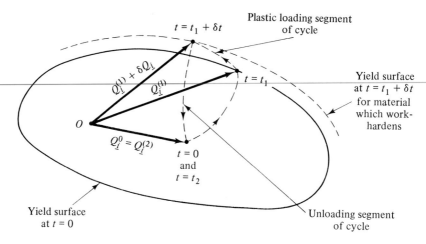

Figure 8.25 Cycle from an external agency.

other point on the initial yield surface. If there is *work hardening*, the stress vector $Q_i^{(1)} + \delta Q_i$ runs to a point on a different yield surface corresponding to time $t_1 + \delta t$ as has been shown in the diagram. The interval $t_1 \leq t \leq t_1 + \delta t$ identifies the *plastic loading* segment of the cycle. Finally, the external agency brings the stress vector to $Q_i^{(2)}$ at the time $t = t_2$, which is *equal* to the original stress vector Q_i^0 inside the initial yield surface. There is no plastic deformation during this *unloading* segment of the cycle.

We now define the following work terms occurring *during the cycle* described above:

W_{ex} = net external work performed by the external agency

W_t = total work done by all stresses

W_0 = work done by the constant initial stress vector Q_i^0

We can then say, by virtue of *Drucker's postulate*,

$$W_{\text{ex}} = W_t - W_0 \geq 0 \tag{8.79}$$

The generalized rate of deformation vector $\dot{q}_i$ is expressed as

$$\dot{q}_i = \dot{q}_i^e + \dot{q}_i^p \tag{8.80}$$

where $\dot{q}_i^e$ is the elastic component and $\dot{q}_i^p$ is the plastic component. We shall now evaluate each of the terms in Eq. (8.79) for the cycle shown in Fig. 8.25. Noting that plastic deformation occurs only during the time interval t_1 to $t_1 + \delta t$, we obtain for W_t,

$$W_t = \oint \dot{W}\, dt = \int_0^{t_1} Q_i \dot{q}_i^e\, dt \; + \; \int_{t_1}^{t_1 + \delta t} Q_i(\dot{q}_i^e + \dot{q}_i^p)\, dt \; + \; \int_{t_1 + \delta t}^{t_2} Q_i \dot{q}_i^e\, dt$$

$$\begin{pmatrix} Q_i \text{ goes from} \\ Q_i^0 \text{ to } Q_i^{(1)} \end{pmatrix} \quad \begin{pmatrix} Q_i \text{ goes from} \\ Q_i^{(1)} \text{ to } (Q_i^{(1)} + \delta Q_i) \end{pmatrix} \quad \begin{pmatrix} Q_i \text{ goes from} \\ (Q_i^{(1)} + \delta Q_i) \text{ to } Q_i^0 \end{pmatrix}$$

Therefore,

$$W_t = \oint Q_i \dot{q}_{\underline{i}}^e \, dt + \int_{t_1}^{t_1 + \delta t} Q_i \dot{q}_{\underline{i}}^p \, dt = W_t^e + \delta W_t^p$$

Note that for a closed cycle the work done involving elastic deformation must be zero, so that the closed line integral above (i.e., W_t^e) vanishes. Hence

$$W_t = \int_{t_1}^{t_1 + \delta t} Q_i \dot{q}_{\underline{i}}^p \, dt = \delta W_t^p \tag{8.81}$$

where δW_t^p is clearly the increment of *plastic* work done by *all* stresses during the interval $t_1 \le t \le t_1 + \delta t$.

As for W_0, we have

$$W_0 = \int_0^{t_1} Q_{\underline{i}}^0 \dot{q}_{\underline{i}}^e \, dt + \int_{t_1}^{t_1 + \delta t} Q_{\underline{i}}^0 (\dot{q}_{\underline{i}}^e + \dot{q}_{\underline{i}}^p) \, dt + \int_{t_1 + \delta t}^{t_2} Q_{\underline{i}}^0 \dot{q}_{\underline{i}}^e \, dt$$

$$= \oint Q_{\underline{i}}^0 \dot{q}_{\underline{i}}^e \, dt + \int_{t_1}^{t_1 + \delta t} Q_{\underline{i}}^0 \dot{q}_{\underline{i}}^p \, dt = W_0^e + \delta W_0^p$$

Clearly, the closed line integral (i.e., W_0^e) again vanishes, and so

$$W_0 = \int_{t_1}^{t_1 + \delta t} Q_{\underline{i}}^0 \dot{q}_{\underline{i}}^p \, dt = \delta W_0^p \tag{8.82}$$

where δW_0^p is the increment of *plastic* work done by the *initial* stresses during the plastic loading segment of the cycle. Now going back to Eq. (8.79), we see from Eqs. (8.81) and (8.82) that

$$W_{\text{ex}} = \delta W_t^p - \delta W_0^p = \delta W_{\text{ex}}^p = \int_{t_1}^{t_1 + \delta t} (Q_i - Q_{\underline{i}}^0) \dot{q}_{\underline{i}}^p \, dt \ge 0 \tag{8.83}$$

where you will note we have used Drucker's postulate to obtain the inequality on the extreme right side of this result. Since δt is arbitrary, we may make it *arbitrarily small* and take the limit $\lim_{\delta t \to 0} \delta W_{\text{ex}}^p / \delta t$, whereupon we finally conclude that*

$$(Q_i^p - Q_{\underline{i}}^0) \dot{q}_{\underline{i}}^p \ge 0 \tag{8.84}$$

where we have introduced the superscript p on Q_i^p to indicate that this vector is directed to a point *on the original plastic yield surface* (i.e., $Q_i^{(1)}$ in Fig. 8.25).

Looking back at definitions (8.76) we see that inequality (8.84) may be rewritten as

$$(\tau_{ij}^p - \tau_{ij}^0) \dot{\varepsilon}_{ij}^p \ge 0 \tag{8.85}$$

Furthermore, for principal axes this simplifies to

$$\boxed{(\tau_i^p - \tau_i^0) \dot{\varepsilon}_i^p \ge 0} \tag{8.86}$$

---

* To prove condition (8.84) rigorously, let $f(t) = (Q_i - Q_{\underline{i}}^0) \dot{q}_{\underline{i}}^p$ and use the mean value theorem to replace the integral in expression (8.83) by $f(\tau) \, \delta t$, where $t_1 \le \tau \le (t_1 + \delta t)$. Then $\lim_{\delta t \to 0^+} \delta W_{\text{ex}}^p / \delta t$ yields condition (8.84).

which is the form that we shall utilize in the remainder of this section. We remind you that τ_i^p is a principal stress vector with components τ_1, τ_2, τ_3 directed from the origin of principal stress space *to any point P* on the original yield surface, whereas τ_i^0 is directed to any point interior to this yield surface. On the other hand, $\dot{\varepsilon}_i^p$ is a principal plastic strain-rate vector with components $\dot{\varepsilon}_1^p, \dot{\varepsilon}_2^p, \dot{\varepsilon}_3^p$, acting *at the point P.*

Normality and Convexity

We will be able to draw two important conclusions about the yield surface as a result of the formulation above. For this purpose consider the yield locus curve in the deviator plane as shown in Fig. 8.26. Inequality (8.86) says that any vector, connecting any point τ_i^0 inside the yield surface with a point τ_i^p on the yield surface, must form an angle with the plastic strain-rate vector $\dot{\varepsilon}_i^p$ of *not more than 90°* because of the dot product. With this in mind, consider in Fig. 8.26 two arbitrary points A and B *inside* the yield surface and a point P *on* the yield surface. Fanning out of point P are two systems of dashed arrows signifying the ranges of permitted directions for $\dot{\varepsilon}_i^p$ to be associated with the points A, B, and P. Thus for A and P the range of permitted directions of plastic strain rate extends 180° from ① to ②, while for B and P the range of permitted directions of plastic strain rate extends 180° from ③ to ④. Note that arrows ① and ② are normal to AP and that arrows ③ and ④ are normal

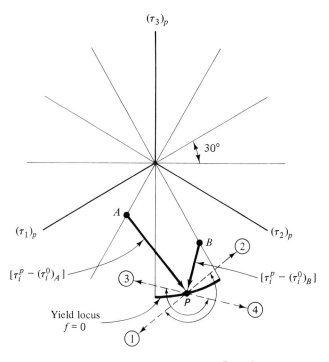

180° range of $\dot{\varepsilon}_i^p$ for AP: ① - ②

180° range of $\dot{\varepsilon}_i^p$ for BP: ③ - ④

Figure 8.26 Deviator plane with two points A and B for τ_i^0.

Plasticity   Chap. 8

to *BP*. For *both* points *A* and *B* simultaneously associated with *P*, the *net* range of permitted plastic strain rate is from ① to ④, which is clearly the *overlap* between the individual ranges for *A* and *B*, respectively, associated with *P*. Now choose point *A* to be *inside but infinitesimally close* to the yield surface *P*. The range of permitted directions for $\dot{\varepsilon}_i^p$ is shown in Fig. 8.27(a). In Fig. 8.27(b) we also have shown the permitted range of $\dot{\varepsilon}_i^p$ for a point *B* inside but infinitesimally close to the yield locus. Then, in Fig. 8.27(c) we show the *net* permitted range of $\dot{\varepsilon}_i^p$ for both points *A* and *B*. As points *A* and *B* approach point *P* along paths inside but infinitesimally close to the yield surface, the net range in Fig. 8.27(c) narrows and approaches normality with the yield locus curve at *P*. In the limit, as $A \rightarrow P$ and $B \rightarrow P$ the range narrows to one direction only, and that direction must be the *outward-directed normal* to the yield locus curve as shown in Fig. 8.27(d).

Note that the curve of the yield locus used in the sequence of Fig. 8.27 was drawn *convex* relative to the interior. Suppose that a *portion* of the yield curve is concave as shown in Fig. 8.28. Shown in the figure are the normal to the yield locus at a point *P* and the tangent to the yield locus at *P*. Also shown are points *A* and *B* lying inside but infinitesimally close to that part of the yield locus which is *interior* to the tangent line, and points *A'* and *B'* lying inside but infinitesimally close to that part of the yield locus which is *exterior* to the tangent line. Proceeding as in Fig.

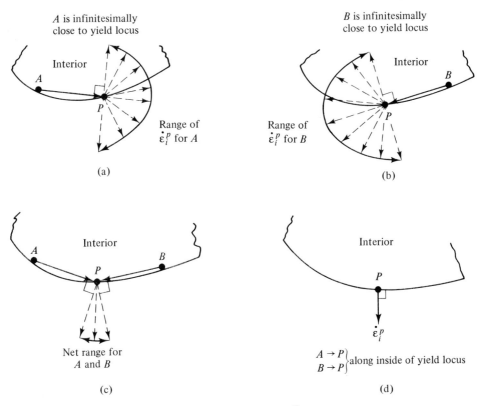

Figure 8.27 Sequence showing normality of $\dot{\varepsilon}_i^p$ to yield locus.

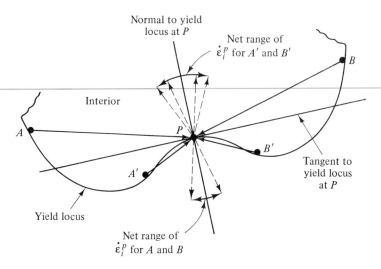

Figure 8.28 Yield locus with concave portion.

8.27, we may determine the permitted net range of $\dot{\varepsilon}_i^p$ at P for τ_i^0 at A and B and also for τ_i^0 at A' and B'. As shown in Fig. 8.28, the net range for A and B contains only *outwardly* directed vectors, whereas the net range for A' and B' contain only *inwardly* directed vectors. Clearly, these two ranges do *not* overlap. Since inequality (8.86) must be satisfied for *all* points inside the yield locus, there is *no acceptable* net range for the configuration shown in Fig. 8.28. Clearly, the presence of a concave portion along the yield locus must be *excluded*.

We may now draw two important conclusions for a plastic material stemming from Drucker's postulate:

1. Because the direction of $\dot{\varepsilon}_i^p$ must satisfy condition (8.86) for *any* and *all* points τ_i^0 *within* the yield surface, $\dot{\varepsilon}_i^p$ must be directed *outwardly normal* to the yield surface. This is called the *normality principle*.

2. The yield surface must be convex since the permitted range of $\dot{\varepsilon}_i^p$ at points of concavity would vanish otherwise.

In the next section we shall further consider the yield surface and the plastic strain rate, making much use of the foregoing results from Drucker's postulate. In particular, conclusion 1 leads directly to important *plastic flow laws*.

8.12 PRANDTL–REUSS EQUATIONS; FLOW LAWS

We will first approach plastic stress-strain rate relations from a historical point of view in order to introduce the subject. After this introduction, we shall present a more *general* approach.

Prandtl–Reuss Equations

In 1870, Saint-Venant proposed that the principal axes of strain rate coincide with the principal axes of stress.[*] Levy in 1871, and independently von Mises much later in 1913, then proposed that the *strain-rate components* $\dot{\varepsilon}_{ij}$ and the *corresponding stress deviator components* s_{ij} at any time t have the *same ratio* $\dot{\Lambda}$. That is,

$$\frac{\dot{\varepsilon}_{11}}{s_{11}} = \frac{\dot{\varepsilon}_{22}}{s_{22}} = \frac{\dot{\varepsilon}_{33}}{s_{33}} = \frac{\dot{\varepsilon}_{12}}{s_{12}} = \frac{\dot{\varepsilon}_{23}}{s_{23}} = \frac{\dot{\varepsilon}_{31}}{s_{31}} = \dot{\Lambda} \tag{8.87}$$

where $\dot{\Lambda}$ is a *positive* scalar parameter (*not* a material constant) which is not necessarily constant in time and is *not determinable* from the stresses. Equation (8.87) may be written in index notation as

$$\dot{\varepsilon}_{ij} = \dot{\Lambda} s_{ij} \tag{8.88}$$

In these equations the strain rates are assumed to consist of only plastic deformation (i.e., the elastic deformation is *ignored*). Thus these plastic results are useful only for large plastic flow. These equations, which are called the *Lévy–Mises* equations, are clearly three-dimensional constitutive relations for a *rigid, perfectly plastic* material. The one-dimensional stress-strain diagram for this idealized material was previously given in Fig. 8.7.

In order to consider elastic, perfectly plastic materials, Prandtl (1925) and then Reuss (1930) arrived at the following equations as a modification of the Lévy–Mises equations:

$$\frac{\dot{\varepsilon}_{11}^{p}}{s_{11}} = \frac{\dot{\varepsilon}_{22}^{p}}{s_{22}} = \frac{\dot{\varepsilon}_{33}^{p}}{s_{33}} = \frac{\dot{\varepsilon}_{12}^{p}}{s_{12}} = \frac{\dot{\varepsilon}_{23}^{p}}{s_{23}} = \frac{\dot{\varepsilon}_{31}^{p}}{s_{31}} = \dot{\Lambda} \tag{8.89}$$

Now the ratios of the *plastic strain rates* to the corresponding deviatoric stress components at any time t have the same positive indeterminate ratio $\dot{\Lambda}$. In index notation, these equations can be written as

$$\boxed{\dot{\varepsilon}_{ij}^{p} = \dot{\Lambda} s_{ij}} \tag{8.90}$$

The preceding equations are known as the *Prandtl–Reuss* equations. Note again that principal axes of plastic strain rate coincide with the principal axes of the stress tensor. Also, note that the plastic strain rates depend on the *current* values of the deviatoric stresses and *not* on the *previous stresses* required to reach this state. Finally, we see that since $s_{kk} \equiv 0$, Eq. (8.90) gives $\dot{\varepsilon}_{kk}^{p} = 0$ (i.e., the plastic deformation is *incompressible*).

We will now add the elastic contribution to Eq. (8.90). The *plastic* deformation is still assumed to be *incompressible*, and thus $\varepsilon_{kk}^{p} = 0$ and $\varepsilon_{ij}^{p} = e_{ij}^{p}$, where e_{ij}^{p} is the plastic strain deviator tensor. Accordingly, Eq. (8.90) may be decomposed into deviatoric and bulk parts as follows:

---

[*] Note that the principal axes for the stress tensor τ_{ij} and for the stress deviator tensor s_{ij} *must* coincide. This is so because *all* axes are principal for the difference $(\tau_{kk}/3)\delta_{ij}$.

$$\dot{e}_{ij}^p = \dot{\Lambda} s_{ij}$$

$$\varepsilon_{kk}^p = 0 \qquad\qquad (8.91)$$

The *elastic* strains are in general *compressible*, and will be assumed to obey *Hooke's Law* in the form

$$e_{ij}^e = \frac{s_{ij}}{2G}$$

$$\varepsilon_{kk}^e = \frac{\tau_{kk}}{3K} \qquad\qquad (8.92)$$

Combining Eqs. (8.91) and (8.92) in accordance with $\varepsilon_{ij} = \varepsilon_{ij}^e + \varepsilon_{ij}^p$, we finally get

$$\boxed{\begin{aligned} \dot{e}_{ij} &= \dot{\Lambda} s_{ij} + \frac{\dot{s}_{ij}}{2G} \\ \varepsilon_{kk} &= \frac{\tau_{kk}}{3K} \end{aligned}} \qquad\qquad (8.93)$$

Equations (8.93) are constitutive equations for a *linear elastic, perfectly plastic* (also called *elastoplastic*) material. The one-dimensional stress-strain diagram for this material was given in Fig. 8.4.

General Flow Law

We shall now proceed to develop a *general incompressible plastic stress-strain rate relation* for the *onset* of yielding. Then we shall show that the Prandtl–Reuss equation is a special case of this general equation, valid only for the case of perfectly plastic behavior according to the *Mises* criterion for yielding. In other words we will show that for Eq. (8.89) [or (8.90)] to be correct, they must be associated with a yield condition corresponding to the Mises criterion.

We have concluded in Sections 8.7 and 8.11 that an initial yield surface represented as

$$f(J_2, J_3) = 0 \qquad\qquad (8.94)$$

is a convex cylinder with generator parallel to the hydrostatic line, and is composed of 12 mirror image 30° segments in the cross section. As a result of Drucker's postulate, the generalized rate of deformation vector $\dot{q}_i$ at the onset of yielding must be outwardly normal to the initial yield surface in the generalized stress space Q_i. Accordingly, we can set forth the following equation, which is called a *flow rule* (or flow law), using the directional property of the gradient of a scalar:

$$\dot{q}_i^p = \dot{\Lambda} \frac{\partial f}{\partial Q_i} \qquad\qquad (8.95)$$

Here $\dot{\Lambda}$ is a *positive* scalar multiplier not necessarily constant, and i runs from 1 to 6. Looking back at definitions (8.76), we see that we may also express Eq. (8.95) as follows:

$$\dot{\varepsilon}_{ij}^p = \dot{\Lambda} \frac{\partial f}{\partial \tau_{ij}} \qquad (8.96)$$

where i, j run as usual from 1 to 3. For principal axes, this equation becomes simply*

$$\dot{\varepsilon}_i^p = \dot{\Lambda} \frac{\partial f}{\partial \tau_i} \qquad (8.97)$$

It is important to realize that in Eq. (8.96) the partial differentiation is with respect to the τ_{ij} regarded as *nine* independent variables. Thus in expressing the function f for this equation the conjugate shear stresses are *not* assumed to be equal a priori. On the other hand, in expressing f for Eq. (8.95) in terms of the *six* independent Q_i we *do* utilize the symmetry of the stress tensor. For this latter approach it was necessary to employ the factor 2 in the definitions of $\dot{q}_4, \dot{q}_5, \dot{q}_6$ [see Eqs. (8.76)]. Note also that Eq. (8.96), as presented above, is applicable to the *onset* of yielding. In the next part of this chapter we extend its range of applicability to *continuing* plastic deformation with hardening. Thus whereas $\dot{\Lambda}$ was chosen indeterminate in the Prandtl–Reuss equation (8.90), it is *not necessarily* indeterminate in Eq. (8.96).

Noting Eq. (8.94), we now use the chain rule for differentiation to obtain from Eq. (8.96) the result

$$\dot{\varepsilon}_{ij}^p = \dot{\Lambda} \left(\frac{\partial f}{\partial J_2} \frac{\partial J_2}{\partial \tau_{ij}} + \frac{\partial f}{\partial J_3} \frac{\partial J_3}{\partial \tau_{ij}} \right) \qquad (8.98)$$

Recall that (see Section 7.11)

$$J_2 = \tfrac{1}{2} s_{pq} s_{pq} = \tfrac{1}{2} \left(\tau_{pq} \tau_{pq} - \tfrac{1}{3} \tau_{pp} \tau_{qq} \right)$$

Hence

$$\frac{\partial J_2}{\partial \tau_{ij}} = \tfrac{1}{2} \left(2\tau_{pq} \delta_{pi} \delta_{qj} - \tfrac{2}{3} \tau_{pp} \delta_{qi} \delta_{qj} \right) = s_{ij} \qquad (8.99)$$

Also, we set

$$\frac{\partial J_3}{\partial \tau_{ij}} = r_{ij} \qquad (8.100)$$

where in Problem 7.20 you were asked to show that

$$r_{ij} = s_{ip} s_{pj} - \tfrac{1}{3} s_{qp} s_{pq} \delta_{ij} \qquad (8.101)$$

We can then state Eq. (8.98) as follows:

$$\dot{\varepsilon}_{ij}^p = \dot{\Lambda} \left(\frac{\partial f}{\partial J_2} s_{ij} + \frac{\partial f}{\partial J_3} r_{ij} \right) \qquad (8.102)$$

---

* Equation (8.97) is sometimes written more generally as $\dot{\varepsilon}_i^p = \dot{\Lambda} \partial \Psi / \partial \tau_i$, where Ψ is called the *plastic potential*. When Ψ is chosen equal to the yield function f, we obtain the present formulation. If Ψ is chosen not equal to f, we obtain so-called *nonassociated* plastic flow laws which are not consistent with Drucker's postulate.

This is the *general relationship* alluded to earlier. It is an easy matter to show that $s_{kk} = r_{kk} = 0$, which is a direct consequence of the fact that they are *both* deviator tensors. It then follows that $\dot{\varepsilon}^p_{kk} = 0$ [i.e., Eq. (8.102) is a constitutive relation for an *incompressible* plastic material]. For a compressible material, yield function (8.94) would have to be modified to include a dependence on the first invariant of stress, I_τ.

Mises Flow Law

Now we shall apply Eq. (8.102) to a material governed by the *Mises* yield condition. For this condition we showed earlier [see Eq. (8.71)] that f is a function of J_2 only given by

$$f(J_2) = J_2 - k_M^2 \tag{8.103}$$

where setting $f = 0$ gives a circular cylindrical yield surface, for which k_M is the yield stress in pure shear k if k_M is determined from a simple shear test. When we use this function in Eq. (8.102) we simply get

$$\dot{\varepsilon}^p_{ij} = \dot{\Lambda} \frac{\partial f(J_2)}{\partial J_2} s_{ij} = \dot{\Lambda} s_{ij} \tag{8.104}$$

which becomes the *Prandtl–Reuss* equation (8.90) if $\dot{\Lambda}$ is considered indeterminate, as predicted earlier. To distinguish Eq. (8.90) (in which $\dot{\Lambda}$ has been chosen indeterminate) from Eq. (8.104) (in which $\dot{\Lambda}$ is *not necessarily* indeterminate), we shall refer to the latter as the *Mises flow law*. For principal axes we have, for Eq. (8.104),

$$\dot{\varepsilon}^p_i = \dot{\Lambda} s_i \tag{8.105}$$

We may also express the above equations in the differential (or "incremental") forms

$$\begin{align} d\varepsilon^p_{ij} &= s_{ij} d\Lambda \quad \text{(a)} \\ d\varepsilon^p_i &= s_i d\Lambda \quad \text{(b)} \end{align} \tag{8.106}$$

where $d\varepsilon^p_{ij}$ and $d\varepsilon^p_i$ are called strain *increments*.* Finally, we note that because of incompressibility we may also express Eqs. (8.104) and (8.105) as

$$\begin{align} \dot{e}^p_{ij} &= \dot{\Lambda} s_{ij} \quad \text{(a)} \\ \dot{e}^p_i &= \dot{\Lambda} s_i \quad \text{(b)} \end{align} \tag{8.107}$$

---

*In general, for large deformation the plastic strain-rate tensor is expressed in terms of the plastic *velocity* V^p_i via

$$\dot{\varepsilon}^p_{ij} = \tfrac{1}{2}(V^p_{i,j} + V^p_{j,i})$$

The differential $d\varepsilon^p_{ij} = \dot{\varepsilon}^p_{ij} dt$ can then be shown to be equal to the *natural strain increment* (see the footnote on p. 101). If deformations are *small*, then $d\varepsilon^p_{ij}$ is *approximately* equal to the increment of the small strain tensor. We also note that since Eqs. (8.105) and (8.106) are equivalent, the present formulation is either called "flow" theory or "incremental deformation" theory. We shall not consider here the so-called "total deformation" theory, wherein $\dot{\varepsilon}^p_{ij}$ in Eq. (8.104) is replaced by ε^p_{ij}, since the incremental theory is considered by most to be more general.

In general, we can say the following about flow rules in the event that the stress state for a material point touches the yield surface. For a *perfectly plastic* material model, there will be an *indeterminate* plastic strain-rate vector along the outward normal to the yield surface at the point where the stress state touches the yield surface. For a *strain-hardening* material, the stress state of a material point coming into contact with and *piercing* the yield surface will cause a *determinate* plastic strain-rate vector, again in the direction of the outward normal to the yield surface at the point of contact. A new yield surface will then be reached, which is a topic we shall discuss in Part C. Experimental evidence indicates that the normality principle we have been discussing is generally valid for many ductile materials.

We will now *attempt* to evaluate $\dot{\Lambda}$ for Mises yielding. To do this we take the inner product of Eq. (8.104) with itself to form from the Mises flow law the equation

$$\dot{\varepsilon}_{ij}^{p}\,\dot{\varepsilon}_{ij}^{p} = \dot{\Lambda}^{2} s_{ij} s_{ij} \tag{8.108}$$

But we already know that $\frac{1}{2} s_{ij} s_{ij} = J_2$, and we can by the same token set $\frac{1}{2}\dot{e}_{ij}^{p}\dot{e}_{ij}^{p} = K_2$, where K_2 is the second tensor invariant of $\dot{e}_{ij}^{p}$ (which equals $\dot{\varepsilon}_{ij}^{p}$ because of incompressibility). Solving for $\dot{\Lambda}$ from above we then get

$$\boxed{\dot{\Lambda} = \frac{\sqrt{K_2}}{\sqrt{J_2}} = \frac{1}{k}\sqrt{K_2}} \tag{8.109}$$

where we have used k to replace $\sqrt{J_2}$ for the Mises yield criterion as per Eq. (8.103). We have already noted that k is the yield stress in pure shear. We have thus formulated an expression for $\dot{\Lambda}$ for Mises yielding, and since K_2 is positive, we see that $\dot{\Lambda}$ must also be *positive*. We also see that if $\dot{\varepsilon}_{ij}^{p}$ is given, we may evaluate $\dot{\Lambda}$ from Eq. (8.109) and then s_{ij} from Eq. (8.104). However, if the s_{ij} are given, $\dot{\Lambda}$ may *not* be determined from Eq. (8.109) *alone*. To determine $\dot{\Lambda}$ we then need an additional condition: for example, a matching condition at an elastic–plastic interface for perfectly plastic behavior, or a hardening law for plastic behavior with strain hardening. In the absence of such a condition, $\dot{\varepsilon}_{ij}^{p}$ is known only to within an arbitrary multiplying factor. This is an *essential characteristic* of the perfectly plastic material.

We have previously introduced the power [see Eq. (8.77)] as

$$\dot{W} = \tau_{ij}\dot{\varepsilon}_{ij} = \tau_{ij}\dot{\varepsilon}_{ij}^{e} + \tau_{ij}\dot{\varepsilon}_{ij}^{p} \tag{8.110}$$

where we have used $\varepsilon_{ij} = \varepsilon_{ij}^{e} + \varepsilon_{ij}^{p}$ in the above. The second term on the right of Eq. (8.110) is the *plastic dissipation power* $\dot{W}_p$. Assuming *incompressible* plastic deformation as usual, it is easily shown that the plastic dissipation power takes on the following alternative forms:

$$\dot{W}_p = \tau_{ij}\dot{\varepsilon}_{ij}^{p} = \tau_{ij}\dot{e}_{ij}^{p} = s_{ij}\dot{e}_{ij}^{p} = s_{ij}\dot{\varepsilon}_{ij}^{p} \tag{8.111}$$

One can also easily show (see Problem 8.20) that $\dot{\Lambda}$ may be expressed in terms of $\dot{W}_p$ as

$$\dot{\Lambda} = \frac{\dot{W}_p}{2k^2} \tag{8.112}$$

Note that $\dot{\Lambda} > 0$ implies $\dot{W}_p > 0$, which is *as expected* for plastic deformation. Finally, we note that for principal axes, Eqs. (8.111) become

$$\dot{W}_p = \tau_i \dot{\varepsilon}_i^P = \tau_i \dot{e}_i^P = s_i \dot{e}_i^P = s_i \dot{\varepsilon}_i^P \tag{8.113}$$

Returning again to the Mises flow law (8.104), we note that it has a formal similarity with the Newton viscosity law of fluid mechanics. Thus expressing both equations side by side we have, for incompressible behavior,

$$\dot{\varepsilon}_{ij}^P = \dot{\Lambda} s_{ij} \quad \text{(a)} \qquad\qquad \dot{\varepsilon}_{ij} = \frac{1}{\zeta} s_{ij} \quad \text{(b)} \tag{8.114}$$

$$\text{Mises flow law} \qquad\qquad \text{Newton's viscosity law}$$

However, we must emphatically point out that unlike the viscosity law there is *no rate dependence* implied by the plasticity equation. To bring out this point we consider the case of *proportional* straining, whereby the components of $\dot{\varepsilon}_{ij}^P$ are changed *in concert*. Accordingly, $\dot{\varepsilon}_{ij}^P$ is changed to $\alpha(t) \dot{\varepsilon}_{ij}^P$, where $\alpha(t)$ is a function of time. Clearly, the corresponding value of the invariant K_2 is changed to $\alpha^2 K_2$. From Eq. (8.109) we also see that $\dot{\Lambda}$ must become $\alpha(t)\dot{\Lambda}$. The result, as seen from the Mises flow law (8.114a), is that there is *no change* in the deviator tensor s_{ij}. This indicates that for such a change in strain rate there is *no rate dependence* in the plasticity equation, whereas the viscosity law (8.114b) is clearly *rate dependent*.

Also, from Mises flow law (8.105) we conclude that $\dot{\varepsilon}_i^P$ is collinear with s_i. Since s_i is radial in the deviator plane [see Eq. (8.40) and Fig. 8.10], we see that to satisfy the flow rule, the Mises yield surface must be a *circular cylinder*, as indicated earlier on several occasions. Furthermore, we see from Eqs. (8.112) and (8.113) that on the Mises yield surface we have $\dot{W}_p / \dot{\Lambda} = s_i \dot{\varepsilon}_i^P / \dot{\Lambda} = 2k^2$. That is, the dot product of the collinear vectors s_i and $\dot{\varepsilon}_i / \dot{\Lambda}$ is invariant along this yield surface. Since the magnitude of s_i is unchanged as a point P moves along the Mises yield locus, it clearly follows that the *magnitude* of $\dot{\varepsilon}_i^P / \dot{\Lambda}$ is also *unchanged* during this process. This has been illustrated in Fig. 8.29.*

Tresca Flow Law

We turn finally to a brief consideration of flow laws associated with the Tresca yield criterion. Let us emphasize at the outset that the Prandtl–Reuss equation should *not* be used in association with Tresca, since the yield function is now *not* given by $f(J_2) = J_2 - k_T^2$. We noted earlier that the Tresca yield function may be given by the complicated expression [see Eq. (8.67)]

$$f(J_2, J_3) = 4J_2^3 - 27J_3^2 - 36k_T^2 J_2^2 + 96k_T^4 J_2 - 64k_T^6 \tag{8.115}$$

One could attempt to substitute this relation into Eq. (8.102) in order to obtain the flow law, but the complexity of f renders this approach impractical. An alternative

*The scalar parameter $\dot{\Lambda}$ may be indeterminate (as in rigid, perfectly plastic behavior), or specified by some condition such as a hardening rule. Since we have yet to specify any such conditions or hardening rules, the variation of $\dot{\Lambda}$ along the yield surface is at present unknown. However, we can still determine the properties of the *ratio* $\dot{\varepsilon}_i^P / \dot{\Lambda}$.

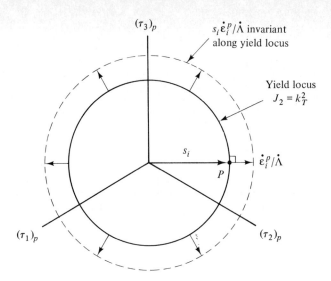

Figure 8.29 For Mises, normality implies $\dot{\varepsilon}_i^P / \dot{\Lambda}$ collinear with s_i.

approach due to W. T. Koiter* (1953) introduces a set of *three* yield functions [see Eqs. (8.64)]

$$f^{(1)}(\tau_1, \tau_2) = |\tau_1 - \tau_2| - 2k_T \qquad \text{(a)}$$

$$f^{(2)}(\tau_2, \tau_3) = |\tau_2 - \tau_3| - 2k_T \qquad \text{(b)} \qquad\qquad (8.116)$$

$$f^{(3)}(\tau_1, \tau_3) = |\tau_3 - \tau_1| - 2k_T \qquad \text{(c)}$$

The plastic strain rate $\dot{\varepsilon}_{ij}^p$ is then expressed as the sum of three components $\dot{\varepsilon}_{ij}^{p(1)}, \dot{\varepsilon}_{ij}^{p(2)}, \dot{\varepsilon}_{ij}^{p(3)}$, which are derivable from $f^{(1)}, f^{(2)}, f^{(3)}$, respectively. Some details of the formulation are presented in Problem 8.21, so we shall develop it no further here.

We simply note that again the vector $\dot{\varepsilon}_i^p$ (and also the "normalized" vector $\dot{\varepsilon}_i^p / \dot{\Lambda}$) is *normal* to the Tresca yield locus. Furthermore, it can be shown that the *normalized* plastic dissipation power (i.e., $\dot{W}_p / \dot{\Lambda} = s_i \dot{\varepsilon}_i^p / \dot{\Lambda}$) is again identical for all $\dot{\varepsilon}_i^p / \dot{\Lambda}$ vectors normal to the *sides* of the Tresca hexagon (see Problem 8.22). At the six "corner points" the direction of $\dot{\varepsilon}_i^p / \dot{\Lambda}$ is *not unique*, that is, a "fan" of permissible $\dot{\varepsilon}_i^p$ vectors exists where each vector in a fan may have a different value of $\dot{\Lambda}$ associated with it. For the purposes of illustration, we may also set $s_i \dot{\varepsilon}_i^p / \dot{\Lambda}$ equal to a constant for all vectors $\dot{\varepsilon}_i^p / \dot{\Lambda}$ in a fan of vectors at a corner point. All of the above has been illustrated in Fig. 8.30. Note in particular that $\dot{\varepsilon}_i^p / \dot{\Lambda}$ and s_i are *not* in general collinear here.

In closing, we mention that the plane stress counterparts of Figs. 8.29 and 8.30 are given by the traces of these diagrams on the $\tau_1 \tau_2$ plane. We discuss this in Chapter 13, on plane stress. We now go on to hardening formulations† in Part C.

---

*For a detailed presentation of Koiter's method, see B. A. Boley and J. H. Weiner, *Theory of Thermal Stresses* (New York: John Wiley & Sons, Inc., 1960; reprinted in 1985 by R. E. Krieger Publishing Company, Melbourne, FL), p. 481.

†From this point on we shall assume (unless specifically noted otherwise) that the Mises and Tresca yield surfaces are correlated in *tension*. Thus $k_M = Y/\sqrt{3}$ and $k_T = Y/2$, so that $k_T = (\sqrt{3}/2)k_M$.

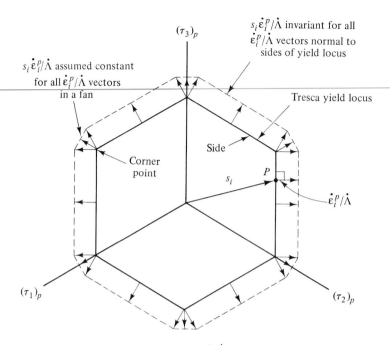

$s_i \dot{\varepsilon}_i^p / \dot{\Lambda}$ assumed constant
for all $\dot{\varepsilon}_i^p / \dot{\Lambda}$ vectors
in a fan

$(\tau_3)_p$

$s_i \dot{\varepsilon}_i^p / \dot{\Lambda}$ invariant for all
$\dot{\varepsilon}_i^p / \dot{\Lambda}$ vectors normal to
sides of yield locus

Tresca yield locus

Side

Corner
point

s_i

P

$\dot{\varepsilon}_i^p / \dot{\Lambda}$

$(\tau_1)_p$

$(\tau_2)_p$

Figure 8.30   Normality of $\dot{\varepsilon}_i^p / \dot{\Lambda}$ for Tresca criterion.

PART C
THREE-DIMENSIONAL PLASTICITY WITH STRAIN
AND STRAIN-RATE HARDENING

8.13 PRELIMINARY REMARKS

In Part B we considered the *onset* of yielding and thus were concerned with the *initial* yield surface. In Part C we first proceed to include the process of *strain hardening* once yielding has begun. We do this by allowing the yield surface to change as plastic deformation occurs. You will recall that for *initial yielding* the conditions for elastic and plastic behavior were stated in terms of the yield function *f* by means of postulate 1 [see Eqs. (8.29) and (8.30)]. We can restate these conditions for initial yielding concisely as follows:

$$\text{Elastic:} \quad \text{if } f < 0, \quad \text{or if } f = 0 \quad \text{and} \quad \dot{f} < 0 \quad \text{(a)}$$

$$\text{Plastic:} \quad \text{if } f = 0 \quad \text{and} \quad \dot{f} \geq 0 \qquad\qquad \text{(b)}$$

(8.117)

You will also recall that here *f* depends on J_2, J_3, which are functions of τ_{ij}, and thus $\dot{f} = (\partial f / \partial \tau_{ij}) \dot{\tau}_{ij}$. If strain hardening is not permitted (i.e., the behavior is *perfectly plastic*), the inequality in Eq. (8.117b) must be replaced by $\dot{f} = 0$.

In stating the conditions for *continuing* plastic flow with hardening, we must modify Eqs. (8.117). Initially we shall focus on *rate-insensitive* plastic flow with *isotropic hardening*, and for this case Eqs. (8.117) are replaced by

$$\text{Elastic:} \quad \text{if } f < K, \quad \text{or if } f = K \quad \text{and} \quad \dot{f} < 0 \quad \text{(a)}$$

$$\text{Plastic:} \quad \text{if } f = K \quad \text{and} \quad \dot{f} \geq 0 \quad \text{(b)}$$

(8.118)

Here f is a function only of the invariants $J_2, J_3,$* and K is a nonnegative *parameter* that is a function of the *plastic strain history* (i.e., a function of *time*) beginning at zero for initial yield. It is the usual practice now to refer to f as the *load function*, thus reserving the designation *yield function* for the initial state (i.e., $K = 0$). The surface $f = K$ in principal stress space is accordingly called the *load surface*. (During a load–unload–reload cycle, plastic deformation recommences during the reload part of the cycle, when the load function f reaches the value of K that was attained at the end of the load part of the cycle.) According to the *isotropic hardening* concept, the load surface expands uniformly about the origin during loading while maintaining its initial shape and orientation. The mechanism that produces isotropic hardening acts equally in *tension and compression*, even if the yielding is entirely due to one-dimensional tension. It clearly follows that during isotropic hardening the load function will satisfy postulates 2, 3, and 4 set down in Section 8.6 for the initial yield function. That is, at *any* stage of plastic deformation the material behavior is isotropic, the plastic flow is independent of hydrostatic stress, and the material behaves identically in tension and compression.

A *basic postulate* here is that flow law (8.96) (i.e., $\dot{\varepsilon}^P_{ij} = \dot{\Lambda}\, \partial f/\partial \tau_{ij}$) be applicable to continuing rate-insensitive plastic flow with strain hardening. But we now use conditions (8.118) on the load function f rather than conditions (8.117), and furthermore, $\dot{\Lambda}$ must be determined from the hardening model. We shall do this in Part C within the framework of *incompressible, rate-independent* yielding according to the *Mises criterion* with *isotropic hardening*. It follows that at *any* stage of plastic deformation for such a material, the *load surface* is a circular cylinder and the plastic strain-rate vector is directed *outwardly normal* to this surface.

In Part C we also make some brief observations on the *kinematic hardening* model, which does *not* produce equal tensile and compressive hardening when a tensile stress is applied. We close Part C with an introductory treatment of three-dimensional *viscoplasticity*, which allows for the inclusion of *rate sensitivity* as well as strain hardening. When *either* nonisotropic strain hardening (e.g., kinematic hardening) or rate sensitivity is considered, conditions (8.118) are again subject to modification. We shall do this as the need arises.

8.14 ISOTROPIC STRAIN HARDENING; UNIVERSAL PLASTIC STRESS-STRAIN CURVE

Here, as noted above, the load surface is assumed to *maintain its shape*, while its size is *increased* under the control of a *single parameter* dependent on the plastic strain history. (The case of *perfect plasticity* may be thought of as a special case where the change of shape and size of the initial yield surface is zero.) There are

---

* We shall later consider more general forms for f, which include a dependence on the plastic strain. In such cases $\dot{f} \neq (\partial f/\partial \tau_{ij})\dot{\tau}_{ij}$, and thus the condition for *loading* is given by $(\partial f/\partial \tau_{ij})\dot{\tau}_{ij} \geq 0$ and for *unloading* by $(\partial f/\partial \tau_{ij})\dot{\tau}_{ij} < 0$. In more precise terminology the case $(\partial f/\partial \tau_{ij})\dot{\tau}_{ij} = 0$ is called *neutral loading*.

two hypotheses that have been widely used to measure the amount of hardening. One hypothesis valid for isotropic hardening involves the formulation of the *universal plastic stress-strain curve*. We shall pursue this hypothesis in detail in this section and will in essence express the parameter K in Eq. (8.118) in terms of an effective plastic strain $\bar{\varepsilon}^p$. A second and more general hypothesis assumes that the amount of work hardening and thus K depend on the plastic work W_p. This is called the hypothesis of *equivalence of plastic work*. For materials with a *Mises* yield criterion we show later that the two hypotheses are *equivalent* for isotropic hardening (i.e., one may be expressed in terms of the other).

We begin by introducing the *effective stress* $\bar{\tau}$ and the *effective plastic strain rate* $\bar{\varepsilon}^p$. These quantities* are *defined* in the following way when used for an *incompressible* material satisfying Mises flow law (8.104):

$$\bar{\tau} \equiv \sqrt{3J_2}$$

$$= \frac{\sqrt{2}}{2} [(\tau_{11} - \tau_{22})^2 + (\tau_{22} - \tau_{33})^2 + (\tau_{33} - \tau_{11})^2 + 6(\tau_{12}^2 + \tau_{23}^2 + \tau_{31}^2)]^{1/2} \tag{a}$$

$$\bar{\dot{\varepsilon}}^p \equiv \tfrac{2}{3}\sqrt{3K_2} \tag{8.119}$$

$$= \frac{\sqrt{2}}{3} \{(\dot{\varepsilon}_{11}^p - \dot{\varepsilon}_{22}^p)^2 + (\dot{\varepsilon}_{22}^p - \dot{\varepsilon}_{33}^p)^2 + (\dot{\varepsilon}_{33}^p - \dot{\varepsilon}_{11}^p)^2 + 6[(\dot{\varepsilon}_{12}^p)^2 + (\dot{\varepsilon}_{23}^p)^2 + (\dot{\varepsilon}_{31}^p)^2]\}^{1/2} \tag{b}$$

Here we have used Eq. (8.48c) for $J_2 \equiv \tfrac{1}{2} s_{ij} s_{ij}$ and an analogous expression for $K_2 \equiv \tfrac{1}{2}\dot{e}_{ij}^p \dot{e}_{ij}^p = \tfrac{1}{2}\dot{\varepsilon}_{ij}^p \dot{\varepsilon}_{ij}^p$ (since incompressible). We shall be concerned here only with the case of *loading* (i.e., $\dot{f} \geq 0$ and $\dot{J}_2 \geq 0$ for Mises yielding), and it then follows from Eq. (8.119a) that $\dot{\bar{\tau}} \geq 0$. Now consider the uniaxial stress case where τ_{11} is the only nonzero stress. Equation (8.119a) for the effective stress reduces for this case to

$$\bar{\tau} = \sqrt{3J_2} = |\tau_{11}| \tag{8.120}$$

For incompressible deformation, we have for this uniaxial stress case

$$\dot{\varepsilon}_{22}^p = \dot{\varepsilon}_{33}^p = -\tfrac{1}{2}\dot{\varepsilon}_{11}^p \tag{a}$$

$$\dot{\varepsilon}_{12}^p = \dot{\varepsilon}_{23}^p = \dot{\varepsilon}_{31}^p = 0 \tag{b}$$

$$\tag{8.121}$$

where as usual the principal axes of stress and strain rate coincide for *isotropic* behavior. Now going back to Eq. (8.119b) and using the results above, we find that the effective plastic strain rate for the uniaxial stress simply becomes

$$\bar{\dot{\varepsilon}}^p = \tfrac{2}{3}\sqrt{3K_2} = |\dot{\varepsilon}_{11}^p| \tag{8.122}$$

Equations (8.120) and (8.122) demonstrate the convenience of definitions (8.119).

Before proceeding further, let us discuss defining Eqs. (8.119) for $\bar{\tau}$ and $\bar{\dot{\varepsilon}}^p$. First we note that $\bar{\tau}$ and $\bar{\dot{\varepsilon}}^p$ are directly related to the tensor invariants J_2 and K_2, respectively. Hence they are also scalar tensor invariants. Also, we see from Eq. (8.120) that $\bar{\tau} = Y$ at initial yield and $\bar{\tau} > Y$ after hardening occurs. Now, by analogy with Eq. (8.119b), one could define an effective plastic strain as follows:

---

* The usual notation for the effective value of a tensor quantity is either $(\bar{})$ or $()_e$. However, we have already used these respective notations for the diagonal average (e.g., bulk stress) and for the elastic component, respectively. Hence we have chosen the notation $(\check{})$.

$$\bar{\varepsilon}^P = \frac{\sqrt{2}}{\sqrt{3}} [\varepsilon_{ij}^P \, \varepsilon_{ij}^P]^{1/2}$$

(8.123)

$$= \frac{\sqrt{2}}{3} \{(\varepsilon_{11}^P - \varepsilon_{22}^P)^2 + (\varepsilon_{22}^P - \varepsilon_{33}^P)^2 + (\varepsilon_{33}^P - \varepsilon_{11}^P)^2 + 6[(\varepsilon_{12}^P)^2 + (\varepsilon_{23}^P)^2 + (\varepsilon_{31}^P)^2]\}^{1/2}$$

However, the time derivative of Eq. (8.123) does *not* yield Eq. (8.119b); that is, *in general*, we have

$$\dot{\bar{\varepsilon}}^P \neq \tilde{\dot{\varepsilon}}^P$$

(8.124)

To avoid the above-noted inconvenience inherent in definition (8.123), we introduce the following *alternative definition* for the *effective plastic strain*:

$$\tilde{\varepsilon}^P \equiv \int_{t_0}^t \tilde{\dot{\varepsilon}}^P(t') \, dt' = \frac{\sqrt{2}}{\sqrt{3}} \int_{t_0}^t [\dot{\varepsilon}_{ij}^P(t') \dot{\varepsilon}_{ij}^P(t')]^{1/2} \, dt'$$

(8.125)

where the plastic deformation for loading begins at $t' = t_0$ and we have used definition (8.119b).* Note that $\tilde{\varepsilon}^P$ is a function of *time* (i.e., it is dependent on the *history* of the plastic deformation). Differentiating expression (8.125) with respect to t, we *now* obtain

$$\dot{\tilde{\varepsilon}}^P = \tilde{\dot{\varepsilon}}^P = \frac{\sqrt{2}}{\sqrt{3}} [\dot{\varepsilon}_{ij}^P \, \dot{\varepsilon}_{ij}^P]^{1/2}$$

(8.126)

Since for uniaxial stress we have $\tilde{\dot{\varepsilon}}^P = |\dot{\varepsilon}_{11}^P|$ [see Eq. (8.122)], it follows from Eq. (8.125) that in this special case we also have

$$\tilde{\varepsilon}^P = |\varepsilon_{11}^P|$$

(8.127)

In obtaining this result we have made use of the fact that for *loading* we have $\operatorname{sgn} \dot{\varepsilon}_{11}^P = \operatorname{sgn} \varepsilon_{11}^P$, and thus $|\dot{\varepsilon}_{11}^P| = \dot{\varepsilon}_{11}^P (\operatorname{sgn} \varepsilon_{11}^P)$.

Assume that we are given a one-dimensional *tensile* stress-strain curve, such that the relation between $\tau_{11} = |\tau_{11}|$ and the plastic strain component $\varepsilon_{11}^P = |\varepsilon_{11}^P|$ is expressed by the function

$$\tau_{11} = H(\varepsilon_{11}^P)$$

(8.128)

Using Eqs. (8.120) and (8.127), we can express Eq. (8.128) in terms of the *effective stress* $\tilde{\tau}$ and the *effective plastic strain* $\tilde{\varepsilon}^P$ as follows:

$$\boxed{\tilde{\tau} = H(\tilde{\varepsilon}^P)}$$

(8.129)

Although Eq. (8.129) has been obtained from a one-dimensional case, we now postulate that it is *equally valid for any multidimensional stress state*. This is the previously mentioned hypothesis of a single *universal plastic stress-strain curve*. For the actual form of H for use in Eq. (8.129), we go back to Eq. (8.128) for the simple one-dimensional tensile test.

---

* Note the use of different forms of epsilon, namely ε and ϵ, on the left sides of Eqs. (8.123) and (8.125), respectively, in order to distinguish between those two definitions of effective plastic strain.

In the next section we shall utilize Eq. (8.129) to determine $\dot{\Lambda}$ in the flow law for isotropic hardening. In so doing it will become clear why it was necessary to establish Eq. (8.129) in terms of $\bar{\varepsilon}^p$ as defined by Eq. (8.125) rather than in terms of $\bar{\varepsilon}^p$ as defined by Eq. (8.123). We shall also examine the special case of power-law isotropic strain hardening in some detail.*

8.15 FLOW LAW FOR ISOTROPIC HARDENING; CASE OF POWER-LAW HARDENING

Go back to the *Mises flow law* (8.104), which we now rewrite on using Eq. (8.109):

$$\dot{\varepsilon}_{ij}^p = \dot{\Lambda}\,s_{ij} = \frac{\sqrt{K_2}}{\sqrt{J_2}}\,s_{ij} \tag{8.130}$$

In this equation we have $J_2 \geq Y^2/3$ and $\dot{J}_2 \geq 0$ for plastic flow during loading. Replacing $\sqrt{K_2}$ and $\sqrt{J_2}$ using Eqs. (8.119), we reach the following form of the Mises flow law:

$$\dot{\varepsilon}_{ij}^p = \dot{\Lambda}s_{ij} = \frac{3}{2}\left(\frac{\dot{\bar{\varepsilon}}^p}{\bar{\tau}}\right)s_{ij} \tag{8.131}$$

For the case of perfectly plastic material, $\bar{\tau} = Y$ in Eq. (8.131) but $\dot{\Lambda}$ is in general indeterminate. For a material that work-hardens, $\bar{\tau}$ may exceed Y, and for isotropic hardening $\dot{\bar{\varepsilon}}^p$ and $\dot{\Lambda}$ are determined from hypothesis (8.129).

We start with the one-dimensional tensile plastic stress-strain curve shown in Fig. 8.31, with ordinate τ_{11} and abscissa $\varepsilon_{11}^p = \varepsilon_{11} - \varepsilon_{11}^e = \varepsilon_{11} - \tau_{11}/E$. The function defining the curve is given as $\tau_{11} = H(\varepsilon_{11}^p)$, and its slope at any point is denoted as

$$\frac{d\tau_{11}}{d\varepsilon_{11}^p} = H' \tag{8.132}$$

In accordance with the hypothesis of a universal plastic stress-strain curve, we note that for three dimensions the ordinate is replaced by the effective stress $\bar{\tau}$ and the abscissa by the effective plastic strain $\bar{\varepsilon}^p$, whereas the function H (and the shape of the curve) is unchanged. Accordingly, Eq. (8.132) becomes

$$\frac{d\bar{\tau}}{d\bar{\varepsilon}^p} = H' \tag{8.133}$$

Using the chain rule for differentiation, we then have

$$\dot{\bar{\tau}} = \frac{d\bar{\tau}}{d\bar{\varepsilon}^p}\,\dot{\bar{\varepsilon}}^p = H'\dot{\bar{\varepsilon}}^p \tag{8.134}$$

Replacing $\dot{\bar{\varepsilon}}^p$ by $\dot{\bar{\varepsilon}}^p$ via Eq. (8.126), we finally obtain

$$\dot{\bar{\varepsilon}}^p = \frac{\dot{\bar{\tau}}}{H'} \tag{8.135}$$

---

* In developing nonlinear rate-sensitive creep laws in Chapter 7, we utilized a "strain-hardening" hypothesis. In the present plasticity formulation "strain hardening" is clearly *not* an equivalent concept, since we are dealing with rate-insensitive (i.e., inviscid) constitutive laws.

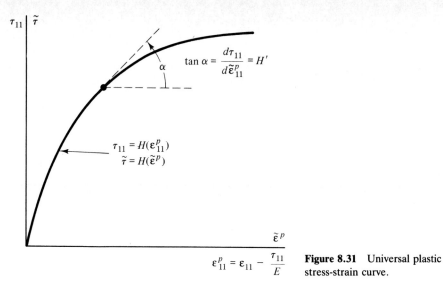

$$\tan \alpha = \frac{d\tau_{11}}{d\tilde{\varepsilon}^p_{11}} = H'$$

$$\tau_{11} = H(\varepsilon^p_{11})$$
$$\tilde{\tau} = H(\tilde{\varepsilon}^p)$$

$$\varepsilon^p_{11} = \varepsilon_{11} - \frac{\tau_{11}}{E}$$

Figure 8.31 Universal plastic stress-strain curve.

Inserting this result into Eq. (8.131), we obtain the desired flow law for *loading* (i.e., $\dot{\tilde{\tau}} \geq 0$) as

$$\dot{\varepsilon}^p_{ij} = \dot{\Lambda} s_{ij} = \frac{3}{2} \frac{\dot{\tilde{\tau}}}{\tilde{\tau} H'} s_{ij} \qquad (8.136)$$

We may replace $\dot{\tilde{\tau}}$ in the above by $(\partial \tilde{\tau}/\partial \tau_{kl})\dot{\tau}_{kl}$ to obtain the alternative form

$$\dot{\varepsilon}^p_{ij} = \dot{\Lambda} s_{ij} = \left[\frac{3}{2\tilde{\tau}H'} \frac{\partial \tilde{\tau}}{\partial \tau_{kl}} \dot{\tau}_{kl} \right] s_{ij} \qquad (8.137)$$

From this we see that $\dot{\Lambda}$ is a *linear* function of *all* of the *stress-rates* $\dot{\tau}_{kl}$, with coefficients that depend on the current state of stress τ_{ij}.

We now illustrate the application of the flow law above to the case of power-law strain hardening.

Example 8.2

Consider as an example of the use of Eq. (8.136) the case of *power-law* strain hardening. The one-dimensional, *rate-independent* plastic stress-strain law for this case was given earlier (for $\tau_{11} \geq Y$ and $\dot{\tau}_{11} \geq 0$) by Eq. (8.2b) as

$$\varepsilon^p_{11} = \varepsilon_{11} - \frac{\tau_{11}}{E} = A(\tau_{11} - Y)^n \qquad (a)$$

where we have set $A = (\mu_p)^{-n}$. For this case determine the expression for $\dot{\varepsilon}^p_{ij}$, with $\dot{\Lambda}$ expressed in terms of J_2 and $\dot{J}_2$. Also, verify that in one dimension this three-dimensional flow law does indeed reduce to rate-independent law (a) above.

The universal curve is obtained directly from Eq. (a) as

$$\tilde{\varepsilon}^p = A(\tilde{\tau} - Y)^n \qquad (b)$$

For use in Eq. (8.136) we will need the reciprocal of the slope (i.e., $1/H'$). Noting Eq.

(8.133), we have for the present case

$$\frac{1}{H'} = \frac{d\bar{\varepsilon}^P}{d\bar{\tau}} = nA(\bar{\tau} - Y)^{n-1} \tag{c}$$

We also see from Eq. (8.119a) that

$$\bar{\tau} = \sqrt{3J_2} \tag{d}$$

and thus Eq. (c) becomes

$$\frac{1}{H'} = nA(\sqrt{3J_2} - Y)^{n-1} \tag{e}$$

We shall also require $\dot{\bar{\tau}}$ for use in Eq. (8.136), and this follows from Eq. (d) as

$$\dot{\bar{\tau}} = \frac{\sqrt{3}}{2}\frac{\dot{J}_2}{\sqrt{J_2}} \tag{f}$$

Note that $\dot{J}_2 \geq 0$, since $J_2 \geq 0$ and $\dot{\bar{\tau}} \geq 0$ for loading. Substituting Eqs. (d) to (f) into Eq. (8.136) and combining terms, we finally obtain for loading

$$\dot{\varepsilon}^P_{ij} = \left[\frac{3nA}{4}\frac{\dot{J}_2}{J_2}(\sqrt{3J_2} - Y)^{n-1}\right]s_{ij} \qquad \dot{J}_2 \geq 0 \tag{g}$$

For the second part of this example, we examine Eq. (g) for the one-dimensional tension case in which τ_{11} is the only nonzero stress. In this case $\bar{\tau} = \tau_{11}$ [see Eq. (8.120)], and thus Eq. (d) gives

$$J_2 = \frac{\tau_{11}^2}{3} \tag{h}$$

It immediately follows that

$$\frac{\dot{J}_2}{J_2} = \frac{2\dot{\tau}_{11}}{\tau_{11}} \tag{i}$$

By definition of the stress deviator tensor, we also have for this case

$$s_{11} = \tfrac{2}{3}\tau_{11} \tag{j}$$

Setting $i = j = 1$ in Eq. (g) and then using Eqs. (h) to (j), we obtain after simplification

$$\dot{\varepsilon}^P_{11} = nA(\tau_{11} - Y)^{n-1}\dot{\tau}_{11} \tag{k}$$

and this result can be rewritten as

$$\dot{\varepsilon}^P_{11} = A\frac{d}{dt}(\tau_{11} - Y)^n \tag{l}$$

which after integration from t_0 to t [with $\tau_{11}(t_0) = Y$ and $\varepsilon^P_{11}(t_0) = 0$] becomes

$$\varepsilon^P_{11} = A(\tau_{11} - Y)^n \tag{m}$$

But this is precisely the one-dimensional, rate-independent law (a) given at the beginning of this example.

In the example above, we developed a three-dimensional flow rule for the case of isotropic power-law strain hardening [i.e., Eq. (g)], and we now rewrite this useful result:

$$\dot{\varepsilon}_{ij}^p = \left[\frac{3nA}{4} \frac{\dot{J}_2}{J_2} (\sqrt{3J_2} - Y)^{n-1} \right] s_{ij} \qquad \dot{J}_2 \geq 0 \qquad (8.138)$$

We also showed that for *one-dimensional* stress this equation reduces as expected to a *rate-independent* equation, that is, one in which ε_{11}^p is a power function in τ_{11} only and is thus independent of $\dot{\tau}_{11}$ (and $\dot{\varepsilon}_{11}^p$). The question naturally arises as to whether ε_{ij}^p for *multidimensional* loading will in general be independent of all the components of $\dot{\tau}_{ij}$. To help answer this question, we first rewrite Eq. (8.138) in the form

$$\dot{\varepsilon}_{ij}^p = \frac{\sqrt{3}A}{2} \frac{d}{dt} (\sqrt{3J_2} - Y)^n \frac{s_{ij}}{\sqrt{J_2}} \qquad (8.139)$$

which you may readily verify. Complete rate independence of ε_{ij}^p is obtained if the factor $s_{ij}/\sqrt{J_2}$ in Eq. (8.139) is *independent of time*, since then the time derivatives in this equation may be removed via an integration. You can easily show that this factor equals $2/\sqrt{3}$ in the *uniaxial tension case* [see Eqs. (h) and (j) in Example 8.2]. However, one can readily construct examples of multidimensional loadings for which this factor is *not* independent of time (see Problem 8.26). We thus conclude that *in general* Eq. (8.138) may exhibit some dependency of components of ε_{ij}^p on components of $\dot{\tau}_{ij}$.

We will now prove that in the *special case* of multidimensional *proportional loading*, the above-mentioned rate dependence is absent. A proportional loading is defined as one for which the *stresses* at any instant t are given by

$$\tau_{ij}(t) = (\tau_{ij})_0 \beta(t) \qquad (8.140)$$

Here $(\tau_{ij})_0$ is the stress tensor at the time of initial yielding t_0, and $\beta(t)$ is a monotonically increasing dimensionless function of time $t \geq t_0$, which equals unity at $t = t_0$ [e.g., $\beta(t) = t/t_0$]. During proportional loading the stresses increase *in concert*, so that at any time $t \geq t_0$ all stress components are the same multiple of their values at the onset of yielding. It follows directly from the use of Eq. (8.140) in the definitions of s_{ij} and J_2 that under proportional loading

$$s_{ij} = (s_{ij})_0 \beta(t) \qquad \text{where} \quad (s_{ij})_0 = (\tau_{ij})_0 - \tfrac{1}{3}(\tau_{kk})_0 \delta_{ij} \qquad \text{(a)}$$

$$J_2 = (J_2)_0 \beta(t)^2 \qquad \text{where} \quad (J_2)_0 = \tfrac{1}{2}(s_{ij})_0 (s_{ij})_0 \qquad \text{(b)} \qquad (8.141)$$

Returning to Eq. (8.139), we see that in this case the factor

$$\frac{s_{ij}}{\sqrt{J_2}} = \frac{(s_{ij})_0 \beta(t)}{\sqrt{(J_2)_0} \beta(t)} = \frac{(s_{ij})_0}{\sqrt{(J_2)_0}} \qquad (8.142)$$

which is seen to be independent of time, and thus our initial assertion is proven.* We emphasize that proportional loading was *not* assumed in the development of Eq. (8.139) or the more general expression (8.136). However, experimental evi-

---

* You may recall that we showed earlier that if in the Mises flow law for the *onset* of yielding $\dot{\varepsilon}_{ij}^p$ is replaced by $\alpha(t) \dot{\varepsilon}_{ij}^p$ (i.e., *proportional straining*), then s_{ij} is *unchanged* [see discussion after Eqs. (8.114)]. This type of rate independence is the *converse* of the discussion of rate independence for Eq. (8.138), which is a special example of strain-hardening Mises flow law (8.130). Note that if in Eq. (8.130) we replace $\dot{\varepsilon}_{ij}^p$ by $\alpha(t) \dot{\varepsilon}_{ij}^p$, the *factor* $s_{ij}/\sqrt{J_2}$ is unchanged.

dence does indicate that these flow laws tend to work better for stress states which do not depart radically from a state of proportional loading.

In Section 8.13 we noted that at *any* stage of plastic deformation during *loading*, the plastic strain-rate vector will be normal to the *current load* surface. We will now demonstrate that this is indeed the case for Eq. (8.138). First, we employ Eq. (8.99) to write

$$s_{ij} = \frac{\partial f}{\partial \tau_{ij}} \tag{8.143}$$

where f is the Mises load function defined as

$$f = J_2 - \frac{Y^2}{3} \tag{8.144}$$

Also note that

$$\dot{f} = \frac{d}{dt}\left(\tfrac{1}{2}s_{kl}s_{kl}\right) = s_{kl}\dot{s}_{kl} \geq 0 \tag{8.145}$$

since we are assuming that *loading* is occurring. Using Eq. (8.143), we may express Eq. (8.138) as

$$\dot{\varepsilon}^p_{ij} = \dot{\Lambda}\,\frac{\partial f}{\partial \tau_{ij}} = \left[\frac{3nA}{4}\,\frac{\dot{J}_2}{J_2}\,(\sqrt{3J_2} - Y)^{n-1}\right]\frac{\partial f}{\partial \tau_{ij}} \tag{8.146}$$

In principal stress (and principal strain-rate) space, this becomes

$$\dot{\varepsilon}^p_i = \dot{\Lambda}\,\frac{\partial f}{\partial \tau_i} = \left[\frac{3nA}{4}\,\frac{\dot{J}_2}{J_2}\,(\sqrt{3J_2} - Y)^{n-1}\right]\frac{\partial f}{\partial \tau_i} \qquad \dot{J}_2 \geq 0 \tag{8.147}$$

where $\dot{\varepsilon}^p_i$ and $\partial f/\partial \tau_i$ are vectors and $\dot{\Lambda}$ is a scalar. Let us say that the *onset* of yielding occurs at the time $t = t_0$, and as t increases beyond t_0 we follow some loading path in principal stress space (see Fig. 8.32). At the onset of yielding we have $J_2 = Y^2/3$ according to the Mises criterion, and thus definition (8.144) gives $f = 0$ [look back at condition (8.117b)]. As additional loading occurs we have $J_2 > Y^2/3$ and thus $f = K > 0$ [see condition (8.118b)], where K is a monotonically increasing positive parameter. Since $\partial f/\partial \tau_i$ is a gradient vector, Eq. (8.147) then tells us that at any instant $\dot{\varepsilon}^p_i$ is *normal* to the load surface $f = K$, where as noted above, $K = 0$ at the onset of yielding and $K > 0$ after hardening occurs. The surface $f = 0$ is the familiar circular cylinder for the onset of Mises yielding, which is seen as a circle in principal stress space when viewed down the hydrostatic line. Clearly, as loading occurs and K increases beyond zero, this circle is growing in size without change in shape or origin. We have illustrated the process described above in Fig. 8.32, and you should note the *normality* of $\dot{\varepsilon}^p_i$ to the *current* load locus. The *magnitude* of $\dot{\varepsilon}^p_i$ follows directly from Eq. (8.147) as

$$|\dot{\varepsilon}^p_i| = \dot{\Lambda}\left|\frac{\partial f}{\partial \tau_i}\right| = \left[\frac{3nA}{4}\,\frac{\dot{J}_2}{J_2}\,(\sqrt{3J_2} - Y)^{n-1}\right]\left|\frac{\partial f}{\partial \tau_i}\right| \tag{8.148}$$

since as previously noted $\dot{\Lambda}$ is a scalar. It is also interesting to note that since $\sqrt{3J_2} = Y$ at $t = t_0$, we have $|\dot{\varepsilon}^p_i| = 0$ at initial yield for this power flow law *if* $n > 1$. Since J_2

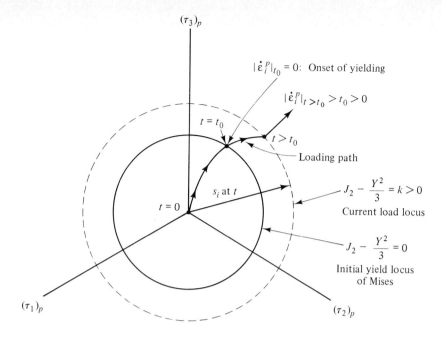

Figure 8.32 Mises yielding using power-law isotropic hardening ($n > 1$).

and $|\partial f/\partial \tau_i|$ (equal to $|s_i|$) are constant along the load locus, Eq. (8.148) also tells us that the *ratio* $|\dot{\varepsilon}_i^p|/\dot{J}_2$ is *invariant* along this load locus.

8.16 ADDITIONAL HARDENING HYPOTHESES AND FLOW LAWS

In this section we discuss three additional topics concerning hardening. First we consider the more general hypothesis of *equivalent plastic work*, and will show that for *Mises yielding* it is equivalent to isotropic hardening via the hypothesis of a universal plastic stress-strain curve. Next we briefly discuss some *more general yield functions*, which are not necessarily of the Mises yield type nor isotropic. Finally, we discuss *kinematic hardening*, which is *not* isotropic and has been used to explore the Bauschinger effect.[*]

Equivalent Plastic Work Hypothesis

According to this hypothesis, the amount of work hardening depends on the plastic work W_p. In essence it says that resistance to further yielding at a material point depends only on the amount of plastic work done to reach the given state. Earlier, we

---

[*] For further information on these and other hardening theories, see: L. E. Malvern, *Introduction to the Mechanics of a Continuous Medium* (Englewood Cliffs, NJ: Prentice-Hall, Inc., 1969), Chap. 6; A. Mendelson, *Plasticity: Theory and Application* (Melbourne, FL: R.E. Krieger Publishing Co., reprint edition, 1983); and also P. M. Naghdi, "Stress-Strain Relations in Plasticity and Thermoplasticity," pp. 121–169 in *Plasticity*, E. H. Lee and P. S. Symonds (eds.) (New York: Pergamon Press, 1960).

gave the *plastic dissipation power* as [see Eq. (8.111)]

$$\dot{W}_p = \tau_{ij}\dot{\varepsilon}^P_{ij} = s_{ij}\dot{\varepsilon}^P_{ij} \tag{8.149}$$

Integrating this result, we obtain the *plastic work* for loading as

$$W_p = \int_{t_0}^{t} \tau_{ij}\dot{\varepsilon}^P_{ij}\,dt' = \int_{t_0}^{t} s_{ij}\dot{\varepsilon}^P_{ij}\,dt' \tag{8.150}$$

where t_0 is the time at which plastic deformation starts. (Note that just as $\bar{\varepsilon}^P$ was a function of time [see Eq. (8.125)], so too is W_p a *history-dependent* function of time.) We wish to show that the plastic work hypothesis is equivalent to the universal curve hypothesis when there is Mises yielding present. Recall that the concept of the universal plastic stress-strain curve is given as [see Eq. (8.129)]

$$\bar{\tau} = H(\bar{\varepsilon}^P) \tag{8.151}$$

where $\bar{\tau}$ and $\bar{\varepsilon}^P$ are defined by Eqs. (8.119a) and (8.125), respectively. Now we have seen that for the Mises flow law with *isotropic* hardening, the *size* of the *current* load surface depends on J_2 [see Eq. (8.144)]. But $\bar{\tau} = \sqrt{3J_2}$ [see Eq. (8.119a)], and thus $\bar{\tau}$ is clearly also a measure of the size of the current load surface. Accordingly, if the size of the current load surface is to depend only on W_p, we must have a function

$$\bar{\tau} = F(W_p) \tag{8.152}$$

We will now show that W_p is a single-valued function of $\bar{\varepsilon}^P$, and thus Eq. (8.152) is *equivalent* to Eq. (8.151).

Consider the *stress deviator vector* s_i [look back at Eq. (8.40) and recall that s_i is the indicial equivalent of the radial stress vector τ_r] in the three-dimensional principal stress space. As we have seen, the axes of this space have the same orientation as the axes for the principal plastic strain-rate space. Now the *magnitude* of s_i is given as

$$|s_i| = (s_i s_i)^{1/2} = \sqrt{2J_2} = \sqrt{\tfrac{2}{3}}\,\bar{\tau} \tag{8.153}$$

where we have used the definition of J_2 for principal axes, and the definition of $\bar{\tau}$ [Eq. (8.119a)]. Similarly, we consider the principal plastic strain-rate vector $\dot{\varepsilon}^P_i$, and determine its magnitude as

$$|\dot{\varepsilon}^P_i| = (\dot{\varepsilon}^P_i \dot{\varepsilon}^P_i)^{1/2} = \sqrt{2K_2} = \sqrt{\tfrac{3}{2}}\,\dot{\bar{\varepsilon}}^P \tag{8.154}$$

where here we have used the definition of K_2 for *incompressible* behavior, and the definition of $\dot{\bar{\varepsilon}}^P$ [see Eq. (8.119b)]. Now go back to the Mises flow law (8.130), which for principal axes becomes

$$\dot{\varepsilon}^P_i = \dot{\Lambda}\,s_i \qquad \dot{\Lambda} > 0 \tag{8.155}$$

and thus we see once more that in this case $\dot{\varepsilon}^P_i$ and s_i are *collinear* and have the same sense.

The plastic dissipation power $\dot{W}_p$, defined by Eq. (8.149), may now be expressed in terms of $\bar{\tau}$ and $\dot{\bar{\varepsilon}}^P$. Thus, for principal axes,

$$\dot{W}_p = s_i\dot{\varepsilon}^P_i = |s_i||\dot{\varepsilon}^P_i| = \bar{\tau}\dot{\bar{\varepsilon}}^P \tag{8.156}$$

where we have used the collinearity of s_i and $\dot{\varepsilon}_i^p$, and also Eqs. (8.153) and (8.154). Replacing $\tilde{\dot{\varepsilon}}^p$ in the above by $\dot{\tilde{\varepsilon}}^p$ [see Eq. (8.126)] and integrating over time, we finally obtain the plastic work as

$$W_p(t) = \int_{t_0}^{t} \tilde{\tau}\dot{\tilde{\varepsilon}}^p \, dt' = \int_{0}^{\tilde{\varepsilon}^P(t)} \tilde{\tau} \, d\tilde{\varepsilon}^p(t') \qquad (8.157)$$

Observing Fig. 8.33 we see that $W_p(t)$ for the plastic state at time t is the area under the universal plastic stress-strain curve in the interval $0 \le \tilde{\varepsilon}^p(t') \le \tilde{\varepsilon}^P(t)$. Clearly, for a given material $W_p(t)$ is a single-valued function of $\tilde{\varepsilon}^p(t)$, which is what we set out to prove. Thus, by enjoining the Mises flow rule with the plastic work-hardening hypothesis, we arrive again at isotropic strain hardening via the universal curve hypothesis.

More General Yield Functions

Thus far we have presented *isotropic* hardening formulations, used in conjunction with the flow law

$$\dot{\varepsilon}_{ij}^p = \dot{\Lambda} \frac{\partial f}{\partial \tau_{ij}} \qquad (8.158)$$

where f is the *Mises load function*

$$f(J_2) = J_2 - \frac{Y^2}{3} = K \ge 0 \qquad (8.159)$$

Using the universal curve and the plastic work concepts, the hardening parameter K may be expressed in terms of $\tilde{\varepsilon}^p$ and W_p, respectively. Following the latter approach, we set [see Eq. (8.152)]

$$\tilde{\tau} = \sqrt{3J_2} = F(W_p) \qquad (8.160)$$

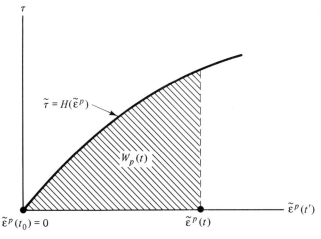

Figure 8.33 Plot showing that $W_p(t)$ is a single-valued function of $\tilde{\varepsilon}^p(t)$.

and thus K follows from Eq. (8.159) as

$$K = \tfrac{1}{3}[F(W_p)^2 - Y^2] = G(W_p) \qquad (8.161)$$

where G is another function of W_p. We may now rewrite Eq. (8.159) as

$$f(J_2) = G(W_p) \qquad (8.162)$$

which clearly shows that W_p determines the *size* of the current Mises load surface.

As indicated by Eq. (8.37) in Part A, an immediate extension of the above is to replace Eq. (8.162) by

$$f(J_2, J_3) = G(W_p) \qquad (8.163)$$

Such a postulate is still *isotropic* since J_2, J_3 are scalar invariants, but it is *not* restricted to Mises yielding. Given the form of $f(J_2, J_3)$, one could then proceed to determine $\dot{\Lambda}$ in flow law (8.158). As shown in Eq. (8.102), this flow law now has the form

$$\dot{\varepsilon}_{ij}^p = \dot{\Lambda}\left(\frac{\partial f}{\partial J_2}\, s_{ij} + \frac{\partial f}{\partial J_3}\, r_{ij}\right) \qquad (8.164a)$$

where

$$r_{ij} = s_{ip}\, s_{pj} - \tfrac{1}{3} s_{qp}\, s_{pq}\, \delta_{ij} \qquad (8.164b)$$

A further generalization is obtained by replacing Eq. (8.163) with

$$f(\tau_{ij}) = G(W_p) = K \qquad (8.165)$$

Since f has not been expressed here in terms of the invariants, this formulation may be used for hardening which is not necessarily isotropic. One may also choose to include an *explicit* dependence of f on the plastic strain in Eq. (8.165), that is,

$$f(\tau_{ij}, \varepsilon_{ij}^p) = K \qquad (8.166)$$

It is also common practice to *imbed* a hardening parameter κ within the load function, and then to write

$$f(\tau_{ij}, \varepsilon_{ij}^p, \kappa) = 0 \qquad (8.167)$$

where κ depends on the plastic strain history. Note that in using Eq. (8.167) rather than Eq. (8.166), we have replaced the condition $f = K$ during loading by $f = 0$. Furthermore, since in Eq. (8.167) f is no longer a function of stress *only*, the condition for loading is now given as $(\partial f/\partial \tau_{ij})\dot{\tau}_{ij} \geq 0$ rather than $\dot{f} \geq 0$. [In fact, $\dot{f} \equiv 0$, since Eq. (8.167) is to be satisfied for *all time* during which plastic deformation occurs.]

There is one particular nonisotropic model called *kinematic hardening* which has seen some use, and thus we shall now discuss this model in a little more detail.

Kinematic Hardening

It is presumed here that the load surface *does not change in shape or size*, but merely *translates* in stress space. Thus, initially, we have for the yield surface

$$f(\tau_{ij}) = 0 \tag{8.168}$$

During loading with hardening this becomes

$$f(\tau_{ij} - \alpha_{ij}) = 0 \tag{8.169}$$

where f here is the same function as in Eq. (8.168) but with τ_{ij} replaced by $\tau_{ij} - \alpha_{ij}$; thus α_{ij} are the coordinates of the origin of a translating reference frame fixed to the current load surface. Also note here that α_{ij} is a *tensor hardening parameter* which depends on the state of deformation and thus on the time. The most generally used formulation for α_{ij} is the *linear hardening* case, where it is assumed that

$$\dot{\alpha}_{ij} = C\dot{\varepsilon}_{ij}^p \tag{8.170}$$

where C is a positive constant. According to Eq. (8.170), the time rate of change of the coordinate tensor for the translating origin is linearly proportional to the plastic strain-rate tensor. Integrating Eq. (8.170) from t_0 to t with $\alpha_{ij}(t_0) = \varepsilon_{ij}^p(t_0) = 0$, and using the result in Eq. (8.169), we finally obtain

$$\boxed{f(\tau_{ij} - C\varepsilon_{ij}^p) = 0} \tag{8.171}$$

Note that this equation is a *special case* of Eq. (8.167), in that the hardening parameter κ is now the *constant* C.

To interpret Eq. (8.171), we once more make use of the *three-dimensional* principal axis space. Equations (8.170) and (8.171) become for such a space

$$\dot{\alpha}_i = C\dot{\varepsilon}_i^p \qquad \text{(a)}$$
$$f(\tau_i - C\varepsilon_i^p) = 0 \qquad \text{(b)} \tag{8.172}$$

We see from Eq. (8.172a) that the $\dot{\alpha}_i$ vector, which represents the rate of change of the three coordinates of the moving origin in this space, is *parallel* to the plastic strain-rate vector $\dot{\varepsilon}_i^p$. Thus at *any instant* the current load surface is translating in a direction parallel to $\dot{\varepsilon}_i^p$ at that instant, which is of course *normal* to the current load surface. We have illustrated the foregoing process in Fig. 8.34 at the instant of initial yielding for a Tresca yield surface, with a loading path that touches the initial yield surface at point P_0. The vector $\dot{\alpha}_i\,dt$ gives the translation of the origin of the moving principal stress axes in the differential increment of time dt. Note that $\dot{\alpha}_i\,dt$ is parallel to $\dot{\varepsilon}_i^p$ at P_0, and the yield locus has simply translated to the right a "distance" in principal stress space equal to $|\dot{\alpha}_i|\,dt$.*

We shall now determine $\dot{\Lambda}$ in flow law (8.158) for the case of linear kinematic hardening. First we rewrite Eq. (8.171) as

$$f(\tau_{ij}^*) = 0 \qquad \text{where } \tau_{ij}^* = \tau_{ij} - C\varepsilon_{ij}^p \tag{8.173}$$

Since this condition is to be satisfied for *all time*, we must have

$$\dot{f} = \frac{\partial f(\tau_{ij}^*)}{\partial \tau_{ij}}\dot{\tau}_{ij} + \frac{\partial f(\tau_{ij}^*)}{\partial \varepsilon_{ij}^p}\dot{\varepsilon}_{ij}^p \equiv 0 \tag{8.174}$$

---

* Prager has proposed an interesting mechanical model for kinematic hardening. For further information, see J. N. Goodier aand P. G. Hodge, Jr., *Elasticity and Plasticity* (New York: John Wiley & Sons, Inc., 1958), p. 65.

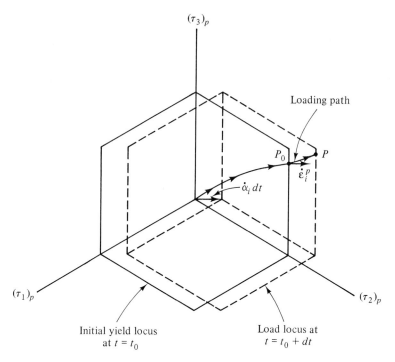

Figure 8.34 Translation of the yield surface in accordance with linear kinematic hardening.

The chain rule gives us

$$\frac{\partial f(\tau_{ij}^*)}{\partial \tau_{ij}} = \frac{\partial f(\tau_{ij}^*)}{\partial \tau_{kl}^*} \frac{\partial \tau_{kl}^*}{\partial \tau_{ij}} = \frac{\partial f(\tau_{ij}^*)}{\partial \tau_{ij}^*} \qquad (a)$$

$$\frac{\partial f(\tau_{ij}^*)}{\partial \varepsilon_{ij}^p} = \frac{\partial f(\tau_{ij}^*)}{\partial \tau_{kl}^*} \frac{\partial \tau_{kl}^*}{\partial \varepsilon_{ij}^p} = -C \frac{\partial f(\tau_{ij}^*)}{\partial \tau_{ij}^*} \qquad (b)$$

(8.175)

where we have used the expressions $\partial \tau_{kl}^*/\partial \tau_{ij} = \delta_{ki}\,\delta_{lj}$ and $\partial \tau_{kl}^*/\partial \varepsilon_{ij}^p = -C\delta_{ki}\,\delta_{lj}$. Using Eq. (8.175a) on the right side of Eq. (8.175b), we then get

$$\frac{\partial f(\tau_{ij}^*)}{\partial \varepsilon_{ij}^p} = -C \frac{\partial f(\tau_{ij}^*)}{\partial \tau_{ij}} \qquad (8.176)$$

whereupon Eq. (8.174) becomes

$$\frac{\partial f(\tau_{ij}^*)}{\partial \tau_{ij}} [\dot{\tau}_{ij} - C\dot{\varepsilon}_{ij}^p] = 0 \qquad (8.177)$$

Finally, using flow law (8.158) [i.e., $\dot{\varepsilon}_{ij}^p = \dot{\Lambda}\partial f(\tau_{ij}^*)/\partial \tau_{ij}$] to replace $\dot{\varepsilon}_{ij}^p$ in the above, and then solving for $\dot{\Lambda}$, we obtain

$$\dot{\Lambda} = \frac{\partial f(\tau_{ij}^*)}{\partial \tau_{ij}} \dot{\tau}_{ij} \bigg/ C \frac{\partial f(\tau_{ij}^*)}{\partial \tau_{kl}} \frac{\partial f(\tau_{ij}^*)}{\partial \tau_{kl}} \qquad (8.178)$$

We thus have the essential features of the constitutive law for linear kinematic hardening.

Look once more at Fig. 8.34, and now consider a *load reversal*. For example, construct an unloading path which goes from point *P back* to the initial origin, followed by a load reversal to some point on the *opposite face* of the *current* Tresca load locus. Since the region inside the current load locus corresponds to purely elastic deformation, the current load locus (shown dashed in the figure) is unaltered during this load reversal. Clearly, whereas the point of yielding *increased* during the loading part of the cycle, this caused a *decrease* in the point of yielding for the load reversal part of the cycle. This is the essential characteristic of the *Bauschinger effect*, which we illustrated in Fig. 8.3 for one-dimensional loading. Kinematic hardening has in fact been used to model the Bauschinger effect, but it is usually difficult to employ. As a result, purely isotropic hardening has seen greater use. We should point out that actual strain hardening is some *combination* of isotropic hardening, kinematic hardening, and possibly some change in shape of the load surface. In a recent review article,[*] Chaboche compares several plasticity models based on generalizations of the classical isotropic and linear kinematic hardening theories.

8.17 THREE-DIMENSIONAL VISCOPLASTICITY

In this section we give an introductory presentation of three-dimensional viscoplasticity, beginning with a rate-dependent material model without strain hardening and then going on to rate-dependent models with strain hardening. For simplicity we consider no load reversal (i.e., loads are either monotonically increasing or monotonically decreasing).

Bingham Material

The most elementary viscoplastic model is the rigid, linear viscoplastic *Bingham* material, which we discussed in Chapter 4 for the case of one-dimensional *tensile* loading [look back at Eq. (4.16) and Fig. 4.22]. Assuming identical tensile and compressive behavior, this equation is easily extended to *arbitrary* uniaxial loading in the x_1 direction as follows:

$$\dot{\varepsilon}_{11} = \begin{cases} 0 & \text{if } |\tau_{11}| < Y \quad (a) \\ \dfrac{|\tau_{11}| - Y}{\eta} \operatorname{sgn} \tau_{11} & \text{if } |\tau_{11}| \geq Y \quad (b) \end{cases} \qquad (8.179)$$

where η and Y are, respectively, the *tensile* viscosity coefficient and the *tensile* yield point. Replacing $\operatorname{sgn} \tau_{11}$ by $\tau_{11}/|\tau_{11}|$ in the above, we obtain the equivalent form

$$\eta \dot{\varepsilon}_{11} = \begin{cases} 0 & \text{if } g_t < 0 \qquad (8.180a) \\ g_t \tau_{11} & \text{if } g_t \geq 0 \qquad (8.180b) \end{cases}$$

[*] J. L. Chaboche, "Time-Independent Constitutive Theories for Cyclic Plasticity," *Int. J. Plasticity*, Vol. 2, No. 2, pp. 149–188 (1986).

where g_t is the dimensionless *tensile load function*

$$g_t = 1 - \frac{Y}{|\tau_{11}|} \qquad (8.180c)$$

Assuming *incompressible* viscoplastic flow and yielding via the *Mises* criterion, the logical generalization of Eqs. (8.180) to three dimensions may be given as*

$$\zeta \dot{\varepsilon}_{ij} = \begin{cases} 0 & \text{if } g < 0 & (8.181a) \\ g s_{ij} & \text{if } g \geq 0 & (8.181b) \end{cases}$$

Here ζ is the *shear* viscosity coefficient, and g is the dimensionless load function for multidimensional Mises yielding,

$$g = 1 - \frac{k}{\sqrt{J_2}} \qquad (8.181c)$$

where k is the yield point for pure shear. In the above, $\dot{\varepsilon}_{ij}$ equals the viscoplastic strain rate $\dot{\varepsilon}_{ij}^p$ since the elastic strain rate $\dot{\varepsilon}_{ij}^e$ has been neglected (i.e., the model is *rigid*, viscoplastic). Note that if we set $k = 0$ in Eq. (8.181c), then Eq. (8.181b) gives the familiar incompressible linear viscous constitutive law $\zeta \dot{\varepsilon}_{ij} = s_{ij}$. You can also easily show that for simple uniaxial loading in the x_1 direction (i.e., $s_{11} = \frac{2}{3}\tau_{11}$ and $J_2 = \tau_{11}^2/3$), Eqs. (8.181) reduce back to Eqs. (8.180) with $Y = \sqrt{3}k$ and $\eta = 3\zeta/2$ (look back at Example 6.4 of Section 6.8). Finally, we note that for simple shear in the $x_1 x_2$ plane, Eqs. (8.181) simplify to

$$\zeta \dot{\varepsilon}_{12} = \begin{cases} 0 & \text{if } g_s < 0 & (8.182a) \\ g_s \tau_{12} & \text{if } g_s \geq 0 & (8.182b) \end{cases}$$

where g_s is the dimensionless simple *shear* load function

$$g_s = 1 - \frac{k}{|\tau_{12}|} \qquad (8.182c)$$

This last result is the equation originally proposed by E. C. Bingham in 1922.† We have shown the corresponding model in Fig. 8.35.

It will be instructive to obtain the inverted form of Eq. (8.181b). We thus first solve for s_{ij} to obtain

$$s_{ij} = \frac{\zeta}{g} \dot{\varepsilon}_{ij} \qquad g \geq 0 \qquad (8.183)$$

To complete the inversion process we must also express g in terms of the invariant K_2, which equals $\frac{1}{2}\dot{\varepsilon}_{ij}\dot{\varepsilon}_{ij}$ for incompressible behavior. Now it immediately follows from Eq. (8.183) that

---

* See W. Prager, *Introduction to Mechanics of Continua* (Boston: Ginn & Company, 1961), Chap. 7. K. Hohenemser and W. Prager generalized Bingham's relation to three dimensions in 1932.

† See E. C. Bingham, *Fluidity and Plasticity* (New York: McGraw-Hill Book Company, 1922), p. 215.

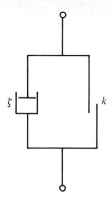

Figure 8.35 Rigid, linear viscoplastic Bingham model for shear.

$$\frac{1}{2} s_{ij} s_{ij} = \frac{\zeta^2}{g^2} \left(\frac{1}{2} \dot{\varepsilon}_{ij} \dot{\varepsilon}_{ij} \right)$$

Therefore,

$$J_2 = \frac{\zeta^2}{g^2} K_2 \tag{8.184}$$

Using this result to substitute for J_2 in Eq. (8.181c), and solving the expression obtained for g then gives

$$g = \frac{\zeta \sqrt{K_2}}{k + \zeta \sqrt{K_2}} \tag{8.185}$$

Finally, inserting this result into Eq. (8.183), we have

$$s_{ij} = \left(\zeta + \frac{k}{\sqrt{K_2}} \right) \dot{\varepsilon}_{ij} \qquad g \geq 0 \tag{8.186}$$

The stress deviator is seen from Eq. (8.186) to be the sum of a viscous component due to Newtonian flow (set $k = 0$) and a classical plastic component due to flow via the Mises flow law (set $\zeta = 0$). This is clearly consistent with the model shown in Fig. 8.35. If in Eq. (8.186) we replace $\dot{\varepsilon}_{ij}$ by $\alpha(t)\dot{\varepsilon}_{ij}$ (i.e., proportional straining), we once more see that the Mises flow term (i.e., the second term $k\dot{\varepsilon}_{ij}/\sqrt{K_2}$) is *unaffected*. Thus the rate sensitivity of a Bingham material arises solely from the linear viscous element in the model. Returning to Eq. (8.181c) for the load function g, we also see that as the load is increased, the associated load surface "grows" in size from its initial yield configuration (i.e., $g = 0$ for $\sqrt{J_2} = k$) to its current state ($g > 0$ for $\sqrt{J_2} > k$). But there is *no strain hardening* in a Bingham material, since the plastic component is *perfectly plastic* (again see Fig. 8.35). Clearly, this growth in the yield surface is entirely due to the rate sensitivity of the viscous component in the model. We shall now go on to a case in which *both* strain hardening and rate sensitivity are included.

Inclusion of Strain Hardening

Before generalizing Eqs. (8.181) to include strain hardening, it is convenient to first rewrite them in the form

$$\dot{\varepsilon}_{ij} = \begin{cases} 0 & \text{if } F < 0 \quad \text{(a)} \\ \gamma F \dfrac{s_{ij}}{\sqrt{J_2}} & \text{if } F \geq 0 \quad \text{(b)} \end{cases} \qquad (8.187)$$

Here $\gamma = k/\zeta$ is a material constant with dimension (sec)$^{-1}$, and the load function is now defined as

$$F = \frac{\sqrt{J_2}}{k} g = \frac{\sqrt{J_2}}{k} - 1 \qquad (8.188)$$

To include *isotropic strain hardening* in Eqs. (8.187) and (8.188), we shall simply modify the definition of the load function F to read

$$F = \frac{\sqrt{3J_2}}{H(\bar{\varepsilon})} - 1 \qquad (8.189)$$

where $\bar{\tau} = H(\bar{\varepsilon})$ is the equation for the universal curve of effective stress versus effective strain [see Eq. (8.129)]. (Recall that here we have $\varepsilon_{ij} = \varepsilon_{ij}^p$ and $\bar{\varepsilon} = \bar{\varepsilon}^p$, since elastic deformation has been ignored.) For perfect plasticity we set $H(\bar{\varepsilon}) = Y = \sqrt{3}k$, and thereby arrive back at definition (8.188). Let us now examine Eqs. (8.187), with Eq. (8.189) for F, in the case of simple uniaxial *tensile* loading in the x_1 direction. In this case we have $s_{11} = \frac{2}{3}\tau_{11}$, $\sqrt{J_2} = \tau_{11}/\sqrt{3}$ [see Eq. (8.119a)] and $H(\bar{\varepsilon})$ becomes $H(\varepsilon_{11})$, where $\tau_{11} = H(\varepsilon_{11})$ is the equation of the stress-strain curve for simple tension [see Eq. (8.128)]. Substituting these values into Eqs. (8.187) with definition (8.189) for F, we obtain

$$\dot{\varepsilon}_{11} = \begin{cases} 0 & \text{if } \tau_{11} < H(\varepsilon_{11}) \\ \dfrac{2\gamma}{\sqrt{3}} \left[\dfrac{\tau_{11}}{H(\varepsilon_{11})} - 1 \right] & \text{if } \tau_{11} \geq H(\varepsilon_{11}) \end{cases} \qquad (8.190)$$

But this is precisely the plastic strain term in Eq. (8.28b) of Part A, with $2\gamma/\sqrt{3} = B$ and $H(\varepsilon_{11}) = g(\varepsilon_{11})$, where $\tau_{11} = g(\varepsilon_{11})$ is the equation for the uniaxial *static* stress-strain curve. We shall accordingly refer to the function F defined by Eq. (8.189) as the *static load function*. Note that $F = 0$ [i.e., $\bar{\tau} = \sqrt{3J_2} = H(\bar{\varepsilon})$] indicates that the stress state lies *on* the static load surface. Rate effects come into play when $F > 0$. You may recall that Eq. (8.28b) is a variation of Eq. (8.27) due to Sokolovsky, which in turn is an extension and variation of power hardening law (8.25). We have thus come *full cycle* in our treatment of viscoplasticity.

As in the case of the Bingham material, we shall find it instructive to invert Eq. (8.187b). Thus, solving for s_{ij}, we have

$$s_{ij} = \frac{\sqrt{J_2}}{\gamma F} \dot{\varepsilon}_{ij} \qquad F \geq 0 \qquad (8.191)$$

from which it immediately follows that

$$J_2 = \frac{J_2}{\gamma^2 F^2} K_2 \quad \text{or} \quad F = \frac{\sqrt{K_2}}{\gamma} \qquad (8.192)$$

Substituting this result into definition (8.189) for F and solving for $\sqrt{J_2}$, we get

$$\sqrt{J_2} = \frac{H(\bar{\varepsilon})}{\sqrt{3}} \left(1 + \frac{\sqrt{K_2}}{\gamma} \right) \qquad (8.193)$$

Finally, using Eqs. (8.192) and (8.193) to replace F and $\sqrt{J_2}$, respectively, in Eq. (8.191), we obtain

$$s_{ij} = \frac{H(\bar{\varepsilon})}{\sqrt{3}}\left(\frac{1}{\gamma} + \frac{1}{\sqrt{K_2}}\right)\dot{\varepsilon}_{ij} \qquad F \geq 0 \qquad (8.194)$$

It will be interesting to show that we can obtain from Eq. (8.194) the previous constitutive equation of Sec. 8.15 for *rate-insensitive* (inviscid) flow with *Mises yielding* and *isotropic hardening*. Since by definition $\gamma = k/\zeta$ [see Eq. (8.187b)], the inviscid case $\zeta = 0$ is obtained by letting $\gamma \to \infty$. Furthermore, since in this case a stress state *must lie on* the static load surface, we have $\bar{\tau} = \sqrt{3J_2} = H(\bar{\varepsilon})$ [see Eqs. (8.119a) and (8.129)] and thus $F = 0$ [Eq. (8.189)]. Inserting these values in Eq. (8.194) then gives

$$s_{ij} = \frac{H(\bar{\varepsilon})}{\sqrt{3K_2}}\dot{\varepsilon}_{ij} = \frac{2\bar{\tau}}{3\bar{\varepsilon}}\dot{\varepsilon}_{ij} \qquad F = 0 \qquad (8.195)$$

where we have also used $\sqrt{3K_2} = \frac{3}{2}\bar{\varepsilon}$ from Eq. (8.119b). Equation (8.195) is precisely our previous equation (8.131), with elastic deformation neglected.

Perzyna's Model

Viscoplastic law (8.187) with the static load function defined by Eq. (8.189) (i.e., the extended Sokolovsky law) is a special case of a viscoplastic law proposed by Perzyna.[*] Since the latter law has received some recognition, we review some of its essential features. The model is linear elastic, viscoplastic, that is,

$$\dot{\varepsilon}_{ij} = \dot{\varepsilon}_{ij}^e + \dot{\varepsilon}_{ij}^p \qquad (8.196)$$

where $\dot{\varepsilon}_{ij}^e$ is the usual linear elastic component and $\dot{\varepsilon}_{ij}^p$ is a viscoplastic (usually chosen incompressible) component. As in the previous extended Sokolovsky model, the viscoplastic component will contain rate-sensitive viscous behavior and rate-independent plastic behavior with strain hardening, but now this is done in a more general way. Thus definition (8.189) for the *static load function* is generalized to read

$$F(\tau_{ij}, \varepsilon_{ij}^p) = \frac{f(\tau_{ij}, \varepsilon_{ij}^p)}{\kappa(W_p)} - 1 \qquad (8.197)$$

where $f(\tau_{ij}, \varepsilon_{ij}^p)$ will be called the *dynamic load surface function*, and $\kappa(W_p)$ is a *work-hardening parameter* expressed in terms of the *plastic work* W_p [see Eq. (8.150)]. With this form for F we can consider isotropic or anisotropic (e.g., kinematic) hardening, with either not necessarily of the Mises yield type.

Perzyna expressed his plastic flow law in terms of the functions F and f as follows:

$$\dot{\varepsilon}_{ij}^p = \gamma\langle\Phi(F)\rangle\frac{\partial f}{\partial \tau_{ij}} \qquad (8.198)$$

[*] See P. Perzyna, "Fundamental Problems in Viscoplasticity," *Adv. Appl. Mech.*, Vol. 9, pp. 243–377 (1966).

where the notation $\langle \Phi(F) \rangle$ is defined in terms of a *function* of F, namely $\Phi(F)$, as follows:

$$\langle \Phi(F) \rangle = \begin{cases} 0 & \text{if } F < 0 \\ \Phi(F) & \text{if } F \geq 0 \end{cases} \tag{8.199}$$

This law reduces in one dimension to a variation of Malvern's law (see the footnote on p. 261 and Problem 8.32), which as noted in Part A, simplifies to a variation of Sokolovsky's law [i.e., Eq. (8.28b)] for $\Phi(F) = CF$, where C is a constant. An examination of Eqs. (8.197) and (8.198) reveals that $\dot{\varepsilon}_{ij}^p$ is a *function* of the *excess* in F above the static load condition [i.e., $F = 0$ or $f(\tau_{ij}, \varepsilon_{ij}^p) = \kappa(W_p)$]. Furthermore, we see from Eq. (8.198) that in principal stress and strain-rate (incompressible) space, the strain-rate vector $\dot{\varepsilon}_i^p$ is *normal* to the dynamic load surface defined by $f > \kappa(W_p)$ and equal to a constant. We have illustrated this in Fig. 8.36. Note that the *initial yield surface* corresponds to the static load surface (i.e., $F = 0$) with no work hardening (i.e., $W_p = 0$ also). The change in geometry from the initial yield surface to the current dynamic load surface is due to both strain hardening ($W_p > 0$) and strain-rate hardening ($F > 0$). Neither surface is necessarily isotropic or of the Mises type.

If we set $\kappa(W_p) = H(\bar{\varepsilon})/\sqrt{3}$ and $f = \sqrt{J_2}$, we go back to the special case of isotropic hardening of the Mises type and Eq. (8.197) simplifies to Eq. (8.189). In this case $\partial f / \partial \tau_{ij} = s_{ij}/(2\sqrt{J_2})$, and if we also set $\Phi(F) = 2F$, flow law (8.198) simplifies to Eq. (8.187). If we go one step further and set $H(\bar{\varepsilon}) = \sqrt{3}k$, we return to the original Bingham (perfectly plastic) model for which F was given by Eq. (8.188). Various expressions for the *function* $\Phi(F)$ have appeared in the literature; for example, the power function

$$\Phi = AF^n \tag{8.200}$$

where A is a constant. For illustration, let $A = 2$ in the above and set $f = \sqrt{J_2}$ (Mises

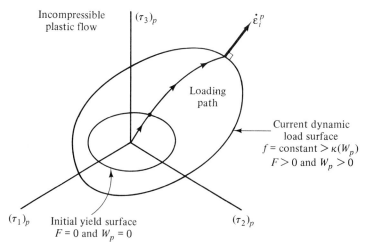

Figure 8.36 Change from initial yield surface to current dynamic load surface–due to isotropic or nonisotropic strain and strain-rate hardening.

Plasticity   Chap. 8

flow) and $\kappa = k$ (perfect plasticity) in Eq. (8.197). Flow law (8.198) then becomes

$$\dot{\varepsilon}_{ij}^{p} = \frac{\gamma}{k^{n}} \langle [\sqrt{J_2} - k]^{n} \rangle \frac{s_{ij}}{\sqrt{J_2}} \qquad (8.201)$$

This is the plastic flow term for a *nonlinear Bingham material*, since for $n = 1$ Eq. (8.201) (with elastic deformation ignored) becomes Eq. (8.187) with definition (8.188).

It will be instructive to compare the *rate-sensitive* power law (8.201) with the *rate-independent* power law (8.139) of similar form. In *both* cases the principal strain-rate vector $\dot{\varepsilon}_i^p$ is *normal* to a circular cylindrical load surface defined by J_2 (or $\sqrt{J_2}$) equal to a constant. However, for the rate-independent law the *ratio* $|\dot{\varepsilon}_i^p|/\dot{J}_2$ is invariant along the circular load locus [see Eq. (8.138)], whereas for rate-dependent law (8.201) $|\dot{\varepsilon}_i^p|$ *itself* is invariant along the load locus. Finally, let $k \to 0$ in Eq. (8.201), and noting that now it is necessarily true that $F \geq 0$ (since the initial yield surface has been reduced to a point at the origin), we get

$$\dot{\varepsilon}_{ij}^{p} = C J_2^{m} s_{ij} \qquad m = \frac{n-1}{2} \qquad (8.202)$$

In the above we have set $\gamma/k^n = C$, since here both γ and $k^n \to 0$. You will recognize Eq. (8.202) as the *nonlinear viscous power law*, derived in Chapter 7 for nonlinear steady creep [see Eq. (7.143)]. We thus see that *this nonlinear viscous flow law is a very special case of viscoplastic law (8.198)*.

Many of the useful applications of viscoplasticity occur in *dynamic problems* (e.g., vibrations and wave propagation). Since in this book we have limited ourselves to *quasi-static* applications of constitutive laws, we shall consider viscoplasticity no further. You will recall that in Part A we noted that many viscoplastic laws have been proposed. Thus the interested reader is referred not only to the work of Perzyna but also to the recent publications in this field. For example, a recent review article by Krempl (see footnote on p. 262) compares Perzyna's model with several other models.

8.18 CLOSURE

In this chapter we have presented the *classical* theory of plasticity and have also introduced the still unfolding area of *viscoplasticity*. All of the constitutive laws presented are characterized by the presence of a plastic yield condition. We demonstrated that classical plastic behavior is deformation-history dependent but not deformation-rate dependent (i.e., during loading there is *strain hardening* but no strain-rate hardening). In the case of viscoplasticity, we in general have the combined difficulties due to both *strain-rate dependence and strain hardening*. If the yield condition and the strain hardening are deleted from the viscoplastic laws presented in this chapter, these laws reduce to special cases of the viscoelastic constitutive laws presented in Chapters 6 and 7.

Part A presented some one-dimensional constitutive laws for rate-independent plastic behavior and for viscoplastic behavior. We first developed a rate-independent plastic constitutive law with power-law strain hardening. We then introduced a rate-sensitive *mechanical model*, which exhibited both strain and strain-rate hardening of the power-law type. Finally, these constitutive laws were extended to more general forms, so as to link up with the recent trends in viscoplasticity.

In Part B we examined *classical* three-dimensional *nonhardening* rate-independent theory in some detail. We first presented certain key postulates for the *onset* of yielding in ductile materials: The assumed material behavior is isotropic, yielding is taken independent of hydrostatic stress, and the behaviors in tension and compression are assumed to be identical. The associated yield surface in principal stress space was shown to be an infinite *cylinder* whose generator is parallel to the hydrostatic line, and whose cross section (*yield locus*) is composed of twelve 30° segments each of which is a mirror image of its contiguous neighbors. Next we presented the celebrated *Tresca* and *Mises* yield criteria, and examined the corresponding yield surfaces forming, respectively, regular hexagonal and circular cylindrical surfaces with axes equally inclined to the principal stress axes. We then presented *Drucker's postulate* for a stable, work-hardening plastic material, from which the important principles of *convexity* and *normality* followed directly. Convexity required that the yield locus be convex, and normality required that the principal strain-rate vector $\dot{\varepsilon}_i^p$ be oriented *outwardly normal* to the yield surface in principal stress space.

With this general background, we then went on in Part B to trace the historical development of the *Prandtl–Reuss* equation for plastic deformation. We next utilized the normality principle to develop a general plastic strain rate-stress constitutive relation (*flow law*), and showed how this degenerated to the Prandtl–Reuss equation when we restricted ourselves to Mises yielding. Finally, we considered Tresca yielding and gave a brief discussion of the associated flow laws.

In Part C we considered three-dimensional plasticity *with strain hardening*. Most of our efforts centered around rate-independent *isotropic* hardening, whereby the initial yield surface deforms into a *load surface* which expands uniformly while maintaining its initial shape and orientation. Isotropic hardening was developed first via the hypothesis of a *universal plastic stress-strain curve*, which hypothesis was later shown to be equivalent to the more general *plastic work hypothesis* for the particular case of Mises yielding. As an illustration of the isotropic hardening concept, the one-dimensional rate-independent plastic constitutive power-law, presented in Part A, was generalized to three dimensions for Mises yielding. We then presented briefly certain key particulars for *kinematic hardening*, whereby the load surface does not change shape or size but merely translates in stress space. The kinematic hardening model is useful for studying the nonisotropic phenomenon called the Bauschinger effect.

Finally, in Part C we gave an introductory treatment of *three-dimensional viscoplasticity*, beginning with only rate dependence and then going on to include strain hardening. We thus followed the progression from the Bingham model, which exhibits no strain hardening, to the constitutive model of Perzyna. We demonstrated that Perzyna's model could be used to generalize the rate-sensitive one-dimensional power-law model with strain hardening, given in Part A, to the case of three dimensions. We concluded by obtaining, as a very special case, the nonlinear viscous flow law obtained in Chapter 7 for *nonlinear steady creep*.

We have thus arrived at the end of Part II of the book, dealing with various important constitutive relations. In Part III we will consider certain classes of *quasi-static* structural problems, whereby we can bring together the kinematics and mechanics of Part I with some of the constitutive laws of Part II.

PROBLEMS

8.1. **(a)** What is the maximum value of P in Fig. P8.1 for linear elastic behavior if the material is linear elastic, plastic with power-law hardening? Neglect the weight of the bar.

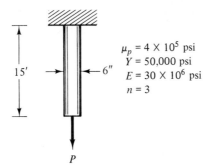

$$\mu_p = 4 \times 10^5 \text{ psi}$$
$$Y = 50,000 \text{ psi}$$
$$E = 30 \times 10^6 \text{ psi}$$
$$n = 3$$

15'   ← 6″

P

Figure P8.1

(b) If this force is increased by the ratio 1.5, what is the elongation of the member? Assume that the plastic response is rate independent.

(c) If the load in part (b) is released, what is the change of length of the bar from its original length?

8.2. In Fig. P8.2, A is a rigid drum on which rods made of rate-independent bilinear material are attached firmly. The stress-strain diagram for the rods is shown in Fig. P8.2b.

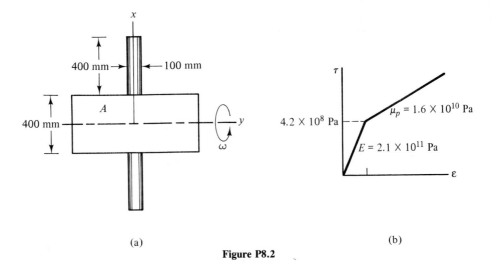

400 mm → ← 100 mm

x

A

400 mm

y

ω

τ

$4.2 \times 10^8 \text{ Pa}$

$\mu_p = 1.6 \times 10^{10} \text{ Pa}$

$E = 2.1 \times 10^{11} \text{ Pa}$

ε

(a)

(b)

Figure P8.2

(a) What is the highest angular speed ω for purely elastic behavior of the rod? What is the elongation of the rods for this speed?

(b) Now increase ω by 1.8 times the preceding value. What is the total elongation of the rods?

(c) When rotation ceases, what is the permanent elongation of the rods?

Take the specific weight $\gamma = 6 \times 10^4$ N/m³. Neglect static weight effects.

8.3. Cylinder A in Fig. P8.3 is a bilinear material and cylinder B is elastic, plastic with power-law hardening having $n = 3$. What is the largest load F_1 for only elastic behavior? Now increase this load twofold. What is the deflection downward of the top surface C? Assume that the plastic response is rate independent. Now release the load at the top of B. What is the position of C? Next release the load on top at C. Also, what is the deflection of C? If we are to load again, what are the new parameters E_A', Y_A', μ_{pA}', E_B', Y_B', and μ_{pB}'?

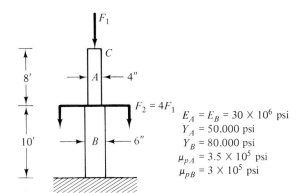

$$E_A = E_B = 30 \times 10^6 \text{ psi}$$
$$Y_A = 50{,}000 \text{ psi}$$
$$Y_B = 80{,}000 \text{ psi}$$
$$\mu_{pA} = 3.5 \times 10^5 \text{ psi}$$
$$\mu_{pB} = 3 \times 10^5 \text{ psi}$$

Figure P8.3

8.4. A rod shown in Fig. P8.4 has the following properties for linear elastic, plastic behavior with power-law hardening:

In tension:	In compression:
$n = 1$	$n = 1$
$E = 30 \times 10^6$ psi	$E = 25 \times 10^6$ psi
$Y = 60{,}000$ psi	$Y = 50{,}000$ psi
$\mu_p = 5 \times 10^5$ psi	$\mu_p = 4 \times 10^5$ psi

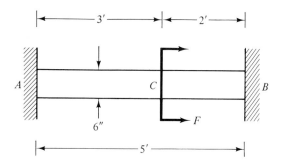

Figure P8.4

Find the force F_e for elastic behavior. Now apply the force

$$F = 2F_e$$

What are the supporting forces for load F above? Assume that the behavior is rate independent.

8.5. Consider the mechanical model of Fig. 8.6. Identify each of the special cases listed below. In each case give the constitutive law and the associated mechanical model. Also indicate for each case whether the model exhibits no hardening, only strain hardening, or only strain-rate hardening (i.e., rate sensitivity).

(a) $t_\varepsilon = 0$

(b) $t_\varepsilon \to \infty$, $\mu_p = 0$, $t_\varepsilon^{1/n} \mu_p \to \lambda_p$

(c) $t_\varepsilon = 0$, $\mu_p = 0$

8.6. Redo Example 8.1 in Section 8.4 for $n = 3$. Check your solution for the static loading case in which the constant stress rate $\dot\tau_0 \to 0$, and for the infinitely rapid loading case $\dot\tau_0 \to \infty$. Compare your conclusions with Eqs. (8.17) and (8.18). [*Hint*: In investigating the case $\dot\tau_0 \to \infty$, expand the term $\exp[-(\tau - Y)/(t_\varepsilon \dot\tau_0)] = e^{-x}$ in a Taylor series in x.]

8.7. Consider a viscoplastic material with a mechanical model behavior as shown in Fig. P8.7. A rod of cross-sectional area A and made of this material has an applied axial load given as

$$F = F_0 e^{\alpha t}$$

where $(F_0/A) < Y$. Neglecting inertia and changes of geometry, what is the strain-stress curve? Let $\alpha \to 0$ and $\alpha \to \infty$ to examine, respectively, the static loading case $\dot\tau \to 0$ and the infinitely rapid loading case $\dot\tau \to \infty$. Compare your results with Eqs. (8.17) and (8.18). Take $n = 3$ for this material.

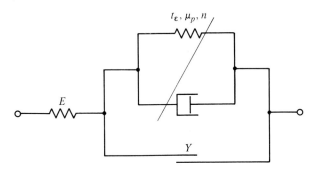

Figure P8.7

8.8. In Problem 8.4, let the material be rate-sensitive viscoplastic. The additional material property t_ε is 1,000 sec for the rod either in tension or in compression. Now the applied force is

$$F = 0.1 F_e e^{0.1t}$$

where $F_e = 2.545 \times 10^6$ lb, as obtained in Problem 8.4. Find the supporting force at time $t = 25$ sec.

8.9. A pile is being pushed into a mud surface at a constant rate of 5 ft/sec. A constant resisting force F_1 is suddenly applied at the time $t = 0$ at the bottom with a value 20,000 lb, while a friction force f is developed on the periphery, given as $f = 2000$ lb/in. (see Fig. P8.9). The pile has the following properties for rate-sensitive viscoplastic behavior:

$$E = 10 \times 10^6 \text{ psi}$$

$$Y = 20{,}000 \text{ psi}$$

$$n = 1$$

$$t_e = 10 \text{ sec}$$

$$\mu_p = 2 \times 10^5 \text{ psi}$$

If the pile just enters the mud at time $t = 0$, what is the change in length of the pile at $t = 2$ sec and $t = 6$ sec? Disregard weight and inertia.

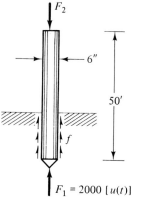

Figure P8.9

8.10. A piston assembly, made from a rod and a hollow sleeve of different materials, is fixed to rigid plates at both ends. The piston is installed in a long cylinder as shown in Fig. P8.10. An external force F is applied to the piston to keep it compressing the air at a constant velocity of $v = 1$ ft/sec. For the air in the cylinder we have $pV = $ constant, and at $t_0 = 0$, $p_0 = 10^4$ psi and $x_0 = 260$ ft.

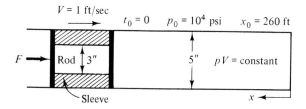

Figure P8.10

(a) Up to what time will both the rod and the sleeve experience elastic behavior?

(b) After one of the materials experiences plastic deformation, what are the governing differential equations for stress in the time interval prior to the onset of plastic deformation in the other material?

(c) Use a numerical method to find the time at which the second material begins to experience plastic deformation.

Assume that both materials are one-dimensional rate-sensitive viscoplastic in accordance with Eqs. (8.15). The data are as follows:

Sleeve:	Rod:
$E_1 = 15 \times 10^6$ psi	$E_2 = 30 \times 10^6$ psi

$$\mu_{p1} = 3 \times 10^5 \text{ psi} \qquad \mu_{p2} = 5 \times 10^5 \text{ psi}$$

$$Y_1 = 40,000 \text{ psi} \qquad Y_2 = 60,000 \text{ psi}$$

$$n_1 = 1 \qquad n_2 = 1$$

$$t_{\varepsilon 1} = 100 \text{ sec} \qquad t_{\varepsilon 2} = 10^5 \text{ sec}$$

8.11. The following state of stress exists at a point in a body:

$$\tau_{ij} = \begin{bmatrix} 20,000 & 15,000 & -30,000 \\ 15,000 & 40,000 & 8,000 \\ -30,000 & 8,000 & 10,000 \end{bmatrix} \text{ psi}$$

What are the stress vectors $\boldsymbol{\tau}_t$ and $\boldsymbol{\tau}_r$ in principal stress space? Evaluate $\boldsymbol{\tau}_t \cdot \hat{\boldsymbol{\varepsilon}}_t$, $\boldsymbol{\tau}_t \times \hat{\boldsymbol{\varepsilon}}_t$, $\boldsymbol{\tau}_r \cdot \hat{\boldsymbol{\varepsilon}}_t$, and $\boldsymbol{\tau}_r \times \hat{\boldsymbol{\varepsilon}}_t$, where $\hat{\boldsymbol{\varepsilon}}_t$ is the unit vector along the hydrostatic line (see Fig. 8.10). Interpret your results.

8.12. The following state of plane stress exists at a point:

$$\tau_{xx} = 30,000 \text{ psi}$$

$$\tau_{yy} = 15,000 \text{ psi}$$

$$\tau_{xy} = -18,000 \text{ psi}$$

If $Y = 30,000$ psi, will there be yielding according to Tresca? According to Mises? The yield criteria are based on the tensile test calibration. Redo this example for $Y = 40,000$ psi.

8.13. Answer the following questions concerning the onset of yielding.
   (a) In a torsion test we find the pure shear yield stress $k = 80,000$ psi. What are k_M and k_T for Mises and Tresca yielding for a pure shear calibration? What is the yield stress predicted by these criteria for simple tension?
   (b) In a tension test we find that $Y = 100,000$ psi. What are k_M and k_T for Mises and Tresca yielding with a tensile test calibration? What is the yield stress predicted by these criteria for pure shear?

8.14. The following is the stress tensor at a point:

$$\tau_{ij} = \begin{bmatrix} 7 \times 10^7 & 0 & 0 \\ 0 & \tau_{yy} & 0 \\ 0 & 0 & -3.5 \times 10^7 \end{bmatrix} \text{ Pa}$$

What are the algebraically largest and smallest values of τ_{yy} for elastic behavior according to Tresca? According to Mises? The one-dimensional tensile yield stress Y is 1.7×10^8 Pa. The yield criteria are based on the tensile test calibration.

8.15. In Chapter 5 [see Eq. (5.59)] the total strain energy density for linear elastic material was given as

$$\mathcal{U}_t = \tfrac{1}{2} \tau_{ij} \varepsilon_{ij}$$

(a) Using this expression, show that $\mathcal{U}_t$ may be expressed as [see Eq. (8.55)]

$$\mathcal{U}_t = \frac{1}{2E} [(\tau_1^2 + \tau_2^2 + \tau_3^2) - 2\nu(\tau_1 \tau_2 + \tau_2 \tau_3 + \tau_3 \tau_1)]$$

(b) Also show that the strain energy density for a hydrostatic state of stress is [see Eq. (8.56)]

$$\mathcal{U}_h = \frac{3}{2E} (1 - 2\nu)\bar{\tau}^2 = \frac{1 - 2\nu}{6E} (\tau_1 + \tau_2 + \tau_3)^2$$

8.16. Prove the following identities for the deviatoric stress invariants:

(a) $J_2 = -\frac{1}{3}[(s_1 - s_2)(s_2 - s_3) + (s_3 - s_1)(s_1 - s_2) + (s_2 - s_3)(s_3 - s_1)]$

(*Hint:* Begin with the expansion of the identity $[(s_1 - s_2) + (s_2 - s_3) + (s_3 - s_1)]^2 = 0$.)

(b) $3J_3^2 - J_2^3 = s_1^3 s_2^3 + s_2^3 s_3^3 + s_3^3 s_1^3$

(*Hint:* First use $J_2 = -s_1 s_2 - s_2 s_3 - s_3 s_1$ and $s_1 + s_2 + s_3 = 0$ to obtain $J_2 s_1 = -J_3 + s_1^3$ and similar expressions for $J_2 s_2$ and $J_3 s_3$. Then multiply these three expressions together.)

8.17. Verify that the general form of the Tresca yield function, as given by Eq. (8.67), is equivalent to Eq. (8.65b). [*Hint:* Expand Eq. (8.65b) and make use of the identities of Problem 8.16.]

8.18. Starting with the Prandtl–Reuss equations as given by Eqs. (8.89), show that the following formulation can be reached:

$$\frac{d\varepsilon_1^P - d\varepsilon_2^P}{s_1 - s_2} = \frac{d\varepsilon_2^P - d\varepsilon_3^P}{s_2 - s_3} = \frac{d\varepsilon_3^P - d\varepsilon_1^P}{s_3 - s_1} = d\Lambda$$

Verify the following two interpretations of the results above.

(a) The three-dimensional Mohr's circles of stress and plastic strain increment are *similar*.

(b) The ratios of the three principal plastic shear strain increments to the *principal shear stresses* are constant at any instant.

8.19. Verify that the Prandtl–Reuss equations (8.89) may be rewritten as

$$\dot{\Lambda} = \frac{\dot{\varepsilon}_{oc}^P}{\tau_{oc}}$$

Here τ_{oc} is the octahedral shear stress, which may be expressed as [see Eq. (8.61)]

$$\tau_{oc} = \frac{1}{3}[(s_1 - s_2)^2 + (s_2 - s_3)^2 + (s_3 - s_1)^2]^{1/2}$$

Similarly, $\dot{\varepsilon}_{oc}^P$ is the plastic octahedral shear strain rate, defined as

$$\dot{\varepsilon}_{oc}^P = \frac{1}{3}[(\dot{\varepsilon}_1^P - \dot{\varepsilon}_2^P)^2 + (\dot{\varepsilon}_2^P - \dot{\varepsilon}_3^P)^2 + (\dot{\varepsilon}_3^P - \dot{\varepsilon}_1^P)^2]^{1/2}$$

8.20. Verify Eqs. (8.111); that is, the plastic dissipation power $\dot{W}_p$ has the following alternative forms:

$$\dot{W}_p \equiv \tau_{ij}\dot{\varepsilon}_{ij}^P = \tau_{ij}\dot{e}_{ij}^P = s_{ij}\dot{e}_{ij}^P = s_{ij}\dot{\varepsilon}_{ij}^P$$

Also, prove that for the Mises yield criterion

$$\dot{\Lambda} = \frac{\dot{W}_p}{2k^2}$$

where k is the Mises yield stress for pure shear calibration.

8.21. According to Koiter's method, a yield condition and its associated flow rule may be stated in terms of a set of n independent yielding functions $f^{(\alpha)}(\tau_i)$, $\alpha = 1, 2, \ldots, n$. If one or more yield functions are zero while the others are negative, the principal plastic strain rates are taken as the sum of n constituents:

$$\dot{\varepsilon}_i^P = \sum_{\alpha=1}^{n} \dot{\varepsilon}_i^{P\,(\alpha)}$$

Here, for perfectly plastic behavior each constituent is given by the flow rule

$$\dot{\varepsilon}_i^{P\,(\alpha)} = \begin{cases} 0 & \text{if } f^{(\alpha)} < 0, \quad \text{or} \quad f^{(\alpha)} = 0 \quad \text{and} \quad \dot{f}^{(\alpha)} < 0 \\ \dot{\Lambda}^{(\alpha)} \dfrac{\partial f^{(\alpha)}}{\partial \tau_i} & \text{if } f^{(\alpha)} = 0 \quad \text{and} \quad \dot{f}^{(\alpha)} = 0 \end{cases}$$

where

$$\dot{\Lambda}^{(\alpha)} \geq 0$$

For the Tresca yield condition, the set of yield functions consists of the three functions given in Eqs. (8.116). Consider the particular stress state

$$f^{(1)} = \tau_1 - \tau_2 - 2k_T = 0, \qquad \dot{f}^{(1)} = 0$$

and

$$f^{(2)} < 0$$

$$f^{(3)} < 0$$

Prove that the constitutive equations for this stress state are given as

$$\dot{s}_1 = \dot{s}_2 = G(\dot{\varepsilon}_1 + \dot{\varepsilon}_2)$$

$$\dot{s}_3 = 2G\dot{\varepsilon}_3$$

where G is the elastic shear modulus for an incompressible linear elastic, perfectly plastic material of the Tresca type.

8.22. Use Koiter's method (refer to Problem 8.21) to prove that along *any side* of the Tresca yield hexagon (see Fig. 8.14)

$$\frac{|\dot{\varepsilon}_i^P|}{\dot{\Lambda}^{(\alpha)}} = \sqrt{2}$$

and

$$\frac{\dot{W}_p}{\dot{\Lambda}^{(\alpha)}} = Y$$

In the above, $|\dot{\varepsilon}_i^P|$ is the magnitude of $\dot{\varepsilon}_i^P$, and $\dot{\Lambda}^{(\alpha)}$ is the parameter in the plastic flow rule for a side

$$\dot{\varepsilon}_i^{P\,(\alpha)} = \dot{\Lambda}^{(\alpha)} \frac{\partial f^{(\alpha)}}{\partial \tau_i}$$

8.23. Consider the onset of yielding in an incompressible plastic material governed by the Mises flow law. In this plastic flow law, let the yield stress for simple tension be 30,000 psi.
  (a) Find the principal deviatoric stress components corresponding to the following plastic principal strain rates:
  (1) $\dot{\varepsilon}_1^P = 0.002$, $\dot{\varepsilon}_2^P = -0.003$, $\dot{\varepsilon}_3^P = 0.001$
  (2) $\dot{\varepsilon}_1^P = -0.01$, $\dot{\varepsilon}_2^P = 0.01$, $\dot{\varepsilon}_3^P = 0$
  (b) Calculate the effective stress $\bar{\tau}$ and the effective plastic strain rate $\dot{\bar{\varepsilon}}^P$ in both of the cases above [see Eqs. (8.119)].

8.24. Consider a state of *loading* for which the plastic strain rates increase *proportionally*. Thus

$$\dot{\varepsilon}_{ij}^P(t) = \alpha(t)\,\dot{\varepsilon}_{ij}^P(t_0)$$

where $\varepsilon_{ij}^P(t_0)$ is the plastic strain rate at the *onset* of yield ($t = t_0$), and $\alpha(t)$ is a monotonically increasing positive function of time with $\alpha(t_0) = 1$.
  (a) Integrate the above from t_0 to t, and thereby obtain

$$\varepsilon_{ij}^P(t) = \gamma(t)\,\dot{\varepsilon}_{ij}^P(t_0)$$

Prove that $\gamma(t)$ is also positive and monotonically increasing, but with $\gamma(t_0) = 0$. As an example, set $\alpha(t) = t/t_0$ and determine the corresponding expression for $\gamma(t)$.

(b) We have noted that in general $\dot{\varepsilon}^P \neq \dot{\bar{\varepsilon}}^P$, where $\bar{\varepsilon}^P$ has been defined by Eq. (8.123) and $\dot{\bar{\varepsilon}}^P$ by Eq. (8.119b). Prove that in the *special case* of proportional straining, as defined above, we have

$$\dot{\varepsilon}^P = \dot{\bar{\varepsilon}}^P$$

8.25. The plastic strain-stress law for a material in simple tension is given by the power law,

$$\varepsilon_{11}^P = \left(\frac{\tau_{11} - Y}{\mu_p} \right)^3$$

where $Y = 80{,}000$ psi and $\mu_p = 3 \times 10^5$ psi. At an instant of time a material point is undergoing plastic deformation, due to the state of stress

$$\tau_{ij} = \begin{bmatrix} 60{,}000 & 40{,}000 & 80{,}000 \\ 40{,}000 & -100{,}000 & 50{,}000 \\ 80{,}000 & 50{,}000 & 70{,}000 \end{bmatrix} \text{ psi}$$

Furthermore, loading is occurring such that the stress-rate tensor is given as

$$\dot{\tau}_{ij} = \begin{bmatrix} -400 & 600 & 300 \\ 600 & 600 & -400 \\ 300 & -400 & 600 \end{bmatrix} \text{ psi/sec}$$

Assume that this material is undergoing Mises flow with isotropic hardening, and then determine the plastic strain-rate tensor at this material point for this instant of time.

8.26. In Section 8.15 we obtained the isotropic strain-hardening power law (8.139). For this law we proved that under *proportional loading*, the components of ε_{ij}^P are *independent* of the components of $\dot{\tau}_{ij}$. Consider the biaxial stress loading state for principal axes

$$\tau_1 = \alpha t$$

$$\tau_2 = \beta$$

$$\tau_3 = 0$$

where α and β are *positive constants*. This is clearly an example of nonproportional loading. Assuming that plastic flow is occurring in accordance with Eq. (8.138), obtain the expressions for $\dot{\varepsilon}_1^P$, $\dot{\varepsilon}_2^P$, and $\dot{\varepsilon}_3^P$. Are the strains ε_1^P, ε_2^P, and ε_3^P independent of $\dot{\tau}_1$?

8.27. The one-dimensional power law employed in Example 8.2 of Section 8.15 [see Eq. (a)] is frequently written in *inverted* form, that is,

$$\tau_{11} = Y + \mu_p (\varepsilon_{11}^P)^{1/n}, \qquad \tau_{11} \geq Y, \quad n \geq 1$$

As an alternative to this equation, consider the hyperbolic tangent law for simple tension

$$\tau_{11} = Y + \sigma_p \tanh \left(\frac{\varepsilon_{11}^P}{\gamma_p} \right), \qquad \tau_{11} \geq Y$$

Here σ_p and γ_p are plastic material constants with the dimensions of stress and strain, respectively.

(a) For the two laws above, evaluate τ_{11} and $d\tau_{11}/d\varepsilon_{11}^P$ at $\varepsilon_{11}^P = 0$ and for $\varepsilon_{11}^P \to \infty$. Use the values obtained to compare the essential characteristics of these functions.

(b) Redo Example 8.2 with the power law replaced by the hyperbolic tangent law above. That is, obtain $\dot{\varepsilon}_{ij}^P$ for Mises flow with isotropic hardening, and verify that this expression reduces to the proper rate-independent law in one dimension.

8.28. As an extension of the Mises yield criterion, let the yield function at initial yield be a *function* of J_2. That is,

$$f(J_2) = 0$$

where here $f(J_2)$ is *not necessarily* $J_2 - Y^2/3$.

(a) Prove that Eq. (8.157) is still valid for the formulation above, that is,

$$W_p(t) = \int_{t_0}^{t} \bar{\tau} \dot{\bar{\varepsilon}}^P \, dt' = \int_{0}^{\bar{\varepsilon}^P(t)} \bar{\tau} \, d\bar{\varepsilon}^P(t')$$

(b) Equation (8.162) then also follows, that is,

$$f(J_2) = G(W_p)$$

Consider a material which under simple tension is governed by the *linear* strain-hardening law

$$\varepsilon_{11}^P = \frac{\tau_{11} - Y}{\mu_p}, \qquad \tau_{11} \geq Y$$

Also assume that the *initial* yield function is given as

$$f(J_2) = \sqrt{J_2} - \frac{Y}{\sqrt{3}} = 0$$

What is the form of the function $G(W_p)$ for this case?

8.29. (a) For linear kinematic hardening the load function has been given by Eq. (8.171), that is,

$$f(\tau_{ij} - C\varepsilon_{ij}^P) = 0$$

Prove that for the Mises yield criterion this function becomes

$$f = \tfrac{1}{2}(s_{ij} - C\varepsilon_{ij}^P)(s_{ij} - C\varepsilon_{ij}^P) - k^2 = 0$$

where k is the yield stress in pure shear.

(b) Use Eq. (8.178) to prove that the flow law for the material above is given as

$$\dot{\varepsilon}_{ij}^P = \frac{(s_{kl} - \alpha_{kl})\dot{s}_{kl}}{2k^2 C}(s_{ij} - \alpha_{ij})$$

where $\alpha_{ij} = C\varepsilon_{ij}^P$.

8.30. Consider a linear kinematic hardening material with Mises yielding, governed by the equations in Problem 8.29. At time $t = 0$ the state of stress at a material point is

$$\tau_{ij} = \begin{bmatrix} 9000 & 0 & 0 \\ 0 & 5000 & 0 \\ 0 & 0 & 3100 \end{bmatrix} \text{ psi}$$

and for $t \geq 0$ the state of stress is increasing at the *constant* rate

$$\dot{\tau}_{ij} = \begin{bmatrix} 20 & 0 & 0 \\ 0 & 45 & 0 \\ 0 & 0 & 40 \end{bmatrix} \text{ psi/sec}$$

The tensor kinematic hardening parameter is given as $\alpha_{ij} = 25\varepsilon_{ij}^P$ psi and the yield stress for pure shear is 40,000 psi.

(a) At what time t_0 does the material at this point begin to yield?

(b) At that time, what are $\dot{\alpha}_{11}$, $\dot{\alpha}_{22}$, and $\dot{\alpha}_{33}$?

(c) Set up three simultaneous nonlinear ordinary differential equations for α_{11}, α_{22}, and α_{33} in the time interval $t \geq t_0$. Use a computer program to find α_{11}, α_{22}, and α_{33} at $t - t_0 = 12$ sec.

8.31. For $F \geq 0$, viscoplastic law (8.198) gives

$$\dot{\varepsilon}_{ij}^p = \gamma \Phi(F) \frac{\partial f}{\partial \tau_{ij}} \tag{a}$$

where

$$F = \frac{f}{\kappa(W_p)} - 1 \tag{b}$$

Prove that f is given by

$$f = \kappa(W_p) \left\{ 1 + \Phi^{-1} \left[\frac{(K_2)^{1/2}}{\gamma} \left(\frac{1}{2} \frac{\partial f}{\partial \tau_{kl}} \frac{\partial f}{\partial \tau_{kl}} \right)^{-1/2} \right] \right\} \tag{c}$$

where $K_2 = \frac{1}{2} \dot{\varepsilon}_{ij}^p \dot{\varepsilon}_{ij}^p$ and Φ^{-1} is the *inverse* operator $\Phi^{-1}[\Phi(F)] = F$. Discuss the physical significance of Eq. (c).

8.32. Consider viscoplastic law (8.198) with isotropic hardening of the Mises type,

$$\dot{\varepsilon}_{ij}^p = \gamma \Phi(F) \frac{s_{ij}}{2\sqrt{J_2}} \qquad F \geq 0$$

where

$$F = \frac{\sqrt{3J_2}}{H(\bar{\varepsilon})} - 1$$

(a) *Prove* that in one dimension this law reduces to a variation of Malvern's law (see the footnote on p. 261).

(b) Let the total strain rate be given as $\dot{\varepsilon}_{ij} = \dot{\varepsilon}_{ij}^e + \dot{\varepsilon}_{ij}^p$, where $\dot{\varepsilon}_{ij}^e$ is an elastic component. Use isotropic Hooke's law to write the expression for $\dot{\varepsilon}_{ij}$, with the assumption that the *total* strain is incompressible.

8.33. Consider nonlinear Bingham law (8.201), that is,

$$\dot{\varepsilon}_{ij}^p = \gamma \left[\frac{\sqrt{J_2}}{k} - 1 \right]^n \frac{s_{ij}}{\sqrt{J_2}} \qquad \sqrt{J_2} \geq k$$

Show that in one dimension this reduces to

$$\dot{\varepsilon}_{11}^p = \gamma^* \left[\frac{|\tau_{11}|}{Y} - 1 \right]^n \operatorname{sgn} \tau_{11} \qquad |\tau_{11}| \geq Y$$

where $\gamma^* = (2/\sqrt{3})\gamma$. Plot τ_{11} (positive) versus $\dot{\varepsilon}_{11}$ for $Y = 40{,}000$ psi, $n = 3$, and $\gamma = 200$ sec^{-1}. Discuss the physical significance of this curve.

Chapter 9

Boundary Value Problems

9.1 INTRODUCTION

Any continuous medium must satisfy the following *basic* laws:

1. Conservation of mass
2. Principle of momentum
3. Principle of moment of momentum
4. First law of thermodynamics
5. Second law of thermodynamics

In addition to these basic laws, there are certain *geometrical* considerations that are important: namely, the concepts of displacement, strain, and the compatibility of strain. Furthermore, certain *constitutive* laws describing material behavior, the form of which depends on the material, must be satisfied. Thus for linear elastic materials we have presented Hooke's law in Chapter 5. In addition, we presented in Chapters 6, 7, and 8 a variety of linear viscoelastic, nonlinear viscoelastic, plastic, and visco-plastic constitutive laws.

It is our first goal in Part A of this chapter to assemble, for linear elastic, linear viscoelastic, nonlinear viscoelastic, and plastic materials all of the governing field equations necessary for the formulation of well-posed boundary value problems. To limit the scope of this endeavor, we employ a number of fundamental simplifying assumptions that we have discussed previously. Thus inertia effects are usually not considered (i.e., conditions are quasi-static), the deformation is small, temperature fields are isothermal, and the materials are isotropic and homogeneous. Further-more, because of the great variety of nonlinear inelastic constitutive laws, we shall focus here on those that are most widely used. Thus, of the many nonlinear viscoelastic laws, we shall concentrate on the case of steady nonlinear viscous creep, and of the various plasticity laws we shall be concerned primarily with perfectly plastic behavior. All of the equations necessary to achieve the above-stated goal were developed in preceding chapters, and thus it will only be necessary for us to assemble these equations in a systematic manner. The equations are given here only for rectangular Cartesian coordinates and are presented in three dimensions both in the compact index notation and in unabridged form.

After assembling the governing field equations, we consider in Part B the formulation of certain key boundary value problems. We first develop in detail two basic formulations of boundary value problems for linear elastic materials, (i.e., the displacement formulation and the stress formulation). We go next to the linear elastic–linear viscoelastic correspondence principle, which enables us to relate problem formulations and solutions for these two materials via the Laplace transform. Finally, we consider some useful analogies between problem formulations for nonlinear viscous behavior, nonlinear elasticity, and plasticity.

We then discuss in Part C uniqueness theorems for the various materials considered. Finally, in Part D we solve several illustrative examples that are formulated within this general framework.

PART A
SUMMARY OF GOVERNING FIELD EQUATIONS

9.2 BASIC LAWS AND GEOMETRIC CONDITIONS

Conservation of mass simply requires that for a given material element we have $\tilde{\rho}\,\tilde{dv} = \rho\,dv$, where $\tilde{\rho}, \tilde{dv}$ and ρ, dv are the mass density and differential volume in *deformed* and *undeformed* geometry, respectively. You will recall that for the case of *small deformation* we have obtained $\tilde{dv}/dv = 1 + \Delta$ [look back at Eq. (3.59)], where Δ is the *cubical dilatation*. Combining this with conservation of mass we now have for small deformation $\tilde{\rho} = \rho/(1 + \Delta)$. In this book we assume that the deformation is small enough for us to neglect Δ in comparison with unity in the expression above. Thus conservation of mass simply becomes $\tilde{\rho} = \rho$ (i.e., the mass density is *independent of time*). With this assumption it will be unnecessary for us to consider conservation of mass any further in this book.

In Chapter 2 we have used the principles of *momentum* and *moment of momentum* to develop the differential equation of motion [see Eq. (2.24)]. You will recall that use of the moment of momentum principle led to the condition that the stress tensor be symmetric (i.e., $\tau_{ij} = \tau_{ji}$). Setting the acceleration $\dot{V}_i = \ddot{u}_i$ equal to zero, we obtain the so-called *equation of equilibrium*, which in index notation for rectangular Cartesian coordinates is given as

$$\tau_{ij,j} + B_i = 0 \qquad (9.1)$$

In unabridged notation we have

$$\frac{\partial \tau_{xx}}{\partial x} + \frac{\partial \tau_{xy}}{\partial y} + \frac{\partial \tau_{zx}}{\partial z} + B_x = 0$$

$$\frac{\partial \tau_{xy}}{\partial x} + \frac{\partial \tau_{yy}}{\partial y} + \frac{\partial \tau_{yz}}{\partial z} + B_y = 0 \tag{9.2}$$

$$\frac{\partial \tau_{zx}}{\partial x} + \frac{\partial \tau_{yz}}{\partial y} + \frac{\partial \tau_{zz}}{\partial z} + B_z = 0$$

where we have set $\tau_{yx} = \tau_{xy}$, $\tau_{zy} = \tau_{yz}$, and $\tau_{xz} = \tau_{zx}$. We leave it as an exercise for you to express these equations for cylindrical coordinates (see Problem 9.1, which is an extension of Problem 2.15). In the equations above we have not taken care to distinguish between original undeformed geometry and current deformed geometry, and accordingly, they are valid only for small deformation as pointed out in Chapter 2. Couple traction and body couple distributions have also been neglected.

Let us now briefly consider the *first law of thermodynamics*. This law yields the so-called energy differential equation, which in its usual form equates the sum of the stress work input and heat influx to the internal energy change. In the most general situation, this energy equation must be solved *simultaneously* with the equation of motion and other relevant equations to determine the temperature and displacement fields. In "uncoupled" theory the stress work term is dropped (see Section 5.6), and these equations are solved *consecutively* (i.e., first solve the energy equation for temperature and then use the equation of motion to find displacement). On the other hand, if the heat flux and internal thermal effects terms are dropped, one can then show that the remaining equation is equivalent to the equation of motion. As confirmation of this, you will recall from earlier courses in solid mechanics and structures that Newton's law and energy methods gave us alternative ways of solving problems with no heat flow. In this chapter we are concerned only with spatially and temporally isothermal problems, wherein the heat flux is identically zero. At a few places in this book we do briefly consider problems with nonuniform temperature fields, but in these cases we simply assume that the temperature field is known a priori. Accordingly, throughout this book we shall not have any occasion to use the first law of thermodynamics.

As for the *second law of thermodynamics*, we note that a consideration of this law leads to the Clausius–Duhem inequality.* For the same reasons cited in the previous paragraphs, we shall have no occasion formally to employ this inequality, except occasionally in an implicit way. For example, the observation that the net work done on an anelastic material during loading and unloading must be positive [e.g., see Fig. 4.21(b) for the Kelvin material] is consistent with the Clausius–Duhem inequality. Note, however, that the Kelvin constitutive law *automatically* gave this effect, and it was not necessary to formally use the Clausius–Duhem inequality. As a second example we note that Drucker's postulate in plasticity (see Section 8.11) is related to the Clausius–Duhem inequality, although they are not equivalent.

---

* For full details on all of the basic laws, see L. E. Malvern, *Introduction to the Mechanics of a Continuous Medium* (Englewood Cliffs, NJ: Prentice-Hall, Inc., 1969), Chap. 5.

To summarize our observations on the use in this book of the five basic laws listed in Section 9.1:

1. It will not be necessary to use the law of conservation of mass, the first law of thermodynamics, and the second law of thermodynamics.

2. The principles of momentum and moment of momentum are embodied in equilibrium equation (9.1) with the condition $\tau_{ij} = \tau_{ji}$.

We now go on to a summary of certain important *geometrical* considerations.

In Chapter 3 we showed that for *small deformation* the strain tensor ε_{ij} was related to the displacement field via the following *strain-displacement* relation:

$$\varepsilon_{ij} = \tfrac{1}{2}(u_{i,j} + u_{j,i}) \tag{9.3}$$

It follows immediately from this relation that $\varepsilon_{ij} = \varepsilon_{ji}$, and $\varepsilon_{kk} = u_{k,k} = \Delta$, where Δ is the cubical dilatation. In unabridged form, Eq. (9.3) is written as

$$
\begin{aligned}
\varepsilon_{xx} &= \frac{\partial u_x}{\partial x}, & \varepsilon_{xy} &= \frac{1}{2}\left(\frac{\partial u_x}{\partial y} + \frac{\partial u_y}{\partial x}\right) \\
\varepsilon_{yy} &= \frac{\partial u_y}{\partial y}, & \varepsilon_{yz} &= \frac{1}{2}\left(\frac{\partial u_y}{\partial z} + \frac{\partial u_z}{\partial y}\right) \\
\varepsilon_{zz} &= \frac{\partial u_z}{\partial z}, & \varepsilon_{zx} &= \frac{1}{2}\left(\frac{\partial u_z}{\partial x} + \frac{\partial u_x}{\partial z}\right)
\end{aligned} \tag{9.4}
$$

In Problem 9.5 you will be asked to express these equations in cylindrical coordinates.

We also showed in Chapter 3 that if displacements are not considered explicitly, the strains had to satisfy conditions called the *compatibility* equations, as a necessary requirement for obtaining single-valued, continuous displacement fields. In their most compact indicial notation form, the compatibility equations for small deformation are expressed as

$$e_{ikm} e_{jln} \varepsilon_{kl,mn} = 0 \tag{9.5}$$

You may recall that these six equations represent three functionally independent conditions, and they are also sufficient for *simply connected* domains.* When fully written out, Eq. (9.5) becomes [see Eqs. (3.67) and (3.68)]

$$\frac{\partial^2 \varepsilon_{xx}}{\partial y^2} + \frac{\partial^2 \varepsilon_{yy}}{\partial x^2} - 2\frac{\partial^2 \varepsilon_{xy}}{\partial x\,\partial y} = 0 \qquad \text{(a)}$$

$$\frac{\partial^2 \varepsilon_{yy}}{\partial z^2} + \frac{\partial^2 \varepsilon_{zz}}{\partial y^2} - 2\frac{\partial^2 \varepsilon_{yz}}{\partial y\,\partial z} = 0 \qquad \text{(b)}$$

$$\frac{\partial^2 \varepsilon_{zz}}{\partial x^2} + \frac{\partial^2 \varepsilon_{xx}}{\partial z^2} - 2\frac{\partial^2 \varepsilon_{zx}}{\partial z\,\partial x} = 0 \qquad \text{(c)}$$

$$-\frac{\partial^2 \varepsilon_{xx}}{\partial y\,\partial z} + \frac{\partial}{\partial x}\left(-\frac{\partial \varepsilon_{yz}}{\partial x} + \frac{\partial \varepsilon_{zx}}{\partial y} + \frac{\partial \varepsilon_{xy}}{\partial z}\right) = 0 \qquad \text{(d)}$$

$$\tag{9.6}$$

*For multiply connected domains, see Appendix I involving Cesàro integrals.

$$-\frac{\partial^2 \varepsilon_{yy}}{\partial z \, \partial x} + \frac{\partial}{\partial y}\left(-\frac{\partial \varepsilon_{zx}}{\partial y} + \frac{\partial \varepsilon_{xy}}{\partial z} + \frac{\partial \varepsilon_{yz}}{\partial x}\right) = 0 \qquad \text{(e)}$$

$$-\frac{\partial^2 \varepsilon_{zz}}{\partial x \, \partial y} + \frac{\partial}{\partial z}\left(-\frac{\partial \varepsilon_{xy}}{\partial z} + \frac{\partial \varepsilon_{yz}}{\partial x} + \frac{\partial \varepsilon_{zx}}{\partial y}\right) = 0 \qquad \text{(f)}$$

The form of these equations for cylindrical coordinates is given in Problem 9.6.

All of the equations presented in this section are valid for *any* continuum satisfying the various stated assumptions. In the next section we summarize the most widely used linear elastic, linear viscoelastic, nonlinear viscoelastic, and plastic constitutive laws. The particular constitutive law that one actually uses in the formulation of a boundary value problem will not only depend on the material being studied, but also on the loading and thermal conditions to which this material is subjected.

9.3 CONSTITUTIVE LAWS

We now turn to a summary of various constitutive laws that we have presented in this book. In so doing we select here only the most commonly used expressions, and present them in three-dimensional form. In all cases we assume isothermal, isotropic, and homogeneous conditions.

Linear Elastic Material

Isotropic Hooke's law in the form of a strain-stress equation is usually expressed in terms of the engineering constants E and ν [see Eq. (5.15)] as follows:

$$\varepsilon_{ij} = \frac{1+\nu}{E}\tau_{ij} - \frac{\nu}{E}\tau_{kk}\,\delta_{ij} \qquad (9.7)$$

When written out, this equation becomes

$$\varepsilon_{xx} = \frac{1}{E}\left[\tau_{xx} - \nu(\tau_{yy} + \tau_{zz})\right]$$

$$\varepsilon_{yy} = \frac{1}{E}\left[\tau_{yy} - \nu(\tau_{zz} + \tau_{xx})\right]$$

$$\varepsilon_{zz} = \frac{1}{E}\left[\tau_{zz} - \nu(\tau_{xx} + \tau_{yy})\right]$$

$$\varepsilon_{xy} = \frac{1}{2G}\,\tau_{xy}$$

$$\varepsilon_{yz} = \frac{1}{2G}\,\tau_{yz}$$

$$\varepsilon_{zx} = \frac{1}{2G}\,\tau_{zx}$$

$$(9.8)$$

where G is the shear modulus given by

$$G = \frac{E}{2(1 + \nu)} \tag{9.9}$$

The inverted stress-strain form of Eq. (9.7) is usually written in terms of the Lamé constants λ and μ [see Eq. (5.41)]:

$$\tau_{ij} = \lambda \, \varepsilon_{kk} \, \delta_{ij} + 2\mu \, \varepsilon_{ij} \tag{9.10}$$

where $\mu = G$. Also, Eq. (9.10) may be decomposed into bulk and deviatoric components [see Eqs. (5.52) and (5.56)] as follows:

$$\bar{\tau} = 3K\bar{\varepsilon} \qquad \text{(a)} \tag{9.11}$$
$$s_{ij} = 2Ge_{ij} \qquad \text{(b)}$$

where K is the bulk modulus

$$K = \frac{3\lambda + 2\mu}{3} \tag{9.12}$$

Note that only two of five constants E, ν, G (or μ), λ, K are independent. In addition to Eqs. (9.9) and (9.12), all of the other relations between these constants were given in Table 5.1.

Linear Viscoelastic Material

The most useful three-dimensional formulation for isotropic linear viscoelastic materials entails the use of a decomposition into bulk and distortional behaviors. Thus, in the differential equation format [see Eqs. (6.86) and (6.89)] we write

$$P^K \bar{\tau} = Q^K \bar{\varepsilon} \qquad \text{(a)} \tag{9.13}$$
$$P^G s_{ij} = Q^G e_{ij} \qquad \text{(b)}$$

where P^K, Q^K and P^G, Q^G are differential operator pairs obtained from pressure and shear tests, respectively. These operators are expressed as

$$P^K = \sum_{j=0}^{m^K} p_j^K \frac{\partial^j}{\partial t^j} \qquad Q^K = \sum_{j=0}^{n^K} q_j^K \frac{\partial^j}{\partial t^j} \qquad \text{(a)} \tag{9.14}$$
$$P^G = \sum_{j=0}^{m^G} p_j^G \frac{\partial^j}{\partial t^j} \qquad Q^G = \sum_{j=0}^{n^G} q_j^G \frac{\partial^j}{\partial t^j} \qquad \text{(b)}$$

where the various p's and q's are constants, and where in the standard normalized form $p_0^K = p_0^G = 1$.

Equations (9.13) are frequently rewritten as hereditary integrals [see Eqs. (6.90)]. Accordingly, we have

$$\bar{\varepsilon}(t) = \int_{0^-}^{t} J^K(t - t') \frac{\partial \bar{\tau}(t')}{\partial t'} dt' \qquad \text{(a)} \tag{9.15}$$
$$e_{ij}(t) = \int_{0^-}^{t} J^G(t - t') \frac{\partial s_{ij}(t')}{\partial t'} dt' \qquad \text{(b)}$$

where $J^K(t)$ and $J^G(t)$ are creep compliance functions for pressure and shear, respectively. Alternatively, we may write

$$\bar{\tau}(t) = \int_{0^-}^t Y^K(t - t')\frac{\partial\bar{\varepsilon}(t')}{\partial t'}\,dt' \qquad \text{(a)}$$

$$s_{ij}(t) = \int_{0^-}^t Y^G(t - t')\frac{\partial e_{ij}(t')}{\partial t'}\,dt' \qquad \text{(b)}$$

(9.16)

where $Y^K(t)$ and $Y^G(t)$ are, respectively, the relaxation modulus functions for pressure and shear.

It will be instructive to write out Eqs. (9.15) in terms of the components of the strain and stress tensors. Thus, upon multiplication by a factor of 3, Eq. (9.15a) yields

$$(\varepsilon_{xx} + \varepsilon_{yy} + \varepsilon_{zz}) = \int_{0^-}^t J^K(t - t')\frac{\partial(\tau_{xx} + \tau_{yy} + \tau_{zz})}{\partial t'}\,dt' \qquad (9.17)$$

Similarly, Eq. (9.15b) yields

$$(2\varepsilon_{xx} - \varepsilon_{yy} - \varepsilon_{zz}) = \int_{0^-}^t J^G(t - t')\frac{\partial(2\tau_{xx} - \tau_{yy} - \tau_{zz})}{\partial t'}\,dt' \qquad \text{(a)}$$

$$(2\varepsilon_{yy} - \varepsilon_{zz} - \varepsilon_{xx}) = \int_{0^-}^t J^G(t - t')\frac{\partial(2\tau_{yy} - \tau_{zz} - \tau_{xx})}{\partial t'}\,dt' \qquad \text{(b)}$$

$$(2\varepsilon_{zz} - \varepsilon_{xx} - \varepsilon_{yy}) = \int_{0^-}^t J^G(t - t')\frac{\partial(2\tau_{zz} - \tau_{xx} - \tau_{yy})}{\partial t'}\,dt' \qquad \text{(c)}$$

$$\varepsilon_{xy} = \int_{0^-}^t J^G(t - t')\frac{\partial\tau_{xy}}{\partial t'}\,dt' \qquad \text{(d)}$$

$$\varepsilon_{yz} = \int_{0^-}^t J^G(t - t')\frac{\partial\tau_{yz}}{\partial t'}\,dt' \qquad \text{(e)}$$

$$\varepsilon_{zx} = \int_{0^-}^t J^G(t - t')\frac{\partial\tau_{zx}}{\partial t'}\,dt' \qquad \text{(f)}$$

(9.18)

where again the first three of these have been multiplied by a factor of 3. Note that Eq. (9.18c) is the negative of the sum of Eqs. (9.18a) and (9.18b), and thus Eqs. (9.15) yield a set of *six* linearly independent equations in the components of strain and stress.

Nonlinear Viscoelastic Material

In Chapter 7 we presented various nonlinear viscoelastic constitutive relations, and we also remarked that many other relations may be found in the literature. At this point we focus on a particular simplified constitutive relation which has seen widespread use. Specifically, we consider *incompressible nonlinear viscous* relation (7.143),

$$\dot{\varepsilon}_{ij} = CJ_2^m s_{ij} \qquad (9.19)$$

where J_2 is the negative of the second invariant of the stress deviator tensor, and is defined as

$$J_2 = \tfrac{1}{2} s_{ij} s_{ij} \tag{9.20}$$

In Eq. (9.19) C is the steady creep constant and m is the stress power. These constants are obtainable from one-dimensional creep tests. You may recall that this equation was obtained by neglecting the elastic and transient creep components of strain and generalizing the remaining *steady creep* component to the case of variable stress. Although the development of Eq. (9.19) also involved a number of additional restrictions (see Sec. 7.12), it has proven to be quite useful in practice.

When Eq. (9.19) is expanded out with the components of s_{ij} expressed in terms of the components of τ_{ij}, we obtain

$$
\begin{align*}
\dot{\varepsilon}_{xx} &= (C/3) J_2^m \left(2\tau_{xx} - \tau_{yy} - \tau_{zz}\right) && \text{(a)} \\
\dot{\varepsilon}_{yy} &= (C/3) J_2^m \left(2\tau_{yy} - \tau_{zz} - \tau_{xx}\right) && \text{(b)} \\
\dot{\varepsilon}_{zz} &= (C/3) J_2^m \left(2\tau_{zz} - \tau_{xx} - \tau_{yy}\right) && \text{(c)} \\
\dot{\varepsilon}_{xy} &= C J_2^m \tau_{xy} && \text{(d)} \\
\dot{\varepsilon}_{yz} &= C J_2^m \tau_{yz} && \text{(e)} \\
\dot{\varepsilon}_{zx} &= C J_2^m \tau_{zx} && \text{(f)}
\end{align*}
\tag{9.21}
$$

Note that the sum of the first three of these equations is equal to zero, in conformity with the condition of incompressibility. As to the invariant J_2, Eq. (9.20) gives J_2 in expanded form as

$$J_2 = \tfrac{1}{2}\left(s_{xx}^2 + s_{yy}^2 + s_{zz}^2\right) + s_{xy}^2 + s_{yz}^2 + s_{zx}^2 \tag{9.22}$$

Since the trace of a deviator tensor must vanish identically, the expression for J_2 above is unaffected if we rewrite it as

$$J_2 = \tfrac{1}{2}\left(s_{xx}^2 + s_{yy}^2 + s_{zz}^2\right) - \tfrac{1}{6}\left(s_{xx} + s_{yy} + s_{zz}\right)^2 + s_{xy}^2 + s_{yz}^2 + s_{zx}^2$$

This last equation can be rewritten more compactly as

$$J_2 = \tfrac{1}{6}\left[(s_{xx} - s_{yy})^2 + (s_{yy} - s_{zz})^2 + (s_{zz} - s_{xx})^2\right] + s_{xy}^2 + s_{yz}^2 + s_{zx}^2$$

Finally, expressing the above in terms of the components of τ_{ij}, we get

$$J_2 = \tfrac{1}{6}\left[(\tau_{xx} - \tau_{yy})^2 + (\tau_{yy} - \tau_{zz})^2 + (\tau_{zz} - \tau_{xx})^2\right] + \tau_{xy}^2 + \tau_{yz}^2 + \tau_{zx}^2 \tag{9.23}$$

The inverted form of Eq. (9.19) was obtained in Section 7.14 [see Eq. (7.148)] as

$$s_{ij} = C^{-1/(2m+1)} K_2^{-m/(2m+1)} \dot{\varepsilon}_{ij} \tag{9.24}$$

where

$$K_2 = \tfrac{1}{2} \dot{e}_{ij} \dot{e}_{ij} = \tfrac{1}{2} \dot{\varepsilon}_{ij} \dot{\varepsilon}_{ij} \tag{9.25}$$

The unabridged forms of Eqs. (9.24) and (9.25) may easily be obtained by the same procedures as those employed in the preceding paragraph.

Plastic Material

In Chapter 8 we studied a variety of plastic constitutive laws, including some with hardening and some with rate sensitivity (i.e., viscoplastic materials). Here we limit ourselves to a summary of the governing three-dimensional constitutive relations for *rigid, perfectly plastic* materials. We shall assume that the material is incompressible and isotropic, and also that the yield function is independent of hydrostatic stress and is the same for loading in compression as for tension. Also, there is no Bauschinger effect.

The yield surface is plotted in a principal stress space (i.e., with coordinates τ_1, τ_2, τ_3), and for the material described above it is in general defined by a yield function

$$f(J_2, J_3) = 0 \tag{9.26}$$

where J_2 and J_3 are the invariants

$$J_2 = \tfrac{1}{2} s_{ij} s_{ji} \qquad \text{(a)}$$
$$J_3 = \tfrac{1}{3} s_{ij} s_{jk} s_{ki} \qquad \text{(b)} \tag{9.27}$$

We showed in Chapter 8 that Eq. (9.26) defines a convex cylinder* whose generator is parallel to the hydrostatic line defined by $\tau_1 = \tau_2 = \tau_3$. We also showed that the cross section of this cylinder is composed of twelve 30° segments, where adjacent segments are mirror images.

For the rigid, perfectly plastic material the strain rate is either zero or entirely plastic (i.e., $\dot{\varepsilon}_{ij} = \dot{\varepsilon}_{ij}^p$), and the constitutive law is written as follows:

$$\dot{\varepsilon}_{ij} = \begin{cases} 0 & \text{if } f < 0, \quad \text{or if } f = 0 \text{ and } \dot{f} < 0 \quad \text{(a)} \\ \Lambda \dfrac{\partial f}{\partial \tau_{ij}} & \text{if } f = 0 \text{ and } \dot{f} = 0 \quad\quad\quad\quad\quad \text{(b)} \end{cases} \tag{9.28}$$

These equations have been called *flow rules* or *flow laws*. Equation (9.28a) indicates that there is no plastic flow if the stress state falls inside the yield surface, or if it is about to leave the yield surface due to unloading. And Eq. (9.28b) indicates that a plastic flow vector exists and is directed outwardly *normal* to the yield surface (see Section 8.11), if the stress state lies on the yield surface and is not about to fall within the yield surface because of unloading. For the perfectly plastic material the positive parameter $\dot{\Lambda}$ is *indeterminate*.

According to the *Mises criterion*, the yield function is given as

$$f = J_2 - \frac{Y^2}{3} = 0 \tag{9.29a}$$

where Y is the yield stress in tension. In this case the yield surface is a circular

---

*The word "cylinder" in this context is meant to represent a uniform prismatic surface.

cylinder (see Section 8.10). When written out in terms of principal stresses, Eq. (9.29a) yields

$$\tau_{oc} = \frac{1}{3}[(\tau_1 - \tau_2)^2 + (\tau_2 - \tau_3)^2 + (\tau_3 - \tau_1)^2]^{1/2} = \frac{\sqrt{2}}{3} Y \qquad (9.29b)$$

where τ_{oc} is the octahedral shear stress. Using Eq. (9.29a), the flow rule in Eq. (9.28b) now simplifies to the Lévy-Mises equation

$$\dot{\varepsilon}_{ij} = \dot{\Lambda} s_{ij} \qquad (9.30)$$

In expanded notation this yields in terms of principal values,

$$\dot{\varepsilon}_1 = \frac{\dot{\Lambda}}{3}(2\tau_1 - \tau_2 - \tau_3)$$

$$\dot{\varepsilon}_2 = \frac{\dot{\Lambda}}{3}(2\tau_2 - \tau_3 - \tau_1) \qquad (9.31)$$

$$\dot{\varepsilon}_3 = \frac{\dot{\Lambda}}{3}(2\tau_3 - \tau_1 - \tau_2)$$

We see that $\dot{\varepsilon}_1 + \dot{\varepsilon}_2 + \dot{\varepsilon}_3 = 0$, as required by incompressibility.

Finally, we consider the *Tresca criterion*, wherein it is expected that yielding occurs when the *maximum shear* stress equals $Y/2$, that is, when

$$\max[(\tau_1 - \tau_2), (\tau_2 - \tau_1), (\tau_2 - \tau_3), (\tau_3 - \tau_2), (\tau_3 - \tau_1), (\tau_1 - \tau_3)] = Y \qquad (9.32)$$

The corresponding yield function is given as

$$f = [(\tau_1 - \tau_2)^2 - Y^2][(\tau_2 - \tau_3)^2 - Y^2][(\tau_3 - \tau_1)^2 - Y^2] = 0 \qquad (9.33)$$

This equation can also be expressed in terms of J_2 and J_3. The Tresca yield surface is a hexagonal cylinder. If we require the Mises and Tresca criteria to reduce to the same condition for simple shear, the Mises circular cylinder must be *inscribed* in the Tresca hexagonal cylinder. On the other hand, if the two criteria are to reduce to the same condition for simple tension, the Mises cylinder must be *circumscribed* about the Tresca cylinder. The latter case is the conventional configuration, and is in fact the one given by Eqs. (9.29a) and (9.32) above (assuming that Y is the *same* in these two equations).

In this section we have reviewed some widely used constitutive laws for elastic, linear viscoelastic, nonlinear viscoelastic, and plastic materials. Although all equations have been written for rectangular Cartesian coordinates only, the extension to orthogonal curvilinear coordinates is trivial. For example, in the case of cylindrical coordinates, we simply associate the subscripts 1, 2, 3 with r, θ, z, respectively. For each material we have obtained *six* independent algebraic, differential or integral equations, relating ε_{ij} (or $\dot{\varepsilon}_{ij}$) to τ_{ij}. In the preceding section we presented the *three* equations of equilibrium, plus the *six* strain-displacement equations. Thus we now have for each type of material *fifteen* field equations in the 15 quantities τ_{ij}, ε_{ij}, and u_i. In Part B we combine these equations with appropriate boundary conditions, in order to formulate convenient *boundary value problems*.

9.4 BOUNDARY VALUE PROBLEM FORMULATIONS FOR LINEAR ELASTICITY

The equations presented in Part A provide the fundamental field equations of quasi-static linear elasticity for a volume in domain D. In addition, the solution to these equations must satisfy the boundary conditions which are stipulated on the boundary surface S. Various types of boundary conditions are physically possible, but it is usually the case that *either* the displacement *or* the traction is specified at a point on S. You will recall that in Chapter 2 we proved that the surface traction $T_i^{(\nu)}$ and the stress are related by the Cauchy formula

$$T_i^{(\nu)} = \tau_{ij}\, \nu_j \tag{9.34}$$

where the ν_j are direction cosines between the normal to an area element and the x_j axes. Accordingly, we may express the boundary conditions as

$$u_i = F_i \qquad \text{on } S_1 \qquad \text{(a)}$$
$$\tau_{ij}\, \nu_j = G_i \qquad \text{on } S_2 \qquad \text{(b)} \tag{9.35}$$

where F_i and G_i are prescribed vector functions.* Note that the traction function G_i on S_2 and the body force B_i in D must be prescribed in such a manner that overall equilibrium is satisfied. Equations (9.35) are illustrated schematically in Fig. 9.1.

It is desirable to reformulate the previously mentioned 15 field equations of elasticity in the variables τ_{ij}, ε_{ij}, and u_i into mathematically more convenient formats. Two such formulations are useful, one in which only u_i appears in the boundary value problem (i.e., the displacement formulation) and one in which only τ_{ij} appears (i.e., the stress formulation). In the displacement formulation u_i is referred to as the *primary* variable, whereas ε_{ij} and τ_{ij} are termed the *secondary*

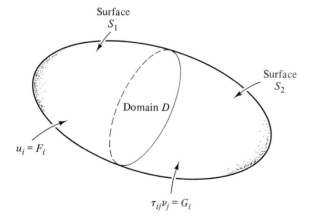

Figure 9.1 Displacement and traction boundary conditions.

---

*This type of boundary condition is called a *mixed* boundary condition.

variables. Similarly, in the stress formulation τ_{ij} is the *primary* variable, whereas ε_{ij} and u_i are the *secondary* variables. In either case, the solution procedure involves first solving a boundary value problem consisting of differential equations and boundary conditions in the primary variable, and then using this solution to determine the secondary variables.

Displacement Formulation

Let us first consider the displacement formulation. We begin by restating governing equations (9.1), (9.3), and (9.10):

$$\tau_{ij,j} + B_i = 0 \qquad \text{(a)}$$

$$\varepsilon_{ij} = \tfrac{1}{2}(u_{i,j} + u_{j,i}) \qquad \text{(b)} \qquad (9.36)$$

$$\tau_{ij} = \lambda \varepsilon_{kk} \delta_{ij} + 2\mu \varepsilon_{ij} \qquad \text{(c)}$$

We first express τ_{ij} in terms of u_i by substituting Eq. (9.36b) into (9.36c). Accordingly,

$$\tau_{ij} = \lambda u_{k,k} \delta_{ij} + \mu(u_{i,j} + u_{j,i})$$

Now substitute this result into Eq. (9.36a) to get

$$\lambda u_{k,kj} \delta_{ij} + \mu u_{i,jj} + \mu u_{j,ij} + B_i = 0$$

which may finally be rewritten* as

$$\boxed{(\lambda + \mu)u_{j,ji} + \mu u_{i,jj} + B_i = 0} \qquad (9.37)$$

Equations (9.37) yield three differential equations in the three u_i, and are associated with the name of *Navier*. Introducing symbolic notation, they may also be expressed as

$$\boxed{(\lambda + \mu)\,\text{grad}\,\Delta + \mu\,\nabla^2\mathbf{u} + \mathbf{B} = 0} \qquad (9.38)$$

where Δ is the cubical dilatation

$$\Delta = \varepsilon_{jj} = u_{j,j} \equiv \text{div}\,\mathbf{u} \qquad (9.39)$$

As for the boundary conditions, we shall consider here only the case in which displacement is specified at each point on the boundary surface S of the domain D. Thus, in Eqs. (9.35), S_1 is the entire surface S and there is no S_2-type surface (see Fig. 9.1). To summarize, the displacement formulation requires the determination of single-valued and continuous functions u_i, which satisfy the equations

$$\boxed{\begin{aligned} (\lambda + \mu)u_{j,ji} + \mu u_{i,jj} + B_i = 0 \qquad &\text{in } D \qquad \text{(a)} \\ u_i = F_i \qquad &\text{on } S \qquad \text{(b)} \end{aligned}} \qquad (9.40)$$

---

* It is assumed here that u_j and its derivatives are continuous, such that $u_{j,ij} = u_{j,ji}$.

where B_i and F_i are prescribed functions.* Once the primary variable u_i has been determined, ε_{ij} follows by simple differentiation in accordance with Eq. (9.36b), and finally, τ_{ij} is obtained by direct substitution of ε_{ij} into Eq. (9.36c).

Stress Formulation

Since displacement is the primary variable in the displacement formulation above, it was not necessary to integrate the strain-displacement equations, and accordingly the compatibility equations played no role. However, in the stress formulation the displacement will be a secondary variable obtained via integration of strain-displacement equation (9.3), and thus compatibility plays a vital role. We shall consider only simply connected domains here, and thus compatibility equation (9.5) is both necessary and sufficient for the existence of single-valued and continuous displacements. Also, to reduce the complexity of our development we shall for now drop the body-force term from equilibrium equation (9.1). Furthermore, since in this formulation strains will be computed from the stresses, we shall employ Hooke's law in the form of Eq. (9.7). Restating all of these governing equations, we have

$$\varepsilon_{ij} = \tfrac{1}{2}(u_{i,j} + u_{j,i}) \qquad \text{(a)}$$

$$e_{pir}\, e_{qjs}\, \varepsilon_{ij,rs} = 0 \qquad \text{(b)}$$

$$\tau_{ij,j} = 0 \qquad \text{(c)}$$

$$\varepsilon_{ij} = \frac{1+\nu}{E}\, \tau_{ij} - \frac{\nu}{E}\, \tau_{kk}\, \delta_{ij} \qquad \text{(d)}$$

(9.41)

Since the stress is the primary variable, our major task is to express compatibility equation (9.41b) in terms of τ_{ij}. Thus we substitute Hooke's law (9.41d) into Eq. (9.41b) and obtain, after multiplying through by E,

$$e_{pir}\, e_{qjs}(1+\nu)\tau_{ij,rs} - e_{pir}\, e_{qjs}\, \nu\tau_{kk,rs}\, \delta_{ij} = 0 \qquad (9.42)$$

In the second term we may employ the well-known properties of the Kronecker delta and the alternating tensor to obtain [see Chapter 1, in particular the e–δ identity (1.42)]

$$e_{pir}\, e_{qjs}\, \delta_{ij} = e_{ipr}\, e_{iqs} = \delta_{pq}\, \delta_{rs} - \delta_{ps}\, \delta_{rq}$$

Equation (9.42) thus becomes, after first replacing $\tau_{kk,rs}$ by $\tau_{kk,sr}$

$$(1+\nu)e_{pir}\, e_{qjs}\, \tau_{ij,rs} + \nu(\tau_{kk,pq} - \tau_{kk,rr}\, \delta_{pq}) = 0 \qquad (9.43)$$

which implies that the second derivatives of τ_{ij} are continuous.†

Equation (9.43) is a form of stress compatibility, but it may be simplified through the use of equilibrium equation (9.41c). To this end we first perform the

---

* For dynamic conditions we need only employ equation of motion (2.24) in place of equilibrium equation (9.36a). The result is simply the addition of the term $\rho \dot{V}_i = \rho \ddot{u}_i$ on the right side of Eq. (9.40a).

† From this point on we shall without comment reverse the order of differentiation or invoke symmetry of τ_{ij} whenever it proves convenient.

contraction $p = q$, and again use $e-\delta$ identity (1.42) to obtain

$$(1 + \nu)(\delta_{ij}\,\delta_{rs} - \delta_{is}\,\delta_{rj})\tau_{ij,\,rs} - 2\nu\tau_{kk,\,pp} = 0$$

which becomes, after simplification,

$$(1 - \nu)\tau_{ii,\,rr} - (1 + \nu)\tau_{ij,\,ji} = 0$$

But the second term in this result drops out since $\tau_{ij,\,j} = 0$ via equilibrium, and thus

$$\boxed{\tau_{ii,\,rr} = \nabla^2\tau_{ii} = 0} \tag{9.44}$$

This important result states that the first invariant of the stress tensor, τ_{ii}, (and also the bulk stress $\tau_{ii}/3$) is harmonic (i.e., it satisfies Laplace's equation). We thus see that we may delete the last term on the left side of Eq. (9.43), giving

$$(1 + \nu)e_{pir}\,e_{qjs}\,\tau_{ij,\,rs} + \nu\tau_{kk,\,pq} = 0 \tag{9.45}$$

The first term in Eq. (9.45) may be written in a more convenient form through the use of generalized $e-\delta$ identity (1.43) in conjunction with equilibrium. Thus we may write

$$e_{pir}\,e_{qjs}\,\tau_{ij,\,rs} = \begin{vmatrix} \delta_{pq} & \delta_{iq} & \delta_{rq} \\ \delta_{pj} & \delta_{ij} & \delta_{rj} \\ \delta_{ps} & \delta_{is} & \delta_{rs} \end{vmatrix} \tau_{ij,\,rs}$$

The expansion of this determinant may be simplified considerably if we first note that any term containing the elements δ_{rj} or δ_{is} will be zero by virtue of equilibrium equation (9.41c).[*] We may thus replace these two elements by zeros, giving

$$\begin{vmatrix} \delta_{pq} & \delta_{iq} & \delta_{rq} \\ \delta_{pj} & \delta_{ij} & 0 \\ \delta_{ps} & 0 & \delta_{rs} \end{vmatrix} \tau_{ij,\,rs} = (\delta_{pq}\,\delta_{ij}\,\delta_{rs} - \delta_{iq}\,\delta_{pj}\,\delta_{rs} - \delta_{rq}\,\delta_{ij}\,\delta_{ps})\tau_{ij,\,rs}$$

Then

$$e_{pir}\,e_{qjs}\,\tau_{ij,\,rs} = \tau_{ii,\,rr}\,\delta_{pq} - \tau_{pq,\,rr} - \tau_{ii,\,pq}$$

But the first term on the right side of this equation vanishes because of condition (9.44), whereupon

$$e_{pir}\,e_{qjs}\,\tau_{ij,\,rs} = -\tau_{pq,\,rr} - \tau_{rr,\,pq} \tag{9.46}$$

We may now substitute Eq. (9.46) into Eq. (9.45), and after simplifying we get the stress compatibility equation

$$(1 + \nu)\tau_{pq,\,rr} + \tau_{rr,\,pq} = 0 \tag{9.47}$$

In Problem 9.9 you will be asked to prove that if the body force B_i is included in the derivation, Eq. (9.47) generalizes to

[*] This follows the approach given in B. A. Boley and J. H. Weiner, *Theory of Thermal Stresses* (Melbourne, FL: R.E. Krieger Publishing Co., reprint edition, 1985), p. 88.

$$\tau_{pq,rr} + \frac{1}{1+\nu}\tau_{rr,pq} + \frac{\nu}{1-\nu}B_{r,r}\delta_{pq} + B_{p,q} + B_{q,p} = 0 \qquad (9.48)$$

These six equations are known as the *Beltrami–Michell* stress compatibility equations. As was the case for the original set of strain compatibility equations, they represent only three functionally independent conditions. Thus, in order to have a properly posed boundary value problem in the six stresses τ_{ij}, Eqs. (9.48) must still be supplemented by the three equations of equilibrium.

For boundary conditions, we restrict ourselves here to the case in which tractions are prescribed at all points on the boundary S of the domain D. Hence, referring to Eqs. (9.35) and Fig. 9.1, we see that now S_2 covers the entire surface S and thus an S_1-type surface does not exist. Summarizing, the stress formulation entails the evaluation of stresses τ_{ij}, satisfying the equations

$$\tau_{ij,kk} + \frac{1}{1+\nu}\tau_{kk,ij} + \frac{\nu}{1-\nu}B_{k,k}\delta_{ij} + B_{i,j} + B_{j,i} = 0 \qquad \text{in } D \qquad (a)$$

$$\tau_{ij,j} + B_i = 0 \qquad \text{in } D \qquad (b) \qquad (9.49)$$

$$\tau_{ij}\nu_j = G_i \qquad \text{on } S \qquad (c)$$

where B_i and G_i are specified functions. After the primary variables τ_{ij} have been evaluated, the strains follow directly from Hooke's law (9.41d). Finally, the displacements are obtained by integrating strain-displacement equations (9.41a). Since compatibility has already been ensured via solution to Eq. (9.49a), this integration will yield the desired single-valued and continuous displacement field.

Alternative Methods of Approach

We shall now enumerate three overall methods of attack in obtaining analytical solutions to boundary value problems in solid mechanics.

1. Carry out a *direct* solution to the pertinent differential equations for the particular boundary value problem. Thus if one uses the displacement formulation, the Navier equations must be solved, whereas if one uses the stress formulation, the Beltrami–Michell equations must be solved. This "head-on" approach is often difficult, because of the complexity of the equations involved.

2. Select certain simple functions for the stress or displacement distributions, which by inspection satisfy the pertinent differential equations. Then examine the behavior of these distributions at the boundary, and thereby determine the boundary value problem for which the selected functions are solutions. This is called the *inverse* method. When several such simple solutions have been established, we may frequently superpose these solutions to form solutions to problems of practical interest.

3. Carry out a combination of the direct and inverse methods. This is called the *semi-inverse* method, and entails selecting some of the displacement or stress variables and then determining the remaining ones by direct solution procedures. When using this approach, it is usually more convenient to work with the original set of 15 governing equations, rather than with a reduced set in displacement alone or stress alone.

There are times when "exact" analytical solutions can be obtained with relative ease by use of the foregoing approaches if the geometry and the load are restricted to certain special cases. From these solutions we can then often formulate judicious a priori approximate assumptions as to the deformation characteristics when more general loadings are applied. Using these approximations of behavior, along with selected basic and constitutive laws, we can in some situations establish some very useful and valuable formulations. Such is the case for the study of beams, shafts, plates, and shells. There is an extensive body of knowledge developed by this means, forming a discipline which we call "strength of materials." Knowing and working within the limitations of the formulations of strength of materials, we can make rapid computations of acceptable accuracy in many problems of engineering interest. In this book we use the approach of developing some of the basic assumptions of strength of materials from the exact theory. By approaching strength of materials in this manner, we shall have the means of viewing the simpler, handier formulations in the proper perspective. That is, we shall have available the means of estimating the limitations of the simple formulations and the degree of error to be expected.

We wish to also point out that an important alternative approach exists to the boundary value problems we have presented in this section, wherein we presented differential equations and associated boundary and initial conditions. Instead, we can often work with *functionals*,* which when extremized with respect to admissible classes of functions of the dependent variables, lead to the solution to the associated boundary value problem. This approach is valuable for approximation methods such as *finite elements*.

In the next section we discuss a correspondence principle, which closely relates linear viscoelasticity to linear elasticity.

9.5 CORRESPONDENCE PRINCIPLE OF LINEAR VISCOELASTICITY

We now consider a linear viscoelastic medium. The basic equilibrium equations (9.1) and strain-displacement equations (9.3) for this or any continuum in domain

---

* A functional is an expression whose value depends on the function used in the functional. For instance, a simple functional could be of the integral form

$$I = \int_{x_1}^{x_2} F\left(x, y, \frac{dy}{dx}\right) dx$$

whose value depends on the function $y(x)$ used in F. For more information, see I. H. Shames and C. L. Dym, *Energy and Finite Element Methods in Structural Mechanics* (New York: Hemisphere Publishing Corp., 1985).

D are restated as

$$\tau_{ij,j} + B_i = 0 \qquad \text{(a)}$$

$$\varepsilon_{ij} = \tfrac{1}{2}(u_{i,j} + u_{j,i}) \qquad \text{(b)}$$

(9.50)

For the linear viscoelastic constitutive law, we shall for now employ the isotropic differential equation format given by Eqs. (9.13), which we repeat below:

$$P^K \bar{\tau} = Q^K \bar{\varepsilon} \qquad \text{(a)}$$

$$P^G s_{ij} = Q^G e_{ij} \qquad \text{(b)}$$

(9.51)

where

$$P^K = \sum_{j=0}^{m^K} p_j^K \frac{\partial^j}{\partial t^j}, \qquad Q^K = \sum_{j=0}^{n^K} q_j^K \frac{\partial^j}{\partial t^j}$$

$$P^G = \sum_{j=0}^{m^G} p_j^G \frac{\partial^j}{\partial t^j}, \qquad Q^G = \sum_{j=0}^{n^G} q_j^G \frac{\partial^j}{\partial t^j}$$

(9.52)

and where the various p_j and q_j coefficients are constants.

As for the *boundary* conditions, we again consider the case in which boundary surface S is composed of S_1-type surface on which displacement is prescribed and S_2-type surface on which traction is prescribed. Accordingly Eqs. (9.35) apply, i.e.

$$u_i = F_i \qquad \text{on } S_1 \qquad \text{(a)}$$

$$\tau_{ij} \nu_j = G_i \qquad \text{on } S_2 \qquad \text{(b)}$$

(9.53)

In a viscoelastic material the dependent variables depend on the time t as well as on the space coordinates x_k, and thus *initial* conditions are also required. As discussed in Chapter 6, we shall always assume that the loads are applied at time $t = 0$ to a medium that is initially free of stress, strain, and displacement. Accordingly, all dependent variables and all their time derivatives vanish at $t = 0^-$ (i.e., at the instant *just before* the load is applied), and the following homogeneous initial conditions apply:

$$\tau_{ij} = \frac{\partial \tau_{ij}}{\partial t} = \cdots = 0 \qquad \text{at } t = 0^-$$

$$\varepsilon_{ij} = \frac{\partial \varepsilon_{ij}}{\partial t} = \cdots = 0 \qquad \text{at } t = 0^-$$

$$u_i = \frac{\partial u_i}{\partial t} = \cdots = 0 \qquad \text{at } t = 0^-$$

(9.54)

Differential equations (9.50) and (9.51) [with boundary conditions (9.53) and initial conditions (9.54)] are a set of 15 independent equations in $\tau_{ij}(x_k, t)$, $\varepsilon_{ij}(x_k, t)$, and $u_i(x_k, t)$. The solution to these equations is closely related to the solution to a corresponding problem for an elastic continuum occupying the same geometric configuration in D, with the same body force B_i in D, and subjected to the same displacement on S_1 and traction on S_2. This relationship will be formally presented in the so-called *linear viscoelastic–linear elastic correspondence principle* (also called the *linear viscoelastic–linear elastic analogy**), which we shall now develop with the use of the Laplace transform over t. Note that the corresponding elastic problem is governed by the same set of equations, with the exception that constitutive equations (9.51) are replaced by the elastic relations [see Eqs. (9.11)]

$$\bar{\tau} = 3K\bar{\varepsilon} \qquad \text{(a)}$$
$$s_{ij} = 2Ge_{ij} \qquad \text{(b)} \tag{9.55}$$

Since the initial conditions are homogeneous at $t = 0^-$, the Laplace transform operator will be employed with 0^- as the lower limit. For example, using the notation presented in Appendix III, the Laplace transform of stress is defined as follows:

$$\mathbf{L}\{\tau_{ij}(x_k, t)\} = \bar{\tau}_{ij}(x_k, s) = \int_{0^-}^{\infty} \tau_{ij}(x_k, t)e^{-st}\, dt \tag{9.56}$$

In the transform s-space, governing equations (9.50) in the domain D then become

$$\bar{\tau}_{ij,j} + \bar{B}_i = 0 \qquad \text{(a)}$$
$$\bar{\varepsilon}_{ij} = \tfrac{1}{2}(\bar{u}_{i,j} + \bar{u}_{j,i}) \qquad \text{(b)} \tag{9.57}$$

And differential linear viscoelastic constitutive equations (9.51) transform, with the use of homogeneous initial conditions (9.54), to the algebraic equations

$$\bar{P}^K \bar{\tau} = \bar{Q}^K \bar{\varepsilon} \qquad \text{(a)}$$
$$\bar{P}^G \bar{s}_{ij} = \bar{Q}^G \bar{e}_{ij} \qquad \text{(b)} \tag{9.58}$$

where the coefficients are the polynomials in s,

$$\bar{P}^K = \sum_{j=0}^{m^K} p_j^K s^j \qquad \bar{Q}^K = \sum_{j=0}^{n^K} q_j^K s^j$$
$$\bar{P}^G = \sum_{j=0}^{m^G} p_j^G s^j \qquad \bar{Q}^G = \sum_{j=0}^{n^G} q_j^G s^j \tag{9.59}$$

Finally, boundary conditions (9.53) become in s-space

$$\bar{u}_i = \bar{F}_i \qquad \text{on } S_1 \qquad \text{(a)}$$
$$\bar{\tau}_{ij}\nu_j = \bar{G}_i \qquad \text{on } S_2 \qquad \text{(b)} \tag{9.60}$$

We also take the Laplace transform of the corresponding elastic problem. Clearly, Eqs. (9.57) and (9.60) are obtained again, but instead of Eqs. (9.58) we now obtain, from Eqs. (9.55),

$$\bar{\bar{\tau}} = 3K\bar{\bar{\varepsilon}} \qquad \text{(a)}$$
$$\bar{s}_{ij} = 2G\bar{e}_{ij} \qquad \text{(b)} \tag{9.61}$$

Thus we see that the two formulations are identical, the only difference being that

---

* This analogy was first given by F. Alfrey in *Mechanical Behavior of High Polymers* (New York: Interscience Publishers, 1948), for the special case of incompressible material. It has since been extended to much more general viscoelastic material.

the elastic constants in the elastic problem are *replaced* in the viscoelastic problem by ratios of polynomials in s. It is therefore clear that the Laplace transform of the viscoelastic *solution* may be obtained from the Laplace transform of the elastic solution by setting

$$3K \to \frac{\overline{Q}^K(s)}{\overline{P}^K(s)}$$

$$2G \to \frac{\overline{Q}^G(s)}{\overline{P}^G(s)} \tag{9.62}$$

in this elastic solution. We leave it as an exercise (Problem 9.10) for you to show that if we use constitutive laws expressed in terms of the axial and'lateral behaviors for tensile loadings [see Eqs. (6.81) and (9.7)], we then set in the elastic solution

$$E \to \frac{\overline{Q}^E(s)}{\overline{P}^E(s)}$$

$$\nu \to \frac{\overline{Q}^\nu(s)}{\overline{P}^\nu(s)} \tag{9.63}$$

We have thus established the linear viscoelastic–linear elastic correspondence principle for quasi-static conditions.[*]

It is often the case that the solution to the corresponding elastic problem is available in the literature. The solution to the viscoelastic problem may then be obtained by preceding through the following steps:

1. Take the Laplace transform of the known elastic solution. If B_i, F_i, and G_i are independent of time, the elastic solution will also be independent of time, and in this case this step is trivial.

2. Replace K and G in this transformed solution by the ratios of the transforms of the differential operators, as specified by relations (9.62). As alternative procedures, we may introduce either the transforms of the creep compliance or the relaxation modulus functions [see Eqs. (9.15), (9.16), and (6.55)] by employing the substitutions

$$3K \to \frac{1}{s\overline{J}^K(s)} = s\overline{Y}^K(s) \qquad \text{(a)}$$

$$2G \to \frac{1}{s\overline{J}^G(s)} = s\overline{Y}^G(s) \qquad \text{(b)} \tag{9.64}$$

On the other hand, if the viscoelastic behavior is known in the axial and lateral directions for tensile loadings, we may employ substitution (9.63) or their equivalent forms in terms of creep compliance or relaxation modulus functions.

3. Invert this solution in the Laplace transform domain back into the time domain. This step may frequently be done in closed form, since relations (9.62)

---

[*] The correspondence principle is easily extended to dynamic conditions. For example, see D. R. Bland, *The Theory of Linear Viscoelasticity* (New York: Pergamon Press, 1960), p. 95.

[or (9.64)] introduce rational algebraic functions in s which are often not difficult to invert. In any event, excellent numerical inversion techniques are also available.*

If the solution to the corresponding elastic problem is not available, the computational procedure above is not useful. However, the correspondence principle is still of considerable value for many fundamental reasons, and we cite three of these below:

1. The existence of the analogy suggests that fundamental theorems in linear elasticity have their counterparts in linear viscoelasticity. We mention in particular theorems on uniqueness of solution, which we will discuss in Section 9.7.
2. The analogy also implies that well-established methods of solution available in elasticity may be adapted to viscoelasticity. For example, approximate solutions based on strain or complementary energy techniques may be developed for the *transform* of a viscoelastic problem.
3. Approximate formulations in elasticity also have their counterparts in viscoelasticity. For example, the kinematic assumptions employed in elastic strength of materials may also be used to develop a viscoelastic strength of materials.

The correspondence principle is thus seen to be of considerable value, but it does have its limitations. If a variable is not defined at a fixed point for *all* time, the Laplace transform of a linear viscoelastic problem cannot be carried out. We shall now enumerate two examples in which this occurs:

1. The boundaries of a viscoelastic problem may be changing with time (i.e., the surface S and domain D are functions of t). These are termed "moving boundary problems," and occur when, for example, the material burns (i.e., ablates) or melts.
2. Tractions and displacements may be prescribed at a point during different time intervals (i.e., the division between S_1 and S_2 types of surfaces is a function of t). This can occur in contact problems involving the motion of an object.

We also mention the important case of temperature-dependent viscoelastic properties, such that the p and q coefficients are functions of time. Although a Laplace transform may still be possible in this case for special types of coefficients, the transformed equation will in general be quite complex and not correspond with a recognizable elastic problem. Finally, we note that if either geometrical nonlinearity (e.g., finite strain) or physical nonlinearity (e.g., nonlinear viscoelasticity) are included, the Laplace transform is of little value. In the next section we consider two analogies having to do with nonlinear viscous flow.

---

*For example, see R. A. Schapery, "Approximate Methods of Transform Inversion for Viscoelastic Stress Analysis," *Proc. 4th U.S. Natl. Cong. Appl. Mech.,* p. 1075 (1962).

9.6 NONLINEAR VISCOUS FLOW; ANALOGIES WITH NONLINEAR ELASTICITY AND PLASTICITY

Nonlinear Viscous–Nonlinear Elastic Analogy

We are concerned in this section with a material governed by *nonlinear viscous* relation (9.19), that is,

$$\dot{\varepsilon}_{ij} = CJ_2^m s_{ij} \tag{9.65}$$

The *equilibrium* equation is as usual

$$\tau_{ij,j} + B_i = 0 \tag{9.66}$$

However, it is preferable now to differentiate strain-displacement equation (9.3) with respect to time, and thereby obtain the following *strain rate–velocity* equation:

$$\dot{\varepsilon}_{ij} = \tfrac{1}{2}(\dot{u}_{i,j} + \dot{u}_{j,i}) \tag{9.67}$$

The *boundary conditions* are now chosen such that *velocity* is prescribed on S_1 and traction is prescribed on S_2,

$$\dot{u}_i = F_i \qquad \text{on } S_1$$
$$\tau_{ij}\nu_j = G_i \qquad \text{on } S_2 \tag{9.68}$$

Equations (9.65) to (9.67) with boundary conditions (9.68) are a set of 15 independent equations in stress τ_{ij}, strain rate $\dot{\varepsilon}_{ij}$, and velocity $\dot{u}_i$. Note that no initial conditions are required in the formulation of this problem.

We now consider an *elastic* problem, formulated as usual in terms of stress τ_{ij}, strain ε_{ij}, and displacement u_i. Thus equilibrium and strain-displacement are given as

$$\tau_{ij,j} + B_i = 0$$
$$\varepsilon_{ij} = \tfrac{1}{2}(u_{i,j} + u_{j,i}) \tag{9.69}$$

while displacement is prescribed on S_1 and traction on S_2:

$$u_i = F_i \qquad \text{on } S_1$$
$$\tau_{ij}\nu_j = G_i \qquad \text{on } S_2 \tag{9.70}$$

However, instead of Hooke's law we assume that the material obeys the *nonlinear elastic* law

$$\varepsilon_{ij} = CJ_2^m s_{ij} \tag{9.71}$$

You should verify that for $m = 0$ this relation is equivalent to isotropic Hooke's law for an *incompressible* linear elastic material.

We require that the geometrical configuration and the functions B_i, F_i, G_i be the same in both of the nonlinear viscous and nonlinear elastic formulations above. Direct comparison of these formulations then shows that the stresses in the two problems are identical, whereas the strain rates and velocities in the nonlinear viscous problem are, respectively, equal to the strains and displacements in the nonlinear elastic problem. We have thus established another analogy, which we shall call the *nonlinear viscous–nonlinear elastic analogy*.* It would again be useful for you to verify that for $m = 0$ this analogy is equivalent to a special application of the linear viscoelastic–linear elastic correspondence principle presented in the preceding section.

The primary value of the nonlinear viscous–nonlinear elastic analogy rests on the fact that it establishes the validity of using techniques developed in elasticity to solve nonlinear viscous problems. For example, by employing definitions (5.57) in Chapter 5 in conjunction with nonlinear elastic constitutive law (9.71), we may derive for this material expressions for the strain energy density $\mathcal{U}(\varepsilon_{ij})$ and complementary energy density $\mathcal{U}^*(\tau_{ij})$ (see Problem 9.12). In contrast with the linear elastic case, $\mathcal{U}(\varepsilon_{ij})$ and $\mathcal{U}^*(\tau_{ij})$ are now *not* numerically equal unless $m = 0$ (i.e., the area under a stress-strain diagram is not equal to the area above the diagram). These expressions for $\mathcal{U}(\varepsilon_{ij})$ and $\mathcal{U}^*(\tau_{ij})$ may then be used with the principles of total potential energy and total complementary energy to develop approximate nonlinear elastic solution techniques. The nonlinear viscous–nonlinear elastic analogy then immediately suggests that these same techniques are applicable to nonlinear viscous materials governed by Eq. (9.65), with the proviso that ε_{ij} be replaced by $\dot{\varepsilon}_{ij}$ and u_i by $\dot{u}_i$.†

Nonlinear Viscous–Plastic Analogy

At this point we go on to still another analogy—this one being between *nonlinear viscous behavior* and *plastic behavior*. We mentioned this analogy in Chapter 7 when we noted that the creep law presented could be expressed in terms of a creep potential. Accordingly, nonlinear viscous law (9.65) is rewritten as

$$\dot{\varepsilon}_{ij} = \frac{\partial \Phi}{\partial \tau_{ij}} \tag{9.72a}$$

where Φ is defined as [see Eq. (7.123)]

$$\Phi = \frac{C}{m+1} J_2^{m+1} \tag{9.72b}$$

Substituting Eq. (9.72b) into (9.72a) gives us

$$\dot{\varepsilon}_{ij} = \frac{\partial \Phi}{\partial J_2} \frac{\partial J_2}{\partial \tau_{ij}} = C J_2^m s_{ij} \tag{9.73}$$

which, as required, brings us back to nonlinear viscous law (9.65). To assist us in developing an analogy with plasticity, we may modify the form of Eq. (9.73) to obtain

---

* This analogy is usually attributed to N. J. Hoff, who gave impetus to its application with his paper, "Approximate Analysis of Structures in the Presence of Moderately Large Creep Deformations," *Quart. Appl. Math.*, Vol. 12, No. 1, p. 49 (1954).

† For example, see S. A. Patel, B. Venkatraman, and P. G. Hodge, Jr., "Torsion of Cylindrical and Prismatic Bars in the Presence of Steady Creep," *J. Appl. Mech.*, Vol. 25, p. 163 (1958).

the equivalent representation

$$\dot{\varepsilon}_{ij} = g(J_2) \frac{\partial f}{\partial \tau_{ij}} \tag{9.74}$$

where

$$f = \sqrt{J_2} \tag{a}$$

$$g = 2C\sqrt{J_2^n} \qquad n = 2m + 1 \tag{b}$$

$$(9.75)$$

When nonlinear viscous law (9.73) is rewritten in the form given by Eq. (9.74), it is seen to be a *viscoplastic* law (see Sec. 8.17). We have in fact noted previously that Eq. (9.73) is equivalent to a nonlinear *Bingham* law with *zero yield stress* [see the discussion of Eq. (8.202)].

Now look back at Eq. (8.138) in Chapter 8, which is the rate-insensitive (i.e., *inviscid*) Mises continuing plastic flow rule with isotropic power-law hardening. Setting $Y = 0$ in this equation, we can rewrite it in the form

$$\dot{\varepsilon}_{ij} = h(J_2, \dot{J}_2) \frac{\partial f}{\partial \tau_{ij}} \tag{9.76a}$$

where as above $f = \sqrt{J_2}$, but now

$$h(J_2, \dot{J}_2) = \frac{3^{(n+1)/2} nA}{2} \dot{J}_2 J_2^{(n-2)/2} \tag{9.76b}$$

Note that Eqs. (9.74) and (9.76a) *both* indicate that the principal strain-rate vector, $\dot{\varepsilon}_i$, is *normal* to the circular cylindrical *potential surface* defined by $\sqrt{J_2}$ equal to a constant. We will call this useful correspondence the *nonlinear viscous–plastic analogy*. This analogy is a limited one for two reasons. First, by setting $Y = 0$ in the above we are saying that there is no lower bound on the size of the potential surface. In inviscid plasticity we of course have $Y \neq 0$, and the lower bound on the potential surface is given by the initial yield surface. Second, it is also important to note that whereas Eq. (9.74) indicates that $|\dot{\varepsilon}_i|$ is invariant on the potential surface defined above, Eqs. (9.76) give the *ratio* $|\dot{\varepsilon}_i|/\dot{J}_2$ invariant on this potential surface.

The main utility of the analogy above lies in the fact that we may take advantage of established concepts in plasticity to help solve nonlinear viscous problems. We give two examples of this below.

1. In plasticity the hexagonal cylinder of Tresca is often used for the yield surface, rather than the circular cylinder of Mises. Correspondingly, we may approximate the circular cylindrical potential surface for nonlinear viscous materials by a hexagonal cylinder. The advantage here is that the surface is now piecewise linear rather than quadratic. This approximation is illustrated in Fig. 9.2, and we shall encounter this concept again in Chapter 13 on plane stress.

2. As $m \to \infty$ in Eq. (9.73), this equation takes on the form $\dot{\varepsilon}_{ij} = \dot{\Lambda} s_{ij}$, where $\dot{\Lambda}$ is *indetermediate*. But this is precisely the form of the Mises flow rule for *perfectly plastic* behavior [see Eq. (9.30)]. Thus, as $m \to \infty$ the solutions for non-

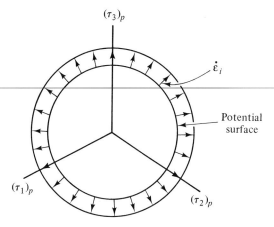

(a) Circular cylindrical potential surface

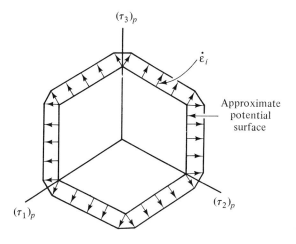

(b) Piecewise linear potential surface of Tresca type

Figure 9.2 Use of nonlinear viscous–plastic analogy to develop approximate potential surface for nonlinear viscous flow.

linear viscous problems approach the solutions for corresponding perfectly plastic problems. We have already pointed this out in Chapter 7 and shall take advantage of this fact at several places in the next part of this book.

PART C
UNIQUENESS THEOREMS

9.7 UNIQUENESS THEOREM FOR LINEAR ELASTICITY

In Part C we are concerned with questions of uniqueness of solution for boundary value problems such as those considered in earlier sections. The usual approach to such questions is to develop *uniqueness theorems*, which give the conditions under which solutions will necessarily be unique. These theorems are very important, since they in effect tell us that if the conditions of a theorem are satisfied, then when a solution is obtained it must be the *correct* solution, no matter what method is used to obtain this solution. A complete presentation of uniqueness theorems for all of the materials considered in this book would be a considerable task and is beyond the scope of our treatment. However, because of the importance of this topic, in this section we present a uniqueness theorem for linear elastic behavior. This will then be followed in the next section by some comments concerning other uniqueness theorems for inelastic behavior.

The starting point for a number of uniqueness theorems is the energy volume integral

$$I = \iiint_D \tau_{ij}\,\varepsilon_{ij}\,dv \tag{9.77}$$

Introducing the rotation tensor Ω_{ij} (see Chapter 3), we may express the integrand of the integral above as follows:

$$\tau_{ij}\,\varepsilon_{ij} = \tau_{ij}(\varepsilon_{ij} + \Omega_{ij}) = \tau_{ij}\,u_{i,j} \tag{9.78}$$

where we have used the symmetry and skew-symmetry properties of τ_{ij} and Ω_{ij}, respectively, and have also employed Eq. (3.49). Thus we can say that

$$\iiint_D \tau_{ij}\,\varepsilon_{ij}\,dv = \iiint_D \tau_{ij}\,u_{i,j}\,dv \equiv \iiint_D (\tau_{ij}\,u_i)_{,j}\,dv - \iiint_D \tau_{ij,j}\,u_i\,dv \tag{9.79}$$

Finally, we use Gauss' theorem [see Eq. (1.66) in Chapter 1] to convert the first integral on the right to a surface integral, and thereby obtain for quasi-static conditions the useful identity

$$\iiint_D \tau_{ij}\,\varepsilon_{ij}\,dv \equiv \oiint_S T_i^{(\nu)}\,u_i\,dA + \iiint_D B_i\,u_i\,dv \tag{9.80}$$

In this result we have used Cauchy's formula (9.34) and equilibrium equation (9.1) to introduce the traction $T_i^{(\nu)}$ and body force B_i.

Now let us focus on linear elastic behavior and the energy integral I for this particular material. Introducing the stress deviator tensor s_{ij} and strain deviator tensor e_{ij} into the integrand of I, we obtain

$$\tau_{ij}\,\varepsilon_{ij} = (s_{ij} + \tfrac{1}{3}\tau_{kk}\,\delta_{ij})(e_{ij} + \tfrac{1}{3}\varepsilon_{ll}\,\delta_{ij}) = s_{ij}\,e_{ij} + \tfrac{1}{3}\tau_{ii}\,\varepsilon_{jj} \tag{9.81}$$

since by definition $e_{ii} = s_{ii} = 0$. Then inserting Hooke's law in the form of Eqs. (9.11) gives us

$$\tau_{ij}\,\varepsilon_{ij} = 2Ge_{ij}\,e_{ij} + K\varepsilon_{ii}\,\varepsilon_{jj} \tag{9.82}$$

We now set the physically reasonable *requirement* that for a *stable* elastic material, the shear modulus be positive (i.e., $G > 0$) and the bulk modulus also be positive (i.e., $K > 0$). This requirement will be a condition for the theorem that is to follow. (By examining the entries in Table 5.1 we may also get the conditions $E > 0$ and $-1 < \nu < \tfrac{1}{2}$). It immediately follows from Eq. (9.82) that $\tau_{ij}\,\varepsilon_{ij}$ is a *positive-definite quadratic form*. That is, it takes on positive values for every set of variables e_{ij} and

$\varepsilon_{ii} = 3\bar{\varepsilon}$ in which these variables are not all zero, and is zero only when e_{ij} and $\bar{\varepsilon}$ are zero. The use of this property will be an essential step in the theorem.

We now turn to the proof of the following theorem for a linear elastic isotropic material under quasi-static conditions:

Theorem. There exists at most one set of single-valued continuous functions τ_{ij}, ε_{ij}, and u_i, which satisfy the following field equations in the domain D:

$$\tau_{ij,j} + B_i = 0 \qquad \text{(a)}$$

$$\varepsilon_{ij} = \tfrac{1}{2}(u_{i,j} + u_{j,i}) \qquad \text{(b)}$$

$$\bar{\tau} = 3K\bar{\varepsilon}, \qquad s_{ij} = 2Ge_{ij} \qquad \text{(c)}$$

where K and G are positive constants, and where the following mixed boundary conditions are prescribed on the surface $S = S_1 + S_2$:

$$u_i = F_i \qquad \text{on } S_1 \qquad \text{(d)}$$

$$\tau_{ij} \nu_j = T_i^{(\nu)} = G_i \qquad \text{on } S_2 \qquad \text{(e)}$$

Proof. Let us for the moment assume that two separate solutions exist, and we designate these as $\tau_{ij}^{(1)}$, $\varepsilon_{ij}^{(1)}$, $u_i^{(1)}$, and $\tau_{ij}^{(2)}$, $\varepsilon_{ij}^{(2)}$, $u_i^{(2)}$. We define *difference* functions according to $\tau_{ij}^d = \tau_{ij}^{(1)} - \tau_{ij}^{(2)}$, $\varepsilon_{ij}^d = \varepsilon_{ij}^{(1)} - \varepsilon_{ij}^{(2)}$, $u_i^d = u_i^{(1)} - u_i^{(2)}$ and similarly for $\bar{\tau}^d$, $\bar{\varepsilon}^d$, s_{ij}^d, e_{ij}^d. By virtue of the linearity of field equations (a, b, c) and boundary conditions (d, e), it follows immediately that these difference functions satisfy the *homogeneous counterparts* of these same equations (i.e., with $B_i^d = F_i^d = G_i^d = 0$). For this "difference problem," identity (9.80) then simplifies to

$$\iiint_D \tau_{ij}^d \, \varepsilon_{ij}^d \, dv = \iint_{S_1} \tau_{ij}^d \nu_j F_i^d \, dA + \iint_{S_2} G_i^d u_i^d \, dA + \iiint_D B_i^d u_i^d \, dv = 0 \qquad \text{(f)}$$

Since the integrand in the integral on the left is for linear elastic material a positive definite quadratic form in e_{ij}^d and $\bar{\varepsilon}^d$, the integral can vanish only when $e_{ij}^d = 0$ and $\bar{\varepsilon}^d = 0$. Clearly, since $\varepsilon_{ij}^d = e_{ij}^d + \bar{\varepsilon}^d \delta_{ij}$ we then have $\varepsilon_{ij}^d = 0$ [i.e., $\varepsilon_{ij}^{(1)} = \varepsilon_{ij}^{(2)}$], which proves that the strain field is *unique*. The uniqueness of the stress field τ_{ij} then follows from constitutive equations (c), and finally the uniqueness of the displacement field u_i follows from strain-displacement relation (b). The theorem is thus proven.

It should be emphasized that the above theorem is applicable to either simply or multiply connected bodies. For dynamic conditions we employ an alternative form of identity (9.80), in which difference functions ε_{ij}^d and u_i^d are replaced by differences of their *rates* $\dot{\varepsilon}_{ij}^d$ and $\dot{u}_i^d$. Furthermore, in this case the use of equation of motion (2.24) in place of the equilibrium equation yields an additional kinetic energy term. For details of the proof of the theorem for dynamic conditions, see *Mathematical Theory of Elasticity* by I. S. Sokolnikoff (New York: McGraw-Hill Book Company, 1956, reprinted by R.E. Krieger Publishing Co., Melbourne, FL, 1987). Extended theorems for thermoelastic behavior (both coupled and uncoupled) are given in *Theory of Thermal Stresses* by B. A. Boley and J. H. Weiner

(New York: John Wiley & Sons, Inc., 1960; reprinted by R.E. Krieger Publishing Co., Melbourne, FL, 1985).

9.8 COMMENTS ON UNIQUENESS FOR INELASTIC MATERIALS

We present now some brief remarks on uniqueness theorems for *linear viscoelastic* materials. In this case the variables depend on time even for quasi-static conditions. One approach for quasi-static problems is to employ the linear viscoelastic–linear elastic correspondence principle presented in Section 9.5, and accordingly utilize the form of identity (9.80) in the Laplace transform domain. Alternatively, we may proceed directly from identity (9.80) and then prove that the difference functions vanish at *every instant of time*. A theorem utilizing the latter approach is given in *Theory of Viscoelasticity: An Introduction* by R. M. Christensen (New York: Academic Press, 1971). In this theorem the conditions $G > 0$ and $K > 0$, which were used above for elastic material, generalize to the conditions that the initial values of the analogous relaxation modulus functions be positive [i.e., $Y^G(0) > 0$ and $Y^K(0) > 0$]. A more general theorem, which includes dynamic and coupling effects, is also developed in this same reference with the use of the Laplace transform.

Uniqueness theorems for *plastic behavior* are presented in *The Mathematical Theory of Plasticity* by R. Hill (London: Oxford University Press, 1950). Theorems are presented for a variety of idealized models, including: rigid, perfectly plastic; linear elastic, perfectly plastic; and linear elastic, plastic with hardening. Identity (9.80) is again utilized, but this time with difference functions τ_{ij}^d, ε_{ij}^d, u_i^d replaced by differences of their *increments* $d\tau_{ij}^d$, $d\varepsilon_{ij}^d$, du_i^d relative to a given state. For idealized models containing perfect plasticity only $d\tau_{ij}$ can be shown to be unique, but if hardening is included, $d\tau_{ij}$, $d\varepsilon_{ij}$, and du_i are uniquely determined. The book by Boley and Weiner cited previously also contains a theorem, for rigid, perfectly plastic materials, which includes thermal effects. A parallel development in terms of the *rates* $\dot{\tau}_{ij}$, $\dot{\varepsilon}_{ij}$, $\dot{u}_i$ rather than the increments is employed.

Finally, we shall make some brief remarks concerning uniqueness for *nonlinear viscoelastic* materials. A theorem for materials governed by nonlinear viscous power law (9.65) is given in the following journal article: J. L. Sackman, "A Uniqueness Theorem for a Nonlinear Steadily Creeping Body," *SIAM Rev.*, Vol. 9, pp. 741–743, (1967).* Once again the proof begins with identity (9.80), but now τ_{ij}^d is retained as a variable while ε_{ij}^d and u_i^d are replaced by differences in their rates $\dot{\varepsilon}_{ij}^d$ and $\dot{u}_i^d$. The critical step in this article is proving that the integrand in I [see Eq. (9.77)] is still composed of positive-definite quadratic forms when the stress power m is nonzero (i.e., the material is nonlinear). You will be asked to prove this in Problem 9.15. Another approach would be to use either the nonlinear viscous–nonlinear elastic analogy or the nonlinear viscous–plastic analogy presented in

---

* For more recent uniqueness theorems on nonlinear creep, see W. S. Edelstein, "On Uniqueness of Solutions for Secondary Creep Problems," *Int. J. Solids Structures*, Vol. 13, p. 807 (1977); and also G. A. Bécus and F. A. Cozzarelli, "A Uniqueness Theorem in Nonlinear Viscoelasticity with Application to Temperature and Irradiation Induced Creep Problems," *Int. J. Solids Structures*, Vol. 17, p. 291 (1981).

Section 9.6. Those interested in uniqueness theorems in solid mechanics will find many in the technical journals.

9.9 SAINT-VENANT'S PRINCIPLE

The various uniqueness theorems mentioned in the preceding section were for the most part based on problem formulations with boundary conditions in the form of Eqs. (d) and (e) in the theorem presented in Section 9.7 for linear elastic material. However, the exact solution of these problems often presents formidable mathematical difficulties because of the complexity of these boundary conditions. It is frequently possible to obtain a solution if the boundary conditions are appropriately modified, and this solution will still give a good approximation to the actual solution. The following principle, due to *Saint-Venant*, specifically refers to such a modification for the traction-type boundary condition:

> If a surface traction distribution over a small part of a boundary is replaced by a statical equivalent, the stress distribution is not significantly altered at points sufficiently far away from this surface traction.

In the principle above, the phrase "statical equivalent" means that the two statically equivalent traction distributions have the same resultant force and resultant couple moment. Thus Saint-Venant's principle indicates that the effects of a localized surface traction distribution at distant points are dependent only on the resultants of this applied traction. In the case of elongated members, such as beams, the phrase "sufficiently far" usually implies distances that exceed the maximum cross-sectional dimension. To illustrate the application of Saint-Venant's principle, consider the cantilever beam of thickness h shown in Fig. 9.3(a). By this principle we can replace the complex supporting force distribution exerted by the wall on the cantilever beam by the single force and single couple moment shown in Fig. 9.3(b), for the purpose of simplifying the evaluation of stress and displacement at sections that are greater than distance h to the right of the supported end. If stresses are desired at sections close to the support, the more complicated "end problem" must be solved.

Although we shall not present them here, it is to be pointed out that mathe-

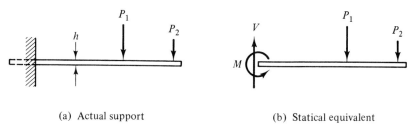

(a) Actual support   (b) Statical equivalent

Figure 9.3 Cantilever beam illustrating use of Saint-Venant's principle.

matical justifications have been advanced for Saint-Venant's principle.* It must also be pointed out that there are cases in which the principle may appear to fail, as was shown by Hoff† for some thin-walled structures. In the remainder of this chapter we solve several boundary value problems to illustrate the formulations we have presented thus far, and we shall have occasion to utilize Saint-Venant's principle.

PART D
CLOSED-FORM SOLUTIONS TO PROBLEMS FOR DIFFERENT CONSTITUTIVE LAWS

9.10 LINEAR ELASTIC PRISMATIC BAR HANGING BY ITS OWN WEIGHT

In this section we examine a prismatic elastic bar supported at one end (see Fig. 9.4) and acted on by its own weight. Note that the z axis runs perpendicular to the uniform but otherwise arbitrary cross section A, with the upper supported end at $z = l$ and the lower free end at $z = 0$. The actual location of the origin $(0, 0, 0)$ is at any convenient point in the free end. We shall choose the *centroid*. The body force stems only from gravity, and for a specific weight γ the body force $\mathbf{B}$ (in units force/volume) is as follows:

$$\mathbf{B} = -\frac{\gamma A l}{A l}\,\hat{\mathbf{k}} = -\gamma\hat{\mathbf{k}}$$

Therefore,

$$B_x = 0, \qquad B_y = 0, \qquad B_z = -\gamma \tag{9.83}$$

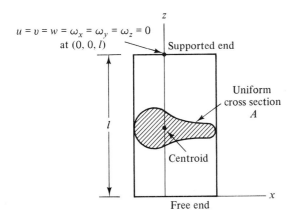

$u = v = w = \omega_x = \omega_y = \omega_z = 0$ at $(0, 0, l)$

Supported end

Uniform cross section A

Centroid

Free end

Figure 9.4 Suspended prismatic bar.

---

*For example, see *Foundations of Solid Mechanics* by Y. C. Fung (Englewood Cliffs, NJ: Prentice-Hall, Inc., 1965), p. 300.

†N. J. Hoff, "The Applicability of Saint-Venant's Principle to Airplane Structures," *J. Aeronaut. Sci.,* Vol. 12, pp. 455–460 (1945).

The surface tractions consist of uniform atmospheric pressure on all surfaces of the bar exposed to the atmosphere, and a traction distribution at the upper supported end whose resultant must be a force $\gamma l A$ in the z direction at the centroidal point $(0, 0, l)$. If we do not get too close to the support, we may employ *any* traction distribution with this same resultant by virtue of Saint-Venant's principle, without requiring an exact knowledge of the nature of the actual traction distribution. Thus we simply assume that the traction is *uniformly* distributed at $z = l$ [i.e., $T_z^{(z)} = \gamma l$]. Furthermore, we shall neglect the contribution to stress due to atmospheric pressure. Accordingly, the traction vanishes on the lateral surface and at the free lower end, while the only nonzero component of traction at the supported upper end we take as $T_z^{(z)} = \gamma l$. Referring to the Cauchy formula (9.34), we see that at the supported end the stresses are prescribed as

$$\tau_{yz} = \tau_{zx} = 0, \qquad \tau_{zz} = \gamma l \quad \text{at } z = l \tag{9.84}$$

since at that end $\nu_x = \nu_y = 0$ and $\nu_z = 1$. Furthermore, the stress components of traction vanish on all other surfaces. Thus we see that we have here a stress boundary value problem, and if we wish to determine the stresses inside the body directly we must obtain the solution to Eqs. (9.49).

However, rather than attempting a direct solution to Eqs. (9.49), we shall employ a *semi-inverse* method of approach here. Consider as a possible stress distribution the following quantities:

$$\tau_{zz} = \gamma z, \qquad \tau_{xx} = \tau_{yy} = \tau_{xy} = \tau_{yz} = \tau_{zx} = 0 \tag{9.85}$$

Clearly, the equations of *equilibrium* (9.2) with body forces (9.83) are satisfied by such a distribution. Next, consider the *boundary conditions* of the problem, and let us first examine the lateral surface of the bar. Since $\nu_z = 0$ on the lateral surface, the stress τ_{zz} does not appear as a component of the traction on this surface [see Cauchy formula (9.34)]. Clearly, then, Eqs. (9.85) indicate that all components of traction vanish on the lateral surface, as required. Consider next the free lower surface, where $z = 0$, $\nu_x = \nu_y = 0$, and $\nu_z = -1$. The components of traction on this surface are τ_{yz}, τ_{zx}, and τ_{zz}, and in accordance with Eqs. (9.85) these also vanish. Finally, since $z = l$ at the supported upper surface, Eqs. (9.85) conform with conditions (9.84) at that surface.

Next we ascertain the strain distributions by employing the *elastic stress-strain law* (9.8). Thus, inserting stresses (9.85), we get

$$\varepsilon_{xx} = -\frac{\nu \gamma z}{E} \qquad \varepsilon_{xy} = 0$$

$$\varepsilon_{yy} = -\frac{\nu \gamma z}{E} \qquad \varepsilon_{yz} = 0 \tag{9.86}$$

$$\varepsilon_{zz} = \frac{\gamma z}{E} \qquad \varepsilon_{zx} = 0$$

We can next check to see whether this strain distribution satisfies the *compatibility* equations (9.6). Substituting the foregoing results into these equations, we see quite readily that since the strains are linear in the coordinates the compatibility equations are indeed satisfied, ensuring us in this case that the strain stems from a single-valued, continuous displacement field. We thus may be assured at this point that we have presented the unique solution to the problem at hand [i.e., stress formulation (9.49)], at least away from the immediate vicinity of the support.

To complete the analysis, we now establish the *displacement* field for this problem. From Eqs. (9.4) and (9.86), we get

$$\frac{\partial u}{\partial x} = -\frac{\nu \gamma z}{E} \qquad \text{(a)}$$

$$\frac{\partial v}{\partial y} = -\frac{\nu \gamma z}{E} \qquad \text{(b)}$$

$$\frac{\partial w}{\partial z} = \frac{\gamma z}{E} \qquad \text{(c)}$$

$$\frac{\partial u}{\partial y} + \frac{\partial v}{\partial x} = 0 \qquad \text{(d)}$$ (9.87)

$$\frac{\partial v}{\partial z} + \frac{\partial w}{\partial y} = 0 \qquad \text{(e)}$$

$$\frac{\partial w}{\partial x} + \frac{\partial u}{\partial z} = 0 \qquad \text{(f)}$$

where $u = u_x$, $v = u_y$, and $w = u_z$. We shall begin by integrating Eq. (9.87c). Thus

$$w = \frac{\gamma z^2}{2E} + f(x, y) \qquad (9.88)$$

where $f(x, y)$ is an arbitrary function of the coordinates x and y. Substituting the foregoing result into Eqs. (9.87e) and (9.87f), we get

$$\frac{\partial v}{\partial z} = -\frac{\partial f}{\partial y} \qquad \text{(a)}$$ (9.89)

$$\frac{\partial u}{\partial z} = -\frac{\partial f}{\partial x} \qquad \text{(b)}$$

Integrate these equations, remembering that f is a function of only x and y. Thus

$$v = -\frac{\partial f}{\partial y} z + g(x, y) \qquad \text{(a)}$$ (9.90)

$$u = -\frac{\partial f}{\partial x} z + h(x, y) \qquad \text{(b)}$$

where g and h are two more arbitrary functions of the coordinates x and y.

Now substitute the preceding results into Eqs. (9.87a) and (9.87b). That is,

$$-\frac{\partial^2 f}{\partial x^2} z + \frac{\partial h}{\partial x} = -\frac{\nu \gamma z}{E} \qquad \text{(a)}$$ (9.91)

$$-\frac{\partial^2 f}{\partial y^2} z + \frac{\partial g}{\partial y} = -\frac{\nu \gamma z}{E} \qquad \text{(b)}$$

Since f, g, and h do not in any way depend on z, we may set $z = 0$ in the preceding equations and thereby obtain

$$\frac{\partial h}{\partial x} = 0 \qquad \text{(a)}$$

$$\frac{\partial g}{\partial y} = 0 \qquad \text{(b)}$$

(9.92)

Subtracting Eqs. (9.92) from Eqs. (9.91) then yields

$$\frac{\partial^2 f}{\partial x^2} = \frac{\nu \gamma}{E} \qquad \text{(a)}$$

$$\frac{\partial^2 f}{\partial y^2} = \frac{\nu \gamma}{E} \qquad \text{(b)}$$

(9.93)

We have yet to consider Eq. (9.87d). Substituting from Eqs. (9.90), we get

$$-2 \frac{\partial^2 f}{\partial y \, \partial x} z + \frac{\partial h}{\partial y} + \frac{\partial g}{\partial x} = 0 \qquad (9.94)$$

Since f, g, and h are functions of only x and y, we can proceed as above and set $z = 0$ to obtain

$$\frac{\partial h}{\partial y} + \frac{\partial g}{\partial x} = 0 \qquad (9.95)$$

which then also requires that

$$\frac{\partial^2 f}{\partial y \, \partial x} = 0 \qquad (9.96)$$

Now from Eqs. (9.92), we see that g and h can be given as

$$g = \alpha(x)$$
$$h = \beta(y)$$

(9.97)

where α and β are functions of x and y, respectively. But Eq. (9.95) then requires that

$$\frac{d\alpha}{dx} = -\frac{d\beta}{dy} \qquad (9.98)$$

Since α is a function of x only and β is a function of y only, Eq. (9.98) leads to an apparent contradiction. However, we avoid such a contradiction by setting both sides of this equation equal to the same separation constant, say C_1. Carrying out the integrations and noting Eqs. (9.97), we finally obtain

$$g = C_1 x + C_2$$
$$h = -C_1 y + C_3$$

(9.99)

where C_2 and C_3 are two more constants. We leave it for you to show as an exercise that Eqs. (9.93) and (9.96) give the function f as (see Problem 9.17)

$$f = \frac{\nu\gamma}{2E}(x^2 + y^2) + C_4 x + C_5 y + C_6 \qquad (9.100)$$

where C_4, C_5, and C_6 are also constants. We can now give the displacement field in terms of the six arbitrary constants. Thus, substituting Eqs. (9.99) and (9.100) into Eqs. (9.88) and (9.90), we finally have

$$u = -\frac{\nu\gamma}{E}xz - C_4 z - C_1 y + C_3 \qquad \text{(a)}$$

$$v = -\frac{\nu\gamma}{E}yz - C_5 z + C_1 x + C_2 \qquad \text{(b)} \qquad (9.101)$$

$$w = \frac{\gamma z^2}{2E} + \frac{\nu\gamma}{2E}(x^2 + y^2) + C_4 x + C_5 y + C_6 \qquad \text{(c)}$$

We may solve for the six constants of integration by ensuring that there is no rigid-body translation or rotation of the bar itself. Up to this point we have simply stipulated that $z = l$ designates the "supported end" of the bar, but we have not indicated the specific nature of this support. We now require that all components of displacement and rotation vanish at the *point* $(0, 0, l)$,* but shall not restrict the movement of any other points in the plane of the supported end. First we set $u = v = w = 0$ in Eqs. (9.101) at $(0, 0, l)$, and thereby obtain the following conditions on the constants:

$$-C_4 l + C_3 = 0$$

$$-C_5 l + C_2 = 0 \qquad (9.102)$$

$$\frac{\gamma l^2}{2E} + C_6 = 0$$

Next we also set the components of rotation ω_x, ω_y, and ω_z [see Eqs. (3.40) to (3.42)] equal to zero at this same point. Accordingly, we require that at the point $(0, 0, l)$

$$\omega_x = \frac{1}{2}\left(\frac{\partial w}{\partial y} - \frac{\partial v}{\partial z}\right) = 0 \qquad \text{or} \qquad \frac{\partial w}{\partial y} = \frac{\partial v}{\partial z}$$

$$\omega_y = \frac{1}{2}\left(\frac{\partial u}{\partial z} - \frac{\partial w}{\partial x}\right) = 0 \qquad \text{or} \qquad \frac{\partial u}{\partial z} = \frac{\partial w}{\partial x} \qquad (9.103)$$

$$\omega_z = \frac{1}{2}\left(\frac{\partial v}{\partial x} - \frac{\partial u}{\partial y}\right) = 0 \qquad \text{or} \qquad \frac{\partial v}{\partial x} = \frac{\partial u}{\partial y}$$

We then get from Eqs. (9.103) and (9.101) the following additional conditions on the constants:

$$C_5 = -C_5$$

$$-C_4 = C_4 \qquad (9.104)$$

$$C_1 = -C_1$$

* In Appendix I we have presented a sufficiency proof for the compatibility equations. This proof requires that if displacements are to be single-valued and continuous, the displacements and rotations must be prescribed at one point.

The foregoing results indicate that $C_1 = C_4 = C_5 = 0$, so going back to Eqs. (9.102), we see that

$$C_3 = 0$$

$$C_2 = 0$$

$$C_6 = -\frac{\gamma l^2}{2E}$$ (9.105)

Using these values for the constants then ensures no rigid-body motion, and displacement field (9.101) then finally becomes

$$u = -\frac{\nu \gamma}{E} xz$$ (a)

$$v = -\frac{\nu \gamma}{E} yz$$ (b) (9.106)

$$w = \frac{\gamma}{2E}(z^2 + \nu x^2 + \nu y^2 - l^2)$$ (c)

Notice that points along the z axis have only vertical displacements given by the expression

$$w = \frac{\gamma}{2E}(z^2 - l^2)$$ (9.107)

which then gives $w = 0$ at the supported end (as required) and the maximum displacement $w = -\gamma l^2/2E$ (i.e., downward) at the free end. Other points also have horizontal displacements due to the Poisson contraction of the member. In Problem 9.18 you will be asked to show that for a circular cross-section, every horizontal plane surface (including the supported end) deforms *essentially* (i.e., with higher-order terms neglected) into a paraboloid of revolution.

In the next section we consider another problem for a linear elastic isotropic material.

9.11 LINEAR ELASTIC BEAM IN PURE BENDING

Consider a linear elastic beam of length L and with a rectangular cross section of width b and height h, as shown in Fig. 9.5. The beam is considered weightless, and the only loads are the indicated linear, antisymmetric traction distributions in the x direction at the ends $x = \pm L/2$. Note that there are no applied or supporting forces in the vertical y direction. Clearly, the resultant shear force V_y and the resultant axial force F_x are zero, and thus the only nonzero resultant is the bending moment M_z, which is independent of x. We shall designate this uniform bending moment simply as M, and for obvious reasons will also say that the beam is in a state of "pure bending."[*]

---

[*] We employ the sign convention that a bending moment is positive if it has a positive sense on a positive area or has a negative sense on a negative area. Thus the moments at the ends $x = \pm L/2$ in Fig. 9.5 are *both* positive.

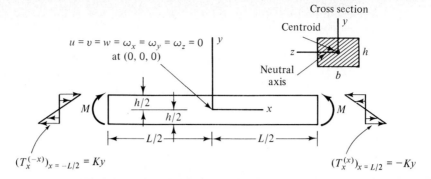

Figure 9.5 Linear elastic beam under pure bending.

Since there are no forces in the transverse z direction, we have here a problem in plane stress (i.e., only the stresses τ_{xx}, τ_{yy}, and τ_{xy} may be nonzero). Our procedure will once again be a *semi-inverse* method, and we begin by assuming that the stresses predicted by strength of materials are valid. Thus we have τ_{xx} as the *only* nonzero stress for reference xyz, and we may write

$$\tau_{xx} = -\frac{My}{I} \tag{9.108}$$

where M is the above-mentioned bending moment resultant of the two end linear traction distributions, and where I is the second moment of area about the neutral axis of the cross section. We may relate M to the magnitude of the slopes of the traction distributions (i.e., K in Fig. 9.5), by equating M with the moment about the neutral axis of the traction $T_x^{(x)} = -Ky$ at the end $x = L/2$. That is,

$$M = -\int_{-h/2}^{h/2} (T_x^{(x)}) by \, dy = -\int_{-h/2}^{h/2} (-Ky) by \, dy = K \int_{-h/2}^{h/2} y^2 \, dA = KI$$

and thus

$$K = \frac{M}{I} \tag{9.109}$$

We first consider *equilibrium* [see Eqs. (9.2)] which for this case becomes simply

$$\frac{\partial \tau_{xx}}{\partial x} = 0 \tag{9.110}$$

Clearly, from Eq. (9.108) we see that this equation is satisfied.

Now we use *Hooke's law* to determine the strains. From Eqs. (9.8) we see that

$$\varepsilon_{xx} = \frac{\tau_{xx}}{E} = -\frac{M}{EI} y$$

$$\varepsilon_{yy} = -\frac{\nu \tau_{xx}}{E} = \frac{\nu M}{EI} y$$

$$\varepsilon_{zz} = -\frac{\nu \tau_{xx}}{E} = \frac{\nu M}{EI} y \tag{9.111}$$

$$\varepsilon_{xy} = \varepsilon_{yz} = \varepsilon_{zx} = 0$$

Because we have been working without explicit use of the displacements, we must also satisfy the *compatibility equations*. Thus going to Eqs. (9.6), we see on inspection that since the strains presented above are either zero or linear in y, they trivially satisfy all six compatibility equations.

Next we check to see if the proposed stress distribution satisfies the *boundary conditions*. For this we use the Cauchy formula given by Eq. (9.34) on all surfaces of the beam. On the four lateral surfaces of the beam, the traction force $T_i^{(\nu)}$ is zero. Thus on the top and bottom we have

$$0 = \tau_{xx}\, \nu_x \tag{9.112}$$

The direction cosines for the upper and lower lateral surfaces are $\nu_x = 0$, $\nu_y = \pm 1$, $\nu_z = 0$, and thus Eq. (9.112) is satisfied. On the front and back lateral surfaces, we again have Eq. (9.112). Now for these surfaces we have for the direction cosines $\nu_x = 0$, $\nu_y = 0$, $\nu_z = \pm 1$, and again we satisfy this boundary condition. Next look at the right end $x = L/2$, where we have

$$T_x^{(x)} = \tau_{xx}\, \nu_x = \left(-\frac{My}{I} \right) \nu_x \tag{9.113}$$

Since $\nu_x = 1$ on the right end, we get on using Eq. (9.109) for M/I,

$$T_x^{(x)} = -Ky$$

which is exactly the prescribed loading shown in Fig. 9.5. Similarly, we have $\nu_x = -1$ for the left end, and we get Ky for $T_x^{(-x)}$ there, which again matches the given condition. It is also easy to demonstrate that $T_y^{(\nu)}$ and $T_z^{(\nu)}$ are zero at the ends, as required.

We thus can say that strength of materials gives an "exact" solution for the pure bending problem. If prescribed traction distributions $T_x^{(\nu)}$ at the ends give the correct resultant (i.e., M only) but are *not* given as $\pm Ky$, we can use Saint-Venant's principle to get the proper stress and displacements *away* from the ends.

We now set out to determine the *displacement field* for this problem. First we make the following definition:

$$\frac{M}{EI} = \frac{1}{R} \tag{9.114}$$

where as you know from strength of materials, R will turn out to be the radius of curvature, which in the present problem is a constant.* Hence, going back to Eqs. (9.111), we have on using the *strain-displacement* equations (9.4) as well as the result above,

$$\varepsilon_{xx} = -\frac{y}{R} = \frac{\partial u}{\partial x} \qquad \text{(a)}$$

$$\varepsilon_{yy} = \frac{\nu y}{R} = \frac{\partial v}{\partial y} \qquad \text{(b)} \tag{9.115}$$

$$\varepsilon_{zz} = \frac{\nu y}{R} = \frac{\partial w}{\partial z} \qquad \text{(c)}$$

* We explore this point more fully at the end of this section.

where $u = u_x$, $v = u_y$, and $w = u_z$. Also we have

$$\frac{\partial u}{\partial y} + \frac{\partial v}{\partial x} = 0 \qquad \text{(a)}$$

$$\frac{\partial v}{\partial z} + \frac{\partial w}{\partial y} = 0 \qquad \text{(b)} \qquad\qquad (9.116)$$

$$\frac{\partial w}{\partial x} + \frac{\partial u}{\partial z} = 0 \qquad \text{(c)}$$

We begin by integrating Eq. (9.115a), and thereby obtain

$$u = -\frac{xy}{R} + F(y, z) \qquad\qquad (9.117)$$

where $F(y, z)$ is an arbitrary function of y and z. Now substitute for u in the first and third of Eqs. (9.116):

$$\frac{\partial v}{\partial x} = \frac{x}{R} - \frac{\partial F(y, z)}{\partial y}, \qquad \frac{\partial w}{\partial x} = -\frac{\partial F(y, z)}{\partial z}$$

Integrating each of these equations, we get

$$v = \frac{x^2}{2R} - \frac{\partial F(y, z)}{\partial y} x + G(y, z), \qquad w = -\frac{\partial F(y, z)}{\partial z} x + H(y, z) \qquad (9.118)$$

where $G(y, z)$ and $H(y, z)$ are two more functions of y and z. Now we substitute for v and w above into the second and third of Eqs. (9.115):

$$\frac{vy}{R} = -\frac{\partial^2 F(y, z)}{\partial y^2} x + \frac{\partial G(y, z)}{\partial y} \qquad \text{(a)}$$

$$\qquad\qquad (9.119)$$

$$\frac{vy}{R} = -\frac{\partial^2 F(y, z)}{\partial z^2} x + \frac{\partial H(y, z)}{\partial z} \qquad \text{(b)}$$

In examining the first of equations (9.119) we note the lone appearance of the variable x. For this equation to be valid for a range of x, the following are necessary conditions:[*]

$$\frac{\partial^2 F(y, z)}{\partial y^2} = 0 \qquad\qquad (9.120a)$$

and

$$\frac{\partial G(y, z)}{\partial y} = \frac{vy}{R} \qquad\qquad (9.120b)$$

which implies

$$G(y, z) = \frac{vy^2}{2R} + g(z) \qquad\qquad (9.120c)$$

---

[*] Since $F(y, z)$ and $G(y, z)$ are independent of x, we may set $x = 0$ in Eq. (9.119a) and thereby obtain Eq. (9.120b). Then subtracting this equation from Eq. (9.119a) gives Eq. (9.120a).

Similarly, in considering the second of Eqs. (9.119), we can conclude that

$$\frac{\partial^2 F(y,z)}{\partial z^2} = 0 \tag{9.121a}$$

and

$$\frac{\partial H(y,z)}{\partial z} = \frac{\nu y}{R} \tag{9.121b}$$

which implies

$$H(y,z) = \frac{\nu yz}{R} + h(y) \tag{9.121c}$$

Note that in the above, $g(z)$ depends only on z, while $h(y)$ depends only on y.

Let us next proceed to the second of Eqs. (9.116). Using Eqs. (9.118) and Eqs. (9.120c) and (9.121c), we get

$$\frac{\partial v}{\partial z} + \frac{\partial w}{\partial y} = \left[-\frac{\partial^2 F(y,z)}{\partial y\, \partial z}x + \frac{dg(z)}{dz} \right] + \left[-\frac{\partial^2 F(y,z)}{\partial y\, \partial z}x + \frac{\nu z}{R} + \frac{dh(y)}{dy} \right] = 0$$

Therefore,

$$-2\frac{\partial^2 F(y,z)}{\partial y\, \partial z}x + \frac{dg(z)}{dz} + \frac{\nu z}{R} + \frac{dh(y)}{dy} = 0 \tag{9.122}$$

Since $F(y,z)$, $g(z)$, and $h(y)$ are independent of x, we may, as explained above, split this equation into two parts. Thus the term containing the lone x must vanish, that is,

$$\frac{\partial^2 F(y,z)}{\partial y\, \partial z} = 0 \tag{9.123}$$

The remaining terms must also vanish, and we write this condition in the form

$$\frac{dg(z)}{dz} + \frac{\nu z}{R} = C_1 \qquad \text{(a)}$$

$$\frac{dh(y)}{dy} = -C_1 \qquad \text{(b)} \tag{9.124}$$

where C_1 is a separation constant, introduced to avoid the apparent contradiction inherent in equating a function of z to a function of y. Integrating these ordinary differential equations, we get

$$h(y) = -C_1 y + C_2$$

$$g(z) = -\frac{\nu z^2}{2R} + C_1 z + C_3 \tag{9.125}$$

where C_2 and C_3 are two constants of integration. Furthermore, we see from Eqs. (9.120a), (9.121a), and (9.123) that all second partial derivatives of F are zero, and thus we conclude that $F(y,z)$ is linear in y and z. That is,

$$F(y,z) = C_4 y + C_5 z + C_6 \tag{9.126}$$

with C_4, C_5, and C_6 as three more constants. Now going back to Eq. (9.117) for u and Eqs. (9.118) for v and w, we have on substituting for F, G, and H from Eqs. (9.126), (9.120c), and (9.121c) with g and h given by Eqs. (9.125):

$$u = -\frac{xy}{R} + C_4 y + C_5 z + C_6$$

$$v = \frac{x^2}{2R} - C_4 x + \frac{\nu y^2}{2R} - \frac{\nu z^2}{2R} + C_1 z + C_3 \qquad (9.127)$$

$$w = -C_5 x + \frac{\nu yz}{R} - C_1 y + C_2$$

Finally, to eliminate rigid-body translation we must fix in space one point of the body. Thus for the origin $(0, 0, 0)$ we will require $u = v = w = 0$, and from Eqs. (9.127) we see that this renders $C_6 = C_3 = C_2 = 0$. Also, to eliminate rigid-body rotation we require that $\omega_x = \omega_y = \omega_z = 0$ at the origin. Thus we have at the point $(0, 0, 0)$

$$\omega_x = \frac{1}{2}\left(\frac{\partial w}{\partial y} - \frac{\partial v}{\partial z}\right) = 0$$

$$\omega_y = \frac{1}{2}\left(\frac{\partial u}{\partial z} - \frac{\partial w}{\partial x}\right) = 0$$

$$\omega_z = \frac{1}{2}\left(\frac{\partial v}{\partial x} - \frac{\partial u}{\partial y}\right) = 0$$

and accordingly, Eqs. (9.127) give, respectively, $C_1 = C_5 = C_4 = 0$. The displacement field is finally fully established as follows:

$$u = -\frac{xy}{R}$$

$$v = \frac{1}{2R}[x^2 + \nu(y^2 - z^2)] \qquad (9.128)$$

$$w = \frac{\nu yz}{R}$$

where as shown previously, $1/R = M/EI$ and $M/I = K$.

It will be of interest to examine the cross section of the beam passing through the origin (look back at Fig. 9.5). For this plane we have $x = 0$, and thus the displacement field is

$$u = 0$$

$$v = \frac{\nu}{2R}(y^2 - z^2) \qquad (9.129)$$

$$w = \frac{\nu yz}{R}$$

Examine the left and right sides of this cross section, where $z = \pm b/2$ and thus we

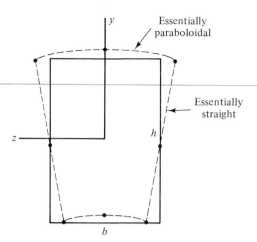

Figure 9.6 Deformed geometry of cross section at the origin.

get

$$v = \frac{\nu}{2R}\left(y^2 - \frac{b^2}{4}\right), \qquad w = \pm\frac{\nu b}{2R}y \qquad (9.130)$$

For small deformation, w will have a much greater effect than v on the deformed shapes of the left and right sides of the cross section. Accordingly, it follows from the linearity of w in Eqs. (9.130) that these sides deform into *essentially* straight lines,* which are no longer vertical (see Fig. 9.6). As for the top and bottom sides of this section, where $y = \pm h/2$, we obtain from Eqs. (9.129) the result

$$v = \frac{\nu}{2R}\left(\frac{h^2}{4} - z^2\right), \qquad w = \pm\frac{\nu h}{2R}z \qquad (9.131)$$

Here v dominates the deformed shapes of the top and bottom sides, and thus we see that these sides become essentially paraboloidal as shown in Fig. 9.6.

For the section at the origin, the axial displacement u was zero [see Eqs. (9.129)]. Now consider a section at some constant nonzero value of x, say x_0. In this case, the first of Eqs. (9.128) gives the linear relation

$$u = -\frac{x_0}{R}y \qquad (9.132)$$

Thus, when viewed along the z axis (see Fig. 9.5), the originally vertical and straight edge of the cross section deforms into another straight line. Hence for *pure bending* the "plane-sections-remain-plane" hypothesis of strength of materials is seen to be strictly valid. Note that in this geometrical consideration we are not including the higher-order effect on the deformation process due to v and w.

Finally, let us examine the deformation of the x axis itself. Setting $y = z = 0$ in Eqs. (9.128) gives us $u = w = 0$, and

$$v = \frac{x^2}{2R} \qquad (9.133)$$

---

* It is permissible to delete the word "essentially," since the higher-order effect due to v is of the same order as the approximation due to the small deformation assumption.

Now, for small deformation the curvature κ is obtained *approximately* from the relation

$$\kappa \approx \frac{d^2 v}{dx^2}$$

Equation (9.133) then gives us $\kappa = 1/R$, which justifies our earlier assertion that R is a constant radius of curvature. The important role of the small-deformation assumption becomes clear when we note that Eq. (9.133) yields a parabolic arc, whereas for R to be *exactly* constant we must have a circular arc.

We have seen in this section that the strength-of-materials solution for a rectangular beam under pure bending is an "exact" solution when viewed from the framework of small-deformation theory. One can also show that this same exact solution is valid for an arbitrary cross section if yz are principal axes of area with origin at the centroid (see Problem 9.21). For more general loading conditions shear stresses are present, and the "plane-sections-remain-plane" assumption of strength of materials is no longer an exact representation of the deformation. The resulting formulation of strength of materials for beams is called the Euler–Bernoulli theory.*

In the next section we go on to a consideration of the use of the linear viscoelastic–linear elastic correspondence principle for the solution of viscoelastic problems.

9.12 APPLICATION OF THE LINEAR VISCOELASTIC CORRESPONDENCE PRINCIPLE

We shall in this section again solve the hanging bar problem of Section 9.10 and the pure bending of Section 9.11, but now for the case of a linear viscoelastic material. Our approach will be based on the correspondence principle presented in Section 9.5.

Linear Viscoelastic Bar Suddenly Hanging under Its Own Weight

Consider again the hanging prismatic bar shown in Fig. 9.4. We shall specify that the bar is hung *suddenly* at time $t = 0$. Furthermore, the bar is of a linear viscoelastic material which exhibits *elastic compressibility* and is *Maxwell under distortion*. The viscoelastic constitutive equations are thus given as (see Problem 6.30)

$$\bar{\tau} = 3K\bar{\varepsilon} \qquad \text{(a)}$$

$$s_{ij} + \frac{\zeta}{2G}\dot{s}_{ij} = \zeta \dot{e}_{ij} \qquad \text{(b)}$$

(9.134)

As in the elastic problem, we seek to determine the only nonzero stress, τ_{zz}, and the displacements u, v, w.

---

* See Chapter 10 and Appendix IV for additional comments on the Euler–Bernoulli theory.

The solution for elastic material is given by Eqs. (9.85) and (9.106). Accordingly,

$$\tau_{zz}^E = \gamma z [u(t)] \tag{a}$$

$$u^E = -\frac{\nu \gamma}{E} xz [u(t)] \tag{b}$$

$$v^E = -\frac{\nu \gamma}{E} yz [u(t)] \tag{c}$$

$$(9.135)$$

$$w^E = \frac{\gamma}{2E} [(z^2 - l^2) + \nu(x^2 + y^2)][u(t)] \tag{d}$$

where we have used the superscript E to indicate elastic solutions and have multiplied by the unit step function because the body force (i.e., the weight) is applied suddenly at $t = 0$. Note that the stress τ_{zz}^E is independent of the elastic material constants E and ν. It follows directly from the correspondence principle that this *same* stress solution is valid for viscoelastic material. Accordingly, from this point on we shall be concerned only with obtaining the viscoelastic displacements, which we shall designate as u^V, v^V, and w^V.

To be able to use the shear and bulk differential operators appearing in viscoelastic constitutive equations (9.134), we must first express E and ν in elastic solutions (9.135) in terms of G and K. Referring back to Table 5.1, we see that

$$\frac{1}{E} = \frac{3K + G}{9KG} \tag{a}$$

$$(9.136)$$

$$\frac{\nu}{E} = \frac{3K - 2G}{18KG} \tag{b}$$

Equations (9.135b, c, d) then become with the use of these relations

$$u^E = -\gamma \left(\frac{3K - 2G}{18KG} \right) xz [u(t)] \tag{a}$$

$$v^E = -\gamma \left(\frac{3K - 2G}{18KG} \right) yz [u(t)] \tag{b} \qquad (9.137)$$

$$w^E = \frac{\gamma}{2} \left[\left(\frac{3K + G}{9KG} \right) (z^2 - l^2) + \left(\frac{3K - 2G}{18KG} \right) (x^2 + y^2) \right] [u(t)] \tag{c}$$

We begin our application of the correspondence principle by taking the Laplace transform of Eqs. (9.137), with homogeneous initial conditions at $t = 0^-$ (see Appendix III). Noting that $\mathbf{L}\{[u(t)]\} = 1/s$, we obtain

$$\bar{u}^E = -\frac{\gamma}{s} \left(\frac{3K - 2G}{18KG} \right) xz \tag{a}$$

$$\bar{v}^E = -\frac{\gamma}{s} \left(\frac{3K - 2G}{18KG} \right) yz \tag{b} \qquad (9.138)$$

$$\bar{w}^E = \frac{\gamma}{2s} \left[\left(\frac{3K + 2G}{9KG} \right) (x^2 - l^2) + \left(\frac{3K - 2G}{18KG} \right) (x^2 + y^2) \right] \tag{c}$$

The next step in the procedure is to replace K and G in Eqs. (9.138) by the appropriate ratios of transformed operators as specified by Eqs. (9.62), which we now repeat:

$$3K \to \frac{\overline{Q}^K}{\overline{P}^K} \qquad 2G \to \frac{\overline{Q}^G}{\overline{P}^G}$$

After some simplification we then find that the groupings of elastic constants, appearing in the parentheses in Eqs. (9.138), must be replaced as follows:

$$\frac{3K - 2G}{18KG} \to \frac{\overline{P}^G \overline{Q}^K - \overline{P}^K \overline{Q}^G}{3\overline{Q}^K \overline{Q}^G} \qquad \text{(a)}$$

$$\frac{3K + G}{9KG} \to \frac{2\overline{P}^G \overline{Q}^K + \overline{P}^K \overline{Q}^G}{3\overline{Q}^K \overline{Q}^G} \qquad \text{(b)}$$

(9.139)

The Laplace transform of the solution for *any* viscoelastic material then follows as

$$\bar{u}^V = -\frac{\gamma}{s} \left(\frac{\overline{P}^G \overline{Q}^K - \overline{P}^K \overline{Q}^G}{3\overline{Q}^K \overline{Q}^G} \right) xz \qquad \text{(a)}$$

$$\bar{v}^V = -\frac{\gamma}{s} \left(\frac{\overline{P}^G \overline{Q}^K - \overline{P}^K \overline{Q}^G}{3\overline{Q}^K \overline{Q}^G} \right) yz \qquad \text{(b) (9.140)}$$

$$\bar{w}^V = \frac{\gamma}{2s} \left[\left(\frac{2\overline{P}^G \overline{Q}^K + \overline{P}^K \overline{Q}^G}{3\overline{Q}^K \overline{Q}^G} \right) (z^2 - l^2) + \left(\frac{\overline{P}^G \overline{Q}^G - \overline{P}^K \overline{Q}^G}{3\overline{Q}^K \overline{Q}^G} \right) (x^2 + y^2) \right] \qquad \text{(c)}$$

where the superscript V indicates viscoelastic solutions.

For the specific linear viscoelastic material under consideration [see Eqs. (9.134)], we have the following differential operators:

$$P^K = 1 \qquad\qquad Q^K = 3K$$

$$P^G = 1 + \frac{\zeta D}{2G} \qquad Q^G = \zeta D$$

(9.141)

In the Laplace transform domain these operators become

$$\overline{P}^K = 1 \qquad\qquad \overline{Q}^K = 3K$$

$$\overline{P}^G = 1 + \frac{\zeta s}{2G} \qquad \overline{Q}^G = \zeta s$$

(9.142)

It then follows that

$$\frac{\overline{P}^G \overline{Q}^K - \overline{P}^K \overline{Q}^G}{3\overline{Q}^K \overline{Q}^G} = \frac{3K(2G + \zeta s) - 2G\zeta s}{18KG\zeta s} = \frac{1}{3\zeta s} + \frac{3K - 2G}{18KG}$$

$$\frac{2\overline{P}^G \overline{Q}^K + \overline{P}^K \overline{Q}^G}{3\overline{Q}^K \overline{Q}^G} = \frac{6K(2G + \zeta s) + 2G\zeta s}{18KG\zeta s} = \frac{2}{3\zeta s} + \frac{3K + G}{9KG}$$

(9.143)

which with the use of Eqs. (9.136) simplify to

$$\frac{\overline{P}^G \overline{Q}^K - \overline{P}^K \overline{Q}^G}{2\overline{Q}^K \overline{Q}^G} = \frac{1}{3\zeta s} + \frac{\nu}{E}$$

$$\frac{2\overline{P}^G \overline{Q}^K + \overline{P}^K \overline{Q}^G}{3\overline{Q}^K \overline{Q}^G} = \frac{2}{3\zeta s} + \frac{1}{E}$$

(9.144)

Substituting Eqs. (9.144) into Eqs. (9.140) finally gives us the following Laplace transforms of the desired viscoelastic solutions:

$$\bar{u}^V = -\frac{\gamma}{s}\left(\frac{1}{3\zeta s} + \frac{\nu}{E}\right)xz \tag{a}$$

$$\bar{v}^V = -\frac{\gamma}{s}\left(\frac{1}{3\zeta s} + \frac{\nu}{E}\right)yz \tag{b} \qquad (9.145)$$

$$\bar{w}^V = \frac{\gamma}{2s}\left[\left(\frac{2}{3\zeta s} + \frac{1}{E}\right)(z^2 - l^2) + \left(\frac{1}{3\zeta s} + \frac{\nu}{E}\right)(x^2 + y^2)\right] \tag{c}$$

Before inverting Eqs. (9.145), it will be instructive to check the limiting behaviors of these solutions by means of the limit theorems given in Appendix III. The long-time asymptotic behaviors follow simply as

$$u^V(\infty) = \lim_{s \to 0} s\bar{u}^V \to \infty$$
$$v^V(\infty) = \lim_{s \to 0} s\bar{v}^V \to \infty \tag{9.146}$$
$$w^V(\infty) = \lim_{s \to 0} s\bar{w}^V \to \infty$$

which are the expected unbounded displacements due to the viscous component in the Maxwell model. Similarly, the short-time behaviors at the instant immediately after load application are obtained as

$$u^V(0^+) = \lim_{s \to \infty} s\bar{u}^V = -\frac{\nu\gamma}{E}xz$$

$$v^V(0^+) = \lim_{s \to \infty} s\bar{v}^V = -\frac{\nu\gamma}{E}yz \tag{9.147}$$

$$w^V(0^+) = \lim_{s \to \infty} s\bar{w}^V = \frac{\gamma}{2E}[(z^2 - l^2) + \nu(x^2 + y^2)]$$

which, as expected, are equal to the elastic solutions [see Eqs. (9.135)].

The inverted forms of Eqs. (9.145) follow directly from the transform properties of the unit step and ramp functions [see Eqs. (III.10) and (III.11) in Appendix III], that is, from

$$\mathbf{L}\{[u(t)]\} = \frac{1}{s}$$

$$\mathbf{L}\{t[u(t)]\} = \frac{1}{s^2}$$

Accordingly, we finally obtain the viscoelastic solutions:

$$u^V = -\gamma\left(\frac{t}{3\zeta} + \frac{\nu}{E}\right)xz[u(t)] \tag{a}$$

$$v^V = -\gamma\left(\frac{t}{3\zeta} + \frac{\nu}{E}\right)yz[u(t)] \tag{b} \qquad (9.148)$$

$$w^V = \frac{\gamma}{2}\left[\left(\frac{2t}{3\zeta} + \frac{1}{E}\right)(z^2 - l^2) + \left(\frac{t}{3\zeta} + \frac{\nu}{E}\right)(x^2 + y^2)\right][u(t)] \tag{c}$$

Note that for $t > 0$ the displacement *rates* are equal to the following *constant* values:

$$\dot{u}^V = -\frac{\gamma}{3\zeta}xz$$

$$\dot{v}^V = -\frac{\gamma}{3\zeta}yz$$

$$\dot{w}^V = \frac{\gamma}{3\zeta}\left[(z^2 - l^2) + \frac{1}{2}(x^2 + y^2)\right]$$

This completes the solution for the hanging viscoelastic bar, and we now go on to the viscoelastic beam under pure bending.

Linear Viscoelastic Beam under Time-Dependent Pure Bending

Consider once more the beam under pure bending shown in Fig. 9.5, but now for the linear viscoelastic material of the hanging bar problem above (i.e., elastic in compression and Maxwell in distortion). The applied bending moment is prescribed as the following function of time:

$$M(t) = M_0\{[u(t)] - [u(t - t_0)]\} \tag{9.149}$$

Accordingly, a constant moment M_0 is suddenly applied at $t = 0$ and then suddenly removed at $t = t_0$ (see Fig. 9.7). We seek the stress τ_{xx} and the displacements u, v, w.

The elastic solutions for *any* applied time-dependent bending moment $M(t)$ were previously given by Eqs. (9.108) and (9.128). In the Laplace transform space these solutions become

$$\overline{\tau}_{xx}^E = -\frac{\overline{M}y}{I} \tag{a}$$

$$\overline{u}^E = -\frac{xy}{E}\frac{\overline{M}}{I} \tag{b}$$

$$\overline{v}^E = \frac{1}{E}[x^2 + \nu(y^2 - z^2)]\frac{\overline{M}}{2I} \tag{c}$$

$$\overline{w}^E = \frac{\nu yz}{E}\frac{\overline{M}}{I} \tag{d}$$

$$(9.150)$$

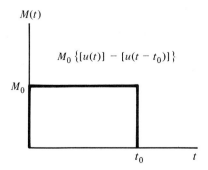

Figure 9.7 Applied bending moment in viscoelastic beam problem.

where $\overline{M}$ is the Laplace transform of $M(t)$. We again have a problem in which the stress is independent of the elastic constants, and thus the same stress solution is valid for viscoelastic material. The viscoelastic displacements u^V, v^V, w^V will not be the same as the elastic displacements.

We have shown in the hanging viscoelastic bar problem that the Laplace transform of the viscoelastic solutions, for the material under consideration, may be obtained by employing the following replacements [see Eqs. (9.144)] in the transformed elastic solutions:

$$\frac{\nu}{E} \to \frac{\nu}{E} + \frac{1}{3\zeta s}$$

$$\frac{1}{E} \to \frac{1}{E} + \frac{2}{3\zeta s}$$

$$(9.151)$$

Furthermore, applying transform formula (III.14a) in Appendix III to Eq. (9.149) for $M(t)$, we get for $\overline{M}$:

$$\overline{M} = \frac{M_0}{s}[1 - \exp(-t_0 s)] \qquad (9.152)$$

Using Eqs. (9.151) and (9.152) in Eqs. (9.150), we then get the following transformed viscoelastic displacements:

$$\overline{u}^V = -xy\left(\frac{1}{E} + \frac{2}{3\zeta s}\right)\frac{M_0}{Is}[1 - \exp(-t_0 s)] \qquad (a)$$

$$\overline{v}^V = \left[x^2\left(\frac{1}{E} + \frac{2}{3\zeta s}\right) + (y^2 - z^2)\left(\frac{\nu}{E} + \frac{1}{3\zeta s}\right)\frac{M_0}{2Is}\right][1 - \exp(-t_0 s)] \qquad (b) \qquad (9.153)$$

$$\overline{w}^V = yz\left(\frac{\nu}{E} + \frac{1}{3\zeta s}\right)\frac{M_0}{Is}[1 - \exp(-t_0 s)] \qquad (c)$$

The initial solutions follow easily from Eqs. (9.153) as

$$u^V(0^+) = \lim_{s \to \infty} s\overline{u}^V = -\left(\frac{xy}{E}\right)\frac{M_0}{I}$$

$$v^V(0^+) = \lim_{s \to \infty} s\overline{v}^V = \frac{1}{E}[x^2 + \nu(y^2 - z^2)]\frac{M_0}{2I} \qquad (9.154)$$

$$w^V(0^+) = \lim_{s \to \infty} s\overline{w}^V = \left(\frac{\nu yz}{E}\right)\frac{M_0}{I}$$

which are the same as the elastic solutions *at the time* $t = 0^+$. In obtaining the long-time asymptotic solutions, we shall make use of the following limits:

$$\lim_{s \to 0}[1 - \exp(-t_0 s)] = 0$$

$$\lim_{s \to 0}\left[\frac{1 - \exp(-t_0 s)}{s}\right] = \lim_{s \to 0} t_0 \exp(-t_0 s) = t_0$$

Accordingly, we get from Eqs. (9.153),

$$u^V(\infty) = \lim_{s \to 0} s\bar{u}^V = -xy \left(\frac{2}{3\zeta}\right) \frac{M_0}{I} t_0$$

$$v^V(\infty) = \lim_{s \to 0} s\bar{v}^V = \left[x^2\left(\frac{2}{3\zeta}\right) + (y^2 - z^2)\left(\frac{1}{3\zeta}\right)\right]\frac{M_0}{2I} t_0 \qquad (9.155)$$

$$w^V(\infty) = \lim_{s \to 0} s\bar{w}^V = yz \left(\frac{1}{3\zeta}\right) \frac{M_0}{I} t_0$$

These displacements are the contributions at time $t = t_0$ due to the viscous component in the model, which is as expected since the contributions due to the elastic component are *recovered* upon removal of the bending moment at $t = t_0$.

The inverted forms of Eqs. (9.153) may now be constructed with the use of the following simple transform formulas, which may all be obtained from Eq. (III.14a) in Appendix III:

$$\mathbf{L}\{[u(t)]\} = \frac{1}{s}$$

$$\mathbf{L}\{t[u(t)]\} = \frac{1}{s^2}$$

$$\mathbf{L}\{[u(t - t_0)]\} = \frac{1}{s} \exp(-t_0 s)$$

$$\mathbf{L}\{(t - t_0)[u(t - t_0)]\} = \frac{1}{s^2} \exp(-t_0 s)$$

Accordingly, we finally obtain

$$u^V = -xy \frac{M_0}{I} \left\langle \frac{1}{E}\{[u(t)] - [u(t - t_0)]\} + \frac{2}{3\zeta}\{t[u(t)] - (t - t_0)[u(t - t_0)]\}\right\rangle$$

$$v^V = \frac{M_0}{2I}\left\langle \frac{1}{E}[x^2 + v(y^2 - z^2)]\{[u(t)] - [u(t - t_0)]\}\right.$$

$$\left. + \frac{2}{3\zeta}\left[x^2 + \frac{1}{2}(y^2 - z^2)\right]\{t[u(t)] - (t - t_0)[u(t - t_0)]\}\right\rangle \qquad (9.156)$$

$$w^V = yz \frac{M_0}{I}\left\langle \frac{v}{E}\{[u(t)] - [u(t - t_0)]\} + \frac{1}{3\zeta}\{t[u(t)] - (t - t_0)[u(t - t_0)]\}\right\rangle$$

Equations (9.156) are consistent with limiting solutions (9.154) and (9.155).

We have in this section solved two simple viscoelastic problems "exactly," by means of the linear viscoelastic–linear elastic correspondence principle. In both problems the stresses in the viscoelastic problem were the same as in the elastic problem. Although this may occur in simple problems such as these, it will not occur in more complicated problems in which the constraints are such that the stresses depend on the material properties. Finally, we note that because of the linearity of the problems formulated in this section, we may superpose the solutions we have obtained. We demonstrate in the next section that superposition is not valid for nonlinear viscoelastic materials.

9.13 NONLINEAR VISCOUS BEHAVIOR; EXAMINATION OF SUPERPOSITION

As another example, consider a nonlinear viscous prismatic bar subjected only to uniform, but time-dependent tensile tractions at the ends $z = 0, L$ (see Fig. 9.8). Specifically, we have for $t \geq 0$,

$$(T_z^{(-z)})_{z=0} = -p(t) = -(p_0 + p_1 t)$$
$$(T_z^{(z)})_{z=L} = p(t) = p_0 + p_1 t$$

(9.157)

where p_0 and p_1 are constants and all other traction components at the ends and on the lateral surface are zero. The origin $(0,0,0)$ is any convenient point in the left end of the bar. At this point we require that the displacement and rotation *rates* (i.e., $\dot{u}, \dot{v}, \dot{w}, \dot{\omega}_x, \dot{\omega}_y, \dot{\omega}_z$) all vanish. We seek the exact solution for the stresses τ_{ij} and the displacement rates $\dot{u}_i$. Clearly, the *only* nonzero resultant force or moment arising from tractions (9.157) is the axial tensile force $F_z = p(t)A$, where A is the cross-sectional area. For nonuniform traction distributions with this same resultant (i.e., with zero bending moment resultants), we seek a solution that in the sense of Saint-Venant's principle is valid at points away from the ends.

We once more employ a *semi-inverse* procedure and consider as a possible stress distribution

$$\tau_{zz} = p_0 + p_1 t, \qquad \tau_{xx} = \tau_{yy} = \tau_{xy} = \tau_{yz} = \tau_{zx} = 0$$

(9.158)

Clearly, *equilibrium* equations (9.2) are satisfied by such a distribution. An examination of Cauchy formula (9.34) at the ends and on the lateral surface easily shows that the prescribed tractions [see Eqs. (9.157)] are also consistent with stress distribution (9.158).

Next we determine the strain-rate distribution from *nonlinear viscous constitutive* law (9.65), that is,

$$\dot{\varepsilon}_{ij} = C J_2^m s_{ij}$$

(9.159)

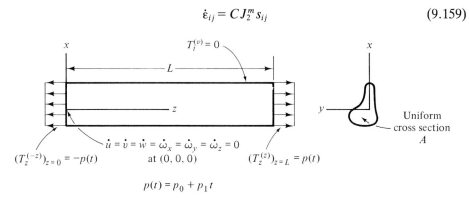

$$p(t) = p_0 + p_1 t$$

Figure 9.8 Nonlinear viscous prismatic bar under uniform tension.

Boundary Value Problems   Chap. 9

We have shown in Chapter 7 (see Section 7.13) that for one-dimensional loadings such as we have here, Eq. (9.159) simplifies to

$$\dot{\varepsilon}_{zz} = A \tau_{zz}^n$$

$$\dot{\varepsilon}_{xx} = \dot{\varepsilon}_{yy} = -\tfrac{1}{2}\dot{\varepsilon}_{zz} \tag{9.160}$$

$$\dot{\varepsilon}_{xy} = \dot{\varepsilon}_{yz} = \dot{\varepsilon}_{zx} = 0$$

where

$$n = 2m + 1$$

$$A = \frac{2C}{3^{m+1}} \tag{9.161}$$

Inserting stresses (9.158) into Eqs. (9.160) we then get

$$\dot{\varepsilon}_{xx} = -\frac{A}{2}(p_0 + p_1 t)^n, \qquad \dot{\varepsilon}_{xy} = 0$$

$$\dot{\varepsilon}_{yy} = -\frac{A}{2}(p_0 + p_1 t)^n, \qquad \dot{\varepsilon}_{yz} = 0 \tag{9.162}$$

$$\dot{\varepsilon}_{zz} = A(p_0 + p_1 t)^n, \qquad \dot{\varepsilon}_{zx} = 0$$

These strain rates are uniform in the spatial coordinates and clearly satisfy the *time derivatives* of *compatibility equations* (9.6). We are thus assured that once the strain rate–displacement rate relations are integrated, we will have obtained the complete exact solution to this problem.

Substituting Eqs. (9.162) for the strain rates appearing in *strain rate–displacement rate* relations (9.67), we now get

$$\frac{\partial \dot{u}}{\partial x} = -\frac{A}{2}(p_0 + p_1 t)^n \qquad \text{(a)}$$

$$\frac{\partial \dot{v}}{\partial y} = -\frac{A}{2}(p_0 + p_1 t)^n \qquad \text{(b)}$$

$$\frac{\partial \dot{w}}{\partial z} = A(p_0 + p_1 t)^n \qquad \text{(c)}$$

$$\frac{\partial \dot{u}}{\partial y} + \frac{\partial \dot{v}}{\partial x} = 0 \qquad \text{(d)} \tag{9.163}$$

$$\frac{\partial \dot{v}}{\partial z} + \frac{\partial \dot{w}}{\partial y} = 0 \qquad \text{(e)}$$

$$\frac{\partial \dot{w}}{\partial x} + \frac{\partial \dot{u}}{\partial z} = 0 \qquad \text{(f)}$$

On comparing these equations with Eqs. (9.87), we see that these two sets of equations are similar in form. Specifically, in each set the right sides of Eqs. (a) and (b) are equal to each other and equal to a constant times the right side of Eq. (c). Furthermore, the right sides of Eqs. (d), (e), and (f) are zero. Accordingly, we may employ the same solution procedure to integrate Eqs. (9.163). We leave it for you to show that we thereby obtain

$$\dot{u} = -\frac{A}{2}(p_0 + p_1 t)^n x - C_4 z + C_1 y + C_3$$

$$\dot{v} = -\frac{A}{2}(p_0 + p_1 t)^n y - C_5 z + C_1 x + C_2 \tag{9.164}$$

$$\dot{w} = A(p_0 + p_1 t)^n z + C_4 x + C_5 y + C_6$$

where $C_1, C_2, C_3, C_4, C_5, C_6$ are constants of integration. Furthermore, we also leave it for you to show that if we set $\dot{u} = \dot{v} = \dot{w} = \dot{\omega}_x = \dot{\omega}_y = \dot{\omega}_z = 0$ at the point $(0,0,0)$, all six constants equal zero. Thus the displacement-rate (i.e., the velocity) field finally becomes

$$\dot{u} = -\frac{A}{2}(p_0 + p_1 t)^n x$$

$$\dot{v} = -\frac{A}{2}(p_0 + p_1 t)^n y \tag{9.165}$$

$$\dot{w} = A(p_0 + p_1 t)^n z$$

We will now comment on the possibility of using *superposition* to obtain velocity solutions (9.165). If the prescribed tractions are simply constant in time, the velocities are obtained by setting $p_1 = 0$ in these equations:

$$\dot{u} = -\frac{A}{2}p_0^n x$$

$$\dot{v} = -\frac{A}{2}p_0^n y \tag{9.166}$$

$$\dot{w} = A p_0^n z$$

On the other hand, if the tractions are linear in time, starting with zero at $t = 0$, the velocities are obtained by setting $p_0 = 0$ in Eqs. (9.165):

$$\dot{u} = -\frac{A}{2}(p_1 t)^n x$$

$$\dot{v} = -\frac{A}{2}(p_1 t)^n y \tag{9.167}$$

$$\dot{w} = A(p_1 t)^n z$$

But since $(p_0 + p_1 t)^n \neq p_0^n + (p_1 t)^n$, except in the special linear viscous case where $n = 1$, the superposition of solutions (9.166) and (9.167) does *not* yield solutions (9.165) for $n \neq 1$.* You may recall that in Chapter 3 (see Section 3.3), we showed

---

*Clearly, superposition is invalid for "combined stress" creep problems (e.g., a tube under internal pressure and axial load). Several combined stress solutions are given in I. Finnie and W. R. Heller, *Creep of Engineering Materials* (New York: McGraw-Hill Book Company, 1959), Chap. 7.

that we may superpose the displacements corresponding to two force inputs if the *deformations are small*. Since the deformations are assumed small here, you may ask why superposition is not valid in the present example. The answer to this question is that for $n \neq 1$ the *input* here is a *nonlinear function* of the load [see the right side of Eqs. (9.163)], and *not* the load itself. Furthermore, if the deformations were large, the left sides of Eqs. (9.163) would be nonlinear in the velocities, and superposition would be invalid even for $n = 1$.

The problem above was very simple since the stresses and strains were *uniform*, and thus we were able to obtain the exact solution. In problems where the stresses are *nonuniform*, the satisfaction of compatibility is no longer trivial, since a stress power $n \neq 1$ gives strains that are nonlinear in the spatial coordinates even if the stresses are linear in the spatial coordinates. For such problems it is frequently necessary to employ approximate solution techniques, such as may be developed by using the nonlinear elastic and plastic analogies presented in Section 9.6.

9.14 ELASTIC, PERFECTLY PLASTIC DEFORMATION OF A THICK-WALLED SPHERE

As a final case in this series, we examine an elastoplastic problem for the thick-walled sphere. The sphere has inner and outer radii of r_i and r_o, respectively. It is subject only to an internal pressure p which can increase monotonically with time. This will be the prescribed traction force system and we shall disregard body forces. Thus it is clear that we have *point symmetry* of geometry and loading. The material will be considered to be isotropic and linear elastic, perfectly plastic. Thus at points in the sphere where the state of stress is below that required for yielding, the strain is obtained from the usual isotropic, compressible Hooke's law. On the other hand, at points where yielding occurs, the strain is the sum of an elastic component and a perfectly plastic component, where in accordance with usual practice the plastic component is incompressible.

Clearly, this study calls for the use of spherical coordinates, and so in Fig. 9.9 we show the spherical coordinate system r, θ, ϕ and the unit vectors $\hat{\epsilon}_r, \hat{\epsilon}_\theta, \hat{\epsilon}_\phi$ in these coordinate directions. Because of the point symmetry of the present problem, the stress, strain, and displacement variables of the problem will depend

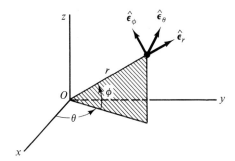

Figure 9.9 Spherical coordinates.

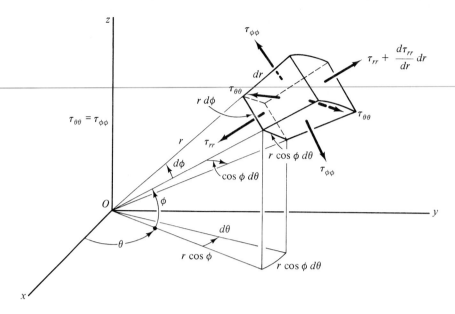

Figure 9.10 Element for spherical coordinates with point symmetry about O.

only on the spatial coordinate r.* Equally clear is the fact that $\tau_{\theta\theta} = \tau_{\phi\phi}$ and that $\tau_{r\theta} = \tau_{\theta\phi} = \tau_{\phi r} = 0$.

We shall first derive the equation of *equilibrium* for this case. Accordingly, we examine the element of the sphere shown in Fig. 9.10. Equilibrium in the direction r requires, on noting the point symmetry, that

$$-\tau_{rr}[(r\,d\phi)(r\,\cos\phi\,d\theta)] + \left[\tau_{rr} + \frac{d\tau_{rr}}{dr}\,dr\right][(r+dr)(d\phi)(r+dr)\,\cos\phi\,d\theta]$$

$$- 2\tau_{\theta\theta}\left[dr(r\,d\phi)\sin\left(\cos\phi\frac{d\theta}{2}\right)\right] - 2\tau_{\phi\phi}\left[dr(r\,\cos\phi\,d\theta)\sin\left(\frac{d\phi}{2}\right)\right] = 0$$

Canceling terms, replacing $\sin(\cos\phi \cdot d\theta/2)$ and $\sin(d\phi/2)$ by $\cos\phi \cdot d\theta/2$ and $d\phi/2$, respectively, and dropping higher-order terms, we then get upon setting $\tau_{\phi\phi} = \tau_{\theta\theta}$

$$\frac{d\tau_{rr}}{dr} = \frac{2}{r}[\tau_{\theta\theta} - \tau_{rr}] \tag{9.168}$$

As for *strains* we have for ε_{rr} the simple obvious result

$$\varepsilon_{rr} = \frac{du_r}{dr} \tag{9.169}$$

Since we cause lateral expansion in the $\hat{\boldsymbol{\epsilon}}_\phi$ direction as a result of radial expansion

---

*For a concise treatment of tensors for spherical and orthogonal curvilinear coordinates in general, see L. E. Malvern, *Introduction to the Mechanics of a Continuous Medium* (Englewood Cliffs, NJ: Prentice-Hall, Inc., 1969), App. II. We shall derive the required results for our special case, since we have not dealt with spherical coordinates up to this point.

in the $\hat{\epsilon}_r$ direction (see Fig. 9.11), we can say for $\varepsilon_{\theta\theta} = \varepsilon_{\phi\phi}$

$$\varepsilon_{\theta\theta} = \varepsilon_{\phi\phi} = \frac{(r+u_r)d\phi - r\,d\phi}{r\,d\phi} = \frac{u_r}{r} \tag{9.170}$$

We can now form a *compatibility* equation by eliminating u_r from the preceding two equations to get

$$\frac{d\varepsilon_{\theta\theta}}{dr} = \frac{1}{r}\left(\varepsilon_{rr} - \varepsilon_{\theta\theta}\right) \tag{9.171}$$

For linear elastic behavior the *constitutive* equations are

$$\varepsilon_{rr} = \frac{1}{E}\left[\tau_{rr} - 2\nu\tau_{\theta\theta}\right]$$

$$\varepsilon_{\theta\theta} = \frac{1}{E}\left[\tau_{\theta\theta}(1-\nu) - \nu\tau_{rr}\right] \tag{9.172}$$

Finally, we shall consider that *yielding* occurs in accordance with the *Mises* criterion. Thus using Eq. (9.29b) we have for this criterion at the onset of yielding

$$(\tau_{rr} - \tau_{\theta\theta})^2 + (\tau_{rr} - \tau_{\phi\phi})^2 + (\tau_{\theta\theta} - \tau_{\phi\phi})^2 = 2Y^2$$

Noting that $\tau_{\theta\theta} = \tau_{\phi\phi}$ this reduces to

$$\tau_{\theta\theta} - \tau_{rr} = \pm Y \tag{9.173}$$

We will soon see that for elastic behavior $\tau_{\theta\theta} > \tau_{rr}$, so we must use the positive value on the right side of Eq. (9.173). Additionally, we note that the yield condition above is also the *Tresca* yield condition [see Eq. (9.32)].

In Problem 9.25 we ask the reader to solve for the purely *elastic* solution to this problem by using the elastic constitutive laws [Eqs.(9.172)], the compatibility equation [Eq. (9.171)] and the equilibrium equation [Eq. (9.168)]. The results obtained

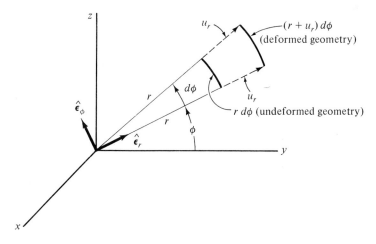

Figure 9.11   Deformation of line segment $r\,d\phi$.

for purely *elastic stress* are

$$\tau_{rr} = C_1 + \frac{C_2}{r^3} \qquad \text{(a)}$$

$$\tau_{\theta\theta} = \tau_{\phi\phi} = C_1 - \frac{C_2}{2r^3} \qquad \text{(b)}$$

(9.174)

We now apply the boundary conditions

$$\tau_{rr}(r_i) = -p$$

$$\tau_{rr}(r_o) = 0$$

(9.175)

This yields

$$C_1 = \frac{pr_i^3}{r_o^3 - r_i^3}$$

$$C_2 = -\frac{pr_i^3 r_o^3}{r_o^3 - r_i^3}$$

(9.176)

We thus have the complete elastic solution for stress. Since C_2 is negative, we see that $\tau_{\theta\theta} > \tau_{rr}$. The elastic displacement then follows directly from these stresses and Eqs. (9.170) and (9.172) as

$$u_r = r\varepsilon_{\theta\theta} = \frac{1}{3K}\left(C_1 - \frac{3K}{4G}\frac{C_2}{r^3}\right)r$$

$$= \frac{p}{3K}\frac{r_i^3}{r_o^3 - r_i^3}\left[\left(\frac{r_o}{r}\right)^3\frac{3K}{4G} + 1\right]r$$

(9.177)

Note that we have expressed E and ν in terms of G and K (see Table 5.1).

To get to the plastic domain we first form $\tau_{\theta\theta} - \tau_{rr}$ from our elastic solution in anticipation of using the Mises (or, equivalently, Tresca in this case) criterion. Thus we have, from Eqs. (9.174) and (9.176),

$$\tau_{\theta\theta} - \tau_{rr} = \frac{3}{2}\left(\frac{r_o^3}{r_i^3 - r_o^3}\right)\left(\frac{r_i}{r}\right)^3 p$$

(9.178)

Clearly, $\tau_{\theta\theta} - \tau_{rr}$ reaches its maximum value at the inner fibers of the sphere where $r = r_i$. Thus, when this value reaches Y as a result of increasing pressure, yielding will start to set in there as indicated by our chosen criterion (9.173). This required pressure is accordingly found from Eq. (9.178) by setting the left side equal to Y and r equal to r_i. Thus the *limiting pressure* for purely elastic behavior, which we denote as p_e, is given as

$$p_e = \frac{2}{3}\frac{(r_i^3 - r_o^3)}{r_o^3}Y$$

(9.179)

Our next task is to determine stresses and displacements in the *elastic zone*, defined by the interval $r \geq R$, for pressures p *exceeding* p_e. We need only go back to Eqs. (9.174) and apply the following boundary conditions to obtain C_1 and C_2:

$$\tau_{\theta\theta} - \tau_{rr} = Y \qquad \text{at } r = R \qquad \text{(a)}$$

$$\tau_{rr} = 0 \qquad \text{at } r = r_o \qquad \text{(b)}$$

(9.180)

Inserting these expressions obtained for C_1 and C_2 into Eq. (9.174) and the first of Eqs. (9.177), we obtain the following results in the *elastic zone, $r \geq R$:*

$$\tau_{rr} = -\frac{2}{3} Y \left(\frac{R}{r}\right)^3 \left[1 - \left(\frac{r}{r_o}\right)^3\right] \qquad \text{(a)}$$

$$\tau_{\theta\theta} = \tau_{\phi\phi} = \frac{1}{3} Y \left(\frac{R}{r}\right)^3 \left[1 + 2\left(\frac{r}{r_o}\right)^3\right] \qquad \text{(b)} \qquad \text{(9.181)}$$

$$u_r = \frac{2Y}{9K} \left(\frac{R}{r}\right)^3 \left[\frac{3K}{4G} + \left(\frac{r}{r_o}\right)^3\right] r \qquad \text{(c)}$$

Next, we investigate the *elastic, perfectly plastic zone,* defined by the interval $r \leq R$. Here we see that the yield condition prevails throughout, so we can replace $\tau_{\theta\theta} - \tau_{rr}$ in the *equilibrium* equation (9.168) by Y in accordance with Eq. (9.180a). We thus have for equilibrium in the elastic, plastic zone

$$\frac{d\tau_{rr}}{dr} = \frac{2Y}{r} \qquad \text{(9.182)}$$

We may integrate this equation to get

$$\tau_{rr} = 2Y \ln r + C_3$$

At $r = r_i$ we have $\tau_{rr} = -p$, so that we may determine C_3 directly as

$$C_3 = -p - 2Y \ln r_i$$

The *stresses* in the *elastic, perfectly plastic zone* are then fully established, and we express them as follows:

$$\tau_{rr} = 2Y \ln \frac{r}{r_i} - p \qquad \text{(a)}$$

$$\tau_{\theta\theta} = \tau_{\phi\phi} = Y + \tau_{rr} = Y\left(1 + 2 \ln \frac{r}{r_i}\right) - p \qquad \text{(b)}$$

(9.183)

Needed yet is the means to determine the value of R marking the transition from linear elastic, perfectly plastic to linear elastic behavior. We find the proper value of R by ensuring the continuity of the stress τ_{rr} as one passes from one domain to the other. Thus setting $r = R$ in Eq. (9.181a) and in Eq. (9.183a) and equating the resulting stresses, τ_{rr}, we get from this continuity requirement:

$$2Y\left\{\frac{1}{3}\left[1 - \left(\frac{R}{r_o}\right)^3\right] + \ln \frac{R}{r_i}\right\} = p \qquad \text{(9.184)}$$

Hence for a given p we can determine R by a trial-and-error procedure. If R should be large enough to equal r_o, we have complete elastic, plastic deformation for the entire sphere. We see from Eq. (9.184) that the required pressure for this extreme, which we denote as p_p, is

$$p_p = 2Y \ln \frac{r_o}{r_i} \qquad \text{(9.185)}$$

Finally, we turn to a determination of u_r in the elastic, plastic zone. As noted previously, the strain in the elastic, plastic zone contains a *compressible* elastic component and an *incompressible* plastic component. Accordingly, the *bulk* behavior obeys the usual elastic relation

$$(\varepsilon_{rr} + 2\varepsilon_{\theta\theta}) = \frac{1}{3K}(\tau_{rr} + 2\tau_{\theta\theta})$$ (9.186)

Employing Eqs. (9.169) and (9.170) on the left side of this equation and Eqs. (9.183) on the right side, we have

$$\frac{du_r}{dr} + \frac{2u_r}{r} = \frac{1}{3K}\left[2Y\ln\frac{r}{r_i} - p + 2Y\left(1 + 2\ln\frac{r}{r_i}\right) - 2p\right]$$

This equation may be rewritten as

$$\frac{1}{r^2}\frac{d}{dr}(r^2 u_r) = \frac{2Y}{3K}\left(1 + 3\ln\frac{r}{r_i} - \frac{3}{2}\frac{p}{Y}\right)$$

Multiplying by r^2 and integrating then gives the displacement

$$u_r = \frac{1}{r^2}\frac{2Y}{3K}\left[\left(\ln\frac{r}{r_i} - \frac{p}{2Y}\right)r^3 + C_4\right]$$ (9.187)

Go back to Eq. (9.184) and use it to replace $p/2Y$ in Eq. (9.187) to obtain

$$u_r = \frac{2Y}{3K}\left\{r\ln\frac{r}{R} - \frac{r}{3}\left[1 - \left(\frac{R}{r_o}\right)^3\right] + \frac{C_4}{r^2}\right\}$$ (9.188)

Meanwhile, for u_r in the elastic zone we have Eq. (9.181c). Set $r = R$ and equate Eqs. (9.188) and (9.181c), thus ensuring the continuity of u_r between the two zones. We get

$$\frac{2Y}{3K}\left\{-\frac{R}{3}\left[1 - \left(\frac{R}{r_o}\right)^3\right] + \frac{C_4}{R^2}\right\} = \frac{2Y}{9K}\left[\frac{3K}{4G} + \left(\frac{R}{r_o}\right)^3\right]R$$ (9.189)

Canceling terms and solving for C_4, we then get

$$C_4 = \left(\frac{K}{4G} + \frac{1}{3}\right)R^3$$ (9.190)

We can now give u_r in the elastic, plastic zone by incorporating Eq. (9.190) into Eq. (9.187). Thus we finally have

$$u_r = \frac{1}{r^2}\frac{2Y}{3K}\left[\left(\ln\frac{r}{r_i} - \frac{p}{2Y}\right)r^3 + \left(\frac{K}{4G} + \frac{1}{3}\right)R^3\right]$$ (9.191)

This is as far as we shall take this problem. One can find in the literature detailed discussions of the thick-walled sphere, including thermal effects as well as discussions including strain hardening in the plastic zone.*

We thus conclude our series of closed-form solutions of boundary value problems for some important constitutive laws.

---

*For instance, see *Plasticity: Theory and Application* by A. Mendelson (Melbourne, FL: R.E. Krieger Publishing Co., reprint edition, 1983), Chap. 8.

9.15 CLOSURE

We thus come to the end of Parts I and II of the book, covering the fundamentals and constitutive laws underlying the study of elastic, viscoelastic, plastic, and viscoplastic materials. The basic equations, constitutive laws, and geometrical considerations were developed at various places in the first eight chapters. These efforts culminated in this chapter in formulating appropriate boundary value problems. We ended by solving some simple problems rigorously using the full theories presented.

In Part III we focus our attention on some simple but important geometries. Certain simplifications can be made as to the manner of the deformation for these geometries. We call these studies strength of materials or structural mechanics. In some instances these simplifications will turn out to be rigorously correct, and then the solutions obtained will be "exact." We shall not use energy or finite element methods in this book but refer you to other books on these important topics.* We will merely point out here that for elastic materials (not necessarily linear elastic) equilibrium is assured by extremizing the *total potential energy functional* with respect to *compatible* deformations consistent with constraints and related to stress via an *elastic constitutive law*. The extremal strain field then yields through the constitutive law the correct stress distribution. Or we can alternatively proceed for the foregoing types of materials to extremize the *complementary energy functional* with respect to stress fields that satisfy *equilibrium* in order to satisfy the *compatibility equations*. The extremal stress is in this case the solution to the problem. Thus we replace a boundary value problem by one of extremizing a functional. The powerful method of finite elements is based on this procedure.

The example in this chapter on pure bending of an elastic beam will be the starting point of Chapter 10, on beam theory.

PROBLEMS

9.1. In Fig. P9.1 we have shown a differential volume element in cylindrical coordinates. The stresses on all faces have been labeled, and in addition, body forces B_r, B_θ, B_z act in the volume. Using this figure, obtain the equations of equilibrium in cylindrical coordinates given below:

$$\frac{\tau_{rr} - \tau_{\theta\theta}}{r} + \frac{\partial \tau_{rr}}{\partial r} + \frac{1}{r}\frac{\partial \tau_{r\theta}}{\partial \theta} + \frac{\partial \tau_{rz}}{\partial z} + B_r = 0 \qquad \text{(a)}$$

$$\frac{2\tau_{\theta r}}{r} + \frac{\partial \tau_{\theta r}}{\partial r} + \frac{1}{r}\frac{\partial \tau_{\theta\theta}}{\partial \theta} + \frac{\partial \tau_{\theta z}}{\partial z} + B_\theta = 0 \qquad \text{(b)}$$

$$\frac{\tau_{zr}}{r} + \frac{\partial \tau_{zr}}{\partial r} + \frac{1}{r}\frac{\partial \tau_{z\theta}}{\partial \theta} + \frac{\partial \tau_{zz}}{\partial z} + B_z = 0 \qquad \text{(c)}$$

---

*For example, see I. H. Shames and C. L. Dym, *Energy and Finite Elements in Structural Mechanics* (New York: Hemisphere Publishing Corp., 1985).

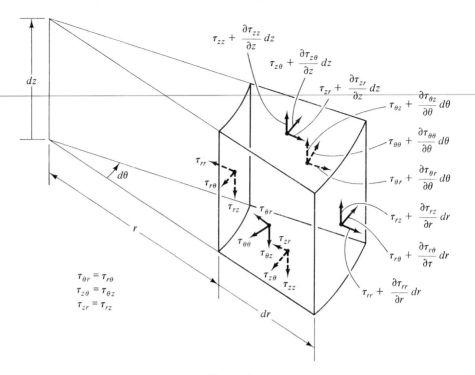

$$\tau_{\theta r} = \tau_{r\theta}$$
$$\tau_{z\theta} = \tau_{\theta z}$$
$$\tau_{zr} = \tau_{rz}$$

Figure P9.1

9.2. Using symbolic notation, equilibrium equation (9.1) may be expressed as

$$\mathbf{\nabla} \cdot \mathbf{T}^{(i)} + \mathbf{B} = \mathbf{0}$$

where $\mathbf{\nabla}$ is the gradient vector operator, $\mathbf{T}^{(i)}$ is the traction vector acting on a coordinate plane with unit normal vector $\hat{\mathbf{\epsilon}}_{(i)}$, and $\mathbf{B}$ is the body force vector. This form of equilibrium is valid for *any* coordinate system and is thus called the *invariant* form.

Use the invariant form above to obtain the equilibrium equations in cylindrical coordinates (see Problem 9.1). *Note*: It will be necessary to employ the following identities:

$$\mathbf{\nabla} \cdot \mathbf{T}^{(i)} = (\hat{\mathbf{\epsilon}}_{(i)} \cdot \mathbf{\nabla} + \mathbf{\nabla} \cdot \hat{\mathbf{\epsilon}}_{(i)})\mathbf{T}^{(i)}$$

$$\mathbf{\nabla} = \hat{\mathbf{\epsilon}}_r \frac{\partial}{\partial r} + \hat{\mathbf{\epsilon}}_\theta \frac{1}{r} \frac{\partial}{\partial \theta} + \hat{\mathbf{\epsilon}}_z \frac{\partial}{\partial z}$$

$$\frac{\partial \hat{\mathbf{\epsilon}}_r}{\partial \theta} = \hat{\mathbf{\epsilon}}_\theta \qquad \frac{\partial \hat{\mathbf{\epsilon}}_\theta}{\partial r} = -\hat{\mathbf{\epsilon}}_r$$

9.3. The first law of thermodynamics may be expressed as

$$\frac{dE}{dt} = \dot{Q} + \dot{W}$$

where E is the total energy of the system, $\dot{Q}$ the rate of heat *input*, and $\dot{W}$ the rate of work done on the system by surface traction $T_i^{(\nu)}$ and body force B_i. Let the domain of the volume be D, which is bounded by surface S.

Consider a linear elastic material under adiabatic conditions, in which case

$\dot{Q} \equiv 0$ and dE/dt is composed entirely of kinetic and strain energies. Prove that under these conditions, the first law is equivalent to the equation of motion

$$\frac{\partial \tau_{ji}}{\partial x_j} + B_i = \rho \frac{dV_i}{dt}$$

[*Hint:* First express the first law in global form (i.e., "in the large"), and then employ Gauss' theorem to obtain the desired result.]

9.4. For a thermodynamic system, the second law of thermodynamics may be expressed as

$$\dot{S} \geq \frac{\dot{Q}}{T}$$

where $\dot{S}$ is the rate of change in total entropy for a process, $\dot{Q}$ the rate of heat input, and T the absolute temperature. The equality sign applies for an ideal *reversible* process. Furthermore, the right-hand side of the expression above may be separated into two parts:

$$\frac{\dot{Q}}{T} = -\oint_S \frac{q_i \nu_i}{T} \, dA + \iiint_D \frac{\rho r}{T} \, dv$$

where q_i is the heat *efflux* vector on the surface S with unit normal ν_i, and r is a distributed heat source in the domain D. Use the formulation above to derive the *Clausius–Duhem inequality*

$$\frac{ds}{dt} \geq \frac{r}{T} - \frac{1}{\rho} \frac{\partial}{\partial x_i} \left(\frac{q_i}{T} \right)$$

where s is the specific entropy (i.e., $S = \iiint_D s\rho \, dv$).

9.5. We shall develop the components of strain in terms of the displacement field for cylindrical coordinates. Let u_r represent the displacement component in the radial direction, u_θ the component in the transverse direction, and u_z the component in the axial direction. Thus

$$\mathbf{u} = u_r \hat{\epsilon}_r + u_\theta \hat{\epsilon}_\theta + u_z \hat{\epsilon}_z$$

Consider the polar coordinate element shown in Fig. P9.5. For element ab in the radial direction, show that

$$\varepsilon_{rr} = \frac{\partial u_r}{\partial r} \tag{a}$$

Now consider element ad. Show that as a result of displacement in the tangential direction as well as in the radial direction

$$\varepsilon_{\theta\theta} = \frac{1}{r} \frac{\partial u_r}{\partial \theta} + \frac{u_r}{r} \tag{b}$$

Finally, consider segments ab and ad. In the deformed state, point a is moved to a'. The segments have rotated α and β from their original orientations. Explain why the shear angle is not $\alpha + \beta$, but the sum of the angles shown shaded. Then show that

$$\varepsilon_{r\theta} = \frac{1}{2} \left(\frac{\partial u_\theta}{\partial r} + \frac{1}{r} \frac{\partial u_r}{\partial \theta} - \frac{u_\theta}{r} \right) \tag{c}$$

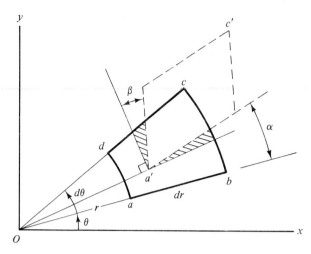

Figure P9.5

By proceeding in similar fashion, obtain the following expressions for ε_{zz}, ε_{zr}, and $\varepsilon_{z\theta}$:

$$\varepsilon_{zz} = \frac{\partial u_z}{\partial z} \tag{d}$$

$$\varepsilon_{zr} = \frac{1}{2}\left(\frac{\partial u_r}{\partial z} + \frac{\partial u_z}{\partial r}\right) \tag{e}$$

$$\varepsilon_{z\theta} = \frac{1}{2}\left(\frac{\partial u_\theta}{\partial z} + \frac{1}{r}\frac{\partial u_z}{\partial \theta}\right) \tag{f}$$

9.6. The compatibility relations, referred to cylindrical coordinates, are given as follows:

$$\frac{2}{r}\frac{\partial^2 \varepsilon_{z\theta}}{\partial z\,\partial\theta} - \frac{1}{r^2}\frac{\partial^2 \varepsilon_{zz}}{\partial\theta^2} - \frac{\partial^2 \varepsilon_{\theta\theta}}{\partial z^2} + \frac{2}{r}\frac{\partial \varepsilon_{rz}}{\partial z} - \frac{1}{r}\frac{\partial \varepsilon_{zz}}{\partial r} = 0 \tag{a}$$

$$2\frac{\partial^2 \varepsilon_{rz}}{\partial r\,\partial z} - \frac{\partial^2 \varepsilon_{rr}}{\partial z^2} - \frac{\partial^2 \varepsilon_{zz}}{\partial r^2} = 0 \tag{b}$$

$$\frac{2}{r}\frac{\partial^2 \varepsilon_{\theta r}}{\partial\theta\,\partial r} - \frac{\partial^2 \varepsilon_{\theta\theta}}{\partial r^2} - \frac{1}{r^2}\frac{\partial^2 \varepsilon_{rr}}{\partial\theta^2} + \frac{1}{r}\frac{\partial \varepsilon_{rr}}{\partial r} + \frac{2}{r^2}\frac{\partial \varepsilon_{r\theta}}{\partial\theta} - \frac{2}{r}\frac{\partial \varepsilon_{\theta\theta}}{\partial r} = 0 \tag{c}$$

$$\frac{1}{r}\frac{\partial^2 \varepsilon_{zz}}{\partial r\,\partial\theta} - \frac{\partial}{\partial z}\left[\frac{1}{r}\frac{\partial \varepsilon_{zr}}{\partial\theta} + \frac{\partial \varepsilon_{\theta z}}{\partial r} - \frac{\partial \varepsilon_{\theta r}}{\partial z}\right] + \frac{1}{r}\frac{\partial \varepsilon_{z\theta}}{\partial z} - \frac{1}{r^2}\frac{\partial \varepsilon_{zz}}{\partial\theta} = 0 \tag{d}$$

$$\frac{1}{r}\frac{\partial^2 \varepsilon_{rr}}{\partial\theta\,\partial z} - \frac{\partial}{\partial r}\left[\frac{\partial \varepsilon_{r\theta}}{\partial z} + \frac{1}{r}\frac{\partial \varepsilon_{zr}}{\partial\theta} - \frac{\partial \varepsilon_{z\theta}}{\partial r}\right] - \frac{2}{r}\frac{\partial \varepsilon_{r\theta}}{\partial z} + \frac{1}{r}\frac{\partial \varepsilon_{z\theta}}{\partial r} - \frac{1}{r^2}\varepsilon_{z\theta} = 0 \tag{e}$$

$$\frac{\partial^2 \varepsilon_{\theta\theta}}{\partial z\,\partial r} - \frac{1}{r}\frac{\partial}{\partial\theta}\left[\frac{\partial \varepsilon_{\theta z}}{\partial r} + \frac{\partial \varepsilon_{r\theta}}{\partial z} - \frac{1}{r}\frac{\partial \varepsilon_{rz}}{\partial\theta}\right] - \frac{1}{r^2}\frac{\partial \varepsilon_{\theta z}}{\partial\theta} - \frac{1}{r}\frac{\partial}{\partial z}(\varepsilon_{rr} - \varepsilon_{\theta\theta}) = 0 \tag{f}$$

Verify that the first and the last of these equations are correct by substituting in the strain displacement relations given in Problem 9.5.

9.7. In Chapter 5 we presented the constitutive law for a linear, isotropic, *thermoelastic* material as (see Section 5.6)

$$\varepsilon_{ij} = \frac{1+\nu}{E}\tau_{ij} - \frac{\nu}{E}\tau_{kk}\delta_{ij} + \alpha\,\Delta T\,\delta_{ij}$$

and in inverted form as

$$\tau_{ij} = 2G\,\varepsilon_{ij} + \lambda\,\varepsilon_{kk}\,\delta_{ij} - \beta\,\Delta T\,\delta_{ij}$$

where

$$\beta = (3\lambda + 2G)\alpha$$

Show that the Navier equation (9.37) for this material becomes

$$(\lambda + G)u_{j,ji} + Gu_{i,jj} - \beta(\Delta T)_{,i} + B_i = 0$$

9.8. In symbolic notation Eqs. (9.44) and (9.47) may be expressed as

$$\nabla^2 \bar{\tau} = 0$$

$$\nabla^2 \tau_{ij} + \left(\frac{3}{1+\nu}\right)\frac{\partial^2 \bar{\tau}}{\partial x_i\,\partial x_j} = 0$$

where $\bar{\tau}$ is the bulk stress. Prove that

$$\nabla^2 \bar{\varepsilon} = 0, \qquad \nabla^4 \tau_{ij} = 0, \qquad \nabla^4 \varepsilon_{ij} = 0$$

That is, if body forces are absent, the bulk stress and cubical dilatation are *harmonic*, whereas the stress and strain tensors are *biharmonic*.

9.9. Prove that if the body force B_i is present, Eqs. (9.44) and (9.47) generalize to

$$\tau_{ii,rr} = -\frac{1+\nu}{1-\nu}B_{i,i}$$

$$\tau_{pq,rr} + \frac{1}{1+\nu}\tau_{rr,pq} + \frac{\nu}{1-\nu}B_{r,r}\,\delta_{pq} + B_{p,q} + B_{q,p} = 0$$

(*Note:* The first of these two equations may be obtained from a contraction of the second equation.)

9.10. (a) Let P and Q be the linear differential operators

$$P = \sum_{i=0}^{m} p_i \frac{\partial^i}{\partial t^i} \qquad Q = \sum_{j=0}^{n} q_j \frac{\partial^j}{\partial t^j}$$

After taking the Laplace transform with respect to t with homogeneous initial conditions, these operators become the polynomials in s:

$$\bar{P}(s) = \sum_{i=0}^{m} p_i s^i \qquad \bar{Q}(s) = \sum_{j=0}^{n} q_j s^j$$

Prove the following identity:

$$\overline{PQ} = \bar{P}\,\bar{Q}$$

(b) If we use constitutive laws expressed in terms of the axial and lateral behaviors for tensile loading, then for linear viscoelastic materials we have

$$Q^E P^V \varepsilon_{ij} = P^E(P^V + Q^V)\tau_{ij} - P^E Q^V \tau_{kk}\,\delta_{ij}$$

and for linear elastic materials we have

$$\varepsilon_{ij} = \frac{1+\nu}{E}\tau_{ij} - \frac{\nu}{E}\tau_{kk}\,\delta_{ij}$$

Using the identity in (a) prove that if we set

$$E = \frac{\overline{Q}^E(s)}{\overline{P}^E(s)}, \qquad \nu = \frac{\overline{Q}^V(s)}{\overline{P}^V(s)}$$

we obtain the linear viscoelastic–linear elastic correspondence principle.

9.11. A nonlinear elastic constitutive law was given by Eq. (9.71) as

$$\varepsilon_{ij} = CJ_2^m s_{ij}$$

(a) Consider a one-dimensional stress state in which τ_{xx} is the only nonzero stress. Express ε_{xx} and ε_{yy} as functions of τ_{xx}. Show that Poisson's ratio ν is equal to 0.5.

(b) Verify that for $m = 0$ the relation above is equivalent to isotropic Hooke's law for an incompressible elastic material.

9.12. Using definitions (5.57) in Chapter 5, obtain expressions for the strain energy density $\mathcal{U}(\varepsilon_{ij})$ and the complementary energy density $\mathcal{U}^*(\tau_{ij})$ for a nonlinear elastic material governed by Eq. (9.71). Verify that for $m = 0$ your results simplify to the usual expressions for incompressible linear elastic material.

9.13. Consider nonlinear elastic constitutive law (9.71), where the stress power m is a nonnegative integer. Prove that for this material the integrand in energy integral (9.77) is the $(m + 1)$ power of a positive definite quadratic form.

9.14. For the linear elastic uniqueness theorem of Section 9.7, it was postulated that $G > 0$ and $K > 0$. Using Table 5.1 in Chapter 5, show that this implies that $E > 0$ and $-1 < \nu < \frac{1}{2}$. Assuming that E is always nonzero and finite, also show that $K \to \infty$ as $\nu \to \frac{1}{2}$ and $G \to \infty$ as $\nu \to -1$. What can you say about the range of the Lamé parameter λ? Consider the simple tension, shear, and pressure tests, and discuss the physical implications of the limiting cases $\nu \to \frac{1}{2}$ and $\nu \to -1$.

9.15. The proof of uniqueness for nonlinear viscous power law (9.65) begins with the energy integral

$$I = \iiint_D \tau_{ij}\dot{\varepsilon}_{ij}\,dv = \iiint_D s_{ij}\dot{\varepsilon}_{ij}\,dv$$

where the form on the right follows from incompressibility.

(a) For the *difference* solution, first express $s_{ij}^d\,\dot{\varepsilon}_{ij}^d$ in terms of the invariants

$$J_2^{(1)} = \tfrac{1}{2}s_{ij}^{(1)}\,s_{ij}^{(1)}$$
$$J_2^{(2)} = \tfrac{1}{2}s_{ij}^{(2)}\,s_{ij}^{(2)}$$
$$J_2^d = \tfrac{1}{2}s_{ij}^d\,s_{ij}^d$$

(b) Then prove $s_{ij}^d \equiv 0$, from which the uniqueness of stress and displacement follow.

9.16. In Chapters 12 and 13 we will introduce the Airy stress function Φ. It will be shown that if body forces are absent and Φ satisfies the biharmonic equation

$$\nabla^4\Phi = 0$$

then Φ is the solution of some plane strain or two-dimensional plane stress problem.

As an example,* show that the following stress function is a proper function for a simply supported rectangular beam carrying a uniform load q_0, as shown in Fig. P9.16.

---

* Numerous examples of this type are developed by inverse methods in S. Timoshenko and J. N. Goodier, *Theory of Elasticity* (New York: McGraw-Hill Book Company, 1951).

$$\Phi = -\frac{q_0}{4}x^2 + \frac{3q_0}{4h}x^2y - \frac{q_0}{h^3}x^2y^3 + \frac{q_0}{h^3}\left(L^2 - \frac{1}{10}h^2\right)y^3 + \frac{q_0}{5h^3}y^5$$

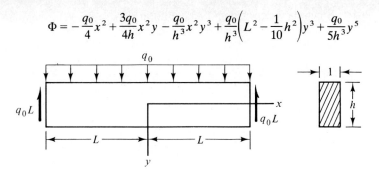

Figure P9.16

9.17. In the hanging elastic bar problem of Section 9.10, the function $f(x,y)$ was shown to satisfy [see Eqs. (9.93) and (9.96)]

$$\frac{\partial^2 f}{\partial x^2} = \frac{\nu\gamma}{E}, \qquad \frac{\partial^2 f}{\partial y^2} = \frac{\nu\gamma}{E}, \qquad \frac{\partial^2 f}{\partial x\,\partial y} = 0$$

Derive the following expression for f [see Eq. (9.100)]:

$$f = \frac{\nu\gamma}{2E}(x^2 + y^2) + C_4 x + C_5 y + C_6$$

[*Hint:* Integrate these three conditions. First show that the third condition precludes the presence of mixed (i.e., xy) terms. Then compare the results from the first two conditions.]

9.18. The displacement field for the elastic bar hanging under its own weight [see Eqs. (9.106)] may be written in *nondimensional* form as

$$\bar{u} = -\nu\bar{x}\bar{z}$$

$$\bar{v} = -\nu\bar{y}\bar{z}$$

$$\bar{w} = \bar{z}^2 + \nu\bar{x}^2 + \nu\bar{y}^2 - 1$$

How have $\bar{u}, \bar{v}, \bar{w}, \bar{x}, \bar{y}, \bar{z}$ been defined? Let the cross section be circular of radius R and let $l/R = 4$, as shown in Fig. P9.18. Compute the nondimensional displacements of points a, b, c, d, e for $\nu = \frac{1}{3}$, and sketch the deformed geometries of the supported and free ends. Note in particular the *directions* of the displacements. Show that horizontal plane surfaces deform into paraboloids of revolution *if* we neglect the higher-order contributions due to $\bar{u}$ and $\bar{v}$.

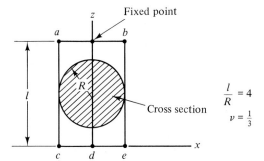

$$\frac{l}{R} = 4$$

$$\nu = \frac{1}{3}$$

Figure P9.18

9.19. An elastic bar of length l and uniform cross section A is rotating with angular speed ω rad/sec about the y axis (see Fig. P9.19).

    (a) Using d'Alembert's principle, convert this dynamic problem to an equivalent static problem, and show that the "body force" is given by $B_x = \rho\omega^2 x$, $B_y = 0$, $B_z = 0$.

    (b) Assume that the stress state in this problem is given by $\tau_{xx} = (\rho\omega^2/2)$ $(l^2 - x^2)$, $\tau_{yy} = \tau_{zz} = \tau_{xy} = \tau_{yz} = \tau_{zx} = 0$. Verify that this stress state satisfies the equations of equilibrium and the traction boundary conditions.

    (c) Compute the strains and show that these strains do *not* satisfy compatibility unless we set $\nu = 0$. How do you explain this apparent contradiction?

    (d) Setting $\nu = 0$, determine the displacements u, v, w.

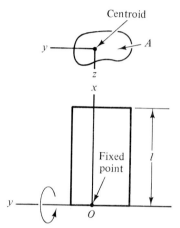

Figure P9.19

9.20. A solid three-dimensional linear elastic body is submerged in a fluid such that every point on its surface is subjected to uniform hydrostatic pressure p (see Fig. P9.20). What is the state of stress at an interior point? Using this state of stress, determine the displacements u, v, w. Set $u = v = w = \omega_x = \omega_y = \omega_z = 0$ at $x = y = z = 0$. Neglect the body forces.

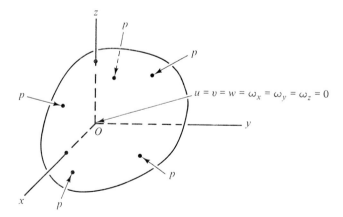

Figure P9.20

9.21. Consider a linear elastic beam of *arbitrary* cross section R, subjected to pure bending M_z about the z axis (see Fig. P9.21). Prove that the flexure formula

$$\tau_{xx} = -\frac{M_z y}{I_{zz}}$$

is *exact* if O is at the centroid and yz are principal axes.

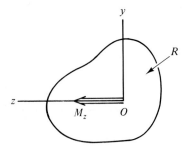

Figure P9.21

9.22. In Section 9.12 we solved the hanging bar problem for a material that is Maxwell under distortion and exhibits elastic compressibility for bulk behavior. Redo this problem for a material that is *Kelvin* under distortion and elastic in bulk behavior:

$$P^K = 1, \qquad Q^K = 3K$$
$$P^G = 1, \qquad Q^G = \zeta D + 2G$$

(*Note:* Obtain the complete time-dependent solutions as well as the limiting behaviors. Also discuss the special case of *incompressible* behavior in bulk.)

9.23. In Section 9.12 we considered the problem of a linear viscoelastic beam under time-dependent pure bending. Consider the same viscoelastic material, but instead of Eq. (9.149) for the bending moment $M(t)$, now consider the linearly decreasing moment shown in Fig. P9.23. Using the Laplace transform limit theorems, find the initial and long-time asymptotic solutions for the displacements with this $M(t)$.

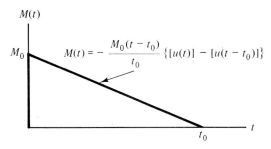

$$M(t) = -\frac{M_0(t - t_0)}{t_0} \{[u(t)] - [u(t - t_0)]\}$$

Figure P9.23

9.24. Consider the prismatic bar hanging under its own weight as shown in Fig. 9.4. But now let the bar be of *nonlinear viscous* material, i.e.,

$$\dot{\varepsilon}_{ij} = C J_2^m s_{ij}$$

Assume as a *possible* stress distribution

$$\tau_{zz} = \gamma z, \qquad \tau_{xx} = \tau_{yy} = \tau_{xy} = \tau_{yz} = \tau_{zx} = 0$$

which satisfies the equations of equilibrium and the boundary conditions.

(a) Compute the strain rates and show that compatibility is *not* satisfied unless we set $m = 0$. What do you think is wrong with the assumed stress distribution above if $m > 0$?

(b) Setting $m = 0$, determine the velocities $\dot{u}, \dot{v}, \dot{w}$.

9.25. Obtain the linear elastic stress solution (9.174) for the thick-walled sphere problem considered in Section 9.14. Use Eqs. (9.172) for the constitutive laws, Eq. (9.171) for compatibility, and Eq. (9.168) for equilibrium.

9.26. Consider again the *elastoplastic* thick-walled sphere problem of Section 9.14, but now with *external* pressure applied at $r = r_o$. Thus boundary conditions (9.175) are replaced by

$$\tau_{rr}(r_i) = 0$$

$$\tau_{rr}(r_o) = -p$$

For $p > p_e$ determine the stresses τ_{rr}, $\tau_{\theta\theta}$ and the displacement u_r for this problem.

Part III

Application to Simple Structural Members

Chapter 10

Flexure of Beams

10.1 INTRODUCTION

In this chapter we consider beams whose material behavior may be linear elastic, linear viscoelastic, nonlinear viscous, and linear elastic, perfectly plastic. Such material models not only represent the behavior of a large number of actual materials, but are also simple enough to permit us to obtain closed-form solutions. We shall restrict our attention to *small deformation* and *quasi-static* loads, that is, loads that are either independent of time or vary so slowly with time that inertial effects may be ignored.

We have already examined the linear elastic beam under static *pure bending* in Section 9.11, and we found that the familiar flexure formula $\tau_{xx} = -My/I$ gave the *exact* stress distribution. (In Appendix IV we prove that the flexure formula is also exact for a linear elastic material when the bending moment is a linear function of position along the beam.) You will recall [see Fig. 10.1(a)] that the longitudinal axis x passed through the centroid of the cross section, and also that axes y, z were principal axes (see Problem 9.21) of the cross section (i.e., $I_{yz} = 0$). Also, in the flexure formula, $I = I_{zz}$ and the couple moment M acts in the xy plane. Furthermore, the strain ε_{xx} was found to be

$$\varepsilon_{xx} = -\frac{y}{R} = -y\kappa \tag{10.1}$$

where, for small deformation, R was the constant radius of curvature equal to EI/M and κ was the constant curvature. This classical result stipulates that for pure bending of a beam *plane sections remain plane* during deformation. Also, x is along the so-called *neutral* surface on which $\varepsilon_{xx} = 0$.

Condition (10.1) on the axial strain ε_{xx} is the foundation of the so-called *Euler–Bernoulli* theory of elastic bending. It will be instructive to investigate the

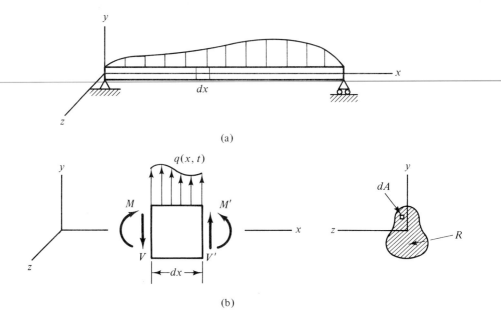

Figure 10.1 Beam element showing positive variables.

relation of this condition to the axial displacement u. If we stipulate that u be a *linear* function of y at a given cross section $x = x_0$ [i.e., $u = f(x)y$ where $f(x)$ is some function of x], then clearly plane sections remain plane during deformation. It immediately follows by simple *differentiation* that $\varepsilon_{xx} = \partial u/\partial x = [df(x)/dx]\,y$, which brings us back to Eq. (10.1) with $1/R = -df(x)/dx$. [It is for this reason that we refer to Eq. (10.1) as the "plane sections remain plane" condition.] Now we have reminded you that for the case of *pure bending* of an isotropic elastic beam, the plane sections remain plane condition (i.e., $\varepsilon_{xx} = -y/R$) yields via *integration* of the strain-displacement equations the axial displacement $u = -xy/R$ [see Eq. (9.128)]. Since this expression for u is *linear* in y at a fixed value of x, it is clear that in this case plane sections do in fact remain plane. However, we must point out that if we follow this *converse* procedure of assuming that ε_{xx} is linear in y and then *integrating* the strain-displacement equations to determine u, it does *not necessarily* follow that u is also linear in y. An example of this is seen in Appendix IV, where as noted above we prove that the flexure formula is exact when the bending moment is a *linear* function in x. It then follows from Hooke's law that ε_{xx} is linear in y, but it does *not* also follow that u is linear in y unless we set the bending moment equal to a constant. Thus plane sections *do not* in general remain plane even if the flexure formula is satisfied, unless we require *in addition* that the bending moment be independent of x.

In Part A of the chapter we review the Euler–Bernoulli theory of bending for linear elastic materials under arbitrarily distributed transverse load, in which case the flexure formula and deformation equation (10.1) are in general only approximate relations. In Parts B and C we then go to linear viscoelastic beams and nonlinear viscous beams, respectively. Finally, in Part D we consider plastic deformation of beams with the work hardening neglected. In all four sections we shall be concerned primarily with the longitudinal stress distribution τ_{xx} and the lateral deflection v_0 of the longitudinal x axis of the beam. Furthermore, the beam cross sections will all have at least one longitudinal plane of symmetry (i.e., xy) and there will be vertical loading in that plane of symmetry. Symmetry relative to plane xy clearly ensures that y, z are principal axes. *The basic approach in all four parts is to assume that the "plane sections remain plane" assumption [i.e., Eq. (10.1)] is at least approximately valid.* * The location of the longitudinal axis x and the form of the stress distribution are then *derived*; they are not assumed a priori. However, in accordance with Eq. (10.1), ε_{xx} must always vanish along the x axis. This approach is called the *technical theory of beams*.

In Fig. 10.1(b) we show at an instant of time t an element of any of the beams that we shall be studying, in order to give the positive directions of loading $q(x,t)$, shear force $V(x,t)$, and bending moment $M(x,t)$. Note that in conformity with the sign convention for stress set forth in Chapter 2, positive V and M have a positive sense on a positive area and a negative sense on a negative area. In all cases you may easily deduce that the following equations of equilibrium (no doubt familiar to you from your earlier studies in strength of materials) are valid:

$$\frac{\partial V}{\partial x} = -q \qquad \text{(a)}$$

$$\frac{\partial M}{\partial x} = -V \qquad \text{(b)} \qquad\qquad (10.2)$$

$$\frac{\partial^2 M}{\partial x^2} = q \qquad \text{(c)}$$

where the partial derivatives are necessary since V and M may depend on t as well as on x. You may also verify that the stress resultants V and M are related to the axial stress τ_{xx} and shear stress τ_{xy}, respectively, in accordance with the following formulations:

$$V = \int_R \tau_{xy}\, dA \qquad \text{(a)}$$

$$M = -\int_R y\tau_{xx}\, dA \qquad \text{(b)} \qquad\qquad (10.3)$$

Here R is the region covered by the cross section [see Fig. 10.1(b)], and the minus sign in Eq. (10.3b) is necessary since a positive τ_{xx} at a positive y position generates a negative M on a positive area.

The loadings for the various beams will be expressed in terms of discontinuity functions. Appendix II gives the properties of the unit step, delta, and doublet functions both in time and in space, and discusses how the delta and doublet functions in x may be used to represent point loads and point couples, respectively. It is rec-

---

* In "strength of materials" you employed symmetry arguments to show that plane sections do in fact remain plane for a beam under *pure bending*. It is important to note that these arguments are valid for *any isotropic* material. For details, see I. H. Shames, *Introduction to Solid Mechanics* (Englewood Cliffs, NJ: Prentice-Hall, Inc., 1988), Chap. 8.

ommended that the reader review Appendix II at this time. One procedure to be used when singularity functions are involved is to imagine the beam to extend in a weightless manner along x from $-\infty$ to $+\infty$. This is shown in Fig. 10.2 for a simple specific case where the dashed lines indicate the aforementioned infinite extensions. The loads shown are suddenly applied at $t = 0$, and the loading function $q(x, t)$ then is given as follows:

$$q(x, t) = \{70[\delta(x)] - 10[u(x)] + 10[u(x - 20)] + 100[\eta(x - 15)]$$
$$+ 50[\delta(x - 10)] + 80[\delta(x - 20)]\}[u(t)]$$

where $-\infty < x < \infty$ and $-\infty < t < \infty$. Note that a positive distributed load is directed *upward* and that a *clockwise* point couple is represented by a positive doublet function. Another procedure that is sometimes useful is to include only the loading over the finite interval *interior* to the supporting forces R_1 and R_2. Thus we can say that for such a case

$$q(x, t) = \{-10[u(x)] + 50[\delta(x - 10)] + 100[\eta(x - 15)]\}[u(t)]$$

where here $0^+ \leq x \leq 20^-$ and $0^- \leq t < \infty$ if we also ignore times less than $t = 0^-$. As we shall see in this chapter in computing the deflection, the former "infinite extension" method allows for the use of boundary conditions at $x = 0^-$ and $x = L^+$ for a beam of length L, whereas the latter "finite interval" method requires boundary conditions at $x = 0^+$ and $x = L^-$.

Finally, we point out that we will be concerned with the curvature κ, which is the reciprocal of the radius of curvature R. The deflection v_0 of the neutral axis of the beam is related to κ and R by the following formulation from analytic geometry:

$$\frac{1}{R} = \kappa = \frac{\partial^2 v_0 / \partial x^2}{[1 + (\partial v_0 / \partial x)^2]^{3/2}}$$

where since y is positive upward (see Fig. 10.1), we have also chosen v_0 as positive upward. For small deformation with $|\partial v_0 / \partial x| \ll 1$, we can reduce the equation above to the form

$$\frac{1}{R} = \kappa \approx \frac{\partial^2 v_0}{\partial x^2} \tag{10.4}$$

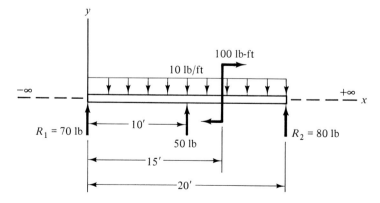

Figure 10.2 Loaded beam with loads applied at $t = 0$.

Flexure of Beams   Chap. 10

We shall use this formulation a number of times in future sections. Note that since v_0 is in general some function of x and t, it follows that R and κ are also in general functions of x and t. However, if v_0 is quadratic in x *and* if we assume small deformation, Eq. (10.4) indicates that R and κ are independent of x. This was precisely the case in the pure bending problem solved exactly in Section 9.11.

We are now ready to consider special materials starting with the Hookean material.

PART A
LINEAR ELASTIC BEAMS

10.2 EULER–BERNOULLI THEORY OF BENDING

We now consider linear elastic beams carrying the time-independent transverse load $q(x)$ and assume as in the pure bending case that plane sections remain plane. As noted previously, this is no longer exactly correct, but for *long slender* beams this approximation does not cause a serious loss of accuracy. Hence the resulting formulas for τ_{xx} and R still hold,

$$\tau_{xx} = -\frac{My}{I} \qquad \text{(a)}$$

$$R = \frac{EI}{M} \qquad \text{(b)}$$

(10.5)

and this forms the basis of the *Euler–Bernoulli* theory of bending that you studied in your earlier courses. As indicated by Eq. (10.1), y is the distance from the *neutral axis*, which for this theory is also that *centroidal* axis of the cross section which is perpendicular to the plane of symmetry. Also, the bending moment M and the radius of curvature R are *local* values corresponding to the position x of the cross section under study.

Substituting for R in Eq. (10.4) by using Eq. (10.5b), we get

$$\frac{d^2 v_0}{dx^2} = \frac{M}{EI}$$

(10.6)

where we have used the ordinary derivative since M and v_0 have been taken independent of t here. This is the basic differential equation for the deflection curve in terms of the bending moment M. Now bringing EI to the left side of the equation and then differentiating twice with respect to x, we get

$$\frac{d^2}{dx^2}\left(EI\frac{d^2 v_0}{dx^2}\right) = \frac{d^2 M}{dx^2} = q$$

(10.7)

where we have used Eq. (10.2c) in the last step. For constant EI we then get for Eq. (10.7),

$$\boxed{\frac{d^4 v_0}{dx^4} = \frac{q}{EI}}$$

(10.8)

This is our basic deflection equation in terms of q. It also follows from Eqs. (10.6) and (10.2b) that

$$\frac{d}{dx}\left(EI\frac{d^2 v_0}{dx^2}\right) = \frac{dM}{dx} = -V \qquad (10.9)$$

For EI constant the above yields the following expression involving the shear:

$$\frac{d^3 v_0}{dx^3} = -\frac{V}{EI} \qquad (10.10)$$

In the next section we shall demonstrate how to integrate Eq. (10.8) for a variety of problems. It is important to note that the deflection v_0 governed by Eq. (10.8) results *only* from *bending actions* and *not* from *shear*. The deflection due to shear in long, slender beams generally is very small compared to bending deflection and will not be considered here.*

10.3 DEFLECTION COMPUTATIONS USING DISCONTINUITY FUNCTIONS

The approach that we shall now follow for the evaluation of the deflection curve $v_0(x)$ is to utilize the infinite beam concept mentioned previously. Accordingly, we shall now examine the boundary considerations for such an approach. Consider a simply supported beam of constant EI loaded by an arbitrary loading distribution $q_1(x)$ as well as point forces and couples as shown in Fig. 10.3(a). We may replace the beam by one of infinite length as shown in Fig. 10.3(b), where the supporting forces R_1 and R_2 are to be considered as a pair of unknown external loads. We next formulate a loading function $q(x)$ for this entire infinite beam making use of the discontinuity functions. Using this loading function in Eq. (10.8), we carry out four integrations from 0^- to x to evaluate v_0 in terms of four unknown constants of integration and two unknown forces R_1 and R_2. These six quantities are all evaluated by examining the boundary conditions associated with the beam, which must take account of the fact that no loads exist in the intervals to the left of $x = 0$ and to the right of $x = L$. Thus, immediately to the left of the origin (i.e., at $x = 0^-$) and immediately to the right of the support ② (i.e., at $x = L^+$), we have zero bending moment and zero shear in our hypothetical beam. From Eq. (10.6) we see that the zero bending moment means that $d^2 v_0/dx^2 = 0$ at these points. Also, Eq. (10.10) indicates that for $V = 0$ it is necessary that $d^3 v_0/dx^3$ also be zero at these points. Furthermore, we know that the deflection v_0 is zero at $x = 0$ and $x = L$ as a result of the constraints. Summarizing the conditions that we must impose on our solution, we have

---

*For the study of shear stress and shear deflection in the Euler–Bernoulli theory and also for the study of other items such as composite beams, shear center, and so on, see I. H. Shames, *Introduction to Solid Mechanics*, 2nd ed. (Englewood Cliffs, NJ: Prentice-Hall, Inc., 1988).

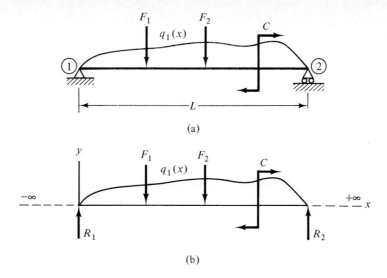

Figure 10.3 Simply supported beam.

At $x = 0^-$:

$$\frac{d^2 v_0}{dx^2} = 0 \qquad \text{(a)}$$

$$\frac{d^3 v_0}{dx^3} = 0 \qquad \text{(b)}$$

At $x = 0$:

$$v_0 = 0 \qquad \text{(c)}$$

At $x = L^+$:

$$\frac{d^2 v_0}{dx^2} = 0 \qquad \text{(d)}$$

$$\frac{d^3 v_0}{dx^3} = 0 \qquad \text{(e)}$$

At $x = L$:

$$v_0 = 0 \qquad \text{(f)}$$

(10.11)

Thus we have the six conditions that permit us to solve for the six unknowns.

Consider next a cantilever beam with constant EI as shown in Fig. 10.4(a). The hypothetical replacement is shown directly below in Fig. 10.4(b). Note that the supporting force system now consists of a force R_1 and a point couple M_1 applied at the origin. As before, the loading function $q(x)$ is formulated for the entire beam and four integrations are again carried out using Eq. (10.8). The boundary conditions are the same as in the simply supported beam except for Eq. (10.11f). Thus,

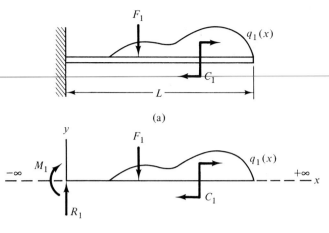

(a)

(b)

Figure 10.4 Cantilever beam.

instead of a zero deflection at $x = L$, we have a zero slope of the deflection curve at $x = 0$. The boundary conditions then become

At $x = 0^-$:

$$\frac{d^2 v_0}{dx^2} = 0 \quad \text{(a)}$$

$$\frac{d^3 v_0}{dx^3} = 0 \quad \text{(b)}$$

At $x = 0$:

$$v_0 = 0 \quad \text{(c)}$$

$$\frac{dv_0}{dx} = 0 \quad \text{(d)}$$

(10.12)

At $x = L^+$:

$$\frac{d^2 v_0}{dx^2} = 0 \quad \text{(e)}$$

$$\frac{d^3 v_0}{dx^3} = 0 \quad \text{(f)}$$

We thus have again six conditions by which we can compute the four constants of integration as well as the unknown quantities R_1 and M_1.

We shall now illustrate the procedure of finding the deflection curve by considering several simple examples. In these examples we shall use the integration formulas for discontinuity functions developed in Appendix II.

Example 10.1

Shown in Fig. 10.5(a) is a simply supported beam. We are to determine the deflection curve $v_0(x)$ and the supporting forces. The infinite hypothetical beam for our calculations is shown in Fig. 10.5(b).

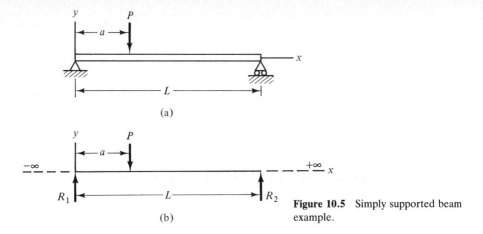

(a)

(b)

Figure 10.5 Simply supported beam example.

We first write the loading function $q(x)$ for the entire infinite beam. Thus

$$q(x) = R_1[\delta(x)] - P[\delta(x-a)] + R_2[\delta(x-L)] \qquad \text{(a)}$$

Substituting into the basic differential equation (Eq. 10.8), we have

$$\frac{d^4 v_0}{dx^4} = \frac{1}{EI}\{R_1[\delta(x)] - P[\delta(x-a)] + R_2[\delta(x-L)]\} \qquad \text{(b)}$$

We shall now carry out four integrations from 0^- to x. The first two integrations will involve $(d^3 v_0/dx^3)_{0^-}$ and $(d^2 v_0/dx^2)_{0^-}$, but because of the boundary conditions (10.11a) and (10.11b) we can always set these equal to zero. The third and fourth integrations will involve $(dv_0/dx)_{0^-}$ and $(v_0)_{0^-}$ on the left-hand side of the equations. We shall denote these quantities as $-C_3$ and $-C_4$ (i.e., as unknown constants $+C_3$ and $+C_4$ on the right-hand side of the equations), and we shall determine them using the boundary conditions.* We now proceed with the integrations as follows:

$$\frac{d^3 v_0}{dx^3} = \frac{1}{EI}\{R_1[u(x)] - P[u(x-a)] + R_2[u(x-L)]\} \qquad \text{(c)}$$

$$\frac{d^2 v_0}{dx^2} = \frac{1}{EI}\{R_1 x[u(x)] - P(x-a)[u(x-a)] + R_2(x-L)[u(x-L)]\} \qquad \text{(d)}$$

$$\frac{dv_0}{dx} = \frac{1}{EI}\left\{R_1 \frac{x^2}{2}[u(x)] - P\frac{(x-a)^2}{2}[u(x-a)]\right.$$
$$\left. + R_2 \frac{(x-L)^2}{2}[u(x-L)] + C_3\right\} \qquad \text{(e)}$$

$$v_0 = \frac{1}{EI}\left\{R_1 \frac{x^3}{6}[u(x)] - P\frac{(x-a)^3}{6}[u(x-a)]\right.$$
$$\left. + R_2 \frac{(x-L)^3}{6}[u(x-L)] + C_3 x + C_4\right\} \qquad \text{(f)}$$

---

* It is permissible to consider that the four integrations generate four constants of integration with the first two, C_1 and C_2, zero for all problems.

The boundary conditions at $x = L^+$ require that

$$\left(\frac{d^3 v_0}{dx^3}\right)_{L^+} = 0 = \frac{1}{EI}(R_1 - P + R_2) = 0$$

which gives

$$R_1 + R_2 = P \tag{g}$$

and

$$\left(\frac{d^2 v_0}{dx^2}\right)_{L^+} = 0 = R_1 L - P(L - a) = 0$$

which gives

$$R_1 = \frac{P(L - a)}{L} \tag{h}$$

Returning to Eq. (g), we then see that*

$$R_2 = P - \frac{P(L - a)}{L} = \frac{Pa}{L} \tag{i}$$

We thus have determined the supporting forces, a job we could have done by inspection for this simple problem.

We shall now proceed to the final boundary conditions requiring v_0 to be zero at $x = 0$ and $x = L$. The first condition renders $C_4 = 0$. The second condition becomes

$$0 = \frac{1}{EI}\left[\frac{R_1 L^3}{6} - \frac{P(L - a)^3}{6} + C_3 L\right] \tag{j}$$

Therefore,

$$C_3 = \frac{P(L - a)^3}{6L} - \frac{R_1 L^2}{6} \tag{k}$$

Now going back to Eq. (f) and putting in the values of R_1, R_2, and the constants of integration, we get

$$v_0 = \frac{P}{EI}\left\{\frac{L - a}{L}\frac{x^3}{6}[u(x)] - \frac{(x - a)^3}{6}[u(x - a)]\right.$$
$$\left.+ \frac{a}{6L}(x - L)^3[u(x - L)] + \left[\frac{(L - a)^3}{6L} - \frac{L(L - a)}{6}\right]x\right\} \tag{ℓ}$$

For the special case of $a = L/2$, Eq. (ℓ) reduces to

$$v_0 = \frac{P}{EI}\left\{\frac{x^3}{12}[u(x)] - \frac{(x - L/2)^3}{6}[u(x - L/2)]\right.$$
$$\left.+ \frac{1}{12}(x - L)^3[u(x - L)] - \frac{L^2}{16}x\right\} \tag{m}$$

---

* Note that Eq. (g) for $(d^3 v_0/dx^3)_{L^+} = 0$ and Eq. (h) for $(d^2 v_0/dx^2)_{L^+} = 0$ are the equations of *equilibrium*, with Eq. (g) corresponding to the summation of forces, and Eq. (h) corresponding to the summing of moments about the right end of the beam.

Finally, we may take advantage of symmetry and only consider the half-interval $0^+ < x \le L/2^-$, whereupon Eq. (m) simplifies considerably to

$$v_0 = -\frac{P}{48EI}(3L^2 x - 4x^3) \tag{n}$$

which is clearly negative (i.e., downward) at all points.

Example 10.2

Consider the cantilever beam shown in Fig. 10.6(a) loaded by a uniform load q_0 over a portion of the beam.

Using an infinite beam [Fig. 10.6(b)], the loading function is

$$q(x) = M_1[\eta(x)] + R_1[\delta(x)] - q_0[u(x-a)] + q_0[u(x-L)] \tag{a}$$

The basic differential equation then becomes

$$\frac{d^4 v_0}{dx^4} = \frac{1}{EI}\{M_1[\eta(x)] + R_1[\delta(x)] - q_0[u(x-a)] + q_0[u(x-L)]\} \tag{b}$$

We now perform four integrations from 0^- to x. Thus

$$\frac{d^3 v_0}{dx^3} = \frac{1}{EI}\{M_1[\delta(x)] + R_1[u(x)] - q_0(x-a)[u(x-a)]$$
$$+ q_0(x-L)[u(x-L)]\} \tag{c}$$

$$\frac{d^2 v_0}{dx^2} = \frac{1}{EI}\left\{M_1[u(x)] + R_1 x[u(x)] - q_0\frac{(x-a)^2}{2}[u(x-a)]\right.$$
$$\left. + q_0\frac{(x-L)^2}{2}[u(x-L)]\right\} \tag{d}$$

$$\frac{dv_0}{dx} = \frac{1}{EI}\left\{M_1 x[u(x)] + R_1\frac{x^2}{2}[u(x)] - \frac{q_0(x-a)^3}{6}[u(x-a)]\right.$$
$$\left. + \frac{q_0(x-L)^3}{6}[u(x-L)] + C_3\right\} \tag{e}$$

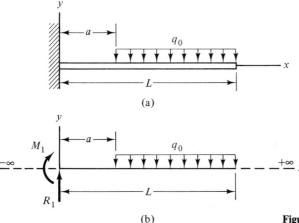

(a)

(b) **Figure 10.6** Cantilever beam example.

$$v_0 = \frac{1}{EI} \left\{ \frac{M_1 x^2}{2} [u(x)] + \frac{R_1 x^3}{6} [u(x)] - \frac{q_0(x-a)^4}{24} [u(x-a)] \right.$$
$$\left. + \frac{q_0(x-L)^4}{24} [u(x-L)] + C_3 x + C_4 \right\} \qquad \text{(f)}$$

At $x = L^+$, we have $d^3 v_0/dx^3 = d^2 v_0/dx^2 = 0$. Thus, we get from (c) and (d)

$$\frac{1}{EI} [R_1 - q_0(L-a)] = 0 \qquad \text{(g)}$$

and

$$\frac{1}{EI} \left[M_1 + R_1 L - \frac{q_0(L-a)^2}{2} \right] = 0 \qquad \text{(h)}$$

We may solve for R_1 and M_1 from these equations:

$$R_1 = q_0(L-a) \qquad \text{(i)}$$

$$M_1 = -q_0 L(L-a) + \frac{q_0(L-a)^2}{2} = \frac{q_0}{2}(a^2 - L^2) \qquad \text{(j)}$$

The boundary conditions at the support requiring $v_0 = dv_0/dx = 0$ at $x = 0$ clearly render $C_3 = C_4 = 0$. We may then give the deflection curve in the following form:

$$v_0 = \frac{q_0}{EI} \left\{ \frac{a^2 - L^2}{4} x^2 [u(x)] + \frac{L-a}{6} x^3 [u(x)] \right.$$
$$\left. - \frac{(x-a)^4}{24} [u(x-a)] + \frac{(x-L)^4}{24} [u(x-L)] \right\} \qquad \text{(k)}$$

For the special case of $a = 0$, Eq. (k) simplifies to

$$v_0 = -\frac{q_0 x^2}{24EI} (6L^2 - 4Lx + x^2) \qquad (\ell)$$

for the finite interval $0^+ \le x \le L^-$.

In using the singularity approach for *statically indeterminate* problems we simply consider all supporting forces and moments as unknowns. These are all subsequently determined from the boundary conditions of the problem. There will be as many new boundary conditions for statically indeterminate beams as there are redundant constraints. We illustrate these comments in the following example.

Example 10.3

Shown in Fig. 10.7(a) is a simply supported beam with a degree of redundancy of unity. We wish to determine the supporting forces R_1, R_2, and R_3, and the deflection curve in terms of E and I.

The loading function for the infinite hypothetical replacement beam is given as

$$q(x) = R_1[\delta(x)] - 100[\delta(x - 10)] + R_2[\delta(x - 20)] + R_3[\delta(x - 40)] \qquad \text{(a)}$$

The basic differential equation for deflection is then

$$\frac{d^4 v_0}{dx^4} = \frac{1}{EI} \{ R_1[\delta(x)] - 100[\delta(x - 10)] + R_2[\delta(x - 20)] + R_3[\delta(x - 40)] \} \qquad \text{(b)}$$

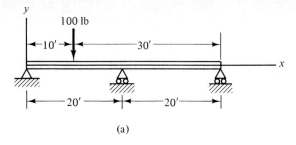

(a)

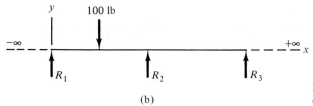

(b)

Figure 10.7 Indeterminate beam example.

Integrating four times, we get

$$\frac{d^3 v_0}{dx^3} = \frac{1}{EI}\{R_1[u(x)] - 100[u(x-10)] + R_2[u(x-20)] + R_3[u(x-40)]\} \qquad (c)$$

$$\frac{d^2 v_0}{dx^2} = \frac{1}{EI}\{R_1 x[u(x)] - 100(x-10)[u(x-10)]$$
$$+ R_2(x-20)[u(x-20)] + R_3(x-40)[u(x-40)]\} \qquad (d)$$

$$\frac{dv_0}{dx} = \frac{1}{EI}\left\{\frac{R_1 x^2}{2}[u(x)] - 100\frac{(x-10)^2}{2}[u(x-10)]\right.$$
$$\left. + R_2\frac{(x-20)^2}{2}[u(x-20)] + R_3\frac{(x-40)^2}{2}[u(x-40)] + C_3\right\} \qquad (e)$$

$$v_0 = \frac{1}{EI}\left\{\frac{R_1 x^3}{6}[u(x)] - 100\frac{(x-10)^3}{6}[u(x-10)]\right.$$
$$+ R_2\frac{(x-20)^3}{6}[u(x-20)] + R_3\frac{(x-40)^3}{6}[u(x-40)]$$
$$\left. + C_3 x + C_4\right\} \qquad (f)$$

Since the deflection is zero at the origin, C_4 must be zero. To the right of the support R_3, we have $d^3 v_0/dx^3 = d^2 v_0/dx^2 = 0$. We then have

$$R_1 - 100 + R_2 + R_3 = 0 \qquad (g)$$

$$40R_1 - 3000 + 20R_2 = 0 \qquad (h)$$

Furthermore, at $x = 20$ and $x = 40$, we have $v_0 = 0$. That gives us the following equations:

$$\frac{8000}{6}R_1 - \frac{100}{6}(10)^3 + C_3(20) = 0 \qquad (i)$$

$$\frac{(40)^3}{6}R_1 - \frac{100}{6}(30)^3 + \frac{(20)^3}{6}R_2 + C_3(40) = 0 \qquad (j)$$

Equations (g), (h), (i), and (j) are now rewritten as follows:

$$R_1 + R_2 + R_3 = 100 \tag{k}$$

$$2R_1 + R_2 = 150 \tag{ℓ}$$

$$1333R_1 + 20C_3 = 16.67 \times 10^3 \tag{m}$$

$$10.67 \times 10^3 R_1 + 1333R_2 + 40C_3 = 450 \times 10^3 \tag{n}$$

We may substitute for R_2 in Eq. (n) using Eq. (ℓ), and we may then eliminate C_3 from Eqs. (m) and (n). This permits us to solve for R_1. We get

$$R_1 = 40.4 \text{ lb} \tag{o}$$

and from Eqs. (k) and (ℓ) we get the other supporting forces. Thus

$$R_2 = 69.3 \text{ lb} \tag{p}$$

$$R_3 = -9.64 \text{ lb} \tag{q}$$

Finally, from Eq. (m) we can compute C_3 as

$$C_3 = -1859 \tag{r}$$

We thus have simultaneously determined the deflection curve [Eq. (f)] and the supporting forces.*

PART B
LINEAR VISCOELASTIC BEAMS

10.4 BASIC CONSIDERATIONS; STRESSES

We remind you that Eqs. (10.1) and (10.2) in Section 10.1 are valid for all materials, so we may use these equations in this section. We point out also that we will be considering homogeneous isothermal beams with a plane of symmetry (i.e., xy) containing loading normal to the neutral axis x [refer back to Fig. 10.1(a)]. Furthermore, the dependent variables V, M, v_0, and κ will now be functions of time as well as of position x, while τ_{xx} and ε_{xx} will in addition also depend on y.

The key equation that is different here is the *constitutive law*, which is given from the one-dimensional test (see Section 6.7) as

$$P^E \tau_{xx} = Q^E \varepsilon_{xx} \tag{10.13}$$

The differential operators above were defined [see Eqs. (6.57)] as

$$P^E = \sum_{i=0}^{mE} p_i^E \frac{\partial^i}{\partial t^i} = \sum_{i=0}^{mE} p_i^E D^i, \qquad Q^E = \sum_{i=0}^{nE} q_i^E \frac{\partial^i}{\partial t^i} = \sum_{i=0}^{nE} q_i^E D^i \tag{10.14}$$

where the coefficients p_i^E and q_i^E are constants for a homogeneous isothermal material. You are reminded that the operators P^E, Q^E include the linear elastic and

---

* For additional problems of this type, see the reference cited in the footnote on page 402 and the problems at the end of this chapter. See also I. H. Shames, *Mechanics of Deformable Solids* (Englewood Cliffs, NJ: Prentice-Hall, Inc., 1964; reprinted by R.E. Krieger Publishing Co., Melbourne, FL, 1979).

linear viscous operators as special cases. We start by stating here the definition of bending moment in cross-sectional region R, which is the same as in other beam problems:

$$M = -\int_R y \tau_{xx} \, dA \qquad (10.15)$$

The limits here are constants since we are concerned only with beams of constant cross section. Now we apply the differential time operator P^E to both sides of the equation. Since P^E and the spatial integral operator clearly commute, we get

$$P^E(M) = -\int_R y P^E(\tau_{xx}) \, dA \qquad (10.16)$$

Next, we use Eq. (10.13) on the right side of Eq. (10.16), giving

$$P^E(M) = -\int_R y Q^E(\varepsilon_{xx}) \, dA = \int_R y Q^E(y\kappa) \, dA$$

where we have replaced ε_{xx} by using Eq. (10.1) in the last integral. Extracting y from the time operator Q^E, we get

$$P^E(M) = \int_R y^2 Q^E(\kappa) \, dA$$

Hence we can write

$$P^E(M) = I Q^E(\kappa) \qquad (10.17)$$

The last step is valid because $Q^E(\kappa)$ is independent of the yz coordinates in the cross section, and thus $Q^E(\kappa)$ may be extracted from the integral leaving only the second moment of area $I = \int_R y^2 \, dA$. Equation (10.17) is called the *moment-curvature* relation for a linear viscoelastic beam.

We now seek an expression for the longitudinal stress τ_{xx}, and to this end we replace κ in Eq. (10.17) by $-\varepsilon_{xx}/y$ [see Eq. (10.1)], and extract $1/y$ from the operator Q^E. Accordingly, we get

$$P^E(M) = -\frac{Q^E(\varepsilon_{xx})}{y} I = -\frac{P^E(\tau_{xx})}{y} I$$

where we have again used the constitutive law Eq. (10.13). The equation above may also be rewritten as

$$P^E \left\{ M + \frac{\tau_{xx} I}{y} \right\} = 0$$

We shall now prove that the expression in braces must vanish for homogeneous initial conditions at $t = 0^-$, that is, for M and τ_{xx} and all of their time derivatives zero at $t = 0^-$. For this purpose we take the Laplace transform of the equation above with 0^- as the lower limit [see Eq. (6.48)], and for the above-mentioned homogeneous conditions we obtain

$$\bar{P}^E \left\{ \bar{M}(s) + \frac{\bar{\tau}_{xx}(s) I}{y} \right\} = 0$$

where $\bar{P}^E$ is a nonzero *polynomial* in the transform variable s [see Eqs. (6.50)]. Finally, dividing the equation above by $\bar{P}^E$ and performing a simple inversion, we get the familiar *flexure formula*

$$\tau_{xx}(x, y, t) = -\frac{M(x, t)y}{I} \qquad (10.18)$$

What about the position of the *neutral axis* for a linear viscoelastic material? We know that for loading perpendicular to the neutral axis there is zero axial force, and this requires that

$$\int_R \tau_{xx}\, dA = 0$$

and thus

$$\int_R P^E(\tau_{xx})\, dA = 0$$

Now we use the constitutive law to replace $P^E(\tau_{xx})$, and accordingly we get

$$\int_R Q^E(\varepsilon_{xx})\, dA = 0$$

Next we replace ε_{xx} using Eq. (10.1), from the plane sections remaining plane hypothesis, and obtain

$$\int_R y Q^E(\kappa)\, dA = Q^E(\kappa) \int_R y\, dA = 0$$

Again the last step is valid because $Q^E(\kappa)$ is independent of y and z. Since $Q^E(\kappa)$ is nonzero, we finally conclude that $\int_R y\, dA = 0$, which makes the *neutral axis coincide with that centroidal axis perpendicular to the plane of symmetry.*

We may now conclude that the *normal stress in a linear viscoelastic beam is the same as the normal stress in a geometrically identical elastic beam with the same bending moment.* On the other hand, the *deflection* will in general clearly *not be the same,* and we shall illustrate this in subsequent sections. And you will recall that the bending moment in a statically indeterminate beam *may* depend on the material properties. This point will also be explored more fully in subsequent sections. It then follows that even if the loads on geometrically identical viscoelastic and elastic beams are the same, the stresses are *not necessarily the same if the beams are statically indeterminate.* You are also reminded that the results above are valid only for homogeneous isothermal materials. For example, if the viscoelastic material properties vary through the beam depth as a result of a temperature gradient, the neutral axis will no longer coincide with the centroid.

10.5 DEFLECTIONS IN LINEAR VISCOELASTIC BEAMS; BASIC EQUATIONS

We start with moment-curvature equation (10.17) and replace κ by $\partial^2 v_0 / \partial x^2$ to get

$$P^E(M) = IQ^E(v_0'') \tag{10.19}$$

where the primes indicate the partial derivative $\partial/\partial x$. Differentiating twice with respect to x, while noting that the operator pair P^E and Q^E are time derivative operators, we get for constant properties

$$P^E(M'') = IQ^E(v_0^{iv}) \tag{10.20}$$

Using Eq. (10.2c), we then get the desired deflection *differential equation* (the corresponding integral equation will soon follow):

$$\boxed{P^E(q) = IQ^E(v_0^{iv})} \tag{10.21}$$

You will note by comparing this equation with Eq. (10.8) that the operator ratio Q^E/P^E corresponds to E for linear elastic behavior. In fact, this is the same "analogy relation" as we discussed in Chapter 6 [see Eq. (6.58a)]. Also, in the Laplace transform space E corresponds to the ratio of polynomials $\overline{Q}^E(s)/\overline{P}^E(s)$, which is precisely the correspondence principle presented in Chapter 9 [see Eqs. (9.63)].

Some useful information can now be obtained by a simple inspection of the equations above. Considering Eq. (10.19), it is clear that if $M = 0$ at a given position for all values of time, it must be true that v_0'' must also be zero at this point for all values of time. This will be important for us when we consider boundary conditions for Eq. (10.21). Now differentiate Eq. (10.19) once with respect to x and use the equation of equilibrium (10.2b) to get

$$-P^E(V) = IQ^E(v_0''') \tag{10.22}$$

where V is the shear force. Again, for consideration of boundary conditions, if $V = 0$ at all times at some position, then v_0''' must be zero at this point for all times.

We shall next consider how to express the basic differential equation (10.21) as an *integral equation*. We first go back to the one-dimensional constitutive law [see Eq. (10.13)], which we now rewrite

$$P^E \tau_{xx} = Q^E \varepsilon_{xx} \tag{10.23}$$

We have shown in Chapter 6 that this equation may be rewritten as a hereditary integral in terms of the creep compliance function $J^E(t)$ as follows [see Eq. (6.46)]:

$$\varepsilon_{xx} = \int_{0^-}^{t} J^E(t - t') \frac{\partial \tau_{xx}(t')}{\partial t'} \, dt' \tag{10.24}$$

where t' is the dummy variable of integration. Now considering Eqs. (10.21) and (10.23), we see that Iv_0^{iv} corresponds to ε_{xx} and q corresponds to τ_{xx}. It therefore follows immediately by analogy with Eq. (10.24) that Eq. (10.21) may be rewritten as

$$v_0^{\text{iv}}(x,t) = \frac{1}{I} \int_{0^-}^{t} J^E(t-t') \frac{\partial q(x,t')}{\partial t'} dt' \qquad (10.25)$$

In solving differential equation (10.21) or the equivalent integral equation (10.25), we may adopt a number of solution techniques. For a given loading function $q(x,t)$ it is frequently more convenient to work from Eq. (10.25), since the time differential operator Q^E appearing in Eq. (10.21) has already been removed by an integration over time. Given the creep compliance function, it is only necessary to evaluate this time integral and then successively integrate out the four spatial derivatives in x. Alternatively, we may employ the Laplace transform over t and then integrate over x in solving either differential equation (10.21) or integral equation (10.25). If the solution to the corresponding linear elastic problem is available, we may avoid the integrations over x by using the correspondence principle presented in Section 9.5. Accordingly, we replace E in the transformed elastic solution by either $\bar{Q}^E(s)/\bar{P}^E(s)$ or $1/[s\bar{J}^E(s)]$, and then perform a Laplace transform inversion. In the problems at the end of the chapter you will be asked to utilize the various solution techniques described above. In the next section we consider in detail a special case that is of some interest.

10.6 CASE OF SUDDENLY APPLIED CONSTANT EXTERNAL AND SUPPORT FORCES

We now consider the special case in which the loading function is expressible in the simple form

$$q(x,t) = q_0(x)[u(t)], \qquad -\infty < x < \infty \qquad (10.26)$$

Note that loading function $q(x,t)$ includes all supporting forces and couple moments in the infinite extended interval. We point out that for some statically indeterminate beams, loadings will not be expressible in this form–as we shall shortly demonstrate. Now substitute this loading into Eq. (10.25), giving

$$v_0^{\text{iv}}(x,t) = \frac{1}{I} \int_{0^-}^{t} J^E(t-t') q_0(x)[\delta(t')] dt'$$

$$= \frac{q_0(x)}{I} J^E(t)[u(t)] \qquad (10.27)$$

Since $J^E(t)$ is assumed known, we see that in the case of the special loading function according to Eq. (10.26), the evaluation of the hereditary integral is trivial.

Now consider a geometrically identical *elastic* beam under the same load for $t > 0$, and assume that its deflection solution is known as $[v_0(x)]_{\text{EL}}$. Noting Eq. (10.8), which is valid for linear elastic beams, we can then replace $q_0(x)$ in Eq. (10.27) by $EI[v_0^{\text{iv}}(x)]_{\text{EL}}$. We thus get

$$v_0^{iv}(x,t) = [v_0^{iv}(x)]_{EL} \, EJ^E(t)[u(t)]$$

Integrating once over x, we obtain

$$v_0'''(x,t) = [v_0'''(x)]_{EL} \, EJ^E(t)[u(t)] + f_1(t)$$

where $f_1(t)$ is a function of integration. But as explained in Section 10.3, the shear force in both beams must be zero at $x = 0^-$ (i.e., $v_0'''(0^-, t) = [v_0'''(0^-)]_{EL} = 0$), and thus $f_1(t) = 0$. Performing a second integration and using the fact that at $x = 0^-$ the bending moment is also zero, we can show that the second function of integration, $f_2(t)$, is also zero and thereby obtain

$$\boxed{v_0''(x,t) = [v_0''(x)]_{EL} \, EJ^E(t)[u(t)]} \tag{10.28}$$

Two more integrations yield the slope as

$$v_0'(x,t) = [v_0'(x)]_{EL} \, EJ^E(t)[u(t)] + f_3(t)$$

and the deflection as

$$v_0(x,t) = [v_0(x)]_{EL} \, EJ^E(t)[u(t)] + f_3(t)x + f_4(t)$$

If the governing boundary conditions are of the *homogeneous* type (i.e., zero deflection and/or slope at one or two points), it immediately follows that $f_3(t) = f_4(t) = 0$. Accordingly, we obtain in this special case

$$v_0(x,t) = [v_0(x)]_{EL} \, EJ^E(t)[u(t)] \tag{10.29}$$

Thus, knowing the deflection equation for an *elastic beam* with the same geometry and loading, and having also the *creep compliance* function $J^E(t)$, we can get the deflection function for a linear viscoelastic beam under loading function (10.26) in a straightforward manner. This statement is nothing more than a special case of the *correspondence principle* which we presented in Chapter 9. We shall now consider a simple example in which we make use of Eq. (10.28).

Example 10.4

Consider a statically determinate, simply supported Maxwell beam acted on by a suddenly applied force $P_0[u(t)]$ (Fig. 10.8). Determine the deflection $v_0(x,t)$.

The loading function for $-\infty < x < \infty$ is given as

$$q(x,t) = \left\{ \frac{P_0(L-a)}{L}\,[\delta(x)] - P_0[\delta(x-a)] + \frac{P_0 a}{L}\,[\delta(x-L)] \right\}[u(t)] \tag{a}$$

where the reactions R_1 and R_2 followed from simple static equilibrium. Clearly, this loading is of the form $q_0(x)[u(t)]$, so we can immediately say

$$v_0''(x,t) = [v_0''(x)]_{EL} \, EJ^E(t)[u(t)] \tag{b}$$

Integrating twice over x, we obtain

$$v_0(x,t) = [v_0(x)]_{EL} \, EJ^E(t)[u(t)] + f_3(t)x + f_4(t) \tag{c}$$

where $f_3(t)$ and $f_4(t)$ are time functions of integration. Since the displacements in both simply supported beams vanish at $x = 0$ and $x = L$, it follows here that $f_4(t) = f_3(t) = 0$.

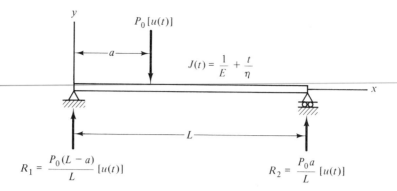

Figure 10.8 Simply supported Maxwell beam example.

The final solution is then obtained by setting $J(t) = 1/E + t/\eta$ for the Maxwell material and by employing Eq. (ℓ) of Example 10.1 for $[v_0(x)]_{\text{EL}}$. Accordingly,

$$
\begin{aligned}
v_0(x,t) = \frac{P_0}{I} \Bigg\{ & \frac{L-a}{L} \frac{x^3}{6} - \frac{(x-a)^3}{6} [u(x-a)] \\
& + \frac{(L-a)^3}{6L} x - \frac{L(L-a)}{6} x \Bigg\} \left(\frac{1}{E} + \frac{t}{\eta} \right) [u(t)]
\end{aligned}
\tag{d}
$$

for the finite interval $0^+ \le x \le L^-$. Note that v_0 is bounded at $t = 0^+$ and unbounded as $t \to \infty$, which is characteristic of a Maxwell material.

Example 10.4 is that of a statically determinate beam, and it was easy to see that the loading function on the infinite extended interval was in the simple form of Eq. (10.26). For statically indeterminate beams the reactions may not be determined from static equilibrium alone, and therefore the form of $q(x,t)$, which includes these reactions, may not be readily apparent. Consider first the case in which the boundary conditions at the supports are of the homogeneous type (i.e., zero deflection and zero slope). For example, look back at statically indeterminate elastic beam Example 10.3 in Section 10.3, for which beam the deflections are zero at the three supports (see Fig. 10.7). Note that because of the homogeneity of these boundary conditions, the elastic modulus E did *not* enter into the calculation of the reactions R_1, R_2, and R_3. It is easy to verify that in general the reactions in a statically indeterminate elastic beam with homogeneous boundary conditions will be independent of E. It follows immediately from the correspondence principle that the calculation of the reactions in a viscoelastic statically indeterminate beam with homogeneous boundary conditions will *not* involve the viscoelastic operators P^E and Q^E. Thus, if the prescribed external load is in the simple form of Eq. (10.26), the reactions are also in this same simple form. In fact, these reactions as well as the bending moment in the beam will be the same as in the corresponding elastic beam under the same prescribed external load.

Now consider the case of a statically indeterminate beam with deformable supports that interact with other materials. In this case the computation of the reaction *will* involve the material properties of *both* the beam and the supports. Even if the applied external load is in the simple form of Eq. (10.26), the reactions will in general *not* be in this simple form. We illustrate this case in the next section.

10.7 STATICALLY INDETERMINATE BEAMS WITH DEFORMABLE SUPPORTS

If the loading function is not in the simple form of Eq. (10.26), the solution to differential equation (10.21) or its equivalent integral equation (10.25) requires a more detailed handling. As mentioned previously, one approach is to take a Laplace transform over t, integrate over x, and then invert the corresponding transformed viscoelastic solution back into time space. Another approach is just to carry out all of the necessary integrations over t and x. We shall follow the latter approach for the following statically indeterminate beam problem which contains a deformable support. In Problem 10.15 you will be asked to solve a similar problem via the method of Laplace transform.

Example 10.5

A linear Maxwell beam is shown in Fig. 10.9 with a suddenly applied (at $t = 0$) uniform load and an elastic midsupport with spring constant k. (a) Formulate the governing differential deflection equation and the appropriate boundary and initial conditions; (b) solve for $v_0(x, t)$. Note that the supports at $x = 0$ and $x = 2L$ are simple supports.

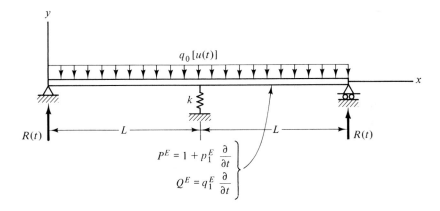

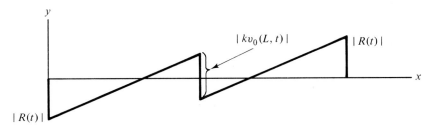

Figure 10.9 Statically indeterminate Maxwell beam example.

To aid us in our analysis we have shown a shear diagram directly below the loading diagram, assuming that the beam deflects downward [i.e., $v_0(x, t) \leq 0$]. The loading function for this beam is given as

$$q(x, t) = \{R(t)[\delta(x)] - q_0[u(x)] + q_0[u(x - 2L)] - kv_0(L, t)[\delta(x - L)]$$
$$+ R(t)[\delta(x - 2L)]\}[u(t)], \qquad -\infty < x < \infty$$

where the reactions at $x = 0$ and $2L$ equal an unknown positive *function of time* $R(t)$ because of the displacement-dependent reaction at $x = L$. Obviously, this loading is *not* in the form of a function only of x times a step function in time.

(a) *Formulation of the problem.* We go back to the basic deflection differential equation (10.21) as our starting point:

$$P^E(q) = IQ^E(v_0^{iv}) \tag{a}$$

The constitutive law for a Maxwell material was expressed in Chapter 6 [see Eq. (6.3)] as

$$\frac{\partial \varepsilon_{xx}}{\partial t} = \frac{1}{E} \frac{\partial \tau_{xx}}{\partial t} + \frac{\tau_{xx}}{\eta}$$

and thus

$$P^E = \left(1 + \frac{\eta}{E} \frac{\partial}{\partial t}\right) = \left(1 + p_1^E \frac{\partial}{\partial t}\right) \tag{b}$$

$$Q^E = \eta \frac{\partial}{\partial t} = q_1^E \frac{\partial}{\partial t} \tag{c}$$

Equation (a) can now be written as

$$\left(1 + p_1^E \frac{\partial}{\partial t}\right)(q) = Iq_1^E \frac{\partial}{\partial t}(v_0^{iv}) \tag{d}$$

For the half-range $0^+ \leq x \leq L^-$ we can express Eq. (d) simply as

$$Iq_1^E \dot{v}_0^{iv} = \left(1 + p_1^E \frac{\partial}{\partial t}\right)\{-q_0[u(t)]\}$$

and thus

$$\dot{v}_0^{iv} = -\frac{q_0}{Iq_1^E} \{[u(t)] + p_1^E [\delta(t)]\} \tag{e}$$

where the dot indicates the partial time derivative $\partial/\partial t$.

Differential equation (e) requires four *boundary* conditions and one *initial* condition. The simple support at $x = 0^+$ and the symmetry at $x = L^-$ yield three of the boundary conditions immediately as

$$v_0(0^+, t) = 0, \qquad v_0''(0^+, t) = 0 \tag{f}$$

$$v_0'(L^-, t) = 0 \tag{g}$$

The fourth boundary condition will be obtained from the shear at $x = L^-$ (see Fig. 10.9), which is given in terms of the deflection as

$$V(L^-, t) = -\tfrac{1}{2} k v_0(L^-, t)$$

where the minus sign is necessary because a negative $v_0(L^-, t)$ (i.e., downward) generates a positive shear force $V(L^-, t)$. Substituting $V(L^-, t)$ as given above into Eq. (10.22), we can say that

$$-P^E[-\tfrac{1}{2}k v_0(L^-, t)] = IQ^E[v_0'''(L^-, t)]$$

Now we replace P^E and Q^E using Eqs. (b) and (c) respectively, and get on rearranging the terms

$$\ddot{v}_0'''(L^-, t) - a[v_0(L^-, t) + p_1^E \dot{v}_0(L^-, t)] = 0 \tag{h}$$

where

$$a = \frac{k}{2q_1^E I} \tag{i}$$

Thus Eqs. (f), (g), and (h) are the four required boundary conditions for differential equation (e). The one initial condition is given simply by the homogeneous condition at $t = 0^-$,

$$v_0(x, 0^-) = 0 \tag{j}$$

which also implies that $v_0'(x, 0^-) = v_0''(x, 0^-) = v_0'''(x, 0^-) = \cdots = 0$.

(b) *Solution to the problem.* Integrating differential Eq. (e) over time first, we obtain

$$v_0^{\mathrm{iv}}(x, t) = -f(t) + G(x) \tag{k}$$

where $f(t)$ from direct integration is

$$f(t) = \frac{q_0}{Iq_1^E}(t + p_1^E)[u(t)] \tag{ℓ}$$

and $G(x)$ is a spatial function of integration, which must vanish by virtue of initial condition (j). Now integrate Eq. (k) with $G(x) = 0$, successively, four times over x:

$$v_0'''(x, t) = -f(t)x + F_1(t) \tag{m}$$

$$v_0''(x, t) = -f(t)\frac{x^2}{2} + F_1(t)x + F_2(t) \tag{n}$$

$$v_0'(x, t) = -f(t)\frac{x^3}{6} + F_1(t)\frac{x^2}{2} + F_2(t)x + F_3(t) \tag{o}$$

$$v_0(x, t) = -f(t)\frac{x^4}{24} + F_1(t)\frac{x^3}{6} + F_2(t)\frac{x^2}{2} + F_3(t)x + F_4(t) \tag{p}$$

where $F_1(t)$, $F_2(t)$, $F_3(t)$, and $F_4(t)$ are time functions of integration to be determined from the boundary conditions. Applying boundary conditions (f) to Eqs. (n) and (p), we immediately see that $F_2(t) = F_4(t) = 0$. The determination of $F_1(t)$ and $F_3(t)$ is more difficult. However, by applying initial condition (j) to Eqs. (m) and (o), we see that they must satisfy the conditions $F_1(0^-) = F_3(0^-) = 0$.

By next applying condition (g) to Eq. (o) with $F_2(t) = 0$, we obtain the following relation between $F_3(t)$ and $F_1(t)$:

$$F_3(t) = f(t)\frac{L^3}{6} - F_1(t)\frac{L^2}{2} \tag{q}$$

Finally, condition (h) in conjunction with Eqs. (m) and (p) with $F_2(t) = F_4(t) = 0$ yields

$$-\dot{f}(t)L + \dot{F}_1(t) - a\left[-f(t)\frac{L^4}{24} + F_1(t)\frac{L^3}{6} + F_3(t)L\right.$$
$$\left. - p_1^E\dot{f}(t)\frac{L^4}{24} + p_1^E\dot{F}_1(t)\frac{L^3}{6} + p_1^E\dot{F}_3(t)L\right] = 0$$

We may now eliminate $F_3(t)$ from this result by means of Eq. (q), and after rearranging terms we get the ordinary differential equation in $F_1(t)$,

$$\dot{F}_1(t) + \lambda F_1(t) = g(t) \tag{r}$$

where λ is the constant

$$\lambda = \frac{aL^3}{3 + ap_1^E L^3} \tag{s}$$

and $g(t)$ is given in terms of known function $f(t)$ as

$$g(t) = \frac{3L(8 + ap_1^E L^3)\dot{f}(t) + 3aL^4 f(t)}{8(3 + ap_1^E L^3)} \tag{t}$$

By introducing an integrating factor we can easily obtain the solution to differential equation (r) as

$$F_1(t) = e^{-\lambda t}\int_{0^-}^{t} e^{\lambda t'} g(t')\, dt' \tag{u}$$

where we have used the previously obtained condition $F_1(0^-) = 0$.

We leave it for you to verify that the evaluation of integral (u), with the use of Eqs. (i), (ℓ), (s), and (t), yields

$$F_1(t) = q_0[u(t)]\left[\frac{15}{4L^2 k} + \frac{3L}{8Iq_1^E}(t + p_1^E) - Ce^{-\lambda t}\right] \tag{v}$$

where C is the constant

$$C = \frac{45Iq_1^E}{2L^2 k(6Iq_1^E + kp_1^E L^3)} \tag{w}$$

Function $F_3(t)$ then follows directly from Eqs. (q), (ℓ) and (v) as

$$F_3(t) = -q_0\frac{L^2}{2}[u(t)]\left[\frac{15}{4L^2 k} + \frac{L}{24Iq_1^E}(t + p_1^E) - Ce^{-\lambda t}\right] \tag{x}$$

The final complete solution then follows from Eq. (p), with $F_2(t) = F_4(t) = 0$ and with $F_1(t)$ and $F_2(t)$ given by Eqs. (v) and (x), as

$$v_0(x, t) = -q_0[u(t)]\left\{\frac{t + p_1^E}{Iq_1^E}\frac{x^4}{24} - \left[\frac{15}{4L^2 k} + \frac{3L}{8Iq_1^E}(t + p_1^E) - Ce^{-\lambda t}\right]\frac{x^3}{6}\right.$$
$$\left. + \frac{L^2}{2}\left[\frac{15}{4L^2 k} + \frac{L}{24Iq_1^E}(t + p_1^E) - Ce^{-\lambda t}\right]x\right\} \tag{y}$$

Note that as t approaches infinity at the center support, solution Eq. (y) yields the finite limit

$$v_0(L, \infty) = -\frac{5q_0 L}{4k}$$

whereas $v_0(x, \infty)$ is unbounded at all other points interior to $x = 0$ and $2L$. How can you explain this interesting result?

Flexure of Beams   Chap. 10

We have seen in Sections 10.6 and 10.7 that deflections in linear, isothermal, homogeneous viscoelastic beams may readily be determined, although the details for indeterminate beams with deformable supports may be somewhat laborious. In the next part we consider stress and deflection in nonlinear viscous beams, with some consideration of inhomogeneous material properties.

PART C
NONLINEAR VISCOUS BEAMS

10.8 STRESS AND STRAIN CONSIDERATIONS

Again we consider beams (see Fig. 10.10) having a longitudinal plane of symmetry (i.e., xy) with constant material and geometric properties. As the constitutive law we shall employ the nonlinear viscous stress power law [see Eq. (7.31)]

$$\dot{\varepsilon}_{xx} = \left(\frac{\tau_{xx}}{\lambda_c}\right)^n, \qquad n = 1, 3, 5, 7, \ldots \tag{10.30}$$

where n is an odd positive integer,* λ_c is a constant viscosity parameter and $\dot{\varepsilon}_{xx}$ represents $\partial \varepsilon_{xx}(x, t)/\partial t$. You will recall that Eq. (10.30) corresponds to the steady creep component, and hence it is applicable to problems in which instantaneous strain and transient creep strain may be ignored. Furthermore, as discussed in Chapter 7, $n = 1$ and $\lambda_c = \eta$ indicates *linear viscous* behavior, whereas $n \to \infty$ approaches *fully perfectly plastic* behavior (see Fig. 7.2). The x axis for the beam as usual will correspond to the plane of zero strain with loading in the plane of symmetry (see Fig. 10.10) and normal to x. We will soon see that in general the neutral axis for this material does *not* go through the centroid.

Accordingly, set the axial force on a section of beam equal to zero. Thus

$$\int_R \tau_{xx}\, dA = 0$$

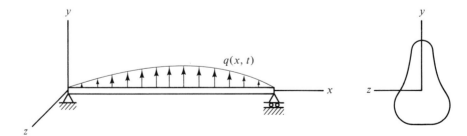

Figure 10.10   Axes for the beam.

---

*This development is easily extended to arbitrary positive n, by replacing Eq. (10.30) with $\dot{\varepsilon}_{xx} = (|\tau_{xx}|/\lambda_c)^n \, \mathrm{sgn}\, \tau_{xx}$. For details, see J. A. Hult, *Creep in Engineering Structures* (New York: Blaisdell Publishing Company, 1966), p. 44.

where the limits of integration are constants because the beam is of uniform cross section. Substituting from the nonlinear constitutive law [Eq. (10.30)], we then have

$$0 = \int_R \lambda_c(\dot{\varepsilon}_{xx})^{1/n}\, dA = -\lambda_c \int_R (\dot{\kappa}y)^{1/n}\, dA$$

where we have used Eq. (10.1) to eliminate $\dot{\varepsilon}_{xx}$ and have also replaced $(-1)^{1/n}$ by -1 since n is an odd positive integer. Extracting $\dot{\kappa}(x, t)$ from the integration, we may thus conclude that

$$\boxed{\int_R y^{1/n}\, dA = 0} \tag{10.31}$$

Upon examination of Eq. (10.31), we may conclude:

1. If $n = 1$, $\int_R y\, dA = 0$ and the neutral axis is at the *centroid* of the area.
2. If $n \to \infty$, $\int_R \operatorname{sgn} y\, dA = 0$ and the neutral axis lies along the *median* of the area.

In item (2) we have used the fact that $\lim\limits_{n \to \infty} y^{1/n} = \operatorname{sgn} y$, where sgn is the signum function. These two extreme cases are illustrated for a particular cross section in Fig. 10.11, and you should note that the median divides the cross section into two equal areas. Obviously, the neutral axis of this cross section for other values of n will lie in between these two extreme axes. However, if there are two axes of symmetry, as for the elliptical cross section shown in Fig. 10.12, the centroidal and median axes will coincide.

Next we seek the *moment-curvature* relation, and thus we consider the moment M about the z axis in the neutral plane. Proceeding in a manner similar to the above, we obtain

$$M = -\int_R y\tau_{xx}\, dA = -\int_R y\lambda_c(\dot{\varepsilon}_{xx})^{1/n}\, dA$$

$$= \int_R y\lambda_c(\dot{\kappa}y)^{1/n}\, dA \tag{10.32}$$

$$= \lambda_c \dot{\kappa}^{1/n} \int_R y^{(n+1)/n}\, dA$$

Let us introduce the definition

$$\boxed{I_n = \int_R y^{(n+1)/n}\, dA, \qquad n = 1, 3, 5, \dots} \tag{10.33}$$

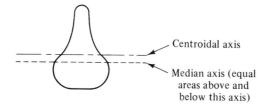

Centroidal axis

Median axis (equal areas above and below this axis)

Figure 10.11 Section showing centroidal axis and the median axis.

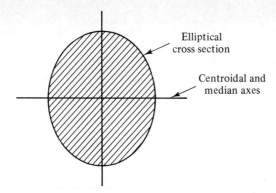

Elliptical
cross section

Centroidal and
median axes

Figure 10.12 Centroidal and median
axes coincide for two axes of symmetry.

For $n = 1$, corresponding to linear viscous behavior, $I_n = I_1 = \int_R y^2 \, dA$ which is the familiar second moment of area I. Furthermore, for $n \to \infty$, $I_n = I_\infty = \int_R |y| \, dA$, where the magnitude in the integrand is necessary since $y^{(n+1)/n}$ is positive for all real values of y if n is restricted to odd positive integers. Using definition (10.33) in Eq. (10.32), we obtain the moment-curvature relation as

$$M = \lambda_c \dot{\kappa}^{1/n} I_n \qquad (10.34)$$

We may now formulate a "flexure" formula. To do this, replace $\dot{\kappa}$ in Eq. (10.34) by $-\dot{\varepsilon}_{xx}/y$ to get

$$M = \lambda_c \left(-\frac{\dot{\varepsilon}_{xx}}{y} \right)^{1/n} I_n$$

Now replace $\dot{\varepsilon}_{xx}$ using the constitutive law [Eq. (10.30)], and after rearranging terms, we get

$$\boxed{\tau_{xx}(x, y, t) = -\frac{M(x,t)y^{1/n}}{I_n}} \qquad (10.35)$$

which is the desired *flexure formula*. If $n = 1$ we get the familiar flexure formula for linear elastic beams, that is,

$$\tau_{xx} = -\frac{My}{I} \qquad \text{for } n = 1 \qquad (10.36)$$

This is no surprise, since we proved in Section 10.4 that the usual flexure formula is obtained for homogeneous linear viscoelastic beams, and linear viscous behavior (i.e., $n = 1$) is a special case of linear viscoelasticity. Also, for $n \to \infty$ we get

$$\tau_{xx} = -\frac{M}{I_\infty} \text{sgn}(y) \qquad \text{for } n \to \infty \qquad (10.37)$$

where sgn is the signum function, and as indicated previously,

$$I_\infty = \int_R |y| \, dA \qquad (10.38)$$

We shall now present two examples that illustrate the results of this section.

Example 10.6

Consider a nonlinear viscous rectangular beam of width b and height h (see Fig. 10.13), subjected to pure bending $M = M_0$. Determine I_n and $\tau_{xx}(y)$ for this beam, and sketch the stress distribution for $n = 1, 3$ and $n \to \infty$ with $M_0 = 1000$ in.-lb, $b = 1$ in., and $h = 2$ in.

Since this particular cross section has two axes of symmetry, the neutral axis coincides with both the centroidal and median axes for all values of n, as shown in Fig. 10.13. Using Eq. (10.33) we may thus compute I_n as follows:

$$I_n = \int_R y^{(n+1)/n}\, dA = b \int_{-h/2}^{h/2} y^{(n+1)/n}\, dy = b \frac{n}{2n+1} y^{(2n+1)/n} \Big|_{-h/2}^{h/2} \tag{a}$$

Since $y^{(2n+1)/n}$ is an even function, Eq. (a) may be given as

$$I_n = 2b \frac{n}{2n+1} \left(\frac{h}{2}\right)^{(2n+1)/n} \tag{b}$$

It then follows from this result that

$$I_1 = I = \frac{bh^3}{12} \tag{c}$$

$$I_\infty = \frac{bh^2}{4} \tag{d}$$

Alternatively, we can obtain Eq. (c) from $\int y^2\, dA$ and Eq. (d) from $\int |y|\, dA$.

The stress distribution now follows from Eq. (10.35) with $M = M_0$ and from Eq. (b) above as

$$\tau_{xx}(y) = -\frac{M_0 y^{1/n}}{2b \dfrac{n}{2n+1} \left(\dfrac{h}{2}\right)^{(2n+1)/n}} \tag{e}$$

For $n = 1$ and $n \to \infty$, Eq. (e) simplifies to

$$\tau_{xx}(y) = -\frac{M_0 y}{bh^3/12} \qquad \text{for } n = 1 \tag{f}$$

$$\tau_{xx}(y) = -\frac{M_0 \, \text{sgn}(y)}{bh^2/4} \qquad \text{for } n \to \infty \tag{g}$$

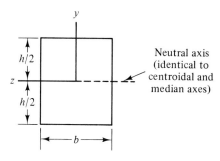

Neutral axis
(identical to
centroidal and
median axes)

Figure 10.13 Rectangular nonlinear viscous beam.

Inserting $M_0 = 1000$ in.-lb, $b = 1$ in. and $h = 2$ in. into Eqs. (e), (f), and (g), we get

$$\tau_{xx} = -1500y \text{ psi} \qquad \text{for } n = 1$$

$$\tau_{xx} = -1167y^{1/3} \text{ psi} \qquad \text{for } n = 3 \qquad\qquad \text{(h)}$$

$$\tau_{xx} = -1000 \text{ sgn}(y) \text{ psi} \qquad \text{for } n \to \infty$$

Equations (h) have been sketched in Fig. 10.14, and you will note that τ_{xx} is highly nonlinear for $n = 3$, and that $n \to \infty$ corresponds with rigid, perfectly plastic behavior with a "yield point" of 1000 psi.

Example 10.7

In Fig. 10.15 we show a nonlinear viscous beam with an isosceles triangular cross section. Locate the neutral axis and determine I_n. Specialize your results to the $n = 1$ and $n \to \infty$ special cases.

In the figure the distance d from the base to the z axis is an unknown distance corresponding to the position of the neutral axis relative to the base. The value of d is determined from Eq. (10.31), which we now rewrite

$$\int_R y^{1/n} dA = 0 \qquad\qquad \text{(a)}$$

To set up the integral, we note that along line $\overline{AC}$ in Fig. 10.15 we have for z as a function of y (using similar triangles gkC and AEC)

$$z = \frac{b}{2h}(h - d - y)$$

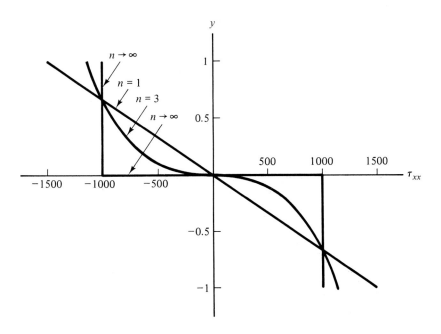

Figure 10.14 Stress distribution for rectangular beam.

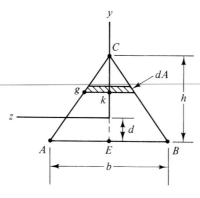

Figure 10.15 Nonlinear viscous triangular beam.

The area element is thus

$$dA = 2z\,dy = \frac{b}{h}(h - d - y)\,dy \tag{b}$$

and Eq. (a) yields

$$\int_{-d}^{h-d} (h - d - y)y^{1/n}\,dy = 0 \tag{c}$$

The integration is straightforward and leads after some manipulation to the following equation:

$$(h - d)^{(2n+1)/n} + d^{(2n+1)/n} - \frac{2n+1}{n}hd^{(n+1)/n} = 0 \tag{d}$$

In this result we have set $(-1)^{(n+1)/n} = 1$ and $(-1)^{(2n+1)/n} = -1$, since n is a positive odd integer. If a specific value of n is given, we can solve for the desired value of d and thus find the position of the neutral axis. You can easily show that

$$d = \begin{cases} \dfrac{h}{3} & \text{for } n = 1 \\[2mm] \left(1 - \dfrac{\sqrt{2}}{2}\right)h = 0.293h & \text{for } n \to \infty \end{cases} \tag{e}$$

in which the first result defines the centroid and the second gives the median. Thus, for any value of n,

$$0.333 \geq \frac{d}{h} > 0.293 \qquad \text{for } 1 \leq n < \infty \tag{f}$$

Now let us determine I_n as defined by Eq. (10.33), that is,

$$I_n = \int_R y^{(n+1)/n}\,dA \tag{g}$$

Inserting dA from Eq. (b) this becomes

$$I_n = \frac{b}{h}\int_{-d}^{h-d} (h - d - y)y^{(n+1)/n}\,dy \tag{h}$$

We get upon carrying out the integration

$$I_n = \frac{b}{h} \left\{ \frac{n(h-d)}{2n+1} [(h-d)^{(2n+1)/n} + d^{(2n+1)/n}] \right.$$

$$\left. + \frac{n}{3n+1} [d^{(3n+1)/n} - (h-d)^{(3n+1)/n}] \right\} \tag{i}$$

where here we have set $(-1)^{(2n+1)/n} = -1$ and $(-1)^{(3n+1)/n} = 1$. Finally, for $n = 1$ and $n \to \infty$, we get with the use of Eqs. (e) for d,

$$I_1 = I = \frac{bh^3}{36} \qquad \text{for } n = 1$$

$$I_\infty = \frac{2-\sqrt{2}}{6} bh^2 \qquad \text{for } n \to \infty \tag{j}$$

It is now a simple matter to get stresses for this problem.

We now consider the *deflection* in nonlinear viscous beams.

10.9 DEFLECTION OF NONLINEAR VISCOUS BEAMS

As is usual, we start with the curvature–deflection relation [Eq. (10.4)], valid for all beams with small deflection slopes. Thus

$$\kappa = \frac{\partial^2 v_0}{\partial x^2}$$

Upon differentiating with respect to time, we get

$$\dot{\kappa} = \frac{\partial^2 \dot{v}_0}{\partial x^2} \tag{10.39}$$

Now substitute for $\dot{\kappa}$ as given above into Eq. (10.34) to get

$$M = \lambda_c \left(\frac{\partial^2 \dot{v}_0}{\partial x^2} \right)^{1/n} I_n = \lambda_c (\dot{v}_0'')^{1/n} I_n$$

Solving for $\dot{v}_0''$, we obtain

$$\boxed{\dot{v}_0'' = \left(\frac{M}{\lambda_c I_n} \right)^n} \tag{10.40}$$

Equation (10.40) is one form of the deflection differential equation. Another form involving the loading function q rather than the bending moment M will be formulated next. Take the nth root and then the second partial derivative of Eq. (10.40) with respect to x. Accordingly, we obtain

$$[(\dot{v}_0'')^{1/n}]'' = \frac{M''}{\lambda_c I_n} \tag{10.41}$$

From equilibrium considerations for all beams having small deformation, we can replace M'' by q [see Eq. (10.2c)]. We then arrive at the second form of the deflection equation

$$[(v_0'')^{1/n}]'' = \frac{q}{\lambda_c I_n} \tag{10.42}$$

Note that for linear viscous behavior, $n = 1$ and $\lambda_c = \eta$. This equation then reduces to linear viscoelastic equation (10.21) for $P^E = 1$ and $Q^E = \eta D$. Also note that no nonzero finite limiting form exists for $n \to \infty$, which is consistent with the fact the deflections are indeterminate for perfectly plastic behavior.

Equation (10.42) is in general more useful than Eq. (10.40), since in many problems the loading function $q(x, t)$ is either known or easily set up in terms of reactions. However, if $M(x, t)$ is known as in the case of statically determinate problems, then Eq. (10.40) may be more convenient. We now illustrate the use of this formulation.

Example 10.8

We have shown in Fig. 10.16 a tip-loaded, nonlinear viscous cantilever beam, where the load P is suddenly applied at $t = 0$. Find the deflection as a function of position and time [i.e., $v_0(x, t)$].

The bending moment is here simply $-Px$ for $0 \le x \le L$ and $t \ge 0^+$. Hence going to Eq. (10.40), we have

$$\dot{v}_0'' = -\left(\frac{Px}{\lambda_c I_n}\right)^n, \qquad n = 1, 3, 5, \dots \tag{a}$$

Integrating with respect to x once, we then get

$$\dot{v}_0' = -\left(\frac{P}{\lambda_c I_n}\right)^n \frac{x^{n+1}}{n+1} + f_1(t) \tag{b}$$

We can obtain the function $f_1(t)$ by noting for all times $\dot{v}_0' = 0$ at the clamped support at $x = L$. Thus we have

$$f_1(t) = \left(\frac{P}{\lambda_c I_n}\right)^n \frac{L^{n+1}}{n+1} \tag{c}$$

and we can write

$$\dot{v}_0' = -\left(\frac{P}{\lambda_c I_n}\right)^n \frac{1}{n+1}(x^{n+1} - L^{n+1}) \tag{d}$$

$P[u(t)]$

x

L

Figure 10.16 Nonlinear viscous cantilever beam.

Integrating a second time with respect to x, we get

$$\dot{v}_0 = -\left(\frac{P}{\lambda_c I_n}\right)^n \frac{1}{n+1}\left[\frac{x^{n+2}}{n+2} - L^{n+1}x\right] + f_2(t) \tag{e}$$

At $x = L$ we have as a second boundary condition $\dot{v}_0 = 0$ at all times. We can then solve for $f_2(t)$ as

$$f_2(t) = \left(\frac{P}{\lambda_c I_n}\right)^n \frac{1}{n+1}\left[\frac{L^{n+2} - (n+2)L^{n+2}}{n+2}\right] \tag{f}$$

$$= -\left(\frac{P}{\lambda_c I_n}\right)^n \frac{L^{n+2}}{n+2}$$

Hence we have for $\dot{v}_0$,

$$\dot{v}_0 = -\left(\frac{P}{\lambda_c I_n}\right)^n\left[\frac{x^{n+2}}{(n+1)(n+2)} - \frac{L^{n+1}x}{n+1} + \frac{L^{n+2}}{n+2}\right] \tag{g}$$

Finally, integrating with respect to time, we get

$$v_0 = -\left(\frac{P}{\lambda_c I_n}\right)^n\left[\frac{x^{n+2}}{(n+1)(n+2)} - \frac{L^{n+1}x}{n+1} + \frac{L^{n+2}}{n+2}\right]t + g(x) \tag{h}$$

For a step loading at $t = 0$ the deflection in a viscous beam will not suddenly "jump," and thus we have the initial condition $v_0(x, 0^+) = 0$. Hence function $g(x) = 0$ and the final result is then

$$v_0(x, t) = -\left(\frac{P}{\lambda_c I_n}\right)^n\left[\frac{x^{n+2}}{(n+1)(n+2)} - \frac{L^{n+1}x}{n+1} + \frac{L^{n+2}}{n+2}\right]t \tag{i}$$

For $n = 1$, Eq. (i) reduces to the same solution obtainable from linear viscoelastic equation (10.21), but as expected, no finite nonzero limiting deflection solution exists for $n \to \infty$.

We conclude this section with some brief remarks about beams on a *continuous elastic foundation*. In some applications a beam will rest on a continuous elastic foundation,* which may be approximated by an infinite number of isolated springs with spring constant k. This is illustrated in Fig. 10.17(a) and is called the *Winkler foundation*. If under some external load $q_e(x, t)$ the beam deflects an amount $v_0(x, t)$, the foundation reacts by exerting a reactive force of magnitude $kv_0(x, t)$ in the direction opposite to $v_0(x, t)$ [see Fig. 10.17(b)]. Clearly, then, the total loading function is given as

$$q(x, t) = q_e(x, t) - kv_0(x, t) \tag{10.43}$$

We may now extend *any* of our previous formulations to include the Winkler foundation, simply by replacing the loading function with Eq. (10.43). Thus equilibrium equations (10.2), which are valid for any material, now become

---

* For additional information, see M. Hetenyi, "Beams on Elastic Foundation," in W. Flügge (ed.), *Handbook of Engineering Mechanics* (New York: McGraw-Hill Book Company, 1962), Chap. 31. The linear viscoelastic foundation is discussed in W. Flügge, *Viscoelasticity* (Berlin: Springer-Verlag, 1975), Chap. 4. The latter reference contains a variety of viscoelastic beam solutions.

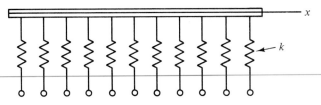

(a) Winkler foundation

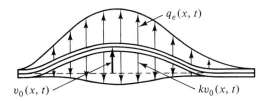

(b) Winkler reactive force

Figure 10.17 Beam on a continuous elastic foundation.

$$V' = -q_e + kv_0 \qquad \text{(a)}$$

$$M' = -V \qquad \text{(b)} \qquad (10.44)$$

$$M'' = q_e - kv_0 \qquad \text{(c)}$$

For the nonlinear viscous beam, Eq. (10.42) becomes with the use of Eq. (10.43):

$$[(\dot{v}_0'')^{1/n}]'' + \frac{k}{\lambda_c I_n} v_0 = \frac{q_e}{\lambda_c I_n} \qquad (10.45)$$

We may also obtain a moment-load formulation by using Eq. (10.44c) to eliminate v_0 from Eq. (10.40). Accordingly, we get

$$\left(\frac{\dot{q}_e - \dot{M}''}{k} \right)'' = \left(\frac{M}{\lambda_c I_n} \right)^n$$

which then yields

$$\dot{M}^{\text{iv}} + \frac{k}{(\lambda_c I_n)^n} M^n = \dot{q}_e'' \qquad (10.46)$$

Equations (10.45) and (10.46) are complicated nonlinear differential equations, which would in general require numerical solutions for $n \neq 1$ to determine the deflection $v_0(x, t)$ and the bending moment M for a given loading $q_e(x)$. The stress τ_{xx} is then obtainable from Eq. (10.35).

In the next section we briefly consider nonlinear viscous beams with inhomogeneous viscosity.

10.10 EXTENSION TO CASE OF INHOMOGENEOUS VISCOSITY

In preceding sections the viscosity parameter λ_c in the constitutive law was a constant. We shall now consider λ_c to be a function of y, where $y = 0$ defines the neutral axis. Since viscosity is highly sensitive to temperature, this variation could typically be the result of a temperature gradient through the height of the cross section.* The viscosity parameter will actually be prescribed as a function of a coordinate measured from some convenient location, such as the base of the cross section. The function $\lambda_c(y)$ is then formulated by a simple variable change, using the *unknown* distance d between the base of the cross section and the neutral axis. The nonlinear viscous constitutive law is then expressed as

$$\dot{\varepsilon}_{xx} = \left(\frac{\tau_{xx}}{\lambda_c(y)}\right)^n, \qquad n = 1, 3, 5, 7, \ldots \tag{10.47}$$

First we consider the location of the *neutral axis*. Thus we have

$$0 = \int_R \tau_{xx}\, dA = \int_R (\dot{\varepsilon}_{xx})^{1/n} \lambda_c(y)\, dA$$

Replace ε_{xx} by $-\kappa y$, where, as noted above, y is measured from the yet unknown *neutral axis*. This is permissible for all beams with small deformations. We then get

$$0 = -(\dot{\kappa})^{1/n} \int_R y^{1/n} \lambda_c(y)\, dA$$

and therefore

$$\int_R y^{1/n} \lambda_c(y)\, dA = 0 \tag{10.48}$$

The neutral axis is generally not at the centroid unless the following two conditions are met:

1. There is a *second axis of symmetry* in addition to the y axis (i.e., there are two axes of symmetry).
2. Viscosity parameter $\lambda_c(y)$ is an *even* function of y.

Now take moments about the neutral axis. We get on using Eq. (10.47) for τ_{xx},

$$M = -\int_R \tau_{xx} y\, dA = -\int_R (\dot{\varepsilon}_{xx})^{1/n} \lambda_c(y) y\, dA = \int_R (\dot{\kappa}y)^{1/n} \lambda_c(y) y\, dA = \dot{\kappa}^{1/n} J_n \tag{10.49}$$

where

$$J_n = \int_R y^{(n+1)/n} \lambda_c(y)\, dA \tag{10.50}$$

Note that if in the equation above, $\lambda_c(y) = \lambda_0$, a constant, then

$$J_n = \lambda_0 I_n \tag{10.51}$$

where I_n has been defined in Eq. (10.33).

---

* An interesting example of this phenomenon is the study of flexure in the Earth's lithospheric crust due to surface loading. The temperature in the lithosphere increases with depth due to the natural geothermal gradient. For example, see R. F. DeRito, F. A. Cozzarelli, and D. S. Hodge, "A Forward Approach to the Problem of Nonlinear Viscoelasticity and the Thickness of the Mechanical Lithosphere," *J. Geophys. Res.*, Vol. 91, No. B8, pp. 8295–8313 (1986).

We are now ready to obtain yet another "flexure" formula. Replacing $\dot{\kappa}$ in Eq. (10.49) by $-\dot{\varepsilon}_{xx}/y$, we get

$$M = -\left(\frac{\dot{\varepsilon}_{xx}}{y}\right)^{1/n} J_n \tag{10.52}$$

Now using the constitutive law to replace $\dot{\varepsilon}_{xx}$ [see Eq. (10.47)], we obtain

$$M = -\frac{\tau_{xx}}{\lambda_c(y)y^{1/n}} J_n$$

Solving for τ_{xx}, we finally get the desired extension of the flexure formula

$$\tau_{xx} = -\frac{M\lambda_c(y)y^{1/n}}{J_n} \tag{10.53}$$

Note that for $\lambda_c(y) = \lambda_0$, $J_n = \lambda_0 I_n$ [Eq. (10.51)] and perforce Eq. (10.53) reduces to Eq. (10.35).

As for the *deflection*, we go back to Eq. (10.49) and replace κ by v_0'', and thus we obtain

$$M = (v_0'')^{1/n} J_n \tag{10.54}$$

which is the moment-deflection equation. Noting from equilibrium that $M'' = q$, we then may get the load-deflection equation:

$$[(v_0'')^{1/n}]'' = \frac{q}{J_n} \tag{10.55}$$

On comparing Eqs. (10.54) and (10.55) with Eqs. (10.40) and (10.42), respectively, we see that they are of the same form except that $\lambda_c I_n$ has now been replaced by J_n. Furthermore, we may immediately extend Eqs. (10.45) and (10.46) (containing the Winkler term) in the same way to the present inhomogeneous case. Accordingly we get for the case of a Winkler foundation

$$[(v_0'')^{1/n}]'' + \frac{k}{J_n} v_0 = \frac{q_e}{J_n}$$

$$\dot{M}^{iv} + \frac{k}{(J_n)^n} M^n = \dot{q}_e'' \tag{10.56}$$

Example 10.9

Again consider the nonlinear viscous rectangular beam of Example 10.6 with $b = 1$ in. and $h = 2$ in., except that now let the viscosity parameter vary as the function $\bar{\lambda}_c(\bar{y}) = \lambda_0(1 + \bar{y})$, where $\bar{y}$ is measured from the base of the cross section (see Fig. 10.18). Obtain the general expression for the location of the neutral axis, and obtain numerical values for $n = 1$ and $n \to \infty$.

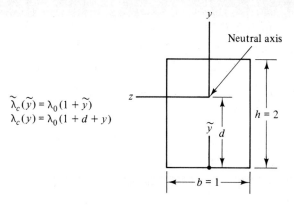

$$\tilde{\lambda}_c(\tilde{y}) = \lambda_0(1 + \tilde{y})$$
$$\lambda_c(y) = \lambda_0(1 + d + y)$$

Figure 10.18 Inhomogeneous rectangular beam.

Since $\lambda_c(y)$ is *not* an *even* function, the neutral axis will *not* coincide with the *centroid*. In Fig. 10.18 we have used d to indicate the unknown distance from the base of the rectangle to the neutral axis. Since $\tilde{y} = y + d$, we obtain $\lambda_c(y) = \lambda_0(1 + d + y)$, and Eq. (10.48) then gives

$$\int_R y^{1/n} \lambda_c(y) \, dA = b\lambda_0 \int_{-d}^{h-d} y^{1/n}(1 + d + y) \, dy = 0 \qquad (a)$$

and thus

$$(1 + d) \int_{-d}^{h-d} y^{1/n} \, dy + \int_{-d}^{h-d} y^{(n+1)/n} \, dy = 0 \qquad (b)$$

The evaluation of these integrals is routine. We get, after some algebra, the relation

$$(1 + d)[(h - d)^{(n+1)/n} - (d)^{(n+1)/n}] + \frac{n+1}{2n+1}[(h - d)^{(2n+1)/n} + (d)^{(2n+1)/n}] = 0 \qquad (c)$$

where we have set $(-1)^{(n+1)/n} = 1$ and $(-1)^{(2n+1)/n} = -1$, because n is restricted to odd positive integers. For $n = 1$ we get

$$(1 + d)[(h - d)^2 - d^2] + \tfrac{2}{3}[(h - d)^3 + d^3] = 0 \qquad (d)$$

Expanding out the terms and canceling terms when possible, we obtain

$$d = \frac{h[1 + (2h/3)]}{2 + h} \qquad (e)$$

Setting $h = 2$, we get for this case

$$d = 1.167 \qquad (f)$$

Thus the neutral axis has shifted above the centroidal axis as a result of the inhomogeneity of the viscosity. Now, letting $n \to \infty$ in Eq. (c), we obtain

$$(1 + d)[(h - d) - d] + \tfrac{1}{2}[(h - d)^2 + d^2] = 0 \qquad (g)$$

which simplifies to

$$d^2 + 2d - h\left(1 + \frac{h}{2}\right) = 0 \qquad (h)$$

Solving for d with $h = 2$, we get in this case

$$d = 1.236 \qquad (i)$$

We have seen in Part C that as $n \to \infty$ we obtain the stress distribution for a fully perfectly plastic material. The corresponding deflection is indeterminate. In Part D we study plastic behavior of beams in greater detail.

PART D
PLASTIC BEHAVIOR OF BEAMS

10.11 THE LINEAR ELASTIC, PERFECTLY PLASTIC CASE WITH PURE BENDING

We shall now turn to the case of linear elastic, perfectly plastic behavior, which we introduced in Sections 4.6 and 8.2. (Later we shall consider the more general case of an elastoplastic material with an arbitrary stress-strain curve.) We shall assume that the material is isotropic and behaves in compression in the same way that it does in tension (see Fig. 10.19). This idealization is meaningful for certain ductile structural materials such as structural steel and aluminum alloys. Furthermore, we shall assume that loading is such that the magnitude of τ_{xx} is a nondecreasing function of time. Accordingly, we will not be concerned with the complexities associated with unloading in the plastic range.

The symmetry arguments traditionally employed in "strength of materials" for pure bending to show that plane sections in beams remain plane are presented without reference to the nature of the stress-strain law for the particular isotropic material, as we have already pointed out in Section 10.1. Thus we can conclude that the normal strain ε_{xx} at a position y above the neutral surface in the undeformed geometry can again be expressed for plastic material as

$$\varepsilon_{xx} = -\frac{y}{R} = -y \frac{d^2 v_0}{dx^2} \tag{10.57}$$

where this is exact only for the case of pure bending with small deformation.

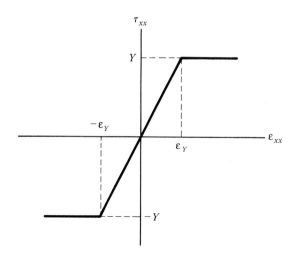

Figure 10.19 Linear elastic, perfectly plastic material, with same behavior in tension and compression.

For simplicity, we shall first consider a beam having a rectangular cross section with *pure couples* applied in a plane of symmetry (i.e., *xy*), as shown in Fig. 10.20. The maximum moment M_e that can be applied without plastic deformation may be computed using the flexure formula [i.e., Eq. (10.5a)] as follows:

$$Y = -\frac{M_e(-h/2)}{bh^3/12}$$

Therefore, M_e is given in terms of known quantities as

$$M_e = \frac{bh^2Y}{6} \tag{10.58}$$

where Y is the yield stress of the material, as shown in Fig. 10.19. When a design is based on this approach, we say we are using the *elastic-limit criterion*. If the applied couple is increased above this value, plastic deformation occurs first at the outer fibers of the beam. For our chosen constitutive law these fibers cannot develop greater stress than that having a magnitude of Y, and so give no increased resistance to further increases in load. Thus as the load is increased, adjacent fibers closer to the neutral axis reach a stress with magnitude Y and remain at this stress, with the result that regions of constant stress magnitude, Y, penetrate from the outer fibers toward the neutral surface in a manner suggested by Fig. 10.21. We denote as d the distance from the neutral surface to the position where the yield stress begins. Clearly, in this problem d must be the same above and below the neutral surface, as indicated in the diagram. Finally, we note that in the elastic range, $-d \leq y \leq d$, ε_{xx} is linearly proportional to y in accordance with Eq. (10.57), and thus Fig. 10.21 also gives the distribution of τ_{xx} versus $-R\varepsilon_{xx}$.

We may use Hooke's law in the interval $-d \leq y \leq d$ so that the strain at $y = -d$, which we denote as ε_Y (see Fig. 10.19), can be given as

$$\varepsilon_Y = \frac{Y}{E} \tag{10.59}$$

Substituting this result into Eq. (10.57) for the position $y = -d$, we then get for $1/R$,

$$\frac{1}{R} = \frac{Y}{Ed} \tag{10.60}$$

We thus have the radius of curvature in terms of Y and E, which are properties of the material, and d, which depends on the applied load M. The stress distribution is also known in terms of these quantities. Thus for $d \leq y \leq h/2$ (i.e., the plastic region on top) we have $\tau_{xx} = -Y$, and for $-d \geq y \geq -h/2$ (i.e., the plastic region at

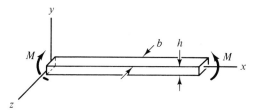

Figure 10.20 Pure bending of plastic beam.

the bottom) we have $\tau_{xx} = Y$. Furthermore, for the elastic region $-d \le y \le d$, we have

$$\tau_{xx} = E\epsilon_{xx} = -E\frac{y}{R} \tag{10.61}$$

wherein we have used Hooke's law and Eq. (10.57). Now replacing $1/R$ in accordance with Eq. (10.60), for τ_{xx} we have

$$\tau_{xx} = -\frac{Yy}{d}, \qquad -d \le y \le d \tag{10.62}$$

Equation (10.62) shows the linear variation of stress in the elastic range and could have been determined by merely inspecting Fig. 10.21.

Our task is now to determine d in terms of the applied moment M. First we note that the stress distribution must have a zero resultant force for this problem. This requires that

$$\int_{-h/2}^{-d} Yb\,dy + \int_{-d}^{d} \tau_{xx} b\,dy + \int_{d}^{h/2} (-Y)b\,dy = 0$$

Clearly, the first and last integrals cancel each other. Substituting for τ_{xx} using Eq. (10.62), we then have

$$-\frac{Y}{d}\int_{-d}^{d} yb\,dy = 0$$

and therefore

$$\int_{-d}^{d} y\,dy = 0 \tag{10.63}$$

This shows that the neutral axis is the *centroidal* axis for this case. (As we learned in Part C on nonlinear viscous behavior, this need not necessarily occur for more complex stress-strain laws.)

Next we take moments of the stress distribution about the neutral axis. Thus

$$M = -\int_{-h/2}^{-d} Yyb\,dy - \int_{-d}^{d} \tau_{xx} yb\,dy - \int_{d}^{h/2} (-Y)yb\,dy$$

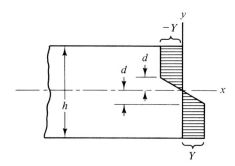

Figure 10.21 Stress distribution.

Substituting for τ_{xx} using Eq. (10.62) and integrating, we get

$$M = -bY \left.\frac{y^2}{2}\right|_{-h/2}^{-d} + \frac{bY}{d}\left.\frac{y^3}{3}\right|_{-d}^{d} + bY \left.\frac{y^2}{2}\right|_{d}^{h/2}$$

Putting in the limits we finally obtain

$$M = bY\left(\frac{h^2}{4} - \frac{d^2}{3}\right) \tag{10.64}$$

We can solve for d from Eq. (10.64) for any given applied moment M, so that we now have a complete statement as to the stress distribution for this problem.

The maximum moment that the beam can withstand with finite deformation occurs when $d = 0$, that is, when the elastic core has shrunk to zero thickness and plastic action pervades the entire section. This bending moment is called the *plastic-hinge moment*, M_p, and when we base a design on M_p we are using the *plastic-limit criterion* to be discussed shortly. Setting $d = 0$ in Eq. (10.64), we see that M_p for the rectangular cross section under consideration is expressed in terms of *known* properties as

$$M_p = \frac{bh^2 Y}{4} \tag{10.65}$$

Note that $M_p = \frac{3}{2}M_e$ [see Eq. (10.58)], and thus we see that by permitting complete plastic deformation the maximum applied moment has been increased by 50%. Also note that as $d \to 0$ the stress distribution in Fig. 10.21 approaches fully perfectly plastic behavior, and that in this case Eq. (10.65) gives the ratio M_p/Y as $bh^2/4$. But this is *precisely* the result obtained in Example 10.6 of Section 10.8, by letting the nonlinear viscous stress power n approach infinity.

Until now, we have considered only the case of *pure bending*. As in our earlier work, we can extend the results above in an approximate sense to loadings which include shear force, provided that we use local values of M. This in turn gives a local value of d, and we say that a *plastic hinge* forms at those points where d vanishes. Furthermore, the radius of curvature R as computed from Eq. (10.60) would then be a local radius of curvature.

10.12 LIMIT ANALYSIS OF ENGINEERING STRUCTURES

For certain purposes one may consider that a structure fails when for a linear elastic material, the yield stress is reached somewhere so that permanent deformation is developed there. It may well be that the structure, despite the permanent deformation developed, can still be capable of withstanding even greater loads. Hence if the presence of a reasonable amount of permanent deformation is acceptable in a structure, one can design on the basis of loads larger than those required by the exclusion of plastic deformation. We shall now introduce the concept of *limit analysis* as a means of ascertaining acceptable maximum loads for a structure in which reasonable plastic deformation is permitted.

To do this let us consider the simply supported beam, shown in Fig. 10.22(a) loaded by a uniform loading q whose value we shall assume can be varied. The bending-moment diagram has been shown as a dashed curve in this diagram. The maximum bending moment occurs at the center of the beam. Clearly, if q is increased sufficiently, a bending moment wherein the yield stress pervades the entire section will first be reached at point B at the center of this beam. This is the maximum *possible* bending moment and is the plastic *hinge moment* which we have denoted as M_p. For further increases in external load, point B acts as a "hinge," offering no increased resistance to bending. In our simply supported beam there would then be a collapse of the beam under such an increase of load. We would say that the beam becomes at this time a *mechanism* and is no longer fulfilling its mission of withstanding the external loading. This has been shown in an exaggerated manner in Fig. 10.22(b). Note that the load has been increased to a degree where the beam acts like two members pinned at points A, B, and C. With C free to move horizontally, the beam then acts like a *mechanism* having certain constraints.

In more complex systems the achievement of the moment M_p at a particular point may not mean that the structure has been reduced to a mechanism. The structure may continue to withstand increased loads with acceptably small deflections. In that case the moment at the aforementioned position remains at the value M_p, but moments elsewhere increase in value as the load is increased further. Clearly, another position in the structure will then eventually reach the value M_p. If a mechanism is formed at this stage, the structure is considered to have failed. If not, one continues to increase the load until enough plastic hinges have been formed as to render the structure a mechanism. The structure "fails" at this particular load. Thus consider the loaded frame shown in Fig. 10.23(a). The bending moment distribution in this frame will be linear between each successive pair of numbered points, and thus the moments will reach their maximum values at these points. Therefore, the plastic yield hinges can occur only at these four numbered points. Consider the case in which a plastic hinge first forms at the clamped support point 1 as the loads P and Q are increased. Clearly, this frame can continue to support increased loads. As loads are increased further, additional plastic hinges

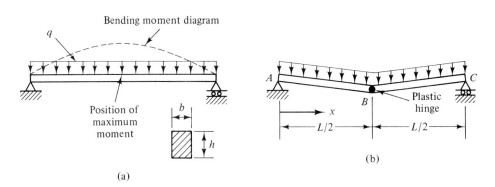

(a)

(b)

Figure 10.22 Development of plastic hinge.

Flexure of Beams   Chap. 10

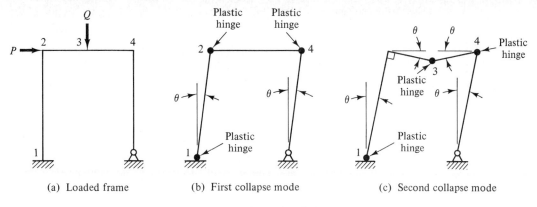

(a) Loaded frame (b) First collapse mode (c) Second collapse mode

Figure 10.23 Collapse of a frame.

are formed so as eventually to form a mechanism. The frame is then said to be in a "collapse mode," and two such possible collapse modes are shown in Fig. 10.23(b) and (c), depending on values of loads, sequence of loading, and geometry. In either case we have failure of the frame to support increased loading.*

You will note that we used the bending moment as the key measure above for beams and frames. In the limit analysis of other engineering structures we also use certain *stress resultants* and corresponding *generalized strains* in conjunction with limit analysis rather than using the usual stress and strain tensors. Thus, for torsion of rods we use the twisting moment (T) at a section, while for plates we use bending moments (M_x, M_y), twisting moment (M_{xy}), and shear forces (V_x, V_y, V_z). Using the stress resultants, we can determine a collapse load when plastic flow occurs in several locations of the structure so as to form a mechanism. For loads up to this collapse (or limit) load the deformation can still be small, and we can use original geometry for the analysis with a rigid, plastic or elastic, perfectly plastic behavior of the material. The method of limit analysis under these conditions provides a relatively simple means of either determining or bracketing the limit load, without the need to investigate the elastic, plastic behavior, which can often be difficult and tedious.

Example 10.10

Compare the maximum intensity of uniform loading q for the simply supported rectangular beam shown in Fig. 10.22, when the elastic-limit criterion is used and when the plastic-limit criterion is used. Also determine the function $d(x)$, which gives the equation of the line that separates elastic from plastic behavior (refer back to Fig. 10.21).

From simple equilibrium the bending moment M at the center of the beam is

$$M = \frac{qL^2}{8} \qquad \text{at } x = \frac{L}{2} \tag{a}$$

---

*For full details on the formation of plastic hinges in beams and frames, see P. G. Hodge, Jr., *Plastic Analysis of Structures* (New York: McGraw-Hill Book Company, 1959), Part I. Plates and shells are considered in Part II of this reference.

Hence, for elastic action, we have for the maximum stress at the center section of the beam

$$\tau_{xx} = \frac{(qL^2/8)(h/2)}{bh^3/12} = \frac{3qL^2}{4bh^2} \tag{b}$$

The maximum load possible with the presence of only *elastic deformation*, q_e, is then found by setting $\tau_{xx} = Y$ and solving for the loading, i.e.,

$$q_e = \frac{4bh^2Y}{3L^2} \tag{c}$$

It should be clear that if $q < q_e$, the beam is everywhere elastic.

Now let us compute the maximum loading for the *plastic-limit criterion*. From Eq. (10.65) we have M_p in terms of given *geometrical* and *material* properties as

$$M_p = \frac{bh^2Y}{4} \tag{d}$$

Substitute the preceding result for M_p into Eq. (a) with q then denoted as the plastic-hinge load q_p. Solving for q_p, we have

$$q_p = \frac{2bh^2Y}{L^2} \tag{e}$$

Note that this corresponds to the formation of a plastic hinge at $x = L/2$, and if $q > q_p$, the beam collapses. The ratio of the maximum loads according to the two criteria is thus again equal to $\frac{3}{2}$. It is up to the designer to decide on which design criterion he should base his work.

Now we consider the variation of stress with the longitudinal coordinate x, assuming that the plastic-hinge load q_p has been achieved. The corresponding bending moment distribution in the interval $L/2 \leq x \leq L$ follows simply from equilibrium as (see Fig. 10.22)

$$M(x) = \frac{q_p x}{2}(L - x) \tag{f}$$

which is a monotonically decreasing function ranging from $q_p L^2/8$ to zero as x runs from $L/2$ to L. As noted above, the stress distribution at $x = L/2$ (i.e., at the plastic hinge) corresponds to fully perfectly plastic behavior. It should also be clear that the stress distribution is *linear elastic, perfectly plastic* in an interval $L/2 < x < x_1$, and *linear elastic* in the remaining interval $x_1 \leq x \leq L$. We shall soon determine x_1.

The moment distribution in the linear elastic, perfectly plastic interval is given by Eq. (10.64) as

$$M(x) = bY\left(\frac{h^2}{4} - \frac{d(x)^2}{3}\right), \qquad \frac{L}{2} < x < x_1 \tag{g}$$

where $d(x)$ is as shown in Fig. 10.21. Equating (f) and (g), we then obtain

$$\frac{q_p x}{2}(L - x) = bY\left(\frac{h^2}{4} - \frac{d(x)^2}{3}\right), \qquad \frac{L}{2} < x < x_1 \tag{h}$$

It is an easy matter to show that after eliminating q_p by means of Eq. (e), we may solve for $d(x)$ as

$$\frac{d(x)}{h} = \sqrt{3}\left(\frac{x}{L} - \frac{1}{2}\right), \qquad \frac{L}{2} < x < x_1 \tag{i}$$

which is the equation of a straight line. Note that, as expected, $d(x) = 0$ at $x = L/2$, and that $d(x)$ increases linearly until the distribution becomes fully elastic when $d(x) = h/2$ at

$$x = x_1 = \left(1 + \frac{\sqrt{3}}{3}\right)\frac{L}{2} = 0.789L \tag{j}$$

We have considered only stresses in elastic, perfectly plastic beams up to this point, and we shall now make a few remarks about determining the deflection $v_0(x)$. For illustration, consider a beam that has been found to be linear elastic, perfectly plastic in the interval $L/2 < x < x_1$ and linear elastic in the interval $x_1 \leq x \leq L$, as in Example 10.10. In the elastic interval the deflection is obtained from Eq. (10.6), which for a rectangular beam becomes

$$\frac{d^2 v_0}{dx^2} = \frac{M(x)}{E(bh^3/12)}, \qquad x_1 \leq x \leq L \tag{10.66}$$

And in the plastic interval we may use Eq. (10.60) with $1/R = d^2 v_0/dx^2$, i.e.,

$$\frac{d^2 v_0}{dx^2} = \frac{Y}{Ed(x)}, \qquad \frac{L}{2} < x < x_1 \tag{10.67}$$

Assuming that $M(x)$ and $d(x)$ are known, we may integrate Eqs. (10.66) and (10.67) to obtain $v_0(x)$ in the appropriate intervals in terms of four constants of integration. Two constants are determined from boundary conditions at the supports, and the remaining two are found by matching solutions v_0 and dv_0/dx of Eqs. (10.66) and (10.67) at $x = x_1$. The procedure above will enable you to solve Problems 10.30 and 10.31. Finally, we note that the results of this section may be extended to beams of nonrectangular cross section.

It should be clear that stresses and deflections in statically indeterminate beams can be difficult to obtain, since $M(x)$, $d(x)$, and the locations of the hinges are in general not easily determined. In the next section we discuss how we may use limit analysis to evaluate the collapse load of such problems.

10.13 LIMIT ANALYSIS OF INDETERMINATE BEAMS

In Section 10.12 we introduced the concept of limit analysis. As an introduction to the application of these concepts and also to show the advantage in design via the limit analysis method, we considered the beam under pure bending and the example of a statically determinate beam under uniform load. We illustrated the difference in maximum loads allowable according to the elastic-limit and plastic-limit criteria. In this section we shall be specifically concerned with the determination of the collapse load in statically indeterminate beams, using the plastic-limit criterion. In such beams several hinges may form, and the locations of some of the hinges are usually not apparent. For illustration we will focus on a particular statically indeterminate beam problem. The problem chosen will be simple enough for us to obtain an analytical solution directly.

Thus, consider the indeterminate beam under a partial uniformly distributed load q shown in Fig. 10.24. For elastic behavior the bending moment of maximum

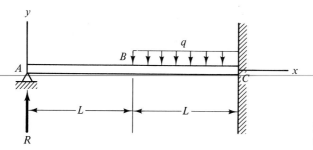

Figure 10.24 Statically indeterminate beam problem.

magnitude occurs at C, and a simple inspection shows that it is negative. Thus, as q is increased, the moment at C will be the first to reach the plastic hinge moment (i.e., $-M_p$), where for a rectangular beam M_p is known as $bh^2Y/4$ [see Eq. (10.65)]. However, a mechanism cannot occur until a second hinge forms, and hence the load may be further increased. As the load is increased, a second hinge will form at some unknown point x_1 where the moment attains the value M_p, and during this process the moment at C remains constant at $-M_p$. We wish to determine the plastic collapse load q_p and the location of the second hinge (i.e., x_1).

Referring to Fig. 10.24, we see that the moment at any point may be written in terms of the redundant reaction R at the left support as

$$M(x) = Rx, \qquad\qquad 0 \le x \le L \qquad \text{(a)}$$

$$M(x) = Rx - \frac{q}{2}(x - L)^2, \qquad L \le x \le 2L \qquad \text{(b)}$$

$$\text{(10.68)}$$

It will be convenient to introduce nondimensional quantities as follows:

$$\bar{x} = \frac{x}{L} \qquad (0 \le \bar{x} \le 2) \qquad \text{(a)}$$

$$\bar{M} = \frac{M}{M_p} \qquad (\bar{M}_p = 1) \qquad \text{(b)}$$

$$\bar{R} = \frac{RL}{M_p} \qquad\qquad\qquad \text{(c)}$$

$$\bar{q} = \frac{qL^2}{M_p} \qquad\qquad\qquad \text{(d)}$$

$$\text{(10.69)}$$

Equations (10.68) then become

$$\bar{M}(\bar{x}) = \bar{R}\bar{x}, \qquad\qquad 0 \le \bar{x} \le 1 \qquad \text{(a)}$$

$$\bar{M}(\bar{x}) = \bar{R}\bar{x} - \frac{\bar{q}}{2}(\bar{x} - 1)^2, \qquad 1 \le \bar{x} \le 2 \qquad \text{(b)}$$

$$\text{(10.70)}$$

We will now determine the location of the second hinge and the value of the plastic collapse load. From Eqs. (10.70) we see immediately that the hinge cannot be in the first interval, because upon extremizing Eq. (10.70a) we get

$$\frac{d\bar{M}}{d\bar{x}} = \bar{R} \ne 0$$

which yields no value of $\bar{x}$ at which $\bar{M}$ is extreme. Clearly, the second hinge forms in the interval $1 \leq \bar{x} \leq 2$, for which Eq. (10.70b) applies. Using this equation we may obtain expressions for the following three conditions: (a) A hinge forms at $\bar{x} = 2$ where $\bar{M}_p = -1$; (b) a second hinge forms at some point $\bar{x}_1$ where $1 \leq \bar{x}_1 \leq 2$ and $\bar{M}_p = 1$; and (c) the moment at $\bar{x}_1$ attains a relative maximum. Accordingly,

$$\bar{M}_p(2) = -1 = \bar{R}_p 2 - \bar{q}_p (1/2) \qquad \text{(a)}$$

$$\bar{M}_p(\bar{x}_1) = 1 = \bar{R}_p \bar{x}_1 - \bar{q}_p \frac{(\bar{x}_1 - 1)^2}{2} \qquad \text{(b)} \qquad (10.71)$$

$$\frac{d\bar{M}}{d\bar{x}}\bigg|_{\bar{x} = \bar{x}_1} = \bar{R}_p - \bar{q}_p(\bar{x}_1 - 1) = 0 \qquad \text{(c)}$$

Equation (10.71c) immediately gives us

$$\bar{x}_1 = 1 + \frac{\bar{R}_p}{\bar{q}_p} \qquad (10.72)$$

Substituting this result into Eq. (10.71b) yields

$$1 = \bar{R}_p\left(1 + \frac{\bar{R}_p}{\bar{q}_p}\right) - \frac{\bar{q}_p}{2}\left(\frac{\bar{R}_p}{\bar{q}_p}\right)^2$$

which may be solved for $\bar{q}_p$ to give

$$\bar{q}_p = \frac{\bar{R}_p^2}{2(1 - \bar{R}_p)} \qquad (10.73)$$

Now substitute into Eq. (10.71a) to get

$$-1 = 2\bar{R}_p - \frac{\bar{R}_p^2}{4(1 - \bar{R}_p)}$$

which can be reformed into the quadratic equation

$$9\bar{R}_p^2 - 4\bar{R}_p - 4 = 0 \qquad (10.74)$$

This equation has one positive and one negative root, and since a negative value of $\bar{R}_p$ is physically unacceptable, the solution is given by the positive root as

$$\bar{R}_p = 0.925 \qquad (10.75)$$

Successive substitution into Eqs. (10.73) and (10.72) finally yields

$$\bar{q}_p = 5.700$$

$$\bar{x}_1 = 1.162$$

The above statically indeterminate beam problem was simple enough to permit an analytical solution. For more complicated problems it may be necessary to employ numerical procedures. One approximate numerical procedure yields bounds on the collapse load through the application of the so-called lower-bound and upper-bound theorems of perfect plasticity. The derivation of these theorems is beyond the scope of this book, but we shall mention some of the key features of these useful theorems. For the lower-bound theorem one considers a sequence of equilibrium states, for which the applied loads are gradually increased by the application of a multiplier α_s. If these equilibrium states also satisfy the condition that they are either below or at the yield stress at every material point, then α_s is called a "statically admissible" multiplier. The lower-bound theorem then states that the *largest* statically admissible multiplier corresponds to collapse. For an illustration of this theorem look back at Fig. 10.23(a), where a frame under loads P and Q has been shown. Let the applied loads be given as $\alpha_s P$ and $\alpha_s Q$; then for all values of α_s less than its largest possible value, a mechanism does not exist and collapse does not occur. When α_s reaches its largest possible value, a mechanism forms and collapse occurs. Now, for the upper-bound theorem one considers a sequence of *possible* collapse modes corresponding to applied loads with multiplier α_k. If the velocity and stress fields satisfy certain kinematic conditions which are given in the statement of the theorem, then α_k is called a "kinematically admissible" multiplier. The upper-bound theorem then states that the *smallest* kinematically admissible multiplier corresponds to the *actual* mode of collapse. To illustrate this theorem, look back at Fig. 10.23(b) and (c), where two possible collapse modes have been illustrated for the frame discussed above. Now let the applied loads be given as $\alpha_k P$ and $\alpha_k Q$, where each mode of collapse has a corresponding value of α_k; then the actual collapse mode corresponds to the smaller value of α_k, whereas the other mode will have a larger value of α_k and does *not* correspond to an equilibrium state. For further details you are referred to the plasticity literature.*

10.14 GENERAL ELASTOPLASTIC BEHAVIOR OF BEAMS

In Sections 10.11, 10.12, and 10.13, we considered materials whose stress-strain diagram could be idealized for certain problems as linear elastic, perfectly plastic with identical tension and compression curves. It was pointed out that structural steel and aluminum alloy can often be treated in this manner. Because such important materials can often be handled this way, there is considerable use for the plastic-limit approach. There are, however, other important materials, such as cast iron and copper, which have stress-strain diagrams for which this idealized stress-strain diagram may have little meaning. Accordingly, let us briefly consider the general elastoplastic stress-strain diagram, such as in Fig. 10.25. Note that the tensile yield stress Y_T and the compressive yield stress Y_C at 0.2% offset are *not* equal (i.e., the tension and compression curves are different), and also that *neither* the elastic nor the plastic intervals are necessarily represented by straight lines.

As explained previously, we may in elementary beam theory always employ the familiar relation for small deformation

$$\varepsilon_{xx} = -\frac{y}{R} \tag{10.76}$$

---

* For example, see B. Venkatraman and S. A. Patel, *Structural Mechanics with Introductions to Elasticity and Plasticity* (New York: McGraw-Hill Book Company, 1970), Chap. 24.

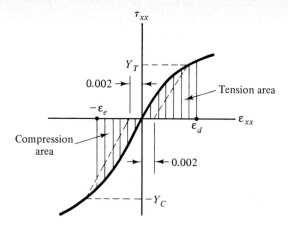

Figure 10.25 General elastoplastic stress-strain diagram.

If d and e represent the distances (positive) from the neutral surface to the outer-most fibers, as shown in Fig. 10.26, we can accordingly say for the magnitudes of the extreme strains, ε_d and ε_e, that

$$\varepsilon_d = \frac{d}{R} \qquad \text{(a)}$$

$$\varepsilon_e = \frac{e}{R} \qquad \text{(b)}$$

(10.77)

where ε_d and ε_e may fall into *either* the elastic or the plastic intervals. Keep in mind that we do not know the position of the neutral surface, and as we learned in Part C on nonlinear viscous behavior, it does not necessarily pass through a centroidal axis of the cross section. As for the stress distribution, we require that τ_{xx} satisfy the following conditions:

$$\int \tau_{xx} \, dA = 0 \qquad \text{(a)}$$

$$\int y\tau_{xx} \, dA = -M \qquad \text{(b)}$$

(10.78)

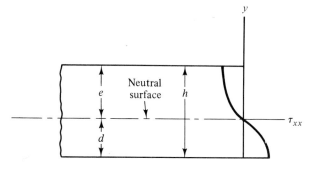

Figure 10.26 Neutral axis showing distances to surfaces of beam.

We have now presented the basic formulations for the determination of the stress τ_{xx} anywhere in the section.

As a simple case, we consider a beam having a rectangular cross section of width b and height h. Noting that $dA = b\,dy$ for this case, and using the differential of Eq. (10.76) to replace dy by $-R\,d\varepsilon_{xx}$, we now rewrite Eq. (10.78a) as follows:

$$\int \tau_{xx}\,dA = \int_{-d}^{e} \tau_{xx}\,b\,dy = -\int_{\varepsilon_d}^{-\varepsilon_e} \tau_{xx}\,bR\,d\varepsilon_{xx} = -bR\int_{\varepsilon_d}^{-\varepsilon_e} \tau_{xx}\,d\varepsilon_{xx} = 0 \qquad (10.79)$$

The last of the preceding equations may also be expressed as

$$\int_{\varepsilon_d}^{-\varepsilon_e} \tau_{xx}\,d\varepsilon_{xx} = -\int_{0}^{\varepsilon_d} \tau_{xx}\,d\varepsilon_{xx} + \int_{0}^{-\varepsilon_e} \tau_{xx}\,d\varepsilon_{xx} = 0$$

and so $\qquad\qquad\qquad\qquad\qquad\qquad\qquad\qquad\qquad\qquad\qquad\qquad\qquad\qquad$ (10.80)

$$\int_{0}^{\varepsilon_d} \tau_{xx}\,d\varepsilon_{xx} = \int_{0}^{-\varepsilon_e} \tau_{xx}\,d\varepsilon_{xx}$$

This means that the magnitude of the compression area for the stress-strain diagram must equal the magnitude of the tension area for the stress-strain diagram. These regions have been crosshatched in Fig. 10.25.* Thus, for any ε_d, we can evaluate ε_e by analytical or numerical procedures. Now in Eqs. (10.77) we can eliminate R by dividing Eq. (10.77b) into Eq. (10.77a). We get

$$\frac{\varepsilon_d}{\varepsilon_e} = \frac{d}{e} \qquad (10.81)$$

Furthermore, using the relation

$$d + e = h \qquad (10.82)$$

we can now determine d and e for the chosen ε_d.

Next consider Eq. (10.78b). Using Eq. (10.76) for y and its differential form for dy, we may write Eq. (10.78b) as

$$\int y\tau_{xx}\,dA = \int_{-d}^{e} y\tau_{xx}\,b\,dy$$
$$= \int_{\varepsilon_d}^{-\varepsilon_e} R^2\,\varepsilon_{xx}\tau_{xx}\,b\,d\varepsilon_{xx} = bR^2\int_{\varepsilon_d}^{-\varepsilon_e} \varepsilon_{xx}\tau_{xx}\,d\varepsilon_{xx} = -M \qquad (10.83)$$

The last integral represents the first moment of the shaded area in the stress-strain diagram about the τ_{xx} axis. By numerical or analytical methods we may then find from this equation the value of M that corresponds to the chosen value ε_d.

By the preceding formulations, we can thus set forth a trial-and-error numerical procedure, choosing values of ε_d until we get the proper bending moment M in accordance with Eq. (10.83). When this has been attained, we have available ε_d as described above, and the position of the neutral surface in terms of the value of d or e is determined from Eqs. (10.81) and (10.82). The radius of curvature R is now

---

* Note that $\int_{-\varepsilon_e}^{0} \tau_{xx}\,d\varepsilon_{xx}$ yields the *negative* compression area shown in Fig. 10.25. Accordingly, $\int_{0}^{-\varepsilon_e} \tau_{xx}\,d\varepsilon_{xx}$ is the magnitude of this area.

available from Eqs. (10.77). The strain at any elevation y from the neutral axis is computed from Eq. (10.76), and the corresponding stress may be read off the stress-strain diagram. Thus we have for a value of M at a section complete information as to stress and strain at that section. Finally, since $1/R = d^2v_0/dx^2$, the deflection may be determined by numerical integration.

10.15 CLOSURE

We have determined in this chapter stresses and deflections in beams, for the idealized cases of linear elastic, linear viscoelastic, nonlinear viscous, and linear elastic, perfectly plastic material behavior, using the framework of quasi-static elementary (i.e., *technical*) beam theory. Such idealized models are not only good approximations for a large class of materials, but they are also frequently simple enough to yield closed-form solutions. These four models are interrelated in a variety of ways; for example, for operators $P^E = 1$ and $Q^E = E$ linear viscoelastic behavior reduces to linear elastic behavior, or in more general terms the Laplace transform of a linear viscoelastic problem corresponds to a linear elastic problem. Also, the nonlinear viscous model reduces to linear viscous behavior (which is of course a special case of linear viscoelastic behavior) for the stress power $n = 1$, and as $n \to \infty$ it approaches fully perfectly plastic behavior. Finally, when studying linear elastic, perfectly plastic beams we observed that as the width of the elastic region d goes to zero at a point the behavior at that point also approaches fully perfectly plastic behavior and a plastic hinge is formed. Thus we see that a solution to a beam problem for any one of these four idealized models can yield useful information pertaining to solutions for the other idealized models.

As we add more complexity to the problem formulation, we are inevitably faced with the necessity of using numerical techniques. We observed this when we briefly touched upon the inclusion of material inhomogeneity and the Winkler foundation for a nonlinear viscous beam, and when we briefly examined general elastoplastic beams. The list of possible additional complexities that we have not considered is very long, and includes consideration of nonlinear viscoelastic behavior, viscoplastic (i.e., rate-sensitive plastic) behavior, thermal effects such as thermal expansion, and viscoelastic foundations. The method of approach for setting up beam problems which include such additional effects is straightforward, but the details of solution can be difficult.

In the next chapter we turn to another simple but important structural member, namely the shaft, wherein we shall study torsion using various constitutive laws.

PROBLEMS

10.1. Find the deflection curve v_0 for the elastic beam shown in Fig. P10.1. What is $v_0(8)$? Give your results in terms of EI.

10.2. Find the deflection curve $v_0(x)$ for the elastic beam shown in Fig. P10.2. Give the shear force V at $x = 18$ m and the bending moment M at $x = 12$ m. Express your results in terms of EI.

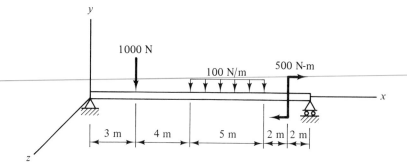

Figure P10.1

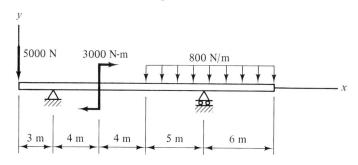

Figure P10.2

10.3. Find the deflection curve $v_0(x)$ and the maximum deflection $(v_0)_{max}$ for the elastic beam shown in Fig. P10.3. Take $E = 30 \times 10^6$ psi. (*Suggestion*: Express the triangular load on the interval $10 \leq x < 16$ as a superposition of uniform and triangular loads which extend to $x \to \infty$.)

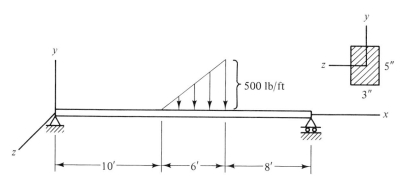

Figure P10.3

10.4. Find the maximum deflection of the simply supported elastic beam shown in Fig. P10.4. Take $E = 3 \times 10^{12}$ Pa.

10.5. Find the supporting forces for the statically indeterminate elastic beam shown in Fig. P10.5. Do these supporting forces depend on EI?

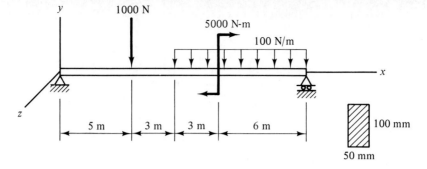

Figure P10.4

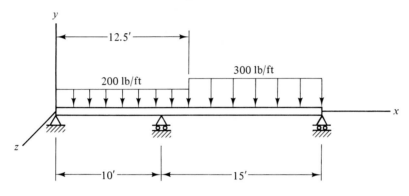

Figure P10.5

10.6. Formulate the deflection curve for the statically indeterminate elastic beam in Fig. P10.6. Evaluate the slope at $x = 15$ ft in terms of EI.

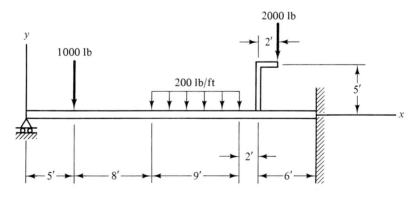

Figure P10.6

10.7. Elastic beam BA and elastic beam AC are joined by a pin at A (see Fig. P10.7), with a simple support at B and a clamped support at C. Determine the deflection of beam AC and of beam BA. (*Hint:* First evaluate the deflection of junction point A by considering beam AC.)

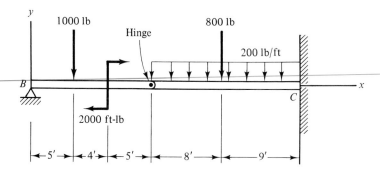

Figure P10.7

10.8. Use the Laplace transform to derive Eq. (10.25) from Eq. (10.21). Also use the Laplace transform to prove that the inverted form of Eq. (10.25) is given by

$$q(x,t) = I \int_{0^-}^{t} Y^E(t-t') \frac{\partial v_0^{iv}(x,t')}{\partial t'} dt'$$

where $Y^E(t)$ is the relaxation modulus function. Then use the equation above to determine the load function $q(x,t)$, which is necessary to generate the deflection function $v_0(x,t) = \sin(\pi x/L)[u(t)]$ for the simply supported Maxwell beam shown in Fig. P10.8.

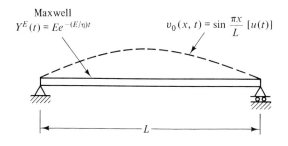

Figure P10.8

10.9. In Section 10.6 we showed that if $q(x,t) = q_0(x)[u(t)]$, then

$$v_0^{iv}(x,t) = [v_0^{iv}(x)]_{EL} EJ^E(t)[u(t)]$$

In a similar manner show the following:

(a) If the loading function is in the separated form

$$q(x,t) = q_0(x) g(t)[u(t)]$$

then

$$v_0^{iv}(x,t) = [v_0^{iv}(x)]_{EL} E\left[J^E(0)g(t) - \int_{0^-}^{t} J^E(t-t')\dot{g}(t') dt' \right][u(t)]$$

where $[v_0(x)]_{EL}$ is the deflection of a geometrically identical elastic beam under the load $q_0(x)$ for $t > 0$.

(b) If the loading function can be written as

$$q(x,t) = q_1(x)[u(t-t_1)] + q_2(x)[u(t-t_2)]$$

then

$$v_0^{iv}(x, t) = [v_1(x)]_{EL} EJ^E(t - t_1)[u(t - t_1)] + [v_2(x)]_{EL} EJ^E(t - t_2)[u(t - t_2)]$$

where $[v_1(x)]_{EL}$ and $[v_2(x)]_{EL}$ are the deflections of a geometrically identical elastic beam under the loads $q_1(x)$ and $q_2(x)$, respectively, for $t > 0$.

10.10. Consider the cantilever beam of Kelvin material shown in Fig. P10.10. The point load P is suddenly applied at $t = 0$ and then held constant. It is known from elastic strength of materials that the deflection of an elastic cantilever beam under this load is given by

$$[v_0(x)]_{EL} = \frac{P}{6EI}x^2(3L - x)$$

It then immediately follows from Eq. (10.29) that the deflection function for the above Kelvin beam is given by

$$v_0(x, t) = \frac{P}{6EI}x^2(3L - x)(1 - e^{-(E/\eta)t})[u(t)]$$

Obtain the same result from differential equation (10.21) by actually carrying out all of the necessary integrations over t and x.

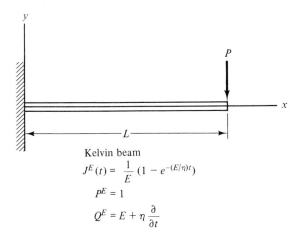

Kelvin beam

$$J^E(t) = \frac{1}{E}(1 - e^{-(E/\eta)t})$$

$$P^E = 1$$

$$Q^E = E + \eta \frac{\partial}{\partial t}$$

Figure P10.10

10.11. What is the deflection function $v_0(x, t)$ for the Maxwell beam AC shown in Fig. P10.11? All loads are applied simultaneously at $t = 0$ and then held constant. Take $E = 25 \times 10^6$ psi and $\eta = 2 \times 10^{10}$ lb-hr/in.^{2}. What is the deflection at C at $t = 100$ hours if $I = 250$ in.^{4}? Also find the deflection of point D if member BD is linear elastic with $E = 30 \times 10^6$ psi and $I = 60$ in.^{4} at a time 80 hours after the loads are applied. (*Suggestion*: Ignore the deformation of the 2-ft section of member BD and use the expression for the deflection of an elastic cantilever beam given in Problem 10.10.)

10.12. A simply supported Maxwell beam is shown in Fig. P10.12. Note that the loads are suddenly applied at $t = 0$ and thereafter vary as $\sin t$. If $E = 30 \times 10^6$ psi and $\eta = 2 \times 10^{10}$ lb-hr/in.^{2}, determine the deflection curve as a function of position x and time. What is the deflection at $t = 200$ hours and at $x = 15$ ft? Take I for the beam as 80 in.^{4}. [*Suggestion*: Use the result given in part (a) of Problem 10.9.]

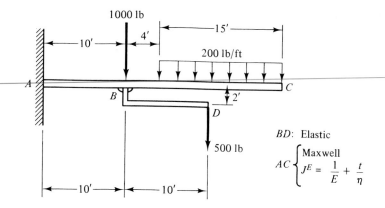

Figure P10.11

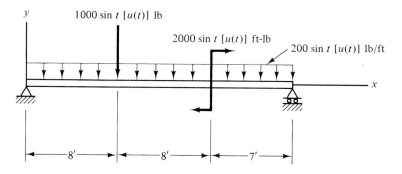

Figure P10.12

10.13. A simply supported beam made from a Maxwell material supports a point load of 1000 lb applied at time $t = 0$, and a uniform load applied at time $t = 100$ hours (see Fig. P10.13). What is the deflection at $x = 10$ ft and $t = 300$ hours? Take $E = 30 \times 10^6$ psi, $\eta = 3 \times 10^{10}$ lb-hr/in.^{2}, and $I = 80$ in.^{4}. [*Suggestion:* Use the result given in part (b) of Problem 10.9.]

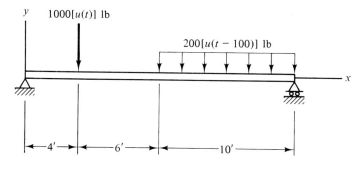

Figure P10.13

10.14. What is the maximum deflection for the beam in Fig. P10.14 after 500 hours? The beam is made of Maxwell material with $\eta = 5 \times 10^{13}$ lb-sec/in.^{2} and $E = 10 \times 10^6$ psi. Take $I = 4.5$ in.^{4}.

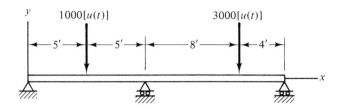

Figure P10.14

10.15. A Kelvin beam with an elastic midsupport (see Fig. P10.15) is subjected to two constant point loads, that are suddenly applied at time $t = 0$. Using the asymptotic limit theorem of Laplace transform theory (see Appendix III), determine the deflection at the midpoint $x = l$ for time $t \to \infty$. Repeat the problem for a beam of Maxwell material.

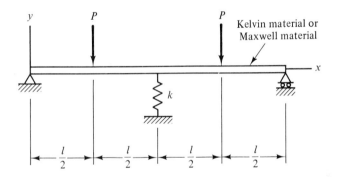

Figure P10.15

10.16. Find the supporting forces and the deflection function for the Maxwell beam shown in Fig. P10.16. Note that Eq. (10.29) is applicable to this statically indeterminate beam problem. (*Suggestion*: Consider the domain from just to the right of support A to just to the left of support C. Find the supporting force at B and the deflection in terms of I, E, and η. Then use the equations of equilibrium to get the supporting forces at A and C.)

10.17. Find the deflection function $v_0(x, t)$ in terms of I, E_1, E_2, η_2 for the beam of standard solid material shown in Fig. P10.17. The loads are applied suddenly at time $t = 0$ and then maintained constant. Note that Eq. (10.29) may be employed for this statically indeterminate beam problem. (*Suggestion*: Set up and solve this problem on the extended infinite x-domain.)

10.18. Refer back to the statically indeterminate Maxwell beam example with a deformable support, shown in Fig. 10.9 and solved by direct integration in Example 10.5 of Section 10.7. Again solve for the deflection function $v_0(x, t)$, but now use the Laplace transform method.

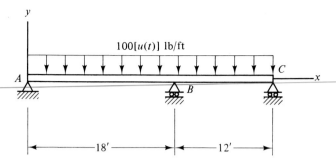

Maxwell beam

$$J^E = \frac{1}{E} + \frac{t}{\eta}$$

Figure P10.16

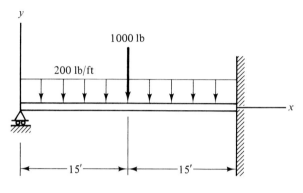

Standard solid material

$$J^E(t) = \frac{1}{E_1} + \frac{1}{E_2}\left(1 - e^{-(E_2/\eta_2)t}\right)$$

Figure P10.17

10.19. A nonlinear viscous beam is shown in Fig. P10.19 with loads applied suddenly at time $t = 0$. What is the maximum normal stress τ_{xx}? Take $n = 3$. What is the radius of curvature at the midpoint of the beam at time 800 hours? Take $\lambda_c = 2.2 \times 10^5$ lb(hr)$^{1/3}$/in.^{2}.

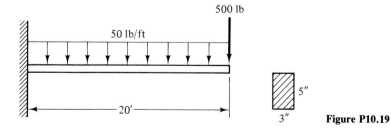

Figure P10.19

10.20. For the nonlinear viscous I-beam shown in Fig. P10.20, determine the maximum normal stress τ_{xx}. Let $n = 3$ and 5.

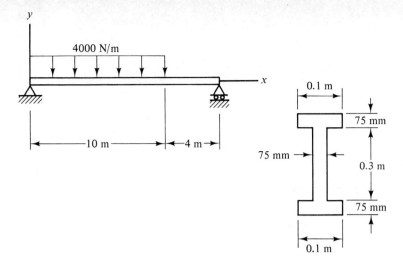

Figure P10.20

10.21. Locate the neutral axis of the cross section of the nonlinear viscous beam shown in Fig. P10.21. Also, determine I_n. Specialize your results for $n = 1$ and $n \to \infty$.

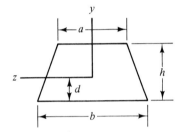

Figure P10.21

10.22. Find the position of the neutral axis and I_n for a nonlinear viscous T-beam with the cross section shown in Fig. P10.22. Specialize your results for $n = 1$ and $n \to \infty$.

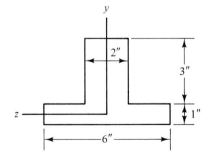

Figure P10.22

10.23. Find the deflection curve for the simply supported, nonlinear viscous beam shown in Fig. P10.23. The load P is applied suddenly. (*Suggestion*: Consider half the domain of the beam.)

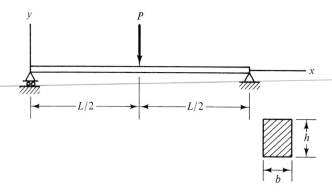

Figure P10.23

10.24. Find the deflection equation for the nonlinear viscous box beam shown in Fig. P10.24. Specialize your result for $n = 3$ and $\lambda_c = 2.2 \times 10^5$ (lb)(hr)$^{1/3}$/in.^{2}. The loading is applied suddenly at time $t = 0$.

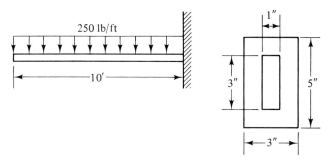

Figure P10.24

10.25. Find the deflection curve for the clamped statically indeterminate beam shown in Fig. P10.25. The beam is nonlinear viscous with $n = 3$. Loading q_0 is applied suddenly. (*Suggestion*: Consider half the domain of the beam.)

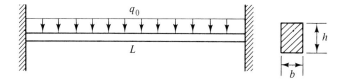

Figure P10.25

10.26. (a) What is the maximum value of P so as to have only elastic behavior in the beam shown in Fig. P10.26, which is elastic, perfectly plastic with $Y = 60{,}000$ psi?
   (b) What is the very largest P possible?
   (c) If a load equal to 80% of the very largest load is applied to the beam, in what interval of x is there complete elastic behavior in a cross section?

10.27. Do Problem 10.26 for the cross section shown in Fig. P10.27. [*Note*: If the applied force is 80% of the very largest load, $d(x)$ may occur either in the web or in the flange.]

10.28. Do Problem 10.26 for the cross section shown in Fig. P10.28.

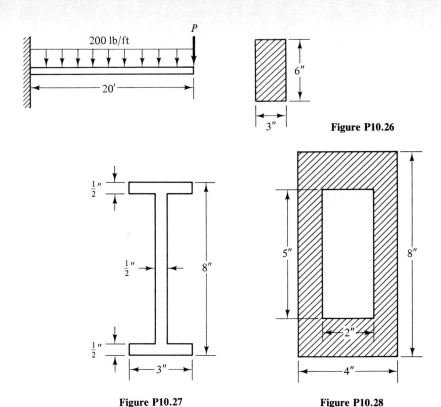

Figure P10.26

Figure P10.27   **Figure P10.28**

10.29. In Fig. P10.29 is shown a cantilever beam, subjected to axial and lateral loads and made from a material that has an elastic, perfectly plastic constitutive law with $Y = 60{,}000$ psi.

 (a) What is the largest value of q_0 for elastic action throughout?

 (b) What is the largest value of q_0, allowing for plastic behavior?

 (c) What is the minimum value of q_0 so that the bottom fibers just begin to yield? What are the depths of plastic penetration d_1 and d_2 for a load q_0 that is 1.1 times the value just calculated?

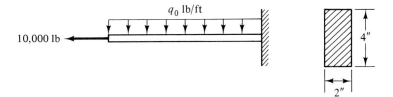

Figure P10.29

10.30. For Example 10.10 in Section 10.12, calculate the deflection curve for the applied uniform lateral load equal to 75% of q_p.

10.31. Calculate the deflection curve for the elastic, perfectly plastic beam shown in Fig. P10.31. Use for the load P a value that is 75% of the very largest load possible. Express the result in terms of h, E, L, and Y.

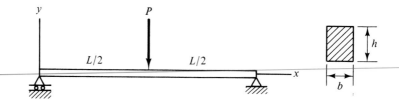

Figure P10.31

10.32. Using a value of q_0 equal to 75% of the very largest loading possible, find the deflection curve for the elastic, perfectly plastic beam shown in Fig. P10.32. Do not evaluate any difficult integrals encountered when computing the constants of integration. Express the result in terms of h, E, L, and Y.

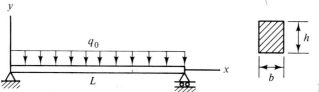

Figure P10.32

10.33. For the beam shown in Fig. P10.33, what is the largest value of the constant K according to the elastic-limit criterion and according to the plastic-limit criterion? Take $Y = 80,000$ psi.

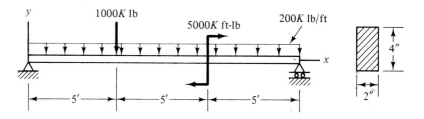

Figure P10.33

10.34. For the indeterminate beam in Fig. P10.34, a plastic hinge first forms at the clamped support as q_0 is increased. As q_0 is increased further, a second plastic hinge is formed and collapse occurs. Determine the location of this second hinge and the value of the plastic collapse load $(q_0)_p$.

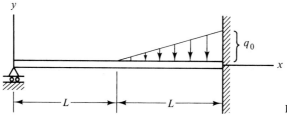

Figure P10.34

10.35. For an elastoplastic constitutive law given by

$$\varepsilon_{xx} = \begin{cases} A\,\tau_{xx}, & \tau_{xx} \geq 0 \\ B\,\tau_{xx}, & \tau_{xx} \leq 0 \end{cases}$$

consider a rectangular beam of base b and height h, subjected to bending moment M at some position x. Using the formulation given in Section 10.14, set up five simultaneous equations in the unknowns d, e, ε_d, ε_e, and R. Obtain the solutions to these equations in terms of b, h, M, A, and B.

11.1 INTRODUCTION

In Part A of this chapter we consider torsion of *circular* shafts, for the cases of the linear elastic, linear viscoelastic, nonlinear viscous, and linear elastic, perfectly plastic material. Because of the simplicity of the circular geometry, the formulation of these problems is relatively straightforward. Then in Part B we consider the general *noncircular* shaft. We first formulate the linear viscoelastic problem from which the linear elastic problem is obtained as a special case, and then briefly consider the more complex nonlinear viscous problem. In all formulations the material is *isotropic*, and the loading is quasi-static so that inertia may be ignored.

PART A
CIRCULAR SHAFTS

11.2 GENERAL CONSIDERATIONS

You may recall when you previously studied *homogeneous*, *isotropic*, *circular* shafts of *constant* cross section (see Fig. 11.1) in strength of materials that, through geometrical arguments, certain deformation statements could be reached for small deformation regardless of the constitutive law.* These statements for the case of a *uniform* torque T are:

---

*See I. H. Shames, *Introduction to Solid Mechanics*, 2nd ed. (Englewood Cliffs, NJ: Prentice-Hall, Inc., 1988), Chap. 14. We shall later verify that these deformation statements are rigorously correct, by showing that they lead to an *exact* solution to the torsion problem for *uniform* torque.

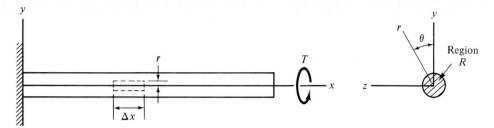

Figure 11.1 Fixed-ended circular shaft with coordinates.

1. Cross sections remain plane (i.e., they do not "warp").
2. The cross sections rotate as rigid surfaces. Accordingly, at time t, all radial lines in a cross section at a position x rotate through the same angle $\phi(x, t)$, which is called the *angle of twist*.
3. The relative rotation $\Delta\phi$ between two sections separated by distance Δx is linearly proportional to Δx. Thus for the fixed-ended shaft in Fig. 11.1 the actual rotation $\phi(x, t)$ is linearly proportional to x, that is, $\phi(x, t) = \alpha(t)x$, where $\alpha(t)$ equals $\partial\phi/\partial x$ and is called the *rate of twist*.

   Now consider a cylindrical element of the shaft of length Δx and of radius r as shown by the dashed lines in Fig. 11.1; this element is shown enlarged in Fig. 11.2. Let us examine the movement of line AB shown in the undeformed geometry in Fig. 11.2. When the torque T is applied, straight line AB becomes the dashed curved line $A'B'$. Line segments dx and ds in the undeformed geometry are shown at A oriented at $\pi/2$ radians from each other. In accordance with geometric considerations, the conclusions of which we have listed above, line segment ds rotates in the original plane of the cross section to ds'. However, dx' ceases to be parallel to the x axis but now forms an angle β with the horizontal line $A'C'$, as shown in the diagram. The rotation of the cross section at the right end relative to the left end is $(\phi + \Delta\phi)$. It is clear that the change in the angle between the line segments dx

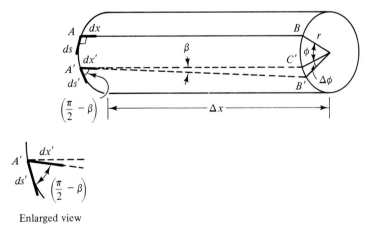

Enlarged view

Figure 11.2 Cylindrical element of radius r.

and ds from that of a right angle is this angle β. Furthermore, β can be found by considering the circular-arc line segment $C'B'$, which is clearly of length $r\,\Delta\phi$ (see cross section at right end) along with distance Δx. Hence we can say that the engineering shear strain $\gamma_{x\theta}$ is given as

$$\gamma_{x\theta} = \beta = \lim_{\Delta x \to 0} \frac{r\,\Delta\phi}{\Delta x} = r\,\frac{\partial\phi}{\partial x} \tag{11.1}$$

You will note that in the limit the curved line $A'B'$ may be considered a straight line, thus ensuring the correctness of the foregoing formulations. Also note that the derivative $\partial\phi/\partial x$ above equals the previously mentioned rate of twist $\alpha(t)$. We can then say that the shear strain is related to the rate of twist by

$$\varepsilon_{x\theta} = \frac{1}{2}\,\gamma_{x\theta} = \frac{1}{2}\,r\,\frac{\partial\phi}{\partial x} \tag{11.2}$$

Using cylindrical coordinates x, r, and θ (see Fig. 11.1), we can conclude from the three geometric conclusions stated at the outset that all other strains are zero, that is,

$$\varepsilon_{ij} = \begin{bmatrix} \varepsilon_{xx} & \varepsilon_{xr} & \varepsilon_{x\theta} \\ \varepsilon_{rx} & \varepsilon_{rr} & \varepsilon_{r\theta} \\ \varepsilon_{\theta x} & \varepsilon_{\theta r} & \varepsilon_{\theta\theta} \end{bmatrix} = \begin{bmatrix} 0 & 0 & \varepsilon_{x\theta} \\ 0 & 0 & 0 \\ \varepsilon_{\theta x} & 0 & 0 \end{bmatrix} \tag{11.3}$$

You will recall that in Section 5.2 we showed that for an isotropic elastic material, a shear stress can only generate the *corresponding* shear strain. The arguments employed were independent of the constitutive law, and thus for *any* isotropic circular shaft Eq. (11.3) also implies for the stress tensor that

$$\tau_{ij} = \begin{bmatrix} \tau_{xx} & \tau_{xr} & \tau_{x\theta} \\ \tau_{rx} & \tau_{rr} & \tau_{r\theta} \\ \tau_{\theta x} & \tau_{\theta r} & \tau_{\theta\theta} \end{bmatrix} = \begin{bmatrix} 0 & 0 & \tau_{x\theta} \\ 0 & 0 & 0 \\ \tau_{\theta x} & 0 & 0 \end{bmatrix} \tag{11.4}$$

The preceding considerations are valid for *all isotropic circular* shafts undergoing small torsional deformation. We now examine the special case of the linear elastic shaft.

11.3 LINEAR ELASTIC CIRCULAR SHAFTS

In Fig. 11.3 we have shown a cross section of a circular shaft under torsion, and have indicated an element of area dA in the region of the cross section R on which the shear stress $\tau_{x\theta}$ acts. *Equilibrium* now dictates that the torsional moment T about x is related to $\tau_{x\theta}$ by

$$T = \int_R \tau_{x\theta}\,r\,dA \tag{11.5}$$

where for simplicity we shall take T as independent of time, so that as a result the twist ϕ will also be independent of time. However, we shall for now *not* also assume

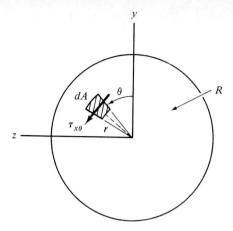

Figure 11.3 Cross section of a circular shaft under torsion.

that T is uniform (i.e., independent of x), which then implies that the three geometric statements previously given may be only *approximately* valid.

For an isotropic *Hookean* (i.e., linear elastic) material, we can replace $\tau_{x\theta}$ by $G\gamma_{x\theta}$ and, using Eq. (11.1) to replace $\gamma_{x\theta}$ by $r\,d\phi/dx$, we have for Eq. (11.5):

$$T = \int_R G\gamma_{x\theta}\,r\,dA = G\frac{d\phi}{dx}\int_R r^2\,dA$$

Therefore,

$$T = G\frac{d\phi}{dx}I_0 \tag{11.6}$$

where I_0 is the *polar moment of area*, which here equals $2I_{zz}$. Solving for the rate of twist, $d\phi/dx$, and denoting it as $\alpha(x)$, we get

$$\boxed{\frac{d\phi(x)}{dx} \equiv \alpha(x) = \frac{T(x)}{GI_0}} \tag{11.7}$$

Note that, for nonuniform torque $T(x)$, this result is *not the differential form of a relation* equivalent to statement (3) in Section 11.2, which is strictly valid only for the case of uniform torque. We shall prove in the next section that for *uniform* torque (i.e., α constant) Eq. (11.7) is *exact*, and thus in the general case of nonuniform torque this equation should be considered as an *approximate relation*.

For the common case of a uniform torque along this circular shaft of constant diameter, we can integrate Eq. (11.7) to give

$$\Delta\phi = \frac{T\,\Delta x}{GI_0} \tag{11.8}$$

where $\Delta\phi$ is the relative rotation between sections a distance Δx apart. If one end of the shaft is fixed at $x = 0$ as in Fig. 11.1, then $\Delta\phi \equiv \phi$, which is the rotation of a section at position x. The equation above then becomes simply

$$\phi = \frac{Tx}{GI_0} \quad \text{(a)}$$

and therefore   (11.9)

$$\alpha = \frac{T}{GI_0} \quad \text{(b)}$$

which is now equivalent to the statement that the rate of twist α is constant for uniform torque. Next using isotropic Hooke's law again and employing Eqs. (11.1) and (11.7), we get

$$\tau_{x\theta} = G\gamma_{x\theta} = Gr\frac{d\phi}{dx} = Gr\frac{T}{GI_0}$$

Then

$$\tau_{x\theta} = \frac{Tr}{I_0} \quad (11.10)$$

Most likely you will recall boxed formulas (11.9) and (11.10) from your earlier studies.

11.4 CONSIDERATION OF EXACTNESS OF ELASTIC SOLUTION

We now wish to show that the results above for uniform, time-independent torque are "exact" when viewed within the context of the classical theory of elasticity. We shall begin by expressing the three deformation statements in Section 11.2 in mathematical form. We will take $\phi = 0$ at $x = 0$ in expressing the displacement field for the shaft. Clearly, we can say that since the warp is zero in accordance with statement (1) of Section 11.2, the axial displacement $u_x = 0$ everywhere. For a section of the shaft at position x in Fig. 11.4, we have shown a point P in the undeformed geometry with cylindrical coordinates r and θ. According to statement (2), the position P' in the deformed geometry is reached by rotating the radius r rigidly through the angle ϕ, the angle of twist. For small deformation (i.e., small ϕ), we can thus give the displacement components u_z and u_y as

$$u_z = r\sin(\theta + \phi) - r\sin\theta \approx r\phi\cos\theta = y\phi \quad (11.11)$$
$$u_y = r\cos(\theta + \phi) - r\cos\theta \approx -r\phi\sin\theta = -z\phi \quad (11.12)$$

where we have employed the double-angle trigonometric formulas. Finally, statement (3) gives $\phi = \alpha x$, where α is the constant rate of twist. The displacement field is thus given as follows:

$$u_x = 0 \quad \text{(a)}$$
$$u_y = -\alpha zx \quad \text{(b)} \quad\quad (11.13)$$
$$u_z = \alpha yx \quad \text{(c)}$$

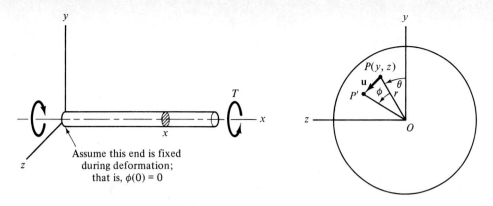

Figure 11.4 Displacement vector in a section.

Now we can get the corresponding strains from the strain displacement equations [see Eq. (9.4)]. Thus

$$\varepsilon_{xx} = 0 \qquad \varepsilon_{xy} = -\frac{\alpha}{2} z$$

$$\varepsilon_{yy} = 0 \qquad \varepsilon_{xz} = \frac{\alpha}{2} y \qquad\qquad (11.14)$$

$$\varepsilon_{zz} = 0 \qquad \varepsilon_{yz} = 0$$

Finally, using Hooke's law we may readily get the stress field as

$$\tau_{xx} = 0 \qquad \tau_{xy} = -G\alpha z$$

$$\tau_{yy} = 0 \qquad \tau_{xz} = G\alpha y \qquad\qquad (11.15)$$

$$\tau_{zz} = 0 \qquad \tau_{yz} = 0$$

We shall now show that the foregoing result is consistent with Eq. (11.10). Thus consider Fig. 11.5, where we have shown shear stress $\tau_{x\theta}$. This stress, according to the preceding section, is the total shear stress at a point (r, θ). The shear stresses τ_{xy} and τ_{xz} then become, with the use of Eqs. (11.10) and (11.9b),

$$\tau_{xy} = -\tau_{x\theta} \sin \theta$$

$$= -\frac{Tr}{I_0} \sin \theta = -G\alpha z$$

$$\tau_{xz} = \tau_{x\theta} \cos \theta$$

$$= \frac{Tr}{I_0} \cos \theta = G\alpha y$$

The preceding results are identical to those of Eqs. (11.15).

We may now check to see whether the strains as given by Eqs. (11.14) satisfy the *compatibility* equations [see Eq. (9.6)]. Since the strains are linear in the coordinates and the compatibility equations are second-order homogeneous, we see

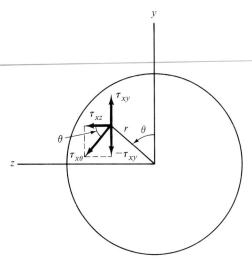

Figure 11.5 Shear stress components.

immediately that the equations of compatibility are identically satisfied. (Actually, since our strains were formulated directly from a single-valued, continuous displacement field, this step is superfluous.) Next consider the *equilibrium* equations as given by Eq. (9.2) for the case of no body forces. Again it is clear by means of simple substitution that these equations are satisfied by Eqs. (11.15).

Finally, we must consider the boundary conditions. On the lateral surface of the shaft, we have zero surface traction $\mathbf{T}^{(\nu)}$ (if we neglect atmospheric pressure), so we have to satisfy Eq. (9.34) for the case where $T_x^{(\nu)} = T_y^{(\nu)} = T_z^{(\nu)} = 0$. Thus

$$\tau_{xx} a_{\nu x} + \tau_{xy} a_{\nu y} + \tau_{xz} a_{\nu z} = 0 \quad \text{(a)}$$

$$\tau_{yx} a_{\nu x} + \tau_{yy} a_{\nu y} + \tau_{yz} a_{\nu z} = 0 \quad \text{(b)} \qquad (11.16)$$

$$\tau_{zx} a_{\nu x} + \tau_{zy} a_{\nu y} + \tau_{zz} a_{\nu z} = 0 \quad \text{(c)}$$

Noting that $a_{\nu x}$, the direction cosine between the normal to the peripheral boundary and the x axis, is zero, and substituting the stresses given by Eqs. (11.15) we get for Eq. (a) of the foregoing set

$$-G\alpha z a_{\nu y} + G\alpha y a_{\nu z} = 0 \qquad (11.17)$$

From Fig. 11.6 we see that since the normal and radial directions are collinear for a circular shaft, $a_{\nu y} = y/r$ and $a_{\nu z} = z/r$ so that the preceding equation becomes

$$-G\alpha z \frac{y}{r} + G\alpha y \frac{z}{r} = 0$$

Note that the terms on the left side cancel. Thus the first of our boundary conditions [Eq. (11.16a)] is satisfied. The other requirements of Eqs. (11.16) are satisfied also, since $\tau_{yy} = \tau_{yz} = \tau_{zz} = a_{\nu x} = 0$.

At the ends of the shaft we must have a resultant which is only a couple $T\hat{\mathbf{i}}$. To show this, note first that since $\tau_{xx} = 0$ the axial force F_x and the bending moments

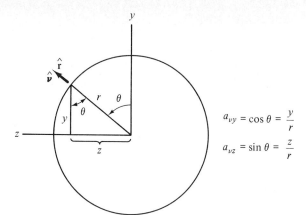

$$a_{vy} = \cos\theta = \frac{y}{r}$$

$$a_{vz} = \sin\theta = \frac{z}{r}$$

Figure 11.6 Direction cosines at a section.

M_y and M_z must vanish. We shall next show that the resultant shear force components V_y and V_z are also zero. Thus

$$V_y = \int_R \tau_{xy}\, dA = \int_R (-G\alpha z)\, dA = -G\alpha \int_R z\, dA \qquad \text{(a)}$$

$$\qquad\qquad\qquad\qquad\qquad\qquad\qquad\qquad\qquad\qquad \text{(11.18)}$$

$$V_z = \int_R \tau_{xz}\, dA = \int_R G\alpha y\, dA = G\alpha \int_R y\, dA \qquad \text{(b)}$$

Since the y and z axes are *centroidal* axes, we see that $\int_R y\, dA = \int_R z\, dA = 0$, so we get a zero resultant shear force at the cross sections of the beam. Finally, we have shown earlier [Eq. (11.9b)] that if we take $\alpha = T/GI_0$, we will get for the torsional moment about the x axis the proper couple T.

We have thus satisfied all of the requirements of the theory of elasticity and have accordingly verified that the three deformation statements of Section 11.2 are indeed correct for linear elastic materials. Furthermore, we may use the uniqueness theorem given in Chapter 9 to conclude that for uniform torque, the displacement and stress solutions given by Eqs. (11.13) and (11.15) are not only correct results but are also the *only* correct results. Note that for these solutions to be exact, the torques at the ends of the shaft must be generated by precisely the stress field given by Eqs. (11.15). It is not likely that this will frequently be the case under actual loading conditions, but in any event we may invoke Saint-Venant's principle and say that the solutions are always sufficiently accurate *if* we do not get close to the ends.

One can also show that the formulations above are correct for the *hollow* circular shaft with a cross section bounded by two concentric circles, if one uses the correct polar moment of area I_0 for such a cross section in Eq. (11.10). We shall not consider linear elastic examples for solid and hollow circular cross sections in this section, since you have probably seen various such examples in your earlier studies. However, for purposes of review several linear elastic problems, including some with variable circular cross sections, are presented at the end of this chapter. In the following section we go directly to the study of torsion in linear viscoelastic circular shafts.

11.5 LINEAR VISCOELASTIC CIRCULAR SHAFTS

You will recall that the deformation equation (11.2) relating $\varepsilon_{x\theta}$ to the twist ϕ is valid for *any* isotropic material, and thus we shall also be able to use it here. It is important to remember here that even if the torque T on a viscoelastic bar is independent of time t, the dependent variables $\varepsilon_{x\theta}$, $\tau_{x\theta}$, ϕ, and α will all be functions of time in general. The primary consideration here is the *constitutive* law which for linear viscoelastic material is

$$P^G \tau_{x\theta} = Q^G \varepsilon_{x\theta} \tag{11.19}$$

where P^G, Q^G is the shear operator pair defined as

$$P^G = \sum_{i=0}^{m^G} p_i^G \frac{\partial^i}{\partial t^i} \qquad Q^G = \sum_{i=0}^{n^G} q_i^G \frac{\partial^i}{\partial t^i} \tag{11.20}$$

Note that coefficients p_i^G and q_i^G are constants for homogeneous isothermal material.

From *equilibrium* we have, as before,

$$T = \int_R \tau_{x\theta} r \, dA \tag{11.21}$$

For polar coordinates $dA = r \, dr \, d\theta$, with the limits in region R constant for the uniform circular cross section. Employing the operator pair from Eq. (11.19) in Eq. (11.21), we then get

$$P^G(T) = \int_R P^G(\tau_{x\theta}) r \, dA = \int_R Q^G(\varepsilon_{x\theta}) r \, dA$$

Now use Eq. (11.2) for $\varepsilon_{x\theta}$, giving

$$P^G(T) = \int_R Q^G \left(\frac{1}{2} r \frac{\partial \phi}{\partial x} \right) r \, dA = \frac{1}{2} Q^G \left(\frac{\partial \phi}{\partial x} \right) \int_R r^2 \, dA$$

Therefore,

$$\boxed{P^G(T) = \frac{I_0}{2} Q^G \left(\frac{\partial \phi}{\partial x} \right) = \frac{I_0}{2} Q^G(\alpha)} \tag{11.22}$$

where α is the usual notation for rate of twist.

Equation (11.22) is called the *torque-rate of twist* relation for a linear viscoelastic circular shaft. You will note, on comparing it with Eq. (11.6) for linear elastic behavior, that the operator ratio (Q^G/P^G) corresponds to $2G$, which is precisely the analogy relation presented in Section 6.5 [see Eq. (6.60)]. As we have done previously on several occasions, we may rewrite a differential equation in the form of Eq. (11.22) as a useful hereditary integral. Proceeding in the usual manner, we obtain

$$\boxed{\alpha(x,t) = \frac{\partial \phi(x,t)}{\partial x} = \frac{2}{I_0} \int_{0^-}^{t} J^G(t - t') \frac{\partial T(x,t')}{\partial t'} \, dt'} \tag{11.23}$$

where $J^G(t)$ is the shear creep compliance function. Note that if the torque is uniform (i.e., independent of x), the rate of twist α is a function of time only. Consider next the case of a *uniform torque suddenly applied* at $t = 0$,

$$T(x,t) = T_0[u(t)] \tag{11.24}$$

where T_0 is a constant. Substituting this equation into Eq. (11.23), we get in this special case the simple result

$$\frac{\partial \phi}{\partial x} = \frac{2T_0}{I_0} \int_{0^-}^{t} J^G(t - t')[\delta(t')] \, dt' = \frac{2T_0}{I_0} J^G(t)[u(t)] \tag{11.25}$$

Now let us return to a consideration of the shear stress $\tau_{x\theta}$. Replacing $\partial \phi/\partial x$ in Eq. (11.22) using deformation Eq. (11.2) and then using constitutive law (11.19), we get

$$P^G(T) = \frac{I_0}{2} \frac{2}{r} Q^G(\varepsilon_{x\theta}) = \frac{I_0}{r} P^G(\tau_{x\theta}) \tag{11.26}$$

which may be rewritten as

$$P^G\left(T - \frac{I_0 \tau_{x\theta}}{r}\right) = 0 \tag{11.27}$$

It will be a simple matter to prove via the use of the Laplace transform that from Eq. (11.27) we may obtain the simple torsional stress equation previously found for linear elastic shafts, namely,

$$\tau_{x\theta}(x, r, t) = \frac{T(x,t)r}{I_0} \tag{11.28}$$

provided that at $t = 0^-$ we have the homogeneous initial conditions*

$$T = \dot{T} = \cdots = \tau_{x\theta} = \dot{\tau}_{x\theta} = \cdots = 0 \tag{11.29}$$

Thus we take the Laplace transform of Eq. (11.27) with 0^- as the lower limit [see Eq. (6.48)] and with the use of initial conditions (11.29) we get

$$\bar{P}^G(s)\left[\bar{T}(s) - \frac{I_0 \bar{\tau}_{x\theta}(s)}{r}\right] = 0$$

Since $\bar{P}^G(s)$ is a nonzero polynomial in s, we may first divide the result by $\bar{P}^G(s)$ and then invert the bracketed expression to obtain the desired equation (11.28). We have thus shown that *the shear stress in a linear viscoelastic shaft is the same as the shear stress in a geometrically identical elastic shaft subjected to the same torque*. The twist of course will in general *not* be the same, as indicated by Eq. (11.23).

We shall now make a few remarks concerning exactness and uniqueness of solution. It is convenient to pursue these points in the Laplace transform domain. Thus we take the Laplace transform of Eqs. (11.23) and (11.28) with homogeneous initial conditions at $t = 0^-$, and obtain with the use of the convolution theorem (see Section III.5 in Appendix III)

---

* As has been our usual practice, we employ the overdot in this chapter to indicate the partial time derivative $\partial/\partial t$.

$$\frac{\partial \overline{\phi}(x,s)}{\partial x} = \frac{2}{I_0} \overline{J}^G(s) s \overline{T}(x,s) \tag{11.30}$$

$$\overline{\tau}_{x\theta}(x,r,s) = \frac{\overline{T}(x,s)\,r}{I_0} \tag{11.31}$$

On comparing Eqs. (11.30) and (11.31) with the transforms of previous elastic equations (11.7) and (11.10), respectively, we see that they are of the identical form except that $1/(2G)$ has now been replaced by $s\,\overline{J}^G(s)$. It follows from this correspondence [see Eq. (9.64b)] that the deductions concerning exactness and uniqueness obtained in Section 11.4 for linear elastic shafts also apply to linear viscoelastic shafts. *Thus, for a uniform torque on a shaft of uniform circular cross section, the solutions obtained from viscoelastic equations (11.23) [or (11.22)] and (11.28) are exact and unique.** It is also common practice to employ these equations for non-uniform torque and/or variable circular cross section, but in such cases they should be considered approximate relations.

The following examples will illustrate the use of the equations developed in this section.

Example 11.1

Find the angle of twist ϕ for a circular shaft of Maxwell material in shear, which is fixed at one end and for which a constant torque T_0 is suddenly applied at the free end (see Fig. 11.7).

The torque in this case is simply

$$T(t) = T_0[u(t)] \tag{a}$$

and thus the solution to differential equation (11.22) is given immediately by Eq. (11.25) as

$$\frac{\partial \phi}{\partial x} = \frac{2T_0}{I_0} J^G(t)[u(t)] \tag{b}$$

For the creep compliance function in shear we shall use the form developed for the Maxwell material in Example 6.5 of Section 6.9,

$$J^G(t) = \frac{1}{2G} + \frac{t}{\zeta} \tag{c}$$

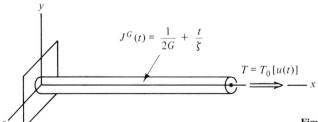

Figure 11.7 Maxwell circular shaft.

Substituting this function into Eq. (b) and integrating the result over x, we get

$$\phi = \frac{2T_0 x}{I_0}\left(\frac{1}{2G} + \frac{t}{\zeta}\right)[u(t)] + f(t) \tag{d}$$

where $f(t)$ is an arbitrary function of time. Noting that $\phi = 0$ at $x = 0$, we conclude that $f(t) = 0$, and thus the final solution is

$$\phi(x,t) = \frac{2T_0 x}{I_0}\left(\frac{1}{2G} + \frac{t}{\zeta}\right)[u(t)] \tag{e}$$

Does this solution look correct? To answer this question we examine the limiting cases $t = 0^+$ and $t \to \infty$:

$$\phi(x,0^+) = \frac{T_0 x}{GI_0} \tag{f}$$

$$\lim_{t \to \infty} \phi(x,t) \to \infty \tag{g}$$

Equation (f) is identical to the solution for an elastic shaft [see Eq. (11.9a)], which is what we would expect for the instantaneous behavior of Maxwell material. Equation (g) is also as expected, since the asymptotic behavior of Maxwell material at large times is that of a fluid.

Example 11.2

In Fig. 11.8 is shown a circular shaft fixed at both ends and loaded at midspan by the suddenly applied constant torque T_0. The first section between the left support and midspan is of linear elastic (Hookean) material, whereas the second section to the right of midspan behaves as linear Maxwell in shear. We wish to determine the reactive torques $T_1(t)$ and $T_2(t)$ (see Fig. 11.8), and also the twist at midspan $\phi(L/2, t)$.

The elastic compliance of the first interval is expressed as

$$J_1^G = \frac{1}{2G} \tag{a}$$

and the creep compliance function in the second interval is given by Eq. (c) of Example 11.1 as,

$$J_2^G(t) = \frac{1}{2G} + \frac{t}{\zeta} \tag{b}$$

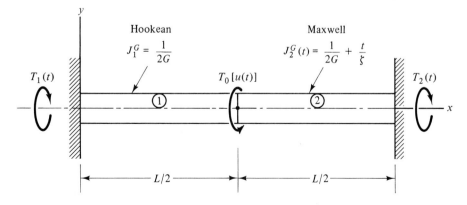

Figure 11.8 Hookean–Maxwell shaft clamped at both ends.

Simple *equilibrium* considerations yield the following torques:*

For $0 \leq x \leq (L/2)^-$: $T = T_1(t) = T_0[u(t)] - T_2(t)$ (c)

For $(L/2)^+ \leq x \leq L$: $T = -T_2(t)$ (d)

Since $T_2(t)$ is not known, this problem is statically indeterminate and the torques will depend on the material behavior. Furthermore, since the torques are functions of time, we may *not* use the simple equation (11.25) in this example.

The simplest way to attack this problem is first to solve it in the Laplace transform domain, and then invert this solution back into the time domain. We begin by transforming Eqs. (a) to (d) (see Appendix III):

$$\bar{J}_1^G(s) = \frac{1}{2Gs} \tag{e}$$

$$\bar{J}_2^G(s) = \frac{1}{2Gs} + \frac{1}{\zeta s^2} \tag{f}$$

$$\bar{T}(s) = \bar{T}_1(s) = \frac{T_0}{s} - \bar{T}_2(s) \qquad 0 \leq x \leq (L/2)^- \tag{g}$$

$$\bar{T}(s) = -\bar{T}_2(s) \qquad (L/2)^+ \leq x \leq L \tag{h}$$

For the governing differential equation in the Laplace transform domain we may employ Eq. (11.30) in each interval; that is, using Eqs. (g) and (h) for $\bar{T}(s)$, we get

$$\frac{\partial \bar{\phi}_1(x,s)}{\partial x} = \frac{2}{I_0} \bar{J}_1^G(s) s \bar{T}_1(s) \qquad 0 \leq x \leq (L/2)^- \tag{i}$$

$$\frac{\partial \bar{\phi}_2(x,s)}{\partial x} = -\frac{2}{I_0} \bar{J}_2^G(s) s \bar{T}_2(s) \qquad (L/2)^+ \leq x \leq L \tag{j}$$

Integrating Eq. (i) from $x = 0$ to some point x in the first interval, we get

$$\bar{\phi}_1(x,s) = \frac{2x}{I_0} \bar{J}_1^G(s) s \bar{T}_1(s) \tag{k}$$

where the constant of integration is zero since $\bar{\phi}_1 = 0$ at $x = 0$. Similarly, we integrate Eq. (j) from $x = (L/2)^+$ to some point x in the second interval, yielding

$$\bar{\phi}_2(x,s) = \frac{2}{I_0}(L - x)\bar{J}_2^G(s) s \bar{T}_2(s) \tag{ℓ}$$

where here we have set $\bar{\phi}_2 = 0$ at $x = L$ to determine the constant of integration.

The critical step in obtaining the solution is the observation that $\bar{\phi}_1$ at $x = (L/2)^-$ must equal $\bar{\phi}_2$ at $x = (L/2)^+$. Accordingly, we obtain from Eqs. (k) and (ℓ) with the use of Eqs. (e) to (g):

$$\frac{L}{2GI_0}\left[\frac{T_0}{s} - \bar{T}_2(s)\right] = \frac{L}{I_0}\left[\frac{1}{2G} + \frac{1}{\zeta s}\right]\bar{T}_2(s) \tag{m}$$

Solving for $\bar{T}_2(s)$, we get

$$\bar{T}_2(s) = \frac{T_0 \zeta}{2(\zeta s + G)} = \frac{T_0}{2}\frac{1}{(s + G/\zeta)} \tag{n}$$

---

* We employ here the sign convention that a torque T is positive if it either has a positive sense on a positive area or a negative sense on a negative area. Thus, taking both $T_1(t)$ and $T_2(t)$ positive, we see that the torque T is positive at $x = 0$, whereas it is negative at $x = L$.

which is readily inverted (see Table III.1 in Appendix III) to yield the solution for the torque at the right support as

$$T_2(t) = \frac{T_0}{2} \exp[-(G/\zeta)t][u(t)] \tag{o}$$

Substituting this result into Eq. (c), we then get for the torque at the left support

$$T_1(t) = T_0 \left\{ 1 - \frac{1}{2} \exp[-(G/\zeta)t] \right\} [u(t)] \tag{p}$$

The governing equation for the twist in the first interval may now be obtained by substituting $\overline{T}_1(s)$, as obtained from Eqs. (g) and (n), back into Eq. (k) with Eq. (e) used for $\overline{J}_1^G(s)$. Accordingly, we get for the point $x = (L/2)^-$

$$\overline{\phi}_1\left[\left(\frac{L}{2}\right)^-, s\right] = \frac{T_0 L}{2 I_0 G}\left[\frac{1}{s} - \frac{1}{2(s + G/\zeta)}\right] \tag{q}$$

which inverts (again see Table III.1) to the desired solution

$$\phi\left(\frac{L}{2}, t\right) = \phi_1\left[\left(\frac{L}{2}\right)^-, t\right] = \frac{T_0 L}{2 I_0 G}\left[1 - \frac{1}{2}\exp\left(\frac{-Gt}{\zeta}\right)\right][u(t)] \tag{r}$$

Since the first interval is elastic, we could have obtained this same result simply by substituting $T_1(t)$ from Eq. (p) into elastic relation (11.9a).

The character of solutions (o), (p), and (r) is quite interesting. For example, at $t = 0^+$ we get

$$T_1(0^+) = T_2(0^+) = \frac{T_0}{2} \tag{s}$$

$$\phi\left(\frac{L}{2}, 0^+\right) = \frac{T_0 L}{4 I_0 G} \tag{t}$$

which is the solution for a fully elastic bar of length L, clamped at both ends and with an applied torque at midspan. Note that the applied torque divides equally between the two supports. Also, in the limit as $t \to \infty$, we obtain

$$T_1(\infty) = T_0, \qquad T_2(0) = 0 \tag{u}$$

$$\phi\left(\frac{L}{2}, \infty\right) = \frac{T_0 L}{2 I_0 G} \tag{v}$$

which is now the solution for an elastic bar of length $L/2$, clamped at only *one* end with the torque T_0 applied at the other end. The torque in the second interval has decayed to zero, and thus the first interval now carries the full load.

11.6 NONLINEAR VISCOUS CIRCULAR SHAFTS; SIMPLE TORSION TEST RESULTS

In Chapter 7 we made use of the simple tensile test to generate the one-dimensional nonlinear viscous power law,[*]

$$\dot{\varepsilon}_{xx} = \left(\frac{\tau_{xx}}{\lambda_c}\right)^n, \qquad n = 1, 3, 5, 7, \ldots \tag{11.32}$$

[*] Equation (11.32) was obtained by extending results from the tensile *creep* test (i.e., constant stress) to the case of *variable* stress. Accordingly, the subscript c was used with the parameter λ_c in Eq. (11.32).

which law we employed in Chapter 10 in our study of nonlinear viscous beams. There is also a simple torsion test that will permit a one-dimensional evaluation of the relation between the shear stress $\tau_{x\theta}$ and the engineering shear strain rate $\dot{\gamma}_{x\theta}$ for a nonlinear viscous material. A torque T is applied to a thin-walled cylindrical specimen (see Fig. 11.9), and the engineering shear strain rate $\dot{\gamma}_{x\theta}$ is measured for an applied shear stress $\tau_{x\theta}$. (Since the specimen is thin-walled, $\tau_{x\theta}$ may be assumed to be independent of the radial coordinate.) As is the case of the one-dimensional tension test, we may formulate a stress power law here for pure shear as

$$\boxed{\dot{\gamma}_{x\theta} = \left(\frac{\tau_{x\theta}}{\lambda_s}\right)^n,} \qquad n = 1,3,5,7,\ldots \qquad (11.33)$$

where the n and λ_s are material constants in shear found from this torsion test. You will note that the *same* stress power n appears in both Eqs. (11.32) and (11.33), which is justified since these two equations are special cases of the same three-dimensional incompressible steady creep power law [see Eq. (7.143)]

$$\dot{\varepsilon}_{ij} = C J_2^m s_{ij} \qquad (11.34)$$

Recall that in Section 7.13 we showed that the material constants in the one-dimensional tensile equation (11.32) and in the three-dimensional equation (11.34) are related as follows:

$$m = \frac{n-1}{2}, \qquad C = \frac{3^{(n+1)/2}}{2\lambda_c^n} \qquad (11.35)$$

where λ_c^{-n} here corresponds with A in Eq. (7.129). We shall now obtain a similar set of relations between m, C and n, λ_s in Eq. (11.33) for the torsion test.

We start with the stress tensor τ_{ij}, which for torsion is given for $x_1 = x$, $x_2 = r$, and $x_3 = \theta$ as

$$\tau_{ij} = \begin{bmatrix} 0 & 0 & \tau_{13} \\ 0 & 0 & 0 \\ \tau_{31} & 0 & 0 \end{bmatrix} = s_{ij} \qquad (11.36)$$

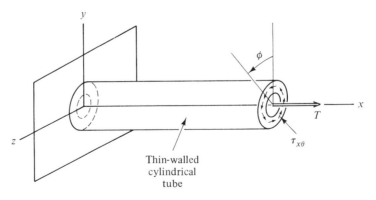

Figure 11.9 Simple torsion test.

where s_{ij} is the stress deviator tensor. Hence the second invariant J_2 in Eq. (11.34) is given simply by

$$J_2 = \tfrac{1}{2} s_{ij} s_{ij} = \tfrac{1}{2}(\tau_{13}^2 + \tau_{31}^2) = \tau_{13}^2 \tag{11.37}$$

Now going to the three-dimensional constitutive law given by Eq. (11.34), we obtain for $i = 1$ and $j = 3$ and with J_2 given by Eq. (11.37)

$$\dot\varepsilon_{13} = \frac{\dot\gamma_{13}}{2} = C(\tau_{13})^{2m}\tau_{13} = C\tau_{13}^{2m+1}$$

Therefore,

$$\boxed{\dot\gamma_{13} = 2C\tau_{13}^{2m+1}} \tag{11.38}$$

Comparing Eq. (11.33) with Eq. (11.38), we see that once again $m = (n-1)/2$, thus justifying our earlier assertion about n being the same for the two tests. Furthermore, we see that

$$C = \frac{1}{2\lambda_s^n} \tag{11.39}$$

Also, we point out that λ_s from the simple torsion test may be related to λ_c from the tensile test by equating the second of Eqs. (11.35) to Eq. (11.39), whereupon we get

$$\lambda_c = 3^{(n+1)/2n}\lambda_s \tag{11.40}$$

In Chapter 6 we expressed the one-dimensional *linear viscous* constitutive laws as

$$\dot\varepsilon_{11} = \frac{\tau_{11}}{\eta}, \qquad \dot\varepsilon_{13} = \frac{\tau_{13}}{\zeta} \tag{11.41}$$

and found that for *incompressible* behavior (see Example 6.4)

$$\zeta = \frac{2}{3}\eta \tag{11.42}$$

This result is completely consistent with Eq. (11.40), since as $n \to 1$ in Eqs. (11.32) and (11.33), we see on comparing with Eqs. (11.41) that $\lambda_c \to \eta$ and $\lambda_s \to \zeta/2$. Thus, replacing λ_c and λ_s in Eq. (11.40) by η and $\zeta/2$, respectively, and also setting $n = 1$, we then get Eq. (11.42).

11.7 USEFUL RELATIONS FOR NONLINEAR VISCOUS CIRCULAR SHAFTS

Let us proceed further toward the development of useful relations specifically for torsion of nonlinear viscous shafts. From *geometric* considerations we have again, as in the preceding sections,

$$\gamma_{x\theta} = r\frac{\partial\phi}{\partial x} \tag{11.43}$$

and from *equilibrium* we have for torque T at a cross section R,

$$T = \int_R r\tau_{x\theta} \, dA \tag{11.44}$$

Now replace $\tau_{x\theta}$ in Eq. (11.44) using the constitutive law [Eq. (11.33)]:

$$T = \int_R r\lambda_s \, \dot{\gamma}_{x\theta}^{1/n} \, dA$$

Next we replace $\dot{\gamma}_{x\theta}$ using Eq. (11.43), and noting that $\partial\phi/\partial x$ is constant over a cross section, we obtain

$$T = \lambda_s \left(\frac{\partial\dot{\phi}}{\partial x}\right)^{1/n} \int_R r^{(n+1)/n} \, dA \tag{11.45}$$

We shall denote the integral in Eq. (11.45) as

$$I_{0n} = \int_R r^{(n+1)/n} \, dA \tag{11.46}$$

and we call this expression the *generalized polar moment of area*. Note that for $n = 1$ (linear viscous behavior), $I_{0n} = I_{01}$ is the usual polar moment of area I_0. Also note that whereas $I_{01} = 2I_1$ (i.e., $I_0 = 2I_{zz}$) for the circular cross section, $I_{0n} \neq 2I_n$ for $n \neq 1$, where I_n was defined in Eq. (10.33). Using definition (11.46) in Eq. (11.45), we then obtain

$$\boxed{\frac{\partial\dot{\phi}}{\partial x} = \left(\frac{T}{\lambda_s I_{0n}}\right)^n} \tag{11.47}$$

and we thus get the time derivative of the rate of twist along the shaft.

To get the *shear stress* formula, we go back to Eq. (11.43) and write, on using Eq. (11.33),

$$\frac{\partial\dot{\phi}}{\partial x} = \frac{\dot{\gamma}_{x\theta}}{r} = \left(\frac{\tau_{x\theta}}{\lambda_s}\right)^n \frac{1}{r} \tag{11.48}$$

Equating the right-hand sides of Eqs. (11.47) and (11.48), we have

$$\left(\frac{\tau_{x\theta}}{\lambda_s}\right)^n \frac{1}{r} = \left(\frac{T}{\lambda_s I_{0n}}\right)^n \tag{11.49}$$

Solving for $\tau_{x\theta}$, we get the following shear stress formula:

$$\boxed{\tau_{x\theta} = \frac{Tr^{1/n}}{I_{0n}}} \tag{11.50}$$

We thus have assembled the key equations for torsion of a nonlinear viscous circular shaft.

Example 11.3

Consider a hollow thick-walled circular shaft with outside radius r_o and inside radius r_i (see Fig. 11.10), subjected to a uniform steady torque T_0. Determine the generalized polar moment of area I_{0n} and the shear stress distribution $\tau_{x\theta}(r)$ for this shaft for any value of n. Discuss the special cases $n = 1$ and $n \to \infty$.

Using Eq. (11.46) and referring to Fig. 11.10, we have

$$I_{0n} = \int_R r^{(n+1)/n} \, dA = \int_0^{2\pi} \int_{r_i}^{r_o} r^{(n+1)/n}(r \, dr \, d\theta)$$

$$= \frac{n2\pi}{3n+1}[r_o^{(3n+1)/n} - r_i^{(3n+1)/n}] \tag{a}$$

It follows from this result that for $n = 1$ and $n \to \infty$,

$$I_{01} = I_0 = \frac{\pi}{2}(r_o^4 - r_i^4)$$

$$I_{0\infty} = \frac{2\pi}{3}(r_o^3 - r_i^3) \tag{b}$$

The general shear stress distribution is then given by Eq. (11.50) with Eq. (a) as

$$\tau_{x\theta}(r) = \frac{T_0 r^{1/n}}{[n2\pi/(3n+1)][r_o^{(3n+1)/n} - r_i^{(3n+1)/n}]} \tag{c}$$

Using Eqs. (b) in the denominator for the special cases $n = 1$ and $n \to \infty$, we also get

$$\tau_{x\theta} = \frac{T_0 r}{(\pi/2)(r_o^4 - r_i^4)} \qquad \text{for } n = 1 \tag{d}$$

$$\tau_{x\theta} = \frac{T_0}{(2\pi/3)(r_o^3 - r_i^3)} \qquad \text{for } n \to \infty \tag{e}$$

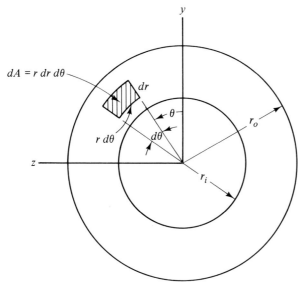

Figure 11.10 Coordinates for hollow thick-walled circular shaft.

We see from Eq. (c) that $\tau_{x\theta}$ is a nonlinear power function of fractional order $1/n$ in the variable r, analogous to the power function in y that we previously obtained for beams [see Eq. (e) of Example 10.6 in Section 10.8]. Equation (d) for $n = 1$ is identical with the well-known radially linear solution of elasticity. This is what we should have expected, since linear viscous behavior (i.e., $n = 1$) is a special case of linear visco-elasticity, and we showed in Section 11.5 that $\tau_{x\theta}$ for a linear viscoelastic shaft is the same as $\tau_{x\theta}$ for a geometrically identical linear elastic shaft. Finally, since $\tau_{x\theta}$ as given by Eq. (e) for $n \to \infty$ is independent of r, it corresponds to perfectly plastic behavior. This same phenomenon occurred in our previous study of beams, and is characteristic of any nonlinear viscous stress solution in which we let $n \to \infty$. In Fig. 11.11, we have shown typical stress profiles for $n = 1$ [Eq. (d)], $n \to \infty$ [Eq. (e)], and $n \neq 1$ or ∞ [Eq. (c)].

11.8 LINEAR ELASTIC, PERFECTLY PLASTIC TORSION

We shall now consider the case of linear elastic, perfectly plastic torsion of a circular shaft, where the cross section and the torque are assumed to be uniform. For the one-dimensional stress problems of Chapter 4 and the bending problems in Chapter 10, we considered yielding to take place when the normal stress in a problem equals the yield stress for the material, as determined from a one-dimensional tensile test. (Such a procedure in bending problems ignores the shear stresses, and it is strictly valid only at the outermost fibers since there the shear stresses are in fact zero.) We considered criteria for yielding for more general states of stress in Chapter 8. In the case of pure torsion of a circular shaft there is only one nonzero stress, the shear stress $\tau_{x\theta}$ for reference x, r, θ, where x is along the centerline of the shaft. We can experimentally relate shear stress $\tau_{x\theta}$ to shear strain $\varepsilon_{x\theta}$ in the way we related normal stress to normal strain in the tensile test by carrying out a simple torsion test on a hollow, thin-walled, circular cylinder. We could in this way find a pure shear yield

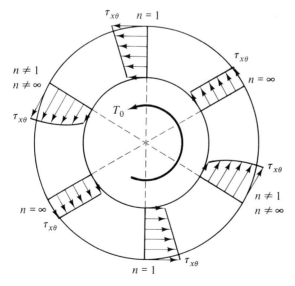

Figure 11.11 Shear stress distributions for various n.

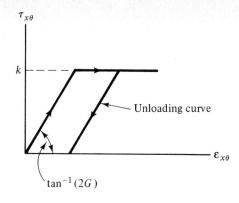

Figure 11.12 Linear elastic, perfectly plastic behavior in shear.

stress, k, analogous to the tensile yield stress Y. We have shown in Chapter 8 that k from the torsion test should be close to one-half the value Y from the tensile test for the same material.* The idealized plot of shear stress versus shear strain for linear elastic, perfectly plastic behavior is shown in Fig. 11.12.

As a uniform torque is increased on a shaft, the outer fiber will eventually reach the yield stress k. What happens when the torque is increased further? We answer this by noting that the statements concerning deformation presented in Section 11.2 for circular shafts under uniform torque can be restated for isotropic plastic deformation—namely, there is no warping in the cross section and sections rotate an angle ϕ, here linearly dependent on x only, in a rigid manner. This means that the shear strain $\varepsilon_{x\theta}$ will vary linearly with the radius [see Eq. (11.2)], and as a consequence a growing torque will result in the yield stress first appearing at the outer boundary, followed by a penetration of the plastic zone in toward the centerline. In regions of the section where the yield stress has been reached, the material simply flows with no change in stress as the section rotates in response to increasing torque. Thus, in Fig. 11.13(a) we have shown a situation wherein there is a *plastic ring* for $r \geq a$ in which $\tau_{x\theta} = k$, and an *elastic core* for $r < a$ in which $\tau_{x\theta} = 2G\varepsilon_{x\theta}$ (with G the elastic shear modulus) varies linearly with r. The stress versus radius diagram is shown in Fig. 11.13(b). The torque can theoretically be increased until plastic action pervades the entire shaft cross section. The shaft can then offer no additional resistance to the applied torque, and we reach the conditions of a fully plastic *torsional hinge* analogous to the plastic hinge of bending discussed in Section 10.11.

It will be of interest to compute the maximum torque T_e for the limiting case of purely elastic behavior, and the torque T_p for the case of a fully plastic torsional hinge. Thus, for a shaft of radius R, we have with the use of Eq. (11.10) for the former case,

$$T_e = \frac{kI_0}{R} = \frac{k[(\pi/2)R^4]}{R} = \frac{\pi}{2}R^3k \qquad \text{(a)}$$

$$T_p = \int_0^{2\pi}\int_0^R kr(r\,d\theta\,dr) = \frac{2\pi}{3}R^3k \qquad \text{(b)}$$

(11.51)

---

* This point was discussed in detail in Section 8.8. We showed that for *ideal* behavior $k = Y/2$ if the Tresca yield criterion is used, whereas $k = Y/\sqrt{3}$ if the Mises yield criterion is used.

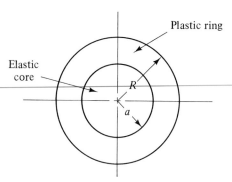

(a) Elastic and plastic zones

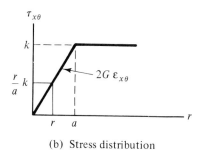

(b) Stress distribution

Figure 11.13 Behavior for applied torque greater than the maximum torque for purely elastic behavior.

The ratio of these quantities is thus

$$\frac{T_p}{T_e} = \frac{4}{3} \tag{11.52}$$

showing that once the yield stress in a shaft has been reached at the outer fibers, there is still a considerable external increase of torque that the shaft can withstand before plastic collapse. You will recall that a design based on T_p is called a *limit design*, and that T_p also corresponds with $n \to \infty$ for a nonlinear viscous material. We can verify this latter statement by noting that, by setting $\tau_{x\theta} = k$, $r_o = R$ and $r_i = 0$ in Eq. (e) of Example 11.3, we get Eq. (11.51b).

Suppose that a torque greater than T_e but less than T_p is applied. How do we get the rate of twist? First we must find the radius a for the radius of the elastic core. We may use Fig. 11.13 in this regard. The torque at the section is related to the stress distribution as follows:

$$T = \int_0^{2\pi} \int_0^a \left[\frac{r}{a} k \right] r^2 \, d\theta \, dr + \int_0^{2\pi} \int_a^R k r^2 \, d\theta \, dr$$

$$= k \frac{2\pi}{a} \frac{a^4}{4} + k \frac{2\pi}{3} (R^3 - a^3) = \frac{\pi k}{3} \left(2R^3 - \frac{a^3}{2} \right)$$

The radius a of the elastic core is then found from the equation above to be

$$a = \left[4R^3 - \frac{6T}{\pi k} \right]^{1/3} \tag{11.53}$$

Note that when $a = 0$ the torque equals T_p as given by Eq. (11.51b). As for the rate of twist, we may return to Eq. (11.2), which is valid for all isotropic constitutive laws as was discussed at the outset, and thus

$$\frac{d\phi}{dx} = \frac{\gamma_{x\theta}}{r} \tag{11.54}$$

Considering the elastic core of the shaft, we can employ for $\gamma_{x\theta}$ the result k/G at $r = a$ [see Fig. 11.13(a)]. For the rate of twist $d\phi/dx$, we then have

$$\boxed{\frac{d\phi}{dx} = \frac{k}{Ga}} \tag{11.55}$$

where a is determined from Eq. (11.53).

11.9 RESIDUAL STRESS AND STRAIN

Let us next consider what occurs when a linear elastic, perfectly plastic shaft, loaded as described above, is unloaded. To understand the unloading process we point out first that on an idealized shear stress-strain diagram, an unloading from the plastic region occurs along a straight line parallel to the elastic part of the loading curve (see Fig. 11.12). That is, the unloading is *elastic*. (This is exactly the same as for the one-dimensional tensile stress case discussed in Chapter 4.) There is, as a result, the possibility of *residual stress* as well as the possibility of a *residual state of strain* remaining in the shaft upon release of the applied torque. To best understand this, consider Fig. 11.14. In part (a) of this figure we have the shear stress $\tau_{x\theta}$ plotted against r for linear elastic, perfectly plastic behavior, as described earlier, for a given torque T. Note that the radius of the elastic core a is related to T via Eq. (11.53). Now imagine that the material behaved purely linear elastically during the loading by the aforestated torque T. The stress diagram would then be as shown in Fig. 11.14(b) with the maximum stress given as TR/I_0. Now when we unload we are *releasing* the given torque T and, as pointed out, the stress-strain relation must be *elastic* during this action. Hence, when unloading we must *subtract* the stress distribution shown in Fig. 11.14(b) from the one shown in Fig. 11.14(a).* The difference between these distributions is shown as the darkened region in Fig. 11.14(c) and is the residual stress. This residual stress distribution is then shown replotted as OAB along the horizontal radius and is denoted as $(\tau_{x\theta})_R$. Notice that the maximum value occurs at either $r = a$ or at $r = R$. Also note that the residual stress distribution must form a *self-equilibrating* system, since the external load has been removed.

---

*The reader may be perplexed by noting from Fig. 11.14(b) that the shear stress to be subtracted is greater than k at and near the outer fibers. Keep in mind that this is a shear-stress distribution that is being *subtracted*; it does not itself exist anywhere. It is the *difference* between the distribution in Fig. 11.14(a) and the distribution in Fig. 11.14(b) that is the *real* distribution [shown as OAB in Fig. 11.14(c)], and it is here that we cannot exceed the value k. For additional information on residual stresses in various structural components, see *Structural Mechanics with Introductions to Elasticity and Plasticity* by B. Venkatraman and S. A. Patel (New York: McGraw-Hill Book Company, 1970), Chap. 22.

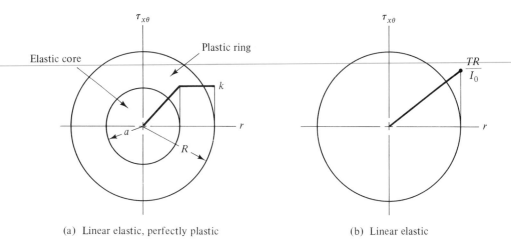

(a) Linear elastic, perfectly plastic

(b) Linear elastic

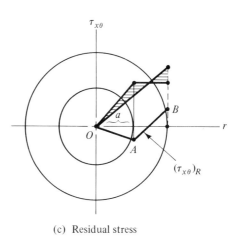

(c) Residual stress

Figure 11.14 Stress distribution upon unloading.

To get to the net *residual rate of twist* $(d\phi/dx)_R$, we subtract from the rate of twist $d\phi/dx$ for the given applied torque T an elastic rate of twist found by the familiar formula $T/(I_0 G)$. Thus

$$\left(\frac{d\phi}{dx}\right)_R = \frac{d\phi}{dx} - \frac{T}{I_0 G} \tag{11.56}$$

We shall now illustrate the formulations above in the following example.

Example 11.4

A shaft of radius 1 in. transmits a uniform torque of 180,000 in.-lb. What is the rate of twist? What is the maximum residual stress on unloading? Finally, what is the residual rate of twist on unloading? Take $G = 15 \times 10^6$ psi and k as 100,000 psi.

We must first find out whether we have completely linear elastic or linear elastic, plastic behavior, or whether we have applied a torque to this shaft in excess of what it can withstand. For this reason we first compute T_e and T_p. Thus, from Eqs. (11.51) we have

$$T_e = \frac{\pi}{2} R^3 k = 157,000 \text{ in.-lb} \tag{a}$$

$$T_p = \frac{2\pi}{3} R^3 k = 209,000 \text{ in.-lb} \tag{b}$$

Clearly, we have both an elastic core and a plastic ring present. The radius of the core a is found by using Eq. (11.53),

$$a = \left[(4)(1)^3 - \frac{6}{\pi} \left(\frac{180,000}{100,000} \right) \right]^{1/3} = 0.825 \text{ in.} \tag{c}$$

The rate of twist from Eq. (11.55) is then

$$\frac{d\phi}{dx} = \frac{k}{Ga} = \frac{100,000}{(15 \times 10^6)(0.825)} = 0.00808 \text{ rad/in.} \tag{d}$$

To get the residual stress distribution we note first that the following is the stress distribution with the given torque applied:

$$\tau_{x\theta} = \begin{cases} \dfrac{r}{0.825}(100,000) = 121,200r \text{ psi} & 0 \le r \le 0.825 \tag{e} \\[2mm] 100,000 \text{ psi} & 0.825 \le r \le 1 \tag{f} \end{cases}$$

From this we subtract the stress

$$\tau_{x\theta} = \frac{Tr}{I_0} = \frac{180,000}{\frac{1}{2}(\pi)(1^4)} r = 114,600r \text{ psi} \tag{g}$$

Hence the residual stress is given as follows:

$$(\tau_{x\theta})_R = \begin{cases} 121,200r - 114,600r = 6600r \text{ psi} & 0 \le r \le 0.825 \tag{h} \\[2mm] 100,000 - 114,600r & 0.825 \le r \le 1 \tag{i} \end{cases}$$

The peak stresses occur at A [see Fig. 11.13(c)], where $r = 0.825$, and at B, where $r = 1$. Thus, from Eqs. (h) and (i),

$$(\tau_{x\theta})_{RA} = (6600)(0.825) = 5400 \text{ psi} \tag{j}$$

$$(\tau_{x\theta})_{RB} = 100,000 - 114,600 = -14,600 \text{ psi} \tag{k}$$

Clearly, we have 14,600 psi as the maximum magnitude of the residual shear stress.

Finally, using Eqs. (11.56) and (d) above, we compute the residual rate of twist on unloading as follows:

$$\left(\frac{d\phi}{dx} \right)_R = 0.00808 - \frac{T}{I_0 G}$$

$$= 0.00808 - \frac{180,000}{\frac{1}{2}\pi(1)^4(15 \times 10^6)}$$

$$= 0.00808 - 0.00764 = 0.00044 \text{ rad/in.} \tag{ℓ}$$

In Part B we go on to a consideration of torsion of shafts with cross sections that are in general *noncircular*. Linear elastic, linear viscoelastic, and nonlinear viscous materials are examined.

PART B
NONCIRCULAR SHAFTS

11.10 SAINT-VENANT THEORY OF TORSION; LINEAR VISCOELASTIC AND LINEAR ELASTIC SHAFTS

We now consider a uniform shaft having an arbitrary cross section and subjected to a time-dependent torque $T(t)$ that is *uniform* in x (see Fig. 11.15). The location of axes x, y, z is *arbitrary* except for the condition that x is to be parallel to the lateral surface, but it is usually convenient for numerical computations to choose x as the *centroidal* axis and the y, z axes as the *principal* axes of area for the cross section. The torque $T(t)$ is due to some shear stress distribution at the ends of the shaft, while the lateral surface is free of traction. We denote the region of the cross section in the yz plane as R and its boundary as C. We will consider linear viscoelastic shafts, with linear elastic shafts coming out as a special case. The Saint-Venant theory of torsion makes the following assumptions on the displacement field:

1. The sections of the shaft rotate as rigid surfaces except for a displacement in the x direction which we call the *warping*. For a shaft fixed* at the point $x = y = z = 0$ (see Fig. 11.15), the rotation ϕ of a section is given as

$$\phi(x, t) = \alpha(t)x \tag{11.57}$$

where

$$\alpha(t) = \frac{\partial \phi(x, t)}{\partial x} \tag{11.58}$$

is the *rate of twist*. For elastic shafts, under time-independent torque, α is a constant.

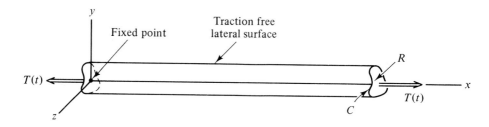

Figure 11.15 Linear viscoelastic shaft with arbitrary cross section.

*By "fixed" we mean that the displacement components u_x, u_y, u_z and the rotation components $\omega_x, \omega_y, \omega_z$ all vanish at the *point*.

2. The so-called *warping* mentioned above is a function of y and z as well as being proportional to $\alpha(t)$. Specifically, the displacement in the x direction is given as

$$u_x = \alpha(t)\Phi(y, z) \tag{11.59}$$

where $\Phi(y, z)$ is called the *warping function*.

The first assumption above is identical with deformation statements (2) and (3) given in Section 11.2 for the circular shaft, while the second assumption is, of course, new. Note that we are following a *semi-inverse* procedure here, since the validity of these two assumptions for the noncircular shaft must be verified by a careful inspection of the governing differential equations and boundary conditions.

The Governing Differential Equation

With these assumptions, the displacements in the y and z directions for small deformation are given by the same equations as were developed for the circular shaft [see Eqs. (11.11) and (11.12)]. Hence the assumed displacement field is given as

$$
\begin{array}{|ll|}
\hline
u_x \equiv u = \alpha(t)\Phi(y, z) & \text{(a)} \\
u_y \equiv v = -\Phi z = -\alpha(t)zx & \text{(b)} \\
u_z \equiv w = \Phi y = \alpha(t)xy & \text{(c)} \\
\hline
\end{array} \tag{11.60}
$$

No further postulates will be necessary for the remainder of our development, since the forms of the strains follow directly from the strain-displacement relations. The forms of the stresses then follow from the constitutive law.

Accordingly, we now obtain the strains directly by substituting displacements (11.60) into *strain-displacement* equation (9.4). We get

$$\varepsilon_{xx} = \frac{\partial u}{\partial x} = 0, \qquad \varepsilon_{yy} = \frac{\partial v}{\partial y} = 0, \qquad \varepsilon_{zz} = \frac{\partial w}{\partial z} = 0 \qquad \text{(a)}$$

$$\varepsilon_{xy} = \frac{1}{2}\left(\frac{\partial u}{\partial y} + \frac{\partial v}{\partial x}\right) = \frac{\alpha}{2}\left(\frac{\partial \Phi}{\partial y} - z\right) \qquad \text{(b)}$$

$$\varepsilon_{yz} = \frac{1}{2}\left(\frac{\partial v}{\partial z} + \frac{\partial w}{\partial y}\right) = \frac{\alpha}{2}(-x + x) = 0 \qquad \text{(c)}$$

$$\tag{11.61}$$

$$\varepsilon_{zx} = \frac{1}{2}\left(\frac{\partial w}{\partial x} + \frac{\partial u}{\partial z}\right) = \frac{\alpha}{2}\left(y + \frac{\partial \Phi}{\partial z}\right) \qquad \text{(d)}$$

Note that all the normal strains plus the shear strain in the cross section (ε_{yz}) vanish (i.e., the cross section rotates rigidly), and thus the shear strains in the longitudinal planes (ε_{xy} and ε_{zx}) are the only nonzero strains.

Next we reproduce multidimensional *constitutive* laws (6.86) and (6.89) for linear viscoelastic behavior:

$$P^K \bar{\tau} = Q^K \bar{\varepsilon} \qquad \text{(a)}$$

$$P^G s_{ij} = Q^G e_{ij} \qquad \text{(b)} \qquad\qquad (11.62)$$

where all of the terms were defined previously. We are considering homogeneous isothermal material, and thus the coefficients appearing in the differential operators above are constants. First, from Eqs. (11.61a) we have $\bar{\varepsilon} = \varepsilon_{kk}/3 = 0$, and thus Eq. (11.62a) implies that $\bar{\tau}$ also vanishes [use the same arguments as those employed in connection with Eq. (11.27)]. Next, since $\bar{\varepsilon} = \bar{\tau} = 0$, we may replace the deviator tensors (s_{ij} and e_{ij}) by the tensors themselves (τ_{ij} and ε_{ij}), and thus Eq. (11.62b) becomes

$$P^G \tau_{ij} = Q^G \varepsilon_{ij} \qquad\qquad (11.63)$$

Finally, since $\varepsilon_{xx} = \varepsilon_{yy} = \varepsilon_{zz} = \varepsilon_{yz} = 0$, the result above gives $\tau_{xx} = \tau_{yy} = \tau_{zz} = \tau_{yz} = 0$, and thus there are left only the following two nontrivial equations:

$$P^G \tau_{xy} = Q^G \varepsilon_{xy}$$

$$P^G \tau_{zx} = Q^G \varepsilon_{zx} \qquad\qquad (11.64)$$

The formulation above clearly also covers as a special case *linear elastic* behavior, wherein for the operator pair we have

$$P^G = 1, \qquad Q^G = 2G \qquad\qquad (11.65)$$

And for the case of linear viscous behavior, the operator pair becomes

$$P^G = 1, \qquad Q^G = \zeta \frac{\partial}{\partial t}$$

where ζ is the shear viscosity coefficient. For general linear viscoelastic behavior, we may use Eqs. (11.61b) and (11.61d) to express the shear strains in terms of the displacements. Accordingly, Eqs. (11.64) become

$$P^G(\tau_{xy}) = \frac{Q^G(\alpha)}{2}\left(\frac{\partial \Phi}{\partial y} - z\right)$$

$$P^G(\tau_{xz}) = \frac{Q^G(\alpha)}{2}\left(\frac{\partial \Phi}{\partial z} + y\right) \qquad\qquad (11.66)$$

where we have used the fact that α is a function of t only, whereas Φ is a function of y and z. Note that Eqs. (11.66) imply that τ_{xy} and τ_{xz} are functions of y, z, and t.

Next, we consider the *equilibrium* equations with no body forces:

$$\frac{\partial \tau_{xx}}{\partial x} + \frac{\partial \tau_{xy}}{\partial y} + \frac{\partial \tau_{xz}}{\partial z} = 0$$

$$\frac{\partial \tau_{xy}}{\partial x} + \frac{\partial \tau_{yy}}{\partial y} + \frac{\partial \tau_{yz}}{\partial z} = 0$$

$$\frac{\partial \tau_{xz}}{\partial x} + \frac{\partial \tau_{yz}}{\partial y} + \frac{\partial \tau_{zz}}{\partial z} = 0$$

Since $\tau_{xx} = \tau_{yy} = \tau_{zz} = \tau_{yz} = 0$ and since τ_{xy} and τ_{xz} are independent of x, the set above simply reduces to

$$\frac{\partial \tau_{xy}}{\partial y} + \frac{\partial \tau_{xz}}{\partial z} = 0 \qquad (11.67)$$

Inserting the time differential operator P^G, we get*

$$\frac{\partial P^G(\tau_{xy})}{\partial y} + \frac{\partial P^G(\tau_{xz})}{\partial z} = 0 \qquad (11.68)$$

Next replace $P^G(\tau_{xy})$ and $P^G(\tau_{xz})$ using Eqs. (11.66), and thereby obtain

$$\frac{Q^G(\alpha)}{2} \left(\frac{\partial^2 \Phi}{\partial y^2} + \frac{\partial^2 \Phi}{\partial z^2} \right) = 0$$

Finally, dividing by the nonzero factor $Q^G(\alpha)/2$, we get

$$\boxed{\nabla^2 \Phi = 0 \qquad \text{in } R} \qquad (11.69)$$

and thus the warping function Φ has been shown to be a *harmonic* function satisfying Laplace's equation in the region of the cross section R.

The Boundary Condition

To complete the statement of the boundary value problem, we must also formulate the *boundary condition* for Φ on the boundary curve C (refer back to Fig. 11.15). For this, we must satisfy Cauchy's formula, which you will recall is

$$T_i^{(\nu)} = \tau_{ij} \nu_j \qquad (11.70)$$

where ν_j are the rectangular components of the unit vector $\hat{\nu}$ in the normal direction ν (see Fig. 11.16). On the lateral surface of the shaft, we have $T_i^{(\nu)} = 0$. Again noting that $\tau_{xx} = \tau_{yy} = \tau_{zz} = \tau_{yz} = 0$ and also that $\nu_x = 0$ since $\hat{\nu}$ is normal to the x axis, we obtain from Eq. (11.70) only one nontrivial condition for the lateral surface:

$$\tau_{xy} \nu_y + \tau_{xz} \nu_z = 0 \qquad \text{on } C \qquad (11.71)$$

Operating on this equation with P^G we get

$$P^G(\tau_{xy})\nu_y + P^G(\tau_{xz})\nu_z = 0$$

We shall now revert to the notation $\nu_y = a_{\nu y}$ and $\nu_z = a_{\nu z}$, and shall also replace $P^G(\tau_{xy})$ and $P^G(\tau_{xz})$ using Eqs. (11.66). Collecting terms, we arrive at the following result:

$$\frac{Q^G(\alpha)}{2} \left[\frac{\partial \Phi}{\partial y} a_{\nu y} - z a_{\nu y} + \frac{\partial \Phi}{\partial z} a_{\nu z} + y a_{\nu z} \right] = 0 \qquad \text{on } C \qquad (11.72)$$

---

* The differential time operator P^G commutes with the spatial derivatives $\partial/\partial y$ and $\partial/\partial z$, since the coefficients in P^G are constants here. Thus we may operate on Eq. (11.67) with P^G and then move P^G past the spatial derivatives, as indicated in Eq. (11.68).

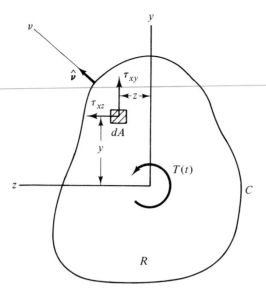

Figure 11.16 Cross section of shaft.

We note that with Φ a function only of y and z, the *directional* derivative in the normal direction is given as

$$\frac{\partial \Phi}{\partial \nu} \equiv \nabla \Phi \cdot \hat{\boldsymbol{\nu}} = \frac{\partial \Phi}{\partial y} a_{\nu y} + \frac{\partial \Phi}{\partial z} a_{\nu z} \tag{11.73}$$

Hence, inserting the result above, Eq. (11.72) can be simplified. Dividing by $Q^G(\alpha)/2$ and solving for $\partial \Phi/\partial \nu$, we then get

$$\boxed{\frac{\partial \Phi}{\partial \nu} = z a_{\nu y} - y a_{\nu z} \qquad \text{on } C} \tag{11.74}$$

For a given boundary curve C the quantities on the right-hand side of this equation are known at all points on C, and thus Eq. (11.74) prescribes the normal derivative $\partial \Phi/\partial \nu$ on C in terms of a given function. In the theory of partial differential equations this type of boundary condition is known as the *Neumann* boundary condition, and thus we must solve Laplace's equation (11.69) with Neumann condition (11.74) to determine the warping function $\Phi(y, z)$. This is a classical problem in applied mathematics that is known to have a solution which is unique to within an arbitrary constant. However, this constant may be set equal to zero by eliminating rigid-body translation with the requirement that $u = 0$ at the fixed point $x = y = z = 0$ [see Fig. 11.15 and Eq. (11.60a)].

The Rate of Twist

We will assume that the boundary value problem above has been solved for $\Phi(y, z)$ by either analytical or numerical methods. We have yet to determine the rate of twist $\alpha(t)$. For this purpose we examine the boundary conditions at the ends of the shaft. We see from Fig. 11.16 that the torque is given by

$$T(t) = \int_R (-\tau_{xy} z + \tau_{xz} y)\, dA \tag{11.75}$$

Hence

$$P^G(T) = \int_R [-zP^G(\tau_{xy}) + yP^G(\tau_{xz})]\, dA \tag{11.76}$$

Using Eqs. (11.66) yet again in Eq. (11.76), we get

$$P^G(T) = \frac{Q^G(\alpha)}{2} \int_R \left(y\frac{\partial\Phi}{\partial z} - z\frac{\partial\Phi}{\partial y} + z^2 + y^2 \right) dA$$

Finally, rewriting the equation above, we get

$$\boxed{P^G(T) = \frac{\bar{I}_0}{2} Q^G(\alpha)} \tag{11.77}$$

where $\bar{I}_0$ is a constant related to the polar moment of area I_0 in accordance with

$$\bar{I}_0 = I_0 + \int_R \left(y\frac{\partial\Phi}{\partial z} - z\frac{\partial\Phi}{\partial y} \right) dA \tag{11.78}$$

Note that for the circular shaft $\bar{I}_0 = I_0$ since $\Phi \equiv 0$ for this case (you are asked to prove this in Problem 11.25). All of the other resultants (i.e., axial force F_x, bending moments M_y and M_z, and shear forces V_y and V_z) *vanish* at the ends. Clearly, F_x, M_y, and M_z vanish because $\tau_{xx} = 0$. In Problem 11.26 you are asked to utilize Green's lemma [see Eq. (1.80)] in proving that V_y and V_z also vanish.

Having evaluated $\bar{I}_0$ from the known function $\Phi(y, z)$ via Eq. (11.78), we may then solve differential equation (11.77) for the rate of twist $\alpha(t)$. This solution may be expressed as the hereditary integral

$$\boxed{\alpha(t) = \frac{2}{\bar{I}_0} \int_{0^-}^t J^G(t - t')\frac{dT(t')}{dt'}\, dt'} \tag{11.79}$$

where $J^G(t)$ is the shear creep compliance function. Note that this result is of the same form as Eq. (11.23) for the circular shaft, except that I_0 has been replaced by $\bar{I}_0$. Following the same procedure employed in Section 11.5, we may show that if

$$T(t) = T_0 [u(t)] \tag{11.80}$$

then Eq. (11.79) simply becomes

$$\alpha(t) = \frac{2T_0}{\bar{I}_0} J^G(t)[u(t)] \tag{11.81}$$

Also, the Laplace transform of integral equation (11.79),

$$\bar{\alpha}(s) = \frac{2}{I_0} \bar{J}^G(s)\, s\, \bar{T}(s)$$

is useful in the evaluation of this integral for general $T(t)$.

We have thus fully presented the Saint-Venant theory of torsion for linear viscoelastic shafts. Since all of the governing differential equations and boundary conditions have been satisfied, we have verified that our initial two assumptions on the displacement field were in fact correct. Clearly, the warping function $\Phi(y,z)$ and the rate of twist $\alpha(t)$ which we have obtained are also correct. It is a simple matter to complete the solution by obtaining displacements from Eqs. (11.60), strains from Eqs. (11.61), and finally, stresses from Eqs. (11.66). The special case of linear elastic behavior is reached simply by setting $P^G = 1$ and $Q^G = 2G$ [or equivalently, $J^G = 1/(2G)$]. Note that the warping function [as determined from Eq. (11.69) with (11.74)] does *not* depend on the constitutive law, and thus we may use a warping function previously obtained for an *elastic shaft* for any *viscoelastic shaft* with the same cross-sectional geometry. Also note that if we use Eq. (11.77) to eliminate $Q^G(\alpha)$ from stress equations (11.66), we obtain after clearing out the P^G operator,

$$
\boxed{
\begin{aligned}
\tau_{xy} &= \frac{T}{I_0}\left(\frac{\partial \Phi}{\partial y} - z\right) \\[2mm]
\tau_{xz} &= \frac{T}{I_0}\left(\frac{\partial \Phi}{\partial z} + y\right)
\end{aligned}
}
\tag{11.82}
$$

Since Φ is the same for all linear viscoelastic shafts (including elastic) with the same geometry and load, it immediately follows from Eqs. (11.82) and (11.78) that *the shear stresses are also the same*. Equations (11.82) are more convenient to use than Eqs. (11.66) for calculating the stresses, since the torque is usually prescribed.

For convenience, we summarize the general solution procedure in the following steps:

1. Solve Laplace's equation (11.69), with Neumann boundary condition (11.74), for $\Phi(y,z)$.
2. Evaluate $\bar{I}_0$ from Eq. (11.78) and then obtain the stresses τ_{xy} and τ_{xz} from Eqs. (11.82).
3. Solve for $\alpha(t)$ using Eq. (11.77) or (11.79).
4. Determine the displacement field components by direct substitution of Φ and α into Eqs. (11.60).

Note that for the solution to be considered "exact," the applied torques at the ends must be due to precisely the shear stress distributions obtained in step 2. Otherwise, the solution is approximate but still accurate away from the ends, in accordance with Saint-Venant's principle. In Problem 11.27 you are asked to verify that the formulation above is essentially independent of the location of the longitudinal x axis.

11.11 ALTERNATIVE FORMULATION IN TERMS OF CONJUGATE WARPING FUNCTION

In this section we shall develop an alternative formulation of the torsion problem for linear viscoelastic shafts, which possesses some computational advantages over the previous formulation. We start by pointing out that for a harmonic function $\Phi(y, z)$ there exists a second harmonic function, which we denote as $\Psi(y, z)$ and which is related to $\Phi(y, z)$ by the well-known *Cauchy–Riemann* equations. That is,

$$\frac{\partial \Phi}{\partial y} = \frac{\partial \Psi}{\partial z} \qquad \text{(a)}$$

$$\frac{\partial \Phi}{\partial z} = -\frac{\partial \Psi}{\partial y} \qquad \text{(b)}$$

$$(11.83)$$

The function Ψ, called the *conjugate warping function*, can readily be shown to be harmonic by taking $\partial/\partial z$ of Eq. (11.83a) and $\partial/\partial y$ of Eq. (11.83b) and subtracting the second from the first. Accordingly, we get

$$\frac{\partial^2 \Phi}{\partial y\, \partial z} - \frac{\partial^2 \Phi}{\partial z\, \partial y} = \frac{\partial^2 \Psi}{\partial z^2} + \frac{\partial^2 \Psi}{\partial y^2}$$

If the mixed second partial derivatives of Φ are continuous, we can interchange the order of the differentiation, thus rendering the value of the left side of the preceding equation zero. We have thus confirmed that Ψ is also harmonic,[*] that is,

$$\nabla^2 \Psi = 0 \qquad \text{in } R \qquad (11.84)$$

Let us next formulate the *boundary conditions* for Ψ on the boundary curve C. First we use Cauchy–Riemann equations (11.83) to replace Φ on the right-hand side of Eq. (11.73) for the normal derivative, yielding

$$\frac{\partial \Phi}{\partial \nu} = \frac{\partial \Psi}{\partial z} a_{\nu y} - \frac{\partial \Psi}{\partial y} a_{\nu z} \qquad (11.85)$$

Next examine Fig. 11.17, in which we have shown a segment of boundary curve C lying in the positive yz quadrant (i.e., $y > 0$ and $z > 0$). The vector **ds** represents the differential element of arc traversed as a point moves along this segment with positive differential increments in y and z (i.e., $dy > 0$ and $dz > 0$), and $\hat{\boldsymbol{\mu}}$ is the unit vector in the tangential direction μ. Also shown is the vector **dA**, which represents an element of area on the lateral surface of length ds and of unit width, and which

---

[*] The Cauchy–Riemann equations are fundamental in the study of an *analytic function of a complex variable*, which in the present formulation would be expressed as $\Phi + i\Psi$. Furthermore, since Φ and Ψ both satisfy Laplace's equation, complex variable theory is closely linked with the mathematical discipline called *potential theory*. For example, see O. D. Kellogg, *Foundations of Potential Theory* (New York: Dover Publications, Inc., 1953).

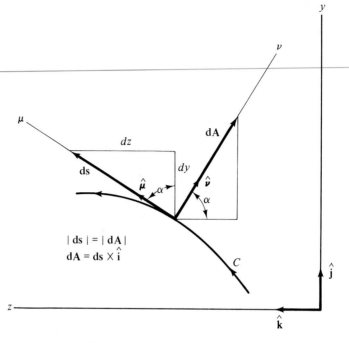

Figure 11.17 Relation between arc vector and lateral area vector.

by convention is normal to ds and hence collinear with the unit normal vector $\hat{\boldsymbol{\nu}}$. Thus, in terms of the unit vectors along y and z we have for $\mathbf{ds}$ from Fig. 11.17

$$\mathbf{ds} = ds\,\hat{\boldsymbol{\mu}} = dy\,\hat{\mathbf{j}} + dz\,\hat{\mathbf{k}}$$

We also see from the figure that $\mathbf{dA} = \mathbf{ds} \times \hat{\mathbf{i}}$, and hence

$$\mathbf{dA} = ds\,\hat{\boldsymbol{\nu}} = dz\,\hat{\mathbf{j}} - dy\,\hat{\mathbf{k}}$$

which then gives

$$\nu_y = a_{\nu y} = \frac{dz}{ds}$$

$$\nu_z = a_{\nu z} = -\frac{dy}{ds}$$

(11.86)

Substituting this result into Eq. (11.85), we then get

$$\frac{\partial \Phi}{\partial \nu} = \frac{\partial \Psi}{\partial z}\frac{dz}{ds} + \frac{\partial \Psi}{\partial y}\frac{dy}{ds} = \frac{\partial \Psi}{\partial s}$$

(11.87)

Now going back to Eq. (11.74) and replacing the left side of this equation using Eq. (11.87), we get

$$\frac{\partial \Psi}{\partial s} = za_{\nu y} - ya_{\nu z}$$

(11.88)

Again using Eqs. (11.86) this becomes

$$\frac{\partial \Psi}{\partial s} = z\frac{dz}{ds} + y\frac{dy}{ds} = \frac{1}{2}\frac{d}{ds}(y^2 + z^2)$$

Noting that on the boundary curve C the functions $\partial \Psi/\partial s$ and Ψ vary only with the curvilinear coordinates, we may integrate the result above to obtain

$$\Psi = \tfrac{1}{2}(y^2 + z^2) + K \qquad \text{on } C$$

where K is a constant of integration. For a solid shaft this constant plays the same role as the arbitrary constant associated with a Neumann boundary condition mentioned previously; that is, it results in only a rigid-body translation and may thus be set equal to zero without any loss in generality.* Accordingly, we have as the boundary condition of Ψ on the lateral surface of the shaft

$$\boxed{\Psi = \tfrac{1}{2}(y^2 + z^2) \qquad \text{on } C} \tag{11.89}$$

The right side of this equation is known at all points on C, and thus Ψ is prescribed on C by Eq. (11.89) in terms of a known function. This type of boundary condition is known as a *Dirichlet* boundary condition, and it is known from potential theory that the solution to Laplace's equation [i.e., Eq. (11.84)] with such a boundary condition is *unique*.

If we use numerical techniques, such as finite differences or finite elements, to solve Laplace's equation, a Dirichlet boundary condition is usually preferable to a Neumann boundary condition. This is so since only the latter requires for finite differences a finite difference approximation in the boundary condition as well as in the differential equation. Furthermore, for finite elements a simpler quadratic functional is needed for the boundary conditions of the Dirichlet problem. In this regard the present Dirichlet formulation is thus more convenient than the former Neumann formulation in Section 11.10.

11.12 ALTERNATIVE FORMULATION IN TERMS OF PRANDTL STRESS FUNCTION

In some cases the viscoelastic torsion problem would be easier to solve if the right side of Eq. (11.89) were zero. This suggests a third formulation of the torsion problem based on the so-called *Prandtl stress function*, which we shall now present. Thus we introduce a function $\psi(y, z)$ related to $\Psi(y, z)$ by

$$\boxed{\psi = \Psi - \tfrac{1}{2}(y^2 + z^2)} \tag{11.90}$$

---

* For full details, see *Mathematical Theory of Elasticity* by I. S. Sokolnikoff (New York: McGraw-Hill Book Company, 1956, p. 115; reprinted by R.E. Krieger Publishing Co., Melbourne, FL, 1987).

and it then follows that

$$\frac{\partial \psi}{\partial y} = \frac{\partial \Psi}{\partial y} - y \qquad \frac{\partial \psi}{\partial z} = \frac{\partial \Psi}{\partial z} - z \qquad \text{(a)}$$

$$\frac{\partial^2 \psi}{\partial y^2} = \frac{\partial^2 \Psi}{\partial y^2} - 1 \qquad \frac{\partial^2 \psi}{\partial z^2} = \frac{\partial^2 \Psi}{\partial z^2} - 1 \qquad \text{(b)}$$

(11.91)

Using Eqs. (11.91b), Laplace's equation (11.84) becomes

$$\boxed{\nabla^2 \psi = -2 \qquad \text{in } R}$$

(11.92)

and on the lateral boundary the use of definition (11.90) transforms boundary condition (11.89) to

$$\boxed{\psi = 0 \qquad \text{on } C}$$

(11.93)

This function ψ is the previously mentioned Prandtl *stress* function, and it is called this because, as we shall soon see, it reduces the equilibrium equation to an identity. Nonhomogeneous differential equation (11.92) is called a *Poisson* equation, and homogeneous boundary condition (11.93) is a Dirichlet-type boundary condition. Later in this section we illustrate the use of this formulation with an example for the case of linear elastic material.*

For linear viscoelastic shafts, the stresses in terms of the warping function Φ were previously given by Eqs. (11.66) as

$$P^G(\tau_{xy}) = \frac{Q^G(\alpha)}{2}\left(\frac{\partial \Phi}{\partial y} - z\right)$$

$$P^G(\tau_{xz}) = \frac{Q^G(\alpha)}{2}\left(\frac{\partial \Phi}{\partial z} + y\right)$$

Replacing Φ by Ψ using the Cauchy–Riemann equations (11.83), and then replacing Ψ by ψ using Eqs. (11.91a), we obtain

$$P^G(\tau_{xy}) = \frac{Q^G(\alpha)}{2}\frac{\partial \psi}{\partial z}$$

$$P^G(\tau_{xz}) = -\frac{Q^G(\alpha)}{2}\frac{\partial \psi}{\partial y}$$

(11.94)

Notice that as asserted previously, Eqs. (11.94) reduce equilibrium equation (11.68) to an *identity*. Finally, replacing the stresses in Eq. (11.76) using Eqs. (11.94), we get for the applied torque

$$P^G(T) = -\frac{Q^G(\alpha)}{2}\int_R \left(z\frac{\partial \psi}{\partial z} + y\frac{\partial \psi}{\partial y}\right) dA$$

(11.95)

---

* In Problems 11.29, 11.30, and 11.31 we develop and utilize a stress function formulation for the problem of torsion in an elastic *circular* shaft of *variable* cross section.

On comparing this result with Eq. (11.77), that is,

$$P^G(T) = \frac{\bar{I}_0}{2} Q^G(\alpha) \tag{11.96}$$

we see that now

$$\bar{I}_0 = -\int_R \left(z \frac{\partial \psi}{\partial z} + y \frac{\partial \psi}{\partial y} \right) dA \tag{11.97}$$

Equations (11.79) and (11.81) of Section 11.10 also follow. Finally, going back to Eqs. (11.82) and replacing Φ by ψ, as described above, we obtain for the stresses

$$\boxed{\begin{aligned} \tau_{xy} &= \frac{T}{\bar{I}_0} \frac{\partial \psi}{\partial z} \\[2mm] \tau_{xz} &= -\frac{T}{\bar{I}_0} \frac{\partial \psi}{\partial y} \end{aligned}} \tag{11.98}$$

There is another form of Eq. (11.97) that will prove more useful. First we rewrite it as

$$\bar{I}_0 = \iint_R \left[-\frac{\partial(y\psi)}{\partial y} - \frac{\partial(z\psi)}{\partial z} \right] dy\,dz + 2 \iint_R \psi\,dy\,dz \tag{11.99}$$

Now refer to Green's lemma, which we derived in Chapter 1 [see Eq. (1.80)]. Replacing x by y and y by z and setting $P = z\psi$ and $Q = -y\psi$, this lemma gives

$$\iint_R \left[-\frac{\partial(y\psi)}{\partial y} - \frac{\partial(z\psi)}{\partial z} \right] dy\,dz = \oint_C (z\psi\,dy - y\psi\,dz) \tag{11.100}$$

The closed line integral in this result can be rewritten as

$$\oint_C \psi \left(z \frac{dy}{ds} - y \frac{dz}{ds} \right) ds = -\oint_C \psi(za_{vz} + ya_{vy})\,ds \tag{11.101}$$

where we have used Eqs. (11.86) in the last step. But according to Eq. (11.93), $\psi = 0$ at all points on C, and thus the line integral in (11.101) must vanish. Equation (11.100) then indicates that the first integral in Eq. (11.99) must also vanish, so the final result for $\bar{I}_0$ is given as

$$\boxed{\bar{I}_0 = 2 \iint_R \psi\,dy\,dz} \tag{11.102}$$

This equation says that if we interpret ψ as the distance above the cross section of a shaft with $\psi = 0$ at the edges, the volume under this ψ-surface equals $\bar{I}_0/2$ (see Fig. 11.18).

The solution procedure in accordance with the Prandtl stress function formulation may be summarized as follows:

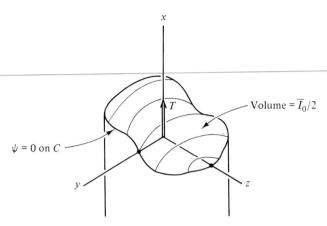

Figure 11.18 The ψ-surface over cross section of shaft.

1. Solve Poisson's equation $\nabla^2 \psi = -2$, with $\psi = 0$ on the boundary, for $\psi(y, z)$.
2. Evaluate $\bar{I}_0$ from Eq. (11.102) and then τ_{xy} and τ_{xz} from Eqs. (11.98).
3. Find $\alpha(t)$ from Eq. (11.96).
4. From ψ get Ψ using Eq. (11.90), and then integrate Cauchy–Riemann equations (11.83) to get the warping function $\Phi(y, z)$.
5. Determine displacements u, v, w by substitution of Φ and α into Eqs. (11.60).

We illustrate the procedure above in the following example, and we again note that ψ, τ_{xy}, and τ_{xz} are the same for all viscoelastic materials, whereas α, u, v, and w depend on the constitutive relation.

Example 11.5

We consider, as an illustration of the use of the theory above, the case of the linear *elastic* shaft having the cross section of an ellipse as shown in Fig. 11.19. The equation of the boundary is given as

$$\frac{y^2}{b^2} + \frac{z^2}{c^2} = 1 \tag{a}$$

where $c > b$. We shall consider for the stress function

$$\psi = k \left(\frac{y^2}{b^2} + \frac{z^2}{c^2} - 1 \right) \tag{b}$$

where k is a constant. Clearly, ψ is zero on the boundary of the cross section as is required by the boundary condition of the problem. Substituting this function ψ into Eq. (11.92), we get

$$\nabla^2 \psi = 2k \left(\frac{1}{b^2} + \frac{1}{c^2} \right) = -2 \tag{c}$$

and thus k is determined as

$$k = -\frac{b^2 c^2}{b^2 + c^2} \tag{d}$$

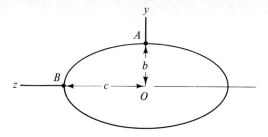

Figure 11.19 Elliptical shaft.

The stress function now becomes

$$\psi = -\frac{b^2c^2}{b^2+c^2}\left(\frac{y^2}{b^2}+\frac{z^2}{c^2}-1\right)$$ (e)

Going to Eq. (11.102), we now find that

$$\bar{I}_0 = 2\iint_R \psi\,dy\,dz = \frac{-2b^2c^2}{b^2+c^2}\iint_R\left(\frac{y^2}{b^2}+\frac{z^2}{c^2}-1\right)dy\,dz$$

$$= \frac{-2}{b^2+c^2}(c^2I_{zz}+b^2I_{yy}-b^2c^2A)$$ (f)

Here I_{zz} and I_{yy} are the second moments of area and A is the area. For an elliptical cross section they are given as

$$A = \pi bc, \qquad I_{zz} = \frac{\pi b^3c}{4}, \qquad I_{yy} = \frac{\pi bc^3}{4}$$ (g)

Inserting these results in Eq. (f), we get

$$\bar{I}_0 = \frac{\pi b^3c^3}{b^2+c^2}$$ (h)

For an *elastic* shaft $P^G = 1$ and $Q^G = 2G$, and accordingly, Eq. (11.96) yields the rate of twist as

$$\alpha = \frac{b^2+c^2}{\pi Gb^3c^3}T$$ (i)

For T constant, α is also constant, as expected for an elastic shaft.

Inserting Eq. (h) for $\bar{I}_0$ and Eq. (e) for ψ into stress equations (11.98), we get

$$\tau_{xy} = -\frac{2Tz}{\pi bc^3}, \qquad \tau_{xz} = \frac{2Ty}{\pi b^3c}$$ (j)

Note that along semiminor axis OA in Fig. 11.19, $z = 0$ and thus

$$\tau_{xy} = 0, \qquad \tau_{xz} = \frac{2Ty}{\pi b^3c} \qquad (0 \le y \le b)$$ (k)

Similarly, along semimajor axis OB we have $y = 0$, whereupon

$$\tau_{xy} = -\frac{2Tz}{\pi bc^3} \qquad (0 \le z \le c), \qquad \tau_{xz} = 0$$ (ℓ)

These stress distributions have been sketched in Fig. 11.20, and with $b < c$ we see that the largest shear stress occurs at A, the point on the boundary *closest* to the origin, and is given by

$$\tau_{\max} = \tau_{xz}\Big|_{\substack{y=b \\ z=0}} = \frac{2T}{\pi b^2c}$$ (m)

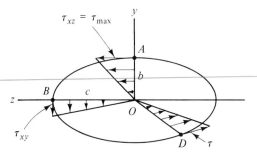

Figure 11.20 Total shear stress along radial lines.

The reader probably expected that point B would be the point of maximum shear stress.

Consider next the shear stresses along an arbitrary radial line such as OD in Fig. 11.20. The ratio z/y must be constant along this line. Furthermore, the ratio of the shear stresses is obtained from Eqs. (j) as

$$\frac{\tau_{xy}}{\tau_{xz}} = -\frac{z}{y}\frac{b^2}{c^2} \tag{n}$$

Thus the ratio of the shear stresses τ_{xy} and τ_{xz} must also be constant along this line. This in turn means that the *direction* of the *total* shear stress τ must be constant along this line. And because of the boundary condition, this direction must be that of the tangent to the boundary at D.[*] We may thus state that along a radial line from O to the boundary, the total shear stress τ in the cross section has a direction corresponding to the tangent of the boundary at the location where this radial line intersects the boundary. This is illustrated in Fig. 11.20 along the line OD.

It will also be of interest to examine the warping of the cross section. First, we get the conjugate warping function Ψ from Eqs. (11.90) and (e) after some algebra as

$$\Psi = \psi + \tfrac{1}{2}(y^2 + z^2)$$
$$= \frac{b^2 - c^2}{2(b^2 + c^2)}(y^2 - z^2) + \frac{b^2 c^2}{b^2 + c^2} \tag{o}$$

Now by use of the Cauchy–Riemann equations we have for the differential of the warping function

$$d\Phi = \frac{\partial \Phi}{\partial y}dy + \frac{\partial \Phi}{\partial z}dz = \frac{\partial \Psi}{\partial z}dy - \frac{\partial \Psi}{\partial y}dz \tag{p}$$

Substituting Eq. (o) for Ψ into this result, we get

$$d\Phi = \frac{c^2 - b^2}{b^2 + c^2}(z\,dy + y\,dz) = \frac{c^2 - b^2}{b^2 + c^2}d(yz) \tag{q}$$

Integrating this equation and eliminating the constant of integration by setting $\Phi = 0$ at $y = z = 0$, we finally obtain

$$\Phi = \frac{c^2 - b^2}{b^2 + c^2}yz \tag{r}$$

---

[*] If the shear stress in the cross section had a component *normal* to the boundary, a complementary shear stress would exist on the lateral surface. But this is not permissible, since the lateral surface is traction-free.

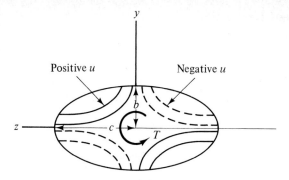

Figure 11.21   Contour lines of constant displacement component u.

Hence the displacement in the x direction becomes

$$u = \alpha\Phi = T\frac{c^2 - b^2}{\pi G b^3 c^3}\, yz \tag{s}$$

where we have used Eq. (i) for α. The contour lines of constant u are thus rectangular hyperbolas, as shown in Fig. 11.21 for $c > b$.

The approach used in Example 11.5 to find Ψ will be successful only for a limited number of cross sections. Another example of this approach is given in Problem 11.33. In general, it will be necessary to use a more formal method, such as the method of separation of variables, to solve the governing partial differential equation. This approach is illustrated in the next section for the case of the rectangular shaft.

11.13 THE ELASTIC RECTANGULAR SHAFT

Consider now a linear elastic shaft with a rectangular cross section of height b and width c, as shown in Fig. 11.22. We shall employ the Prandtl stress function formulation, that is, the Poisson equation

$$\nabla^2 \psi = -2, \qquad -b/2 \le y \le b/2, \qquad -c/2 \le z \le c/2 \tag{11.103}$$

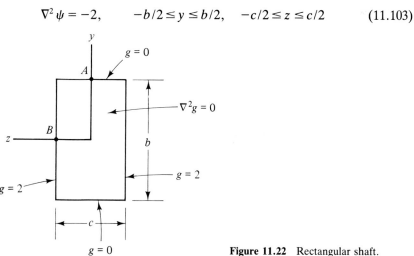

Figure 11.22   Rectangular shaft.

with the homogeneous boundary conditions

$$\psi\left(\pm\frac{b}{2}, z\right) = \psi\left(y, \pm\frac{c}{2}\right) = 0 \qquad (11.104)$$

We seek to solve this problem by the method of separation of variables, but for that method it would be convenient to have a homogeneous differential equation with boundary conditions which are homogeneous on one pair of opposite sides. To accomplish this, we introduce a function $g(y, z)$ defined as

$$g \equiv \frac{\partial^2 \psi}{\partial y^2} + 2 = -\frac{\partial^2 \psi}{\partial z^2} \qquad (11.105)$$

which definition clearly implies that $\nabla^2 \psi = -2$. Operating on g with the ∇^2 operator, we have

$$\nabla^2 g = \frac{\partial^2}{\partial y^2}\left(-\frac{\partial^2 \psi}{\partial z^2}\right) + \frac{\partial^2}{\partial z^2}\left(\frac{\partial^2 \psi}{\partial y^2} + 2\right) = 0 \qquad (11.106)$$

and thus we now have Laplace's equation in g. Boundary conditions (11.104) require that

$$\frac{\partial^2 \psi}{\partial z^2}\left(\pm\frac{b}{2}, z\right) = \frac{\partial^2 \psi}{\partial y^2}\left(y, \pm\frac{c}{2}\right) = 0$$

Now using definition (11.105) to replace the derivatives above, we get for boundary conditions on g,

$$g\left(\pm\frac{b}{2}, z\right) = 0 \qquad \text{(a)}$$
$$\qquad\qquad\qquad\qquad\qquad\qquad (11.107)$$
$$g\left(y, \pm\frac{c}{2}\right) = 2 \qquad \text{(b)}$$

These conditions have been indicated in Fig. 11.22. You should note that the problem is symmetric in both y and z.

We seek solutions to Eq. (11.106) in the separated form

$$g(y, z) = Y(y)Z(z)$$

where Y is a function of y only and Z is a function of z only. Substituting this form into differential equation (11.106), we get

$$Y''Z + YZ'' = 0$$

where the prime indicates differentiation with respect to the appropriate independent variable. Rearranging the equation above, we obtain

$$\frac{Y''}{Y} = -\frac{Z''}{Z} = -\lambda^2 \qquad (11.108)$$

where the separation constant, $-\lambda^2$, has been chosen negative so as to yield a periodic function in y which can vanish at the boundaries.* Note that boundary condition (11.107a) requires that

$$Y\left(\pm\frac{b}{2}\right) = 0 \tag{11.109}$$

The problem now reduces to the solution of the two ordinary differential equations

$$\begin{align} Y'' + \lambda^2 Y &= 0 \qquad \text{(a)} \\ Z'' - \lambda^2 Z &= 0 \qquad \text{(b)} \end{align} \tag{11.110}$$

Equations (11.110) have the well-known solutions

$$Y = A \cos \lambda y + B \sin \lambda y$$
$$Z = C \cosh \lambda z + D \sinh \lambda z$$

Since the problem is symmetric, it is clear that $B = D = 0$, and thus

$$\begin{align} Y &= A \cos \lambda y \qquad \text{(a)} \\ Z &= C \cosh \lambda z \qquad \text{(b)} \end{align} \tag{11.111}$$

Homogeneous boundary condition (11.109) requires that

$$A \cos \frac{\lambda b}{2} = 0$$

and since A cannot be zero for a nontrivial solution, we must have

$$\frac{\lambda b}{2} = \left(\frac{2n + 1}{2}\right)\pi, \qquad n = 0, 1, 2, \ldots$$

We thus have the infinite set of *eigenvalues*

$$\lambda_n = \frac{(2n + 1)\pi}{b}, \qquad n = 0, 1, 2, \ldots \tag{11.112}$$

and the associated *eigenvectors*

$$\begin{align} Y_n &= A_n \cos \lambda_n y \qquad \text{(a)} \\ Z_n &= C_n \cosh \lambda_n z \qquad \text{(b)} \end{align}$$

Taking a linear combination of all solutions, we obtain for the general solution

$$g(y, z) = \sum_{n=0}^{\infty} D_n \cos \lambda_n y \cosh \lambda_n z \tag{11.113}$$

where $A_n C_n$ has been replaced by D_n.

---

* The separation constant is introduced to avoid the apparent contradiction inherent in equating a function of y to a function of the independent variable z. This is the crucial step in the method of separation of variables.

Now go to the nonhomogeneous boundary condition (11.107b). For this condition Eq. (11.113) requires that

$$2 = \sum_{n=0}^{\infty} D_n \cos \lambda_n y \, \cosh \frac{\lambda_n c}{2}$$

To determine D_n we multiply both sides by $\cos \lambda_m y$ ($m = 0, 1, 2, \ldots$) and integrate over y from $-b/2$ to $b/2$, that is,

$$\int_{-b/2}^{b/2} 2 \cos \lambda_m y \, dy = \sum_{n=0}^{\infty} D_n \left[\int_{-b/2}^{b/2} \cos \lambda_n y \cos \lambda_m y \, dy \right] \cosh \frac{\lambda_n c}{2} \quad (11.114)$$

Since differential equation (11.110a) with boundary condition (11.109) falls within the class of Sturm–Liouville equations,[*] functions $\cos \lambda_m y$ must form an orthogonal set, that is,

$$\int_{-b/2}^{b/2} \cos \lambda_n y \, \cos \lambda_m y \, dy = \begin{cases} 0 & m \neq n \\ \dfrac{b}{2} & m = n \end{cases}$$

Accordingly, only the term on the right-hand side of Eq. (11.114) which corresponds with $m = n$ is nonzero, yielding

$$D_m \frac{b}{2} \cosh \frac{\lambda_m c}{2} = \int_{-b/2}^{b/2} 2 \cos \lambda_m y \, dy \quad (11.115)$$

Also, since $\lambda_m = (2m + 1)\pi/b$,

$$\int_{-b/2}^{b/2} \cos \lambda_m y \, dy = \frac{1}{\lambda_m} \sin \lambda_m y \Big|_{-b/2}^{b/2} = \frac{b}{(2m + 1)\pi} \left[\sin \frac{(2m + 1)\pi}{2} \right] 2$$

$$= (-1)^m \frac{2b}{(2m + 1)\pi}$$

Now Eq. (11.115) gives, after replacing m by n,

$$D_n = \frac{8(-1)^n}{(2n + 1)\pi} \frac{1}{\cosh(\lambda_n c/2)}$$

Substituting this result into Eq. (11.113), we get for our final solution

$$g(y, z) = \frac{8}{\pi} \sum_{n=0}^{\infty} \frac{(-1)^n}{2n + 1} \frac{\cosh \lambda_n z}{\cosh(\lambda_n c/2)} \cos \lambda_n y \quad (11.116)$$

Now we return to Eqs. (11.105), and after substituting for $g(y, z)$ using Eq. (11.116) with Eq. (11.112), we obtain for the first derivatives of the stress function,

$$\frac{\partial \psi}{\partial y} = -2y + \frac{8b}{\pi^2} \sum_{n=0}^{\infty} \frac{(-1)^n}{(2n + 1)^2} \frac{\cosh \lambda_n z}{\cosh(\lambda_n c/2)} \sin \lambda_n y + F(z) \quad \text{(a)}$$

$$(11.117)$$

$$\frac{\partial \psi}{\partial z} = -\frac{8b}{\pi^2} \sum_{n=0}^{\infty} \frac{(-1)^n}{(2n + 1)^2} \frac{\sinh \lambda_n z}{\cosh(\lambda_n c/2)} \cos \lambda_n y + G(y) \quad \text{(b)}$$

[*] For details, see *Advanced Engineering Mathematics* by C. R. Wylie and L. C. Barrett (New York: McGraw-Hill Book Company, 1982). This reference gives a more than adequate presentation of the mathematical techniques used in the present section.

where $F(z)$ and $G(y)$ are functions of integration. For the stresses we use Eqs. (11.98), that is,

$$\tau_{xy} = \frac{T}{\bar{I}_0} \frac{\partial \psi}{\partial z} \quad \text{and} \quad \tau_{xz} = -\frac{T}{\bar{I}_0} \frac{\partial \psi}{\partial y} \tag{11.118}$$

and since τ_{xy} must vanish at point A in Fig. 11.22 (where $z = 0$), while τ_{xz} must vanish at point B (where $y = 0$), it follows that $F(z) = G(y) = 0$. Integrating Eq. (11.117b), we then get

$$\psi = -\frac{8b^2}{\pi^3} \sum_{n=0}^{\infty} \frac{(-1)^n}{(2n+1)^3} \frac{\cosh \lambda_n z}{\cosh(\lambda_n c/2)} \cos \lambda_n y + H(y)$$

where $H(y)$ is yet another function of integration. We may readily find $H(y)$ by inserting $z = \pm c/2$ for the boundary condition $\psi = 0$ along $z = \pm c/2$, and thereby eliminating the cosh terms. The final solution for the stress function then becomes

$$\psi = \frac{8b^2}{\pi^3} \sum_{n=0}^{\infty} \frac{(-1)^n}{(2n+1)^3} \left[1 - \frac{\cosh \lambda_n z}{\cosh(\lambda_n c/2)} \right] \cos \lambda_n y \tag{11.119}$$

We may now evaluate $\bar{I}_0$ by means of Eq. (11.102), which here becomes

$$\bar{I}_0 = 2 \int_{-c/2}^{c/2} \int_{-b/2}^{b/2} \psi \, dy \, dz$$

Substituting for ψ from Eq. (11.119) and carrying out the integrations, we get

$$\bar{I}_0 = \frac{16b^2}{\pi^3} \left[\frac{bc}{\pi} \sum_{n=0}^{\infty} \frac{(-1)^n}{(2n+1)^4} \sin \lambda_n y \Big|_{-b/2}^{b/2} - \frac{b^2}{\pi^2} \sum_{n=0}^{\infty} \frac{(-1)^n}{(2n+1)^5} \right.$$

$$\left. \times \frac{\sinh \lambda_n z \Big|_{-c/2}^{c/2} \sin \lambda_n y \Big|_{-b/2}^{b/2}}{\cosh(\lambda_n c/2)} \right]$$

Putting in the limits, we then obtain, since $\sin \lambda_n (b/2) = (-1)^n$ and $(-1)^{2n} = 1$

$$\bar{I}_0 = \frac{16b^2}{\pi^3} \left[\frac{2bc}{\pi} \sum_{n=0}^{\infty} \frac{1}{(2n+1)^4} - \frac{4b^2}{\pi^2} \sum_{n=0}^{\infty} \frac{\tanh(\lambda_n c/2)}{(2n+1)^5} \right]$$

Standard tables* give

$$\sum_{n=0}^{\infty} \frac{1}{(2n+1)^4} = \frac{\pi^4}{96}$$

and thus we have for the final result

$$\bar{I}_0 = \frac{b^3 c}{3} - \frac{64b^4}{\pi^5} \sum_{n=0}^{\infty} \frac{\tanh(\lambda_n c/2)}{(2n+1)^5} \tag{11.120}$$

We now have the rate of twist α in terms of the torque T from Eq. (11.96) (with $P^G = 1$ and $Q^G = 2G$) as

* See E. R. Hansen, *A Table of Series and Products* (Englewood Cliffs, NJ: Prentice-Hall, Inc., 1975), p. 52.

$$\alpha = \frac{T}{G\bar{I}_0} = T / \left[\frac{Gb^3c}{3} - \frac{64Gb^4}{\pi^5} \sum_{n=0}^{\infty} \frac{\tanh(\lambda_n c/2)}{(2n+1)^5} \right] \qquad (11.121)$$

Stresses now follow directly from Eqs. (11.117) [with $F(z) = G(y) = 0$] and Eqs. (11.118) as

$$\tau_{xy} = -\frac{8bT}{\pi^2 \bar{I}_0} \sum_{n=0}^{\infty} \frac{(-1)^n}{(2n+1)^2} \frac{\sinh \lambda_n z}{\cosh(\lambda_n c/2)} \cos \lambda_n y \qquad (a)$$

$$\tau_{xz} = \frac{2Ty}{\bar{I}_0} - \frac{8bT}{\pi^2 \bar{I}_0} \sum_{n=0}^{\infty} \frac{(-1)^n}{(2n+1)^2} \frac{\cosh \lambda_n z}{\cosh(\lambda_n c/2)} \sin \lambda_n y \qquad (b)$$

$$(11.122)$$

where $\bar{I}_0$ has been given by Eq. (11.120). We can show that the largest shear stress for $b > c$ equals τ_{xy} at point B in Fig. 11.22, which is at the midpoint of the *longer* side, and it is given by

$$\tau_{max} = \tau_{xy}\Big|_{\substack{y=0 \\ z=c/2}} = -\frac{8bT}{\pi^2 \bar{I}_0} \sum_{n=0}^{\infty} \frac{(-1)^n}{(2n+1)^2} \tanh \frac{\lambda_n c}{2} \qquad (11.123)$$

This series converges very rapidly and it is necessary to compute only the first few terms. Shear stress τ_{xz} is, of course, zero at point B.

We now seek to determine the warping function Φ, and using Eqs. (11.83) and (11.90), we have the following relations for the derivatives of Φ:

$$\frac{\partial \Phi}{\partial y} = \frac{\partial \Psi}{\partial z} = \frac{\partial \psi}{\partial z} + z$$

$$\frac{\partial \Phi}{\partial z} = -\frac{\partial \Psi}{\partial y} = -\frac{\partial \psi}{\partial y} - y$$

Substituting Eqs. (11.117) for the derivatives of ψ into the above, we obtain the following expression for the differential of Φ:

$$d\Phi = \frac{\partial \Phi}{\partial y} dy + \frac{\partial \Phi}{\partial z} dz$$

$$= \left[z - \frac{8b}{\pi^2} \sum_{n=0}^{\infty} \frac{(-1)^n}{(2n+1)^2} \frac{\sinh \lambda_n z}{\cosh(\lambda_n c/2)} \cos \lambda_n y \right] dy$$

$$+ \left[y - \frac{8b}{\pi^2} \sum_{n=0}^{\infty} \frac{(-1)^n}{(2n+1)^2} \frac{\cosh \lambda_n z}{\cosh(\lambda_n c/2)} \sin \lambda_n y \right] dz$$

Using $\lambda_n = (2n+1)\pi/b$, the two terms on the right of the equality above may be combined as follows into an exact differential:

$$d\Phi = d\left[yz - \frac{8b^2}{\pi^3} \sum_{n=0}^{\infty} \frac{(-1)^n}{(2n+1)^3} \frac{\sinh \lambda_n z}{\cosh(\lambda_n c/2)} \sin \lambda_n y \right]$$

Integrating this result and noting that the constant of integration vanishes if we set $\Phi = 0$ at $y = z = 0$, we finally obtain for the warping displacement

$$u = \alpha\Phi = \alpha yz - \frac{8\alpha b^2}{\pi^3} \sum_{n=0}^{\infty} \frac{(-1)^n}{(2n+1)^3} \frac{\sinh \lambda_n z}{\cosh(\lambda_n c/2)} \sin \lambda_n y \qquad (11.124)$$

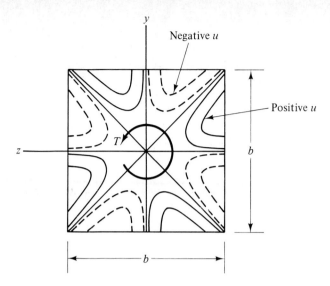

y

Negative u

Positive u

T

z

b

b

Figure 11.23 Contour lines of constant warp for square elastic shaft.

where α has been given by Eq. (11.121). It is interesting to note that for the *square* cross section shown in Fig. 11.23, the section divides into eight 45° triangles, which warp as shown by the constant warp contour lines indicated in the figure.

11.14 NONLINEAR VISCOUS NONCIRCULAR SHAFTS

We shall proceed here by using the *warping* function approach, introduced in Section 11.10 for linear viscoelastic materials. The *geometrical* considerations here are the same as in that section (refer back to Figs. 11.15 and 11.16), and thus the displacement field will be given as [see Eqs. (11.60)]

$$u = \alpha(t)\Phi(y, z)$$

$$v = -\alpha(t)zx \tag{11.125}$$

$$w = \alpha(t)xy$$

where $\Phi(y, z)$ is the warping function and $\alpha(t)$ is the rate of twist. Again, we find from the strain-displacement equations that ε_{xy} and ε_{xz} are the *only* nonzero strains, and they are given by Eqs. (11.61) as

$$\varepsilon_{xy} = \frac{\alpha}{2}\left(\frac{\partial\Phi}{\partial y} - z\right)$$

$$\tag{11.126}$$

$$\varepsilon_{xz} = \frac{\alpha}{2}\left(\frac{\partial\Phi}{\partial z} + y\right)$$

We are now ready for the main change to be made, and that is the *constitutive* law. We shall employ the incompressible multidimensional nonlinear viscous stress power law given by Eq. (11.34) as

$$\dot{e}_{ij} = \dot{\varepsilon}_{ij} = CJ_2^m s_{ij} \tag{11.127}$$

where

$$J_2 = \tfrac{1}{2} s_{ij} s_{ij} \qquad (11.128)$$

The inverted form of this constitutive law was obtained previously as Eq. (7.148), and that equation is

$$s_{ij} = C^{-1/(2m+1)} K_2^{-m/(2m+1)} \dot{\varepsilon}_{ij} \qquad (11.129)$$

where

$$K_2 = \tfrac{1}{2} \dot{\varepsilon}_{ij} \dot{\varepsilon}_{ij} \qquad (11.130)$$

It immediately follows from Eq. (11.129) that since $\varepsilon_{xx} = \varepsilon_{yy} = \varepsilon_{zz} = \varepsilon_{yz} = 0$ for all times, then $s_{xx} = s_{yy} = s_{zz} = s_{yz} = 0$. Using the definition of the stress deviator tensor,

$$s_{ij} = \tau_{ij} - \tfrac{1}{3} \tau_{kk} \delta_{ij}$$

we then obtain

$$s_{xx} = \tfrac{2}{3} \tau_{xx} - \tfrac{1}{3}(\tau_{yy} + \tau_{zz}) = 0$$

$$s_{yy} = \tfrac{2}{3} \tau_{yy} - \tfrac{1}{3}(\tau_{zz} + \tau_{xx}) = 0$$

$$s_{zz} = \tfrac{2}{3} \tau_{zz} - \tfrac{1}{3}(\tau_{xx} + \tau_{yy}) = 0$$

$$s_{yz} = \tau_{yz} = 0$$

These equations have only the trivial solution $\tau_{xx} = \tau_{yy} = \tau_{zz} = \tau_{yz} = 0$, and thus we have proven that τ_{xy} and τ_{xz} are again the *only* nonzero stresses. The equation of *equilibrium* is thus unchanged from that given by Eq. (11.67), that is,

$$\frac{\partial \tau_{xy}}{\partial y} + \frac{\partial \tau_{xz}}{\partial z} = 0 \qquad (11.131)$$

Clearly, the resultant torque $T(t)$ at a section is also the same as given by Eq. (11.75), and we rewrite this here:

$$T(t) = \int_R (-z\tau_{xy} + y\tau_{xz})\, dA \qquad (11.132)$$

Since $\tau_{kk} = 0$ we may replace s_{ij} in Eq. (11.129) by τ_{ij}, and we then have for the nonzero stresses of this development

$$\begin{aligned} \tau_{xy} &= C^{-1/(2m+1)} K_2^{-m/(2m+1)} \dot{\varepsilon}_{xy} \\ \tau_{xz} &= C^{-1/(2m+1)} K_2^{-m/(2m+1)} \dot{\varepsilon}_{xz} \end{aligned} \qquad (11.133)$$

Note further that from Eq. (11.130),

$$K_2 = \tfrac{1}{2}(\dot{\varepsilon}_{xy}^2 + \dot{\varepsilon}_{yx}^2 + \dot{\varepsilon}_{xz}^2 + \dot{\varepsilon}_{zx}^2) = \dot{\varepsilon}_{xy}^2 + \dot{\varepsilon}_{xz}^2 \qquad (11.134)$$

Hence, Eqs. (11.133) become

$$\begin{aligned} \tau_{xy} &= C^{-1/(2m+1)}(\dot{\varepsilon}_{xy}^2 + \dot{\varepsilon}_{xz}^2)^{-m/(2m+1)} \dot{\varepsilon}_{xy} \\ \tau_{xz} &= C^{-1/(2m+1)}(\dot{\varepsilon}_{xy}^2 + \dot{\varepsilon}_{xz}^2)^{-m/(2m+1)} \dot{\varepsilon}_{xz} \end{aligned}$$

Now substitute for the strains in the equations above using Eqs. (11.126), whereupon we get

$$\tau_{xy} = \left(\frac{\dot{\alpha}}{2C}\right)^{1/(2m+1)}\left[\left(\frac{\partial\Phi}{\partial y}-z\right)^2 + \left(\frac{\partial\Phi}{\partial z}+y\right)^2\right]^{-m/(2m+1)}\left(\frac{\partial\Phi}{\partial y}-z\right) \quad\text{(a)}$$

$$\tau_{xz} = \left(\frac{\dot{\alpha}}{2C}\right)^{1/(2m+1)}\left[\left(\frac{\partial\Phi}{\partial y}-z\right)^2 + \left(\frac{\partial\Phi}{\partial z}+y\right)^2\right]^{-m/(2m+1)}\left(\frac{\partial\Phi}{\partial z}+y\right) \quad\text{(b)}$$

(11.135)

Finally, we substitute these stresses into the equation of equilibrium as given by Eq. (11.131), and get

$$\frac{\partial}{\partial y}\left\{\frac{\frac{\partial\Phi}{\partial y}-z}{\left[\left(\frac{\partial\Phi}{\partial y}-z\right)^2 + \left(\frac{\partial\Phi}{\partial z}+y\right)^2\right]^{m/(2m+1)}}\right\}$$
$$+ \frac{\partial}{\partial z}\left\{\frac{\frac{\partial\Phi}{\partial z}+y}{\left[\left(\frac{\partial\Phi}{\partial y}-z\right)^2 + \left(\frac{\partial\Phi}{\partial z}+y\right)^2\right]^{m/(2m+1)}}\right\} = 0 \quad\text{in } R$$

(11.136)

Equation (11.136) is a nonlinear partial differential equation, which would in general require solution by numerical techniques. Note that if $m = 0$ (linear viscous behavior), this equation simplifies to the linear differential equation $\nabla^2\Phi = 0$. This is consistent with the previous result that Φ is harmonic for linear viscoelastic materials, which of course includes the linear viscous material as a special case. Now let $m \to \infty$ (fully perfectly plastic behavior), in which case Eq. (11.136) becomes

$$\frac{\partial}{\partial y}\left\{\frac{\frac{\partial\Phi}{\partial y}-z}{\left[\left(\frac{\partial\Phi}{\partial y}-z\right)^2 + \left(\frac{\partial\Phi}{\partial z}+y\right)^2\right]^{1/2}}\right\} + \frac{\partial}{\partial z}\left\{\frac{\frac{\partial\Phi}{\partial z}+y}{\left[\left(\frac{\partial\Phi}{\partial y}-z\right)^2 + \left(\frac{\partial\Phi}{\partial z}+y\right)^2\right]^{1/2}}\right\} = 0 \quad\text{in } R$$

(11.137)

This again is a nonlinear differential equation that is not readily solved by analytical methods.

The *boundary condition* on the lateral surface states that [refer back to Eq. (11.71) and Fig. (11.16)]

$$\tau_{xy}\nu_y + \tau_{xz}\nu_z = 0 \quad\text{on } C$$

Substituting from Eqs. (11.135) we get

$$\left(\frac{\dot{\alpha}}{2C}\right)^{1/(2m+1)}\left[\left(\frac{\partial\Phi}{\partial y}-z\right)^2 + \left(\frac{\partial\Phi}{\partial z}+y\right)^2\right]^{-m/(2m+1)}\left[\left(\frac{\partial\Phi}{\partial y}-z\right)\nu_y + \left(\frac{\partial\Phi}{\partial z}+y\right)\nu_z\right] = 0 \quad\text{on } C$$

The first bracketed term cannot vanish for nonzero strain rates since it was obtained from K_2 [see Eq. (11.130)], which is nonnegative, and thus to satisfy the equation above we require that

$$\left(\frac{\partial \Phi}{\partial y} - z\right) v_y + \left(\frac{\partial \Phi}{\partial z} + y\right) v_z = 0$$

and so

$$\left(\frac{\partial \Phi}{\partial y} v_y + \frac{\partial \Phi}{\partial z} v_z\right) = zv_y - yv_z$$

Finally, using Eq. (11.73) we can say for the equation above that

$$\boxed{\frac{\partial \Phi}{\partial \nu} = zv_y - yv_z \qquad \text{on } C} \tag{11.138}$$

which is the same Neumann boundary condition obtained previously for linear viscoelastic shafts. The warping function is then determined by solving nonlinear partial differential equation (11.136) with boundary condition (11.138).

Assuming that $\Phi(y, z)$ has been determined, it remains for us to express the unknown rate of twist $\alpha(t)$ in terms of the prescribed torque $T(t)$. We accomplish this by simply substituting Eqs. (11.135) for the stresses into Eq. (11.132), which gives

$$\boxed{T(t) = \left(\frac{\dot{\alpha}}{2C}\right)^{1/(2m+1)} \int_R \frac{\left(y\frac{\partial \Phi}{\partial z} + y^2 - z\frac{\partial \Phi}{\partial y} + z^2\right)}{\left[\left(\frac{\partial \Phi}{\partial z} + y\right)^2 + \left(\frac{\partial \Phi}{\partial y} - z\right)^2\right]^{m/(2m+1)}} \, dA} \tag{11.139}$$

You may easily verify on noting Eq. (11.78) that for $m = 0$, Eq. (11.139) reduces to Eq. (11.77) with $P^G = 1$ and $Q^G = (1/C)(\partial/\partial t)$. Also note that as $m \to \infty$, the $\dot{\alpha}$ variable drops from this equation, since for $\dot{\alpha}$ nonzero and finite,

$$\lim_{m \to \infty} \left(\frac{\dot{\alpha}}{2C}\right)^{1/(2m+1)} = 1$$

Thus, in this case α and all of the displacements are indeterminate [see Eqs. (11.125)]. It is characteristic of fully perfectly plastic behavior that the displacement solutions contain an indeterminate factor.*

The procedure for solving nonlinear viscous torsion problems may be summarized as follows:

1. Solve nonlinear differential Eq. (11.136) for $\Phi(y, z)$ satisfying the Neumann boundary condition set forth by Eq. (11.138).

---

*The more general elastoplastic problem (e.g., linear elastic, perfectly plastic) can be quite complicated. For a discussion of the analytical difficulties inherent in this torsion problem, see W. Prager and P. G. Hodge, Jr., *Theory of Perfectly Plastic Solids* (New York: John Wiley & Sons, Inc., 1951), pp. 62–71.

2. Substitute this Φ into Eq. (11.139) where, for a given $T(t)$, we can get $\dot{\alpha}$ and then $\alpha(t)$ via an integration over t.

3. Compute the stresses from Eqs. (11.135).

4. Finally, compute the displacement components using Eqs. (11.125).

In the formulation above the displacement equations (11.125) were given at the outset, and thus it was unnecessary to utilize the compatibility equations. Nonetheless, it is instructive to see what form compatibility takes for torsion of non-circular nonlinear viscous shafts. Recall that the only nonzero strains are ε_{xy} and ε_{xz}, and that these strains are independent of x. Referring back to the six compatibility equations (9.6) in Chapter 9, we see that the first three of these equations are trivially satisfied, whereas the last three will be satisfied if we set

$$\frac{\partial \varepsilon_{xz}}{\partial y} - \frac{\partial \varepsilon_{xy}}{\partial z} = f(t) \tag{11.140}$$

where $f(t)$ is a function of time which is independent of x, y, z. By substituting Eqs. (11.126) into Eq. (11.140), we find that $f(t)$ is equal to the rate of twist $\alpha(t)$, that is,

$$\boxed{\frac{\partial \varepsilon_{xz}}{\partial y} - \frac{\partial \varepsilon_{xy}}{\partial z} = \alpha(t)} \tag{11.141}$$

Since neither Eqs. (11.126) nor (11.140) involve the constitutive law, it follows that compatibility condition (11.141) is valid for torsion of a bar made from *any material* for which displacement equations (11.125) are applicable. In Problem 11.36 you will be asked to employ Eq. (11.141) in the development of a stress function formulation for torsion in nonlinear viscous shafts.

11.15 CLOSURE

In Part A we started the study of torsion by making certain key geometric statements for homogeneous isotropic circular shafts of uniform cross section, and we showed that for uniform torque the resulting familiar formulations from strength of materials for *linear elastic* behavior were *exact* from the viewpoint of the theory of elasticity. These geometric statements resulted in the relation

$$\varepsilon_{x\theta} = \frac{1}{2} r \frac{\partial \phi}{\partial x} \tag{11.142}$$

and the familiar formulations that followed for linear elastic circular shafts were

$$\alpha = \frac{\partial \phi}{\partial x} = \frac{T}{GI_0} \tag{11.143}$$

$$\tau_{x\theta} = \frac{Tr}{I_0} \tag{11.144}$$

Next we considered *linear viscoelastic* circular shafts for a torque $T(x,t)$. For small deformation, Eq. (11.142) is still valid. We showed that we could get the rate of twist from the following equation analogous to Eq. (11.143):

$$Q^G(\alpha) = \frac{2P^G(T)}{I_0} \tag{11.145}$$

In integral form this equation becomes

$$\alpha(x,t) = \frac{2}{I_0} \int_{0^-}^{t} J^G(t-t') \frac{\partial T(x,t')}{\partial t'} dt' \tag{11.146}$$

Furthermore, the shear stress formula is the same as Eq. (11.144) for the linear elastic case, and thus we have

$$\tau_{x\theta}(x,r,t) = \frac{T(x,t)r}{I_0} \tag{11.147}$$

Hence the stress for a linear viscoelastic circular shaft is the *same* as in a geometrically identical elastic shaft with the same torque. As in the elastic case, Eqs. (11.146) and (11.147) are *exact* if the torque is *uniform* (i.e., independent of x).

Next we considered the *nonlinear viscous* circular shaft using the stress power law. The formulation analogous to Eq. (11.143) now becomes

$$\dot{\alpha} = \frac{\partial \dot{\phi}}{\partial x} = \left(\frac{T}{\lambda_s I_{0n}}\right)^n \tag{11.148}$$

where $I_{0n} = \int_R r^{(n+1)/n} dA$ and λ_s is a material constant from a torsion test for which $\dot{\gamma}_{x\theta} = (\tau_{x\theta}/\lambda_s)^n$. And analogous to stress formula (11.144) we have the relation

$$\tau_{x\theta} = \frac{Tr^{1/n}}{I_{0n}} \tag{11.149}$$

We then finished our discussion of circular shafts with the case of *plastic* deformation by considering elastic, perfectly plastic behavior.

In Part B we looked at *noncircular shafts allowing now for warping*. We went directly to the linear viscoelastic material and from it extracted the *linear elastic case* as a special case. In this study we set up three related boundary value problems. First we worked with the *warping* function $\Phi(y,z)$ where

$$
\begin{aligned}
\nabla^2 \Phi &= 0 && \text{in } R && \text{(a)} \\
\frac{\partial \Phi}{\partial \nu} &= za_{\nu y} - ya_{\nu z} && \text{on } C && \text{(b)}
\end{aligned}
\tag{11.150}
$$

Then we introduced the *conjugate warping function* $\Psi(y,z)$, where

$$
\begin{aligned}
\nabla^2 \Psi &= 0 && \text{in } R && \text{(a)} \\
\Psi &= \tfrac{1}{2}(y^2 + z^2) && \text{on } C && \text{(b)}
\end{aligned}
\tag{11.151}
$$

Finally, we introduced the *Prandtl stress function* $\psi(y,z)$ such that

$$
\begin{aligned}
\nabla^2 \psi &= -2 && \text{in } R && \text{(a)} \\
\psi &= 0 && \text{on } C && \text{(b)}
\end{aligned}
\tag{11.152}
$$

In general, numerical methods are needed to solve these boundary value problems, although analytical solutions are possible for simple cross sections.

Using the warping function approach for linear viscoelastic material, we can get α from the equation

$$P^G(T) = \frac{\bar{I}_0}{2} Q^G(\alpha) \tag{11.153}$$

where

$$\bar{I}_0 = I_0 + \int_R \left(y \frac{\partial \Phi}{\partial z} - z \frac{\partial \Phi}{\partial y} \right) dA \tag{11.154}$$

For the Prandtl stress function approach the $\bar{I}_0$ of Eq. (11.153) becomes

$$\bar{I}_0 = 2 \iint_R \psi \, dy \, dz \tag{11.155}$$

We illustrated the use of the Prandtl stress function approach for torsion of a linear elastic elliptical shaft, as well as for a rectangular elastic shaft. We completed our discussion on noncircular shafts with a brief treatment of nonlinear viscous shafts. As noted above, the stresses are the same for all *linear* viscoelastic shafts (including linear elastic) with the same geometry and torque. However, we found that stresses in *nonlinear* viscous shafts vary with the stress power m.

In Chapter 12 we go on to a consideration of plane strain.

PROBLEMS

11.1. (a) What are the supporting torques at A and B (see Fig. P11.1) for $G = 12 \times 10^{11}$ Pa? The shaft is linear elastic and of circular cross section.
(b) Determine $d\phi/dx$ and ϕ as functions of x.

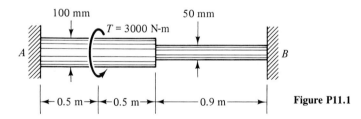
Figure P11.1

11.2. What are the maximum torsional shear stresses in each of the domains of the linear elastic circular shaft in Fig. P11.2? What is the twist at A from the indicated torques for $G = 20 \times 10^6$ psi?

11.3. In Fig. P11.3 is shown a tapered circular shaft made of linear elastic material. Assuming that the theory of torsion of constant diameter shafts can be used locally for the tapered shaft, what is the twist at B from the 2000 N-m torque? In Problem 11.31 we will solve this problem exactly and will compare results for this problem with the proposed approximate approach. The error will be found to be small.

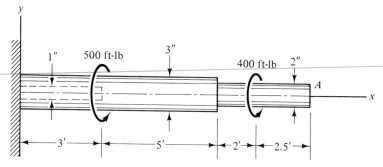

Figure P11.2

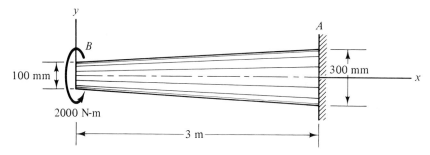

Figure P11.3

11.4. A circular shaft AC is fixed at A (see Fig. P11.4) and is connected at C to a rigid disk that is glued firmly to an elastic rubber grommet. This grommet has a torsional spring constant of 200,000 ft-lb/rad. A second circular shaft goes from the rigid disk at C to a second rigid disk at D, which connects to a rubber grommet with a torsional spring constant of 300,000 ft-lb/rad. Determine the supporting torque at A and the twist at B. The shafts are linear elastic with $G = 10 \times 10^6$ psi.

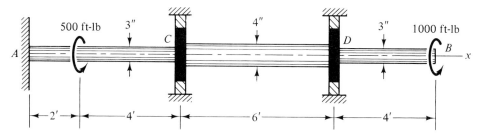

Figure P11.4

11.5. Two circular rods are welded together as shown in Fig. P11.5. For linear elastic behavior, find the displacement of point A as a result of the loads. Use the following data:

$$\text{Rod } BC: \quad E = 30 \times 10^6 \text{ psi}, \quad G = 15 \times 10^6 \text{ psi}$$

$$\text{Rod } BA: \quad E = 35 \times 10^6 \text{ psi}$$

(*Note:* Rod BA is parallel to the y axis and deforms by stretching and bending, whereas rod BC deforms by stretching, bending, *and* twisting.)

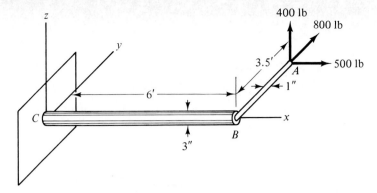

Figure P11.5

11.6. For linear elastic behavior with $G = 1.5 \times 10^{11}$ Pa, determine the very largest normal tensile stress and the very largest compressive stress in circular member AB in Fig. P11.6. (*Note*: The stress in AB is due to stretching, bending, *and* torsion.)

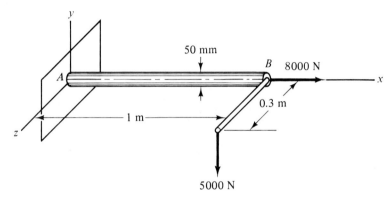

Figure P11.6

11.7. Find the angle of twist at A for the circular shaft in Fig. P11.7 at 500 hours for a Maxwell material in shear for which $G = 20 \times 10^6$ psi and $\zeta = 3 \times 10^9$ lb-hr/in.^{2}. The load is suddenly applied. (*Hint*: See Example 11.1.)

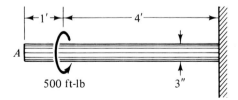

Figure P11.7

11.8. Do Problem 11.7 for a Kelvin material (in shear) for which $G = 20 \times 10^6$ psi and $\zeta = 3 \times 10^9$ lb-hr/in.^{2}. The creep compliance function in shear for a Kelvin material is $J^G(t) = [(1/2G)]\{1 - \exp[-(2G/\zeta)t]\}$.

11.9. In Section 11.5 we showed that if $T(x,t) = T_0[u(t)]$, then

$$\frac{\partial \phi}{\partial x} = \frac{2T_0}{I_0} J^G(t)[u(t)]$$

In a similar manner, show that:

(a) If the loading function can be written as

$$T(x,t) = T_1[u(t-t_1)] + T_2[u(t-t_2)]$$

then

$$\frac{\partial \phi}{\partial x} = \frac{2T_1}{I_0} J^G(t-t_1)[u(t-t_1)] + \frac{2T_2}{I_0} J^G(t-t_2)[u(t-t_2)]$$

(b) If the loading function is in the separated form

$$T(x,t) = T_0(x) f(t)[u(t)]$$

then

$$\frac{\partial \phi}{\partial x} = \frac{2T_0(x)}{I_0} \left[J^G(0) f(t) - \int_{0^-}^{t} f(t') \frac{\partial J^G(t-t')}{\partial t'} dt' \right] [u(t)]$$

11.10. In the torsion problem for linear viscoelastic circular shafts, we may also use a correspondence principle to calculate the rate of twist. Eq. (11.25) may be written as

$$\alpha(x,t) = [\alpha(x)]_{EL} (2G) J^G(t)[u(t)]$$

where $[\alpha(x)]_{EL}$ is the rate of twist of a linear elastic shaft with the same geometry and loading, and $J^G(t)$ is the shear creep compliance function. Using the correspondence principle above, do Problem 11.1 for a torque $T = 3000$ N-m, which is suddenly applied at the position $x = 0.5$ m. The shaft is of Maxwell material in shear, where $J^G(t) = 1/(2G) + t/\zeta$ with $\zeta = 2 \times 10^{14}$ N-hr/m^2 and with G the same as in Problem 11.1.

11.11. In Fig. P11.11 a torque T_1 is applied suddenly at time $t_1 = 0$ and torque T_2 is applied suddenly at time $t_2 = 200$ hours. What is the twist ϕ at the end A at 500 hours for a Maxwell material in shear? Take $G = 1.4 \times 10^{11}$ Pa and $\zeta = 2 \times 10$ N-hr/m^2. [*Hint*: See Problem 11.9(a).]

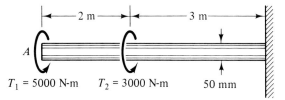

$T_1 = 5000$ N-m $T_2 = 3000$ N-m   50 mm

Figure P11.11

11.12. Do Problem 11.11 for a Kelvin material in shear for $G = 1.4 \times 10^{11}$ Pa and $\zeta = 2 \times 10^{14}$ N-hr/m^2. For $J^G(t)$, see Problem 11.8.

11.13. Circular shafts A and B in Fig. P11.13 are made of Maxwell material in shear with $G = 15 \times 10^6$ psi and $\zeta = 4 \times 10^9$ lb-hr/in.^{2}, while C is of linear elastic material with $G = 15 \times 10^6$ psi. The torque is applied suddenly at the center of C. What are the supporting torques at $t = 200$ hours after loading?

11.14. Shaft AC in Fig. P11.14 is linear elastic with shear modulus G_1. Shaft CB is Maxwell material in shear with viscoelastic constants G_2 and ζ. Find the supporting torques $T_1(t)$ and $T_2(t)$ at A and B and the twist at C. The torque T_0 is applied suddenly at $t = 0$.

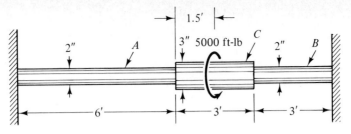

Figure P11.13

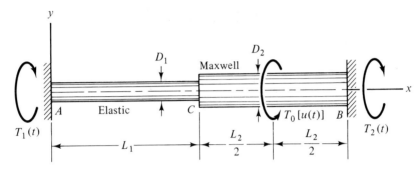

Figure P11.14

11.15. Do Problem 11.14 for a Kelvin material in shear in place of.the Maxwell material in shear. For the form of $J^G(t)$ for shaft CB, see Problem 11.8.

11.16. Find the twist $\phi(t)$ at A for a suddenly applied torque T, as shown in Fig. P11.16. The tapered shaft is of Maxwell material in shear with $G = 20 \times 10^6$ psi and $\zeta = 3 \times 10^9$ lb-hr/in.^{2}. Assume that the simple theory of uniform diameter circular shafts can be extrapolated to a shaft with small taper.

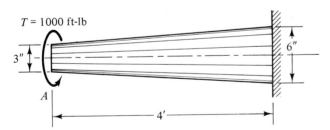

Figure P11.16

11.17. Find the rate of twist as a function of time for the nonlinear viscous circular shaft shown in Fig. P11.17, with $n = 3$ and $\lambda_s = 7 \times 10^6$ lb/(hr-ft^7)$^{1/3}$. What is the maximum shear stress as a function of x and t? Originally there is no rate of twist when the torque distribution is applied. The torque *distribution per unit length* is given by

$$\frac{dT}{dx} = (2x)(2 + 0.001t^{1/2}) \text{ ft-lb/ft}$$

with x in feet and t in seconds.

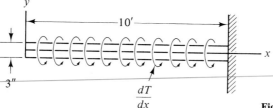

Figure P11.17

11.18. For the nonlinear viscous shaft in Fig. P11.18, with $n = 3$ and $\lambda_s = 8 \times 10^6$ N/(hr-m^7)$^{1/3}$, what is the stress at each section as a function of x and r? What is the rate of twist α as a function of x and t if the 1000 N-m torque is applied at $t = 0$ with $\alpha = 0$ at $t = 0^-$? Assume that the theory of uniform diameter circular shafts can be extrapolated to tapered shafts of small taper.

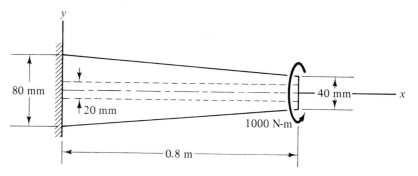

Figure P11.18

11.19. A torque equal to 1.2 times T_e is applied to a linear elastic, perfectly plastic circular cylindrical shaft (see Fig. P11.19) with $G = 20 \times 10^6$ psi and $k = 50,000$ psi. What is the maximum residual shear stress and the residual rate of twist on unloading?

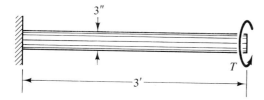

Figure P11.19

11.20. Shafts A and B in Fig. P11.20 are solid circular cylinders. Shaft A is linear elastic, perfectly plastic with $G = 20 \times 10^6$ psi and $k = 50,000$ psi. Shaft B is also linear elastic, perfectly plastic with $G = 25 \times 10^6$ psi and $k = 40,000$ psi.

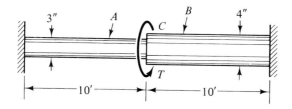

Figure P11.20

Torsion of Shafts   Chap. 11

(a) What is the very largest torque T that can be applied with elastic behavior everywhere? (*Hint*: Cut combined shaft at C and consider separate shafts.) What are the supporting torques?

(b) If one of the shafts has plastic deformation to some degree and the other shaft is just starting to deform plastically, what is the required torque? Determine the supporting torques for this case.

(c) If the torque in part (a) is increased by 30%, what are the supporting torques?

11.21. Consider a linear elastic, perfectly plastic circular shaft (see Fig. P11.21) with $G = 20 \times 10^6$ psi and $k = 60,000$ psi. What is the maximum value of T_1 acting *alone* to cause only elastic deformation, and also what is the very largest value of T_1 possible? We denote these respective results as T_{1e} and T_{1p}. Now apply T_{1e} and apply $T_2 = 0.4(T_{1p} - T_{1e})$. What is the maximum shear stress for $x > 2$ and $x < 2$? What is the twist at A? What is the residual twist at A when the torques are removed?

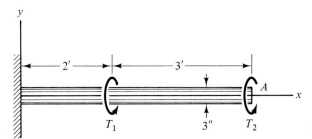

Figure P11.21

11.22. What is the very largest value of torque T that can be applied to the linear elastic, perfectly plastic tapered shaft of Fig. P11.22, with $G = 1.5 \times 10^{11}$ Pa and $k = 3 \times 10^8$ Pa? As an approximation, assume that the theory for uniform diameter shafts can be used in this problem. Now apply a torque that is 0.9 times the largest value T_p above. What is the radius of the elastic core as a function of x? What is the twist at B? Do not attempt to carry out the integration.

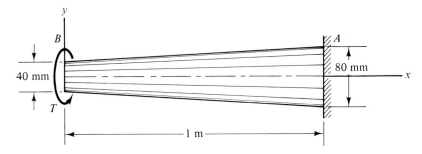

Figure P11.22

11.23. A linear torque *distribution* dT/dx acts on a linear elastic, perfectly plastic circular shaft (see Fig. P11.23). The torque distribution intensity is zero at $x = 0$ and it is T_0 ft-lb/ft at $x = 5$ ft. What is the value of T_0 for a torsional hinge to form? If this loading is reduced by 10%, what is the radius of the elastic core as a function of x? Find the twist at A by means of numerical integration. What is the maximum residual stress as a function of x upon unloading? Take $G = 30 \times 10^6$ psi and $k = 50,000$ psi.

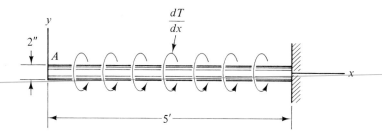

Figure P11.23

11.24. Develop formulas for a linear elastic, perfectly plastic *hollow* circular shaft with inside radius r_i and outside radius r_o, for the following quantities: T_e, T_p, a, and $d\phi/dx$.

11.25. In Section 11.10 we proved that for any arbitrary cross section, the warping function Φ for linear viscoelastic material satisfies Laplace's equation in the region of the cross section R. Thus the governing differential equation is

$$\nabla^2 \Phi = 0 \qquad \text{in } R$$

with the Neumann boundary condition

$$\frac{\partial \Phi}{\partial \nu} = z a_{\nu y} - y a_{\nu z} \qquad \text{on } C$$

where ν is normal to the boundary curve C, and $a_{\nu y}$ and $a_{\nu z}$ are direction cosines of the unit normal vector $\hat{\boldsymbol{\nu}}$.

Prove that if the cross section is circular, the warping function, as obtained by solving the boundary value problem above, is simply $\Phi = 0$.

11.26. Utilize Green's lemma [see Eq. (1.80)] to prove that the shear forces

$$V_y = \int_R \tau_{xy} \, dA$$

$$V_z = \int_R \tau_{xz} \, dA$$

both vanish in the linear viscoelastic torsion problem. *Hint*: Utilize the warping function approach, and set

$$\frac{\partial \Phi}{\partial y} - z = \frac{\partial}{\partial y}\left[y\left(\frac{\partial \Phi}{\partial y} - z\right)\right] + \frac{\partial}{\partial z}\left[y\left(\frac{\partial \Phi}{\partial z} + y\right)\right]$$

$$\frac{\partial \Phi}{\partial z} + y = \frac{\partial}{\partial y}\left[z\left(\frac{\partial \Phi}{\partial y} - z\right)\right] + \frac{\partial}{\partial z}\left[z\left(\frac{\partial \Phi}{\partial z} + y\right)\right]$$

11.27. It is clear that our formulation of the linear viscoelastic torsion problem is independent of the location of the longitudinal x axis, since the location of the origin of yz in no way entered into the derivation. Verify that this is indeed so by introducing the coordinate translation (see Fig. P11.27)

$$x' = x$$

$$y' = y - y_1$$

$$z' = z - z_1$$

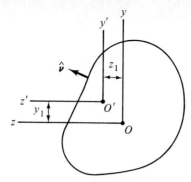

Figure P11.27

where (y_1, z_1) is the position of the origin O' of a new parallel set of axes $y'z'$. Let $\Phi_0(y, z)$ be the warping function in coordinates xyz with the x axis at O. Note that $\nabla^2 \Phi_0(y, z) = 0$ and that the Neumann boundary condition applies. That is,

$$\frac{\partial \Phi_0(y, z)}{\partial \nu} = z\nu_y - y\nu_z$$

Now consider $\Phi_{0'}'(y', z')$, which we take as the warping function in coordinates $x'y'z'$ with the x' axis at O' as shown in the diagram. Prove that

$$\Phi_{0'}'(y', z') \equiv \Phi_{0'}(y, z) = \Phi_0(y, z) - z_1 y + y_1 z + \text{const}$$

where $\Phi_0(y, z)$ is the warping function in y and z with the x axis taken at O. Discuss the significance of this result.

11.28. In Eqs. (11.83) we gave the Cauchy–Riemann equations in rectangular Cartesian coordinates as

$$\frac{\partial \Phi}{\partial y} = \frac{\partial \Psi}{\partial z}$$

$$\frac{\partial \Phi}{\partial z} = -\frac{\partial \Psi}{\partial y}$$

Now derive the forms of the Cauchy–Riemann equations for polar coordinates. In the above, $\Phi(y, z)$ and $\Psi(y, z)$ are, respectively, the warping and conjugate warping functions for linear viscoelastic material.

11.29. In this problem we develop a stress function formulation of torsion for a circular shaft of *variable* cross section. Assume (semi-inverse method) that $u_r = u_x = 0$ so that for axial symmetry:

$$\varepsilon_{rr} = \varepsilon_{\theta\theta} = \varepsilon_{xx} = \gamma_{rx} = 0$$

$$\gamma_{r\theta} = \frac{\partial u_\theta}{\partial r} - \frac{u_\theta}{r}, \qquad \gamma_{\theta x} = \frac{\partial u_\theta}{\partial x}$$

The equilibrium equation in cylindrical coordinates is

$$\frac{\partial \tau_{r\theta}}{\partial r} + 2\frac{\tau_{r\theta}}{r} + \frac{\partial \tau_{\theta x}}{\partial x} = 0$$

The other equations of equilibrium are identically satisfied. Show that a stress function $\bar{\psi}$ defined as follows, satisfies the equation above:

$$\tau_{r\theta} = -\frac{1}{r^2}\frac{\partial \bar{\psi}}{\partial x}, \qquad \tau_{\theta x} = \frac{1}{r^2}\frac{\partial \bar{\psi}}{\partial r} \tag{a}$$

For a linear elastic material, show that

$$\tau_{r\theta} = Gr\frac{\partial}{\partial r}\left(\frac{u_\theta}{r}\right) = -\frac{1}{r^2}\frac{\partial\bar\psi}{\partial x}$$

(b)

$$\tau_{\theta x} = Gr\frac{\partial}{\partial x}\left(\frac{u_\theta}{r}\right) = \frac{1}{r^2}\frac{\partial\bar\psi}{\partial r}$$

(c)

By eliminating (u_θ/r) from the equations above, we form a compatibility equation in the form

$$\frac{\partial^2\bar\psi}{\partial r^2} - \frac{3}{r}\frac{\partial\bar\psi}{\partial r} + \frac{\partial^2\bar\psi}{\partial x^2} = 0$$

(d)

Next show that on the boundary $\bar\psi$ must be constant. Finally, show that at any section the torque is related to $\bar\psi$ as follows:

$$T = 2\pi\bar\psi\,\Big|_0^R$$

(e)

where R is the radius of the section. We have thus formulated the boundary value problem for circular shafts with variable diameter.

11.30. Using the results of Problem 11.29, consider a tapered shaft (see Fig. P11.30). Show that

$$\bar\psi = C\left\{\frac{x}{(r^2+x^2)^{1/2}} - \frac{1}{3}\left[\frac{x}{(r^2+x^2)^{1/2}}\right]^3\right\}$$

Figure P11.30

qualifies as a stress function by satisfying Eq. (d) of Problem 11.29 and being constant on the boundary (look at $\cos\alpha$). Show that

$$\tau_{\theta x} = -\frac{Crx}{(r^2+x^2)^{5/2}}$$

and that the twist for linear elastic material is given by

$$\phi = \frac{u_\theta}{r} = \frac{C}{3G(r^2+x^2)^{3/2}}$$

Finally, show that

$$C = -\frac{T}{2\pi(\frac{2}{3}-\cos\alpha+\frac{1}{3}\cos^3\alpha)}$$

11.31. Using the results of Problem 11.30, solve Problem 11.3 and compare results at B for $r = 0$ and $r = R$. In Problem 11.3 we got $\phi_B = 7.0\times10^{-4}$ rad for a linear elastic material.

11.32. Consider the following warping function:

$$\Phi = -\frac{1}{2a}(3y^2z - z^3)$$

where a is a constant. What is the conjugate warping function? Show that it is harmonic. What is the corresponding Prandtl stress function?

11.33. In Problem 11.32 we showed that a possible Prandtl stress function can be given as

$$\psi = \left[\frac{1}{2a} (y^3 - 3yz^2) - \frac{1}{2} (y^2 + z^2) - \frac{k}{2} \right] \tag{a}$$

where k and a are constants. We use for the equation of the boundary curve C the following expression:

$$(y^2 + z^2) - \frac{1}{a} (y^3 - 3yz^2) + k = 0 \tag{b}$$

Explain why this is acceptable. Now choosing $k = -(\frac{4}{27})a^2$ show that the equation

$$\left(y - \sqrt{3}\, z - \frac{2}{3} a \right)\left(y + \sqrt{3}\, z - \frac{2}{3} a \right)\left(y + \frac{a}{3} \right) = 0 \tag{c}$$

is the same as Eq. (b). Finally, show that the boundary curve C given by Eq. (c) is that for an equilateral triangle, as shown in Fig. P11.33 with the origin of yz at the centroid. Thus Eq. (b) with $k = -\frac{4}{27} a^2$ is the Prandtl stress function for this equilateral triangle. Finally, compute the shear stresses at $y = -a/3, z = 0$ for a rate of twist α of 0.05 rad/ft. Take the material as linear elastic with $G = 15 \times 10^6$ psi and set $a = 6$ in.

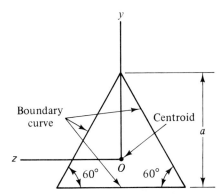

Figure P11.33

11.34. In Example 11.5 of Section 11.12 we solved the problem of torsion in a linear elastic shaft of elliptical cross section. Redo this example for the case of a material that is Maxwell in shear. Note that ψ, τ_{xy}, and τ_{xz} are unchanged, and thus it is only necessary to recompute α.

11.35. Consider Eqs. (11.121) and (11.124) for the rate of twist α and warping displacement u in a *square* linear elastic shaft (i.e., $c = b$). Set $T = 1000$ ft-lb, $G = 12 \times 10^6$ psi, and $b = 1$ in., and then evaluate α using only the first three terms in the series in the expression for $\bar{I}_0$. Comment on the rate of convergence of this series. Now write out an expression for u using only the first five terms in the series in Eq. (11.124) for the warping displacement. Finally, write a computer program to verify that the contour lines of constant warp are as shown in Fig. 11.23.

11.36. In Section 11.14 we formulated the torsion problem for nonlinear viscous noncircular shafts in terms of the warping function $\Phi(y, z)$. This problem may also be formulated in terms of a stress function $\psi(y, z)$. First we define the stress function as follows:

$$\tau_{xy} = \left(\frac{\dot{\alpha}}{2C}\right)^{1/(2m+1)} \frac{\partial \psi}{\partial z}$$

$$\tau_{xz} = -\left(\frac{\dot{\alpha}}{2C}\right)^{1/(2m+1)} \frac{\partial \psi}{\partial y}$$

Verify that with these equations, equilibrium is identically satisfied. Next, utilize the nonlinear viscous constitutive law to express $\dot{\varepsilon}_{xy}$ and $\dot{\varepsilon}_{xz}$ in terms of ψ. Finally, using the compatibility condition [see Eq. (11.141)],

$$\frac{\partial \dot{\varepsilon}_{xz}}{\partial y} - \frac{\partial \dot{\varepsilon}_{xy}}{\partial z} = \dot{\alpha}$$

obtain the governing nonlinear differential equation in the stress function $\psi(y, z)$. Verify that for $m = 0$ your result reduces to the previously obtained linear relation $\nabla^2 \psi = -2$.

Chapter 12
Plane Strain

12.1 INTRODUCTION

In Chapter 3 we defined *plane strain* as a state of strain where, for some axis usually chosen to be the x_3 axis, the strains ε_{13}, ε_{23}, and ε_{33} are zero in the domain of interest. Furthermore, the remaining strains (i.e., $\varepsilon_{11}, \varepsilon_{22}, \varepsilon_{12}$) are defined as being *independent* of x_3. The geometric configurations of interest are *long prismatic* bodies of *uniform* cross section (i.e., *cylinders* of generally noncircular cross section). Portions of such bodies located away from two rigid end constraints may be considered to be in such a state of plane strain under the following conditions:

1. Taking the x_3 direction to correspond to the axis of the prism, the surface tractions on the lateral surface and the body forces must be oriented normal to this axis.
2. These lateral surface tractions and body forces must be functions of only x_1 and x_2.

Thus the dam shown in Fig. 12.1 may be considered to be under a state of plane strain in regions away from the rigid constraining walls.* Also, the long thick-walled pipe under either internal pressure or external pressure while constrained at the ends (see Fig. 12.2) can be considered a problem in plane strain away from the ends.

---

* We shall soon see that for plane strain to be *strictly* valid, the tractions at the ends of the prism must be normal and equal to $\tau_{33} = \nu(\tau_{11} + \tau_{22})$, where τ_{11} and τ_{22} are *determined* functions of x_1, x_2. It is very unlikely that the normal tractions at the end constraints will be distributed precisely in this manner in an actual situation. However, plane strain is valid in such cases at positions away from the ends in the sense of Saint-Venant's principle, since the *resultants* of the normal end traction equal the resultants of the determined τ_{zz} distribution.

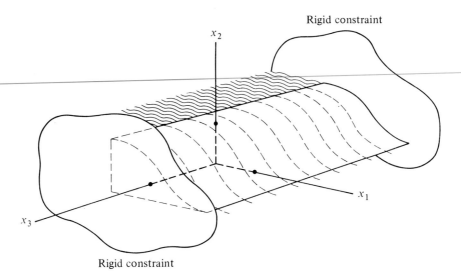

Figure 12.1 Dam in plane strain.

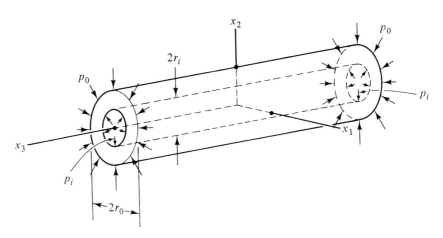

Figure 12.2 Thick-walled circular cylinder constrained at ends.

(We shall study this problem later.) Now we present the basic strain-displacement equations for plane strain under the restrictions just stated.

Let us first examine the *plane displacement* field defined as

$$u_1 = u_1(x_1, x_2)$$
$$u_2 = u_2(x_1, x_2) \qquad (12.1)$$
$$u_3 = 0$$

It follows immediately by substitution into the strain-displacement equations (9.3) that

$$\varepsilon_{13} = \varepsilon_{23} = \varepsilon_{33} = 0 \qquad \text{(a)}$$

$$\varepsilon_{11}(x_1, x_2) = \frac{\partial u_1}{\partial x_1} \qquad \text{(b)}$$

$$\varepsilon_{22}(x_1, x_2) = \frac{\partial u_2}{\partial x_2} \qquad \text{(c)} \qquad (12.2)$$

$$\varepsilon_{12}(x_1, x_2) = \frac{1}{2}\left(\frac{\partial u_1}{\partial x_2} + \frac{\partial u_2}{\partial x_1}\right) \qquad \text{(d)}$$

which is a *plane strain* field. Accordingly, we see that plane displacement also implies plane strain. We shall use Greek letters here for indices with the understanding that such indices take on values 1 and 2 only. Thus Eqs. (12.2b,c,d) are also given as

$$\varepsilon_{\alpha\beta}(x_1, x_2) = \tfrac{1}{2}(u_{\alpha,\beta} + u_{\beta,\alpha}) \qquad (12.3)$$

Equations (12.2) may be considered the mathematical representation of the definition of plane strain. Subsequent governing equations for the various materials (e.g., elastic, viscoelastic, nonlinear viscous, plastic) will be developed with this set of equations as the basic hypothesis. We begin now with a consideration of *elastic* plane strain.

PART A
ELASTIC PLANE STRAIN

12.2 BASIC EQUATIONS

For an isotropic linear elastic material, *Hooke's law* in the form of strain-stress equations has been given by Eqs. (9.8). Inserting the strains according to Eqs. (12.2), we get

$$\varepsilon_{11}(x_1, x_2) = \frac{1}{E}\left[\tau_{11} - \nu(\tau_{22} + \tau_{33})\right] \qquad \text{(a)}$$

$$\varepsilon_{22}(x_1, x_2) = \frac{1}{E}\left[\tau_{22} - \nu(\tau_{33} + \tau_{11})\right] \qquad \text{(b)}$$

$$0 = \frac{1}{E}\left[\tau_{33} - \nu(\tau_{11} + \tau_{22})\right] \qquad \text{(c)} \qquad (12.4)$$

$$\varepsilon_{12}(x_1, x_2) = \frac{1+\nu}{E}\,\tau_{12} \qquad \text{(d)}$$

$$0 = \tau_{13} \qquad \text{(e)}$$

$$0 = \tau_{23} \qquad \text{(f)}$$

Note that $\tau_{13} = \tau_{23} = 0$ whereas Eqs. (a) to (d) imply that τ_{11}, τ_{22}, τ_{33}, and τ_{12} are in general nonzero functions of x_1 and x_2. It is not surprising that τ_{33} is nonzero, since an axial stress is required to eliminate any axial strain due to the Poisson effect. Moreover, Eq. (c) enables us to express τ_{33} in terms of τ_{11} and τ_{22} as

$$\tau_{33} = \nu(\tau_{11} + \tau_{22}) \tag{12.5}$$

We seek to obtain a two-dimensional form of Hooke's law in index notation which is valid for plane strain. Thus we use Eq. (12.5) to eliminate τ_{33} from Eq. (12.4a), yielding

$$\varepsilon_{11} = \frac{1 - \nu^2}{E}\tau_{11} - \frac{\nu(1 + \nu)}{E}\tau_{22} \tag{12.6}$$

Rearranging terms, we get

$$\varepsilon_{11} = \frac{1 + \nu}{E}\tau_{11} - \frac{\nu(1 + \nu)}{E}(\tau_{11} + \tau_{22}) \tag{12.7}$$

which may also be rewritten as

$$\varepsilon_{11} = \frac{1 + \nu_1}{E_1}\tau_{11} - \frac{\nu_1}{E_1}(\tau_{11} + \tau_{22}) \tag{12.8}$$

where E_1 and ν_1 are *modified elastic constants* defined as

$$E_1 = \frac{E}{1 - \nu^2}, \qquad \nu_1 = \frac{\nu}{1 - \nu} \tag{12.9}$$

Proceeding in a similar fashion, Eqs. (12.4b,d) become

$$\varepsilon_{22} = \frac{1 + \nu_1}{E_1}\tau_{22} - \frac{\nu_1}{E_1}(\tau_{11} + \tau_{22}) \qquad \text{(a)}$$
$$\tag{12.10}$$
$$\varepsilon_{12} = \frac{1 + \nu_1}{E_1}\tau_{12} \qquad \text{(b)}$$

Finally, Eqs. (12.8) and (12.10) may be expressed in two-dimensional index notation as

$$\varepsilon_{\alpha\beta} = \frac{1 + \nu_1}{E_1}\tau_{\alpha\beta} - \frac{\nu_1}{E_1}\tau_{\gamma\gamma}\delta_{\alpha\beta} \tag{12.11}$$

where α, β are free to take on values 1 and 2 and γ is summed from 1 to 2.*

To obtain the inverted form of Eq. (12.11), it is best to go back to the three-dimensional isotropic Hooke's law,

$$\tau_{ij} = \lambda\varepsilon_{kk}\delta_{ij} + 2\mu\varepsilon_{ij} \tag{12.12}$$

---

*Note that when we contract the two-dimensional Kronecker delta, $\delta_{\alpha\beta}$, we get $\delta_{\alpha\alpha} = \delta_{11} + \delta_{22} = 2$. You will recall that in three dimensions $\delta_{ii} = \delta_{11} + \delta_{22} + \delta_{33} = 3$.

where λ and μ are the Lamé constants. All strains on the right side of this equation containing the index 3 are by definition zero, and thus if we restrict i, j on the left side to $1, 2$, we immediately get

$$\boxed{\tau_{\alpha\beta} = \lambda \varepsilon_{\gamma\gamma} \delta_{\alpha\beta} + 2\mu \varepsilon_{\alpha\beta}} \tag{12.13}$$

We see that Eqs. (12.11) and (12.13) are both in the same form as their three-dimensional counterparts, with the former requiring the introduction of modified elastic constants. You should verify that a formal inversion of Eq. (12.11) does indeed yield Eq. (12.13) (see Problem 12.1). Since $\varepsilon_{11}, \varepsilon_{22}, \varepsilon_{12}$ are functions of x_1, x_2 only, Eq. (12.13) directly confirms the fact that τ_{11}, τ_{22}, and τ_{12} are also functions of x_1, x_2 only. Furthermore, Eq. (12.5) then gives τ_{33} as a function of x_1, x_2. Summarizing what we have learned about the functional forms of the stresses, we can say that

$$\tau_{11} = \tau_{11}(x_1, x_2), \qquad \tau_{22} = \tau_{22}(x_1, x_2), \qquad \tau_{12} = \tau_{12}(x_1, x_2),$$
$$\tau_{33} = \tau_{33}(x_1, x_2), \qquad \tau_{13} = \tau_{23} = 0 \tag{12.14}$$

Inserting conditions (12.14) into the equations of *equilibrium* [Eqs. (9.2)], we then obtain

$$\frac{\partial \tau_{11}}{\partial x_1} + \frac{\partial \tau_{12}}{\partial x_2} + B_1 = 0$$
$$\frac{\partial \tau_{21}}{\partial x_1} + \frac{\partial \tau_{22}}{\partial x_2} + B_2 = 0 \tag{12.15}$$

which in two-dimensional index notation is given as

$$\boxed{\frac{\partial \tau_{\alpha\beta}}{\partial x_\beta} + B_\alpha = 0 \qquad \text{or} \qquad \tau_{\alpha\beta,\beta} + B_\alpha = 0} \tag{12.16}$$

Note that the body-force component B_3 has been set equal to zero, in accordance with previously stated condition 1 in Section 12.1. It is frequently the case that the body-force distribution B_α is conservative (i.e., $\mathbf{B} = -\text{grad } V$), or in index notation,

$$B_\alpha = -\frac{\partial V}{\partial x_\alpha} = -V_{,\alpha} \tag{12.17}$$

where $V(x_1, x_2)$ is a scalar potential. Equilibrium equations (12.16) then become

$$\frac{\partial \tau_{\alpha\beta}}{\partial x_\beta} - \frac{\partial V}{\partial x_\alpha} = 0 \qquad \text{or} \qquad \tau_{\alpha\beta,\beta} - V_{,\alpha} = 0 \tag{12.18}$$

Next we consider traction-type *boundary conditions* on the *lateral surface* of a prism (such as shown in Fig. 12.3). On this surface we apply Cauchy's formula,

$$T_i^{(\nu)} = \tau_{ij} \nu_j$$

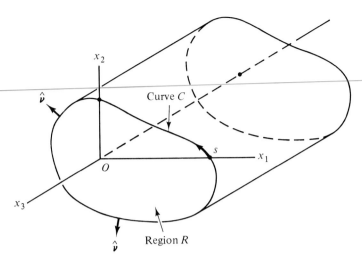

Figure 12.3 Long prismatic body undergoing plane strain.

or in expanded form,*

$$T_1^{(v)} = \tau_{11} v_1 + \tau_{12} v_2 + \tau_{13} v_3$$
$$T_2^{(v)} = \tau_{21} v_1 + \tau_{22} v_2 + \tau_{23} v_3 \qquad (12.19)$$
$$T_3^{(v)} = \tau_{31} v_1 + \tau_{32} v_2 + \tau_{33} v_3$$

Setting $\tau_{31} = \tau_{32} = 0$ [Eqs. (12.14)], $T_3^{(v)} = 0$ (condition 1 of Section 12.1) and $v_3 = 0$ (see Fig. 12.3), we end up with the indicial equation

$$\boxed{T_\alpha^{(v)}(s) = \tau_{\alpha\beta}(s)v_\beta(s) \qquad \text{on } C} \qquad (12.20)$$

where, as shown in Fig. 12.3, s is a curvilinear coordinate on the boundary curve C enclosing the region at the cross section R.

Finally, we come to the *compatibility* equations which in three dimensions are [see Eq. (9.5)]

$$e_{ikm} e_{jln} \frac{\partial^2 \varepsilon_{kl}}{\partial x_m \partial x_n} = 0 \qquad (12.21)$$

Because $\varepsilon_{33} = \varepsilon_{13} = \varepsilon_{23} = 0$ and also because $\partial/\partial x_3 \equiv 0$, we conclude that for any nonzero term the indices k, l, m, and n cannot equal 3. This in turn means that for nonzero terms, i and j must have the value 3. Thus Eq. (12.21) becomes

$$e_{3\alpha\gamma} e_{3\beta\delta} \frac{\partial^2 \varepsilon_{\alpha\beta}}{\partial x_\gamma \partial x_\delta} = 0 \qquad (12.22)$$

where we remind you that the Greek indices above run from 1 to 2. The six compatibility equations have thus been reduced to a single equation.

We may now make effective use of the *two-dimensional alternating tensor* $e_{\alpha\beta}$ defined as follows:

---

*The direction cosine v_1 should not be confused with the modified elastic constant v_1 defined in Eqs. (12.9).

$$e_{\alpha\beta} = e_{3\alpha\beta} = \begin{cases} 1 & \text{if } \alpha = 1, \ \beta = 2 \\ 0 & \text{if } \alpha = \beta \\ -1 & \text{if } \alpha = 2, \ \beta = 1 \end{cases} \tag{12.23}$$

Then Eq. (12.22) can be expressed as

$$e_{\alpha\gamma} e_{\beta\delta} \frac{\partial^2 \varepsilon_{\alpha\beta}}{\partial x_\gamma \partial x_\delta} = 0 \qquad \text{or} \qquad e_{\alpha\gamma} e_{\beta\delta} \varepsilon_{\alpha\beta,\,\gamma\delta} = 0 \tag{12.24}$$

Expanding out the summations over α and β for the equation above, we get

$$e_{1\gamma} e_{1\delta} \frac{\partial^2 \varepsilon_{11}}{\partial x_\gamma \partial x_\delta} + e_{1\gamma} e_{2\delta} \frac{\partial^2 \varepsilon_{12}}{\partial x_\gamma \partial x_\delta} + e_{2\gamma} e_{1\delta} \frac{\partial^2 \varepsilon_{21}}{\partial x_\gamma \partial x_\delta} + e_{2\gamma} e_{2\delta} \frac{\partial^2 \varepsilon_{22}}{\partial x_\gamma \partial x_\delta} = 0$$

The only nonzero terms when we sum over γ and δ are as follows:

$$e_{12} e_{12} \frac{\partial^2 \varepsilon_{11}}{\partial x_2 \partial x_2} + e_{12} e_{21} \frac{\partial^2 \varepsilon_{12}}{\partial x_2 \partial x_1} + e_{21} e_{12} \frac{\partial^2 \varepsilon_{21}}{\partial x_1 \partial x_2} + e_{21} e_{21} \frac{\partial^2 \varepsilon_{22}}{\partial x_1 \partial x_1} = 0$$

Putting in values for the two-dimensional alternating tensor and rearranging terms, we get the following familiar equation:

$$\frac{\partial^2 \varepsilon_{11}}{\partial x_2^2} + \frac{\partial^2 \varepsilon_{22}}{\partial x_1^2} = 2 \frac{\partial^2 \varepsilon_{12}}{\partial x_1 \partial x_2} \tag{12.25}$$

We thus have set forth in this section the basic equations for elastic plane strain.

12.3 AIRY STRESS FUNCTION

As explained in Chapter 9, it is convenient to formulate a boundary value problem either entirely in terms of displacement or entirely in terms of stress. For the displacement formulation we utilize strain-displacement equation (12.3), equilibrium equation (12.16), and stress-strain equation (12.13), all of which we reproduce below:

$$\varepsilon_{\alpha\beta} = \tfrac{1}{2}(u_{\alpha,\,\beta} + u_{\beta,\,\alpha}) \qquad \text{(a)}$$
$$\tau_{\alpha\beta,\,\beta} + B_\alpha = 0 \qquad \text{(b)} \tag{12.26}$$
$$\tau_{\alpha\beta} = \lambda \varepsilon_{\gamma\gamma} \delta_{\alpha\beta} + 2\mu \varepsilon_{\alpha\beta} \qquad \text{(c)}$$

First we substitute Eq. (12.26a) into (12.26c) to obtain

$$\tau_{\alpha\beta} = \lambda u_{\gamma,\,\gamma} \delta_{\alpha\beta} + \mu(u_{\alpha,\,\beta} + u_{\beta,\,\alpha})$$

Then substituting this result into Eq. (12.26b) and grouping terms, we get the final result:

$$(\lambda + \mu)u_{\beta,\,\beta\alpha} + \mu u_{\alpha,\,\beta\beta} + B_\alpha = 0 \tag{12.27}$$

Note that Eq. (12.27) is in the same form as the three-dimensional Navier equation (9.37), except that here indices run from 1 to 2. However, in most plane strain problems the boundary conditions are given in terms of *stress*, and thus Eq. (12.27) is of limited usefulness. From this point on we shall only be concerned with the more useful stress formulation. We shall first focus on the equations of equilibrium.

We may *identically* satisfy the equations of *equilibrium* with *no body forces* [Eqs. (12.15) with $B_1 = B_2 = 0$] if we express the stresses in terms of a function $\Phi(x_1, x_2)$, which is called the *Airy stress function*,* in the following manner:

$$\tau_{11} = \frac{\partial^2 \Phi}{\partial x_2^2}, \qquad \tau_{22} = \frac{\partial^2 \Phi}{\partial x_1^2}, \qquad \tau_{12} = -\frac{\partial^2 \Phi}{\partial x_1 \partial x_2} \tag{12.28}$$

In index notation we can express the relations above as

$$\tau_{\alpha\beta} = \frac{\partial^2 \Phi}{\partial x_\gamma \partial x_\gamma} \delta_{\alpha\beta} - \frac{\partial^2 \Phi}{\partial x_\alpha \partial x_\beta} \tag{12.29}$$

We may also express the equation above in terms of the two-dimensional alternating tensor presented earlier. First recall the $e-\delta$ identity [see Eq. (1.42)]:

$$e_{ijl} e_{ikm} = \delta_{jk} \delta_{lm} - \delta_{jm} \delta_{lk}$$

If j, k, l, m are restricted to values $1, 2$, then i must equal 3 and the identity above becomes

$$e_{3\alpha\gamma} e_{3\beta\delta} = e_{\alpha\gamma} e_{\beta\delta} = \delta_{\alpha\beta} \delta_{\gamma\delta} - \delta_{\alpha\delta} \delta_{\gamma\beta} \tag{12.30}$$

Also, if we perform a contraction and set $\alpha = \beta$, we get the following result, which we will use later:

$$e_{\alpha\gamma} e_{\alpha\delta} = 2\delta_{\gamma\delta} - \delta_{\gamma\delta} = \delta_{\gamma\delta} \tag{12.31}$$

Now go back to Eq. (12.29) and first rewrite it as

$$\tau_{\alpha\beta} = \frac{\partial^2 \Phi}{\partial x_\gamma \partial x_\delta} [\delta_{\alpha\beta} \delta_{\gamma\delta} - \delta_{\alpha\delta} \delta_{\gamma\beta}] \tag{12.32}$$

We can then use identity (12.30) to finally express the result above as

$$\tau_{\alpha\beta} = e_{\alpha\gamma} e_{\beta\delta} \frac{\partial^2 \Phi}{\partial x_\gamma \partial x_\delta} \qquad \text{or} \qquad \tau_{\alpha\beta} = e_{\alpha\gamma} e_{\beta\delta} \Phi_{,\gamma\delta} = 0 \tag{12.33}$$

---

* The stress function Φ was first introduced by G. B. Airy in 1862. We shall present the Airy stress function formulation in two-dimensional *index notation*. A similar development, with thermal expansion included, may be found in B. A. Boley and J. H. Weiner, *Theory of Thermal Stresses* (Melbourne, FL: R.E. Krieger Publishing Co., reprint edition, 1985), p. 107.

Substituting Eq. (12.33) into equilibrium equation (12.16) with $B_\alpha \equiv 0$, we get the required result:

$$\tau_{\alpha\beta,\beta} = e_{\alpha\gamma} e_{\beta\delta} \Phi_{,\gamma\delta\beta} \equiv 0$$

The identical equality on the extreme right of this result follows from the antisymmetry of $e_{\beta\delta}$ and the symmetry of $\Phi_{,\gamma\delta\beta}$ with respect to β, δ. We thus see that the use of any of the relations above to express $\tau_{\alpha\beta}$ in terms of Φ in a formulation ensures that equilibrium is satisfied.

We must consider compatibility* as it pertains to the Airy stress function Φ, and to do this we first examine the plane strain Hooke's law as given by Eq. (12.11). Using Eq. (12.29) for $\tau_{\alpha\beta}$ to introduce the Airy stress function, we get

$$\varepsilon_{\alpha\beta} = \frac{1+\nu_1}{E_1} \tau_{\alpha\beta} - \frac{\nu_1}{E_1} \tau_{\delta\delta} \delta_{\alpha\beta}$$

$$= \frac{1+\nu_1}{E_1}\left(\frac{\partial^2 \Phi}{\partial x_\gamma \partial x_\gamma} \delta_{\alpha\beta} - \frac{\partial^2 \Phi}{\partial x_\alpha \partial x_\beta} \right) - \frac{\nu_1}{E_1}\left(\frac{\partial^2 \Phi}{\partial x_\gamma \partial x_\gamma} \delta_{\delta\delta} - \frac{\partial^2 \Phi}{\partial x_\delta \partial x_\delta} \right) \delta_{\alpha\beta}$$

Since $\delta_{\delta\delta} = 2$, we then have for the equation above,

$$\varepsilon_{\alpha\beta} = \frac{1+\nu_1}{E_1}\left(\frac{\partial^2 \Phi}{\partial x_\gamma \partial x_\gamma} \delta_{\alpha\beta} - \frac{\partial^2 \Phi}{\partial x_\alpha \partial x_\beta} \right) - \frac{\nu_1}{E_1} \frac{\partial^2 \Phi}{\partial x_\gamma \partial x_\gamma} \delta_{\alpha\beta} \tag{12.34}$$

Now substitute the result above for $\varepsilon_{\alpha\beta}$ into the compatibility equation (12.24), to obtain

$$e_{\alpha\gamma} e_{\beta\delta}\left[\frac{1+\nu_1}{E_1}\left(\frac{\partial^4 \Phi}{\partial x_\epsilon \partial x_\epsilon \partial x_\gamma \partial x_\delta} \delta_{\alpha\beta} - \frac{\partial^4 \Phi}{\partial x_\alpha \partial x_\beta \partial x_\gamma \partial x_\delta} \right) - \frac{\nu_1}{E_1} \frac{\partial^4 \Phi}{\partial x_\epsilon \partial x_\epsilon \partial x_\gamma \partial x_\delta} \delta_{\alpha\beta} \right] = 0$$

Combining terms, we then get

$$e_{\alpha\gamma} e_{\beta\delta}\left(\frac{1}{E_1} \frac{\partial^4 \Phi}{\partial x_\epsilon \partial x_\epsilon \partial x_\gamma \partial x_\delta} \delta_{\alpha\beta} - \frac{1+\nu_1}{E_1} \frac{\partial^4 \Phi}{\partial x_\alpha \partial x_\beta \partial x_\gamma \partial x_\delta} \right) = 0 \tag{12.35}$$

We first note that with the use of identity (12.31),

$$e_{\alpha\gamma} e_{\beta\delta} \delta_{\alpha\beta} = e_{\alpha\gamma} e_{\alpha\delta} = \delta_{\gamma\delta} \tag{12.36}$$

In addition, note that

$$e_{\alpha\gamma} e_{\beta\delta} \frac{\partial^4 \Phi}{\partial x_\alpha \partial x_\beta \partial x_\gamma \partial x_\delta} = 0 \tag{12.37}$$

since $e_{\beta\delta}$ is antisymmetric and, assuming continuous fourth derivatives of Φ, $\Phi_{,\alpha\beta\gamma\delta}$ is symmetric with respect to the $\beta\delta$ indices. Now carry out the multiplication in Eq. (12.35) of $e_{\alpha\gamma} e_{\beta\delta}$ with each expression in the bracketed quantity; in the first term use Eq. (12.36) and in the second term use Eq. (12.37). The result of these operations is

$$\frac{1}{E_1} \frac{\partial^4 \Phi}{\partial x_\epsilon \partial x_\epsilon \partial x_\gamma \partial x_\delta} \delta_{\gamma\delta} - \frac{1+\nu_1}{E_1}(0) = 0$$

---

* We learned in Chapter 9 that the use of compatibility is essential in the formulation of stress boundary value problems. For plane strain we shall formulate a *stress function boundary value problem*, and accordingly, compatibility will play a vital role in our development.

and therefore

$$\frac{\partial^4 \Phi}{\partial x_\epsilon \partial x_\epsilon \partial x_\gamma \partial x_\gamma} = 0 \tag{12.38}$$

In symbolic notation we have for the above

$$\boxed{\nabla^4 \Phi = 0 \qquad \text{in } R} \tag{12.39}$$

where R is the region of the cross section (see Fig. 12.3). We see here that the Airy stress function must be a *biharmonic* function for elastic materials when no body forces are present.

Suppose we have a *conservative* body force distribution given as $B_\alpha = -\partial V/\partial x_\alpha$ [see equilibrium equation (12.18)]. In that case, we define the Airy stress function in the following manner:

$$\tau_{11} = V + \frac{\partial^2 \Phi}{\partial x_2^2} \qquad \text{(a)}$$

$$\tau_{22} = V + \frac{\partial^2 \Phi}{\partial x_1^2} \qquad \text{(b)} \tag{12.40}$$

$$\tau_{12} = -\frac{\partial^2 \Phi}{\partial x_1 \partial x_2} \qquad \text{(c)}$$

Then Eq. (12.33) becomes

$$\tau_{\alpha\beta} = e_{\alpha\gamma} e_{\beta\delta} \frac{\partial^2 \Phi}{\partial x_\gamma \partial x_\delta} + V\delta_{\alpha\beta} = e_{\alpha\gamma} e_{\beta\delta} \Phi_{,\gamma\delta} + V\delta_{\alpha\beta} \tag{12.41}$$

from which the desired result $\tau_{\alpha\beta,\beta} - V_{,\alpha} = 0$ easily follows. Upon substituting the expression for $\tau_{\alpha\beta}$ above into Hooke's law [Eq. (12.11)] and using the resulting formulation in the compatibility equation [Eq. (12.24)], it then follows (see Problem 12.3) that instead of Eq. (12.39), we now get

$$\nabla^4 \Phi = -(1 - \nu_1)\nabla^2 V = -\frac{1 - 2\nu}{1 - \nu} \nabla^2 V \qquad \text{in } R \tag{12.42}$$

Finally, we present the *boundary conditions* in terms of Φ. Thus going back to Eq. (12.20), we have

$$T_1^{(\nu)} = \tau_{11} \nu_1 + \tau_{12} \nu_2$$

$$T_2^{(\nu)} = \tau_{21} \nu_1 + \tau_{22} \nu_2 \qquad \text{on } C$$

Using the definition of the Airy stress function with body forces present [Eqs. (12.40)], we get

$$T_1^{(\nu)} = \left(V + \frac{\partial^2 \Phi}{\partial x_2^2}\right)\nu_1 - \frac{\partial^2 \Phi}{\partial x_1 \partial x_2} \nu_2$$

$$T_2^{(\nu)} = -\frac{\partial^2 \Phi}{\partial x_1 \partial x_2} \nu_1 + \left(V + \frac{\partial^2 \Phi}{\partial x_1^2}\right)\nu_2 \qquad \text{on } C \tag{12.43}$$

It is possible to prove that Eqs. (12.43) are equivalent to specifying Φ *and its normal derivative* on the boundary curve C. You are referred to Appendix V for a development of this assertion.

For a *multiply connected* domain, in addition to the compatibility equations we must also satisfy certain integral relations to ensure that we have compatible strains. These integral conditions are discussed in general in Appendix I, and for plane strain and two-dimensional plane stress with body forces in Appendix VI. They are called the Cesàro integral conditions.* For the case of plane strain in a multiply connected domain with n cavities, in addition to Eq. (12.42) the following line integrals [see Eqs. (VI.17)] must be satisfied for the n closed curves C_i at the *boundaries* of the cavities:

$$
\oint_{C_i} x_\beta \left[\delta_{\alpha\beta} \frac{\partial \nabla^2 \Phi}{\partial s} - e_{\alpha\beta} \frac{\partial \nabla^2 \Phi}{\partial \nu} \right] ds = (1 + \nu_1) \oint_{C_i} e_{\alpha\beta} [G_\beta^{(i)}(s) - V(s)\nu_\beta(s)] ds
$$
$$
- (1 - \nu_1) \oint_{C_i} x_\beta \left[\delta_{\alpha\beta} \frac{\partial V}{\partial s} - e_{\alpha\beta} \frac{\partial V}{\partial \nu} \right] ds \qquad \text{(a)} \qquad (12.44)
$$
$$
\oint_{C_i} \frac{\partial \nabla^2 \Phi}{\partial \nu} ds = -(1 - \nu_1) \oint_{C_i} \frac{\partial V}{\partial \nu} ds, \qquad i = 1, \ldots, n \qquad \text{(b)}
$$

In the above, s and ν are curvilinear coordinates which are respectively tangent and normal to C_i; x_β is the position vector to points along the curve C_i; and $G_\beta^{(i)}$ is the prescribed traction vector function on C_i.

We now have the key equations for plane strain in terms of the Airy stress function in rectangular Cartesian coordinates.

12.4 ELASTIC PLANE STRAIN IN POLAR COORDINATES

There are problems of interest in plane strain that may be best investigated with the use of polar coordinates rather than rectangular coordinates. Accordingly, we shall now set forth in polar coordinates the basic equations presented in the preceding section. In the interest of simplicity, we shall consider only the case of zero body force. We shall need the transformation formulas

$$
x = r \cos \theta, \qquad r = (x^2 + y^2)^{1/2}
$$
$$
y = r \sin \theta, \qquad \theta = \tan^{-1} \frac{y}{x}
$$
(12.45)

where $x_1 = x$, $x_2 = y$, $x_{1'} = r$, and $x_{2'} = \theta$, as shown in Fig. 12.4.

As a first step we shall formulate τ_{rr} in terms of the stresses τ_{xx}, τ_{yy}, and τ_{xy}. Employing tensor transformation law (1.9), we have

$$
\tau_{rr} = a_{rx} a_{rx} \tau_{xx} + a_{ry} a_{ry} \tau_{yy} + a_{rz} a_{rz} \tau_{zz} + 2(a_{ry} a_{rx} \tau_{yx} + a_{ry} a_{rz} \tau_{yz} + a_{rz} a_{rx} \tau_{zx}) \quad (12.46)
$$

---

* The *two-dimensional* forms of the Cesàro integral conditions are often referred to as Michell's conditions.

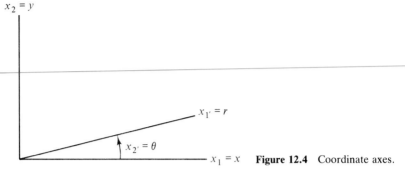

$x_2 = y$

$x_{1'} = r$

$x_{2'} = \theta$

$x_1 = x$ **Figure 12.4** Coordinate axes.

Noting that $a_{rz} = 0$, $a_{rx} = \cos\theta$, and $a_{ry} = \sin\theta$, we have, on collecting terms

$$\tau_{rr} = \tau_{xx}\cos^2\theta + \tau_{yy}\sin^2\theta + 2\tau_{xy}\sin\theta\cos\theta \qquad (12.47)$$

Now replace the stresses on the right side of Eq. (12.47), using Eqs. (12.28) for the case where there are no body forces:

$$\tau_{rr} = \frac{\partial^2\Phi}{\partial y^2}\cos^2\theta + \frac{\partial^2\Phi}{\partial x^2}\sin^2\theta - 2\frac{\partial^2\Phi}{\partial x\,\partial y}\sin\theta\cos\theta \qquad (12.48)$$

To have τ_{rr} expressed entirely in polar coordinates in the foregoing equation, evaluate the partial derivatives of Φ in terms of polar coordinates. Thus considering Φ not to depend on z and using Eqs. (12.45), we get

$$\frac{\partial\Phi}{\partial x} = \frac{\partial\Phi}{\partial r}\frac{\partial r}{\partial x} + \frac{\partial\Phi}{\partial\theta}\frac{\partial\theta}{\partial x} = \frac{\partial\Phi}{\partial r}\frac{x}{r} + \frac{\partial\Phi}{\partial\theta}\left(-\frac{y}{r^2}\right) = \frac{\partial\Phi}{\partial r}\cos\theta - \frac{\partial\Phi}{\partial\theta}\frac{\sin\theta}{r}$$

$$\frac{\partial^2\Phi}{\partial x^2} = \left[\frac{\partial}{\partial r}\left(\frac{\partial\Phi}{\partial x}\right)\right]\frac{\partial r}{\partial x} + \left[\frac{\partial}{\partial\theta}\left(\frac{\partial\Phi}{\partial x}\right)\right]\frac{\partial\theta}{\partial x} = \left[\frac{\partial}{\partial r}\left(\frac{\partial\Phi}{\partial x}\right)\right]\cos\theta - \left[\frac{\partial}{\partial\theta}\left(\frac{\partial\Phi}{\partial x}\right)\right]\frac{\sin\theta}{r}$$

$$= \frac{\partial^2\Phi}{\partial r^2}\cos^2\theta - 2\frac{\partial^2\Phi}{\partial r\,\partial\theta}\frac{\sin\theta\cos\theta}{r} + 2\frac{\partial\Phi}{\partial\theta}\frac{\sin\theta\cos\theta}{r^2}$$

$$+ \frac{\partial\Phi}{\partial r}\frac{\sin^2\theta}{r} + \frac{\partial^2\Phi}{\partial\theta^2}\frac{\sin^2\theta}{r^2} \qquad (12.49)$$

By a similar procedure, we may also get

$$\frac{\partial^2\Phi}{\partial y^2} = \frac{\partial^2\Phi}{\partial r^2}\sin^2\theta + 2\frac{\partial^2\Phi}{\partial r\,\partial\theta}\frac{\sin\theta\cos\theta}{r} - 2\frac{\partial\Phi}{\partial\theta}\frac{\sin\theta\cos\theta}{r^2}$$

$$+ \frac{\partial\Phi}{\partial r}\frac{\cos^2\theta}{r} + \frac{\partial^2\Phi}{\partial\theta^2}\frac{\cos^2\theta}{r^2} \qquad (12.50)$$

$$\frac{\partial^2\Phi}{\partial x\,\partial y} = \frac{\partial^2\Phi}{\partial r^2}\sin\theta\cos\theta + \frac{\partial^2\Phi}{\partial r\,\partial\theta}\frac{1 - 2\sin^2\theta}{r} - \frac{\partial^2\Phi}{\partial\theta^2}\frac{\sin\theta\cos\theta}{r^2}$$

$$- \frac{\partial\Phi}{\partial r}\frac{\sin\theta\cos\theta}{r} - \frac{\partial\Phi}{\partial\theta}\frac{(1 - 2\sin^2\theta)}{r^2} \qquad (12.51)$$

Note that Eq. (12.50) also follows simply by replacing θ in Eq. (12.49) with $\theta + \pi/2$. Substituting Eqs. (12.49), (12.50), and (12.51) into Eq. (12.48), we may obtain the following result after some rearrangement and cancellation of terms:

$$\tau_{rr} = \frac{1}{r}\frac{\partial \Phi}{\partial r} + \frac{1}{r^2}\frac{\partial^2 \Phi}{\partial \theta^2} \tag{12.52}$$

By similar procedures, we may get corresponding relations for $\tau_{\theta\theta}$ and $\tau_{r\theta}$. We now present the following complete set of relations:

$$\tau_{rr} = \frac{1}{r}\frac{\partial \Phi}{\partial r} + \frac{1}{r^2}\frac{\partial^2 \Phi}{\partial \theta^2} \quad \text{(a)}$$

$$\tau_{\theta\theta} = \frac{\partial^2 \Phi}{\partial r^2} \quad \text{(b)} \tag{12.53}$$

$$\tau_{r\theta} = \frac{1}{r^2}\frac{\partial \Phi}{\partial \theta} - \frac{1}{r}\frac{\partial^2 \Phi}{\partial r \partial \theta} \quad \text{(c)}$$

You may readily demonstrate that this formulation for stress satisfies the equations of equilibrium in polar coordinates with no body forces (see Problem 12.5).

We may also arrive at the *compatibility* equation for Φ in polar coordinates by employing the Laplacian operator in polar coordinates (see Problem 12.6), and accordingly, we obtain

$$\nabla^4 \Phi = \nabla^2(\nabla^2 \Phi) = \left(\frac{\partial^2}{\partial r^2} + \frac{1}{r}\frac{\partial}{\partial r} + \frac{1}{r^2}\frac{\partial^2}{\partial \theta^2}\right)\left(\frac{\partial^2 \Phi}{\partial r^2} + \frac{1}{r}\frac{\partial \Phi}{\partial r} + \frac{1}{r^2}\frac{\partial^2 \Phi}{\partial \theta^2}\right) = 0 \tag{12.54}$$

Finally, we point out (see Problem 9.5) that the strain displacement relations for polar coordinates are

$$\varepsilon_{rr} = \frac{\partial u_r}{\partial r} \quad \text{(a)}$$

$$\varepsilon_{\theta\theta} = \frac{1}{r}\frac{\partial u_\theta}{\partial \theta} + \frac{u_r}{r} \quad \text{(b)} \tag{12.55}$$

$$\varepsilon_{r\theta} = \frac{1}{2}\left[\frac{\partial u_\theta}{\partial r} + \frac{1}{r}\frac{\partial u_r}{\partial \theta} - \frac{u_\theta}{r}\right] \quad \text{(c)}$$

We have thus obtained in polar coordinates the basic formulations for the computation of stress and displacement in plane-strain problems where the body forces are zero. In the next section we consider the solutions to these equations for the special case of axial symmetry.

12.5 PROBLEMS WITH AXIAL SYMMETRY

We limit our discussion here to the case of axial symmetry where the z axis will be considered the axis of symmetry. This means that all derivatives with respect to θ are by definition zero. For no body forces, basic equations (12.53), (12.54), and (12.55) for this case reduce to the following forms:

$$\tau_{rr} = \frac{1}{r}\frac{d\Phi}{dr} \qquad (a)$$

$$\tau_{\theta\theta} = \frac{d^2\Phi}{dr^2} \qquad (b)$$

$$\tau_{r\theta} = 0 \qquad (c)$$

$$
\nabla^4\Phi = \left(\frac{d^2}{dr^2} + \frac{1}{r}\frac{d}{dr}\right)\left(\frac{d^2\Phi}{dr^2} + \frac{1}{r}\frac{d\Phi}{dr}\right)
$$
$$
= \left[\frac{1}{r}\frac{d}{dr}\left(r\frac{d}{dr}\right)\right]\left[\frac{1}{r}\frac{d}{dr}\left(r\frac{d\Phi}{dr}\right)\right] = 0 \qquad (d)
$$

(12.56)

$$\varepsilon_{rr} = \frac{du_r}{dr} \qquad (e)$$

$$\varepsilon_{\theta\theta} = \frac{u_r}{r} \qquad (f)$$

$$\varepsilon_{r\theta} = \frac{1}{2}\left[\frac{du_\theta}{dr} - \frac{u_\theta}{r}\right] = 0 \qquad (g)$$

Note that $\tau_{r\theta} = 0$ since $\partial/\partial\theta \equiv 0$, and so $\varepsilon_{r\theta} = 0$ via Hooke's law.

We shall now find the *general solution* of the axially symmetric, biharmonic equation by integrating it successively over r. Thus, in Eq. (12.56d), multiply by r to eliminate the first $1/r$ in the first bracket, and then integrate to eliminate the first d/dr derivative. Accordingly, we get

$$
\left(r\frac{d}{dr}\right)\left[\frac{1}{r}\frac{d}{dr}\left(r\frac{d\Phi}{dr}\right)\right] = C_1
$$

where C_1 is a constant of integration. Dividing by r, we then get

$$
\frac{d}{dr}\left[\frac{1}{r}\frac{d}{dr}\left(r\frac{d\Phi}{dr}\right)\right] = \frac{d}{dr}[\nabla^2\Phi] = \frac{C_1}{r} \qquad (12.57)
$$

A second integration and a subsequent multiplication by r gives us

$$
\frac{d}{dr}\left(r\frac{d\Phi}{dr}\right) = r[\nabla^2\Phi] = rC_1\ln r + C_2 r
$$

where C_2 is a second constant of integration. A third integration with the use of an integration by parts yields the following:

$$
r\frac{d\Phi}{dr} = \frac{1}{2}\left(r^2\ln r - \frac{r^2}{2}\right)C_1 + C_2\frac{r^2}{2} + C_3
$$

It is not necessary for the evaluation of stresses and displacements to actually carry out a fourth integration [see Eqs. (12.56)], and thus we simply divide by r and express our solution as

$$
\frac{d\Phi}{dr} = \frac{C_1}{2}r\left(\ln r - \frac{1}{2}\right) + \frac{C_2}{2}r + \frac{C_3}{r} \qquad (12.58)
$$

The stresses for this case then become by means of Eqs. (12.56a,b),

$$\tau_{rr} = \frac{1}{r}\frac{d\Phi}{dr} = \frac{C_1}{2}\left(\ln r - \frac{1}{2}\right) + \frac{C_2}{2} + \frac{C_3}{r^2} \qquad \text{(a)}$$

$$\tau_{\theta\theta} = \frac{d^2\Phi}{dr^2} = \frac{C_1}{2}\left(\ln r + \frac{1}{2}\right) + \frac{C_2}{2} - \frac{C_3}{r^2} \qquad \text{(b)}$$

(12.59)

Turning next to the evaluation of *displacements*, we see that Eq. (12.56f), in conjunction with Hooke's law [Eq. (12.11)], gives

$$u_r = \frac{r}{E_1}(\tau_{\theta\theta} - \nu_1 \tau_{rr}) \qquad (12.60)$$

Substituting for the stresses from Eqs. (12.59) and combining terms, we then obtain for the radial displacement component

$$u_r = \frac{r}{E_1}\left\{\frac{C_1}{2}\left[(1-\nu_1)\ln r + \frac{1}{2}(1+\nu_1)\right] + \frac{C_2}{2}(1-\nu_1) - \frac{C_3}{r^2}(1+\nu_1)\right\} \quad (12.61)$$

Finally, going back to Eq. (12.56g), we write

$$\frac{du_\theta}{dr} - \frac{u_\theta}{r} \equiv r\frac{d}{dr}\left(\frac{1}{r}u_\theta\right) = 0$$

Integrating, we then get

$$u_\theta = C_4 r$$

and to avoid rigid-body rotation we set the constant $C_4 = 0$. Thus we see that as expected, $u_\theta = 0$ in an axially symmetric problem.

We shall now make some remarks about the constants of integration C_1, C_2, and C_3. For a simply connected domain (i.e., a domain without cavities), we require that the stresses and displacements be *finite* at $r = 0$. Equations (12.59) and (12.61) for τ_{rr}, $\tau_{\theta\theta}$, and u_r then require that we set $C_1 = C_3 = 0$. The remaining constant, C_2, follows directly from the boundary condition. Thus, for a solid cylinder of radius $r = a$ under uniform external pressure p at $r = a$, we have the boundary condition

$$-p = \tau_{rr}|_{r=a} \qquad (12.62)$$

and Eq. (12.59a) then yields $C_2 = -2p$. Equations (12.59) and (12.61) then give the simple solutions

$$\tau_{rr} = \tau_{\theta\theta} = -p$$

$$u_r = -\frac{1-\nu_1}{E_1}pr$$

(12.63)

which are independent of the radius a.

Now consider the *hollow* cylinder of inner radius r_i and outer radius r_o (i.e., $r_i \leq r \leq r_o$). In this case there is no boundedness condition at $r = 0$, but there are two boundary conditions–one at r_i and one at r_o. We thus have only two conditions for the evaluation of the three constants C_1, C_2, and C_3. But this should have been

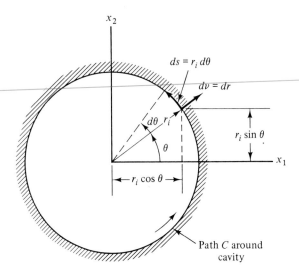

$ds = r_i \, d\theta$

$dv = dr$

$r_i \sin \theta$

x_1

$d\theta \quad r_i$

θ

$r_i \cos \theta$

Path C around cavity

Figure 12.5 Path around boundary of cavity in hollow cynlinder.

expected, since the hollow cylinder is a multiply connected domain and in such a case the compatibility equation [here Eq. (12.56d)] is necessary but *not sufficient* for a unique solution (see Section 12.3). We must also satisfy Eqs. (12.44) for the path around the boundary of the cavity (see Fig. 12.5). In Problem 12.7 we ask you to show that Eq. (12.44a) is identically satisfied with no further adjustments of the constants. However, Eq. (12.44b) does yield a condition as follows:

$$\int_0^{2\pi} \frac{d\nabla^2 \Phi(r)}{dr} \, r_i \, d\theta = 2\pi r_i \frac{d\nabla^2 \Phi}{dr} = 0$$

Therefore,

$$\frac{d\nabla^2 \Phi}{dr} = 0 \tag{12.64}$$

Equation (12.57) then immediately gives $C_1 = 0$. A detailed evaluation of the constants C_2 and C_3 is given in the following example.

Example 12.1

We shall now determine τ_{rr}, $\tau_{\theta\theta}$, τ_{zz}, and u_r for the particular case of a constrained hollow thick-walled elastic cylinder under internal and external pressures, p_i and p_o, respectively (refer back to Fig. 12.2). The inner and outer radii are denoted as r_i and r_o, respectively. The boundary conditions for this problem are thus the following:

$$\tau_{rr}|_{r = r_i} = -p_i \tag{a}$$

$$\tau_{rr}|_{r = r_o} = -p_o \tag{b}$$

Imposing these conditions on the stress distribution given by Eq. (12.59a), we have

$$-p_i = \frac{C_1}{2}\left(\ln r_i - \frac{1}{2}\right) + \frac{C_2}{2} + \frac{C_3}{r_i^2} \tag{c}$$

$$-p_o = \frac{C_1}{2}\left(\ln r_o - \frac{1}{2}\right) + \frac{C_2}{2} + \frac{C_3}{r_o^2} \tag{d}$$

Plane Strain   Chap. 12

As explained above, it follows from Eq. (12.64) that we must require the constant C_1 to be zero. We can then solve for the remaining constants to get

$$C_3 = \frac{r_i^2 r_o^2 (p_o - p_i)}{r_o^2 - r_i^2} \tag{e}$$

$$\frac{C_2}{2} = \frac{p_i r_i^2 - p_o r_o^2}{r_o^2 - r_i^2} \tag{f}$$

We thus have for the stress distributions, from Eqs. (12.59),

$$\tau_{rr} = \frac{r_i^2 r_o^2 (p_o - p_i)}{r_o^2 - r_i^2} \frac{1}{r^2} + \frac{p_i r_i^2 - p_o r_o^2}{r_o^2 - r_i^2} \tag{g}$$

$$\tau_{\theta\theta} = -\frac{r_i^2 r_o^2 (p_o - p_i)}{r_o^2 - r_i^2} \frac{1}{r^2} + \frac{p_i r_i^2 - p_o r_o^2}{r_o^2 - r_i^2} \tag{h}$$

If we add the foregoing pair of equations, we see that the sum of τ_{rr} and $\tau_{\theta\theta}$ is a constant, that is,

$$\tau_{rr} + \tau_{\theta\theta} = 2 \frac{p_i r_i^2 - p_o r_o^2}{r_o^2 - r_i^2} \tag{i}$$

Using the preceding equation in Eq. (12.5), we see that τ_{zz} must then be a constant for this case with the following value:

$$\tau_{zz} = \nu(\tau_{rr} + \tau_{\theta\theta}) = \frac{2\nu(p_i r_i^2 - p_o r_o^2)}{r_o^2 - r_i^2} \tag{j}$$

Finally, the radial displacement is obtained by inserting $\tau_{rr}, \tau_{\theta\theta}$ from Eqs. (g) and (h) into Eq. (12.60), giving

$$u_r = -\frac{1 + \nu_1}{E_1} \left(\frac{r_i^2 r_o^2 (p_o - p_i)}{r_o^2 - r_i^2} \right) \frac{1}{r} + \frac{1 - \nu_1}{E_1} \left(\frac{p_i r_i^2 - p_o r_o^2}{r_o^2 - r_i^2} \right) r \tag{k}$$

In the following section we analyze the stress distribution generated by a *positive edge dislocation* of strength b in an initially stress-free elastic medium. We no longer have axial symmetry for this case.

12.6 STRESS FIELD OF AN EDGE DISLOCATION IN AN ELASTIC MEDIUM

We have shown in Fig. 12.6 an elastic medium with a positive edge dislocation along the z axis, as discussed in some detail in Sections VII.8 and VII.9 of Appendix VII. Cylindrical coordinates have been used for convenience and a *small core* of material has been removed, such that we have a hollow cylinder which has been "cut" and displaced along the $y = 0$ and $x > 0$ plane. On careful inspection we find that this is a mixed boundary value problem. Stresses estimating the effect of the removed core are to be prescribed at the inside surface, which for small deformation may be defined simply by $r = r_i$, where r_i is the radius of a cylindrical hole in the unde-formed geometry. The stress field we shall determine will not be very sensitive to

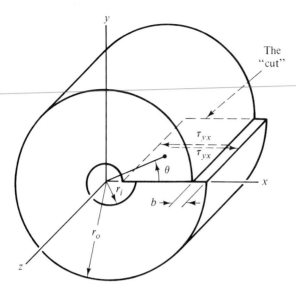

Figure 12.6 Deformed configuration around edge dislocation.

this boundary condition,* and we shall first assume that the stresses vanish at $r = r_i$. Similarly, stresses are to be prescribed at the outer surface, which in the undeformed geometry is at $r = r_o$. Here we shall simply require that the stresses vanish as $r_o \rightarrow \infty$, since the medium is assumed to be initially stress-free. Finally, displacements are prescribed on each face of the cut so that the relative displacement is equal to b. Note that the presence of the cut results in a *simply connected domain*.

The boundary conditions just stated are consistent with the viewpoint that the deformed configuration, shown in Fig. 12.6, is maintained by a pair of oppositely directed shear stress distributions, τ_{yx}, which act on the faces of the cut. However, these shear stress distributions are not known a priori. Note that the displacement and stress fields are single-valued and continuous in the simply connected domain defined by the intervals $r_i \leq r \leq r_o$ and $0^+ \leq \theta \leq 2\pi^-$. When we have obtained the complete solution, we will find that the stress distribution is in fact the same on both faces of the cut.

Now, if we assume that the dislocation line along the z axis is long compared to b, this becomes an example of plane strain, for which Eqs. (12.53), (12.54), and (12.55) are valid since we do not have axial symmetry. A close examination of Fig. 12.6 reveals probable symmetry of τ_{rr} and $\tau_{\theta\theta}$ about the yz plane, and probable symmetry of $\tau_{r\theta}$ about the zx plane. This suggests that Φ has a form, which later results will verify, given by†

---

*For further discussion of this point, see A. H. Cottrell, *Dislocations and Plastic Flow in Crystals* (London: Oxford University Press, 1953). Although the problem discussed in this section is intended primarily for readers interested in the microscopic study of materials, it is also in itself an interesting problem in macroscopic elasticity theory. Additional problems of the latter type are discussed in S. Timoshenko and J. N. Goodier, *Theory of Elasticity* (New York: McGraw-Hill Book Company, 1951), Chap. 4.

†To understand this, note that Eqs. (12.53) and (12.65) indicate that τ_{rr} and $\tau_{\theta\theta}$ are proportional to $\sin \theta$, ensuring symmetry with respect to the yz plane, while $\tau_{r\theta}$ is proportional to $\cos \theta$, ensuring symmetry with respect to the zx plane.

$$\Phi = f(r) \sin \theta \qquad (12.65)$$

Substituting Eq. (12.65) into Eq. (12.54), we find that $f(r)$ satisfies the ordinary differential equation

$$\left(\frac{d^2}{dr^2} + \frac{1}{r}\frac{d}{dr} - \frac{1}{r^2}\right)\left(\frac{d^2 f}{dr^2} + \frac{1}{r}\frac{df}{dr} - \frac{f}{r^2}\right) = 0 \qquad (12.66)$$

By changing the independent variable in Eq. (12.66) from r to t in accordance with the definition, $r = e^t$, we can form a differential equation with constant coefficients. Such equations belong to the Euler–Cauchy class of differential equations. Thus we proceed as follows:

$$\frac{d}{dr} = \frac{d}{dt}\frac{dt}{dr} = e^{-t}\frac{d}{dt}$$

$$\frac{d^2}{dr^2} = e^{-t}\frac{d}{dt}\left(e^{-t}\frac{d}{dt}\right) = e^{-t}\left(e^{-t}\frac{d^2}{dt^2} - e^{-t}\frac{d}{dt}\right) = e^{-2t}\left(\frac{d^2}{dt^2} - \frac{d}{dt}\right)$$

It immediately follows that

$$\frac{d^2}{dr^2} + \frac{1}{r}\frac{d}{dr} - \frac{1}{r^2} = e^{-2t}\left(\frac{d^2}{dt^2} - 1\right)$$

and Eq. (12.66) becomes, upon canceling the leading e^{-2t} factor,

$$\left(\frac{d^2}{dt^2} - 1\right)\left[e^{-2t}\left(\frac{d^2 f}{dt^2} - f\right)\right] = 0 \qquad (12.67)$$

In expanded form, each term in Eq. (12.67) would contain the e^{-2t} factor, which may then be canceled to give the above-mentioned differential equation with constant coefficients. However, it is simpler to substitute the typical trial solution $f(t) = e^{pt}$ for such equations directly into Eq. (12.67). In so doing, we obtain the auxiliary equation

$$\left(\frac{d^2}{dt^2} - 1\right)[e^{(p-2)t}(p^2 - 1)] = 0$$

which, after now carrying out the differentiations and canceling the $e^{(p-2)t}$ factor, gives

$$(p^2 - 1)[(p-2)^2 - 1] = (p+1)(p-1)(p-3)(p-1) = 0$$

The general solution to Eq. (12.67) is thus

$$f(t) = Ae^{3t} + Be^{-t} + Ce^t + Dte^t \qquad (12.68)$$

where A, B, C, D are constants of integration. Replacing t using $r = e^t$, we finally obtain the solution to Eq. (12.66) as

$$f(r) = Ar^3 + \frac{B}{r} + Cr + Dr \ln r \qquad (12.69)$$

Equations (12.65) and (12.53) then yield the stresses as

$$\tau_{rr} = \left(2Ar - \frac{2B}{r^3} + \frac{D}{r}\right) \sin\theta$$

$$\tau_{\theta\theta} = \left(6Ar + \frac{2B}{r^3} + \frac{D}{r}\right) \sin\theta \qquad (12.70)$$

$$\tau_{r\theta} = -\left(2Ar - \frac{2B}{r^3} + \frac{D}{r}\right) \cos\theta$$

Now let us proceed to evaluate A, B, and D from the boundary conditions. Setting $r = r_o$ in Eqs. (12.70) and requiring that τ_{rr} and $\tau_{r\theta} \to 0$ as $r_o \to \infty$ results in $A = 0$ for an initially stress-free medium. As we pointed out earlier, a second condition on stress will be obtained by first setting $\tau_{rr} = \tau_{r\theta} = 0$ and $r = r_i$. Accordingly, since $A = 0$ we first obtain $2B = r_i^2 D$, and Eqs. (12.70) become

$$\tau_{rr} = D\left(\frac{1}{r} - \frac{r_i^2}{r^3}\right) \sin\theta$$

$$\tau_{\theta\theta} = D\left(\frac{1}{r} + \frac{r_i^2}{r^3}\right) \sin\theta \qquad (12.71)$$

$$\tau_{r\theta} = -D\left(\frac{1}{r} - \frac{r_i^2}{r^3}\right) \cos\theta$$

Since r_i is to be chosen *small*, the $1/r^3$ terms in the parentheses in the above will decay very rapidly in comparison with the $1/r$ terms, as we move away from the dislocation at the origin. For example, if we select $r_i = 2b$, then at the small distance $r = 10\,r_i = 20b$ the $1/r^3$ terms are only 1% of the $1/r$ terms. It is thus reasonable to *drop* the $1/r^3$ terms from Eqs. (12.71) [i.e., *finally* set $B = 0$ in Eqs. (12.70)], and accordingly take the following for the stress distributions:

$$\tau_{rr} = \tau_{\theta\theta} = \frac{D}{r} \sin\theta$$

$$(12.72)$$

$$\tau_{r\theta} = -\frac{D}{r} \cos\theta$$

This leaves D to be determined from the displacement boundary conditions.

We let u_r represent the radial displacement component and u_θ the transverse component. Now ε_{rr}, $\varepsilon_{\theta\theta}$, and $\varepsilon_{r\theta}$ can be determined by substituting Eqs. (12.72) into plane-strain Hooke's law. Thus we go back to Eq. (12.11) using $x_1 = r$ and $x_2 = \theta$ and set $\tau_{\theta\theta} = \tau_{rr}$ to obtain

$$\varepsilon_{rr} = \varepsilon_{\theta\theta} = \frac{1 - \nu_1}{E_1} \tau_{rr} = \frac{(1 - 2\nu)(1 + \nu)}{E} \tau_{rr} = \frac{1 - 2\nu}{2G} \tau_{rr}$$

$$(12.73)$$

$$\varepsilon_{r\theta} = \frac{1 + \nu_1}{E_1} \tau_{r\theta} = \frac{1 + \nu}{E} \tau_{r\theta} = \frac{1}{2G} \tau_{r\theta}$$

In the above we have used definitions (12.9) for E_1 and ν_1, and have replaced $(1 + \nu)/E$ by $1/(2G)$. With the use of Eqs. (12.72) and (12.73), Eqs. (12.55) take on the form

$$\varepsilon_{rr} = \frac{1-2\nu}{2G} \frac{D \sin\theta}{r} = \frac{\partial u_r}{\partial r} \qquad \text{(a)}$$

$$\varepsilon_{\theta\theta} = \frac{1-2\nu}{2G} \frac{D \sin\theta}{r} = \frac{1}{r}\frac{\partial u_\theta}{\partial\theta} + \frac{u_r}{r} \qquad \text{(b)} \qquad (12.74)$$

$$\gamma_{r\theta} = 2\varepsilon_{r\theta} = -\frac{1}{G}\frac{D \cos\theta}{r} = \left(\frac{\partial u_\theta}{\partial r} + \frac{1}{r}\frac{\partial u_r}{\partial\theta} - \frac{u_\theta}{r}\right) \qquad \text{(c)}$$

Before we can determine the constant D, we must first integrate the above equations for u_r and u_θ.

We begin by integrating Eq. (12.74a) for u_r, and thereby obtain

$$u_r = \frac{1-2\nu}{2G} D \sin\theta \ln r + f'(\theta) \qquad (12.75)$$

where $f'(\theta)$ is a function of integration equal to the derivative of $f(\theta)$ with respect to θ. Next substitute Eq. (12.75) for u_r into Eq. (12.74b) and solve for $\partial u_\theta/\partial\theta$:

$$\frac{\partial u_\theta}{\partial\theta} = \frac{(1-2\nu)D}{2G} \sin\theta\,(1 - \ln r) - f'(\theta)$$

Integrating this result, we get

$$u_\theta = -\frac{(1-2\nu)D}{2G} \cos\theta\,(1 - \ln r) - f(\theta) + g(r) \qquad (12.76)$$

where $g(r)$ is another function of integration. Now turning to Eq. (12.74c), we substitute for u_r and u_θ using Eqs. (12.75) and (12.76), and after some manipulation we obtain the condition

$$f''(\theta) + f(\theta) + \frac{2(1-\nu)D}{G} \cos\theta = -rg'(r) + g(r) \qquad (12.77)$$

where the primes indicate differentiations with respect to the indicated arguments.

Since the left side of Eq. (12.77) is a function of only θ while the right side is a function of only the *independent* variable r, we have an *apparent* contradiction. We avoid any contradiction by equating each side to a constant E, which is called the separation constant. Accordingly, we obtain the following two ordinary differential equations:

$$rg'(r) - g(r) = r^2\left[\frac{g(r)}{r}\right]' = -E \qquad \text{(a)}$$

$$\qquad (12.78)$$

$$f''(\theta) + f(\theta) = E - \frac{2(1-\nu)D}{G} \cos\theta \qquad \text{(b)}$$

Equation (12.78a) is solved by a straightforward integration, and Eq. (12.78b) is a second-order inhomogeneous differential equation with constant coefficients, which may be solved by superposing the complementary solution and a particular solution found by the method of undetermined coefficients. We leave the details as an exercise for the reader and simply give the final results below:

$$g(r) = E + Fr$$

$$(12.79)$$

$$f(\theta) = H \cos\theta + I \sin\theta + E - \frac{(1-\nu)D}{G}\theta \sin\theta$$

where F, H, and I are constants of integration. Finally, we substitute Eqs. (12.79) into Eqs. (12.75) and (12.76), and thereby obtain the displacement solutions

$$u_r = \frac{D}{G}\left[\frac{1-2\nu}{2}\ln r \sin\theta - (1-\nu)\theta \cos\theta\right] + I \cos\theta + J \sin\theta \qquad \text{(a)}$$

$$(12.80)$$

$$u_\theta = \frac{D}{G}\left[\frac{1-2\nu}{2}\ln r \cos\theta + \frac{1}{2}\cos\theta\right] + (1-\nu)\theta \sin\theta + J \cos\theta - I \sin\theta + Fr \qquad \text{(b)}$$

where we have set $-H - [(1-\nu)D]/G = J$.

We may now enforce the displacement boundary conditions at the two faces of the cut (see Fig. 12.6), i.e.,

$$u_r = \begin{cases} 0 & \text{at } \theta = 0^+ \qquad \text{(a)} \\ b & \text{at } \theta = 2\pi^- \qquad \text{(b)} \end{cases}$$

$$(12.81)$$

Using these conditions in Eq. (12.80a), we obtain two of the constants as

$$I = 0$$

$$(12.82)$$

$$D = -\frac{bG}{2\pi(1-\nu)}$$

Since D is now determined, the stresses are obtained from Eqs. (12.72) in their final forms as

$$\tau_{rr} = \tau_{\theta\theta} = -\frac{bG}{2\pi(1-\nu)}\frac{\sin\theta}{r} \qquad \text{(a)}$$

$$(12.83)$$

$$\tau_{r\theta} = \frac{bG}{2\pi(1-\nu)}\frac{\cos\theta}{r} \qquad \text{(b)}$$

The constants F and J in Eqs. (12.80) for the displacements have yet to be determined. We do this by eliminating rigid-body translations and rotation. Boundary condition (12.81a) has already eliminated rigid-body translation in the x direction, and it is valid for *any* point along the face of the cut at $\theta = 0^+$. Rigid-body translation in the y direction and rigid-body rotation about the z axis may also be eliminated, if we enforce the following conditions at the point $r = r_i$ on this same face:

$$u_\theta = 0 \qquad \text{at } r = r_i \text{ and } \theta = 0^+$$

$$(12.84)$$

$$\omega_z = 0 \qquad \text{at } r = r_i \text{ and } \theta = 0^+$$

In Problem 12.15 you will be asked to prove that these conditions yield the following values for the remaining constants:

$$F = \frac{b}{2\pi r_i}$$

$$(12.85)$$

$$J = -\frac{b(1-2\nu)}{4\pi(1-\nu)}(1 - \ln r_i)$$

Our solution is now complete.

Note that the stresses given by Eqs. (12.83) are equal on the two faces at $\theta = 0^+$ and $\theta = 2\pi^-$, resulting in continuity of stress across the cut as anticipated earlier. It is a simple matter to use the tensor transformation law to determine τ_{xx}, τ_{yy}, and τ_{xy} from τ_{rr}, $\tau_{\theta\theta}$, and $\tau_{r\theta}$. These results would indicate a state of compression for τ_{xx} above the $y = 0$ plane and tension for τ_{xx} below this plane. Furthermore, the shear stress τ_{xy} would be maximum along this plane. Also note that all stresses approach zero at infinity. Now examine the displacement component u_θ as given by Eq. (12.80b), and note that

$$u_\theta\big|_{\theta=0^+} = u_\theta\big|_{\theta=2\pi^-}$$

This indicates that after the two faces of the cut have been subjected to a relative radial displacement equal to b, no additional stresses are required to "reseal" the cut. The displacements and stresses in the *multiply connected* domain are thus given by Eqs. (12.80) and (12.83), with τ_{rr}, $\tau_{\theta\theta}$, $\tau_{r\theta}$, and u_θ continuous across the $\theta = 0$ plane and u_r discontinuous across this plane. The properties enumerated in this paragraph are completely consistent with the essential characteristics of an edge dislocation in a crystal, as discussed in Appendix VII.

This completes our discussion of elastic plane strain. In Part B we consider linear viscoelastic materials.

PART B
LINEAR VISCOELASTIC PLANE STRAIN

12.7 GOVERNING EQUATIONS

You will recall that in Chapter 6 we showed that each elastic constant is analogous to an operator ratio for a corresponding linear viscoelastic material. Thus we may convert the previously developed basic equations of isotropic linear elastic plane strain to the case of isotropic linear viscoelastic plane strain, simply by replacing the elastic constants by the appropriate operator ratios. Furthermore, it should be clear that any result which does not contain at least one elastic constant may be employed here without change. Also, we note that all dependent variables will now in general depend on time t as well as on the coordinates x_1, x_2.

Thus, since the *displacement* field is now a function of time as well as space, we shall modify Eqs. (12.1) to read

$$u_\alpha = u_\alpha(x_1, x_2, t) \qquad \text{with } u_3 = 0 \tag{12.86}$$

As before, the following *strains* are *zero*:

$$\varepsilon_{13} = \varepsilon_{23} = \varepsilon_{33} = 0$$

And the *strain-displacement* relation [Eq. (12.3)] still applies,

$$\boxed{\varepsilon_{\alpha\beta}(x_1, x_2, t) = \tfrac{1}{2}(u_{\alpha,\beta} + u_{\beta,\alpha})} \tag{12.87}$$

The stresses $\tau_{\alpha\beta}$ and τ_{33} are now related to the strains $\varepsilon_{\alpha\beta}$ via the linear viscoelastic counterparts to elastic constitutive equations (12.13) and (12.5), respectively. We shall soon develop these viscoelastic constitutive relations, but it is clear at this juncture that we now have

$$\tau_{\alpha\beta} = \tau_{\alpha\beta}(x_1, x_2, t)$$

$$\tau_{33} = \tau_{33}(x_1, x_2, t) \tag{12.88}$$

$$\tau_{13} = \tau_{23} = 0$$

The form of the traction *boundary condition* on the lateral surface is thus unchanged, except for the time dependency [see Eq. (12.20)], and hence

$$\boxed{T_\alpha^{(\nu)}(s, t) = \tau_{\alpha\beta}(s, t)\, \nu_\beta(s) \qquad \text{on } C} \tag{12.89}$$

Turning next to compatibility, it immediately follows that since $\varepsilon_{\alpha\beta} = \varepsilon_{\alpha\beta}(x_1, x_2, t)$ [Eq. (12.87)], we again arrive at Eq. (12.24),

$$\boxed{e_{\alpha\gamma} e_{\beta\delta} \frac{\partial^2 \varepsilon_{\alpha\beta}(x_1, x_2, t)}{\partial x_\gamma \partial x_\delta} = 0} \tag{12.90}$$

We can still use the *Airy stress function* $\Phi(x_1, x_2, t)$ (now time dependent), as defined by Eqs. (12.28), to satisfy the equations of equilibrium. Thus, for *zero body forces*, the stress function compatibility equation remains as Eq. (12.39),

$$\boxed{\nabla^4 \Phi(x_1, x_2, t) = 0 \qquad \text{in } R} \tag{12.91}$$

If conservative body forces are present, the governing equation in Φ for viscoelastic behavior is *not* the same as Eq. (12.42) for elastic behavior, because of the presence of Poisson's ratio ν in this equation. However, the applicable viscoelastic relation is easily obtained from Eq. (12.42), through the introduction of the appropriate operator ratio. In Problem 12.18 you are asked to obtain this relation and express it in various alternative forms.

We shall now focus on the form of the *linear viscoelastic constitutive* relation. In Section 6.7 we gave the details on how we may extrapolate from elastic behavior to linear viscoelastic behavior by establishing equivalences between the time operator ratios and the elastic constants. When using the tensile test approach, we presented the following analogy relations [see Eqs. (6.58)]:

$$\nu \sim \frac{Q^\nu}{P^\nu}, \qquad E \sim \frac{Q^E}{P^E} \tag{12.92}$$

Hence going first to Eq. (12.5), which is part of Hooke's law, we deduce for the linear viscoelastic case that

$$\tau_{33} = \frac{Q^\nu}{P^\nu}(\tau_{11} + \tau_{22})$$

Therefore,

$$\boxed{P^V \tau_{33} = Q^V(\tau_{11} + \tau_{22})} \tag{12.93}$$

We wish next to introduce viscoelastic operators into the plane-strain linear elastic constitutive law [Eq. (12.11)]. We have noted earlier [see Eqs. (12.9)] that the modified elastic constants ν_1 and E_1 used in Eq. (12.11) are related to ν and E from the tensile test as follows:

$$\nu_1 = \frac{\nu}{1 - \nu}, \qquad E_1 = \frac{E}{1 - \nu^2} \tag{12.94}$$

We have also previously noted that [compare Eqs. (12.7) and (12.8)]

$$\frac{1 + \nu_1}{E_1} = \frac{1 + \nu}{E}, \qquad \frac{\nu_1}{E_1} = \frac{\nu(1 + \nu)}{E} \tag{12.95}$$

Hence, using analogy relations (12.92) and noting the equations above, we obtain

$$\frac{1 + \nu_1}{E_1} \sim \frac{1 + Q^V/P^V}{Q^E/P^E} = \frac{P^E(P^V + Q^V)}{P^V Q^E} \tag{12.96}$$

Also,

$$\frac{\nu_1}{E_1} \sim \frac{(Q^V/P^V)(1 + Q^V/P^V)}{Q^E/P^E} = \frac{P^E Q^V(P^V + Q^V)}{P^V Q^E P^V} \tag{12.97}$$

We can now go back to Eq. (12.11) and introduce the operators above to form the *linear viscoelastic constitutive law*. Thus

$$\varepsilon_{\alpha\beta} = \frac{P^E(P^V + Q^V)}{P^V Q^E} \tau_{\alpha\beta} - \frac{P^E Q^V(P^V + Q^V)}{P^V Q^E P^V} \tau_{\gamma\gamma}\delta_{\alpha\beta}$$

and therefore

$$\boxed{P^V P^V Q^E \varepsilon_{\alpha\beta} = P^V P^E(P^V + Q^V)\tau_{\alpha\beta} - P^E Q^V(P^V + Q^V)\tau_{\gamma\gamma}\delta_{\alpha\beta}} \tag{12.98}$$

The inverted form of this equation is a viscoelastic counterpart to Eq. (12.13).

We now have assembled the essential equations to solve a linear viscoelastic plane-strain problem for the case of *no body forces*. The steps are outlined in broad terms below:

1. Solve the biharmonic stress function compatibility equation $\nabla^4\Phi = 0$ for $\Phi(x_1, x_2, t)$. For multiply connected domains, the viscoelastic plane-strain Cesàro integral conditions must also be satisfied. The viscoelastic Cesàro integral conditions follow from Eqs. (12.44) with ν_1 replaced by the appropriate operator ratio (see Problem 12.19).

2. Find $\tau_{\alpha\beta}(x_1, x_2, t)$ by substitution into the definition of the Airy stress function Φ [see Eqs. (12.28)]. Then determine $\tau_{33}(x_1, x_2, t)$ from Eq. (12.93).

3. Solve for the strains $\varepsilon_{\alpha\beta}(x_1, x_2, t)$ from constitutive law (12.98).
4. Find the displacement field $u_\alpha(x_1, x_2, t)$ by integrating the strain-displacement relation [Eq. (12.87)]. The integrability of these *three* equations for the *two* displacement components is assured by the satisfaction of compatibility in step 1.

12.8 ALTERNATIVE FORM FOR THE CONSTITUTIVE LAW; APPLICATION TO THICK-WALLED VISCOELASTIC CYLINDERS

As we discussed in Section 6.8, it is frequently most convenient in viscoelastic problem formulations to employ a *pair* of constitutive relations, where one equation gives the behavior in *distortion* (e.g., under pure shear) while the other gives the behavior in *bulk* (e.g., under hydrostatic pressure). Thus in this section we first decompose linear elastic plane-strain constitutive law (12.11) into its distortional and bulk components, and then introduce operator pairs to obtain an alternative form of the viscoelastic law given by Eqs. (12.98). We then utilize this alternative form in obtaining the solution for a viscoelastic thick-walled cylinder under internal pressure.

For convenience we reproduce linear elastic plane-strain constitutive law (12.11):

$$\varepsilon_{\alpha\beta} = \frac{1 + \nu_1}{E_1} \tau_{\alpha\beta} - \frac{\nu_1}{E_1} \tau_{\gamma\gamma} \delta_{\alpha\beta} \tag{12.99}$$

For $\varepsilon_{\gamma\gamma}$ we then have from the above,

$$\varepsilon_{\gamma\gamma} = \frac{1 + \nu_1}{E_1} \tau_{\gamma\gamma} - \frac{\nu_1}{E_1} (\tau_{\gamma\gamma})(2) = \frac{1 - \nu_1}{E_1} \tau_{\gamma\gamma} \tag{12.100}$$

Referring to Eqs. (12.94), we can say that

$$\frac{1 - \nu_1}{E_1} = \frac{1 - \nu/(1 - \nu)}{E/(1 - \nu^2)} = \frac{(1 + \nu)(1 - 2\nu)}{E} \tag{12.101}$$

Furthermore, from Table 5.1 we have

$$\nu = \frac{1}{2}\left(\frac{3K - 2G}{3K + G}\right), \qquad E = \frac{9KG}{3K + G} \tag{12.102}$$

and thus after some algebra we obtain by using the results above on the right-hand side of Eq. (12.101),

$$\frac{(1 + \nu)(1 - 2\nu)}{E} = \frac{3}{2(3K + G)} \tag{12.103}$$

Hence Eq. (12.100) becomes

$$\boxed{\varepsilon_{\gamma\gamma} = \frac{3}{2(3K + G)} \tau_{\gamma\gamma}} \tag{12.104}$$

This equation gives the two-dimensional bulk behavior, but you should note that since $\tau_{zz} \neq 0$, the quantity $\tau_{\gamma\gamma}$ is *not* equal to three times the bulk stress.

Let us now define the *strain and stress deviator* tensors in *two dimensions* as follows:

$$e_{\alpha\beta} = \varepsilon_{\alpha\beta} - \tfrac{1}{2}\varepsilon_{\gamma\gamma}\delta_{\alpha\beta} \qquad \text{(a)}$$

$$s_{\alpha\beta} = \tau_{\alpha\beta} - \tfrac{1}{2}\tau_{\gamma\gamma}\delta_{\alpha\beta} \qquad \text{(b)}$$

(12.105)

where you should note that $e_{\gamma\gamma} = s_{\gamma\gamma} \equiv 0$. Now substitute for $\varepsilon_{\alpha\beta}$ in Eq. (12.105a) using Eq. (12.99), and for $\varepsilon_{\gamma\gamma}$ using Eq. (12.100). We get

$$e_{\alpha\beta} = \left(\frac{1+\nu_1}{E_1}\tau_{\alpha\beta} - \frac{\nu_1}{E_1}\tau_{\gamma\gamma}\delta_{\alpha\beta}\right) - \frac{1}{2}\left(\frac{1-\nu_1}{E_1}\right)\tau_{\gamma\gamma}\delta_{\alpha\beta}$$

$$= \frac{1+\nu_1}{E_1}\left(\tau_{\alpha\beta} - \frac{1}{2}\tau_{\gamma\gamma}\delta_{\alpha\beta}\right) \qquad (12.106)$$

Using Eq. (12.105b) on the right side of Eq. (12.106), we get

$$e_{\alpha\beta} = \frac{1+\nu_1}{E_1}s_{\alpha\beta} \qquad (12.107)$$

But using the first of Eqs. (12.95) and Table 5.1, we note that

$$\frac{1+\nu_1}{E_1} = \frac{1+\nu}{E} = \frac{1}{2G} \qquad (12.108)$$

and thus Eq. (12.107) finally becomes

$$\boxed{e_{\alpha\beta} = \frac{s_{\alpha\beta}}{2G}} \qquad (12.109)$$

Equations (12.104) and (12.109) represent the two-dimensional *bulk* and *distortional* components, respectively, of linear elastic plane-strain equation (12.99), with the coefficients expressed in terms of the shear modulus G and the bulk modulus K. We will now convert these equations to the corresponding viscoelastic equations by employing the following analogy relations (see Section 6.7):

$$2G \sim \frac{Q^G}{P^G}, \qquad 3K \sim \frac{Q^K}{P^K} \qquad (12.110)$$

Accordingly, Eq. (12.104) yields

$$\varepsilon_{\gamma\gamma} = \frac{3}{2Q^K/P^K + Q^G/P^G}\tau_{\gamma\gamma}$$

and thus

$$\boxed{(2Q^K P^G + P^K Q^G)\varepsilon_{\gamma\gamma} = 3P^K P^G \tau_{\gamma\gamma}} \qquad (12.111)$$

Similarly, using the first of analogy relations (12.110), Eq. (12.109) yields immediately

$$\boxed{Q^G e_{\alpha\beta} = P^G s_{\alpha\beta}}$$
(12.112)

You may readily show (see Problem 12.20) that if Eqs. (12.111) and (12.112) are combined with the use of definitions (12.105), and if the (P^G, Q^G) and (P^K, Q^K) operator pairs are expressed in terms of the (P^E, Q^E) and (P^ν, Q^ν) operator pairs, we arrive back at Eq. (12.98).

It will also be convenient to express here the (P^ν, Q^ν) operator pair, appearing in Eq. (12.93) for τ_{33}, in terms of the (P^G, Q^G) and (P^K, Q^K) operator pairs. For this purpose, note the first of Eqs. (12.102), which gives for the elastic case

$$\nu = \frac{1}{2}\left(\frac{3K - 2G}{3K + G}\right)$$

Replacing ν, K, and G by the associated ratios for linear viscoelastic behavior [see analogy relations (12.92) and (12.110)], we obtain

$$\frac{Q^\nu}{P^\nu} = \frac{Q^K/P^K - Q^G/P^G}{2Q^K/P^K + Q^G/P^G}$$
(12.113)

Equation (12.93) then becomes

$$\tau_{33} = \frac{Q^K/P^K - Q^G/P^G}{2Q^K/P^K + Q^G/P^G}(\tau_{11} + \tau_{22})$$

which after rearrangement of the operators finally gives the desired result

$$\boxed{(2Q^K P^G + Q^G P^K)\tau_{33} = (Q^K P^G - Q^G P^K)(\tau_{11} + \tau_{22})}$$
(12.114)

Example 12.2

We now reexamine the thick-walled axially constrained cylinder previously studied in Example 12.1 in Section 12.5, but this time for a linear viscoelastic material. We wish to determine the stresses τ_{rr}, $\tau_{\theta\theta}$, and τ_{zz} for an internal pressure p_i. We have shown this cylinder in Fig. 12.7. The pressure p_i is suddenly applied, so that we have a pressure function $p(t)$ given as

$$p(t) = p_i[u(t)] \qquad \text{at } r = r_i$$
(a)

Furthermore, we consider a special viscoelastic material that is *Kelvin* in *distortion* and *elastic* in *bulk*. Accordingly, the operator pairs are given as [see Eqs. (6.98)]

$$P^G = 1 \qquad Q^G = 2G + \zeta\frac{\partial}{\partial t}$$
$$P^K = 1 \qquad Q^K = 3K$$
(b)

We first consider the Airy stress function, for which $\nabla^4 \Phi = 0$. For axial symmetry we have solved this equation by successive integration [see Eq. (12.58)], and thus we have

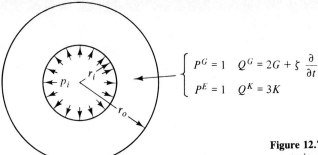

$$\begin{cases} P^G = 1 & Q^G = 2G + \zeta \dfrac{\partial}{\partial t} \\ P^E = 1 & Q^K = 3K \end{cases}$$

Figure 12.7 Viscoelastic axially constrained thick-walled cylinder.

$$\frac{\partial \Phi}{\partial r} = \frac{C_1(t)}{2} r \left(\ln r - \frac{1}{2} \right) + \frac{C_2(t)}{2} r + \frac{C_3(t)}{r} \tag{c}$$

But now $\partial \Phi / \partial r$ is a *partial* derivative and $C_1(t)$, $C_2(t)$, and $C_3(t)$ are in general functions of *time*, since Φ is a function of r and t. As discussed previously, for a unique single-valued displacement field we must set C_1 equal to zero.[*] The stresses associated with $\partial \Phi / \partial r$, as given by Eq. (c) with $C_1 = 0$, are then [see Eqs. (12.56a,b)]

$$\tau_{rr} = \frac{1}{r} \frac{\partial \Phi}{\partial r} = \frac{C_2(t)}{2} + \frac{C_3(t)}{r^2} \tag{d}$$

$$\tau_{\theta\theta} = \frac{\partial^2 \Phi}{\partial r^2} = \frac{C_2(t)}{2} - \frac{C_3(t)}{r^2} \tag{e}$$

The boundary conditions on the inside and outside surfaces are

$$\begin{aligned} \tau_{rr} &= -p_i[u(t)] & \text{at } r = r_i \\ \tau_{rr} &= 0 & \text{at } r = r_o \end{aligned} \tag{f}$$

Applying these conditions to Eq. (d), we get

$$-p_i[u(t)] = \frac{C_2(t)}{2} + \frac{C_3(t)}{r_i^2}$$

$$0 = \frac{C_2(t)}{2} + \frac{C_3(t)}{r_o^2}$$

We may then solve for $C_2(t)$ and $C_3(t)$, and finally get from Eqs. (d) and (e),

$$\tau_{rr} = \frac{r_i^2}{r_o^2 - r_i^2} \left(1 - \frac{r_o^2}{r^2} \right) p_i[u(t)] \tag{g}$$

$$\tau_{\theta\theta} = \frac{r_i^2}{r_o^2 - r_i^2} \left(1 + \frac{r_o^2}{r^2} \right) p_i[u(t)] \tag{h}$$

Note that for $t \geq 0^+$ these stresses *are the same as those previously reached for an elastic material* [see Eqs. (g) and (h) in Example 12.1 with the external pressure $p_o = 0$]. This should have been expected, since the *governing differential equation* ($\nabla^4 \Phi = 0$) is valid

---

[*] This result followed from the *elastic* Cesàro integral condition (12.44b) with $V \equiv 0$. Since this condition contains no elastic constants, it is equally valid for *linear viscoelastic* materials.

for *any viscoelastic material* (*including elastic*) because its form is *independent* of the constitutive law.*

Turning finally to the axial stress τ_{zz}, we note that in accordance with Eq. (12.114),

$$(2Q^K P^G + Q^G P^K)\tau_{zz} = (Q^K P^G - Q^G P^K)(\tau_{rr} + \tau_{\theta\theta}) \tag{i}$$

Now using the assumed viscoelastic behavior as prescribed by Eqs. (b), Eq. (i) becomes

$$\left[2(3K)(1) + \left(2G + \zeta\frac{\partial}{\partial t}\right)(1)\right]\tau_{zz} = \left[(3K)(1) - \left(2G + \zeta\frac{\partial}{\partial t}\right)(1)\right](\tau_{rr} + \tau_{\theta\theta})$$

Substituting for $\tau_{rr} + \tau_{\theta\theta}$ using Eqs. (g) and (h), we then get for the equation above,

$$\frac{\partial \tau_{zz}}{\partial t} + \frac{6K + 2G}{\zeta}\tau_{zz} = \left\{\frac{3K - 2G}{\zeta}[u(t)] - [\delta(t)]\right\}\frac{2r_i^2}{r_o^2 - r_i^2}p_i \tag{j}$$

This equation may be rewritten as

$$\frac{\partial}{\partial t}(e^{\lambda t}\tau_{zz}) = \left\{\frac{3K - 2G}{\zeta}[u(t)] - [\delta(t)]\right\}e^{\lambda t}\frac{2r_i^2}{r_o^2 - r_i^2}p_i \tag{k}$$

where

$$\lambda = \frac{6K + 2G}{\zeta} \tag{ℓ}$$

Integrating Eq. (k) from 0^- to t, and noting that the function of integration $f(r)$ must vanish since $\tau_{zz}(0^-) = 0$, we finally obtain

$$\tau_{zz} = \frac{2r_i^2}{r_o^2 - r_i^2}p_i[u(t)]\left[\frac{3K - 2G}{6K + 2G}(1 - e^{-\lambda t}) - e^{-\lambda t}\right] \tag{m}$$

In contrast with τ_{rr} and $\tau_{\theta\theta}$, the viscoelastic axial stress τ_{zz} *is not* the same as the elastic solution. However, note that [see first of Eqs. (12.102)]

$$\lim_{t \to \infty} \tau_{zz} = \frac{2r_i^2}{r_o^2 - r_i^2}p_i\left(\frac{3K - 2G}{6K + 2G}\right) = \frac{2\nu r_i^2}{r_o^2 - r_i^2}p_i \tag{n}$$

which *is* the same as the elastic solution [i.e., Eq. (j) in Example 12.1 with $p_o = 0$].

We could have obtained the solution for τ_{zz} in Example 12.2 by using the correspondence principle, as discussed in Section 9.5 (see Problem 12.21). In the next example we employ this procedure to determine the displacement.

Example 12.3

We shall now determine the radial displacement u_r, which results from the stresses determined in Example 12.2 for the viscoelastic thick-walled cylinder. Employing the linear elastic–linear viscoelastic correspondence principle, we shall develop this solution from the elastic solution obtained in Example 12.1. You will recall that the *correspondence principle states that the Laplace transform of the elastic solution for a given problem is identical with the Laplace transform of the viscoelastic solution for the same geometry and loading if one replaces 3K by $\overline{Q}^K/\overline{P}^K$ and 2G by $\overline{Q}^G/\overline{P}^G$.*

---

*Of course, for the stresses to be the same for any two viscoelastic (including elastic) materials, the *prescribed* boundary stresses must be identical. The stresses at the boundaries will in general *not* be identical if *displacements* are prescribed (as in Problem 12.23).

We begin by setting the external pressure $p_o = 0$ and by replacing p_i by $p_i[u(t)]$ in Eq. (k) of Example 12.1 in Section 12.5, which then gives us the following elastic solution u_r^E for a thick-walled cylinder subjected to a suddenly applied internal pressure:

$$u_r^E = \frac{r_i^2}{r_o^2 - r_i^2}\, p_i[u(t)]\left[\frac{1 + \nu_1}{E_1}\frac{r_o^2}{r} + \frac{1 - \nu_1}{E_1}r\right] \tag{a}$$

Next, using Eqs. (12.108), (12.101), and (12.103), we express this solution in terms of K and G as

$$u_r^E = \frac{r_i^2}{r_o^2 - r_i^2}\, p_i[u(t)]\left[\frac{r_o^2}{2Gr} + \frac{3r}{2(3K + G)}\right] \tag{b}$$

Now, taking a Laplace transform (here we choose 0^+ as the lower limit on t) and replacing $3K$ and $2G$ as described earlier, we obtain the following Laplace transform of the corresponding viscoelastic solution $\bar{u}_r^V(s)$:

$$\bar{u}_r^V(s) = \frac{r_i^2}{r_o^2 - r_i^2}\frac{p_i}{s}\left[\frac{r_o^2}{(\overline{Q}^G/\overline{P}^G)r} + \frac{3r}{2(\overline{Q}^K/\overline{P}^K) + (\overline{Q}^G/\overline{P}^G)}\right] \tag{c}$$

For the viscoelastic material of interest here we have the operators given by Eqs. (b) of Example 12.2, which in Laplace transform space become the polynomials

$$\begin{aligned}\overline{P}^G &= 1, &\overline{Q}^G &= 2G + \zeta s\\ \overline{P}^K &= 1, &\overline{Q}^K &= 3K\end{aligned} \tag{d}$$

Finally, substituting Eqs. (d) into Eq. (c), we get

$$\bar{u}_r^V(s) = \frac{r_i^2}{r_o^2 - r_i^2}\frac{p_i}{s}\left[\frac{r_o^2}{(2G + \zeta s)r} + \frac{3r}{6K + 2G + \zeta s}\right] \tag{e}$$

which after inversion will yield the desired solution.

For the purpose of inversion, we first multiply Eq. (e) by s and use the formula for the transform of the derivative [see Eq. (III.4) in Appendix III]. Equation (e) with initial conditions at $t = 0^+$ then yields (for convenience we now delete the super-script V):

$$s\bar{u}_r(s) = \mathbf{L}\left\{\frac{\partial u_r}{\partial t}\right\} + u_r(0^+) = \frac{r_i^2 p_i}{r_o^2 - r_i^2}\left[\frac{r_o^2}{(2G + \zeta s)r} + \frac{3r}{6K + 2G + \zeta s}\right] \tag{f}$$

If we now pause to apply limit theorem (III.22) using the right side of Eq. (f) for $s\bar{u}_r(s)$, we get

$$\lim_{s\to\infty} s\bar{u}_r(s) = u_r(0^+) = 0 \tag{g}$$

As a result, we see that we may drop the initial condition from Eq. (f). To facilitate inversion we now rewrite Eq. (f) as

$$\mathbf{L}\left\{\frac{\partial u_r}{\partial t}\right\} = \frac{r_i^2 p_i}{r_o^2 - r_i^2}\left[\frac{r_o^2/(\zeta r)}{s + 2G/\zeta} + \frac{3r/\zeta}{s + (6K + 2G)/\zeta}\right] \tag{h}$$

Table III.1 then yields the inverse as

$$\frac{\partial u_r}{\partial t} = \frac{r_i^2 p_i}{r_o^2 - r_i^2}\left[\frac{r_o^2}{\zeta r}e^{-(2G/\zeta)t} + \frac{3r}{\zeta}e^{-(6K + 2G)t/\zeta}\right] \tag{i}$$

Finally, integrating this result from $t = 0^+$ to t and again using initial condition (g), we get the desired solution

$$u_r = \frac{r_i^2 p_i}{r_o^2 - r_i^2} \left[\frac{r_o^2}{2Gr} (1 - e^{-(2G/\zeta)t}) + \frac{3r}{6K + 2G} (1 - e^{-(6K + 2G)t/\zeta}) \right] \qquad \text{(j)}$$

Note that if we let $t \to \infty$, we arrive back at the elastic solution as given by Eq. (b).

This completes our study of linear viscoelastic plane strain. In the next part we briefly consider plane strain in nonlinear viscous and perfectly plastic materials.

PART C
NONLINEAR VISCOUS AND PERFECTLY PLASTIC PLANE STRAIN

12.9 FORMULATION OF GOVERNING EQUATIONS

In the next three sections we briefly consider nonlinear viscous behavior, with fully perfectly plastic behavior falling out as a special case. By the definition of plane strain we of course still will require that at any instant of time

$$\varepsilon_{13} = \varepsilon_{23} = \varepsilon_{33} = 0 \qquad (12.115a)$$

which implies that

$$\dot{\varepsilon}_{13} = \dot{\varepsilon}_{23} = \dot{\varepsilon}_{33} = 0 \qquad (12.115b)$$

We employ the usual *incompressible nonlinear* viscous constitutive law [see Eq. (9.19)]

$$\dot{\varepsilon}_{ij} = C J_2^m s_{ij} \qquad (12.116)$$

where

$$J_2 = \tfrac{1}{2} s_{kl} s_{kl} \qquad (12.117)$$

In expanded form, Eq. (12.116) together with requirements (12.115b) give the following:

$$
\begin{aligned}
\dot{\varepsilon}_{11} &= C J_2^m s_{11} & \text{(a)} \\
\dot{\varepsilon}_{22} &= C J_2^m s_{22} & \text{(b)} \\
\dot{\varepsilon}_{33} &= C J_2^m s_{33} = 0 & \text{(c)} \\
\dot{\varepsilon}_{12} &= C J_2^m s_{12} & \text{(d)} \\
\dot{\varepsilon}_{23} &= C J_2^m s_{23} = 0 & \text{(e)} \\
\dot{\varepsilon}_{31} &= C J_2^m s_{31} = 0 & \text{(f)}
\end{aligned}
\qquad (12.118)
$$

Employing the definition of the stress deviator tensor,

$$s_{ij} = \tau_{ij} - \tfrac{1}{3} \tau_{kk} \delta_{ij} \qquad (12.119)$$

we get, on noting that $s_{33} = 0$ according to Eqs. (12.118c),

$$s_{33} = 0 = \tau_{33} - \tfrac{1}{3}(\tau_{11} + \tau_{22} + \tau_{33}) = \tfrac{2}{3}\tau_{33} - \tfrac{1}{3}(\tau_{11} + \tau_{22})$$

Therefore,

$$\tau_{33} = \tfrac{1}{2}(\tau_{11} + \tau_{22}) \tag{12.120}$$

On comparing this result with Eq. (12.5) for the elastic case, we see that here we have the same result except that now the viscous Poisson coefficient equals $\tfrac{1}{2}$ since the material is incompressible. Equations (12.118e) and (12.118f) with definition (12.119) also give

$$\tau_{23} = \tau_{31} = 0 \tag{12.121}$$

Turning next to the invariant J_2 [Eq. (12.117)] we have

$$J_2 = \tfrac{1}{2}(s_{11}^2 + s_{22}^2 + 2s_{12}^2) \tag{12.122}$$

where we have set $s_{33} = s_{23} = s_{31} = 0$. Also, from definition (12.119) and Eq. (12.120) for τ_{33}, we get

$$s_{11} = \tau_{11} - \tfrac{1}{3}(\tau_{11} + \tau_{22} + \tau_{33}) = \tau_{11} - \tfrac{1}{3}[(\tau_{11} + \tau_{22}) + \tfrac{1}{2}(\tau_{11} + \tau_{22})]$$
$$= \tau_{11} - \tfrac{1}{2}(\tau_{11} + \tau_{22}) = \tfrac{1}{2}(\tau_{11} - \tau_{22}) \tag{12.123}$$

Similarly,

$$s_{22} = \tfrac{1}{2}(\tau_{22} - \tau_{11}) \tag{12.124}$$

Then, upon substituting Eqs. (12.123) and (12.124) into (12.122), we have, since $s_{12} = \tau_{12}$,

$$J_2 = \tfrac{1}{2}[\tfrac{1}{4}(\tau_{11} - \tau_{22})^2 + \tfrac{1}{4}(\tau_{22} - \tau_{11})^2 + 2\tau_{12}^2]$$
$$= \tfrac{1}{4}(\tau_{11} - \tau_{22})^2 + \tau_{12}^2 \tag{12.125}$$

Finally, using Eqs. (12.123), (12.124), and (12.125) in Eqs. (12.118a,b,d) we obtain the plane strain *constitutive* relations

$$\boxed{\begin{aligned}
\dot{\varepsilon}_{11} &= \frac{C}{2}\left[\frac{1}{4}(\tau_{11} - \tau_{22})^2 + \tau_{12}^2\right]^m (\tau_{11} - \tau_{22}) \qquad &\text{(a)} \\[2mm]
\dot{\varepsilon}_{22} &= \frac{C}{2}\left[\frac{1}{4}(\tau_{11} - \tau_{22})^2 + \tau_{12}^2\right]^m (\tau_{22} - \tau_{11}) \qquad &\text{(b)} \\[2mm]
\dot{\varepsilon}_{12} &= C\left[\frac{1}{4}(\tau_{11} - \tau_{22})^2 + \tau_{12}^2\right]^m \tau_{12} \qquad &\text{(c)}
\end{aligned}} \tag{12.126}$$

Note that $\dot{\varepsilon}_{11} + \dot{\varepsilon}_{22} = 0$, which is as expected for incompressible material. In two-dimensional index notation, we may rewrite Eqs. (12.125) and (12.126) more compactly as

$$J_2 = \tfrac{1}{2}s_{\gamma\delta}s_{\gamma\delta} = \tfrac{1}{2}(\tau_{\gamma\delta}\tau_{\gamma\delta} - \tfrac{1}{2}\tau_{\gamma\gamma}\tau_{\delta\delta}) \qquad \text{(a)}$$
$$\dot{\varepsilon}_{\alpha\beta} = CJ_2^m s_{\alpha\beta} \qquad \text{(b)} \tag{12.127}$$

Here $s_{\alpha\beta}$ is the *two-dimensional* stress deviator tensor

$$s_{\alpha\beta} = \tau_{\alpha\beta} - \tfrac{1}{2}\tau_{\gamma\gamma}\delta_{\alpha\beta} \tag{12.128}$$

By the definition of plane strain, $\dot{\varepsilon}_{11}$, $\dot{\varepsilon}_{22}$, and $\dot{\varepsilon}_{12}$ are functions of x_1, x_2, and thus Eqs. (12.126) and (12.120) imply that τ_{11}, τ_{22}, τ_{12}, and τ_{33} are also functions of x_1, x_2. This property, coupled with our previous result that $\tau_{23} = \tau_{31} = 0$, reduces equilibrium equations (9.2) to the usual *equilibrium equations of plane strain* for zero body forces

$$\frac{\partial \tau_{11}}{\partial x_1} + \frac{\partial \tau_{12}}{\partial x_2} = 0$$

$$\frac{\partial \tau_{12}}{\partial x_1} + \frac{\partial \tau_{22}}{\partial x_2} = 0$$

(12.129)

or in index notation

$$\tau_{\alpha\beta, \beta} = 0 \tag{12.130}$$

Although the equations above are the same as the familiar equilibrium equations of plane stress, you are reminded that $\tau_{33} = 0$ for plane stress while $\tau_{33} \neq 0$ for plane strain. Since *compatibility* is independent of the constitutive law it is also unchanged; that is, for plane strain [see Eqs. (12.25)] we have after differentiation with respect to time

$$\frac{\partial^2 \dot{\varepsilon}_{11}}{\partial x_2^2} + \frac{\partial^2 \dot{\varepsilon}_{22}}{\partial x_1^2} = 2 \frac{\partial^2 \dot{\varepsilon}_{12}}{\partial x_1 \, \partial x_2}$$

(12.131)

and in index notation [see Eqs. (12.24)]

$$e_{\alpha\gamma} e_{\beta\delta} \dot{\varepsilon}_{\alpha\beta, \gamma\delta} = 0 \tag{12.132}$$

We may now proceed in the usual manner to obtain a stress formulation. That is, we first reduce equilibrium equations (12.129) to an identity by introducing the usual *Airy* stress function Φ. We then replace the stresses in constitutive Eqs. (12.126) by inserting their definitions in terms of Φ. Finally, we substitute the resulting strain rates into compatibility equation (12.131). The result is a rather complicated nonlinear partial differential equation in Φ. For the sake of brevity, in the following section we carry out the steps only for the special case of *axially symmetric* plane strain.

12.10 FORMULATIONS FOR THE CASE OF AXIAL SYMMETRY

Let us consider a cylindrical coordinate system, with index 1 identified with r, index 2 with θ, and index 3 with z. Equations (12.115a) and (12.121) then immediately give

$$\varepsilon_{rz} = \varepsilon_{\theta z} = \varepsilon_{zz} = \tau_{rz} = \tau_{\theta z} = 0 \tag{12.133}$$

For plane strain, ε_{rr}, $\varepsilon_{\theta\theta}$, and $\varepsilon_{r\theta}$ are required to be independent of z, and it follows from constitutive equations (12.126) and (12.120) that τ_{rr}, $\tau_{\theta\theta}$, $\tau_{r\theta}$, and τ_{zz} must also be independent of z. Clearly, we have $\partial/\partial z \equiv 0$, and for axial symmetry, we also have $\partial/\partial\theta \equiv 0$. In Problem 9.1 we have presented the three equations of equilibrium in cylindrical coordinates. Setting $\tau_{rz} = \tau_{\theta z} = \partial/\partial z = \partial/\partial\theta = 0$ in these equations, we may obtain the following *equilibrium* equation for zero body forces:

$$\frac{d\tau_{rr}}{dr} + \frac{\tau_{rr} - \tau_{\theta\theta}}{r} = 0 \qquad (12.134)$$

This equation stems from the first of the three equilibrium equations [Eq. (a) in Problem 9.1], and represents equilibrium in the radial direction. An integration of the second equilibrium equation [Eq. (b)–equilibrium in the transverse direction] leads to the requirement that $\tau_{r\theta}$ be zero. Finally, the third equilibrium equation [Eq. (c)–equilibrium in the axial direction] is a trivial identity.

As to *compatibility*, we note that in Problem 9.6 we have also given the six compatibility equations in cylindrical coordinates. If we set $\varepsilon_{rz} = \varepsilon_{\theta z} = \varepsilon_{zz} = \partial/\partial z = \partial/\partial\theta = 0$ in these equations, five of them reduce to trivial identities while the remaining one [Eq. (c) in Problem 9.6] yields the *compatibility* equation in terms of the strain rates as

$$\dot{\varepsilon}_{\theta\theta} - \dot{\varepsilon}_{rr} + r\frac{d\dot{\varepsilon}_{\theta\theta}}{dr} = 0 \qquad (12.135)$$

The result above is first obtained with a constant of integration on the right-hand side, but by using the strain-displacement relations one can show that this constant must be zero. In Problem 12.26 you will be asked to not only prove this assertion, but also to prove that the second equilibrium equation integrates to the solution $\tau_{r\theta} = 0$ as asserted above.

Let us again identify index 1 with r and index 2 with θ, and note that since $\tau_{r\theta} = 0$ Eqs. (12.126) simplify in this case to $\dot{\varepsilon}_{r\theta} = 0$ and

$$\dot{\varepsilon}_{rr} = C\left(\frac{\tau_{rr} - \tau_{\theta\theta}}{2}\right)^n \qquad \text{(a)}$$

$$\dot{\varepsilon}_{\theta\theta} = C\left(\frac{\tau_{\theta\theta} - \tau_{rr}}{2}\right)^n \qquad n = 2m + 1 = 1, 3, 5, \ldots \qquad \text{(b)}$$

$$(12.136)$$

Since we have not introduced the signum function, we must restrict n to odd positive integers.* Furthermore, we see from Eq. (12.125) that here

$$J_2 = \tfrac{1}{4}(\tau_{rr} - \tau_{\theta\theta})^2 \qquad (12.137)$$

---

* For *arbitrary* positive n, we may easily extend our results by rewriting Eq. (12.136a) as

$$\dot{\varepsilon}_{rr} = \frac{C}{2^n}|\tau_{rr} - \tau_{\theta\theta}|^{n-1}(\tau_{rr} - \tau_{\theta\theta}) = \frac{C}{2^n}|\tau_{rr} - \tau_{\theta\theta}|^n \, \text{sgn}(\tau_{rr} - \tau_{\theta\theta})$$

As in Section 12.5, we let [see Eqs. (12.56a,b)]

$$\tau_{rr} = \frac{1}{r}\frac{d\Phi}{dr} \qquad (a)$$

$$\tau_{\theta\theta} = \frac{d^2\Phi}{dr^2} \qquad (b)$$

(12.138)

where $\Phi(r)$ is the *Airy stress function*. You may readily verify that equilibrium equation (12.134) is identically satisfied with the introduction of definitions (12.138). The strain rates [Eqs. (12.136)] now become

$$\dot{\varepsilon}_{rr} = -\dot{\varepsilon}_{\theta\theta} = \frac{C}{2^n}\left(\frac{1}{r}\frac{d\Phi}{dr} - \frac{d^2\Phi}{dr^2}\right)^n \qquad (12.139)$$

Finally, inserting Eqs. (12.139) into compatibility Eq. (12.135), we obtain

$$2\left(\frac{1}{r}\frac{d\Phi}{dr} - \frac{d^2\Phi}{dr^2}\right)^n + r\frac{d}{dr}\left(\frac{1}{r}\frac{d\Phi}{dr} - \frac{d^2\Phi}{dr^2}\right)^n = 0 \qquad (12.140)$$

You may readily verify that for $n = 1$ (linear viscous) this equation is identical with the first integral of $\nabla^4\Phi = 0$, with the constant of integration C_1 set equal to zero [see Eq. (12.57) in Section 12.5]. We have previously noted that for an axially symmetric problem in a linear viscoelastic medium, we must set C_1 equal to zero for single-valued displacements (see footnote on p. 551). In an axially symmetric problem displacements *must* be single-valued since *no variations* with θ are permitted (thus avoiding the problem of possible multivaluedness when θ exceeds 2π). In the next section we obtain solutions for any n that is an odd positive integer and will then examine the behavior of these solutions for $n = 1$ and $n \to \infty$ (perfectly plastic).

12.11 SOLUTIONS TO NONLINEAR VISCOUS AXIALLY SYMMETRIC GOVERNING EQUATIONS

In preparation for solving Eq. (12.140), we note first that after multiplication by $-r$, this equation may be rewritten as

$$\frac{d}{dr}\left\{r^2\left[r\frac{d}{dr}\left(\frac{1}{r}\frac{d\Phi}{dr}\right)\right]^n\right\} = 0 \qquad (12.141)$$

Integrating over r and dividing by r^2, we get

$$\left[r\frac{d}{dr}\left(\frac{1}{r}\frac{d\Phi}{dr}\right)\right]^n = \frac{(2A)^n}{r^2}$$

where for later convenience the constant of integration has been expressed as $(2A)^n$. It then follows directly that

$$\frac{d}{dr}\left(\frac{1}{r}\frac{d\Phi}{dr}\right) = 2Ar^{-(2+n)/n}$$

A second integration finally gives the result [see Eq. (12.138a)]

$$\tau_{rr} = \frac{1}{r}\frac{d\Phi}{dr} = B - Anr^{-(2/n)}$$

(12.142a)

where B is another constant of integration. It also easily follows by differentiation [see Eq. (12.138b)] that

$$\tau_{\theta\theta} = \frac{d^2\Phi}{dr^2} = B - A(n-2)r^{-(2/n)}$$

(12.142b)

To obtain the radial velocity $\dot{u}_r$, we first obtain the transverse strain rate $\dot{\varepsilon}_{\theta\theta}$ by substituting stresses (12.142) into Eq. (12.136b). Accordingly,

$$\dot{\varepsilon}_{\theta\theta} = C\left(\frac{\tau_{\theta\theta} - \tau_{rr}}{2}\right)^n = CA^n r^{-2}$$

(12.143)

Since $\dot{u}_r = r\dot{\varepsilon}_{\theta\theta}$ via Eq. (12.56f), we finally get

$$\dot{u}_r = CA^n r^{-1}$$

(12.144)

We have previously shown that Eq. (12.56g) for axially symmetric problems implies that $u_\theta = 0$, and thus $\dot{u}_\theta = 0$.

Equations (12.142) and (12.144) give the complete stress and velocity solutions for a nonlinear viscous material. The special case of linear viscous behavior is obtained by setting $n = 1$, while the case of *fully* perfectly plastic behavior is found by letting $n \to \infty$. You will recall that in Section 9.6 we presented the *nonlinear elastic–nonlinear viscous analogy*, which includes a linear elastic–linear viscous analogy as a special case. The use of this analogy affords a check of stress and velocity solutions obtained here for $n = 1$, against previously obtained linear elastic stress and displacement solutions. We have also previously noted that although the $n \to \infty$ limiting process does yield meaningful results for stresses, it is not meaningful for velocities since they are generally indeterminate in fully perfectly plastic behavior. Furthermore, you will also recall that in Section 9.6 we showed that nonlinear viscous law (12.116) is analogous to the Mises plastic flow rule with isotropic power-law hardening (i.e., the *nonlinear viscous-plastic analogy*). According to the Mises criterion, yielding occurs when the invariant J_2 reaches a critical value [see Eq. (9.29a)]. In *fully* perfectly plastic plane strain *all* points in the cross section are simultaneously at yield, and thus as $n \to \infty$ the invariant J_2 must approach the same positive constant at all points. Referring to Eq. (12.137), we accordingly have for polar coordinates with axial symmetry

$$\lim_{n\to\infty} J_2 = \lim_{n\to\infty} \frac{1}{4}(\tau_{rr} - \tau_{\theta\theta})^2 = \kappa^2$$

(12.145)

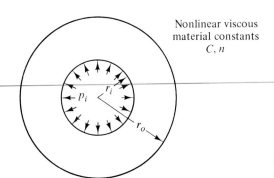

Figure 12.8 Nonlinear viscous thick-walled cylinder.

where κ^2 is the above-mentioned positive constant.* In the following example we illustrate the various points presented above.

Example 12.4

We shall once more examine the thick-walled hollow cylinder under internal pressure p_i, but this time the material is nonlinear viscous with material constants C and n (see Fig. 12.8). We shall determine τ_{rr}, $\tau_{\theta\theta}$, and $\dot{u}_r$ for any value of n, including $n = 1$ and the fully perfectly plastic limiting case $n \to \infty$.

The boundary conditions in this problem are

$$\tau_{rr} = -p_i \qquad \text{at } r = r_i$$
$$\tau_{rr} = 0 \qquad \text{at } r = r_o \tag{a}$$

Using these conditions in Eq. (12.142a), we get

$$-p_i = B - Anr_i^{-(2/n)}$$
$$0 = B - Anr_o^{-(2/n)} \tag{b}$$

Solving for the constants A and B, we then obtain

$$A = \frac{p_i (r_i r_o)^{2/n}}{n(r_o^{2/n} - r_i^{2/n})}$$
$$B = \frac{p_i r_i^{2/n}}{r_o^{2/n} - r_i^{2/n}} \tag{c}$$

which are clearly functions of the stress power n. Substituting the constants above back into Eqs. (12.142) and (12.144), we get the following solutions:

$$\tau_{rr} = \frac{p_i[1 - (r_o/r)^{2/n}]}{[(r_o/r_i)^{2/n} - 1]} \tag{d}$$

$$\tau_{\theta\theta} = \frac{p_i\{1 - [(n-2)/n](r_o/r)^{2/n}\}}{[(r_o/r_i)^{2/n} - 1]} \tag{e}$$

$$\dot{u}_r = \frac{Cr_o^2}{r} \left\{ \frac{p_i}{n[(r_o/r_i)^{2/n} - 1]} \right\}^n \tag{f}$$

---

* For a given problem the constants A and B, appearing in Eqs. (12.142), will be functions of n. Accordingly, the limiting process $n \to \infty$ can only be carried out *after* A and B have been determined from the boundary conditions.

For the special case $n = 1$ (*linear viscous*), the stresses above are identical with those determined in Example 12.2, which you may recall were valid for any linear viscoelastic material, including linear viscous. The velocity $\dot{u}_r$ for $n = 1$ is of course *not* the same as the velocity obtained for viscoelastic material in Example 12.3, since velocity depends on the form of the constitutive law. However, the *viscous-elastic analogy* given in Section 9.6 tells us that the *velocity* in a viscous problem equals the *displacement* in the analogous elastic problem. Indeed, if we set the external pressure $p_o = 0$ and let $\nu_1 = 1, E_1 = 2/C$ in Eq. (k) of linear elastic Example 12.1, we arrive at the right side of Eq. (f) above for $n = 1$. These choices for the material properties are readily justified by matching the right sides of constitutive equations (12.109) and (12.127b) for the case of *incompressible* ($\nu = \frac{1}{2}$) *linear* ($m = 0$) material.

For *fully perfectly plastic* behavior we let $n \to \infty$ in Eqs. (d) to (f), and applying l'Hospital's rule to Eq. (d), we obtain first for τ_{rr},

$$\tau_{rr} = p_i \lim_{n \to \infty} \frac{1 - (r_o/r)^{2/n}}{(r_o/r_i)^{2/n} - 1} = p_i \lim_{n \to \infty} \frac{-(r_o/r)^{2/n} [\ln(r_o/r)] (-2/n^2)}{(r_o/r_i)^{2/n} [\ln(r_o/r_i)] (-2/n^2)}$$

$$= -p_i \frac{\ln(r_o/r)}{\ln(r_o/r_i)} \qquad \text{for } n \to \infty \qquad \text{(g)}$$

Proceeding in a similar manner with Eq. (e) (see Problem 12.30), we may then get for $\tau_{\theta\theta}$,

$$\tau_{\theta\theta} = -p_i \frac{[\ln(r_o/r) - 1]}{\ln(r_o/r_i)} \qquad \text{for } n \to \infty \qquad \text{(h)}$$

In considering Eq. (f) for $\dot{u}_r$, we find that the quantity in braces approaches a finite limit as $n \to \infty$. Thus as the power n outside the braces approaches infinity, $\dot{u}_r$ will approach either zero or infinity. In other words, $\dot{u}_r$ is indeterminate as $n \to \infty$, which is as expected for fully perfectly plastic behavior.

Finally, consider condition (12.145), which with the use of limits (g) and (h) yields

$$\lim_{n \to \infty} J_2 = \frac{1}{4} \left\{ -p_i \frac{\ln(r_o/r)}{\ln(r_o/r_i)} + p_i \frac{[\ln(r_o/r) - 1]}{\ln(r_o/r_i)} \right\}^2$$

$$= \left[\frac{p_i}{2 \ln(r_o/r_i)} \right]^2 = \kappa^2 \qquad \text{for } n \to \infty \qquad \text{(i)}$$

Thus we see that as $n \to \infty$ the invariant J_2 approaches a positive constant which is independent of r, as required.

One may also obtain stress and velocity solutions for the case of the *elastic, perfectly plastic* thick-walled *cylinder* under internal pressure p_i, using either the Mises or the Tresca yield criterion. These solutions can be fairly complicated and we shall not present them here. We refer you to the plasticity literature,[*] and to Problems 12.31 and 12.32. We simply point out that the solution to this problem exhibits the same essential features, which we observed in solving the elastic, perfectly plastic thick-walled *sphere* under internal pressure in Section 9.14. That is, for $p_i < p_e$ (critical elastic pressure) the *entire* cylinder is in a state of elastic

---

[*] For example, see B. Venkatraman and S. A. Patel, *Structural Mechanics with Introduction to Elasticity and Plasticity* (New York: McGraw-Hill Book Company, 1970), Chap. 21.

deformation. Then, for $p_e \le p_i \le p_p$ (critical plastic pressure) a zone in the interval $r_i \le r \le \eta$ is in a state of elastic, plastic deformation, where η is the elastic–plastic junction radius. Finally, for $p_i = p_p$ the *entire* cylinder is in the state of elastic, plastic deformation. If we neglect the contribution of elastic deformation in the latter case, we arrive at the $n \to \infty$ limiting case discussed in Example 12.4.

12.12 CLOSURE

Using the thick-walled hollow cylinder under pressure as examples, we have studied in this chapter the case of plane strain in various types of materials. Introducing the Airy stress function, we set up the stress boundary value problem in rectangular and polar coordinates for *linear elastic* behavior in Part A. We then solved this boundary value problem for the case of axial symmetry and examined in particular the classic problem of the thick-walled cylinder. We also solved for the stress field around an edge dislocation, which is *not* an axially symmetric problem. Note that the Airy stress function for *no body force* satisfies the biharmonic equation $\nabla^4 \Phi = 0$, and this equation does not involve the elastic material constants.

We then turned our attention to the case of *linear viscoelastic* behavior in Part B. Because the definition of Φ is not related to the constitutive law, its defining equation retains the same form as in Part A, and furthermore, for no body force Φ satisfies the same partial differential equation: namely, $\nabla^4 \Phi = 0$. Our main effort was to establish the viscoelastic plane strain constitutive law. This we did by using equivalences between the time operator pairs and the elastic constants. Indeed, we did this two different ways, the first by using the tensile test approach to arrive at a single two-dimensional tensor differential equation. We then proceeded to employ a pair of constitutive relations, where one gives behavior in distortion (e.g., under pure shear) while the other gives behavior in bulk (e.g., under hydrostatic pressure). We then arrived at an equivalent pair of tensor differential equations for viscoelastic plane strain. Again we considered the thick-walled cylinder, using the second approach for a material that is Kelvin in distortion and elastic in bulk. Note that we got the same radial and transverse stresses as in the elastic case, but the axial stress and the displacement were different dependent as they are on the constitutive law.

Finally, in Part C we considered a *nonlinear viscous* incompressible material, and employed the stress power law for this purpose. We developed plane-strain constitutive relations for this case, but for simplicity only examined the axisymmetric boundary value problem in detail using the familiar Airy stress function. The governing equation for Φ is now given in terms of the stress power n of the constitutive law. We noted that $n = 1$ yields the special case of linear viscous behavior, while $n \to \infty$ yields the special case of fully perfectly plastic behavior. We considered once again the thick-walled cylinder for nonlinear viscous behavior. In particular, we noted that for $n = 1$ (linear viscous) we got the same radial and transverse stresses as in the linear viscoelastic case, which were valid for any linear viscoelastic material, including of course the extremes of linear viscous and linear elastic behavior. The radial *velocity* for linear viscous material was also found to be the same as the radial *displacement* for linear *incompressible* elastic material.

We now turn to the final case to be considered in this book, namely, the important case of structural components in a state of plane stress. You will see that many but not all of the results reached in our study of plane strain can be carried over to plane stress.

PROBLEMS

12.1. Invert Eq. (12.13) to get $\varepsilon_{\alpha\beta}$ in terms of $\tau_{\alpha\beta}$, E_1, and ν_1 as given by Eq. (12.11).

12.2. Given the following stress distribution for plane strain in an elastic material:

$$\tau_{xx} = (3x^2 + y) \times 10^3 \text{ psi}$$

$$\tau_{yy} = (10xy + y^2) \times 10^3 \text{ psi}$$

$$\tau_{xy} = -1.2xy \times 10^3 \text{ psi}$$

where x and y are in feet.
(a) What is the strain field for $E = 30 \times 10^6$ psi, $\nu = 0.3$?
(b) Does this stress distribution satisfy compatibility?
(c) What is τ_{zz}?
(d) What must the body force distribution be for equilibrium?
(e) What should be the traction forces on the boundary curve shown in Fig. P12.2?

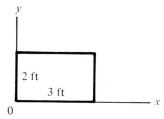

Figure P12.2

12.3. Starting with Eq. (12.41) relating stress to the Airy stress function Φ for conservative body forces, show that as a result of compatibility Φ must satisfy the following partial differential equation for elastic behavior:

$$\nabla^4 \Phi = -\frac{1 - 2\nu}{1 - \nu} \nabla^2 V$$

12.4. Consider a function Φ which is given as the product of two functions f and g,

$$\Phi = fg$$

where g is a harmonic function.
(a) Let $f = x$ and show that $\nabla^4 \Phi = 0$ for this case. That is, the product of x times a harmonic function gives a biharmonic function.
(b) Let

$$f = r^2 = x^2 + y^2$$

Show that

$$\nabla^2 \Phi = 4g + 4\mathbf{r} \cdot \nabla g$$

$$= 4g + 4\left(x \frac{\partial g}{\partial x} + y \frac{\partial g}{\partial y}\right)$$

Now show that $\nabla^4 \Phi = 0$. Thus the product of $r^2 g$, with g a harmonic function, is a biharmonic function.

12.5. Demonstrate that the stresses τ_{rr}, $\tau_{\theta\theta}$, and $\tau_{r\theta}$, when expressed in terms of the Airy stress function according to Eqs. (12.53), will identically satisfy the equations of equilibrium in polar coordinates with no body forces:

$$\frac{\partial \tau_{rr}}{\partial r} + \frac{\tau_{rr} - \tau_{\theta\theta}}{r} + \frac{1}{r}\frac{\partial \tau_{r\theta}}{\partial \theta} = 0$$

$$\frac{\partial \tau_{r\theta}}{\partial r} + \frac{1}{r}\frac{\partial \tau_{\theta\theta}}{\partial \theta} + \frac{2\tau_{r\theta}}{r} = 0$$

12.6. Consider linear elastic plane strain with no body forces. Prove that in polar coordinates the compatibility equation in Φ is given by

$$\nabla^4 \Phi = \left(\frac{\partial^2}{\partial r^2} + \frac{1}{r}\frac{\partial}{\partial r} + \frac{1}{r^2}\frac{\partial^2}{\partial \theta^2}\right)\left(\frac{\partial^2 \Phi}{\partial r^2} + \frac{1}{r}\frac{\partial \Phi}{\partial r} + \frac{1}{r^2}\frac{\partial^2 \Phi}{\partial \theta^2}\right) = 0$$

Do this by obtaining the Laplacian operator in polar coordinates.

12.7. Consider a hollow elastic cylinder of inner radius r_i, with the boundary condition at the cavity

$$\tau_{rr}|_{r=r_i} = -p_i$$

where p_i is a constant. Show that the Cesàro integral condition (12.44a) is identically satisfied by the Airy stress function Φ, for any values of C_1, C_2, and C_3. Refer to Eq. (12.58) and Fig. 12.5.

12.8. Consider a long thick-walled elastic cylinder with an inner radius of 1 ft and an outer radius of $1\frac{1}{4}$ ft. A pressure of 1000 psig is maintained inside the cylinder. If the cylinder is completely constrained at its ends, what is the maximum normal stress? What is the maximum shear stress? Note that $\tau_{zz} \neq 0$. Take $\nu = 0.3$.

12.9. A long elastic cylinder with fixed ends is constructed from two hollow cylinders of the same material. Before assembly, the inner radius of the outside cylinder is 0.005 in. less than the outer radius of the inside cylinder. Assembly is accomplished by applying heat to the outside cylinder so as to produce thermal expansion, and then inserting the inside cylinder. After cooling the final dimensions are as shown in Fig. P12.9. Also, $E = 30 \times 10^6$ psi and $\nu = 0.3$.

(a) What is the contact pressure between the outside and the inside cylinders? What are the stress distributions in both cylinders?

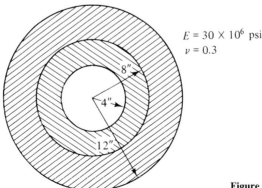

$E = 30 \times 10^6$ psi
$\nu = 0.3$

Figure P12.9

(b) Now let a pressure $p = 30,000$ psi be applied at the inner radius of the inside cylinder. What are the new stress distributions?

12.10. A long, hollow, *thick* elastic cylinder is surrounded by a *thin* elastic band made of different material. The fit is ideal, such that neither a gap nor a prestress exists. An internal pressure p is then applied at the inside radius ($r = a$) of the thick cylinder, as shown in Fig. P12.10. Assuming that the radial displacement is continuous at the interface ($r = b$), prove that the stresses in the thick cylinder are given by

$$\tau_{rr} = -p\,\frac{\beta[1 + (b/r)^2] + (1 - (b/r)^2]}{\beta[1 + (b/a)^2] + [1 - (b/a)^2]}$$

$$\tau_{\theta\theta} = -p\,\frac{\beta[1 - (b/r)^2] + [1 + (b/r)^2]}{\beta[1 + (b/a)^2] + [1 - (b/a)^2]}$$

where

$$\beta = \frac{1 - \nu^2}{(1 + \nu)\nu - (bE)(1 - \nu_b^2)/E_b\,h}$$

Here E, ν are elastic constants for the thick cylinder, and E_b, ν_b are elastic constants for the thin band. In obtaining these stresses, the tangential stress in the thin band is assumed to be uniform, and further simplification is obtained by assuming that $h/b \ll 1$.

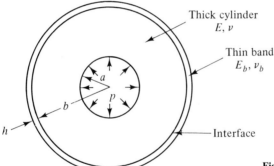

Thick cylinder
E, ν

Thin band
E_b, ν_b

Interface

Figure P12.10

12.11. Using the vector transformation law, verify that for cylindrical coordinates

$$u_1 = u = u_r \cos\theta - u_\theta \sin\theta$$

$$u_2 = v = u_r \sin\theta + u_\theta \cos\theta$$

$$u_3 = w = u_z$$

Also verify that for the components of rotation,

$$\omega_r = \omega_1 \cos\theta + \omega_2 \sin\theta$$

$$\omega_\theta = -\omega_1 \sin\theta + \omega_2 \cos\theta$$

$$\omega_z = \omega_3$$

Then use the chain rule for differentiation to prove that

$$\nabla \cdot \mathbf{u} \equiv \text{div }\mathbf{u} \equiv u_{i,i} = \frac{u_r}{r} + \frac{\partial u_r}{\partial r} + \frac{1}{r}\frac{\partial u_\theta}{\partial \theta} + \frac{\partial u_z}{\partial z}$$

and

$$\omega_r = \frac{1}{2}\left(\frac{1}{r}\frac{\partial u_z}{\partial \theta} - \frac{\partial u_\theta}{\partial z}\right)$$

$$\omega_\theta = \frac{1}{2}\left(\frac{\partial u_r}{\partial z} - \frac{\partial u_z}{\partial r}\right)$$

$$\omega_z = \frac{1}{2r}\left(\frac{\partial(ru_\theta)}{\partial r} - \frac{\partial u_r}{\partial \theta}\right)$$

12.12. The Navier equation for plane strain was given by Eq. (12.27) as

$$(\lambda + \mu)u_{\beta,\beta\alpha} + \mu u_{\alpha,\beta\beta} + B_\alpha = 0$$

(a) Show that this equation may be expressed in terms of the components of rotation as

$$(\lambda + 2\mu)u_{\beta,\beta\alpha} - 2\mu e_{\alpha\beta}\omega_{3,\beta} + B_\alpha = 0$$

(b) Then show that for polar coordinates the plane strain Navier equations become

$$(\lambda + 2\mu)\frac{\partial}{\partial r}\left(\frac{u_r}{r} + \frac{\partial u_r}{\partial r} + \frac{1}{r}\frac{\partial u_\theta}{\partial \theta}\right) - 2\mu\frac{1}{r}\frac{\partial \omega_z}{\partial \theta} + B_r = 0$$

$$(\lambda + 2\mu)\frac{1}{r}\frac{\partial}{\partial \theta}\left(\frac{u_r}{r} + \frac{\partial u_r}{\partial r} + \frac{1}{r}\frac{\partial u_\theta}{\partial \theta}\right) + 2\mu\frac{\partial \omega_z}{\partial r} + B_\theta = 0$$

(*Hint*: Use the results given in Problem 12.11.)

12.13. Use the results given in Problems 12.11 and 12.12 to prove that for axially symmetric polar coordinates the Navier equations simplify to

$$\frac{d}{dr}\left[\frac{1}{r}\frac{d(ru_r)}{dr}\right] = 0$$

Body forces have also been neglected. Solve this equation for u_r, and then obtain τ_{rr} and $\tau_{\theta\theta}$. Then compare your results with Eqs. (12.59) and note that C_1 automatically equals zero via this approach. Explain why we obtained this result here without recourse to the Cesàro integral condition.

12.14. Refer to Section 12.6 on the edge dislocation. Prove that the solutions to ordinary differential equations (12.78),

$$r^2\left[\frac{g(r)}{r}\right]' = -E \qquad \text{(a)}$$

$$f''(\theta) + f(\theta) = E - \frac{2(1-\nu)D}{G}\cos\theta \qquad \text{(b)}$$

are given as

$$g(r) = E + Fr$$

$$f(\theta) = H\cos\theta + I\sin\theta + E - \frac{(1-\nu)D}{G}\theta\sin\theta$$

For (a) use a straightforward integration, and for (b) superpose the complementary solution and a particular solution found by the method of undetermined coefficients.

12.15. For the stress field of an edge dislocation in an elastic medium (see Sec. 12.6), the kinematic boundary conditions were given by Eq. (12.84) as

$$u_\theta = \theta \qquad \text{at } r = r_i \text{ and } \theta = 0^+$$

$$\omega_z = 0 \qquad \text{at } r = r_i \text{ and } \theta = 0^+$$

Show that, with these conditions, the constants F and J in Eq. (12.80) are given by

$$F = \frac{b}{2\pi r_i}$$

$$J = -\frac{b(1-2v)}{4\pi(1-v)}(1 - \ln r_i)$$

Make use of the expression for ω_z given in Problem 12.11.

12.16. **(a)** Show that a polynomial Φ given as

$$\Phi = \frac{C_1}{6} x_1^3 + \frac{C_2}{2} x_1^2 x_2 + \frac{C_3}{2} x_1 x_2^2 + \frac{C_4}{6} x_2^3 + \frac{C_5}{2} x_1^2 + C_6 x_1 x_2 + \frac{C_7}{2} x_2^2$$

is biharmonic for all values of these coefficients. Then show that for an elastic material with an Airy stress function given by this polynomial, all stresses are *linear* in x_1 and x_2.

(b) In Fig. P12.16 is shown a long dam of triangular cross section. Linearly increasing hydrostatic pressure acts along the face OA, face OB is traction-free, and along the base AB normal and shear stresses act in reaction to the weight of the dam and the water pressure. First show that for this particular body force we have $\nabla^2 V = 0$, and thus for a linear elastic dam the stress function Φ is *biharmonic*. If we set $C_5 = C_6 = C_7 = 0$ in part (a), we may use this polynomial as the Airy stress function in solving this prismatic dam problem. Using elastic plane-strain theory, show that the stresses in the dam are given by

$$\tau_{xx} = -\gamma_w y$$

$$\tau_{yy} = \left(\frac{\gamma_d}{\tan \beta} - \frac{2\gamma_w}{\tan^3 \beta}\right)x + \left(\frac{\gamma_w}{\tan^2 \beta} - \gamma_d\right)y$$

$$\tau_{xy} = -\frac{\gamma_w}{\tan^2 \beta} x$$

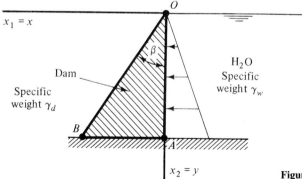

$x_1 = x$

Dam

Specific weight γ_d

β

H_2O
Specific weight γ_w

B

A

$x_2 = y$

Figure P12.16

12.17. The Airy stress function for a semi-infinite body under a knife-edge load (see Fig. P12.17) may be given as

$$\Phi = \frac{Pr}{\pi} \theta \sin \theta$$

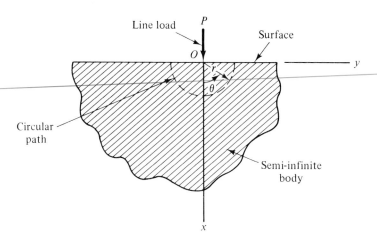

Figure P12.17

The force P is a uniform line load per unit length along the z axis, and extends over the interval $-\infty < z < \infty$.

(a) Show that Φ is biharmonic.

(b) Assuming elastic plane strain, determine the stresses τ_{rr}, $\tau_{\theta\theta}$, and $\tau_{r\theta}$.

(c) Show that the resultant of the traction acting on any circular path about 0 in the interval $-\pi/2 \le \theta \le \pi/2$ (again see Fig. P12.17) is equal to P.

12.18. In Problem 12.3 you were asked to derive

$$\nabla^4 \Phi = -\frac{1-2\nu}{1-\nu}\, \nabla^2 V$$

for the case of elastic behavior with conservative body forces. First prove that for linear viscoelastic behavior the result above generalizes to the differential equation

$$(P^\nu - Q^\nu)\nabla^4 \Phi(x_1, x_2, t) = -(P^\nu - 2Q^\nu)\nabla^2 V(x_1, x_2, t)$$

Rewrite this result in terms of the operator pairs P^K, Q^K and P^G, Q^G. Also, take the Laplace transform of the equation above, and introduce the definition

$$\frac{\bar{P}^\nu(s) - 2\bar{Q}^\nu(s)}{\bar{P}^\nu(s) - \bar{Q}^\nu(s)} = \bar{K}(s)$$

Then use the convolution theorem to express $\nabla^4 \Phi$ as a hereditary integral over the history of $\nabla^2 V$.

12.19. (a) In Sec. 12.3 we gave the Cesàro integral conditions [Eqs. (12.44)] for the case of plane strain in a multiply connected *elastic* medium. It is clear that for zero body force, equation (12.44b) is equally valid for a linear viscoelastic medium, since it then contains no material constants. Prove that for a linear viscoelastic material with zero body force, Eq. (12.44a) generalizes to

$$(P^\nu - Q^\nu)\oint_{C_i} x_\beta \left[\delta_{\alpha\beta} \frac{\partial \nabla^2 \Phi}{\partial s} - e_{\alpha\beta} \frac{\partial \nabla^2 \Phi}{\partial \nu} \right] ds = P^\nu \oint_{C_i} e_{\alpha\beta} G_\beta \, ds$$

Rewrite this result in terms of the P^G, Q^G and P^K, Q^K operator pairs. Note that if the cavities are *traction-free*, the Cesàro condition above is identical for all viscoelastic materials (including elastic).

(b) Viscoelastic constitutive laws (12.111) and (12.112) may be rewritten as

$$Q^{KG} \varepsilon_{\gamma\gamma} = P^{KG} \tau_{\gamma\gamma}$$

$$Q^G e_{\alpha\beta} = P^G s_{\alpha\beta}$$

where we have set

$$Q^{KG} = 2Q^K P^G + P^K Q^G \qquad \text{and} \qquad P^{KG} = 3P^K P^G$$

In Chapter 6 we showed how such differential constitutive laws may also be rewritten as hereditary integrals [e.g., see Eqs. (6.90) and (6.91)]. Using this approach, rewrite the two differential relations above as four hereditary integrals, expressed in terms of creep compliance functions $J^{KG}(t)$ and $J^G(t)$ and relaxation modulus functions $Y^{KG}(t)$ and $Y^G(t)$.

12.20. Obtain viscoelastic Eq. (12.98) from Eqs. (12.111) and (12.112). Do this by using definitions (12.105), and expressing the operator pairs (P^G, Q^G) and (P^K, Q^K) in terms of (P^E, Q^E) and (P^ν, Q^ν).

12.21. In viscoelastic Example 12.2 the stress τ_{zz} was obtained as Eq. (m), by direct integration over time. Obtain this same expression by using the correspondence principle, as discussed in Section 9.5.

12.22. **(a)** In Example 12.2 of Section 12.8, we have obtained the stresses τ_{rr} and $\tau_{\theta\theta}$. Now, using the viscoelastic plane strain constitutive relations for distortional and bulk behaviors [i.e., Eqs. (12.111) and (12.112)], solve for the strains ε_{rr} and $\varepsilon_{\theta\theta}$. Then use Eq. (12.56f) to find the radial displacement u_r. Compare this result with the solution obtained in Example 12.3 by means of the correspondence principle.

(b) In part (a) you obtained an expression for e_{rr} by integrating differential equation (12.112). In Problem 12.18 you were asked to rewrite this differential equation as the hereditary integral

$$e_{\alpha\beta}(t) = \int_{0^-}^{t} J^G(t - t') \frac{\partial s_{\alpha\beta}(t')}{\partial t'} \, dt'$$

Now use this hereditary integral to evaluate e_{rr}, and compare your result with that obtained in part (a).

12.23. For the elastic dislocation problem solved in Section 12.6, a displacement b was applied at the "cut." Now consider a viscoelastic material that exhibits elastic compressibility for bulk and is a Kelvin-type material under distortion, as in Example 12.2. Also assume that the displacement at the cut is suddenly applied (i.e., $b[u(t)]$). Use the correspondence principle to find the stresses $\tau_{rr}, \tau_{\theta\theta}, \tau_{r\theta}$ for this problem.

12.24. Reconsider the problem of the long, hollow, thick cylinder surrounded by a thin band, which we presented in Problem 12.10. But now, let the thick cylinder be linear viscoelastic, whereas the thin band is still elastic with material constants, E_b, ν_b. In particular, let the material of the thick cylinder be incompressible in bulk, and Kelvin in distortion with elastic shear modulus G and shear viscosity coefficient ζ. Assume that the internal pressure is suddenly applied at $t = 0$, and then use the correspondence principle to find τ_{rr} and $\tau_{\theta\theta}$ in the thick cylinder.* In carrying out the Laplace transform inversion, make use of the simple formulas

---

* An interesting application of this problem is to solid-fuel propellant rocketry. The propellant is a hollow cylinder of linear viscoelastic material, subjected to internal pressure due to combustion in the cavity. A thin steel band is placed around the cylinder to prevent rupture of the propellant. For details, see E. H. Lee, J. R. Radok, and W. B. Woodward, "Stress Analysis for Linear Viscoelastic Materials," *Trans. Soc. Rheology*, Vol. 3, pp. 41–59 (1959).

$$\mathbf{L}(e^{-bt}) = \frac{1}{s+b}$$

$$\mathbf{L}(1 - e^{-dt}) = \frac{d}{s(s+d)}$$

12.25. Redo Example 12.2 in Section 12.8 for the following linear viscoelastic materials:
  (a) Incompressible Poisson effect, and Maxwell in tension with tensile elastic modulus E and tensile viscosity coefficient η
  (b) Elastic compressibility with bulk modulus K, and Maxwell in distortion with shear elastic modulus G and shear viscosity coefficient ζ

12.26. Refer to the equations of equilibrium in cylindrical coordinates, presented in Problem 9.1. Show that for axially symmetric plane strain, the second of these equations [Eq. (b)] integrates to $\tau_{r\theta} = 0$. Then refer to the compatibility equations in cylindrical coordinates, presented in Problem 9.6. Again consider axially symmetric plane strain and prove that the third of these equations [Eq. (c)] integrates to yield Eq. (12.135).

12.27. Consider nonlinear viscous plane strain, as formulated in Section 12.9 for rectangular Cartesian coordinates x_1, x_2. First reduce equilibrium equations (12.129) to a trivial identity by introducing the Airy stress function $\Phi(x_1, x_2)$. Then proceed to express the stresses in constitutive equations (12.126) in terms of Φ. Finally, substitute the resulting strain rates into compatibility equation (12.131), and thereby obtain a single stress function compatibility equation. Verify that this equation simplifies to $\nabla^4 \Phi = 0$ for the special case $m = 0$. (*Hint*: Let $J_2^m = F$, and express your result in terms of F and spatial derivatives of F.)

12.28. Equations (12.142) and (12.144), for the stresses τ_{rr}, $\tau_{\theta\theta}$ and the radial velocity $\dot{u}_r$ in the case of axial symmetry, were obtained by employing *steady* nonlinear viscous constitutive law (12.116). Consider now the power time *transient* creep law for constant stress

$$\varepsilon_{ij} = C(J_2)_o^m (s_{ij})_o t^{1/q}$$

In Problem 7.26 you obtained the *time-hardening* generalization of this law for variable stress as

$$\dot{\varepsilon}_{ij} = \frac{C}{q} J_2^m s_{ij} t^{-[(q-1)/q]}$$

which simplifies to Eq. (12.116) in the special case $q = 1$. Using this equation in place of Eq. (12.116), rederive the expressions for τ_{rr}, $\tau_{\theta\theta}$, and $\dot{u}_r$. Note that whereas $\dot{u}_r$ varies with q *and* t, the stresses τ_{rr}, $\tau_{\theta\theta}$, and the stress function Φ are *independent* of q and t.

12.29. A hollow thick cylinder of linear viscoelastic material is encased in a thin band (thickness h) of nonlinear viscous material. Assume that the linear viscoelastic material is Maxwell in tension (tensile modulus E and tensile viscosity η) with incompressible Poisson effect [see Eq. (12.98)]. The nonlinear viscous constitutive law for the band is given by Eq. (12.127b) as

$$\dot{\varepsilon}_{\alpha\beta} = CJ_2^m s_{\alpha\beta}$$

An internal pressure $p(t)$ is applied at the inner radius $(r = a)$ of the thick cylinder, which generates an unknown contact pressure $f(t)$ at the interface $(r = b)$ between the thick viscoelastic cylinder and the thin viscous band.[*] Beginning with Eqs. (d) and (e) of Example 12.2, determine τ_{rr} and $\tau_{\theta\theta}$ in terms of $p(t)$ and $f(t)$. Assuming that the radial displacement is continuous at the interface $(r = b)$, prove that the contact pressure $f(t)$ obeys the nonlinear differential equation

$$\dot{f} + \frac{E}{\eta} f - \alpha f^n = \frac{-a^2 E}{b^2 \eta}\left[p(t) + \frac{\eta}{E}\dot{p}(t)\right]$$

where $n = 2m + 1$ and

$$\alpha = \frac{CE(b^2 - a^2)(b + h)^n}{3(2^{n-1})b^2 h^n}$$

12.30. In Example 12.4 of Section 12.11 we obtained stress distributions for *fully perfectly plastic* behavior by letting $n \to \infty$. Prove that as $n \to \infty$ the transverse stress distribution $\tau_{\theta\theta}$ as given by Eq. (e) goes to Eq. (h). Also show that as $n \to \infty$ the radial velocity as given by Eq. (f) goes to the *indeterminate* result

$$\dot{u}_r = \frac{C r_o^2}{r} \lim_{n \to \infty}\left\{\frac{p_i}{2\ln(r_o/r_i)}\right\}^n$$

Equation (i) for κ^2 was obtained by inserting the limiting values for τ_{rr} and $\tau_{\theta\theta}$ for $n \to \infty$ into Eq. (12.145). Obtain this same result by first forming the difference $\tau_{rr} - \tau_{\theta\theta}$ from Eqs. (d) and (e), and *then* letting $n \to \infty$.

12.31. An axially constrained long thick-walled cylinder is subjected to a uniform internal pressure $p(t)$, which is *monotonically increasing* with time (see Fig. P12.31). The material behavior is linear elastic, perfectly plastic, and the Mises yield criterion, $J_2 = Y^2/3$, determines the onset of plastic behavior. For simplicity we assume that the elastic (as well as the plastic) deformation is *incompressible* (i.e., $\nu = \frac{1}{2}$ and $E = 3G$). For $p(t) \le p_e$ (the critical elastic pressure) the *entire* cylinder is in a state of elastic deformation. Show that for this case we have

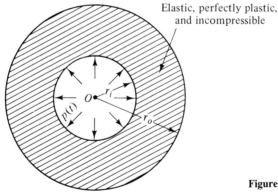

Elastic, perfectly plastic, and incompressible

Figure P12.31

[*] A hollow cylinder of ceramic nuclear fuel (e.g., U_2O) encased in metallic cladding (e.g., stainless steel) is a widely used configuration for a nuclear fuel rod. Pressure is transmitted to the central hole and the rod is subjected to high levels of temperature and neutron flux, thereby generating temperature and irradiation induced creep. The ceramic fuel behaves essentially as a linear viscoelastic material while the metallic cladding is nonlinear viscoelastic. For further information, see S. Huang and F. A. Cozzarelli, "Some Analytical and Numerical Results for Cladded Fuel Rods Subjected to Thermo-Irradiation Induced Creep," *Nuclear Eng. Des.*, Vol. 55, pp. 97–122 (1979).

$$\tau_{rr} = \frac{p(t)\,r_i^2}{r_o^2 - r_i^2}\left(1 - \frac{r_o^2}{r^2}\right) \qquad \tau_{\theta\theta} = \frac{p(t)\,r_i^2}{r_o^2 - r_i^2}\left(1 + \frac{r_o^2}{r^2}\right)$$

$$u_r = \frac{p(t)\,r_i^2\,r_o^2}{2G(r_o^2 - r_i^2)\,r} \qquad p(t) < p_e = \frac{(r_o^2 - r_i^2)Y}{\sqrt{3}\,r_o^2}$$

(*Note*: You may utilize the results obtained in Example 12.1.)

12.32. Consider again the elastic, perfectly plastic cylinder of Problem 12.31, but now let $p_e \le p(t) \le p_p$, where p_p is the critical plastic pressure. For this case a zone in the interval $r_i \le r \le \eta$ is in a state of elastic, plastic deformation, whereas the region $\eta \le r \le r_o$ is in a state of purely elastic deformation. Employing the assumption of *complete* incompressibility (coupled with strain displacement), prove that the radial displacement at *any* value of r is given by $u_r = f(\eta)/r$, where $f(\eta)$ is found to be a function of the elastic–plastic radius. Now consider the elastic zone $\eta \le r \le r_o$; for the stresses in this zone go back to Eqs. (12.59) (with $C_1 = 0$). The constants C_2 and C_3 may be evaluated by setting $\tau_{rr} = 0$ at $r = r_o$ and $J_2 = Y^2/3$ at $r = \eta$. (You *must* choose C_3 negative. Why?) Show that the solutions for τ_{rr}, $\tau_{\theta\theta}$, and u_r in this elastic zone are again given by the results presented in Problem 12.31, but with $p_e(t)r_i^2/(r_o^2 - r_i^2)$ replaced by $Y\eta^2/(\sqrt{3}\,r_o^2)$. The *displacement* solution is now *complete* for *all* r, with the function $f(\eta) = Y\eta^2/(2\sqrt{3}\,G)$. [The *stresses* in the elastic, perfectly plastic zone, $r_i \le r \le \eta$, may be determined from the Mises yield criterion, equilibrium, and continuity of stress at the elastic, plastic boundary. Finally, an equation for η may be obtained by utilizing the final boundary condition, $\tau_{rr} = -p(t)$ at $r = r_i$. For full details you are referred to the literature (e.g., see footnote on p. 561).]

Chapter 13
Plane Stress

13.1 INTRODUCTION

You will recall that in Chapter 12 we defined plane strain as a state of strain in which $\varepsilon_{13} = \varepsilon_{23} = \varepsilon_{33} = 0$ and in which the remaining strains are independent of x_3. We found that these assumptions were rigorously realized in long prismatic bodies of uniform cross section, that are *constrained* at the ends and loaded in a direction *normal* to the x_3 axis by tractions on the lateral surface that *do not* vary with x_3. The associated boundary value problem was strictly two-dimensional, and its analytical solution could be considered to be "exact."

We now define *plane stress* as a stress distribution in which

$$\tau_{13} = \tau_{23} = \tau_{33} = 0 \tag{13.1}$$

but we shall *not*, in general, require that the remaining stresses be independent of x_3. We will prove in this chapter that if a prismatic body with a centerline parallel to x_3 is loaded normal to x_3 but now with its ends *free of traction*, we obtain a plane stress problem in which the nonzero stresses vary with x_3 even if the loads are independent of x_3. This three-dimensionality of plane stress is directly linked to the fact that in contrast with plane strain, conditions (13.1) no longer lead to a single non-trivial compatibility equation.

The above-mentioned dependence on x_3 becomes especially meaningful as the "length" of the "prism" decreases to the point where this length is in fact the "thickness" of a flat "plate." For such a plate we refer to the ends of the prism as "faces," and the lateral surface of the prism is now the "edge" of the plate. The simplest physical problem, for which conditions (13.1) are a good approximation, is the flat plate loaded symmetrically with respect to the midplane of the plate as shown in Fig. 13.1. We have shown in part (a) of this diagram a traction distribution

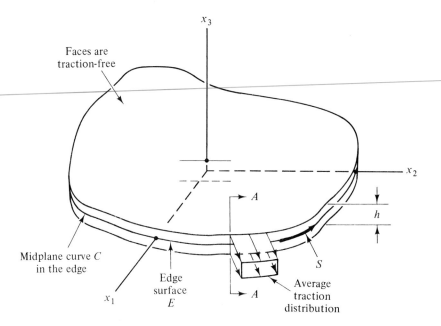

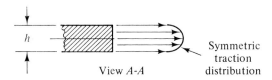

(a) Plate with average traction distribution

(b) Symmetric traction distribution that is the source of the average traction distribution

Figure 13.1 Flat plate with traction distribution symmetric to the midplane of the plate. This is an example of plane stress.

that is an *average* over x_3, and in part (b) the symmetric loading distribution over the thickness h that is the source of this average distribution.* We shall concentrate on this case in this chapter, and for linear elastic material shall obtain general expressions for the nonzero stresses

$$\tau_{\alpha\beta} = \tau_{\alpha\beta}(x_1, x_2, x_3), \qquad \alpha, \beta = 1, 2 \tag{13.2}$$

---

* The average traction distribution is uniformly distributed over x_3 and is evaluated as

$$\overline{T}_i^{(\nu)}(s) = \frac{1}{h} \int_{-h/2}^{h/2} T_i^{(\nu)}(s, x_3)\, dx_3$$

It is similar but not equivalent to the *resultant* force

$$F(s) = \int_{-h/2}^{h/2} T_i^{(\nu)}(s, x_3)\, dx_3$$

which in this case acts *only* along the midplane curve C.

We will find that the *average* of these stresses over x_3, that is,

$$\bar{\tau}_{\alpha\beta} = \bar{\tau}_{\alpha\beta}(x_1, x_2) \tag{13.3}$$

is obtained from a *two-dimensional* formulation which is very similar to the formulation for plane strain. Furthermore, we will show that such an average stress distribution is a good approximation to the actual stress distribution, for the case of *a very thin plate* with traction-free faces and loaded symmetrically with respect to the midplane around the edge.

In Part A of this chapter we present the aforementioned *general x_3*-dependent plane-stress solution for a linear elastic material. Although the primary focus is on the symmetric loading distribution, the general asymmetric loading distribution is considered first. Then in Part B we consider the simplified case of two-dimensional elastic plane stress, which is also mentioned above. Linear viscoelastic behavior is considered first in Part C, which considers inelastic two-dimensional plane stress. Finally, in Part C we also consider plates made of perfectly plastic material, followed by a related analysis of those made of nonlinear viscous material.

PART A
ELASTIC GENERAL PLANE STRESS

13.2 BASIC EQUATIONS

In this section we set forth the basic equations of *general* linear elastic plane stress with the x_3 dependence *included* [i.e., as defined by Eqs. (13.1) and (13.2)]. The geometry under consideration is the flat plate of thickness h, which is traction-free on its faces ($x_3 = \pm h/2$) and subjected to loading around its edge (see Fig. 13.1). In a later section we focus on the symmetric loading case illustrated in view A-A of the figure, but for now the loading is unrestricted. Also, there is no restriction on the magnitude of the thickness h, although in a later section we shall look into the special case of a "thin" plate.

To determine if the tractions on the edge must be restricted in any way, we begin with the *Cauchy formula*

$$T_i^{(\nu)} = \tau_{ij}\,\nu_j \tag{13.4}$$

Because of Eqs. (13.1), we have for plane stress

$$T_1^{(\nu)} = \tau_{11}\,\nu_1 + \tau_{12}\,\nu_2$$

$$T_2^{(\nu)} = \tau_{21}\,\nu_1 + \tau_{22}\,\nu_2 \tag{13.5}$$

$$T_3^{(\nu)} = 0$$

Since $\nu_1 = \nu_2 = 0$ on the upper and lower faces, these equations applied to these *faces* immediately confirm our earlier assertion that the faces are *traction-free*. As for the *edge*, we note that on this surface ν_1 and ν_2 vary only with the curvilinear coordinate s (again see Fig. 13.1), whereas the stresses may vary with x_3 as well as s. Introducing two-dimensional index notation, as was done in Chapter 12, the first two of Eqs. (13.5) therefore become

$$T_\alpha^{(\nu)}(s, x_3) = \tau_{\alpha\beta}(s, x_3)\nu_\beta(s) \qquad \text{on } E \qquad (13.6)$$

where E indicates the edge surface area. This equation with the third of Eqs. (13.5) indicate that although the surface traction on the edge must be directed *perpendicular* to the x_3 axis (i.e., its x_3 component must vanish), it *may* vary with the x_3 coordinate.

If the traction is *symmetric* with respect to the midplane of the plate, it is sometimes useful to examine *average values* over the x_3 coordinate. Computing such averages in the usual way, Eq. (13.6) then yields

$$\overline{T}_\alpha^{(\nu)}(s) = \overline{\tau}_{\alpha\beta}(s)\nu_\beta(s) \qquad \text{on } C \qquad (13.7)$$

where the overbar indicates average value, and C is the midplane curve of the edge (see Fig. 13.1). We shall have more to say about this later.

We now write *Newton's law* for the state of plane stress in the case of equilibrium:

$$\frac{\partial \tau_{11}}{\partial x_1} + \frac{\partial \tau_{12}}{\partial x_2} + B_1 = 0$$

$$\frac{\partial \tau_{21}}{\partial x_1} + \frac{\partial \tau_{22}}{\partial x_2} + B_2 = 0 \qquad (13.8)$$

$$B_3 = 0$$

We see that the third equilibrium condition requires that the body force be directed *normal* to x_3. The first two equilibrium conditions are written compactly as

$$\tau_{\alpha\beta,\beta} + B_\alpha = 0 \qquad (13.9)$$

Clearly, the equations of equilibrium for plane stress are the same as for plane strain [see Eq. (12.16)], except that here $\tau_{\alpha\beta}$ and B_α may depend on x_3 as well as x_1, x_2. In the special case where the body force is independent of x_3 and derivable from a potential, we can write

$$B_\alpha(x_1, x_2) = -\frac{\partial V(x_1, x_2)}{\partial x_\alpha} \qquad (13.10)$$

Equation (13.9) then becomes

$$\tau_{\alpha\beta,\beta} - V_{,\alpha} = 0 \qquad (13.11)$$

Isotropic Hooke's law has been given by Eqs. (9.8). By setting $\tau_{13} = \tau_{23} = \tau_{33} = 0$, in accordance with Eq. (13.1), we obtain

$$\varepsilon_{11} = \frac{1}{E}(\tau_{11} - \nu\tau_{22}) \qquad \text{(a)}$$

$$\varepsilon_{22} = \frac{1}{E}(\tau_{22} - \nu\tau_{11}) \qquad \text{(b)}$$

$$\varepsilon_{33} = -\frac{\nu}{E}(\tau_{11} + \tau_{22}) \qquad \text{(c)} \qquad\qquad (13.12)$$

$$\varepsilon_{12} = \frac{1+\nu}{E}\,\tau_{12} \qquad\qquad \text{(d)}$$

$$\varepsilon_{23} = 0 \qquad\qquad \text{(e)}$$

$$\varepsilon_{13} = 0 \qquad\qquad \text{(f)}$$

Note that $\varepsilon_{23} = \varepsilon_{13} = 0$ whereas ε_{33} is in general a nonzero function of x_1, x_2, x_3, which is computed from τ_{11} and τ_{22} via Eq. (13.12c),

$$\varepsilon_{33}(x_1, x_2, x_3) = -\frac{\nu}{E}\left[\tau_{11}(x_1, x_2, x_3) + \tau_{22}(x_1, x_2, x_3)\right] \qquad (13.13)$$

In two-dimensional index notation, we may give Eqs. (13.12a, b, d) as follows:

$$\varepsilon_{\alpha\beta} = \frac{1+\nu}{E}\,\tau_{\alpha\beta} - \frac{\nu}{E}\,\tau_{\gamma\gamma}\,\delta_{\alpha\beta} \qquad\qquad (13.14)$$

Note that Eq. (13.14) is very similar to the corresponding relation obtained for plane strain [see Eq. (12.11)], but it does differ in two important respects. First, we see that for plane strain we use the *modified* elastic constants ν_1 and E_1, whereas for plane stress we use ν and E. Second, in plane strain $\varepsilon_{\alpha\beta}$ and $\tau_{\alpha\beta}$ are functions of x_1, x_2, whereas in plane stress they may also depend on x_3. In Problem 13.1 you are asked to express the inverted form of Eq. (13.14) in terms of modified Lamé constants λ_1 and μ_1.

Setting $\varepsilon_{23} = \varepsilon_{13} = 0$ in *strain-displacement equations* (9.4), we obtain for plane stress

$$\varepsilon_{\alpha\beta} = \tfrac{1}{2}(u_{\alpha,\beta} + u_{\beta,\alpha}) \qquad\qquad (13.15)$$

and also

$$0 = u_{2,3} + u_{3,2} \qquad \text{(a)}$$

$$0 = u_{1,3} + u_{3,1} \qquad \text{(b)} \qquad\qquad (13.16)$$

$$\varepsilon_{33} = u_{3,3} \qquad\qquad \text{(c)}$$

As a *necessary* condition for the *compatibility* of strain for plane stress, we now go back to Eqs. (9.6) and set $\varepsilon_{23} = \varepsilon_{13} = 0$. Equation (9.6a) can then be written in the following form, identical to Eq. (12.24) for plane strain:

$$e_{\alpha\gamma}e_{\beta\delta}\,\varepsilon_{\alpha\beta,\gamma\delta} = 0 \qquad\qquad (13.17)$$

In addition, Eqs. (9.6b–f) require that

$$\varepsilon_{22,33} + \varepsilon_{33,22} = 0 \qquad \text{(a)}$$

$$\varepsilon_{33,11} + \varepsilon_{11,33} = 0 \qquad \text{(b)}$$

$$\varepsilon_{11,23} - \varepsilon_{12,13} = 0 \qquad \text{(c)} \qquad\qquad (13.18)$$

$$\varepsilon_{22,31} - \varepsilon_{12,23} = 0 \qquad \text{(d)}$$

$$\varepsilon_{33,12} = \varepsilon_{12,33} = 0 \qquad \text{(e)}$$

Consider for the moment the special case in which all of the stresses $\tau_{\alpha\beta}$ are *independent* of x_3. Equations (13.13) and (13.14) immediately tell us that all of the strains (ε_{33} *and* $\varepsilon_{\alpha\beta}$) are also independent of x_3. For this special case, Eq. (13.17) is unchanged, whereas Eqs. (13.18) simplify considerably to

$$\varepsilon_{33,22} = 0$$

$$\varepsilon_{33,11} = 0 \qquad\qquad (13.19)$$

$$\varepsilon_{33,12} = 0$$

These equations are easily integrated to yield the linear relation

$$\varepsilon_{33} = C_1 x_1 + C_2 x_2 + C_3 \qquad\qquad (13.20)$$

where C_1, C_2, C_3 are constants of integration.*

For *multiply connected* regions, we have additional requirements for compatibility (see Appendix I). These are the *Cesàro* line integral conditions around the N cavities of the body, causing the multiplicity of connectivity. At the present time we shall state these equations in generality. After we have introduced a stress function Φ in a later section, we shall present these integral conditions formulated in terms of Φ for the case of two-dimensional plane stress. Thus the $6N$ Cesàro line integral conditions as given by Eqs. (I.22) are

$$\oint_{\Gamma_\alpha} (\varepsilon_{ik} - x_j e_{rij} e_{rpq} \varepsilon_{pk,q})\, dx_k = 0, \qquad \alpha = 1, \ldots, N$$

$$\qquad\qquad (13.21)$$

$$\oint_{\Gamma_\alpha} e_{tpq} \varepsilon_{pk,q}\, dx_k = 0, \qquad \alpha = 1, \ldots, N$$

where x_j are position vectors to points along the individual paths Γ_α around the cavities. In Fig. 13.2 we have shown a plate with N holes, illustrating such a position vector to the path Γ_N. Note that because of the general x_3 dependence of the strains, the x_j vectors are in general position vectors in three dimensions. However, when using *average* strains we may confine x_j to the plate midplane, and then these vectors are two-dimensional position vectors.

We have in this section presented the basic governing equations of general x_3-dependent plane stress. As in the case of plane strain, we can make good use of an Airy stress function Φ, and we shall do so in the next section.

13.3 AIRY STRESS FUNCTION FOR GENERAL PLANE STRESS

Development of Stress Function Φ

We again can use the *Airy stress function* Φ defined exactly as in Section 12.3 on plane strain, by virtue of the fact that the equations of equilibrium are identical for both cases [see Eq. (13.9)]. Hence for *zero body forces* we once again have

---

*By averaging compatibility equation (13.17) over x_3, we obtain this same equation with $\varepsilon_{\alpha\beta}$ replaced by $\bar{\varepsilon}_{\alpha\beta}$. However, in averaging compatibility Eqs. (13.18) we do *not* obtain Eqs. (13.19) with ε_{33} replaced by $\bar{\varepsilon}_{33}$. Thus, although $\bar{\varepsilon}_{33}$ is clearly independent of x_3, it is *not* in general a linear function of x_1 and x_2.

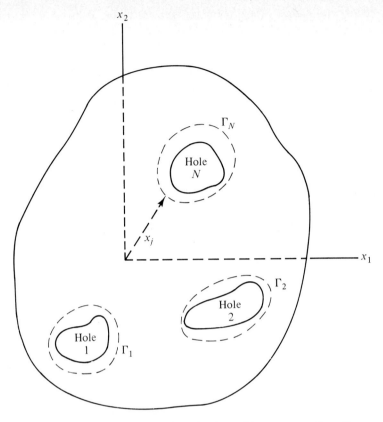

Figure 13.2 Multiply connected plate showing arbitrary curves Γ_α with one around each hole. Position vector x_j is in general three-dimensional.

$$\tau_{11} = \frac{\partial^2 \Phi}{\partial x_2^2}, \qquad \tau_{22} = \frac{\partial^2 \Phi}{\partial x_1^2}, \qquad \tau_{12} = -\frac{\partial^2 \Phi}{\partial x_1 \, \partial x_2} \qquad (13.22)$$

but where now Φ is a function of x_1, x_2, *and* x_3. In two-dimensional index notation we have for the above

$$\tau_{\alpha\beta} = \Phi_{,\gamma\gamma} \delta_{\alpha\beta} - \Phi_{\alpha\beta} = e_{\alpha\gamma} e_{\beta\delta} \Phi_{,\gamma\delta} \qquad (13.23)$$

With this definition equilibrium is identically satisfied in the case of zero body forces. We now proceed to develop the boundary value problem for general x_3-dependent plane stress in terms of Φ for simply connected domains with body forces absent.[*]

In the preceding section we have seen that all six compatibility equations must be satisfied when considering x_3-dependent plane stress. Rather than using the usual strain compatibility equations, it is more convenient for plane stress to employ the

---

[*] For a fundamental paper on plane stress with body forces included, see L.N.G. Filon, "Plane Stress and Generalized Plane Stress," *Quart. J. Math.*, Oxford Series, pp. 289ff. (1930).

Beltrami–Michell stress compatibility equations derived in Section 9.4 [see Eq. (9.48)]. For $B_i = 0$ these equations become

$$(1 + \nu)\tau_{ij,kk} + \Theta_{,ij} = 0 \tag{13.24}$$

where $\Theta = \tau_{kk}$, the first invariant of stress. You are reminded that we have also proven that for $B_i = 0$, the invariant Θ is *harmonic* [see Eq. (9.44)],* that is,

$$\nabla^2 \Theta \equiv \Theta_{,kk} = 0 \tag{13.25}$$

For the case of plane stress we have $\tau_{13} = \tau_{23} = \tau_{33} = 0$. Consequently, in unabridged form we obtain from Eq. (13.24):

$$(1 + \nu)\nabla^2 \tau_{11} + \frac{\partial^2 \Theta}{\partial x_1^2} = 0 \qquad \text{(a)}$$

$$(1 + \nu)\nabla^2 \tau_{22} + \frac{\partial^2 \Theta}{\partial x_2^2} = 0 \qquad \text{(b)}$$

$$\frac{\partial^2 \Theta}{\partial x_3^2} = 0 \qquad \text{(c)}$$

$$(1 + \nu)\nabla^2 \tau_{12} + \frac{\partial^2 \Theta}{\partial x_1 \partial x_2} = 0 \qquad \text{(d)} \tag{13.26}$$

$$\frac{\partial^2 \Theta}{\partial x_2 \partial x_3} = 0 \qquad \text{(e)}$$

$$\frac{\partial^2 \Theta}{\partial x_3 \partial x_1} = 0 \qquad \text{(f)}$$

First considering Eqs. (13.26c, e, f) we can conclude that

$$\frac{\partial \Theta}{\partial x_3} = \alpha$$

where α is a constant. Integrating this result, we then get

$$\boxed{\Theta = \alpha x_3 + f(x_1, x_2)} \tag{13.27}$$

where f is a function of x_1, x_2. Operating on Eq. (13.27) with the Laplacian operator and noting Eq. (13.25), we see that

$$\nabla^2 f(x_1, x_2) = 0 \tag{13.28}$$

Thus f is also harmonic. Returning to the remaining equations of Eqs. (13.26) and introducing the stress function Φ as defined in Eqs. (13.22), we get

$$(1 + \nu)\nabla^2 \left(\frac{\partial^2 \Phi}{\partial x_2^2} \right) + \frac{\partial^2 \Theta}{\partial x_1^2} = 0$$

$$(1 + \nu)\nabla^2 \left(\frac{\partial^2 \Phi}{\partial x_1^2} \right) + \frac{\partial^2 \Theta}{\partial x_2^2} = 0$$

$$(1 + \nu)\nabla^2 \left(\frac{\partial^2 \Phi}{\partial x_1 \partial x_2} \right) - \frac{\partial^2 \Theta}{\partial x_1 \partial x_2} = 0$$

*You may easily verify this again by contracting the indices i and j in Eq. (13.24).

Since $\nabla^2 \Theta = 0$, we can replace $\partial^2 \Theta / \partial x_1^2$ by $-\partial^2 \Theta / \partial x_2^2$ and $\partial^2 \Theta / \partial x_2^2$ by $-\partial^2 \Theta / \partial x_1^2$ in the preceding equations to arrive at

$$\frac{\partial^2}{\partial x_2^2}\left[\nabla^2 \Phi - \frac{1}{1+\nu}\Theta\right] = 0$$

$$\frac{\partial^2}{\partial x_1^2}\left[\nabla^2 \Phi - \frac{1}{1+\nu}\Theta\right] = 0$$

$$\frac{\partial^2}{\partial x_1 \partial x_2}\left[\nabla^2 \Phi - \frac{1}{1+\nu}\Theta\right] = 0$$

A careful inspection of these equations reveals that the quantity in brackets must be a linear function of x_1 and x_2, with coefficients that may be functions of x_3. Accordingly, we can say that

$$\left[\nabla^2 \Phi - \frac{1}{1+\nu}\Theta\right] = g_1''(x_3)x_1 + g_2''(x_3)x_2 + g_3''(x_3) \tag{13.29}$$

where for later convenience we have set the three coefficients equal to the second x_3 derivatives of functions of x_3.

We will at this time introduce the *two-dimensional* Laplacian operator, ∇_1^2, defined as

$$\nabla_1^2 = \frac{\partial^2}{\partial x_1^2} + \frac{\partial^2}{\partial x_2^2}$$

so that

$$\nabla^2 \Phi(x_1, x_2, x_3) = \nabla_1^2 \Phi(x_1, x_2, x_3) + \frac{\partial^2 \Phi(x_1, x_2, x_3)}{\partial x_3^2} \tag{13.30}$$

For plane stress we have $\tau_{33} = 0$, so

$$\nabla_1^2 \Phi = \frac{\partial^2 \Phi}{\partial x_1^2} + \frac{\partial^2 \Phi}{\partial x_2^2} = \tau_{22} + \tau_{11} = \Theta \tag{13.31}$$

Returning to Eq. (13.29) and using Eq. (13.30) with Eq. (13.31) to replace $\nabla^2 \Phi$, we obtain after combining terms:

$$\frac{\partial^2 \Phi}{\partial x_3^2} + \frac{\nu}{1+\nu}\Theta = g_1''(x_3)x_1 + g_2''(x_3)x_2 + g_3''(x_3) \tag{13.32}$$

Replacing Θ using Eq. (13.27), we have for the equation above,

$$\frac{\partial^2 \Phi}{\partial x_3^2} = g_1''(x_3)x_1 + g_2''(x_3)x_2 + g_4''(x_3) - \frac{\nu}{1+\nu}f(x_1, x_2) \tag{13.33}$$

where

$$g_4''(x_3) = g_3''(x_3) - \frac{\nu}{1+\nu}\alpha x_3$$

Integrating Eq. (13.33) twice with respect to x_3, we get

$$\Phi(x_1, x_2, x_3) = g_1(x_3)x_1 + g_2(x_3)x_2 + g_4(x_3) - \frac{\nu}{1+\nu}f(x_1, x_2)\frac{x_3^2}{2}$$

$$+ \Phi_1(x_1, x_2)x_3 + \Phi_2(x_1, x_2) \tag{13.34}$$

where Φ_1 and Φ_2 are functions of integration. Now, since the first three terms on the right side of Eq. (13.34) do not affect the computation of the stresses τ_{11}, τ_{22}, and τ_{12}, we will drop these terms. We thus finally have

$$\Phi(x_1, x_2, x_3) = \Phi_2(x_1, x_2) + x_3\,\Phi_1(x_1, x_2) - \frac{\nu}{2(1+\nu)}\,x_3^2 f(x_1, x_2) \qquad (13.35)$$

It will be very useful to express Eq. (13.35) in terms of the *average* value of Φ over x_3:

$$\overline{\Phi}(x_1, x_2) = \frac{1}{h}\int_{-h/2}^{h/2} \Phi(x_1, x_2, x_3)\, dx_3 \qquad (13.36)$$

Computing this average value from Eq. (13.35), we get

$$\overline{\Phi}(x_1, x_2) = \Phi_2(x_1, x_2) - \frac{\nu}{2(1+\nu)}\,\frac{(h/2)^2}{3}f(x_1, x_2)$$

Now use this equation to substitute for Φ_2 in Eq. (13.35), and thereby obtain the final form

$$\boxed{\Phi(x_1, x_2, x_3) = \overline{\Phi}(x_1, x_2) + x_3\,\Phi_1(x_1, x_2) - \frac{\nu}{2(1+\nu)}\,f(x_1, x_2)\left[x_3^2 - \frac{h^2}{12}\right]}$$

$$(13.37)$$

The first term on the right side of this equation is the aforementioned average value of the Airy stress function. It will be useful to also assign a physical interpretation to the function Φ_1 in the second term. To this end we multiply Eq. (13.37) by x_3 and integrate over x_3 from $-h/2$ to $h/2$. We get

$$\int_{-h/2}^{h/2} x_3\,\Phi(x_1, x_2, x_3)\, dx_3 = \int_{-h/2}^{h/2} x_3^2\,\Phi_1(x_1, x_2)\, dx_3 = \frac{2(h/2)^3}{3}\,\Phi_1(x_1, x_2)$$

and hence

$$\Phi_1(x_1, x_2) = \frac{12}{h^3}\int_{-h/2}^{h/2} x_3\Phi(x_1, x_2, x_3)\, dx_3 \qquad (13.38)$$

which is the *first-order moment* of Φ over x_3, normalized with respect to the average value of x_3^2. We will be able to use Eqs. (13.36) and (13.38) later in our discourse, when we relate solution (13.37) to certain physical problems.

Differential Equations for $\overline{\Phi}$ and Φ_1

Our next step is to obtain explicit differential equations for $\overline{\Phi}$ and Φ_1. Going back to Eq. (13.37) and operating on this equation with the two-dimensional Laplacian operator ∇_1^2, we get

$$\nabla_1^2\,\Phi(x_1, x_2, x_3) = \nabla_1^2\overline{\Phi}(x_1, x_2) + x_3\nabla_1^2\,\Phi_1(x_1, x_2) - \frac{\nu}{2(1+\nu)}\,[\nabla_1^2 f(x_1, x_2)]\left[x_3^2 - \frac{h^2}{12}\right]$$

Recalling that f is a harmonic function [see Eq. (13.28)], and noting that $\nabla_1^2 \Phi = \Theta = \alpha x_3 + f(x_1, x_2)$ via Eqs. (13.31) and (13.27), we have from the above,

$$\alpha x_3 + f(x_1, x_2) = \nabla_1^2 \overline{\Phi}(x_1, x_2) + x_3 \nabla_1^2 \Phi_1(x_1, x_2) \tag{13.39}$$

Since f, $\overline{\Phi}$, and Φ_1 are independent of x_3, we may set $x_3 = 0$ in Eq. (13.39) and thereby obtain the fundamental result

$$\boxed{\nabla_1^2 \overline{\Phi}(x_1, x_2) = f(x_1, x_2)} \tag{13.40}$$

Subtracting Eq. (13.40) from Eq. (13.39), we also obtain

$$\boxed{\nabla_1^2 \Phi_1(x_1, x_2) = \alpha} \tag{13.41}$$

Finally, operating on Eq. (13.40) with the ∇_1^2 operator, we see that since $\nabla_1^2 f = 0$,

$$\boxed{\nabla_1^4 \overline{\Phi}(x_1, x_2) = 0} \tag{13.42}$$

Thus, in the case of general x_3-dependent plane stress the *average value* of the stress function is *biharmonic*, whereas in plane strain you will recall that the stress function itself was biharmonic.

A procedure for solving general x_3-dependent plane stress problems is now outlined. We first determine $\overline{\Phi}$ and Φ_1 by obtaining solutions to differential equations (13.42) and (13.41). Knowing $\overline{\Phi}$ then permits us to determine $f(x_1, x_2)$ by direct substitution into Eq. (13.40). Finally, the stress function $\Phi(x_1, x_2, x_3)$ is found by substituting $\overline{\Phi}$, Φ_1, and f into Eq. (13.37). Stresses follow from Eqs. (13.22). These stresses will in general be expressed in terms of the constant α introduced in Eq. (13.27) and appearing on the right side of differential equation (13.41). Also, these stresses will be expressed in terms of the constants of integration encountered in solving differential equations (13.41) and (13.42). All of these constants are to be determined from the boundary conditions. Assuming that the boundary conditions of a given problem have been completely satisfied, we now have an "exact" x_3-dependent solution to this general plane-stress problem. We shall have more to say about the boundary conditions in the next section.

13.4 PLANE-STRESS PROBLEMS; CASE OF SYMMETRIC LOADING

We now have all the formulations in place for solving plane-stress problems of simple connectivity and with *zero body force*. It will be convenient first to split the stress function Φ into odd and even functions, which we will denote, respectively, as Φ_a(a for "antisymmetric") and Φ_s(s for "symmetric"). This symmetry and antisymmetry is with respect to the $x_1 x_2$ midplane where $x_3 = 0$. Thus for antisymmetry we have

$$\Phi_a(x_1, x_2, x_3) = -\Phi_a(x_1, x_2, -x_3)$$

and for symmetry,

$$\Phi_s(x_1, x_2, x_3) = \Phi_s(x_1, x_2, -x_3)$$

This can be accomplished in general by defining Φ_a and Φ_s in the following manner:

$$\Psi_a = \tfrac{1}{2}[\Phi(x_1, x_2, x_3) - \Phi(x_1, x_2, -x_3)] \qquad \text{(a)}$$
$$\Phi_s = \tfrac{1}{2}[\Phi(x_1, x_2, x_3) + \Phi(x_1, x_2, -x_3)] \qquad \text{(b)}$$

$$(13.43)$$

The function Φ can then readily be seen by inspection to be the sum of Φ_a and Φ_s,

$$\Phi = \Phi_s + \Phi_a \qquad (13.44)$$

Now let us go back to Eq. (13.37) to examine Φ with the concept of antisymmetry and symmetry in mind. We see that Φ is a second-order polynomial in x_3 with coefficients that depend on x_1, x_2. It is easy to identify by inspection the even and odd functions with respect to x_3 that we seek. Thus

$$\Phi_a(x_1, x_2, x_3) = x_3 \, \Phi_1(x_1, x_2) \qquad \text{(a)}$$
$$\Phi_s(x_1, x_2, x_3) = \overline{\Phi}(x_1, x_2) - \frac{\nu}{2(1+\nu)} f(x_1, x_2)\left[x_3^2 - \frac{h^2}{12} \right] \qquad \text{(b)}$$

$$(13.45)$$

Two special cases for Φ are immediately apparent, the antisymmetric case and the symmetric case. In the *antisymmetric* case we have $\Phi_s = 0$ such that $\Phi = \Phi_a$. It follows from Eq. (13.45b) that in this case we must require that $\overline{\Phi} = f = 0$. Similarly, in the *symmetric* case we set $\Phi_a = 0$ and $\Phi = \Phi_s$. Equation (13.45a) then gives $\Phi_1 = 0$, which also requires that $\alpha = 0$ [see Eq. (13.41)].

We shall not consider the antisymmetric case any further in this book, but in Problem 13.4 you will be asked to demonstrate how this case may be used in the study of *pure bending* of flat plates. From this point on in this chapter we shall only be concerned with the *symmetric plane stress* case, and you are reminded that as yet we have introduced *no restrictions* on the magnitude of the plate thickness h.

We shall accordingly focus our attention now on the symmetric case, where as noted above,

$$\Phi(x_1, x_2, x_3) = \overline{\Phi}(x_1, x_2) - \frac{\nu}{2(1+\nu)}\left[x_3^2 - \frac{h^2}{12} \right] f(x_1, x_2) \qquad (13.46)$$

In the preceding section we showed that $\overline{\Phi}$ is the average value of Φ, which is obtained by solving the biharmonic differential equation

$$\nabla^4 \overline{\Phi}(x_1, x_2) = 0 \qquad (13.47)$$

and f is obtained by substituting this solution for $\overline{\Phi}$ into*

$$\nabla^2 \overline{\Phi}(x_1, x_2) = f(x_1, x_2) \qquad (13.48)$$

What are the proper *traction boundary* conditions for this boundary value problem? In Section 13.2 we showed that the x_3 component of the traction vector

---

* Note that we have replaced ∇_1^4 and ∇_1^2 by ∇^4 and ∇^2 in Eqs. (13.47) and (13.48), respectively. This is permissible since $\overline{\Phi}$ is independent of x_3.

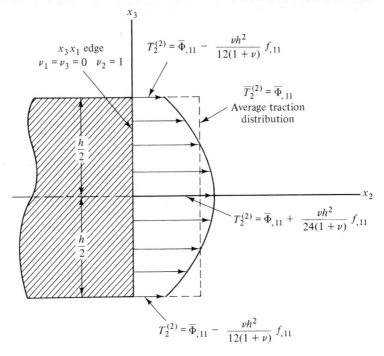

Figure 13.3 Parabolic traction distribution on edge of plate for exact solution. The thickness h is arbitrary.

on the edge of the plate must vanish, whereas the other two components are prescribed in accordance with [see Eq. (13.6)]

$$T_\alpha^{(\nu)}(s, x_3) = \tau_{\alpha\beta}(s, x_3)\nu_\beta(s) \qquad \text{on } E \qquad (13.49)$$

where E designates the edge of the plate. Now substitute Eq. (13.46) for Φ into Eq. (13.23) to obtain $\tau_{\alpha\beta}$, and then substitute this result into Eq. (13.49). Accordingly, we obtain for the traction vector

$$T_\alpha^{(\nu)}(s, x_3) = e_{\alpha\gamma}e_{\beta\delta}\left[\overline{\Phi}_{,\gamma\delta}(s) - \frac{\nu}{2(1+\nu)}\left(x_3^2 - \frac{h^2}{12}\right)f_{,\gamma\delta}(s)\right]\nu_\beta(s) \qquad \text{on } E \qquad (13.50)$$

Thus for solution (13.46) to be an *exact* solution, the components of the traction vector on E must vary *parabolically* with x_3, as prescribed by Eq. (13.50).* This distribution has been illustrated in Fig. 13.3 for an $x_3 x_1$ edge, and the values of $T_2^{(2)}$ at $x_3 = 0$ and at $x_3 = \pm h/2$ have been indicated. The *average* value of the traction follows directly from Eq. (13.50) as

$$\overline{T}_\alpha^{(\nu)}(s) = e_{\alpha\gamma}e_{\beta\delta}\overline{\Phi}_{,\gamma\delta}(s)\nu_\beta(s) \qquad (13.51)$$

and the value $\overline{T}_2^{(2)}$ has also been shown in Fig. 13.3.

---

* In the special case, $f_{,\gamma\delta} \equiv 0$, the components of $T_\alpha^{(\nu)}$ will be *uniformly* distributed over x_3. This case occurs if f is a constant or a linear function of x_1 and x_2.

We have thus found an exact x_3-dependent plane stress solution for the parabolic traction distribution (13.50), and this solution is valid for *any* plate thickness h. However, it is extremely unlikely that we will actually encounter in practice a traction vector with precisely this parabolic distribution over x_3. Accordingly, let us for the moment consider the case of a traction vector which is *uniformly distributed* over x_3 but with an arbitrary distribution over s. Such a uniform distribution is to be chosen to be the *statical equivalent* of the parabolic distribution shown in Fig. 13.3. This can be achieved since the mean (i.e., the zeroth-order moment) of the parabolic distribution is equivalent to a uniform distribution and the first-order moments are zero in both cases. If the thickness h is *small* compared to overall plate dimensions in the x_1x_2 plane, such that we now have a *thin plate*, we may invoke Saint-Venant's principle (see Section 9.9) and conclude that x_3-dependent solution (13.46) is a good approximation for uniform traction, except in a thin rim near the edge. Finally, we may carry our conclusion one step further and say that Eq. (13.46) is approximately valid in the sense of Saint-Venant for a *thin* plate subjected to *any symmetric* traction distribution on its edge, since again such a distribution is the statical equivalent of some parabolic distribution of the form (13.50). Note that in invoking Saint-Venant's principle we are saying that biharmonic differential equation (13.47) may be solved for $\overline{\Phi}$, using the *average traction* on the edge.

At this point we will reiterate the restrictions inherent in x_3-dependent solution (13.46), when Saint-Venant's principle is invoked:

1. Body forces are absent.
2. Tractions are applied only along the edge in a direction normal to x_3, and these tractions are symmetrically distributed with respect to the midplane. The average stress function $\overline{\Phi}$ is determined by using the average traction.
3. The plate is thin and x_3-dependent solution (13.46) for Φ is approximately valid, where this is a good approximation except in a thin rim near the edge.
4. The domain is simply connected, since we have not utilized the Cesàro integral conditions.

In the next part we simplify the development further to strictly *two-dimensional plane stress*.

PART B
ELASTIC TWO-DIMENSIONAL PLANE STRESS

13.5 TWO-DIMENSIONAL PLANE STRESS BOUNDARY VALUE PROBLEM

Case A: No Body Force; Simply Connected Domains

We shall consider here the case of zero body force using the results of the preceding section, which you will recall was limited to no body force and simply connected domains. Since that development is for practical purposes also limited to thin plates, an additional simplification suggests itself. Specifically, for a *very thin* plate the expression $x_3^2 - h^2/12$ in Eq. (13.46) is *very small*, and accordingly it is usually justified to completely drop the second expression on the right side of this equation. This then means that the stress function is approximated by

$$\Phi = \overline{\Phi}(x_1, x_2) \tag{13.52}$$

which is the average value over the thickness and thus *independent of* x_3. It is thus no longer necessary to compute the function $f(x_1, x_2)$. Replacing $\overline{\Phi}$ by Φ in Eqs. (13.47) and (13.51), we now have the following boundary value problem:

$$\boxed{\nabla^4 \Phi(x_1, x_2) = 0 \qquad \text{in } R} \tag{a}$$

$$\tag{13.53}$$

$$\boxed{\overline{T}_\alpha^{(\nu)}(s) = e_{\alpha\gamma} e_{\beta\delta} \Phi_{,\gamma\delta}(s) \nu_\beta(s) \qquad \text{on } C} \tag{b}$$

where R is the region covered by the midplane, and C is the boundary of the midplane at the edge of the plate. Note that $\overline{T}_\alpha^{(\nu)}(s)$ is the *average traction* over x_3, and thus formulation (13.53) is strictly two-dimensional. We shall henceforth refer to the formulation above as the *two-dimensional plane stress* boundary value problem.

The stresses $\tau_{11}, \tau_{22}, \tau_{12}$ now follow directly from Eq. (13.23),

$$\tau_{\alpha\beta}(x_1, x_2) = e_{\alpha\gamma} e_{\beta\delta} \Phi_{,\gamma\delta}(x_1, x_2) \tag{13.54}$$

Since in the above the stress function Φ has been approximated by its average value over x_3, it follows from Eq. (13.54) that the stresses $\tau_{\alpha\beta}$ have also been approximated by their average values. Because the plate is very thin, this approximation is intuitively reasonable, especially if the symmetrically distributed traction distribution varies only slightly with x_3. The strains $\varepsilon_{\alpha\beta}$ and ε_{33} follow next from Eqs. (13.14) and (13.12c) as

$$\varepsilon_{\alpha\beta}(x_1, x_2) = \frac{1+\nu}{E} \tau_{\alpha\beta}(x_1, x_2) - \frac{\nu}{E} \tau_{\gamma\gamma}(x_1, x_2)\delta_{\alpha\beta} \tag{a}$$

$$\tag{13.55}$$

$$\varepsilon_{33}(x_1, x_2) = -\frac{\nu}{E} \left[\tau_{11}(x_1, x_2) + \tau_{22}(x_1, x_2)\right] \tag{b}$$

where again these are all approximating average values over x_3.* Finally, the corresponding displacements $u_i(x_1, x_2, x_3)$, which depend on x_3, may be obtained from the strains $\varepsilon_{ij}(x_1, x_2)$ by integrating the *full set* of strain-displacement relations [i.e., Eqs. (13.15) *and* (13.16)]. However, it is simpler and usually sufficient to consider only the *average* of the *partial set* of equations (13.15),

$$\overline{\varepsilon}_{\alpha\beta}(x_1, x_2) = \varepsilon_{\alpha\beta}(x_1, x_2) = \tfrac{1}{2}\left[\overline{u}_{\alpha,\beta}(x_1, x_2) + \overline{u}_{\beta,\alpha}(x_1, x_2)\right] \tag{13.56}$$

---

*We proved previously that if the stresses are all independent of x_3, then ε_{33} must be linear in x_1 and x_2 [see Eq. (13.20)]. However, Eq. (13.55b) will *not* in general yield values of ε_{33} which are linear functions of x_1 and x_2. There is no contradiction here, since τ_{11} and τ_{22} in Eq. (13.55b) are average value approximations to stresses that actually vary with x_3.

An integration of Eq. (13.56) then yields the average in-plane displacements over x_3 [i.e., $\bar{u}_1(x_1, x_2)$ and $\bar{u}_2(x_1, x_2)$]. If $u_3(x_1, x_2, x_3)$ is of interest, it may be obtained by integrating $\varepsilon_{33}(x_1, x_2) = \partial u_3(x_1, x_2, x_3)/\partial x_3$, where ε_{33} is obtained from Eq. (13.55b).

At this point let us compare the formulation above for elastic *two-dimensional plane stress* with the formulation given in Chapter 12 for *plane strain*. (We remind you that we have yet to include body forces and multiply connected domains in our present development.) We immediately see that formulation (13.53) for the stress function Φ is *mathematically identical* to our previously obtained formulation for plane strain [see Eqs. (12.20), (12.33), and (12.39)]. Accordingly, the *stresses* $\tau_{\alpha\beta}(x_1, x_2)$ in both problems will be the same if the geometry and tractions are the same. In saying that the tractions are "the same," we mean that the traction vector $T_\alpha^{(\nu)}(s)$ in plane strain (which *must* be independent of x_3) is the same function as the *average* traction vector $\bar{T}_\alpha^{(\nu)}(s)$ in two-dimensional plane stress (which must be symmetric with respect to the plate midplane). The identical nature of the two formulations follows directly from the fact that both formulations stem from the single compatibility equation

$$e_{\alpha\gamma} e_{\beta\delta}\, \varepsilon_{\alpha\beta,\gamma\delta}(x_1, x_2) = 0$$

where $\varepsilon_{\alpha\beta}(x_1, x_2)$ is the exact strain field in the case of plane strain, whereas it is the approximate average strain field for two-dimensional plane stress. In the latter case, the remaining five compatibility equations are in effect being ignored.[*] Despite this, we may get quite good solutions for many symmetric plane-stress thin-plate problems. Thus for no body forces and for simply connected domains, a solution to Eq. (13.53a) leads to an exact stress solution for some problem in plane strain and an approximate solution to the corresponding problem in plane stress. We shall thus be able to carry over some of our results from Chapter 12 to the present chapter. It is important to note, however, that the stress τ_{33}, the strains $\varepsilon_{\alpha\beta}$ and ε_{33}, and the displacements u_i will *not* be the same for the two problems. In the case of $\varepsilon_{\alpha\beta}$, the two-dimensional plane-stress solutions may be obtained from the plane-strain solutions, simply by replacing ν_1 and E_1 with ν and E, respectively [see Eqs. (13.55a) and (12.11)].

Boundary conditions (13.53b) are two conditions on the boundary curve C, which involve second derivatives of Φ. In Appendix V we have presented an alternative and more convenient pair of boundary conditions, where one is on Φ itself and one is on its normal derivative $\partial\Phi/\partial\nu$. For the sake of completeness, we reproduce Eqs. (V.10) here:

$$\Phi(s) = \int_0^s [x_\beta(s) - x_\beta(s')] e_{\alpha\beta} G_\alpha(s')\, ds' \qquad \text{on } C \qquad \text{(a)}$$

$$\frac{\partial\Phi}{\partial\nu}(s) = \nu_\beta \int_0^s e_{\alpha\beta} G_\alpha(s')\, ds' \qquad \text{on } C \qquad \text{(b)}$$

$$(13.57)$$

In Eqs. (13.57) $G_\alpha(s)$ is the prescribed function for the average traction vector on C [i.e., $\bar{T}_\alpha^{(\nu)}(s)$]. For multiply connected domains, Eqs. (13.57) must be supple-

---

[*] When these five compatibility equations are averaged over x_3, we do *not* obtain the usual compatibility relations with strains replaced by average strains (see the footnote on p. 578). Clearly, then, the full set of average strains will not satisfy the usual full set of compatibility equations.

mented by similar pairs of conditions around the cavities, and we shall enumerate these in the next case (Case B) of this section.

Case B: Nonzero Body Force; Multiply Connected Domains

What happens if body forces and multiple connectivity are included in the development of general x_3-dependent plane stress and two-dimensional plane stress? For simplicity, we consider the case in which the body force is independent of x_3 and derivable from the potential $V(x_1, x_2)$ [see Eq. (13.10)]. *Equilibrium* is then given by Eq. (13.11):

$$\tau_{\alpha\beta,\beta} - V_{,\alpha} = 0 \qquad (13.58)$$

As in plane strain [see Eq. (12.41)], the definition of the *stress function* must now be modified to read

$$\tau_{\alpha\beta} = e_{\alpha\gamma} e_{\beta\delta} \Phi_{,\gamma\delta} + V \delta_{\alpha\beta} \qquad (13.59)$$

so that Eq. (13.58) reduces to an identity. Replacing Eq. (13.23) by Eq. (13.59), one could develop an Airy stress function for x_3-dependent plane stress, but the development is tedious.[*] However, if we immediately restrict ourselves to very thin plates in which the average stress distributions are good approximations, we may proceed directly to two-dimensional plane stress with body forces present. In so doing, it may be easily shown that governing differential equation (13.53a) generalizes to

$$\nabla^4 \Phi(x_1, x_2) = -(1 - \nu) \nabla^2 V(x_1, x_2) \qquad \text{in } R \qquad (13.60)$$

Note that Eq. (13.60) is identical to Eq. (12.42) for plane strain, *except* that ν_1 has been replaced by ν. Thus when body forces are included, the stresses for two-dimensional plane stress are *not* equal to the stresses for the corresponding plane strain problem, but the former can be obtained from the latter by replacing ν_1 with ν.

Now let us extend our two-dimensional development of Case A to include the multiply connected plate with body forces (i.e., a plate with n cavities as shown in Fig. 13.4). Tractions are also prescribed on the boundary of each cavity, and thus Φ and its normal derivative are also given on these boundaries. Referring to Eqs. (V.13) in Appendix V, we have

$$\Phi(s) = \int_0^s [x_\beta(s) - x_\beta(s')] e_{\alpha\beta} [G_\alpha^{(i)}(s') - V(s') \nu_\alpha(s')] \, ds' + a_\beta^{(i)} x_\beta + b^{(i)}$$

$$\frac{\partial \Phi}{\partial \nu}(s) = \nu_\beta \int_0^s e_{\alpha\beta} [G_\alpha^{(i)}(s') - V(s') \nu_\alpha(s')] \, ds' + a_\beta^{(i)} \nu_\beta \qquad \text{on } C_i \qquad i = 1, \dots, n$$

where $G_\alpha^{(i)}$ is the prescribed function for the average traction vector on the boundary curve C_i for the ith cavity. Note that C_i must conform to the *actual boundary* of the

---

[*] See the footnote on page 579 pertaining to the paper by L.N.G. Filon.

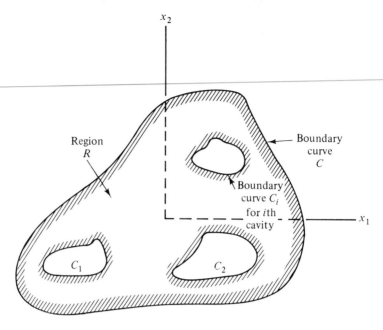

Figure 13.4 Multiply connected plate showing boundary curves conforming to the actual cavity boundaries. For two-dimensional plane stress, R, C, and C_i lie in the midplane of the plate.

cavity. Also note that Eqs. (13.61) contain the $3n$ constants $a_\beta^{(i)}$ and $b^{(i)}$. These constants may be evaluated via the Cesàro line integral condition, which we presented in general form as Eqs. (13.21). For the special case of two-dimensional plane stress, these conditions simplify to the following $3n$ conditions developed in Appendix VI [see Eqs. (VI.18)]:

$$\oint_{C_i} x_\beta \left[\delta_{\alpha\beta} \frac{\partial \nabla^2 \Phi}{\partial s} - e_{\alpha\beta} \frac{\partial \nabla^2 \Phi}{\partial \nu} \right] ds = (1+\nu) \oint_{C_i} e_{\alpha\beta} [G_\beta^{(i)}(s) + V(s)\nu_\beta(s)] ds$$

$$- (1-\nu) \oint_{C_i} x_\beta \left[\delta_{\alpha\beta} \frac{\partial V}{\partial s} - e_{\alpha\beta} \frac{\partial V}{\partial \nu} \right] ds \qquad \text{(a)} \qquad (13.62)$$

$$\oint_{C_i} \frac{\partial \nabla^2 \Phi}{\partial \nu} ds = -(1-\nu) \oint_{C_i} \frac{\partial V}{\partial \nu} ds, \qquad i = 1, \dots, n \qquad \text{(b)}$$

Note that Eqs. (13.62) differ from their plane-strain counterparts, Eqs. (12.44), in that the material constant ν has replaced ν_1.

From this point on in this chapter, we shall be working only within the framework of *two-dimensional plane stress*, with extensions to inelastic behavior. It is important to note that various other plane stress theories exist on the literature. One approach, known as *generalized plane stress*, is based on the definition

$$\tau_{13} = \tau_{23} = 0 \qquad \text{at } x_3 = \pm \frac{h}{2}$$

$$\tau_{33} = 0 \qquad \text{at all points} \qquad (13.63)$$

which is clearly *less restrictive* than definition (13.1). Some of the governing equations are then integrated over x_3, to obtain expressions for the average values of $\tau_{\alpha\beta}$, $\varepsilon_{\alpha\beta}$, and u_α. The term "generalized" may be a little misleading, since not all of the governing equations are explored in eliminating the x_3 dependence. An alternative approach is to define plane stress as

$$\tau_{13} = \tau_{23} = \tau_{33} = 0 \qquad \text{at } x_3 = \pm\frac{h}{2}$$

$$\tau_{33,3} = 0 \qquad \text{at } x_3 = \pm\frac{h}{2}$$

(13.64)

One then assumes that the solution may be expanded in a power series in the thickness coordinate, and thereby obtains plate theories of various "order."[*]

We shall now consider some problems in two-dimensional plane stress for linear elastic material.

13.6 STRETCHED PLATE WITH A SMALL HOLE

In Fig. 13.5 we have shown a very thin rectangular plate loaded at two ends by the constant traction distribution S, such that the plate is stretched in the y direction.

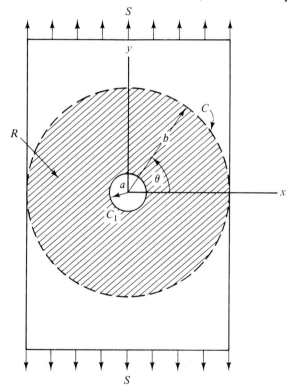

Figure 13.5 Stretched plate with small hole.

* Plate theories of various order with thermal expansion included are developed by power series in *Theory of Thermal Stresses* by B. Boley and J. H. Weiner (Melbourne, FL: R.E. Krieger Publishing Co., reprinted in 1985), p. 125. For further details on generalized plane stress, see *Mathematical Theory of Elasticity* by I. S. Sokolnikoff (Melbourne, FL: R.E. Krieger Publishing Co., reprinted in 1983), p. 253.

The quantity S represents the mean value over z of some traction distribution, which is symmetric with respect to the plate midplane. A *small* traction-free central circular hole of radius a is also shown. We will solve for the approximate two-dimensional plane stress distribution, and pay special attention to the stresses in the neighborhood of the small hole, in order to estimate a stress concentration factor K of the kind you have seen in strength of materials.

Since the hole is circular, it will be convenient to set up this problem in polar coordinates. It will be our first task to convert the given boundary conditions, on the four sides of the rectangular plate, to an equivalent boundary condition $G_\alpha(s)$ on the large inscribed circular boundary shown dashed in Fig. 13.5. Then we will solve the two-dimensional plane stress boundary value problem in the doubly connected region R (shown crosshatched in the figure). The outer boundary of R is the circle C of radius b, and the inner boundary is the concentric circle C_1 of radius a, where $a \ll b$. The governing equations for this problem, as given in the preceding section, are listed below:

$$\nabla^4 \Phi = 0 \qquad \text{in } R \qquad (a)$$

$$\tau_{\alpha\beta}\nu_\beta = G_\alpha(s) \qquad \text{on } C \qquad (b)$$

$$\tau_{\alpha\beta}\nu_\beta = 0 \qquad \text{on } C_1 \qquad (c)$$

$$\oint_{C_1} x_\beta \left[\delta_{\alpha\beta} \frac{\partial \nabla^2 \Phi}{\partial s} - e_{\alpha\beta} \frac{\partial \nabla^2 \Phi}{\partial \nu} \right] ds = 0 \qquad (d) \qquad (13.65)$$

$$\oint_{C_1} \frac{\partial \nabla^2 \Phi}{\partial \nu} ds = 0 \qquad (e)$$

Note that the body force potential $V = 0$ here, and we have chosen to express boundary conditions (b) and (c) in terms of $\tau_{\alpha\beta}$ via Cauchy's formula rather than in terms of Φ and $\partial\Phi/\partial\nu$. Also note that in boundary condition (c) and in Cesàro line integral condition (d), we have set $G_\alpha^{(1)}(s) = 0$ since the hole is traction-free. In Eqs. (13.65) it will be necessary to express ∇^4, ∇^2, $\partial/\partial s$, $\partial/\partial \nu$, ds, and $\tau_{\alpha\beta}(\Phi)$ *all* in polar coordinates. In this regard we may utilize results obtained in Chapter 12.

If there were no hole in the plate, we would have the uniform stress field $\tau_{yy} = S$, $\tau_{xx} = \tau_{xy} = 0$. The presence of the hole will cause a nonuniform stress distribution near the hole, but the stress far from this small hole will approach the aforestated uniform value. As noted previously, we shall employ polar coordinates. With the above in mind, we consider the domain R inside the hypothetical *large* circle C of radius b shown dashed in Fig. 13.5. To express boundary condition (13.65b) on C, we need only give τ_{rr} and $\tau_{r\theta}$ at $r = b$. Employing the tensor transformation formulas for plane stress [e.g., see Eqs. (1.7)], and considering the r direction to correspond with x' and the θ direction to correspond with y', we have for large b,

$$\tau_{rr}|_{r=b} = \frac{S}{2}(1 - \cos 2\theta) \qquad (a)$$

$$\tau_{r\theta}|_{r=b} = \frac{S}{2}\sin 2\theta \qquad (b) \qquad (13.66)$$

The boundary condition just presented can profitably be considered as being composed of two parts. First, there is a uniform radial stress at $r = b$ equal to $S/2$. For this part, the domain R between the concentric circles is the problem of a very thin hollow disk, having uniform radial stress $S/2$ and zero shear stress at its outer edge and zero radial and shear stresses at its inner edge. The remaining stresses on the boundary C give rise to the problem of a very thin hollow disk, having on the outside edge a variable radial stress $-(S/2) \cos 2\theta$ and a variable shear stress $(S/2) \sin 2\theta$, whereas on the inside edge the radial and shear stresses are again zero. These two problems have been illustrated in Fig. 13.6. We shall now proceed to present stress solutions for these two boundary value problems, and when this has been done the results will be superposed for the case of an *infinitely large* plate (i.e., $b \to \infty$).

In seeking solutions to the two plane-stress boundary value problems illustrated in Fig. 13.6, it is important to note first that since Eqs. (13.65) do *not* involve Poisson's ratio ν, a corresponding plane-strain problem will have the *identical* stress solution. Let us now turn to the first boundary value problem illustrated in Fig. 13.6(a) (i.e., the axisymmetric problem of a thin hollow disk subjected only to a uniform radial stress $S/2$ at its outer edge). The corresponding problem in plane strain is a thick-walled hollow cylinder, constrained at its ends and subjected to radial stress at its outer surface. This is in fact a special case of the problem solved in Example 12.1 of Section 12.5 on axially symmetric plane strain problems. Accordingly, we set $p_i = 0$, $p_o = -S/2$, $r_i = a$, and $r_o = b$ in Eqs. (g) and (h) of Example 12.1, and thereby immediately obtain the following solution for the first of our two-dimensional plane stress boundary value problems:

$$\tau'_{rr} = -\frac{a^2 b^2 (S/2)}{b^2 - a^2} \frac{1}{r^2} + \frac{(S/2)b^2}{b^2 - a^2} \qquad \text{(a)}$$

$$\tau'_{\theta\theta} = \frac{a^2 b^2 (S/2)}{b^2 - a^2} \frac{1}{r^2} + \frac{(S/2)b^2}{b^2 - a^2} \qquad \text{(b)} \qquad \text{(13.67)}$$

$$\tau'_{r\theta} = 0 \qquad \text{(c)}$$

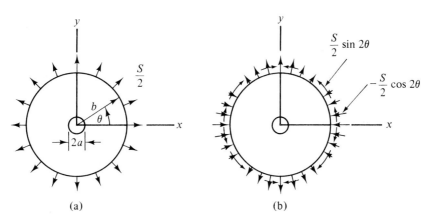

(a)   (b)

Figure 13.6 Two parts of boundary condition on C leading to two boundary value problems.

You may recall that in obtaining this solution, the second Cesàro line integral condition [i.e., Eq. (13.65e)] was used to show that one of the constants of integration had to be set equal to zero.

Now let us turn to the second boundary value problem illustrated in Fig. 13.6(b). This problem does *not* have axial symmetry. In solving this problem we begin by expressing the governing partial differential equation (13.65a) in polar coordinates. Referring back to Eq. (12.54), we have

$$\nabla^4\Phi = \left(\frac{\partial^2}{\partial r^2} + \frac{1}{r}\frac{\partial}{\partial r} + \frac{1}{r^2}\frac{\partial^2}{\partial\theta^2}\right)\left(\frac{\partial^2\Phi}{\partial r^2} + \frac{1}{r}\frac{\partial\Phi}{\partial r} + \frac{1}{r^2}\frac{\partial^2\Phi}{\partial\theta^2}\right) = 0 \qquad (13.68)$$

where the stresses were given by Eqs. (12.53) as

$$\tau_{rr} = \frac{1}{r}\frac{\partial\Phi}{\partial r} + \frac{1}{r^2}\frac{\partial^2\Phi}{\partial\theta^2} \qquad \text{(a)}$$

$$\tau_{\theta\theta} = \frac{\partial^2\Phi}{\partial r^2} \qquad \text{(b)} \qquad (13.69)$$

$$\tau_{r\theta} = \frac{1}{r^2}\frac{\partial\Phi}{\partial\theta} - \frac{1}{r}\frac{\partial^2\Phi}{\partial r\,\partial\theta} \qquad \text{(c)}$$

A careful inspection of Fig. 13.6(b) and Eqs. (13.69a, c) reveals that the correct θ dependence of τ_{rr} and $\tau_{r\theta}$ at $r = b$ will be obtained if we set

$$\Phi(r, \theta) = f(r)\cos 2\theta \qquad (13.70)$$

where $f(r)$ is a function of r that is to be determined. Substituting the preceding form for Φ into Eq. (13.68), we get the following ordinary differential equation in $f(r)$:

$$\left(\frac{d^2}{dr^2} + \frac{1}{r}\frac{d}{dr} - \frac{4}{r^2}\right)\left(\frac{d^2f}{dr^2} + \frac{1}{r}\frac{df}{dr} - \frac{4f}{r^2}\right) = 0 \qquad (13.71)$$

Equation (13.71) has variable coefficients and is of the Euler–Cauchy class, similar to Eq. (12.66), which we solved previously. Proceeding in a manner similar to what we did earlier, we first simplify the given differential equation to one with constant coefficients via the variable change $r = e^t$, and then insert the trial solution $f(r)|_{r=e^t} = g(t) = e^{pt}$. Taking care not to expand out the differential operations prematurely, we may obtain the auxiliary equation in factored form as

$$(p - 2)(p + 2)\,p\,(p - 4) = 0$$

where the details are left for you as an exercise. Accordingly, we have for the solution

$$g(t) = A_1 + A_2 e^{2t} + A_3 e^{4t} + A_4 e^{-2t}$$

In terms of r we have for $f(r)$

$$f(r) = A_1 + A_2 r^2 + A_3 r^4 + \frac{A_4}{r^2} \qquad (13.72)$$

The stress function then follows from Eq. (13.70) as

$$\Phi(r, \theta) = \left(A_1 + A_2 r^2 + A_3 r^4 + \frac{A_4}{r^2}\right) \cos 2\theta \qquad (13.73)$$

where the constants of integration A_1, A_2, A_3, A_4 are to be determined from the boundary conditions on τ_{rr} and $\tau_{r\theta}$ at $r = a$ and at $r = b$.

Since there are four boundary conditions, it is clear that we may proceed to evaluate the four constants of integration *without* recourse to the Cesàro line integral conditions (13.65d, e). Nonetheless, it will be instructive to verify that these conditions are indeed identically satisfied for *any* values of A_1, A_2, A_3, A_4. We shall do this only for condition (13.65d) with free index $\alpha = 1$, and leave it for you to verify that the remaining two conditions [i.e., Eq. (13.65d) with free index $\alpha = 2$, and Eq. (13.65e)] are also identically satisfied. Looking back at Fig. 13.5 we see that the boundary curve of the cavity C_1 is defined by the circle $r = a$. Thus, on C_1 we have $\partial/\partial s = (1/a)(\partial/\partial\theta)$, $\partial/\partial\nu = \partial/\partial r$, $ds = a\,d\theta$, $x = a\cos\theta$ and $y = a\sin\theta$. The integral in Eq. (13.65d) then becomes, for $\alpha = 1$,

$$\int_0^{2\pi} \left\{(a\cos\theta)\left[\frac{1}{a}\frac{\partial\nabla^2\Phi}{\partial\theta}\right]_{r=a} - (a\sin\theta)\left[\frac{\partial\nabla^2\Phi}{\partial r}\right]_{r=a}\right\} a\,d\theta \qquad (13.74)$$

Since $\Phi = f(r)\cos 2\theta$, where $f(r)$ is given by Eq. (13.72), we have

$$\nabla^2\Phi = \frac{\partial^2\Phi}{\partial r^2} + \frac{1}{r}\frac{\partial\Phi}{\partial r} + \frac{1}{r^2}\frac{\partial^2\Phi}{\partial\theta^2} = h(r)\cos 2\theta$$

where

$$h(r) = \frac{d^2 f}{dr^2} + \frac{1}{r}\frac{df}{dr} - \frac{4f}{r^2}$$

Integral (13.74) thus becomes

$$-2ah(a)\int_0^{2\pi}\cos\theta\sin 2\theta\,d\theta - a^2 h'(a)\int_0^{2\pi}\sin\theta\cos 2\theta\,d\theta \qquad (13.75)$$

where $h(a)$ and $h'(a)$ are, respectively, the values of $h(r)$ and its derivative at $r = a$. Both integrals in (13.75) vanish because of the orthogonality of the trigonometric functions $\cos n\theta$ and $\sin n\theta$ over the interval $(0, 2\pi)$. We have thus verified our earlier assertion and will now return to Eq. (13.73) and evaluate the constants of integration.

Substituting Eq. (13.73) for Φ into Eqs. (13.69) for the stresses, we get after collecting terms

$$\tau_{rr} = -\left(2A_2 + \frac{4A_1}{r^2} + \frac{6A_4}{r^4}\right)\cos 2\theta$$

$$\tau_{\theta\theta} = \left(2A_2 + 12A_3 r^2 + \frac{6A_4}{r^4}\right)\cos 2\theta \qquad (13.76)$$

$$\tau_{r\theta} = \left(2A_2 + 6A_3 r^2 + \frac{2A_1}{r^2} - \frac{6A_4}{r^4}\right)\sin 2\theta$$

We now subject this stress distribution to the boundary conditions for this problem. Thus

$$\tau_{rr} = \tau_{r\theta} = 0 \qquad \text{at } r = a$$

$$\tau_{rr} = -\frac{S}{2}\cos 2\theta \qquad \text{at } r = b \qquad (13.77)$$

$$\tau_{r\theta} = \frac{S}{2}\sin 2\theta \qquad \text{at } r = b$$

We then have

$$\frac{4}{a^2}A_1 + 2A_2 + 0 + \frac{6}{a^4}A_4 = 0 \qquad (a)$$

$$\frac{4}{b^2}A_1 + 2A_2 + 0 + \frac{6}{b^4}A_4 = \frac{S}{2} \qquad (b)$$

$$\hspace{6cm} (13.78)$$

$$-\frac{2}{a^2}A_1 + 2A_2 + 6a^2 A_3 - \frac{6}{a^4}A_4 = 0 \qquad (c)$$

$$-\frac{2}{b^2}A_1 + 2A_2 + 6b^2 A_3 - \frac{6}{b^4}A_4 = \frac{S}{2} \qquad (d)$$

We may solve for the four constants of integration by Cramer's rule to get the following results:

$$A_1 = \frac{72S}{\Delta}\left(\frac{a^2}{b^4} - \frac{b^2}{a^4}\right)$$

$$A_2 = \frac{36S}{\Delta}\left(-\frac{4}{b^4} + \frac{3}{a^2 b^2} + \frac{b^2}{a^6}\right)$$

$$A_3 = \frac{72S}{\Delta}\left(\frac{1}{a^2 b^4} - \frac{1}{b^2 a^4}\right) \qquad (13.79a)$$

$$A_4 = \frac{36S}{\Delta}\left(\frac{b^2}{a^2} - \frac{a^2}{b^2}\right)$$

where

$$\Delta = \left(-\frac{576}{b^4} + \frac{144a^2}{b^6} + \frac{864}{a^2 b^2} + \frac{144b^2}{a^6} - \frac{576}{a^4}\right) \qquad (13.79b)$$

You will recall that our formulation is valid for the case of a *small* hole in a *large* rectangular plate, such that the radius of the large inscribed circle can safely be said to be much greater than the radius of the hole. We can be assured that this condition is satisfied, and at the same time considerably simplify our results, by now considering the special case of an *infinitely large* plate (i.e., let $b \to \infty$). Equations (13.79) then simplify to

$$A_1 = -\frac{a^2}{2}S, \qquad A_2 = \frac{S}{4}, \qquad A_3 = 0, \qquad A_4 = \frac{a^4}{4}S \qquad (13.80)$$

Solution (13.76) to the second subsidiary problem then becomes

$$\tau_{rr}'' = \frac{S}{2}\left(-1 + 4a^2\frac{1}{r^2} - 3a^4\frac{1}{r^4}\right)\cos 2\theta$$

$$\tau_{\theta\theta}'' = \frac{S}{2}\left(1 + 3a^4\frac{1}{r^4}\right)\cos 2\theta \qquad (13.81)$$

$$\tau_{r\theta}'' = \frac{S}{2}\left(1 + 2a^2\frac{1}{r^2} - 3a^4\frac{1}{r^4}\right)\sin 2\theta$$

We can now superpose our subsidiary solutions to give the solution to the problem at hand. But we must first adjust Eqs. (13.67) to reflect the fact that now the plate is infinitely large. Thus, dividing through by b^2 and letting $a/b = 0$, we get

$$\tau_{rr}' = \frac{S}{2}\left(1 - \frac{a^2}{r^2}\right)$$

$$\tau_{\theta\theta}' = \frac{S}{2}\left(1 + \frac{a^2}{r^2}\right) \qquad (13.82)$$

$$\tau_{r\theta}' = 0$$

The total solution then becomes

$$\tau_{rr} = \tau_{rr}' + \tau_{rr}'' = \frac{S}{2}\left[\left(1 - \frac{a^2}{r^2}\right) + \left(-1 + 4\frac{a^2}{r^2} - 3\frac{a^4}{r^4}\right)\cos 2\theta\right]$$

$$\tau_{\theta\theta} = \tau_{\theta\theta}' + \tau_{\theta\theta}'' = \frac{S}{2}\left[\left(1 + \frac{a^2}{r^2}\right) + \left(1 + 3\frac{a^4}{r^4}\right)\cos 2\theta\right] \qquad (13.83)$$

$$\tau_{r\theta} = \tau_{r\theta}' + \tau_{r\theta}'' = \frac{S}{2}\left(1 + 2\frac{a^2}{r^2} - 3\frac{a^4}{r^4}\right)\sin 2\theta$$

Let us now examine the foregoing stress distribution in regions far from the hole and at the hole itself. Note, as we get far from the hole, we can drop terms in the preceding equations having r in the denominator. We thus approach the following state of stress as $r \to \infty$:

$$\tau_{rr} = \frac{S}{2}(1 - \cos 2\theta)$$

$$\tau_{\theta\theta} = \frac{S}{2}(1 + \cos 2\theta) \qquad (13.84)$$

$$\tau_{r\theta} = \frac{S}{2}\sin 2\theta$$

This checks with Eqs. (13.66), which correspond to the uniform stress field $\tau_{yy} = S$, $\tau_{xx} = 0$, and $\tau_{xy} = 0$. Next, let us consider the stress at the hole. Thus, setting $r = a$ in Eqs. (13.83), we get

$$\tau_{rr}|_{r=a} = 0$$

$$\tau_{\theta\theta}|_{r=a} = S(1 + 2\cos 2\theta) \qquad (13.85)$$

$$\tau_{r\theta}|_{r=a} = 0$$

The radial and transverse stresses are clearly principal stresses over the entire periphery of the hole, and thus the maximum normal stress occurs at $\theta = 0$ and π. We see that at these points we have the tensile stress $\tau_{\theta\theta} = \tau_{yy} = 3S$. Here is a vivid example of the danger of a stress concentration. A small hole, probably quite harmless in appearance to the layman, causes a stress *three times* greater than the largest stress were the hole not present. Clearly, great care must be taken when designing for such situations.

In this problem, we have been able to compute the *stress concentration factor* K as equal to 3. Thus we can say that the stress τ_{max} is expressible as

$$\tau_{max} = K\tau = 3S \tag{13.86}$$

where τ is the maximum normal stress without the hole. You may find lists of concentration factors in handbooks for other common situations. Some have been computed from the theory using numerical methods such as finite elements.*

13.7 PURE BENDING OF A CURVED BEAM

In the problems at the end of this chapter, you will have the opportunity to use the methods presented to solve several straight, rectangular, thin-beam problems.† Here we shall consider the thin curved beam having upper and lower edges as concentric circular arcs and loaded at the ends AB and CD only by pure couples M, as has been shown in Fig. 13.7. The beam is of rectangular cross section having a thickness t which is very small compared to the other dimensions of the beam.

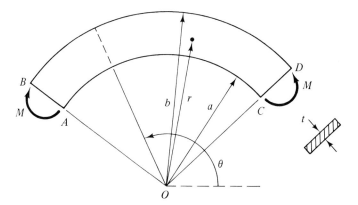

Figure 13.7 Curved thin beam.

* This same problem has been solved by finite elements in *Energy and Finite Element Methods in Structural Mechanics* by I. H. Shames and C. L. Dym, (New York: Hemisphere Publishing Corp., 1985), Chap. 12.

† Problems 13.14 to 13.17 are beam problems of this type, and for each problem the thickness t has been assumed to be small. However, we should mention that if we allow t to become very large and also introduce constraints at the two ends, these thin-beam problems become "plane-strain plate" problems. The stresses $\tau_{\alpha\beta}$ are the same for both classes of problems, but of course τ_{zz} and u_α are in general different.

By considering free bodies of portions of the curved beam in the shape of radial segments, as is shown in Fig. 13.8, we can conclude from equilibrium considerations that the resultants of the traction distributions on the exposed internal surfaces must be pure couples with a magnitude M. Thus the resultants at internal sections are not a function of θ. And furthermore, it can be concluded that the stresses themselves on these exposed faces should not vary with θ. We thus have here a two-dimensional plane-stress problem with axial symmetry about 0. Since we have no body forces and the domain of the beam is simply connected, we may utilize without modification the general solution to the biharmonic equation for axially symmetric plane strain, which we developed in Section 12.5. Accordingly, we simply reproduce Eqs. (12.59) for the radial and transverse stresses below:

$$\tau_{rr} = \frac{1}{r}\frac{d\Phi}{dr} = \frac{C_1}{2}\left(\ln r - \frac{1}{2}\right) + \frac{C_2}{2} + \frac{C_3}{r^2} \qquad \text{(a)}$$

$$\tau_{\theta\theta} = \frac{d^2\Phi}{dr^2} = \frac{C_1}{2}\left(\ln r + \frac{1}{2}\right) + \frac{C_2}{2} - \frac{C_3}{r^2} \qquad \text{(b)}$$

(13.87)

Referring to Fig. 13.7, we see that we have for the boundary conditions of this problem,

$$\tau_{rr} = 0, \qquad \text{at } r = a \text{ and } r = b \qquad \text{(a)}$$

$$\tau_{r\theta} = 0, \qquad \text{at } r = a \text{ and } r = b \qquad \text{(b)}$$

$$\int_S \tau_{\theta\theta}\, dA = 0, \qquad \text{at end surfaces} \qquad \text{(c)}$$

$$\int_S r\tau_{\theta\theta}\, dA = -M, \qquad \text{at end surfaces} \qquad \text{(d)}$$

(13.88)

where S is the surface covered by the end areas. We shall now proceed to show that Eqs. (13.88) yield three independent conditions for the determination of constants C_1, C_2, C_3 in Eqs. (13.87).

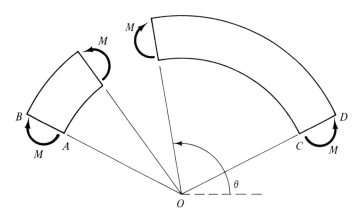

Figure 13.8 Free-body diagrams.

Using Eq. (13.87a), conditions (13.88a) immediately give

$$\frac{C_1}{2}\left(\ln a - \frac{1}{2}\right) + \frac{C_2}{2} + \frac{C_3}{a^2} = 0 \qquad \text{(a)}$$

$$\frac{C_1}{2}\left(\ln b - \frac{1}{2}\right) + \frac{C_2}{2} + \frac{C_3}{b^2} = 0 \qquad \text{(b)}$$

(13.89)

The conditions given by Eq. (13.88b) are identically satisfied since $\tau_{r\theta} = 0$ everywhere in an axisymmetric problem. Next we examine condition (13.88c). We may state on replacing dA by $t\,dr$ and using the first part of Eq. (13.87b),

$$\int_S \tau_{\theta\theta}\, dA = t\int_a^b \frac{d^2\Phi}{dr^2}\, dr = 0$$

Canceling t, we have for the preceding equation,

$$\int_a^b \frac{d^2\Phi}{dr^2}\, dr = \left.\frac{d\Phi}{dr}\right|_a^b = b\left[\frac{C_1}{2}\left(\ln b - \frac{1}{2}\right) + \frac{C_2}{2} + \frac{C_3}{b^2}\right]$$

$$- a\left[\frac{C_1}{2}\left(\ln a - \frac{1}{2}\right) + \frac{C_2}{2} + \frac{C_3}{a^2}\right] = 0$$

where we have used Eq. (13.87a) to substitute for $d\Phi/dr$. But this equation adds nothing new, since it will be satisfied if Eqs. (13.89) are satisfied. We now go to the last of our boundary conditions [i.e., Eq. (13.88d)]. Using Eq. (13.87b) to substitute for $\tau_{\theta\theta}$, we have

$$\int_S r\tau_{\theta\theta}\, dA = t\int_a^b \left[\frac{C_1}{2}\left(r\ln r + \frac{r}{2}\right) + \frac{C_2}{2}r - \frac{C_3}{r}\right]dr = -M$$

Integrating, we obtain upon dividing by t,

$$\left.\frac{C_1}{2}\left(\frac{r^2}{2}\ln r\right) + \frac{C_2}{4}r^2 - C_3 \ln r\right|_a^b = -\frac{M}{t}$$

Inserting the limits, we finally obtain

$$\frac{C_1}{4}(b^2 \ln b - a^2 \ln a) + \frac{C_2}{4}(b^2 - a^2) - C_3 \ln\frac{b}{a} = -\frac{M}{t} \qquad (13.90)$$

Equations (13.89) and (13.90) may now be solved simultaneously for the constants C_1, C_2, and C_3. We obtain

$$C_1 = -\frac{2M}{B}(b^2 - a^2)$$

$$C_2 = -\frac{M}{B}[(b^2 - a^2) - 2(b^2 \ln b - a^2 \ln a)] \qquad (13.91a)$$

$$C_3 = -\frac{M}{B}a^2 b^2 \ln\frac{b}{a}$$

where B is the constant

$$B = \frac{t}{4}\left[(b^2 - a^2)^2 - 4a^2 b^2\left(\ln\frac{b}{a}\right)^2\right] \qquad (13.91b)$$

Substituting the foregoing values for the integration constants into Eqs. (13.87), we then get the following formulation for the state of stress at a point:

$$\tau_{rr} = -\frac{M}{B}\left(\frac{a^2 b^2}{r^2}\ln\frac{b}{a} + b^2\ln\frac{r}{b} + a^2\ln\frac{a}{r}\right) \tag{a}$$

$$\tau_{\theta\theta} = -\frac{M}{B}\left(-\frac{a^2 b^2}{r^2}\ln\frac{b}{a} + b^2\ln\frac{r}{b} + a^2\ln\frac{a}{r} + b^2 - a^2\right) \tag{b} \quad (13.92)$$

$$\tau_{r\theta} = 0 \tag{c}$$

The stress distributions above can be considered correct for the entire beam if the applied normal tractions on the ends are distributed over r in precisely the same manner as the solution for τ_{rr} [i.e., Eq. (13.92a)]. If the applied tractions do not have this distribution (as will usually be the case), the results we have developed are valid in regions away from the ends of the beam in accordance with Saint-Venant's principle.

Let us now compare solution (13.92b) for $\tau_{\theta\theta}$ with the elementary flexure formula from strength of materials (i.e., $\tau_{xx} = -My/I$). It is a simple matter to show that for the present rectangular cross section the flexure formula yields

$$\tau_{\theta\theta} = -\frac{6M(2r - a - b)}{t(b - a)^3} \tag{13.93a}$$

and thus at $r = a$ (and at $r = b$) the stress of maximum magnitude is obtained as

$$|\tau|_{max} = \frac{6M}{t(b - a)^2} \tag{13.93b}$$

One can show that Eq. (13.92b) always yields a value for $|\tau_{\theta\theta}|$, at $r = a$, *greater* than the $|\tau|_{max}$ above, and a value *less* than $|\tau|_{max}$ at $r = b$. Accordingly, the stress $\tau_{\theta\theta}$ of maximum magnitude, as obtained from two-dimensional plane stress theory, always occurs at the *inner* fiber $r = a$. We have illustrated solutions (13.92b) and (13.93a) for $\tau_{\theta\theta}$ in Fig. 13.9. Also illustrated in this figure is τ_{rr} according to Eq. (13.92a). We note that its maximum value is much less than the maximum value of $\tau_{\theta\theta}$. You will recall that in elementary beam theory we assumed that $\tau_{rr} = 0$. Considerable error can be expected from strength of materials here if the depth of the beam $b - a$ is not small compared with the mean radius of the curvature $(b + a)/2$.*

13.8 AXIALLY SYMMETRIC PROBLEMS WITH BODY FORCES

Consider a flat circular disk of radius R and thickness t, where R is much larger than t. The disk is loaded by a constant radial traction S at its edge $r = R$, and also by a radial conservative body force $B(r)$ which may vary only with r (see Fig. 13.10). We express $B(r)$ in terms of the potential $V(r)$ as follows:

$$B(r) = -\frac{dV(r)}{dr} \tag{13.94}$$

---

*For further details and references pertaining to this curved beam problem, see S. Timoshenko and J. N. Goodier, *Theory of Elasticity* (New York: McGraw-Hill Book Company, 1951), p. 61. This book also contains many solutions for straight, rectangular, thin beams.

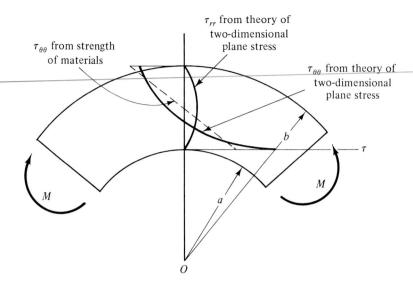

Figure 13.9 Stresses in curved beam for pure bending.

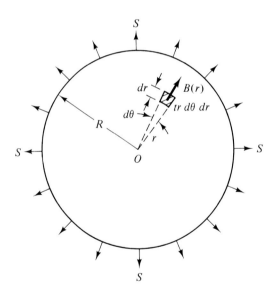

Figure 13.10 Thin circular disk under constant traction and with radial body force acting on volume element $tr\,d\theta\,dr$.

We will assume that S and $V(r)$ are uniform over the thickness. Accordingly, this is an axially symmetric two-dimensional plane-stress problem. We shall use polar coordinates in seeking the stresses τ_{rr} and $\tau_{\theta\theta}$ and the displacement u_r. As explained in Section 13.5 these quantities represent *average* values over the thickness coordinate.

When body forces are present, the Airy stress function must satisfy differential equation (13.60),

$$\nabla^4\Phi = -(1-\nu)\nabla^2 V \tag{13.95}$$

where for rectangular Cartesian coordinates the stresses are obtained from Eq. (13.59),

$$\tau_{\alpha\beta} = e_{\alpha\gamma} e_{\beta\delta} \, \Phi_{,\gamma\delta} + V\delta_{\alpha\beta} \tag{13.96}$$

In the present axially symmetric problem Φ is a function of r only, and so expressing the ∇^2 operator in polar coordinates with axial symmetry [e.g., see Eq. (12.56d)], Eq. (13.95) becomes

$$\left[\frac{1}{r}\frac{d}{dr}\left(r\frac{d}{dr}\right)\right]\left[\frac{1}{r}\frac{d}{dr}\left(r\frac{d\Phi}{dr}\right)\right] = -(1-\nu)\left[\frac{1}{r}\frac{d}{dr}\left(r\frac{dV}{dr}\right)\right] \tag{13.97}$$

Looking back at Eqs. (12.56a, b) for the stresses in polar coordinates when body forces are absent, it follows that with a radial body force present Eq. (13.96) becomes for polar coordinates with axial symmetry

$$\tau_{rr} = \frac{1}{r}\frac{d\Phi}{dr} + V \qquad \text{(a)}$$

$$\tau_{\theta\theta} = \frac{d^2\Phi}{dr^2} + V \qquad \text{(b)} \tag{13.98}$$

$$\tau_{r\theta} = 0 \qquad \text{(c)}$$

We may readily verify that Eqs. (13.98) are indeed the correct representations* of stress by substitution into the equilibrium equation

$$\frac{d\tau_{rr}}{dr} + \frac{\tau_{rr} - \tau_{\theta\theta}}{r} - \frac{dV}{dr} = 0 \tag{13.99}$$

which is the previously obtained Eq. (12.134) with a radial body-force term added. After differential equation (13.97) has been integrated for $\Phi(r)$, the stresses $\tau_{rr}(r)$ and $\tau_{\theta\theta}(r)$ follow directly from Eqs. (13.98). Finally, the radial displacement is obtained from Eq. (12.56f) as

$$u_r(r) = r\varepsilon_{\theta\theta} \tag{13.100}$$

where in accordance with Eq. (13.55a) for polar coordinates,

$$\varepsilon_{\theta\theta} = \frac{1}{E}\left(\tau_{\theta\theta} - \nu\tau_{rr}\right) \tag{13.101}$$

The integration of Eq. (13.97) is straightforward. Multiplying both sides by r and then integrating over r, we obtain after dividing the result by r,

$$\frac{d}{dr}\left[\frac{1}{r}\frac{d}{dr}\left(r\frac{d\Phi}{dr}\right)\right] = -(1-\nu)\frac{dV}{dr} + \frac{C_1}{r}$$

---

* An alternative stress function Ψ may be defined by $\Psi = d\Phi/dr + rV$. Equations (13.98) then become

$$\tau_{rr} = \frac{\Psi}{r}$$

$$\tau_{\theta\theta} = \frac{d\Psi}{dr} - r\frac{dV}{dr}$$

where C_1 is a constant of integration. Now integrate the above over r and multiply by r to obtain

$$\frac{d}{dr}\left(r\frac{d\Phi}{dr}\right) = -(1-\nu)rV + C_1 r \ln r + C_2 r$$

where C_2 is another constant of integration. Finally, we integrate a third time and then divide by r to get

$$\frac{d\Phi}{dr} = -\frac{1-\nu}{r}\int_0^r \eta V(\eta)\,d\eta + \frac{C_1}{2} r\left(\ln r - \frac{1}{2}\right) + \frac{C_2}{2} r + \frac{C_3}{r} \qquad (13.102)$$

where C_3 is a third constant and η is a dummy variable of integration. The radial stress now follows from Eq. (13.98a) as

$$\tau_{rr} = -\frac{1-\nu}{r^2}\int_0^r \eta V(\eta)\,d\eta + V(r) + \frac{C_1}{2}\left(\ln r - \frac{1}{2}\right) + \frac{C_2}{2} + \frac{C_3}{r^2} \qquad (13.103)$$

For τ_{rr} to be finite at $r = 0$ we must set $C_1 = C_3 = 0$, and thus we now have

$$\tau_{rr} = -\frac{1-\nu}{r^2}\int_0^r \eta V(\eta)\,d\eta + V(r) + \frac{C_2}{2} \qquad (13.104)$$

Setting $\tau_{rr} = S$ at $r = R$ (see Fig. 13.10), we may solve for $C_2/2$ and thereby get

$$\frac{C_2}{2} = S + \frac{1-\nu}{R^2}\int_0^R \eta V(\eta)\,d\eta - V(R) \qquad (13.105)$$

where $V(R)$ is the value of $V(r)$ at $r = R$. Inserting this result into Eq. (13.104), we finally obtain for the radial stress

$$\boxed{\tau_{rr} = -\frac{1-\nu}{r^2}\int_0^r \eta V(\eta)\,d\eta + \frac{1-\nu}{R^2}\int_0^R \eta V(\eta)\,d\eta + V(r) - V(R) + S} \qquad (13.106)$$

To obtain the tangential stress, we first go back to Eq. (13.102) and set $C_1 = C_3 = 0$ and then substitute for $C_2/2$ in accordance with Eq. (13.105). Thus

$$\frac{d\Phi}{dr} = -\frac{1-\nu}{r}\int_0^r \eta V(\eta)\,d\eta + \frac{(1-\nu)r}{R^2}\int_0^R \eta V(\eta)\,d\eta + Sr - rV(R) \qquad (13.107)$$

With the use of Leibnitz's rule, we now obtain the second derivative as

$$\frac{d^2\Phi}{dr^2} = \frac{1-\nu}{r^2}\int_0^r \eta V(\eta)\,d\eta - (1-\nu)V(r) + \frac{1-\nu}{R^2}\int_0^R \eta V(\eta)\,d\eta + S - V(R)$$

Finally, the tangential stress follows from Eq. (13.98b) as

$$\boxed{\tau_{\theta\theta} = \frac{1-\nu}{r^2}\int_0^r \eta V(\eta)\,d\eta + \frac{1-\nu}{R^2}\int_0^R \eta V(\eta)\,d\eta + \nu V(r) - V(R) + S} \qquad (13.108)$$

We may now substitute Eqs. (13.106) and (13.108) into Eq. (13.101) to obtain the tangential strain $\varepsilon_{\theta\theta}$. Inserting this result into Eq. (13.100) and combining terms, we get for the radial displacement

$$u_r = \frac{r}{E} \left[\frac{1-\nu^2}{r^2} \int_0^r \eta V(\eta) \, d\eta + \frac{(1-\nu)^2}{R^2} \int_0^R \eta V(\eta) \, d\eta \right. $$
$$\left. + (1-\nu)S - (1-\nu)V(R) \right]$$

(13.109)

It will be useful to evaluate τ_{rr}, $\tau_{\theta\theta}$, and u_r at $r = R$ and at $r = 0$. Thus setting $r = R$ in Eqs. (13.106), (13.108), and (13.109), we obtain after combining terms

$$\tau_{rr}(R) = S \tag{a}$$

$$\tau_{\theta\theta}(R) = \frac{2(1-\nu)}{R^2} \int_0^R \eta V(\eta) \, d\eta - (1-\nu)V(R) + S \tag{b}$$

(13.110)

$$u_r(R) = \frac{1}{E} \left[\frac{2(1-\nu)}{R} \int_0^R \eta V(\eta) \, d\eta + (1-\nu)RS - (1-\nu)RV(R) \right] \tag{c}$$

In order to get τ_{rr}, $\tau_{\theta\theta}$, and u_r at $r = 0$, it is first necessary to verify the following limiting values via l'Hospital's rule:

$$\lim_{r\to0} \frac{1}{r^2} \int_0^r \eta V(\eta) \, d\eta = \lim_{r\to0} \frac{rV(r)}{2\,r} = \frac{V(0)}{2} \tag{a}$$

(13.111)

$$\lim_{r\to0} \frac{1}{r} \int_0^r \eta V(\eta) \, d\eta = \lim_{r\to0} \frac{rV(r)}{1} = 0 \tag{b}$$

where we have assumed that the value of the potential at $r = 0$ [i.e., $V(0)$] is bounded. Utilizing these results, we may then get from Eqs. (13.106), (13.108), and (13.109)

$$\tau_{rr}(0) = \tau_{\theta\theta}(0) = \frac{1-\nu}{R^2} \int_0^R \eta V(\eta) \, d\eta + \frac{1+\nu}{2} V(0) - V(R) + S \tag{a}$$

(13.112)

$$u_r(0) = 0 \tag{b}$$

The formulation above is readily extended to the case of the disk with a central hole, and this will be explored in the problems at the end of the chapter. We now go on to a practical example of the application of the results above.

Example 13.1

Evaluate τ_{rr}, $\tau_{\theta\theta}$, and u_r for a rotating flat thin disk having an angular velocity ω (see Fig. 13.11).

This is a dynamic problem, which may be converted to an equivalent static problem via d'Alembert's principle. Accordingly, we transpose the inertia term on the right side of the equation of motion to the left side, and thereby obtain equilibrium equation (13.99) with a body "force" term. In the present example this body force is equal to the centrifugal "force" per unit volume [i.e., $B(r) = \rho r \omega^2$, where ρ is the mass density]. The edge of the disk at $r = R$ is free of traction, and thus we set $S = 0$ in our previous development.

Referring to Eq. (13.94), we see that in this example the potential is given by

$$V(r) = -\frac{\rho\omega^2}{2} r^2 \tag{a}$$

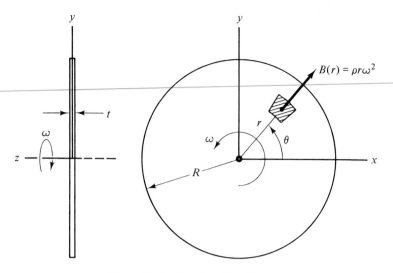

Figure 13.11 Rotating thin disk.

and thus

$$V(R) = -\frac{\rho\omega^2}{2}R^2 \tag{b}$$

Furthermore, we have

$$\int_0^r \eta V(\eta)\,d\eta = -\frac{\rho\omega^2}{2}\int_0^r \eta^3\,d\eta = -\frac{\rho\omega^2}{8}r^4 \tag{c}$$

and then

$$\int_0^R \eta V(\eta)\,d\eta = -\frac{\rho\omega^2}{8}R^4 \tag{d}$$

We may now substitute Eqs. (a) to (d) into Eq. (13.106) to get

$$\tau_{rr} = -\frac{1-\nu}{r^2}\left[-\frac{\rho\omega^2}{8}r^4\right] + \frac{1-\nu}{R^2}\left[-\frac{\rho\omega^2}{8}R^4\right] - \frac{\rho\omega^2}{2}r^2 + \frac{\rho\omega^2}{2}R^2$$

Combining terms, we obtain for the radial stress

$$\tau_{rr} = \frac{\rho\omega^2}{8}(3+\nu)[R^2 - r^2] \tag{e}$$

In a similar manner, we substitute Eqs. (a) to (d) into Eq. (13.108) and combine terms to obtain the tangential stress as

$$\tau_{\theta\theta} = \frac{\rho\omega^2}{8}[(3+\nu)R^2 - (1+3\nu)r^2] \tag{f}$$

Finally, we substitute Eqs. (b) to (d) into Eq. (13.109) and get for the radial displacement

$$u_r = \frac{\rho\omega^2}{8}\frac{r}{E}[(1-\nu)(3+\nu)R^2 - (1-\nu^2)r^2] \tag{g}$$

Note that at $r = 0$, Eqs. (e) and (f) give

$$\tau_{rr}(0) = \tau_{\theta\theta}(0) = \frac{\rho\omega^2}{8}(3+\nu)R^2 \tag{h}$$

which is the *maximum stress*. The *maximum displacement* occurs at $r = R$, and is obtained from Eq. (g) as

$$u_r(R) = \frac{\rho\omega^2}{4}\frac{R^3}{E}(1-\nu) \tag{i}$$

We leave it for you to verify that Eqs. (h) and (i) may also be obtained from Eqs. (13.112a) and (13.110c), respectively.

We shall later consider the case of an elastic, perfectly plastic disk, for which the elastic deformation (as well as the plastic deformation) is incompressible. For such a material $\nu = \frac{1}{2}$ and $E = 2(1+\nu)G = 3G$. Equations (e) to (g) for elastic behavior then simplify to

$$\tau_{rr} = \frac{7\rho\omega^2}{16}(R^2 - r^2) \tag{j}$$

$$\tau_{\theta\theta} = \frac{\rho\omega^2}{16}(7R^2 - 5r^2) \tag{k}$$

$$u_r = \frac{\rho\omega^2}{96}\frac{r}{G}(7R^2 - 3r^2) \tag{ℓ}$$

We have thus established the solution for the solid rotating elastic disk. In Problem 13.23, you will be asked to consider the case where there is a central hole in the disk. This problem is of special interest, since one can show that as the radius of the hole becomes vanishingly small we get a stress concentration factor K of 2 for this problem. As mentioned previously, the elastic, perfectly plastic solid disk will be considered in the next part of the chapter. We shall also look at this problem for the case of linear viscoelastic material.

PART C
INELASTIC TWO-DIMENSIONAL PLANE STRESS

13.9 LINEAR VISCOELASTIC PLANE STRESS

In this section we set forth the basic equations of two-dimensional plane stress for linear viscoelastic materials. We presented in Section 6.7 the following analogy relations:

$$E \sim \frac{Q^E}{P^E}, \qquad \nu \sim \frac{Q^\nu}{P^\nu}, \qquad 2G \sim \frac{Q^G}{P^G}, \qquad 3K \sim \frac{Q^K}{P^K} \tag{13.113}$$

We shall use these relations to convert previously developed equations for elastic behavior to the case of viscoelastic behavior. We remind you that any elastic result that does not contain an elastic constant is also applicable without modification to linear viscoelastic material. Also, it is important to realize that now all dependent variables depend on time t as well as on x_1, x_2.

Let us first consider the *constitutive relations* of two-dimensional plane stress. For linear elastic isotropic behavior we have, according to Eq. (13.55a),

$$\varepsilon_{\alpha\beta} = \frac{1+\nu}{E}\tau_{\alpha\beta} - \frac{\nu}{E}\tau_{\gamma\gamma}\delta_{\alpha\beta} \qquad (13.114)$$

Before utilizing relations (13.113), it is useful to obtain various alternate forms of Eq. (13.114). We begin with the contraction

$$\varepsilon_{\gamma\gamma} = \frac{1+\nu}{E}\tau_{\gamma\gamma} - \frac{2\nu}{E}\tau_{\gamma\gamma} = \frac{1-\nu}{E}\tau_{\gamma\gamma} \qquad (13.115)$$

Now use this result to substitute for $\tau_{\gamma\gamma}$ in Eq. (13.114), and then solve for $\tau_{\alpha\beta}$ to obtain the inverted form

$$\tau_{\alpha\beta} = \frac{E}{1-\nu^2}[(1-\nu)\varepsilon_{\alpha\beta} + \nu\varepsilon_{\gamma\gamma}\delta_{\alpha\beta}] \qquad (13.116)$$

It is easy to show, furthermore, that Eqs. (13.114) and (13.115) may be combined to obtain

$$e_{\alpha\beta} = \frac{1+\nu}{E}s_{\alpha\beta} \qquad (13.117)$$

where $e_{\alpha\beta}$ and $s_{\alpha\beta}$ are the *two-dimensional* strain and stress deviator tensors, respectively [refer back to Eqs. (12.105)]. Finally, referring to Table 5.1, we may rewrite Eqs. (13.117) and (13.114) in terms of G and K as follows:

$$e_{\alpha\beta} = \frac{1}{2G}s_{\alpha\beta} \qquad \text{(a)}$$

$$\qquad\qquad\qquad\qquad\qquad\qquad\qquad\qquad\qquad (13.118)$$

$$\varepsilon_{\gamma\gamma} = \frac{3K+4G}{18KG}\tau_{\gamma\gamma} \qquad \text{(b)}$$

Note that in Eq. (13.118b) we did not get $\varepsilon_{\gamma\gamma} = \tau_{\gamma\gamma}/3K$, since the volume dilatation ε_{kk} is *not* equal to $\varepsilon_{\gamma\gamma}$ because $\varepsilon_{33} \neq 0$ here.

Beginning with Eq. (13.114) and noting the analogy relations (13.113), we see that

$$\frac{1+\nu}{E} \sim \frac{1+Q^\nu/P^\nu}{Q^E/P^E} = \frac{P^E(P^\nu + Q^\nu)}{P^\nu Q^E} \qquad \text{(a)}$$

$$\qquad\qquad\qquad\qquad\qquad\qquad\qquad\qquad\qquad (13.119)$$

$$\frac{\nu}{E} \sim \frac{Q^\nu/P^\nu}{Q^E/P^E} = \frac{P^E/Q^\nu}{P^\nu/Q^E} \qquad \text{(b)}$$

Using the above in Eq. (13.114), we get, for linear viscoelastic material, upon "clearing" fractions,

$$P^\nu Q^E \varepsilon_{\alpha\beta} = P^E(P^\nu + Q^\nu)\tau_{\alpha\beta} - P^E Q^\nu \tau_{\gamma\gamma}\delta_{\alpha\beta} \qquad (13.120)$$

In expanded form this equation gives

$$P^\nu Q^E \varepsilon_{11} = P^E P^\nu \tau_{11} - P^E Q^\nu \tau_{22}$$

$$P^\nu Q^E \varepsilon_{22} = P^E P^\nu \tau_{22} - P^E Q^\nu \tau_{11} \qquad (13.121)$$

$$P^\nu Q^E \varepsilon_{12} = P^E(P^\nu + Q^\nu)\tau_{12}$$

Now consider the inverted equation (13.116), which we first rewrite as

$$\frac{1+\nu}{E}\tau_{\alpha\beta} = \varepsilon_{\alpha\beta} + \frac{\nu}{1-\nu}\varepsilon_{\gamma\gamma}\delta_{\alpha\beta} \tag{13.122}$$

The operator ratio analogous to the factor $(1 + \nu)/E$ has already been given in Eq. (13.119a), and thus it is only necessary to consider the factor $\nu/(1 - \nu)$. Hence

$$\frac{\nu}{1-\nu} \sim \frac{Q^\nu/P^\nu}{1-Q^\nu/P^\nu} = \frac{Q^\nu}{P^\nu - Q^\nu} \tag{13.123}$$

Using relations (13.119a) and (13.123) in Eq. (13.122) and clearing fractions, we obtain the viscoelastic constitutive law,

$$P^E(P^\nu + Q^\nu)(P^\nu - Q^\nu)\tau_{\alpha\beta} = P^\nu Q^E[(P^\nu - Q^\nu)\varepsilon_{\alpha\beta} + Q^\nu\varepsilon_{\gamma\gamma}\delta_{\alpha\beta}] \tag{13.124}$$

In unabridged notation we have for the above,

$$P^E(P^\nu + Q^\nu)(P^\nu - Q^\nu)\tau_{11} = P^\nu Q^E(P^\nu \varepsilon_{11} - Q^\nu \varepsilon_{22})$$

$$P^E(P^\nu + Q^\nu)(P^\nu - Q^\nu)\tau_{22} = P^\nu Q^E(P^\nu \varepsilon_{22} - Q^\nu \varepsilon_{11}) \tag{13.125}$$

$$P^E(P^\nu + Q^\nu)\tau_{12} = P^\nu Q^E \varepsilon_{12}$$

In a similar manner, Eqs. (13.118) may be converted to the analogous viscoelastic laws through the use of the last two of analogy relations (13.113). Furthermore, *any* of these constitutive laws are readily converted to hereditary integrals, either in terms of creep compliance functions or in terms of relaxation modulus functions. The reader may wish to carry out some of the above as exercises.

We may now work with the viscoelastic laws presented above to formulate well-posed boundary value problems. We begin with the formulation of the *displacement boundary value problem*. The key equations here are the viscoelastic law in the form given by Eq. (13.124), as well as the previously developed equilibrium equation [see Eq. (13.58)] and strain-displacement equation [see Eq. (13.56)]. We reproduce Eqs. (13.58) and (13.56) below:

$$\tau_{\alpha\beta,\beta} - V_{,\alpha} = 0 \qquad \text{(a)}$$
$$\varepsilon_{\alpha\beta} = \tfrac{1}{2}(u_{\alpha,\beta} + u_{\beta,\alpha}) \qquad \text{(b)} \tag{13.126}$$

where we remind you that $\tau_{\alpha\beta}$, $\varepsilon_{\alpha\beta}$, and u_α represent average values over x_3. First we use Eq. (13.126b) to substitute for $\varepsilon_{\alpha\beta}$ in Eq. (13.124), giving us

$$P^E(P^\nu + Q^\nu)(P^\nu - Q^\nu)\tau_{\alpha\beta} = P^\nu Q^E[\tfrac{1}{2}(P^\nu - Q^\nu)(u_{\alpha,\beta} + u_{\beta,\alpha})$$
$$+ Q^\nu u_{\gamma,\gamma}\delta_{\alpha\beta}] \tag{13.127}$$

Then we operate on Eq. (13.126a) with the differential operator $P^E(P^\nu + Q^\nu)(P^\nu - Q^\nu)$, and thereby obtain

$$P^E(P^\nu + Q^\nu)(P^\nu - Q^\nu)\tau_{\alpha\beta,\beta} = P^E(P^\nu + Q^\nu)(P^\nu - Q^\nu)V_{,\alpha} \tag{13.128}$$

Next we substitute Eq. (13.127) into Eq. (13.128) to get

$$P^\nu Q^E[\tfrac{1}{2}(P^\nu - Q^\nu)(u_{\alpha,\beta\beta} + u_{\beta,\alpha\beta}) + Q^\nu u_{\gamma,\gamma\beta}\delta_{\alpha\beta}] = P^E(P^\nu + Q^\nu)(P^\nu - Q^\nu)V_{,\alpha}$$

With the usual continuity assumptions we may combine terms in the equation above to obtain the final result,

$$P^\nu Q^E[(P^\nu - Q^\nu)u_{\alpha,\beta\beta} + (P^\nu + Q^\nu)u_{\beta,\beta\alpha}] = 2P^E(P^\nu + Q^\nu)(P^\nu - Q^\nu)V_{,\alpha} \qquad (13.129)$$

Assuming that the boundary and initial conditions are prescribed in terms of displacement, differential equation (13.129) may be solved for the displacement field $u_\alpha(x_1, x_2, t)$. Strains $\varepsilon_{\alpha\beta}(x_1, x_2, t)$ and then stresses $\tau_{\alpha\beta}(x_1, x_2, t)$ follow from Eqs. (13.126b) and (13.124), respectively. Note that if body forces are absent, Eq. (13.129) simplifies to

$$(P^\nu - Q^\nu)u_{\alpha,\beta\beta} + (P^\nu + Q^\nu)u_{\beta,\beta\alpha} = 0 \qquad (13.130)$$

Most plane-stress problems are given with *tractions* prescribed along the edges, and for such problems it is much more convenient to use the formulation of the *stress boundary value problem*. Proceeding as in Section 13.5 on elastic two-dimensional plane stress, we first reduce equilibrium equation (13.126a) to an identity by introducing the Airy stress function $\Phi(x_1, x_2, t)$, which is defined by [see Eq. (13.59)]

$$\tau_{\alpha\beta} = e_{\alpha\gamma}e_{\beta\delta}\,\Phi_{,\gamma\delta} + V\delta_{\alpha\beta} \qquad (13.131)$$

Since displacement is now a secondary variable to be obtained via integration of the strain-displacement equations, clearly then the compatibility equation (13.17) must play a key role. Accordingly, we reproduce this equation below:

$$e_{\alpha\gamma}e_{\beta\delta}\,\varepsilon_{\alpha\beta,\gamma\delta} = 0 \qquad (13.132)$$

As for the constitutive law, it is now more convenient to work with viscoelastic law (13.120) rather than its inverted form (13.124). One may now proceed to introduce Φ into Eq. (13.120) by substituting for $\tau_{\alpha\beta}$ via Eq. (13.131), and then to substitute the result into Eq. (13.132) after it has been operated upon by $P^\nu Q^E$.

However, it is unnecessary to actually carry out the details as described above, since we may work directly from the result already presented for elastic material [see Eq. (13.60)]:

$$\nabla^4 \Phi = -(1 - \nu)\nabla^2 V \qquad (13.133)$$

Thus, using the second of analogy relations (13.113), we have

$$(1 - \nu) \sim 1 - \frac{Q^\nu}{P^\nu} = \frac{P^\nu - Q^\nu}{P^\nu}$$

Proceeding in the usual manner, we immediately obtain for viscoelastic material

$$P^\nu \nabla^4 \Phi(x_1, x_2, t) = -(P^\nu - Q^\nu)\nabla^2 V(x_1, x_2, t) \qquad (13.134)$$

which is a necessary and sufficient condition for simply connected domains. After Φ has been obtained via solution of differential equation (13.134), the stresses $\tau_{\alpha\beta}(x_1, x_2, t)$ follow from Eq. (13.131); the strains from viscoelastic law (13.120); and finally, the displacements $u_\alpha(x_1, x_2, t)$ via integration of Eq. (13.126b).

If body forces are *absent*, Eq. (13.134) simplifies to

$$\nabla^4 \Phi(x_1, x_2, t) = 0 \qquad (13.135)$$

which is the same differential equation obtained for elastic material. Thus, in a simply connected domain with zero body forces, the stress distributions in two-dimensional plane stress are of the *same form* for elastic and viscoelastic material. This is not necessarily so for multiply connected bodies, since the Cesàro integral conditions may involve a material parameter [e.g., see Eq. (13.62a) for elastic material]. Displacements will, of course, not be the same for elastic and viscoelastic materials.

13.10 VISCOELASTIC SOLUTION VIA THE CORRESPONDENCE PRINCIPLE

The solutions to the boundary value problems presented in the preceding section may be difficult to obtain. However, if the solution to the corresponding elastic problem is available, we may take advantage of the correspondence principle presented in Section 9.5. Once again, this principle states that if we know the Laplace transform of the solution for a linear elastic problem, the Laplace transform of the solution for the corresponding viscoelastic problem can be found by replacing the elastic constants with ratios of operator polynomials in s-space. The appropriate substitutions are summarized below:

$$E \to \frac{\overline{Q}^E(s)}{\overline{P}^E(s)}, \qquad \nu \to \frac{\overline{Q}^\nu(s)}{\overline{P}^\nu(s)},$$

$$3K \to \frac{\overline{Q}^K(s)}{\overline{P}^K(s)}, \qquad 2G \to \frac{\overline{Q}^G(s)}{\overline{P}^G(s)}$$

(13.136)

After inverting the resulting equations we get the desired solution to the viscoelastic problem in the time domain.

In considering the elastic two-dimensional plane-stress problems undertaken in Part B of this chapter, we note that the stretched plate with a small hole (see Section 13.6) and the curved beam under pure bending (see Section 13.7) gave stresses that were independent of the elastic constants. Hence the stress solutions for the corresponding viscoelastic problems will not differ from the elastic solutions already presented. However, the case of the rotating elastic thin disk (see Example 13.1 in Section 13.8) gave stresses that depend on ν. Here the viscoelastic stress solutions will differ from the corresponding elastic stress solutions. The elastic displacement solutions for all three of the problems above will depend on E and ν [e.g., see Eq. (g) in Example 13.1], and clearly the viscoelastic displacement solutions for any of these problems will not be the same as the corresponding elastic displacement solutions.

In the following example we shall use the correspondence principle to calculate the stress and displacement solutions for a rotating viscoelastic thin disk.

Example 13.2

We shall use the correspondence principle to find τ_{rr}, $\tau_{\theta\theta}$, and u_r for a rotating disk, for which there is *elastic* behavior in *bulk* and *viscous* behavior in *distortion*. Accordingly,

$$\frac{Q^K}{P^K} = 3K \qquad \text{and} \qquad \frac{\overline{Q}^K}{\overline{P}^K} = 3K$$

$$\frac{Q^G}{P^G} = \zeta \frac{\partial}{\partial t} \qquad \text{and} \qquad \frac{\overline{Q}^G}{\overline{P}^G} = \zeta s \qquad \text{(a)}$$

To facilitate the solution of this problem, we will assume that the centrifugal body "force" is suddenly applied at $t = 0$ by means of a step increase in angular velocity from zero to a constant value ω_0. Thus

$$\omega(t) = \omega_0[u(t)] \qquad \text{(b)}$$

We shall disregard any inertial effects that may be present in this process, other than the radial centrifugal body force distribution which is suddenly attained at the prescribed angular speed ω_0.

We start with the elastic solutions for this case, as given by Eqs. (e) to (g) in Example 13.1. These solutions are valid for *any* angular velocity function $\omega(t)$, assuming of course that tangential inertial effects may be ignored. Employing Eq. (b) above and noting that $[u(t)]^2 = [u(t)]$, we have

$$\tau_{rr}^E = \frac{\rho\omega_0^2}{8}(3+\nu)[R^2 - r^2][u(t)]$$

$$\tau_{\theta\theta}^E = \frac{\rho\omega_0^2}{8}[(3+\nu)R^2 - (1+3\nu)r^2][u(t)] \qquad \text{(c)}$$

$$u_r^E = \frac{\rho\omega_0^2}{8}r\left(\frac{1-\nu}{E}\right)[(3+\nu)R^2 - (1+\nu)r^2][u(t)]$$

where the superscript E indicates the elastic solutions. To be able to utilize Eqs. (a), we must first express E, ν in Eqs. (c) in terms of K, G. Referring back to Table 5.1, we obtain

$$1 + \nu = \frac{9K}{6K + 2G}$$

$$3 + \nu = 2 + (1 + \nu) = 2 + \frac{9K}{6K + 2G}$$

$$1 + 3\nu = -2 + 3(1 + \nu) = -2 + 3\left(\frac{9K}{6K + 2G}\right) \qquad \text{(d)}$$

$$\frac{1 - \nu}{E} = \frac{3K + 4G}{18KG}$$

After substituting Eqs. (d) into Eqs. (c), we can take the Laplace transform of these equations. (Throughout this problem we will take the lower limit of the transform operator at $t = 0^-$, and accordingly *all* initial conditions are homogeneous.) We then get after regrouping terms

$$\overline{\tau}_{rr}^E = \frac{\rho\omega_0^2}{8}\left[2 + \frac{9K}{6K + 2G}\right][R^2 - r^2]\frac{1}{s}$$

$$\overline{\tau}_{\theta\theta}^E = \frac{\rho\omega_0^2}{8}\left\{2[R^2 + r^2] + \frac{9K}{6K + 2G}[R^2 - 3r^2]\right\}\frac{1}{s} \qquad \text{(e)}$$

$$\overline{u}_r^E = \frac{\rho\omega_0^2}{8}r\left(\frac{3K + 4G}{18KG}\right)\left\{2R^2 + \frac{9K}{6K + 2G}[R^2 - r^2]\right\}\frac{1}{s}$$

Now refer back to substitutions (13.136). Utilizing Eqs. (a) for the present problem we have for these substitutions,

$$3K \to \frac{\bar{Q}^K}{\bar{P}^K} = 3K, \qquad 2G \to \frac{\bar{Q}^G}{\bar{P}^G} = \zeta s \qquad \text{(f)}$$

It then follows that the two ratios of elastic constants on the right side of Eqs. (d) undergo the following substitutions:

$$\frac{9K}{6K + 2G} \to \frac{9K}{6K + \zeta s}, \qquad \frac{3K + 4G}{18KG} \to \frac{3K + 2\zeta s}{9K\zeta s} \qquad \text{(g)}$$

The Laplace transforms of the viscoelastic solutions are obtained by utilizing substitutions (g) in Eqs. (e). Thus

$$s\bar{\tau}_{rr} = \frac{\rho\omega_0^2}{8}\left[2 + \frac{9K}{6K + \zeta s}\right][R^2 - r^2]$$

$$s\bar{\tau}_{\theta\theta} = \frac{\rho\omega_0^2}{8}\left\{2[R^2 + r^2] + \frac{9K}{6K + \zeta s}[R^2 - 3r^2]\right\} \qquad \text{(h)}$$

$$s\bar{u}_r = \frac{\rho\omega_0^2}{8} r \left(\frac{3K + 2\zeta s}{9K\zeta s}\right)\left\{2R^2 + \frac{9K}{6K + \zeta s}[R^2 - r^2]\right\}$$

By using the limit theorems given in Appendix III, we may immediately obtain the initial limit solutions at $t = 0^+$ and the asymptotic solutions as $t \to \infty$. Accordingly, at $t = 0^+$ we get

$$\tau_{rr}(0^+) = \lim_{s \to \infty} s\bar{\tau}_{rr} = \frac{\rho\omega_0^2}{4}[R^2 - r^2]$$

$$\tau_{\theta\theta}(0^+) = \lim_{s \to \infty} s\bar{\tau}_{\theta\theta} = \frac{\rho\omega_0^2}{4}[R^2 + r^2] \qquad \text{(i)}$$

$$u_r(0^+) = \lim_{s \to \infty} s\bar{u}_r = \frac{\rho\omega_0^2}{18K} rR^2$$

For $t \to \infty$ we obtain

$$\tau_{rr}(\infty) = \lim_{s \to 0} s\bar{\tau}_{rr} = \frac{7\rho\omega_0^2}{16}[R^2 - r^2]$$

$$\tau_{\theta\theta}(\infty) = \lim_{s \to 0} s\bar{\tau}_{\theta\theta} = \frac{\rho\omega_0^2}{16}[7R^2 - 5r^2] \qquad \text{(j)}$$

$$u_r(\infty) = \lim_{s \to 0} s\bar{u}_r \to \infty$$

$$\dot{u}_r(\infty) = \lim_{s \to 0} s^2\bar{u}_r = \frac{\rho\omega_0^2}{48} \frac{r}{\zeta}[7R^2 - 3r^2]$$

where $\dot{u}_r$ is the radial velocity. Note that $u_r(0^+)$ is finite, whereas $u_r(\infty)$ is unbounded. Thus the short-time behavior is that of an elastic solid, whereas the long-time behavior is that of a viscous fluid. Furthermore, on comparing Eqs. (i) above with elastic solutions (c), we see that the initial solution corresponds with $\nu = -1$.

We now return to the inversion of Eqs. (h). Since an s factor has been multiplied throughout, these inversions will yield the time derivatives $\dot{\tau}_{rr}$, $\dot{\tau}_{\theta\theta}$, and $\dot{u}_r$. Subsequent integrations will then give τ_{rr}, $\tau_{\theta\theta}$, and u_r. Starting with the stress rates, we use the results given in Appendix III (e.g., see Table III.1) and obtain for $t \geq 0^-$,

$$\dot{\tau}_{rr} = \frac{\rho\omega_0^2}{8}\left\{2[\delta(t)] + \frac{9K}{\zeta}\exp(-6Kt/\zeta)\right\}[R^2 - r^2]$$

$$\dot{\tau}_{\theta\theta} = \frac{\rho\omega_0^2}{8}\left\{2[\delta(t)][R^2 + r^2] + \frac{9K}{\zeta}\exp(-6Kt/\zeta)[R^2 - 3r^2]\right\} \tag{k}$$

Integrating over t, we have

$$\tau_{rr} = \frac{\rho\omega_0^2}{8}\left\{2[u(t)] - \frac{3}{2}\exp(-6Kt/\zeta)\right\}[R^2 - r^2] + f(r)$$

$$\tau_{\theta\theta} = \frac{\rho\omega_0^2}{8}\left\{2[u(t)][R^2 + r^2] - \frac{3}{2}\exp(-6Kt/\zeta)\right\}[R^2 - 3r^2] + g(r) \tag{ℓ}$$

where $f(r)$ and $g(r)$ are functions of integration. Now, using the homogeneous initial conditions $\tau_{rr}(0^-) = \tau_{\theta\theta}(0^-) = 0$, we find

$$f(r) = \frac{\rho\omega_0^2}{8}\left(\frac{3}{2}\right)[R^2 - r^2]$$

$$g(r) = \frac{\rho\omega_0^2}{8}\left(\frac{3}{2}\right)[R^2 - 3r^2] \tag{m}$$

The final stress solutions for $t \geq 0^-$ are then given as

$$\tau_{rr} = \frac{\rho\omega_0^2}{8}\left\{2[u(t)] + \frac{3}{2}[1 - \exp(-6Kt/\zeta)]\right\}[R^2 - r^2]$$

$$\tau_{\theta\theta} = \frac{\rho\omega_0^2}{8}\left\{2[u(t)][R^2 + r^2] + \frac{3}{2}[1 - \exp(-6Kt/\zeta)][R^2 - 3r^2]\right\} \tag{n}$$

which are consistent with the limiting solutions in Eqs. (i) and (j).

We finally consider the inversion of the last of Eqs. (h) for the radial velocity $\dot{u}_r$. First we multiply out the leading factor in terms of K and ζ to get

$$s\bar{u}_r = \frac{\rho\omega_0^2}{8}r\left\{\frac{2R^2}{2\zeta s} + \frac{4R^2}{9K} + \frac{3K}{\zeta s(6K + \zeta s)}[R^2 - r^2] + \frac{2}{6K + \zeta s}[R^2 - r^2]\right\} \tag{o}$$

By carrying out a partial fractions expansion, we can easily show that

$$\frac{3K}{\zeta s(6K + \zeta s)} = \frac{1}{2\zeta s} - \frac{1}{2(6K + \zeta s)} \tag{p}$$

Substituting this result for the coefficient of the third term in the braces of Eq. (o), we obtain after collecting terms

$$s\bar{u}_r = \frac{\rho\omega_0^2}{8}r\left\{\frac{4R^2}{9K} + \frac{1}{6\zeta s}[7R^2 - 3r^2] + \frac{3}{2(6K + \zeta s)}[R^2 - r^2]\right\} \tag{q}$$

The inversion of this equation is straightforward. We get for $t \geq 0^-$,

$$\dot{u}_r = \frac{\rho\omega_0^2}{8}r\left\{\frac{4}{9K}[\delta(t)]R^2 + \frac{1}{6\zeta}[u(t)][7R^2 - 3r^2] + \frac{3}{2\zeta}\exp(-6Kt/\zeta)[R^2 - r^2]\right\} \tag{r}$$

An integration over t yields the radial displacement as

$$u_r = \frac{\rho\omega_0^2}{8}r\left\{\frac{4}{9K}[u(t)]R^2 + \frac{1}{6\zeta}t[u(t)][7R^2 - 3r^2] - \frac{1}{4K}\exp(-6Kt/\zeta)[R^2 - r^2]\right\} + h(r) \tag{s}$$

where $h(r)$ is another function of integration. Now we utilize the homogeneous initial condition $u_r(0^-) = 0$ to find $h(r)$, and thereby obtain the final solution for $t \geq 0^-$ as

$$u_r = \frac{\rho \omega_0^2}{8} r \left\{ \frac{4}{9K} [u(t)]R^2 + \frac{1}{6\zeta} t[u(t)][7R^2 - 3r^2] + \frac{1}{4K} [1 - \exp(-6Kt/\zeta)][R^2 - r^2] \right\}$$

(t)

You can easily show that solutions (r) and (t) are consistent with the limiting solutions given in Eqs. (i) and (j).

13.11 CONSTITUTIVE LAWS FOR PERFECTLY PLASTIC PLANE STRESS

We will now make some observations on perfect plasticity in two-dimensional plane stress. First we ask you to recall the three-dimensional plastic flow rule given in Sections 8.12 and 9.3. We rewrite this key equation [e.g., see Eq. (8.96)] below:

$$\dot{\varepsilon}_{ij}^p = \dot{\Lambda} \frac{\partial f}{\partial \tau_{ij}}$$

(13.137)

where $\dot{\Lambda}$ is a *positive* scalar multiplier and f is the yield surface function. You will recall that for principal axes this equation becomes [see Eq. (8.97)]

$$\dot{\varepsilon}_i^p = \dot{\Lambda} \frac{\partial f}{\partial \tau_i}$$

(13.138)

This equation stipulates that in principal stress space the plastic strain-rate vector is oriented outwardly normal to the yield surface (a consequence of Drucker's postulate). Another important quantity is the *plastic dissipation power*, defined as [see Eq. (8.111)]

$$\dot{W}_p = \tau_{kl} \dot{\varepsilon}_{kl}^p$$

(13.139)

which is also *positive*. Finally, for principal axes, Eq. (13.139) becomes

$$\dot{W}_p = \tau_k \dot{\varepsilon}_k^p$$

(13.140)

Now, for the case of *plane stress* we set $\tau_{13} = \tau_{23} = \tau_{33} = 0$ in the constitutive relations above, or for principal axes we equivalently set $\tau_3 = 0$. Accordingly, Eq. (13.138) yields

$$\dot{\varepsilon}_1^p = \dot{\Lambda} \left. \frac{\partial f}{\partial \tau_1} \right|_{\tau_3 = 0} \qquad \text{(a)}$$

$$\dot{\varepsilon}_2^p = \dot{\Lambda} \left. \frac{\partial f}{\partial \tau_2} \right|_{\tau_3 = 0} \qquad \text{(b)} \qquad \qquad (13.141)$$

$$\dot{\varepsilon}_3^p = \dot{\Lambda} \left. \frac{\partial f}{\partial \tau_3} \right|_{\tau_3 = 0} \qquad \text{(c)}$$

The principal strain-rate component $\dot{\varepsilon}_3^p$ is of little interest, and thus we shall ignore Eq. (13.141c). Furthermore, in Eqs. (13.141a, b) the results are unaffected if we set $\tau_3 = 0$ in the function f and *then* carry out the indicated differentiations. Introducing two-dimensional index notation, these two equations then become

$$\dot{\varepsilon}_\alpha^p = \dot{\Lambda} \frac{\partial f_0}{\partial \tau_\alpha} \qquad (13.142)$$

where f_0 is the plane-stress yield curve function obtained by setting $\tau_3 = 0$ in the yield surface function f. Similarly, for plane stress Eq. (13.137) becomes

$$\dot{\varepsilon}_{\alpha\beta}^p = \dot{\Lambda} \frac{\partial f_0}{\partial \tau_{\alpha\beta}} \qquad (13.143)$$

where here f_0 is obtained by setting $\tau_{13} = \tau_{23} = \tau_{33} = 0$ in f. Finally, setting $\tau_3 = 0$ in Eq. (13.140) and $\tau_{13} = \tau_{23} = \tau_{33} = 0$ in Eq. (13.139), we obtain the plastic dissipation power for plane stress as

$$\dot{W}_p = \tau_{\gamma\delta} \dot{\varepsilon}_{\gamma\delta}^p = \tau_\gamma \dot{\varepsilon}_\gamma^p \qquad (13.144)$$

We shall examine Eqs. (13.142) to (13.144) for the cases of yielding according to Mises and Tresca.

Case A: Yielding According to Mises

For the onset of yielding the Mises criterion gives for the yield surface function [e.g., see Eq. (9.29a)]

$$f = J_2 - \frac{Y^2}{3} = 0 \qquad (13.145)$$

where Y is the yield stress in tension. The invariant J_2 is given by

$$J_2 = \tfrac{1}{2} s_{kl} s_{kl} = \tfrac{1}{2} \left(\tau_{kl} \tau_{kl} - \tfrac{1}{3} \tau_{kk} \tau_{ll} \right)$$

and thus

$$f = \tfrac{1}{2} \left(\tau_{kl} \tau_{kl} - \tfrac{1}{3} \tau_{kk} \tau_{ll} \right) - \frac{Y^2}{3} \qquad (13.146)$$

Turning now to the special case of plane stress, we set $\tau_{13} = \tau_{23} = \tau_{33} = 0$ in Eq. (13.146), and thereby obtain the yield curve function as

$$f_0 = \frac{1}{2} \left(\tau_{\gamma\delta} \tau_{\gamma\delta} - \frac{1}{3} \tau_{\gamma\gamma} \tau_{\delta\delta} \right) - \frac{Y^2}{3} \qquad (13.147)$$

In expanded form Eq. (13.147) gives

$$f_0 = \frac{1}{3} \left(\tau_{11}^2 + \tau_{22}^2 - \tau_{11} \tau_{22} + 3\tau_{12}^2 \right) - \frac{Y^2}{3} \qquad (13.148)$$

Finally, for principal axes we have

$$f_0 = \frac{1}{3} \left(\tau_1^2 + \tau_2^2 - \tau_1 \tau_2 \right) - \frac{Y^2}{3} \qquad (13.149)$$

In Section 8.10 we showed that in principal stress space the equation $f_0 = 0$ yields an ellipse symmetric about axes which are rotated $45°$ relative to the $\tau_1 \tau_2$ axes. The

616

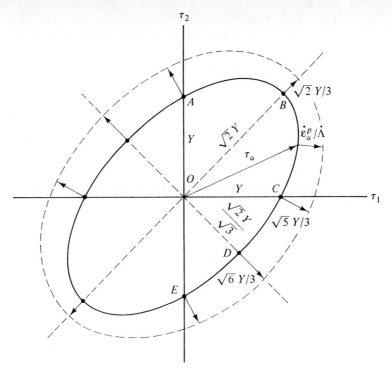

Figure 13.12 Principal normalized strain-rate vectors $\dot{\varepsilon}_\alpha^p/\dot{\Lambda}$ for plane stress via Mises.

semimajor and semiminor diameters of this ellipse are $\sqrt{2}\,Y$ and $\sqrt{2}\,Y/\sqrt{3}$, respectively,* as shown in Fig. 13.12.

We may now substitute Eq. (13.147) into flow rule (13.143), and thereby obtain

$$\dot{\varepsilon}_{\alpha\beta}^p = \frac{\dot{\Lambda}}{2}\left(2\tau_{\gamma\delta}\delta_{\gamma\alpha}\delta_{\delta\beta} - \frac{1}{3}\,\tau_{\gamma\gamma}\delta_{\delta\alpha}\delta_{\delta\beta} - \frac{1}{3}\,\delta_{\gamma\alpha}\delta_{\gamma\beta}\tau_{\delta\delta}\right)$$

$$= \dot{\Lambda}\left(\tau_{\alpha\beta} - \frac{1}{3}\,\tau_{\gamma\gamma}\delta_{\alpha\beta}\right) \tag{13.150}$$

Clearly, for principal axes, Eq. (13.150) gives

$$\dot{\varepsilon}_1^p = \frac{\dot{\Lambda}}{3}\,(2\tau_1 - \tau_2) \qquad \text{(a)}$$

$$\tag{13.151}$$

$$\dot{\varepsilon}_2^p = \frac{\dot{\Lambda}}{3}\,(2\tau_2 - \tau_1) \qquad \text{(b)}$$

---

*Note that we are using the *circumscribed* configuration previously shown in Fig. 8.24, with $k_M = Y/\sqrt{3}$. Accordingly, the Mises and Tresca formulations will correspond for the case of simple tension.

Note that this same result is obtained by substituting Eq. (13.149) into Eq. (13.142). The *magnitude* of the principal strain-rate vector follows from Eqs. (13.151) as

$$|\dot{\varepsilon}_\alpha^p| = \frac{\dot{\Lambda}}{3}\,[(2\tau_1 - \tau_2)^2 + (2\tau_2 - \tau_1)^2]^{1/2} \tag{13.152}$$

Its *direction* is of course normal to the yield curve. The plastic dissipation power on the yield curve is obtained by substituting Eq. (13.150) into Eq. (13.144). Accordingly, we obtain

$$\dot{W}_p = \tau_{\gamma\delta}\,\dot{\varepsilon}_{\gamma\delta}^p = \tau_\gamma\dot{\varepsilon}_\gamma^p = \dot{\Lambda}\left(\tau_{\gamma\delta}\tau_{\gamma\delta} - \tfrac{1}{3}\tau_{\gamma\gamma}\tau_{\delta\delta}\right)$$

But since $f_0 = 0$ on the yield curve, the use of Eq. (13.147) in the above gives

$$\dot{W}_p = \tau_\gamma\dot{\varepsilon}_\gamma^p = \frac{2\dot{\Lambda}Y^2}{3} \tag{13.153}$$

We thus see that on the yield curve we have $\dot{W}_p/\dot{\Lambda} = \tau_\gamma\dot{\varepsilon}_\gamma^p/\dot{\Lambda} = 2Y^2/3$, that is, the dot product of the vectors τ_γ and $\dot{\varepsilon}_\gamma^p/\dot{\Lambda}$ is invariant along the yield curve.*

Using Eqs. (13.151), the principal strain-rate components were calculated for points A, B, C, D, E in Fig. 13.12. The results are tabulated in Table 13.1, and the ratio $\dot{\varepsilon}_\alpha^p/\dot{\Lambda}$ is illustrated in Fig. 13.12. We shall henceforth refer to $\dot{\varepsilon}_\alpha^p/\dot{\Lambda}$ as the *normalized* strain-rate vector. Note that $|\dot{\varepsilon}_\alpha^p/\dot{\Lambda}|_{min}$ occurs at points of $|\tau_\alpha|_{max}$ (e.g., point B), and conversely $|\dot{\varepsilon}_\alpha^p/\dot{\Lambda}|_{max}$ occurs at $|\tau_\alpha|_{min}$ (e.g., point D). Also note that in accordance with Eq. (13.153), the product of $|\tau_\alpha|$ with the projection of the normalized strain-rate vector $\dot{\varepsilon}_\alpha^p/\dot{\Lambda}$ onto τ_α is a constant along the yield curve.

Case B: Yielding According to Tresca

Because the Mises plane stress yield curve is smooth, we found that there was a unique direction for the plastic strain-rate vector at each point on the yield curve. However, you will recall from Chapter 8 that the Tresca plane stress yield curve is

TABLE 13.1 Strain Rates via Mises

Point (Fig. 13.12)	τ_1/Y	τ_2/Y	$\dot{\varepsilon}_1^p/(\dot{\Lambda}Y)$	$\dot{\varepsilon}_2^p/(\dot{\Lambda}Y)$	$|\dot{\varepsilon}_\alpha^p|/(\dot{\Lambda}Y)$
A	0	1	$-\dfrac{1}{3}$	$\dfrac{2}{3}$	$\dfrac{\sqrt{5}}{3}$
B	1	1	$\dfrac{1}{3}$	$\dfrac{1}{3}$	$\dfrac{\sqrt{2}}{3}$
C	1	0	$\dfrac{2}{3}$	$-\dfrac{1}{3}$	$\dfrac{\sqrt{5}}{3}$
D	$\dfrac{\sqrt{3}}{3}$	$-\dfrac{\sqrt{3}}{3}$	$\dfrac{\sqrt{3}}{3}$	$-\dfrac{\sqrt{3}}{3}$	$\dfrac{\sqrt{6}}{3}$
E	0	-1	$\dfrac{1}{3}$	$-\dfrac{2}{3}$	$\dfrac{\sqrt{5}}{3}$

* A similar result was obtained in Section 8.12 for the case of the three-dimensional Mises yield surface [see Eqs. (8.112) and (8.113)].

not smooth, and accordingly, the direction of the plastic strain-rate vector will not be unique at points of discontinuous slope. We shall have to investigate this complicating factor in the present development. Now, in Section 8.10 we showed that in principal stress space the plane stress Tresca yield curve is a polygon, which runs along adjacent sides of squares in the first and third quadrants and along the hypotenuses of isosceles right triangles in the second and fourth quadrants (e.g., look back at Fig. 8.24). We have redrawn this plane-stress polygon (i.e., $\tau_3 = 0$) in Fig. 13.13, and you should note that the "corner" points A, B, C, D, E, F are points of discontinuous slope. Because of the symmetry of this polygon, it will suffice for us to determine the nature of $\dot{\varepsilon}_\alpha^p$ only along the three sides AB, BC, and CD and at the three corner points A, B, and C.

For the sides of Tresca polygon we employ flow rule (13.142),

$$\dot{\varepsilon}_\alpha^p = \dot{\Lambda} \frac{\partial f_0}{\partial \tau_\alpha} \tag{13.154}$$

Rather than using a complicated function f_0 valid for the entire yield curve, it is more convenient to employ separate simpler functions f_{0i} for each side. Each such function must vanish when the equation for the corresponding side is substituted into the function. Furthermore, in order to establish a correspondence between the present Tresca and Mises formulations, we shall select functions f_{0i} that for the case

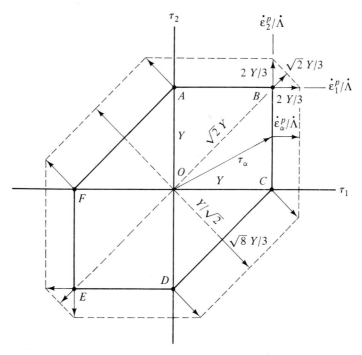

Figure 13.13 Principal normalized strain-rate vectors $\dot{\varepsilon}_\alpha^p/\dot{\Lambda}$ for plane stress via Tresca.

of simple tension take on the same form as does Eq. (13.149) for Mises yielding under simple tension.* The following functions obey the conditions above:

Along AB $(\tau_2 = Y)$: $\qquad f_{01} = \frac{1}{3}(\tau_2^2 - Y^2)$ $\qquad$ (a)

Along BC $(\tau_1 = Y)$: $\qquad f_{02} = \frac{1}{3}(\tau_1^2 - Y^2)$ $\qquad$ (b) $\qquad$ (13.155)

Along CD $(\tau_1 - \tau_2 = Y)$: $\qquad f_{03} = \frac{1}{3}[(\tau_1 - \tau_2)^2 - Y^2]$ $\qquad$ (c)

You may readily verify that Eqs. (13.149) and (13.155) take on the same form, when the appropriate variable τ_1 or τ_2 is set equal to zero so as to yield simple tension (or compression). Using flow law (13.154) with yield curve functions (13.155), we determined the strain-rate components $\dot{\varepsilon}_\alpha^p$ for sides AB, BC, and CD shown in Fig. 13.13. The results are tabulated in Table 13.2, and the normalized strain-rate vector $\dot{\varepsilon}_\alpha^p/\dot{\Lambda}$ is illustrated on all six sides in Fig. 13.13. By utilizing the values labeled in the figure, one can easily see that on *all sides* we have the invariant

$$\frac{\dot{W}_p}{\dot{\Lambda}} = \frac{\tau_\alpha \dot{\varepsilon}_\alpha^p}{\dot{\Lambda}} = \frac{2Y^2}{3} \qquad (13.156)$$

This is the *same* result as that obtained for yielding via Mises [see Eq. (13.153)].

Let us now look at the corner points, where as noted previously, a *range* of normalized strain-rate vectors $\dot{\varepsilon}_\alpha^p/\dot{\Lambda}$ is permitted. In obtaining conditions on these vectors, we shall first logically assume that the vectors at the two limits of a range are equal to the vectors obtained at the adjacent edges via application of flow rule (13.154). In addition, we shall assume that the normalized strain-rate vectors $\dot{\varepsilon}_\alpha^p/\dot{\Lambda}$ within a range are such that $\dot{W}_p/\dot{\Lambda}$ is *invariant*, which is certainly very reasonable since we have already shown that $\dot{W}_p/\dot{\Lambda}$ is invariant along the sides of the Tresca yield curve [see Eq. (13.156)]. Accordingly, the projections of the $\dot{\varepsilon}_\alpha^p/\dot{\Lambda}$ vectors within a range onto the τ_α vector to the corner point must all be equal. Clearly, the conditions above are satisfied when we simply join the tips of the $\dot{\varepsilon}_\alpha^p/\dot{\Lambda}$ vectors at the ends of the adjacent edges by a *straight line*. We have done so at all six corner points in Fig. 13.13. We may now deduce the necessary conditions on $\dot{\varepsilon}_\alpha^p/\dot{\Lambda}$ at each corner point. We shall illustrate the procedure for point B at which point we have

TABLE 13.2 Strain Rates along Sides of Tresca Polygon

Side (Fig. 13.13)	f_{0i}	$\dot{\varepsilon}_1^p/(\dot{\Lambda}Y)$	$\dot{\varepsilon}_2^p/(\dot{\Lambda}Y)$	$|\dot{\varepsilon}_\alpha^p|/(\dot{\Lambda}Y)$
AB $(\tau_2 = Y)$	$\frac{1}{3}(\tau_2^2 - Y^2)$	0	$\frac{2}{3}$	$\frac{2}{3}$
BC $(\tau_1 = Y)$	$\frac{1}{3}(\tau_1^2 - Y^2)$	$\frac{2}{3}$	0	$\frac{2}{3}$
CD $(\tau_1 - \tau_2 = Y)$	$\frac{1}{3}[(\tau_1 - \tau_2)^2 - Y^2]$	$\frac{2}{3}$	$-\frac{2}{3}$	$\frac{\sqrt{8}}{3}$

* Since $\dot{\Lambda}$ is undetermined, many forms may be chosen for the f_0. It is only necessary that the *ratio* $\dot{\varepsilon}_1^p/\dot{\varepsilon}_2^p$ be independent of the particular forms chosen.

TABLE 13.3 Conditions on Strain Rates at Tresca Corner Points

Corner Point (Fig. 13.13)	Locus of $\dot{\varepsilon}_1^p \dot{\varepsilon}_2^p$ Points	Permitted Ranges
A	$\dot{\varepsilon}_2^p = \dfrac{2\dot{\Lambda}Y}{3}$	$-\dfrac{2\dot{\Lambda}Y}{3} \leq \dot{\varepsilon}_1^p \leq 0$
B	$\dot{\varepsilon}_1^p + \dot{\varepsilon}_2^p = \dfrac{2\dot{\Lambda}Y}{3}$	$0 \leq \dot{\varepsilon}_1^p \leq \dfrac{2\dot{\Lambda}Y}{3},\ 0 \leq \dot{\varepsilon}_2^p \leq \dfrac{2\dot{\Lambda}Y}{3}$
C	$\dot{\varepsilon}_1^p = \dfrac{2\dot{\Lambda}Y}{3}$	$-\dfrac{2\dot{\Lambda}Y}{3} \leq \dot{\varepsilon}_2^p \leq 0$

shown a local $\dot{\varepsilon}_1^p/\dot{\Lambda}, \dot{\varepsilon}_2^p/\dot{\Lambda}$ coordinate system with origin at B. Clearly, the *locus* of all points defining the tips of the $\dot{\varepsilon}_\alpha^p/\dot{\Lambda}$ vectors at B is defined by the line

$$\frac{\dot{\varepsilon}_1^p}{\dot{\Lambda}} + \frac{\dot{\varepsilon}_2^p}{\dot{\Lambda}} = \frac{2Y}{3} \tag{13.157}$$

Furthermore, since this line is restricted to the first quadrant of the local $\dot{\varepsilon}_1^p/\dot{\Lambda}, \dot{\varepsilon}_2^p/\dot{\Lambda}$ plane, the components of $\dot{\varepsilon}_\alpha^p/\dot{\Lambda}$ satisfy the *conditions of range*

$$0 \leq \frac{\dot{\varepsilon}_1^p}{\dot{\Lambda}} \leq \frac{2Y}{3}$$
$$0 \leq \frac{\dot{\varepsilon}_2^p}{\dot{\Lambda}} \leq \frac{2Y}{3} \tag{13.158}$$

This same procedure may be applied to corner points A and C. The results for corner points A, B, and C are presented in Table 13.3.

We will now return to the rotating disk problem of Sections 13.8 and 13.10, but now for elastic, perfectly plastic behavior using the Tresca condition for the onset of plastic behavior.

13.12 PLASTIC BEHAVIOR OF THE ROTATING DISK

We once again return to the thin rotating disk, and now consider incompressible elastic, incompressible perfectly plastic behavior. From Eqs. (j) to (ℓ) of Example 13.1 in Section 13.8, we have for the *incompressible* elastic case (i.e., $\nu = \frac{1}{2}$, $E = 3G$):

$$\tau_{rr}(r) = \frac{7\rho\omega_0^2}{16}(R^2 - r^2) \qquad \text{(a)}$$

$$\tau_{\theta\theta}(r) = \frac{7\rho\omega_0^2}{16}\left(R^2 - \frac{5}{7}r^2\right) \qquad \text{(b)} \tag{13.159}$$

$$u_r(r) = \frac{7\rho\omega_0^2}{96G}r\left(R^2 - \frac{3}{7}r^2\right) \qquad \text{(c)}$$

Here ρ and R are, respectively, the density and outside radius of the disk (see Fig. 13.11), and ω_0 is the asymptotic angular velocity reached after the disk has been brought slowly up to speed.

In observing Eqs. (13.159a, b), it should be clear that $\tau_{\theta\theta} > \tau_{rr} \geq 0$ except at the origin ($r = 0$) where $\tau_{rr} = \tau_{\theta\theta}$. Also, since these are principal stresses ($\tau_{r\theta} = 0$), we see that $\tau_{max} = \tau_{\theta\theta}$ and $\tau_{min} = \tau_{zz} = 0$. We can thus readily use the *Tresca condition*, according to which the onset of yielding takes place when

$$\tau_{max} - \tau_{min} = \tau_{\theta\theta} = Y \qquad (13.160)$$

where Y is the tensile yield stress. Setting $\tau_1 = \tau_{\theta\theta}$, $\tau_2 = \tau_{rr}$, and $\tau_3 = \tau_{zz}$ such that $\tau_1 \geq \tau_2 \geq \tau_3 = 0$, we see that yielding occurs along the vertical line BC of the Tresca polygon in Fig. 13.13. The largest stress occurs at $r = 0$ [see Eqs. (13.159)], which in the principal stress space of Fig. 13.13 corresponds to the point B where $\tau_1 = \tau_2 = Y$. Accordingly, yielding begins first at this point as the value of ω_0 is increased. Let ω_e be the largest asymptotic angular velocity for entirely *elastic* behavior, which of course is the angular velocity at which yielding first appears at $r = 0$. Accordingly, in Eq. (13.159b) we set $\omega_0 = \omega_e$, $r = 0$, and $\tau_{\theta\theta} = Y$ [via Eq. (13.160)], and thereby obtain

$$\omega_e = \frac{4}{R}\left(\frac{Y}{7\rho}\right)^{1/2} \qquad (13.161)$$

As the value of ω_0 is increased above ω_e, the plastic zone in the disk penetrates radially out from the origin so that we have a plastic disk surrounded by an elastic annulus. We shall designate the radius separating these two zones as η, and call it the *elastic–plastic junction radius*. In Fig. 13.14 we have drawn the Tresca polygon, showing the locus of points in principal stress space for the case of ω_0 somewhat greater than ω_e. Note that the plastic zone begins at the corner point B, for which $r = 0$, and then moves down the vertical side to point G, for which $r = \eta$. The elastic zone then proceeds from G along a curve to point H, for which $r = R$. At the latter point we have $\tau_{rr} = 0$, since the outer edge of the disk is traction-free.

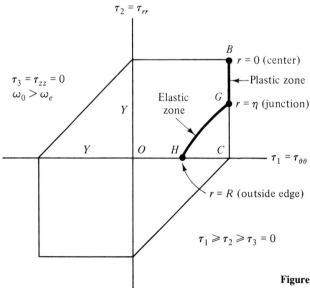

Figure 13.14 Locus of stress points for rotating disk when $\omega_0 > \omega_e$.

Equations (13.159) are valid only if $\omega_0 \le \omega_e$, since then the *entire* plate is elastic. What about the elastic annular region $\eta \le r \le R$, which exists when we have $\omega_0 > \omega_e$? Equations (13.159) are *not* applicable to this region, since such an annular region is *multiply connected*. For this region we must return to Eq. (13.102) in Section 13.8 for the Airy stress function Φ, with the potential $V(r)$ for the rotating disk and its integral given by Eqs. (a) and (c) respectively in Example 13.1 of that same section. Accordingly, we have for incompressible elastic behavior ($\nu = \frac{1}{2}$),

$$\frac{d\Phi}{dr} = \frac{\rho\omega_0^2}{16} r^3 + \frac{C_1}{2} r \left(\ln r - \frac{1}{2}\right) + \frac{C_2}{2} r + \frac{C_3}{r} \tag{13.162}$$

It then follows (e.g., see Problem 13.29) that, for incompressible elastic behavior ($\nu = \frac{1}{2}$ and $E = 3G$) in this doubly connected region of the rotating disk, we have

$$\tau_{rr}(r) = -\frac{7\rho\omega_0^2}{16} r^2 + \frac{C_2}{2} + \frac{C_3}{r^2} \tag{a}$$

$$\tau_{\theta\theta}(r) = -\frac{5\rho\omega_0^2}{16} r^2 + \frac{C_2}{2} - \frac{C_3}{r^2} \tag{b} \tag{13.163}$$

$$u_r(r) = -\frac{\rho\omega_0^2}{32G} r^3 + \frac{C_2 r}{12G} - \frac{C_3}{2Gr} \tag{c}$$

Note that $C_1 = 0$ by virtue of the Cesàro integral conditions. For $\omega_0 > \omega_e$ and $\eta \le r \le R$, we may now determine the functions C_2 and C_3 in Eqs. (13.163) by enforcing the following boundary conditions:

$$\tau_{rr}(R) = 0, \qquad \tau_{\theta\theta}(\eta) = Y \tag{13.164}$$

Submitting Eqs. (13.163a, b) to the conditions above, we find after some algebra that

$$C_2 = \frac{16Y\eta^2 + \rho\omega_0^2(5\eta^4 + 7R^4)}{8(\eta^2 + R^2)} \tag{a}$$

$$C_3 = -\frac{\eta^2 R^2[16Y + \rho\omega_0^2(5\eta^2 - 7R^2)]}{16(\eta^2 + R^2)} \tag{b} \tag{13.165}$$

where η is some as yet undetermined function of ω_0.

Next let us consider the constitutive laws in the plastic zone $0 \le r \le \eta$. It will be sufficient to focus on the radial strain-rate component $\dot{\varepsilon}_{rr}$. First we note that the *total* strain rate is composed of elastic and plastic components, that is,

$$\dot{\varepsilon}_{rr} = \dot{\varepsilon}_{rr}^e + \dot{\varepsilon}_{rr}^p \tag{13.166}$$

Also, since *both* the elastic and plastic strain components are assumed to be incompressible, we have

$$\dot{\varepsilon}_{rr}^e = \dot{e}_{rr}^e \tag{a} \tag{13.167}$$

$$\dot{\varepsilon}_{rr}^p = \dot{e}_{rr}^p \tag{b}$$

where e_{rr}^e and e_{rr}^p are the elastic and plastic radial strain-rate *deviators*, respectively. For the Tresca plastic yield condition $\tau_{\theta\theta} = Y$ [Eq. (13.160)], we are in the interval

BG along the side *BC* of the polygon in Fig. 13.14. We see from Table 13.2 that for this part of the Tresca polygon we have the plastic flow rules

$$\dot{\varepsilon}_{rr}^p = 0 \qquad \text{(a)}$$

$$\dot{\varepsilon}_{\theta\theta}^p = \frac{2Y\dot{\Lambda}}{3} \qquad \text{(b)}$$

$$(13.168)$$

As for the elastic strain-rate deviator component, the time derivative of plane-stress Hooke's law gives [e.g., see Eq. (13.118a)]

$$\dot{e}_{rr}^e = \frac{\dot{s}_{rr}}{2G} \tag{13.169}$$

Utilizing Eqs. (13.167a), (13.166), and (13.168a), we see that

$$\dot{e}_{rr}^e = \dot{\varepsilon}_{rr}^e = \dot{\varepsilon}_{rr} - \dot{\varepsilon}_{rr}^p = \dot{\varepsilon}_{rr} \tag{13.170}$$

Accordingly, Eq. (13.169) becomes

$$\dot{\varepsilon}_{rr} = \frac{\dot{s}_{rr}}{2G} \tag{13.171}$$

Integrating this result over time, we finally obtain

$$\varepsilon_{rr} = \frac{s_{rr}}{2G} + C_4 \tag{13.172}$$

where C_4 is a constant.* You will recognize the first term in Eq. (13.172) as e_{rr}^e, which equals ε_{rr}^e, and thus the second term C_4 clearly gives ε_{rr}^p, which is independent of time [see Eq. (13.168a)].

To determine the radial stress in the plastic region, we go back to the *equilibrium* equation [see Eq. (13.99) and Eq. (a) in Example 13.1]. Thus

$$\frac{d\tau_{rr}}{dr} + \frac{\tau_{rr} - \tau_{\theta\theta}}{r} + \rho\omega_0^2 r = 0 \tag{13.173}$$

Setting $\tau_{\theta\theta} = Y$ [Eq. (13.160)] and regrouping terms, we have

$$\frac{d}{dr}(r\tau_{rr}) = Y - \rho\omega_0^2 r^2$$

Integrating this equation and solving for τ_{rr} gives

$$\tau_{rr} = Y - \frac{\rho\omega_0^2 r^2}{3} + \frac{C_5}{r}$$

where C_5 is another constant of integration. In order that τ_{rr} be finite at $r = 0$ we must set $C_5 = 0$, and thus τ_{rr} is fully determined as

$$\tau_{rr} = Y - \frac{\rho\omega_0^2 r^2}{3} \tag{13.174}$$

---

*The integration of Eq. (13.171) would in general permit C_4 to be a function of r. However, subsequent analysis will show that it is in fact a constant, which is obtained by matching u_r at the elastic–plastic junction radius.

Now consider the deviator stress s_{rr}, which we shall require for use in Eq. (13.172). Since $\tau_{zz} = 0$, we have

$$s_{rr} = \tau_{rr} - \frac{1}{3}(\tau_{rr} + \tau_{\theta\theta}) = \frac{2}{3}\tau_{rr} - \frac{Y}{3} \tag{13.175}$$

Substituting Eq. (13.174) into Eq. (13.175), we thus get

$$s_{rr} = \frac{Y}{3} - \frac{2\rho\omega_0^2 r^2}{9} \tag{13.176}$$

Finally, inserting the expression above for s_{rr} into Eq. (13.172) and replacing ε_{rr} by du_r/dr [see Eq. (12.56e)], we arrive at the following equation:

$$\frac{du_r}{dr} = \frac{Y}{6G} - \frac{\rho\omega_0^2 r^2}{9G} + C_4$$

Integrating, we then get

$$u_r = \frac{Yr}{6G} - \frac{\rho\omega_0^2 r^3}{27G} + C_4 r + C_6 \tag{13.177}$$

where C_6 is one more constant of integration. Clearly, $u_r = 0$ at $r = 0$, so $C_6 = 0$ in Eq. (13.177).

We now summarize our results for the plastic region $0 \le r \le \eta$ with $\omega_0 > \omega_e$ by restating Eqs. (13.160), (13.174), and (13.177) (with $C_6 = 0$):

$$\tau_{rr}(r) = Y - \frac{\rho\omega_0^2 r^2}{3} \qquad \text{(a)}$$

$$\tau_{\theta\theta}(r) = Y \qquad \text{(b)} \tag{13.178}$$

$$u_r(r) = \frac{Yr}{6G} - \frac{\rho\omega_0^2 r^3}{27G} + C_4 r \qquad \text{(c)}$$

To get the value of C_4 we set $u_r(\eta)$ from Eq. (13.178c) equal to $u_r(\eta)$ from Eq. (13.163c) [with C_2, C_3 given by Eqs. (13.165)], and this ensures that u_r is continuous at the transition from the plastic to the elastic zone. After some algebraic manipulation, we obtain

$$C_4 = \frac{1}{3G(\eta + R^2)}\left[YR^2 + \frac{\rho\omega_0^2}{144}(25\eta^4 + 70\,\eta^2 R^2 - 63R^4) \right] \tag{13.179}$$

If we substitute $\eta = 0$ and $\omega_0 = \omega_e$ using Eq. (13.161) we find that $C_4 = 0$, which indicates that ε_{rr}^p vanishes for this case [see the comment after Eq. (13.172)].

Elastic solutions (13.163) and plastic solutions (13.178), for $\omega_0 \ge \omega_e$ and with the constants of integration evaluated, are expressed in terms of the radius η of the elastic–plastic boundary. The relation between this radius and the angular velocity ω_0 is obtained from the condition that τ_{rr} be continuous at $r = \eta$. Accordingly, we set $\tau_{rr}(\eta)$ from Eq. (13.178a) equal to $\tau_{rr}(\eta)$ from Eq. (13.163a) [using C_2, C_3 from Eqs. (13.165)], and thereby obtain after simplification

$$\omega_0^2 = \frac{48YR^2}{\rho(5\eta^4 - 10\eta^2 R^2 + 21R^4)} \tag{13.180}$$

Given a value for $\omega_0 \geq \omega_e$, this equation must be solved numerically for η. If we set $\eta = 0$ in Eq. (13.180), we obtain $\omega_0 = \omega_e$ [see Eq. (13.161)] as required. Furthermore, if we set $\eta = R$ in Eq. (13.180) (i.e., the *entire* disk is plastic), we obtain the *plastic* angular velocity

$$\omega_p = \frac{1}{R}\left(\frac{3Y}{\rho}\right)^{1/2} \tag{13.181}$$

This value is the *largest* angular velocity that the disk can sustain and still remain within the framework of the present incompressible elastic, incompressible perfectly plastic formulation.*

13.13 NONLINEAR VISCOUS PLANE STRESS

In this section we make some brief remarks about the constitutive laws for *nonlinear viscous plane stress*. We begin with the three-dimensional *incompressible* nonlinear viscous constitutive law [see Eq. (9.19)]

$$\dot{\varepsilon}_{ij} = CJ_2^m s_{ij} = CJ_2^m(\tau_{ij} - \tfrac{1}{3}\tau_{kk}\delta_{ij}) \tag{13.182}$$

where

$$J_2 = \tfrac{1}{2}s_{lm}s_{lm} \tag{13.183}$$

For plane stress we set $\tau_{13} = \tau_{23} = \tau_{33} = 0$. It immediately follows from Eq. (13.182) that $\dot{\varepsilon}_{13} = \dot{\varepsilon}_{23} = 0$. Since $\dot{\varepsilon}_{33}$ is usually of little interest, we will restrict the free indices in Eq. (13.182) to $1, 2$. Accordingly, introducing two-dimensional index notation this equation gives us for plane stress

$$\dot{\varepsilon}_{\alpha\beta} = C(J_2^0)^m(\tau_{\alpha\beta} - \tfrac{1}{3}\tau_{\gamma\gamma}\delta_{\alpha\beta}) \tag{13.184}$$

In Eq. (13.184)† the quantity J_2^0 is obtained by setting $\tau_{13} = \tau_{23} = \tau_{33} = 0$ in Eq. (13.183). It can easily be shown that

$$J_2^0 = \tfrac{1}{2}\left(\tau_{\delta\epsilon}\tau_{\delta\epsilon} - \tfrac{1}{3}\tau_{\delta\delta}\tau_{\epsilon\epsilon}\right) \tag{13.185}$$

In unabridged form, Eq. (13.184) with Eq. (13.185) gives

$$\dot{\varepsilon}_{11} = \frac{C}{3}\left[\frac{1}{3}\left(\tau_{11}^2 + \tau_{22}^2 - \tau_{11}\tau_{22} + 3\tau_{12}^2\right)\right]^m (2\tau_{11} - \tau_{22}) \qquad \text{(a)}$$

$$\dot{\varepsilon}_{22} = \frac{C}{3}\left[\frac{1}{3}\left(\tau_{11}^2 + \tau_{22}^2 - \tau_{11}\tau_{22} + 3\tau_{12}^2\right)\right]^m (2\tau_{22} - \tau_{11}) \qquad \text{(b)} \qquad (13.186)$$

$$\dot{\varepsilon}_{12} = C\left[\frac{1}{3}\left(\tau_{11}^2 + \tau_{22}^2 - \tau_{11}\tau_{22} + 3\tau_{12}^2\right)\right]^m \tau_{12} \qquad \text{(c)}$$

Note that these equations are *not* the same as Eqs. (12.126) for plane strain.

---

*The presentation of this example is similar to that given on pp. 571–578 of *Structural Mechanics with Introductions to Elasticity and Plasticity*, by B. Venkatraman and S. A. Patel (New York: McGraw-Hill Book Company, 1970).

†We have not set the term $\tau_{\alpha\beta} - \tfrac{1}{3}\tau_{\gamma\gamma}\delta_{\alpha\beta}$ in Eq. (13.184) equal to $s_{\alpha\beta}$, since we have previously defined $s_{\alpha\beta}$ as $\tau_{\alpha\beta} - \tfrac{1}{2}\tau_{\gamma\gamma}\delta_{\alpha\beta}$ [see Eq. (12.128)]. Note that this definition gives $s_{\gamma\gamma} = 0$.

For Eqs. (13.186) the principal axes of stress and strain rate clearly coincide, since $\tau_{12} = 0$ implies that $\dot{\varepsilon}_{12} = 0$. Thus for *principal axes* these equations simplify to

$$\dot{\varepsilon}_1 = \frac{C}{3}\left[\frac{1}{3}(\tau_1^2 + \tau_2^2 - \tau_1\tau_2)\right]^m (2\tau_1 - \tau_2) \qquad \text{(a)}$$

$$\dot{\varepsilon}_2 = \frac{C}{3}\left[\frac{1}{3}(\tau_1^2 + \tau_2^2 - \tau_1\tau_2)\right]^m (2\tau_2 - \tau_1) \qquad \text{(b)}$$

(13.187)

where the quantity in brackets is J_2^0 for principal axes. We see by inspection of Eqs. (13.187) that these equations may be rewritten in the compact form

$$\dot{\varepsilon}_\alpha = C(J_2^0)^m \frac{\partial J_2^0}{\partial \tau_\alpha} \qquad (13.188)$$

Now, we have previously shown that the perfectly plastic, plane-stress flow law according to *Mises* [see Eqs. (13.142) and (13.149)] is given by

$$\dot{\varepsilon}_\alpha^p = \dot{\Lambda} \frac{\partial f_0}{\partial \tau_\alpha} \qquad (13.189)$$

where

$$f_0 = J_2^0 - \frac{Y^2}{3} \qquad (13.190)$$

Since $\partial J_2^0/\partial \tau_\alpha = \partial f_0/\partial \tau_\alpha$ and $C(J_2^0)^m$ becomes indeterminate as $m \to \infty$, we see that Eq. (13.188) approaches Eq. (13.189) for this limiting case. We have noted this interesting phenomenon on several previous occasions in this book.

We have also noted previously (e.g., see Section 9.6) that the nonlinear viscous constitutive law exhibits a "normality" property, analogous to the normality property for perfectly plastic flow based on the Mises yield criterion. Thus, just as Eq. (13.189) yields plastic strain-rate vectors that are normal to the Mises yield ellipse, so does Eq. (13.188) exhibit normality of the $\dot{\varepsilon}_\alpha$ vectors to curves that are elliptical. To illustrate this point, consider a nonlinear viscous plane stress problem for which the solution in principal stress space is given by the locus of points along curve ab in Fig. 13.15. At point a we have taken $\tau_1 = \tau_2$, whereas at point b we have $\tau_2 = 0$. Shown in the figure is the elliptical curve $J_2^0 = \frac{1}{3}(\tau_1^2 + \tau_2^2 - \tau_1\tau_2) = C_1^2/3$, which intersects the τ_1 axis at $\tau_1 = C_1$ and crosses the stress locus at point a where $\tau_1 = \tau_2 = C_1$. Using *either* Eqs. (13.187) or Eq. (13.188), we find for the strain-rate components at point a,

$$\dot{\varepsilon}_1 = \dot{\varepsilon}_2 = \frac{C}{3^{m+1}}\tau_1^{2m+1} \qquad (\tau_1 = \tau_2) \qquad (13.191)$$

The strain-rate vector at point a (i.e., $\dot{\varepsilon}_{aa}$) is clearly normal to the indicated elliptical curve, as shown in Fig. 13.15. Also shown in the figure is another elliptical curve, $J_2^0 = \frac{1}{3}(\tau_1^2 + \tau_2^2 - \tau_1\tau_2) = C_2^2/3$, which intersects the stress locus and the τ_1 axis at the point b, where $\tau_1 = C_2$ and $\tau_2 = 0$. For this point Eqs. (13.187) give

$$\dot{\varepsilon}_1 = \frac{2C}{3^{m+1}}\tau_1^{2m+1}, \qquad \dot{\varepsilon}_2 = -\frac{C}{3^{m+1}}\tau_1^{2m+1} \qquad (\tau_2 = 0) \qquad (13.192)$$

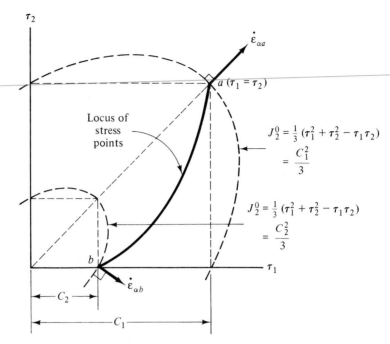

Figure 13.15 Normality of nonlinear viscous strain-rate vector.

and the normality of the vector $\dot{\varepsilon}_{\alpha b}$ is again evident in the figure. The strain-rate vector at *any* point along stress locus ab will also exhibit normality to the local elliptical curve.

Equation (13.188) is of the class

$$\dot{\varepsilon}_\alpha = C\phi^m \frac{\partial \phi}{\partial \tau_\alpha} \tag{13.193}$$

where ϕ equal to a constant defines a potential curve to which the $\dot{\varepsilon}_\alpha$ vectors are normal. If we set $\phi = J_2^0$, we obtain elliptical potential curves, which then leads to constitutive equations (13.187). If we replace the elliptical potential curve by a piecewise linear curve, we would obtain *approximate* constitutive equations of *simplified* form. To do this it is only necessary to determine the appropriate ϕ function along each side of the piecewise linear curve, for use in Eq. (13.193). This immediately suggests that we inscribe a Tresca-type polygon inside the Mises-type ellipse. We can then generate tables similar to Tables 13.2 and 13.3 for perfectly plastic flow, except that now the quantity $\dot{\Lambda}Y$ is replaced by a determined power function of stress. We leave the details for you as an exercise.

13.14 CLOSURE

In Part A of this chapter we considered linear elastic general x_3-dependent plane stress. We obtained Airy stress functions Φ which were either odd or even with respect to the coordinate x_3 normal to the faces of the plate. The odd functions could be used to study pure bending of plates wherein the shear stresses τ_{13} and τ_{23} could be neglected. However, we did not proceed along this direction, in order to keep the size of the chapter from being excessive. We did examine the symmetric case in some detail. In this case edge tractions are distributed symmetrically with respect to $x_3 = 0$. We showed that by using the *average* traction distribution over x_3, we obtain an x_3-dependent solution which is a very good approximation for thin plates except in a narrow rim near the edge.

In Part B we simplified the formulation of Part A to the case of elastic *two-dimensional* plane stress. We did this by dropping the x_3-dependent term in the Airy stress function for symmetric loading, thereby approximating this function by its *average* value. The differential equation for Φ then simplified to $\nabla^4 \Phi = 0$ for the case of no body forces, which is the *same* equation obtained for plane strain in Chapter 12. It was thus clear that in two-dimensional plane stress we are ignoring all compatibility equations other than the simple compatibility equation that was also valid for plane strain. Nonetheless, the results obtained from this formulation are still quite good for plates that are *very thin* and loaded around the edge symmetrically with respect to $x_3 = 0$. We then solved a series of two-dimensional plane stress problems, including the stretched plate with a hole, the curved thin beam, and the rotating thin disk.

In Part C we turned to *inelastic* two-dimensional plane stress. We first considered linear viscoelastic materials, and used the familiar *analogy relations* to convert constitutive relations from elastic behavior to viscoelastic behavior. We also discussed once again the use of the *correspondence principle*, wherein we can utilize the linear elastic solution to obtain the Laplace transform of the corresponding viscoelastic problem. And for the rotating disk problem of Part B, we used this principle to find the viscoelastic stress and displacement solutions for a material that is elastic in bulk and viscous in distortion. Next in Part C we turned to perfectly plastic behavior, discussing first the Mises and Tresca flow rules for two-dimensional plane stress. Care had to be taken for the Tresca case, because of the nonuniqueness of the normal direction at corner points of the yield curve. We then once again looked at the rotating disk for linear elastic, perfectly plastic behavior with a Tresca polygon as the yield curve. Finally, we discussed nonlinear viscous plane stress, taking special care to correlate this behavior with perfectly plastic behavior. In this concluding chapter we have made much use of earlier materials in Chapter 9, which enable us to interrelate elastic, viscoelastic, perfectly plastic, and nonlinear viscous behavior.

PROBLEMS

13.1. Express the inverted form of Eq. (13.14) in terms of the modified Lamé constants λ_1 and μ_1. Compare λ_1 and μ_1 with λ and μ.

13.2. The following plane stress distribution exists in a linear elastic rectangular plate:

$$\tau_{11} = \tau_{22} = A + Bx_3$$

$$\tau_{12} = 0$$

Compute $\Phi(x_1, x_2, x_3)$ from Eqs. (13.22) and drop terms which are linear in x_1 and x_2, since such terms do not affect the stresses. Compare your result with Eq. (13.37), and thereby determine $\overline{\Phi}$, Φ, and f. Note that this is an *exact* solution for a plate of arbitrary thickness. Finally, determine the resultant forces and moments along the four edges of the plate.

13.3. A linear elastic rectangular plate is subjected to *uniformly* distributed normal tractions over two opposite edges (see Fig. P13.3). Use the general x_3-dependent theory of plane stress to determine the stress function $\Phi(x_1, x_2, x_3)$ for this case (i.e., first determine $\overline{\Phi}$ and f). In solving differential equation (13.47) for $\overline{\Phi}(x_1, x_2)$, assume that $\overline{\Phi} = Ax_1^2 + Bx_1x_2 + Cx_2^2$ where A, B, C are constants. Then calculate the stresses τ_{11}, τ_{22}, and τ_{12}. Are these stresses consistent with what you might expect from simple strength of materials? Is this solution an exact solution for a plate of arbitrary thickness?

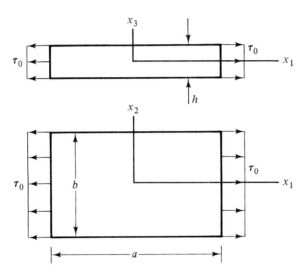

Figure P13.3

13.4. Consider the antisymmetric case of plane stress [i.e., $\Phi(x_1, x_2, x_3) = x_3 \Phi_1(x_1, x_2)$]. Apply this case to a rectangular plate subjected to couples M_o (moment per unit length) along two opposite edges, as shown in Fig. P13.4. Determine the stresses for this case, assuming that the material is linear elastic. Under what condition is this solution an exact solution for a plate of arbitrary thickness?

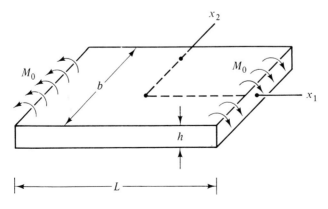

Figure P13.4

13.5. Given a linear elastic rectangular plate (see Fig. P13.5) for which

$$\overline{\Phi}(x_1, x_2) = x_1^2 x_2^3 - \tfrac{1}{5} x_2^5$$

Verify that $\nabla^4 \overline{\Phi} = 0$. Then determine $f(x_1, x_2)$, $\Phi(x_1, x_2, x_3)$, and the stresses τ_{11}, τ_{22}, τ_{12}. Sketch the traction distributions $T_1^{(1)}$ and $T_2^{(1)}$ at point A in Fig. P13.5. Explain why this is an exact solution for a plate of arbitrary thickness.

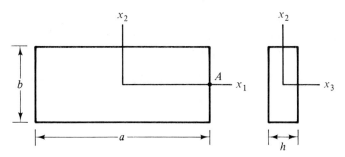

Figure P13.5

13.6. In Problem 13.3 the normal tractions were uniformly distributed in both the x_2 and x_3 directions. Now consider the case where these tractions vary linearly with x_3 as shown in Fig. P13.6, while still being uniformly distributed with respect to x_2. Furthermore, the plate is now *thin* (i.e., $h \ll a$ and $h \ll b$). Use Saint-Venant's principle, in conjunction with the general x_3-dependent theory of plane stress, to determine the stress distributions for this case.

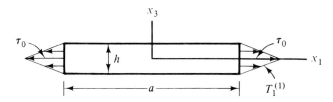

Figure P13.6

13.7. Redo Problem 13.6 for normal traction $T_1^{(1)}$ still uniform over x_2, but with the following distributions over x_3.

(a) $T_1^{(1)} = \tau_0 \cos \dfrac{\pi x_3}{h}$

(b) $T_1^{(1)} = \begin{cases} \tau_0, & -\dfrac{h}{4} \le x_3 \le \dfrac{h}{4} \\ 0, & \text{elsewhere} \end{cases}$

(c) $T_1^{(1)} = \tau_0 \, e^{-|x_3/h|}$

13.8. Consider the x_3-dependent theory of plane stress, with tractions symmetrically distributed over x_3. Prove that ε_{33} is independent of x_3. Then prove that the average value of the displacement u_3 over x_3 is zero. Set $u_3 = 0$ at $x_3 = 0$.

13.9. Consider the special case where the stresses $\tau_{\alpha\beta}$, in the x_3-dependent theory of plane stress, are *independent* of x_3. Starting with Eq. (13.37), prove that for this case Φ_1 and f are linear functions in x_1 and x_2. Then show that $\nabla^2 \Phi$ is also linear in x_1 and x_2.

13.10. In "generalized" plane stress $\tau_{13} = \tau_{23} = \tau_{33} = 0$ at $x_3 = \pm h/2$. Using equilibrium in the x_3 direction for no body force, show that τ_{33} must be small over the thickness of the plate for very thin plates. Generalized plane stress approximates this by setting $\tau_{33} = 0$ *everywhere*. (*Hint*: Use a Taylor series expansion in the x_3 direction at the point $x_3 = h/2$.)

13.11. Refer to the example of the stretched elastic plate with a small hole, presented in Section 13.6. Starting with Eq. (13.71), find the solution $f(r)$ as given by Eq. (13.72).

13.12. In the example of the stretched elastic plate with a small hole (see Section 13.6), show that the Cesàro integral condition (13.65d) is valid for arbitrary constants A_1, A_2, A_3, and A_4 with $\alpha = 2$. Do the same for Cesàro integral condition (13.65e).

13.13. Show that the stress concentration for a very small hole in the elastic plate loaded as shown in Fig. P13.13 is 4. The quantity S is a stress magnitude.

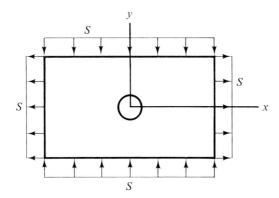

Figure P13.13

13.14. Use the following polynomial as an Airy stress function for an elastic rectangular beam:

$$\Phi = C_1 x_1^3 + C_2 x_1^2 x_2 + C_3 x_1 x_2^2 + C_4 x_2^3$$

Evaluate the constants and $\tau_{\alpha\beta}$ and ε_{33}, so that for two-dimensional plane stress this represents a beam under "in-plane" pure bending (see Fig. P13.14). Note that T is the maximum magnitude of the applied linear traction distributions. Also recall that these traction distributions are the average over x_3 of some symmetric distributions, and also assume that $L \gg t$ and $h \gg t$.

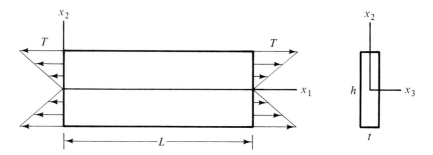

Figure P13.14

13.15. Given the following polynomial for the Airy stress function:

$$\Phi(x_1, x_2) = C_1 x_1^4 + C_2 x_1^3 x_2 + C_3 x_1^2 x_2^2 + C_4 x_1 x_2^3 + C_5 x_2^4$$

Make any adjustments in the coefficients required to render Φ a biharmonic function. Now, adjust the remaining constants to give a two-dimensional plane-stress solution to the elastic rectangular cantilever beam shown in Fig. P13.15. Note that uniform distributed shear tractions τ_0 are applied on the upper and lower surfaces, and a resultant shear force V is applied at the tip. How are V and τ_0 related? The thickness t is assumed small.

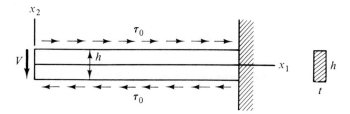

Figure P13.15

13.16. In Fig. P13.16 is shown a rectangular elastic beam of depth h and thickness t, carrying a uniformly distributed load q_0 on its upper surface and resultant forces V at its ends (due to *simple supports*). Although t is assumed small, h is not necessarily small. In Problem 9.16 we showed that the following function is the proper Airy stress function for this two-dimensional plane stress problem:

$$\Phi = -\frac{q_0}{4} x_1^2 + \frac{3q_0}{4h} x_1^2 x_2 - \frac{q_0}{h^3} x_1^2 x_2^3 + \frac{q_0}{h^3}\left(L^2 - \frac{1}{10} h^2\right) x_2^3 + \frac{q_0}{5h^3} x_2^5$$

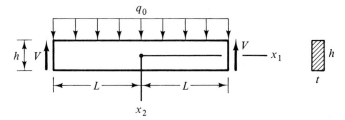

Figure P13.16

Show that

$$\tau_{11} = -\frac{q_0}{2I} (x_1^2 - L^2)x_2 + \frac{q_0}{2I}\left(\frac{2}{3} x_2^3 - \frac{h^2}{10} x_2\right)$$

$$\tau_{22} = -\frac{q_0}{2I}\left(\frac{1}{3} x_2^3 - \frac{h^2}{4} x_2 + \frac{h^3}{12}\right)$$

$$\tau_{12} = -\frac{q_0}{2I}\left(\frac{h^2}{4} - x_2^2\right) x_1$$

where $I = h^3/12$. Also, check the resultant shear forces, normal forces, and bending moments at the ends.

13.17. Consider the tip-loaded elastic cantilever beam shown in Fig. P13.17. Using the following Airy stress function

$$\Phi = Ax_2^3 + Bx_1 x_2^3 + Cx_1 x_2$$

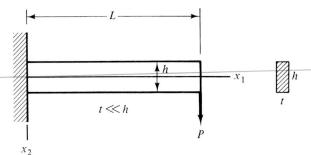

Figure P13.17

show that the constants A, B, and C, for a two-dimensional plane-stress solution, are given by

$$A = -\frac{2PL}{th^3}, \qquad B = \frac{2P}{th^3}, \qquad C = -\frac{3P}{2th}$$

Show that simple strength of materials gives the same *stresses* $\tau_{11}, \tau_{22}, \tau_{12}$ as this two-dimensional plane stress formulation. Also prove that the displacement field is given by

$$u_1 = -\frac{P}{EI}\left[L x_1 x_2 - \frac{1}{2} x_1^2 x_2 - \frac{1+2\nu}{3} x_2^3 + (1+\nu)\frac{h^2 x_2}{8} \right]$$

$$u_2 = \frac{P}{EI}\left[\nu\left(\frac{L-x_1}{2}\right) x_2^2 + \frac{x_1^2}{2} - \frac{x_1^3}{6} - (1+\nu)\frac{h^2 x_1}{8} \right]$$

[*Hint:* Use the boundary conditions $u_1 = u_2 = \omega_3 = 0$ at $x_1 = x_2 = 0$, where $\omega_3 = \frac{1}{2}(\partial u_2/\partial x_1 - \partial u_1/\partial x_2)$.]

13.18. Consider a curved thin elastic beam, such as shown in Fig. 13.17, with

$$a = 4 \text{ ft}$$
$$b = 5 \text{ ft}$$
$$M = 1000 \text{ ft-lb}$$
$$t = 0.3 \text{ ft}$$

Determine the maximum tangential stress $\tau_{\theta\theta}$, arising from the action of the couples. Compare this result with that using the elementary flexure formula for straight beams. Compute the relative error of straight-beam theory for this example, as compared to curved beam theory. If a and b are varied such that the depth $b - a = 1$ ft. while M and t are unchanged, find the minimum value of b such that the relative error is less than 3%. Use a numerical procedure to obtain your answer.

13.19. In Section 13.7 we derived the stress distributions for a curved thin elastic beam. Using constitutive law (13.55a) for polar coordinates and also strain-displacement relations (12.55), determine the displacement fields u_r and u_θ for this curved beam. Set $u_r = u_\theta = \partial u_\theta/\partial r = 0$ at the point $\theta = 0$ and $r = (a + b)/2$ (refer to Fig. 13.7).

13.20. A spinning elastic thin disk has a mass density ρ, which varies linearly from $\rho = 300$ lbm/ft^3 at $r = 0$ to $\rho = 500$ lbm/ft^3 at $r = 5$ ft. If $\nu = 0.3$ and $\omega = 1000$ rpm, what are the stresses τ_{rr}, $\tau_{\theta\theta}$ for the disk? The thickness is uniform.

13.21. In Fig. P13.21 is shown a thin elastic disk ($t \ll R$) surrounded by a thin elastic ring, for which both the thickness t and the width h are small. The fit is ideal, so that there is no initial contact pressure between the disk and the ring. The device is then rotated

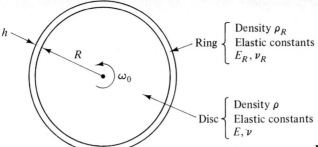

Density ρ_R
Ring $\left\{ \begin{array}{l} \text{Elastic constants} \\ E_R, \nu_R \end{array} \right.$

Density ρ
Disc $\left\{ \begin{array}{l} \text{Elastic constants} \\ E, \nu \end{array} \right.$

Figure P13.21

about an axis at its center with a constant angular speed ω_0. Show that the contact pressure f due to this spinning action is

$$f = \frac{[\rho\nu(1-\nu) - (4E/E_R)\rho_R]\omega_0^2 R^2}{4[(1-\nu) + (E/E_R)(R/h - \nu_R)]}$$

In obtaining this result, assume that the tangential stress and the body force are uniformly distributed across the width of the ring, h. Obtain an inequality relating ρ_R to ρ, such that contact is maintained between the disk and the ring.

13.22. Consider a flat elastic thin ring with a conservative radial body force distribution, which is a function only of r. A uniform radial pressure p_i acts at its inner edge $r = r_i$, and uniform radial pressure p_o acts at its outer edge $r = r_o$ (see Fig. P13.22). Starting from Eq. (13.102), prove that the stress distributions τ_{rr} and $\tau_{\theta\theta}$ are given as

$$\tau_{rr} = -\frac{1-\nu}{r^2}\int_{r_i}^{r} \eta V(\eta)\,d\eta + V(r) + \frac{C_2}{2} + \frac{C_3}{r^2}$$

$$\tau_{\theta\theta} = \frac{1-\nu}{r^2}\int_{r_i}^{r} \eta V(\eta)\,d\eta + \nu V(r) + \frac{C_2}{2} - \frac{C_3}{r^2}$$

where

$$C_2 = -\frac{2}{r_o^2 - r_i^2}\left[p_o r_o^2 - p_i r_i^2 + r_o^2 V(r_o) - r_i^2 V(r_i) - (1-\nu)\int_{r_i}^{r_o} \eta V(\eta)\,d\eta\right]$$

$$C_3 = \frac{r_i^2 r_o^2}{r_o^2 - r_i^2}\left[p_o - p_i + V(r_o) - V(r_i) - \frac{1-\nu}{r_o^2}\int_{r_i}^{r_o} \eta V(\eta)\,d\eta\right]$$

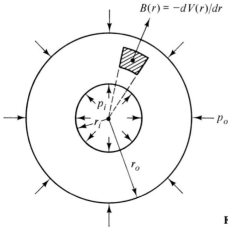

$B(r) = -dV(r)/dr$

Figure P13.22

[*Hint*: Use the Cesàro integral conditions (13.62) to prove that $C_1 = 0$ in Eq. (13.102).]

13.23. Refer to the stress solutions given in Problem 13.22 for the thin elastic ring. Consider the case where $p_i = p_o = 0$, and the body force is due to spinning of the ring at an angular velocity ω about an x_3 axis at $r = 0$ (see Fig. P13.22). For this case find τ_{rr} and $\tau_{\theta\theta}$, and also determine their maximum values. Let $r_i \to 0$ and show that the maximum value of $\tau_{\theta\theta}$ is twice the value of $\tau_{\theta\theta}$ at the corresponding point for the solid spinning disk. (*Note*: This shows that a very small hole at $r = 0$ produces a stress concentration factor of $K = 2$.)

13.24. Use the last two of analogy relations (13.113) to convert elastic constitutive relations (13.118) to the analogous viscoelastic laws. Compare your result with the corresponding set of equations for plane strain [see Eqs. (12.111) and (12.112)]. Next, rewrite these two-dimensional viscoelastic plane stress equations in the form

$$\mathcal{Q}^{KG}\varepsilon_{\gamma\gamma} = \mathcal{P}^{KG}\tau_{\gamma\gamma}$$

$$Q^G e_{\alpha\beta} = P^G s_{\alpha\beta}$$

where $\mathcal{Q}^{KG}$ and $\mathcal{P}^{KG}$ are appropriately defined in terms of P^G, Q^G, P^K, and Q^K. Finally, rewrite the above two differential relations as four hereditary integrals, expressed in terms of creep compliance functions $\mathcal{J}^{KG}$ and $J^G(t)$ and relaxation modulus functions $\mathcal{Y}^{KG}(t)$ and $Y^G(t)$. How does this result differ from the corresponding result obtained in Problem 12.19 for plane strain?

13.25. Refer to Example 13.2 in Section 13.10 on the viscoelastic spinning disk. Obtain expressions for $s\bar{\tau}_{rr}$, $s\bar{\tau}_{\theta\theta}$, and $s\bar{u}_r$ for the following linear viscoelastic materials.
  (a) Elastic compressibility with bulk modulus K, and Kelvin behavior in distortion with shear elastic modulus G and shear viscosity coefficient ζ
  (b) Incompressible Poisson effect, and Maxwell behavior in tension with tensile elastic modulus E and tensile viscosity coefficient η

Also, carry out the Laplace transform inversions to obtain $\tau_{rr}(t)$, $\tau_{\theta\theta}(t)$, and $u_r(t)$ for both of the cases above.

13.26. A thin disk of linear viscoelastic material is very quickly brought up to the constant angular speed $\omega_0 = 2000$ rpm. The disk rotates inside a rigid stationary ring, and there is an initial gap of 0.001 in. when the disk is stationary (see Fig. P13.26). What is the

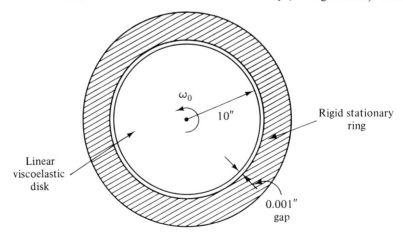

ω_0

10"

Rigid stationary ring

Linear viscoelastic disk

0.001" gap

Figure P13.26

clearance immediately after the disk is first brought up to speed? At what time will the disk first touch the rigid stationary ring? Assume that the disk behaves as an elastic material in bulk and as a viscous material in distortion. The following data apply:

$$\rho = 460 \text{ lbm/ft}^3$$

$$K = 2.5 \times 10^7 \text{ psi}$$

$$\zeta = 3 \times 10^9 \text{ psi-hr}$$

13.27. Reconsider the tip-loaded cantilever beam of Problem 13.17, but now the material is linear viscoelastic. Specifically, let the material be elastic in bulk and Maxwell in distortion, that is,

$$\bar{\tau} = 3K\bar{\varepsilon}$$

$$\left(1 + \frac{\zeta}{2G} \frac{\partial}{\partial t}\right) s_{ij} = \zeta \frac{\partial}{\partial t} e_{ij}$$

The tip load is suddenly applied (i.e., $P = P_0[u(t)]$). Using the solutions given in Problem 13.17, determine the displacements u_1 and u_2 for this viscoelastic problem.

13.28. In Problem 13.21 let the disk be linear viscoelastic, whereas the ring is still elastic. In particular, the material of the disk is incompressible in bulk and Kelvin in distortion, that is,

$$P^G = 1, \qquad Q^G = 2G + \zeta \frac{\partial}{\partial t}$$

The angular speed increases linearly with time (i.e., $\omega(t) = At[u(t)]$ where A is a constant). Use the correspondence principle to determine the variation of the contact pressure f with time, assuming that $f = 0$ at $t = 0$. [*Hint*: Invert the quantity $s^3 \bar{f}(s)$ and then integrate three times over t.] Investigate the *sign* of $\dot{f}$ in order to determine whether the ring becomes loose.

13.29. Starting from Eq. (13.162), show that for the incompressible elastic, perfectly plastic spinning disk, the stress distribution in the elastic region $\eta \leq r \leq R$ is given by

$$\tau_{rr} = -\frac{7\rho\omega_0^2}{16} r^2 + \frac{C_2}{2} + \frac{C_3}{r^2}$$

$$\tau_{\theta\theta} = -\frac{5\rho\omega_0^2}{16} r^2 + \frac{C_2}{2} - \frac{C_3}{r^2}$$

where $\omega_e < \omega_0 < \omega_p$, and

$$C_2 = \frac{16Y\eta^2 + \rho\omega_0^2 (5\eta^4 + 7R^4)}{8(\eta^2 + R^2)}$$

$$C_3 = -\frac{\eta^2 R^2 [16Y + \rho\omega_0^2 (5\eta^2 - 7R^2)]}{16(\eta^2 + R^2)}$$

The constant C_1 in Eq. (13.162) equals zero by virtue of the Cesàro integral conditions (refer to Problem 13.22).

Also, using Eqs. (13.100) and (13.101), prove that

$$u_r = -\frac{\rho\omega_0^2}{32G} r^3 + \frac{C_2 r}{12G} - \frac{C_3}{2Gr}$$

13.30. Consider an elastic, perfectly plastic thin hollow disk, with inside radius r_i and infinitely large outside radius (i.e., $r_o \to \infty$). A uniform radial pressure p_i is applied at the inside radius (see Fig. P13.30).

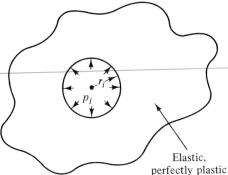

Elastic,
perfectly plastic   **Figure P13.30**

(a) Using results given in Example 12.1 of Section 12.5, show that if $p_i < p_e$, the stress distributions are given by

$$\tau_{\theta\theta} = p_i \left(\frac{r_i}{r}\right)^2 = -\tau_{rr}, \qquad \tau_{r\theta} = 0$$

The quantity p_e is the limiting pressure for complete elastic behavior.

(b) Using the Tresca yield criterion, express p_e in terms of the yield stress Y.

(c) For $p_i > p_e$ determine the stress distribution in terms of η, the plastic–elastic junction radius.

13.31. A thin hollow ring with inside radius r_i and outside radius r_o is rotating at constant angular speed ω_0. The material of the ring is elastic, perfectly plastic, and exhibits both plastic and elastic incompressibility.

(a) Using the Tresca yield condition with yield stress Y, show that the largest angular velocity for entirely elastic deformation is given by

$$\omega_e = \left[\frac{8Y}{\rho(7r_o^2 + r_i^2)}\right]^{1/2}$$

Refer to Problem 13.22.

(b) Let $\omega_0 > \omega_e$ such that there is an elastic–plastic junction radius η, where $r_i < \eta < r_o$. Show that in the plastic zone $r_i \le r \le \eta$, the stress distributions are given by

$$\tau_{rr} = Y\left(1 - \frac{r_i}{r}\right) - \frac{\rho\omega_0^2}{3}\left(r^2 - \frac{r_i^3}{r}\right)$$

$$\tau_{\theta\theta} = Y$$

(c) Obtain expressions for the elastic–plastic junction radius η and for the fully plastic angular velocity ω_p.

13.32. Nonlinear viscous plane-stress constitutive law (13.184) was given as

$$\dot\varepsilon_{\alpha\beta} = C(J_2^0)^m \left(\tau_{\alpha\beta} - \tfrac{1}{3}\tau_{\gamma\gamma}\delta_{\alpha\beta}\right)$$

where

$$J_2^0 = \tfrac{1}{2}\left(\tau_{\delta\epsilon}\tau_{\delta\epsilon} - \tfrac{1}{3}\tau_{\delta\delta}\tau_{\epsilon\epsilon}\right)$$

Although this material is incompressible, we see that $\dot\varepsilon_{\gamma\gamma} \ne 0$. Explain this apparent contradiction. Then show that this constitutive law for $m = 0$ (linear viscous) is analogous to linear elastic constitutive law (13.14) for $\nu = \tfrac{1}{2}$ (incompressible). Finally, prove that the inverted form of the nonlinear viscous constitutive law above is given as

$$\tau_{\alpha\beta} = \left[\frac{2^m}{C(\dot{\varepsilon}_{\delta\epsilon}\dot{\varepsilon}_{\delta\epsilon})^m} \right]^{1/(2m+1)} (\dot{\varepsilon}_{\alpha\beta} + \dot{\varepsilon}_{\gamma\gamma}\delta_{\alpha\beta})$$

(*Hint*: First obtain an expression relating J_2^0 to $\dot{\varepsilon}_{\delta\epsilon}\dot{\varepsilon}_{\delta\epsilon}$.)

13.33. The nonlinear viscous constitutive equations in polar coordinates for axially symmetric two-dimensional plane stress follow directly from Eqs. (13.186) as

$$\dot{\varepsilon}_{rr} = \frac{C}{3}\left[\frac{1}{3}(\tau_{rr}^2 + \tau_{\theta\theta}^2 - \tau_{rr}\tau_{\theta\theta})\right]^m (2\tau_{rr} - \tau_{\theta\theta})$$

$$\dot{\varepsilon}_{\theta\theta} = \frac{C}{3}\left[\frac{1}{3}(\tau_{rr}^2 + \tau_{\theta\theta}^2 - \tau_{rr}\tau_{\theta\theta})\right]^m (2\tau_{\theta\theta} - \tau_{rr})$$

The compatibility equation and the definition of the Airy stress function Φ for this case are the same as for plane strain. Thus, neglecting body forces, we have [see Eqs. (12.135) and (12.138)]

$$\dot{\varepsilon}_{\theta\theta} - \dot{\varepsilon}_{rr} + r\frac{d\dot{\varepsilon}_{\theta\theta}}{dr} = 0$$

$$\tau_{rr} = \frac{1}{r}\frac{d\Phi}{dr}, \qquad \tau_{\theta\theta} = \frac{d^2\Phi}{dr^2}$$

Combine the equations above to obtain a *single* differential equation in Φ. Verify that for $m = 0$ (linear viscous) this equation reduces to the first integral of $\nabla^4\Phi = 0$.

13.34. Refer to the nonlinear viscous constitutive law in the form of Eq. (13.193), that is,

$$\dot{\varepsilon}_\alpha = C\phi^m \frac{\partial\phi}{\partial\tau_\alpha}$$

Verify that if we set $\phi = \frac{1}{3}(\tau_1^2 + \tau_2^2 - \tau_1\tau_2)$, we get constitutive relations (13.187). In Fig. P13.34 we have plotted the elliptical curve $\phi = \frac{1}{3}(\tau_1^2 - \tau_1\tau_2 + \tau_2^2) = a^2/3$, where a

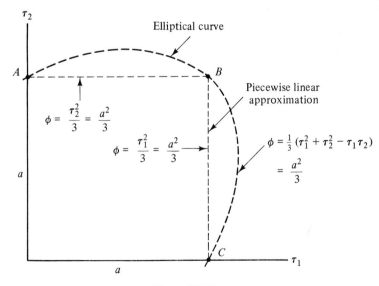

Figure P13.34

is a constant. Evaluate the components of $\dot{\varepsilon}_\alpha$ at points A, B, and C. Also shown in the figure is an inscribed piecewise linear approximation to the elliptical curve. Along the side AB we have replaced ϕ by $\tau_2^2/3$, and along the side BC it has been replaced by $\tau_1^2/3$. Verify that $\phi = a^2/3$ yields the indicated straight-line approximations, while still being coincident with the original ϕ function at points A, B, and C. Now, using these approximate expressions for ϕ, evaluate the components of $\dot{\varepsilon}_\alpha$ along the straight *sides AB* and *BC*. Next, for the *corner point B* obtain conditions on the components of the strain-rate vector. [*Hint*: Use a procedure analogous to that employed in developing Table 13.3 for the Tresca polygon of plasticity.] Finally, draw careful sketches analogous to Figs. 13.12 and 13.13 (first quadrants only) showing a comparison of the $\dot{\varepsilon}_\alpha$ vectors, as obtained by the two methods.

Appendixes

Appendix I

Sufficiency Conditions for Compatibility

I.1 SIMPLY CONNECTED DOMAINS

We shall now consider the *sufficiency* of the compatibility equations for generating a single-valued, continuous displacement field for the case of simply connected regions. It is assumed that deformations are small.

Let $P^0(x_1^0, x_2^0, x_3^0)$ be a point at which the displacement u_i^0 and rotation Ω_{ij}^0 are known. Then the displacement of *any other point* $P^*(x_1^*, x_2^*, x_3^*)$ in the domain is representable by a line integral along a continuous curve C from P^0 to P^* in the following way:

$$u_i^* = u_i^0 + \int_{P^0}^{P^*} du_i = u_i^0 + \int_{P^0}^{P^*} u_{i,j} \, dx_j$$

We now employ Eq. (3.49) in the last expression to give us

$$u_i^* = u_i^0 + \int_{P^0}^{P^*} \varepsilon_{ij} \, dx_j + \int_{P^0}^{P^*} \Omega_{ij} \, dx_j \tag{I.1}$$

Since x_j^* is constant as far as integration is concerned, we may employ $d(x_j - x_j^*)$ in the last line integral. Integrating this expression by parts, we obtain

$$\int_{P^0}^{P^*} \Omega_{ij} \, d(x_j - x_j^*) = \Omega_{ij}(x_j - x_j^*)\Big|_{P^0}^{P^*} - \int_{P^0}^{P^*} (x_j - x_j^*) \, d\Omega_{ij}$$

$$= -\Omega_{ij}^0(x_j^0 - x_j^*) - \int_{P^0}^{P^*} (x_j - x_j^*)\Omega_{ij,k} \, dx_k \tag{I.2}$$

Now the expression $\Omega_{ij,k}$ can be written as follows:

$$\Omega_{ij,k} = \tfrac{1}{2}(u_{i,jk} - u_{j,ik}) = \tfrac{1}{2}(u_{i,jk} + u_{k,ij}) - \tfrac{1}{2}(u_{j,ik} + u_{k,ij})$$

where we have added and subtracted $\tfrac{1}{2}u_{k,ij}$. From this we conclude

$$\Omega_{ij,k} = \tfrac{1}{2}(u_{i,kj} + u_{k,ij}) - \tfrac{1}{2}(u_{j,ki} + u_{k,ji})$$

$$= \varepsilon_{ik,j} - \varepsilon_{jk,i} \tag{I.3}$$

Substituting Eq. (I.2) with Eq. (I.3) into Eq. (I.1), we get

$$u_i^* = u_i^0 - \Omega_{ij}^0(x_j^0 - x_j^*) + \int_{P^0}^{P^*} U_{ik}\, dx_k \qquad \text{(a)}$$

(I.4)

where

$$U_{ik} = \varepsilon_{ik} - (x_j - x_j^*)(\varepsilon_{ik,j} - \varepsilon_{jk,i}) \qquad \text{(b)}$$

If u_i^* is to be single-valued and continuous, the integral in Eq. (I.4a) must be independent of the path C. This in turn requires that the integral around *any closed* curve Γ must vanish, that is,

$$\oint_\Gamma U_{ik}\, dx_k = 0 \qquad (I.5)$$

We now employ Stokes' theorem for a tensor field in a *simply connected* domain [see Eq. (1.82)] to rewrite Eq. (I.5) as the surface integral

$$\iint_S e_{mlk}\, U_{ik,l}\, dA_m = 0 \qquad (I.6)$$

The necessary and sufficient condition for this to be satisfied for *every* surface S is

$$e_{mlk}\, U_{ik,l} = 0 \qquad (I.7)$$

It then follows that $U_{ik,l}$ is symmetric in kl since e_{mlk} is skew-symmetric in kl, that is,

$$U_{ik,l} - U_{il,k} = 0 \qquad (I.8)$$

Using Eq. (I.4b) in Eq. (I.8) and noting that $x_{j,l} = \delta_{jl}$, we find that

$$\varepsilon_{ik,l} - \delta_{jl}(\varepsilon_{ik,j} - \varepsilon_{jk,i}) - (x_j - x_j^*)(\varepsilon_{ik,jl} - \varepsilon_{jk,il})$$
$$- \varepsilon_{il,k} + \delta_{jk}(\varepsilon_{il,j} - \varepsilon_{jl,i}) + (x_j - x_j^*)(\varepsilon_{il,jk} - \varepsilon_{jl,ik}) = 0$$

Rearranging this equation, we get

$$\varepsilon_{ik,l} - \varepsilon_{il,k} - (\varepsilon_{ik,l} - \varepsilon_{lk,i}) + (\varepsilon_{il,k} - \varepsilon_{kl,i}) + (x_j - x_j^*)(\varepsilon_{il,jk} + \varepsilon_{jk,il} - \varepsilon_{ik,jl} - \varepsilon_{jl,ik}) = 0$$

The first six terms cancel each other, and since $(x_j - x_j^*)$ is arbitrary, it follows that

$$\varepsilon_{il,jk} + \varepsilon_{jk,il} - \varepsilon_{ik,jl} - \varepsilon_{jl,ik} = 0$$

Employing symmetry and reordering terms, we finally obtain

$$\varepsilon_{il,kj} + \varepsilon_{kj,il} - \varepsilon_{jl,ki} - \varepsilon_{ki,jl} = 0 \qquad (I.9)$$

But these are the compatibility equations (3.65) presented earlier, and thus we have proved that these equations are *both necessary* and *sufficient* for a *simply connected* domain.

The alternative form of compatibility given by Eq. (3.68) may also be obtained from the formulation above. To this end we first rewrite Eq. (I.4b) for U_{ik} as follows:

$$U_{ik} = \varepsilon_{ik} - (x_j - x_j^*)\varepsilon_{pk,q}(\delta_{pi}\delta_{qj} - \delta_{pj}\delta_{qi})$$

Using the e–δ identity [Eq. (1.42)] this becomes

$$U_{ik} = \varepsilon_{ik} - (x_j - x_j^*)\varepsilon_{pk,q}\, e_{rpq}\, e_{rij} \qquad (I.10)$$

Now go back and substitute Eq. (I.10) into Eq. (I.7):

$$e_{mlk}[\varepsilon_{ik,l} - \delta_{jl}\varepsilon_{pk,q}\, e_{rpq}\, e_{rij} - (x_j - x_j^*)\varepsilon_{pk,ql}\, e_{rpq}\, e_{rij}] = 0 \qquad (I.11)$$

In the second term in the brackets we may set

$$\delta_{jl} e_{rpq} e_{rij} = e_{rpq} e_{ril} = \delta_{pi} \delta_{ql} - \delta_{pl} \delta_{qi}$$

and thus Eq. (I.11) becomes

$$e_{mlk}[\varepsilon_{ik,l} - \varepsilon_{ik,l} + \varepsilon_{lk,i} - (x_j - x_j^*)\varepsilon_{pk,ql} e_{rpq} e_{rij}] = 0$$

The first two terms in the brackets cancel and the third term drops since e_{mlk} is skew-symmetric in kl, whereas $\varepsilon_{lk,i}$ is symmetric in these same indices. Furthermore, since $(x_j - x_j^*)$ is arbitrary we have

$$e_{mlk} e_{rpq} e_{rij} \varepsilon_{pk,ql} = 0 \tag{I.12}$$

Now multiply this result by e_{tij} and note that

$$e_{tij} e_{rij} = e_{jti} e_{jri} = \delta_{tr} \delta_{ii} - \delta_{ti} \delta_{ir} = 3 \delta_{tr} - \delta_{tr} = 2 \delta_{tr} \tag{I.13}$$

Accordingly, Eq. (I.12) becomes

$$2 e_{tpq} e_{mlk} \varepsilon_{pk,ql} = 0$$

Dividing by -2 and replacing e_{mlk} by $-e_{mlk}$, we finally obtain

$$e_{tpq} e_{mkl} \varepsilon_{pk,ql} = 0 \tag{I.14}$$

which is the desired compatibility equation (3.68).† We can easily demonstrate that the six equations given by this relation are the only nontrivial equations generated by Eq. (I.12).

In the development above we showed that [see Eqs. (I.5) and (I.10)] the integral expression for *any* closed path Γ

$$\oint_{\Gamma} U_{ik} \, dx_k \equiv \oint_{\Gamma} [\varepsilon_{ik} - (x_j - x_j^*) e_{rij} e_{rpq} \varepsilon_{pk,q}] \, dx_k \tag{I.15}$$

must vanish for compatible strains. The three integrals given by Eq. (I.15) are called the Cesàro integrals. The condition that they vanish is not restricted to simply connected domains, and thus we shall make full use of this condition in the next section on multiply connected domains.

I.2 MULTIPLY CONNECTED DOMAINS

Consider now a multiply connected domain as shown in Fig. I.1, where there are N cavities labeled $\alpha = 1, 2, \ldots, N$, so as to form a "fat pretzel." As explained in Section 1.12 on Stokes' theorem, we can form a simply connected domain in this body by inserting surfaces (shown dashed) between the outside boundary and each cavity, and staying within all boundaries and these surfaces. Let us first consider any closed path *inside* this simply connected domain such as curve $\bar{\Gamma}$ in Fig. I.1. Setting the Cesàro integral for such a path equal to zero and utilizing Stokes' theorem as discussed in the preceding section, we obtain again [see Eq. (I.7)] the condition

$$e_{mlk} U_{ik,l} = 0 \tag{I.16}$$

† The derivation of Eq. (I.14) above is similar to the treatment given in *Theory of Thermal Stresses* by B. A. Boley and J. H. Wiener (Melbourne, FL: R.E. Krieger Publishing Co., reprint edition, 1985), pp. 86–87. Also, the preceding derivation of Eq. (I.9) is similar to that given in *Mathematical Theory of Elasticity* by I. S. Sokolnikoff (Melbourne, FL: R.E. Krieger Publishing Co., reprint edition, 1983), pp. 25–28.

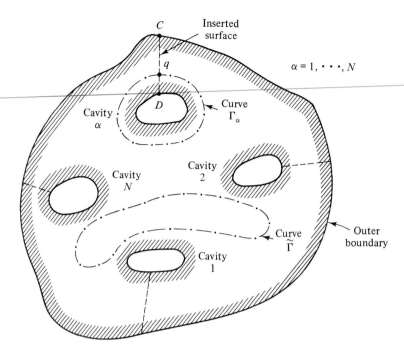

Figure I.1 Multiply connected domain resembling a fat pretzel. Curve Γ_α cuts through inserted surface.

which again yields [see Eq. (I.14)] the compatibility equations

$$e_{tpq}\, e_{mkl}\, \varepsilon_{pk,ql} = 0 \tag{I.17}$$

Clearly, these compatibility equations are necessary but *not sufficient* for multiply connected domains, because we have excluded closed paths that *cut through* the inserted dashed surfaces. To extend the sufficiency condition to multiply connected domains, we must also require that the Cesàro integrals vanish for *all possible* closed paths that cut through the inserted surfaces. Such a closed path is shown in Fig. I.1 as curve Γ_α around cavity α, cutting the surface CD at the point q. In accordance with Eq. (I.15), we require for this curve

$$\oint_{\Gamma_\alpha} [\varepsilon_{ik} - (x_j - x_j^*)\, e_{rij}\, e_{rpq}\, \varepsilon_{pk,q}]\, dx_k = 0 \tag{I.18}$$

where you will recall that x_j^* designates *any* fixed point on the curve Γ_α.

Let us for a moment go back to a simply connected domain formed as described above with the aid of inserted (dashed) surfaces (see Fig. I.2). Consider a particular closed path $\bar{\Gamma}$ that goes inside the outer boundary (counterclockwise), along one side of an inserted surface to a cavity, around the cavity (clockwise), and then back out to the outer boundary along the other side of the inserted surface for each cavity. The portions of the path along the inserted surfaces are taken infinitesimally close to these surfaces, so that in the limit, the curves Γ_α, $\alpha = 1, 2, \ldots, N$, around the cavities and the curve Γ_0 inside the outer boundary are all in themselves closed curves. The Cesàro integrals [Eq. (I.15)] for such a path become

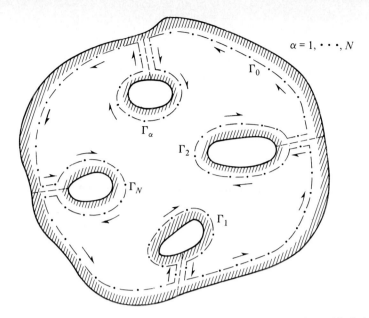

Figure I.2 Closed path that does not cut across inserted boundaries and includes curves inside the outer boundary and around all cavities.

$$\oint_{\Gamma} U_{ik}\, dx_k = \oint_{\Gamma_0} U_{ik}\, dx_k - \sum_{\alpha=1}^{N} \oint_{\Gamma_\alpha} U_{ik}\, dx_k$$

where counterclockwise integrals around closed curves are positive, and the contributions along the inserted surfaces have canceled in the limit. Using Stokes' theorem [see Eq. (1.82)] for this simply connected domain, we obtain

$$\oint_{\Gamma_0} U_{ik}\, dx_k - \sum_{\alpha=1}^{N} \oint_{\Gamma_\alpha} U_{ik}\, dx_k = \iint_{S} e_{mlk}\, U_{ik,l}\, dA_m$$

But we have already concluded that the integrand of the surface integral above is identically zero [see Eq. (I.16)], and thus we have

$$\oint_{\Gamma_0} U_{ik}\, dx_k = \sum_{\alpha=1}^{N} \oint_{\Gamma_\alpha} U_{ik}\, dx_k \tag{I.19}$$

From Eq. (I.19) we may immediately conclude that *if* we set all the Cesàro integrals equal to zero for paths around each cavity α as discussed previously [see Eq. (I.18)], the Cesàro integral for the path enclosing *all* of the cavities must necessarily also vanish. In a similar manner we can also show that the Cesàro integrals for paths enclosing any subgroup of cavities will also vanish. Furthermore, we see that we may alter any one of the closed paths about a cavity while maintaining all other closed paths intact without invalidating Eq. (I.19). This leads us to conclude that $\oint_{\Gamma_\alpha} U_{ik}\, dx_k$ has the *same* value for *all* possible closed curves about a single cavity α. Hence if Eq. (I.18) is valid for *any one* path about cavity α cutting surface CD at *one* particular point q, as shown in Fig. I.1, it is valid for closed paths solely about cavity α cutting through any other point on the surface CD. Thus for multiply connected domains it is sufficient for us to require condition (I.18) for *every* cavity, where Γ_α is *any* one path enclosing *only* the cavity α.

How then do we ensure that Eq. (I.18) is valid for at least one closed path solely about each of the N cavities? Note first that x_j^* is constant as far as integration is concerned, and thus we may rewrite Eq. (I.18) in the form

$$\oint_{\Gamma_\alpha} (\varepsilon_{ik} - x_j e_{rij} e_{rpq} \varepsilon_{pk,q}) \, dx_k + x_j^* \oint_{\Gamma_\alpha} e_{rij} e_{rpq} \varepsilon_{pk,q} \, dx_k = 0 \tag{I.20}$$

But as noted previously, x_j^* are the coordinates of an *arbitrary* fixed point on Γ_α, and thus it is necessary that each integral in Eq. (I.20) vanish *separately*,† that is,

$$\oint_{\Gamma_\alpha} (\varepsilon_{ik} - x_j e_{rij} e_{rpq} \varepsilon_{pk,q}) \, dx_k = 0 \qquad \text{(a)}$$
$$\oint_{\Gamma_\alpha} e_{rij} e_{rpq} \varepsilon_{pk,q} \, dx_k = 0 \qquad \text{(b)} \tag{I.21}$$

Now multiply Eq. (I.21b) by e_{tij}, and since $e_{tij} e_{rij} = 2 \delta_{tr}$ [see Eq. (I.13)], we finally obtain the Cesàro integral conditions

$$\boxed{\begin{aligned} &\oint_{\Gamma_\alpha} (\varepsilon_{ik} - x_j e_{rij} e_{rpq} \varepsilon_{pk,q}) \, dx_k = 0 \qquad \alpha = 1, \ldots, N \\ &\oint_{\Gamma_\alpha} e_{tpq} \varepsilon_{pk,q} \, dx_k = 0 \qquad \alpha = 1, \ldots, N \end{aligned}} \tag{I.22}$$

where the second of these relations gives the only nontrivial equations generated by Eq. (I.21b). We point out again that Γ_α is a set of closed paths each solely about each of the N cavities.

We can now conclude that for a multiply connected domain it is *necessary and sufficient* that the six partial differential equations (I.17) and the $6N$ Cesàro integral conditions (I.22) be satisfied. If one is able to first solve compatibility equations (I.17) with the other field equations in terms of $6N$ undetermined parameters, then Eqs. (I.22) may be used to evaluate these parameters. A curve Γ_α may be chosen to conform with the cavity itself, but for irregularly shaped cavities it is much more convenient to choose some simple curve (such as a circle) around the cavity.

---

† To show this, first set $x_j^* = 0$ (i.e., place the point P^* at the origin). Equation (I.21a) then follows immediately. Next let $x_j^* \neq 0$, which then requires that Eq. (I.21b) also be satisfied.

Discontinuity Functions

II.1 INTRODUCTION

In this book we will make frequent use of discontinuity functions (also denoted as singularity functions). Specifically, we consider in this appendix the unit step function, the ramp function, the delta function, and the doublet function.

II.2 THE UNIT STEP FUNCTION AND THE RAMP FUNCTION

The unit step function in time, $[u(t - t_0)]$, is defined in the following way:

$$[u(t - t_0)] \equiv \begin{cases} 1 & \text{for } t > t_0 \\ \frac{1}{2} & \text{for } t = t_0 \\ 0 & \text{for } t < t_0 \end{cases} \tag{II.1}$$

A plot of this function is shown in Fig. II.1. Of great importance is the way the unit step function acts during an integration. Thus, considering any integrable function of time $f(t)$, it should be clear to the reader that

$$\int_{-\infty}^{t} f(t')[u(t' - t_0)] \, dt' = [u(t - t_0)] \int_{t_0}^{t} f(t') \, dt' \tag{II.2}$$

Let us now consider the case where $f(t) = (t - t_0)^n$. Equation (II.2) with the use of this function becomes, for $n = 0, 1, 2, \ldots$,

$$\int_{-\infty}^{t} (t' - t_0)^n [u(t' - t_0)] \, dt' = [u(t - t_0)] \frac{(t - t_0)^{n+1}}{n+1} \tag{II.3}$$

647

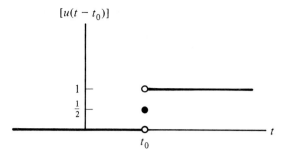

Figure II.1 The unit step function.

When we use $n = 0$, the formulation above becomes $[u(t - t_0)](t - t_0)$, which is shown in Fig. II.2. This function, as might be expected, is called a *ramp* function.

Up to this point, we have used time t as the independent variable. Clearly, we can use the step function and the ramp function for a spatial coordinate x. Thus the unit step in space, $[u(x - x_0)]$, is defined in a manner analogous to Eq. (II.1). Note that both $[u(t - t_0)]$ and $[u(x - x_0)]$ are dimensionless. It is usual practice to express $[u(t - t_0)]$ at $t_0 = 0$ simply as $[u(t)]$, and $[u(x - x_0)]$ at $x_0 = 0$ as $[u(x)]$. This same practice is followed for the delta and doublet functions, which we will discuss in the next sections.

II.3 THE DIRAC DELTA FUNCTION

In defining the step function, we established a one-to-one correspondence between the dependent and the independent variables. The Dirac delta function, by contrast, will not be defined by such a correspondence between dependent and independent variables. Indeed, it may be said justifiably that we are using the word "function" very loosely in conjunction with the Dirac delta function. Rather than relating dependent and independent variables, we instead define the Dirac delta function in time, $[\delta(t - t_0)]$, by an integral condition on a function $f(t)$, which is continuous at t_0. We give this integral condition as

$$\int_{-\infty}^{t} f(t')[\delta(t' - t_0)] \, dt' = f(t_0)[u(t - t_0)] \tag{II.4}$$

and since $[u(\infty)] = 1$ it follows that

$$\int_{-\infty}^{\infty} f(t')[\delta(t' - t_0)] \, dt' = f(t_0) \tag{II.5}$$

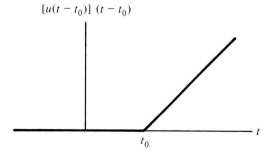

Figure II.2 The ramp function.

The Dirac delta function above is described as "acting" at time $t = t_0$. We note from Eq. (II.5) that when the Dirac delta function appears in an integrand multiplied by a function $f(t')$ for an integral with *infinite* limits, it "extracts" the value of this function at the time t_0 at which the Dirac delta function acts. Because of the step function on the right side of Eq. (II.4), the *indefinite* integral on the left side of this equation is zero for $t < t_0$, has the value $f(t_0)/2$ at $t = t_0$, and thereafter has the constant value $f(t_0)$ for $t > t_0$.

In the special case where $f(t) = 1$, Eq. (II.4) reduces to

$$\int_{-\infty}^{t} [\delta(t' - t_0)]\, dt' = [u(t - t_0)] \tag{II.6}$$

Thus the Dirac delta function is simply related via integration to the unit step function. If now we differentiate Eq. (II.6) with respect to time, we obtain via Leibnitz's rule,

$$[\delta(t - t_0)] = \frac{d}{dt}[u(t - t_0)] \tag{II.7}$$

The derivative above is undefined at the point $t = t_0$ because of the discontinuity in the step function as t goes through t_0 (see Fig. II.1). Furthermore, we see from Eq. (II.7) that $[\delta(t - t_0)]$ is zero when $t \ne t_0$, and, as just indicated, is undefined (actually unbounded) at $t = t_0$. By convention, it is represented as an infinite "spike" at $t = t_0$ (see Fig. II.3). The delta function in space, $[\delta(x - x_0)]$, is defined in a manner analogous to Eq. (II.4). One can easily see from Eq. (II.7) that the dimension of $[\delta(t - t_0)]$ is $(T)^{-1}$. The dimension of $[\delta(x - x_0)]$, it then follows, is $(L)^{-1}$.

To find a meaning and use of the delta function, consider $I_0[\delta(t - t_0)]$ where the constant I_0 has the dimension $(F)(T)$. Clearly, then, the dimension of $I_0[\delta(t - t_0)]$ is $(F)(T)/(T) = (F)$. Thus $I_0[\delta(t - t_0)]$ is some kind of *force* function varying with time. We shall denote this function as $P(t)$. [We realize that because of the delta function, $P(t)$ is not a time function in the usual sense.] What then is the nature of this time "function"? We can ascertain this only by considering the integral of $I_0[\delta(t - t_0)]$, since the meaning of a delta function is embodied in the integral from $t' = -\infty$ to $t' = t$. Thus

$$\int_{-\infty}^{t} I_0[\delta(t' - t_0)]\, dt' = \int_{-\infty}^{t} P(t')\, dt' = I_0[u(t - t_0)] \tag{II.8}$$

You will recognize that the integrals above represent an *impulse* $I(t)$, which using the extreme right side above is plotted in Fig. II.4. We now ask what is the *only force function of time* that will yield the impulse function $I(t)$ shown in the diagram, this being a step increase of I_0 in $I(t)$ at time t_0. The answer is a force of value I_0 applied at time t_0 and maintained constant thereafter. Thus the expression $100[\delta(t - 20)]$ represents a force of value 100 applied to a body at time $t = 20$ with the dimension of 100 being $(F)(T)$.

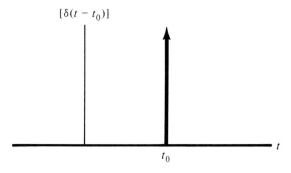

$[\delta(t - t_0)]$

t_0

t

Figure II.3 Representation of the Dirac delta function.

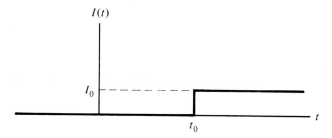

$I(t)$

I_0

t_0

t

Figure II.4 Plot of $\int_{-\infty}^{t} I_0[\delta(t'-t_o)]$, which is a plot of an impulse.

To further illustrate the meaning of the delta function, this time using x as the independent variable, consider the expression $P_0[\delta(x-x_0)]$ where P_0 has the dimension of (F). Clearly, then, the expression $P_0[\delta(x-x_0)]$, with dimension $(F)/(L)$, represents some kind of loading "function" $q(x)$, the quotes being used because of the presence of the delta function. Again, for meaning we must integrate. Thus

$$\int_{-\infty}^{x} P_0[\delta(x'-x_0)]\,dx' = \int_{-\infty}^{x} q(x')\,dx' = P_0[u(x-x_0)] \qquad (II.9)$$

Before proceeding further, let us pause to understand the meaning of the integrals above. Recall from strength of materials that from equilibrium conditions on a beam, we have $dV(x)/dx = -q(x)$, where $V(x)$ is the familiar shear force function. We can then conclude from this relation that

$$\int_{-\infty}^{x} q(x')\,dx' = -V(x) \qquad (II.10)$$

Thus the integrals of Eq. (II.9) represent the negative of a shear force function. For our specific integral of Eq. (II.9) we have plotted $V(x)$ using the extreme right side of Eq. (II.9). This is shown in Fig. II.5. We now ask the important question as to what is the only *loading distribution* that will yield this shear force function. The answer is a positive point force P_0 acting at position $x = x_0$ on the beam. Thus we can readily express the loading function for a 100-lb point force acting downward at position $x = 10$ ft as $-100[\delta(x-10)]$. This is shown in Fig. II.6.

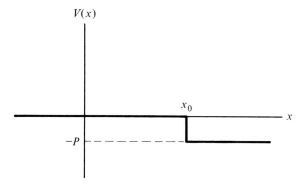

$V(x)$

x_0

x

$-P$

Figure II.5 Plot of $\int_{-\infty}^{x} P_o[\delta(x'-x_o)]\,dx'$, which is the plot of shear force function.

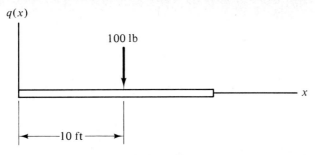

$q(x)$

100 lb

x

10 ft

Figure II.6 The expression $-100[\delta(x - 10)]$ represents the loading of a 100-lb point force acting downward on a beam.

II.4 THE DOUBLET FUNCTION

Like the Dirac delta function, the doublet function in time, denoted as $[\eta(t - t_0)]$, is not in the usual sense a function. We define it via an integration as

$$\int_{-\infty}^{t} f(t')[\eta(t' - t_0)]\, dt' = f(t)[\delta(t - t_0)] - \dot{f}(t_0)[u(t - t_0)] \qquad (\text{II.11})$$

where $f(t)$ is continuous at t_0 and $\dot{f}(t_0)$ is the value of its time derivative at that point. Letting $t \to \infty$ in Eq. (II.11) and noting that $[\delta(\infty)] = 0$ and $[u(\infty)] = 1$, we obtain

$$\int_{-\infty}^{\infty} f(t')[\eta(t' - t_0)]\, dt' = -\dot{f}(t_0) \qquad (\text{II.12})$$

We see from this result that an integration of the product $f(t)[\eta(t - t_0)]$ over the infinite t axis extracts *minus* the value of $\dot{f}(t_0)$. Returning to definition (II.11), we can conclude from the presence of $[\delta(t - t_0)]$ in the first term on the right, that *two* integrations of $f(t)[\eta(t - t_0)]$ are required to obtain a result in terms of well-defined functions. Accordingly, using Eqs. (II.11), (II.4), and (II.3) we obtain

$$\int_{-\infty}^{t}\int_{-\infty}^{t''} f(t')[\eta(t' - t_0)]\, dt'\, dt'' = f(t_0)[u(t - t_0)] - \dot{f}(t_0)(t - t_0)[u(t - t_0)] \qquad (\text{II.13})$$

In the special case where $f(t) = 1$, definition (II.11) simplifies to the useful expression

$$\int_{-\infty}^{t} [\eta(t' - t_0)]\, dt' = [\delta(t - t_0)] \qquad (\text{II.14})$$

which is an alternative, commonly used definition of the doublet function. It follows immediately via differentiation that

$$[\eta(t - t_0)] = \frac{d}{dt}[\delta(t - t_0)] \qquad (\text{II.15})$$

which shows that $[\eta(t - t_0)]$ is undefined at $t = t_0$ since $[\delta(t - t_0)]$ is undefined at that point. Since $[\delta(t - t_0)] = 0$ at all points excluding $t = t_0$, it follows that $[\eta(t - t_0)] = 0$ for $t \neq t_0$, whereas it is unbounded at $t = t_0$. [It is interesting to note that one can obtain the right side

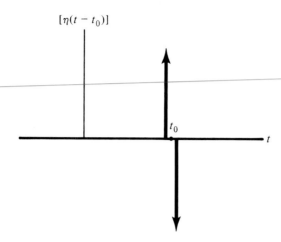

Figure II.7 Representation of the doublet function.

of Eq. (II.11) by substituting Eq. (II.15) into the left side of Eq. (II.11), performing an integration by parts, and then using Eq. (II.4).] A doublet function may be represented as a pair of infinite spikes forming a couple as shown in Fig. II.7. (The logic behind this convention will soon become clear.) Upon considering Eqs. (II.15) and (II.6), we see that the dimension of $[\eta(t - t_0)]$ is $(T)^{-2}$. We can introduce via similar procedures the doublet function in space, $[\eta(x - x_0)]$, which then has the dimension $(L)^{-2}$.

We will now explore the meaning of the doublet function as it pertains to loading on a beam. For this purpose consider the expression $M_0[\eta(x - x_0)]$, where M_0 has the dimension of $(F)(L)$. Clearly, considering the dimension of $M_0[\eta(x - x_0)]$, it represents some loading "function" $q(x)$. To find the meaning of this loading function we will integrate twice as follows:

$$\int_{-\infty}^{x} \int_{-\infty}^{x''} M_0[\eta(x' - x_0)]\, dx'\, dx'' = \int_{-\infty}^{x} \int_{-\infty}^{x''} q(x')\, dx'\, dx'' = M_0[u(x - x_0)] \qquad \text{(II.16)}$$

We pause again to go back to strength of materials where you will recall that for the bending moment function $M(x)$ we have

$$\frac{d^2M(x)}{dx^2} = q(x)$$

If we integrate twice, we get for $M(x)$,

$$M(x) = \int_{-\infty}^{x} \int_{-\infty}^{x''} q(x')\, dx'\, dx'' \qquad \text{(II.17)}$$

Thus we can conclude from the result above that the double integrals of Eq. (II.16) represents a bending moment distribution, which using the right side of Eq. (II.16), is plotted in Fig. II.8. We next ask the key question as to what is the only loading function $q(x)$ that will yield this specific bending moment distribution. The answer is a clockwise point couple of value M_0 applied at $x = x_0$ on the beam. Thus the expression $500[\eta(x - 8)]$ represents the loading function of a clockwise 500-unit point couple, applied at position $x = 8$ on the beam. This is shown in Fig. II.9 using SI units.

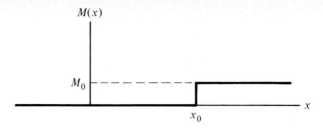

Figure II.8 Plot of $\int_{-\infty}^{x} \int_{-\infty}^{x''} M_o[\eta(x' - x_o)]\, dx'\, dx''$ which is the plot of a bending moment distribution.

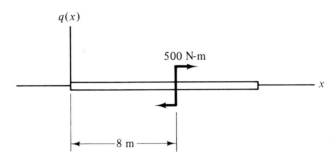

Figure II.9 The expression $500\,[\eta(x - 8)]$ represents the loading of a 500 N-m clockwise couple-moment.

II.5 VEHICLE FUNCTIONS FOR OBTAINING DELTA AND DOUBLET FUNCTIONS

The *delta* function $[\delta(x - x_o)]$ may also be obtained by performing a limiting process on a function with unit area that is even relative to x_o. In carrying out the limit, the amplitude is made to approach infinity, while the width of the function approaches zero in such a manner that the unit area is maintained. The *doublet* function $[\eta(x - x_o)]$ may be obtained by a similar limiting process applied to an odd function relative to x_o with unit first moment of area about x_o. The functions chosen for such limiting processes are not unique, and various examples may be found in the literature. We next present some specific examples of such functions, to further clarify the physical meanings of the delta and doublet functions.

As mentioned above, one can employ various functions as a "vehicle" for arriving at the *delta* function. For example, in Fig. II.10(a) we have shown a function $g_1(t)$ that is zero from $-\infty$ to $[t_0 - (\Delta/2)]$, then forms a rectangle of height $1/\Delta$ and base Δ, and finally is zero again from $[t_0 + (\Delta/2)]$ to $+\infty$. Note that the *area* under the curve is *unity* for *all values* of Δ. A way to obtain the delta function is to consider this function in the limit as $\Delta \to 0$. Clearly, the peak of the curve goes to infinity as the base goes to zero, and we end up with an infinite spike at $t = t_0$ (see Fig. II.3) enclosing a unit area. The latter is true since

$$\lim_{\Delta \to 0} \left\{ \int_{-\infty}^{\infty} g_1(t)\, dt \right\} = \lim_{\Delta \to 0} \left\{ \Delta\left(\frac{1}{\Delta}\right) \right\} = 1 \tag{II.18}$$

where we have used the expression for the area of a rectangle.

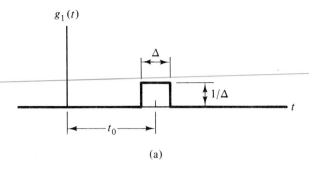

(a)

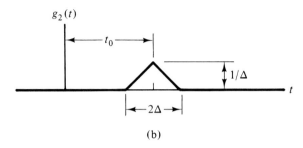

(b)

Figure II.10 Vehicle functions for the delta function.

We will now verify that as $\Delta \to 0$ the function $g_1(t)$ described above does in fact satisfy *defining* Eq. (II.4). Introducing step functions, we have [see Fig. II.10(a)]

$$\lim_{\Delta \to 0} g_1(t) = \lim_{\Delta \to 0} \frac{1}{\Delta} \left\langle \left[u \left\{ t - \left(t_0 - \frac{\Delta}{2} \right) \right\} \right] - \left[u \left\{ t - \left(t_0 + \frac{\Delta}{2} \right) \right\} \right] \right\rangle \qquad (II.19)$$

Now examine the integral

$$\lim_{\Delta \to 0} \int_{-\infty}^{t} f(t') g_1(t') \, dt' = \lim_{\Delta \to 0} \frac{1}{\Delta} \int_{-\infty}^{t} f(t') \left\langle \left[u \left\{ t' - \left(t_0 - \frac{\Delta}{2} \right) \right\} \right] - \left[u \left\{ t' - \left(t_0 + \frac{\Delta}{2} \right) \right\} \right] \right\rangle dt' \qquad (II.20)$$

where $f(t)$ is any function that is continuous at t_0, and where we have assumed that the limit and integral operators commute. Using Eq. (II.2), the right side becomes

$$\lim_{\Delta \to 0} \left\{ \frac{[u\{t - (t_0 - (\Delta/2))\}]}{\Delta} \int_{t_0 - (\Delta/2)}^{t} f(t') \, dt' - \frac{[u\{t - (t_0 + (\Delta/2))\}]}{\Delta} \int_{t_0 + (\Delta/2)}^{t} f(t') \, dt' \right\}$$

which is easily shown to be equivalent to

$$[u(t - t_0)] \lim_{\Delta \to 0} \left\{ \frac{\int_{-\infty}^{t_0 + (\Delta/2)} f(t') \, dt' - \int_{-\infty}^{t_0 - (\Delta/2)} f(t') \, dt'}{\Delta} \right\}$$

But you will recognize the limit in the above as the derivative

$$\frac{d}{dt_0} \int_{-\infty}^{t_0} f(t') \, dt' = f(t_0)$$

and thus Eq. (II.20) becomes

$$\lim_{\Delta \to 0} \int_{-\infty}^{t} f(t')g_1(t')\,dt' = f(t_0)[u(t-t_0)] \tag{II.21}$$

On comparing Eqs. (II.21) and (II.4), we see that as $\Delta \to 0$, the function $g_1(t)$ does have the necessary properties of $[\delta(t-t_0)]$.

Another vehicle for the delta function is the function $g_2(t)$ shown in Fig. II.10(b). In this case the function is zero from $-\infty$ to $(t_0 - \Delta)$, forms an isosceles triangle of height $1/\Delta$ and base 2Δ from $(t_0 - \Delta)$ to $(t_0 + \Delta)$, and is zero again for $t > (t_0 + \Delta)$. The area under this function is again unity for all Δ, and using the same approach employed above it may be shown that as $\Delta \to 0$ function $g_2(t)$ also satisfies defining Eq. (II.4). Many other functions that are even with respect to t_0 and have unit area may be similarly employed. Any of these functions is simply a vehicle toward arriving at the delta function, and can then be discarded as long as the conditions embodied in Eq. (I.4) are obeyed.

Turning now to the *doublet* function, consider the function $h(t)$ shown in Fig. II.11 and examine its behavior as $\Delta \to 0$. Note that we have a rectangle of positive area with base Δ and height $1/\Delta^2$ from $(t_0 - \Delta)$ to t_0, a rectangle of negative area with the same dimensions from t_0 to $(t_0 + \Delta)$, and that $h(t)$ is zero elsewhere. Thus, for any Δ, including $\Delta \to 0$, the net *area* under $h(t)$ is *zero*, that is,

$$\lim_{\Delta \to 0}\left\{ \int_{-\infty}^{\infty} h(t)\,dt \right\} = 0 \tag{II.22}$$

However, the *first moment* of area relative to t_0 is clearly nonzero, and defining clockwise as positive, we obtain

$$\lim_{\Delta \to 0}\left\{ \int_{-\infty}^{\infty} (t_0 - t)\,h(t)\,dt \right\} = \lim_{\Delta \to 0}\left\{ 2\left[\Delta\left(\frac{1}{\Delta^2}\right)\frac{\Delta}{2}\right] \right\} = 1 \tag{II.23}$$

where we have used the well-known properties of rectangles. Clearly, as $\Delta \to 0$ we end up with two infinitesimally close infinite spikes forming a *clockwise couple* at $t = t_0$ (see Fig. II.7), which generates a *unit first moment* of area about t_0.

We shall now prove that as $\Delta \to 0$, the function $h(t)$ does indeed satisfy the integral *definition* of the doublet function given by Eq. (II.11). First note that $h(t)$ as shown in Fig. II.11 is equal to the *derivative* of the function $g_2(t)$ shown in Fig. II.10(b) [i.e., $h(t) \equiv \dot{g}_2(t)$]. It then follows from an integration by parts that

$$\int_{-\infty}^{t} f(t')\,h(t')\,dt' = f(t)\,g_2(t) - \int_{-\infty}^{t} g_2(t')\dot{f}(t')\,dt' \tag{II.24}$$

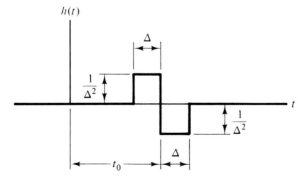

Figure II.11   Vehicle function for the doublet function.

where as previously noted, $f(t)$ is any function that is continuous at t_0. Now take the limit as $\Delta \to 0$,

$$\lim_{\Delta \to 0} \int_{-\infty}^{t} f(t') h(t') \, dt' = f(t)[\delta(t - t_0)] - \dot{f}(t_0)[u(t - t_0)] \tag{II.25}$$

where we have used our previous observation that as $\Delta \to 0$ the function $g_2(t)$ yields the delta function as defined by Eq. (II.4). Comparing Eq. (II.25) with Eq. (II.11) and commuting the limit and integral operators appearing on the left side of Eq. (II.25), we see that

$$\lim_{\Delta \to 0} h(t) = [\eta(t - t_0)]$$

which is what we sought to prove. Again, many other functions, which are odd relative to t_0 and generate unit first moment of area about t_0, may be used as vehicle functions for the doublet function.

II.6 CLOSURE

This concludes our treatment of the step, ramp, delta, and doublet functions, which are called discontinuity or singularity functions. One can continue the process to higher orders of singularity and define triplet, quadruplet, and so on, functions, but we have no need for these in this book.* Some additional properties of the step, delta, and doublet functions are developed in Appendix III on the Laplace transform.

---

*For further information on singularity functions, see C. R. Wylie and L. C. Barrett, *Advanced Engineering Mathematics*, 5th ed. (New York: McGraw-Hill Book Company, 1982), pp. 456–460.

Appendix III
The Laplace Transform

III.1 INTRODUCTION

The Laplace transform will enable us to achieve better insight into linear viscoelastic constitutive laws. In addition, it provides a powerful method for solving the associated stress analysis problems. Accordingly, in this appendix we present a brief survey of those topics that will be most useful to us in our study of linear viscoelastic behavior.

III.2 BASIC CONSIDERATIONS

The Laplace transform of a function of time $f(t)$ will be denoted here as $\mathbf{L}\{f(t)\}$, and it is defined on the interval $t \geq 0$ as

$$\boxed{\mathbf{L}\{f(t)\} = \int_0^\infty f(t)e^{-st}\,dt \equiv \bar{f}(s)} \tag{III.1}$$

where in this book s is a nonnegative, real parameter termed the *transform parameter*. For this integral to exist, it is sufficient (but not necessary) that the function be *piecewise regular* [*] and of *exponential order*. The latter requires that

$$|f(t)| < Me^{at} \qquad \text{for all } t > T$$

for some choice of positive constants M, a, and T. One can also express the Laplace transform for a function of a space coordinate [i.e., $f(x)$], as stated in Eq. (III.1), by simply replac-

---

[*] Function $f(t)$ is said to be *piecewise regular* if, in every interval $0 \leq t_1 \leq t$, $f(t)$ is bounded and has at most a finite number of local maxima and minima and a finite number of finite discontinuities. Some of the functions considered in this appendix are not piecewise regular, and the Laplace transform of these functions will require special scrutiny.

ing t with x. However, x must not be negative [i.e., $f(x)$ may be defined only in the half-space $x \geq 0$]. In either case, it follows from the definition of the Laplace transform that the operation is distributive. That is,

$$\mathbf{L}\{f(t) + g(t)\} = \bar{f}(s) + \bar{g}(s) \tag{III.2}$$

which indicates that the Laplace transform is a *linear operator*. Also, the Laplace transform of the product of a constant a times the function $f(t)$ is given as

$$\mathbf{L}\{af(t)\} = a\bar{f}(s) \tag{III.3}$$

Next, consider the Laplace transform of the derivative, $\dot{f}(t)$. Using integration by parts, we get

$$\mathbf{L}\{\dot{f}(t)\} = \int_0^\infty \dot{f}(t)e^{-st}\,dt = f(t)e^{-st}\Big|_0^\infty + \int_0^\infty sf(t)e^{-st}\,dt$$

and thus

$$\mathbf{L}\{\dot{f}(t)\} = -f(0) + s\bar{f}(s) \tag{III.4}$$

For this important theorem it is sufficient (but not necessary) that $\dot{f}(t)$ be piecewise regular, $f(t)$ be continuous, and both $\dot{f}(t)$ and $f(t)$ be of exponential order. Note we have used Eq. (III.3) in the determination of the last expression. We can continue the process above to apply to higher-order derivatives in the following manner:

$$\mathbf{L}\{\ddot{f}(t)\} = \int_0^\infty \ddot{f}(t)e^{-st}\,dt = -\dot{f}(0) - sf(0) + s^2\bar{f}(s) \tag{a}$$
$$\mathbf{L}\{\overset{(n)}{f}(t)\} = \int_0^\infty \overset{(n)}{f}(t)e^{-st}\,dt = -\overset{(n-1)}{f}(0) - \cdots - s^{n-1}f(0) + s^n\bar{f}(s) \tag{b}$$
$$\tag{III.5}$$

where $(n), (n-1), \ldots$ above f in the second of the equations above represent orders of differentiation. From these formulations, we can discern a very important property of the Laplace transform. It is that the Laplace transform of a derivative is simply related to $\bar{f}(s)$, and the initial conditions up to one order less than the order of the derivative of the function $f(t)$. The results above are also valid for the *partial time derivative* of a function of time t and other independent variables.

III.3 THE LAPLACE TRANSFORM OF DISCONTINUITY FUNCTIONS

Let us consider that the function $f(t)$ or any of its derivatives for which we are taking the Laplace transform has a *discontinuity* at $t = 0$. In such cases, if the transform exists we may consider the possibility of using initial conditions at the time *just before* the discontinuity, $t = 0^-$, or at the time *just after* the discontinuity, $t = 0^+$. In many problems, the initial conditions will be homogeneous* at $t = 0^-$ while being nonhomogeneous at $t = 0^+$. For such problems, it is usually more convenient to choose $t = 0^-$ as the lower limit in the transform. The reason for such a choice is that Eq. (III.5b) then apparently simplifies to the following form:

$$\mathbf{L}\{\overset{(n)}{f}(t)\} = s^n\bar{f}(s) \tag{III.6}$$

However, since $\overset{(n)}{f}(t)$ is not continuous here, the validity of Eq. (III.5b) is not obvious.

---

*By homogeneous initial conditions at $t = 0^-$ we mean that $f(t)$ and all its derivatives are zero at $t = 0^-$.

To explore the point above, let $f(t)$ be zero at $t = 0^-$ and have the finite value $f(0^+)$ at $t = 0^+$. In this case we ask whether Eq. (III.4) is still valid with 0^- as the lower limit for the **L** operator and with $f(0) = f(0^-) = 0$. To answer this question, let

$$f(t) = g(t)[u(t)] \tag{III.7}$$

where $g(t)$ is continuous everywhere on the *infinite* interval $-\infty < t < \infty$. It is easily seen from the definition of the Laplace transform that

$$\mathbf{L}\{f(t)\} = \mathbf{L}\{g(t)\} \tag{III.8}$$

Now differentiate Eq. (III.7),

$$\dot{f}(t) = \dot{g}(t)[u(t)] + g(t)[\delta(t)]$$

and then form the Laplace transform with $t = 0^-$ as the lower limit

$$\mathbf{L}\{\dot{f}(t)\} = \int_{0^-}^{\infty} \dot{g}(t')[u(t')]e^{-st'}\, dt' + \int_{0^-}^{\infty} g(t')[\delta(t')]e^{-st'}\, dt'$$

Using Eqs. (II.2) and (II.4) in Appendix II (with $t_0 = 0$ and $t \to \infty$), we get for the above

$$\mathbf{L}\{\dot{f}(t)\} = \mathbf{L}\{\dot{g}(t)\} + g(0) \tag{III.9}$$

where you are reminded that here 0^- is the lower limit for **L**. But since $g(t)$ is continuous, we may use Eq. (III.4) for $\mathbf{L}\{\dot{g}(t)\}$ and Eq. (III.8) to obtain

$$\mathbf{L}\{\dot{f}(t)\} = s\mathbf{L}\{g(t)\} - g(0) + g(0) = s\mathbf{L}\{f(t)\}$$

We have thus confirmed that Eq. (III.6) is valid for $n = 1$ if $f(t)$ is at the form given by Eq. (III.7); the proof for $n > 1$ follows in a similar manner.

Let us next consider the *unit step function* at $t = 0$, $[u(t)]$, and evaluate the Laplace transform of this piecewise regular function:

$$\mathbf{L}\{[u(t)]\} = \int_0^{\infty} [u(t)]e^{-st}\, dt = \int_0^{\infty} e^{-st}\, dt = -\frac{1}{s}e^{-st}\Big|_0^{\infty}$$

Therefore,

$$\mathbf{L}\{[u(t)]\} = \frac{1}{s} \tag{III.10}$$

It should be clear that the result above is valid both for 0^- and 0^+ as a lower limit. In a similar manner, consider the *ramp function* $t[u(t)]$; we get for the Laplace transform of this function

$$\mathbf{L}\{t[u(t)]\} = \int_0^{\infty} t[u(t)]e^{-st}\, dt = \frac{1}{s^2} \tag{III.11}$$

Again, the result above is valid with a 0^- or a 0^+ lower limit.

We turn next to the Dirac delta function and the doublet function.* Here we must distinguish between the two aforementioned lower limits. Accordingly, for the *delta function* we have by means of Eq. (II.4) of Appendix II,

---

*Although the delta and doublet functions are of exponential order, they are not piecewise regular since they are unbounded at the singularity. However, one may proceed by *transforming bounded* "vehicle" functions (such as those given in Section II.5 of Appendix II) and then letting the width parameter Δ *approach zero*. Alternatively, one may simply employ integral definitions (II.4) and (II.11), which have been shown to be satisfied by these vehicle functions in the limit as $\Delta \to 0$.

$$\int_{0^+}^{\infty} [\delta(t)]e^{-st}\,dt = 0 \qquad\qquad (a)$$

$$\int_{0^-}^{\infty} [\delta(t)]e^{-st}\,dt = \int_{-\infty}^{\infty} [\delta(t-0)]e^{-st}\,dt = [u(\infty)]e^{-st}\Big|_{t=0} = 1 \qquad (b)$$

(III.12)

Note that for a 0^+ lower limit the delta function "spike" is not within the interval of integration, and thus its transform is zero. As for the *doublet function* we will show that

$$\int_{0^+}^{\infty} [\eta(t)]e^{-st}\,dt = 0 \qquad (a)$$

$$\int_{0^-}^{\infty} [\eta(t)]e^{-st}\,dt = s \qquad (b)$$

(III.13)

Again, for the 0^+ lower limit the doublet double spike lies outside the range of integration and we get zero for the transform. To verify Eq. (III.13b), we employ Eq. (II.11) in Appendix II with $f(t) = e^{-st}$, $t_0 = 0$ and $t \to \infty$. Thus we get

$$\int_{0^-}^{\infty} [\eta(t)]e^{-st}\,dt = \int_{-\infty}^{\infty} [\eta(t-0)]e^{-st}\,dt = e^{-\infty}[\delta(\infty - 0)] - (-s)e^{-0}[u(\infty - 0)] = s$$

as indicated previously.

III.4 TRANSFORM PAIRS

The functions $f(t)$ and $\bar{f}(s)$ are termed Laplace *transform pairs*. In the preceding section, we developed transform pairs for discontinuity functions at $t = 0$. Some useful transform pairs (obtained by simple integrations) encountered frequently in solid mechanics are listed in Table III.1.

TABLE III.1   Laplace Transform Pairs

(1)	e^{-at}	$\dfrac{1}{s+a}$
(2)	$\cos at$	$\dfrac{s}{s^2 + a^2}$
(3)	$\sin at$	$\dfrac{a}{s^2 + a^2}$
(4)	$t^n,\ n = 0, 1, 2, \ldots$	$\dfrac{n!}{s^{n+1}}$

The results in Table III.1 can be extended via the use of the following easily derived formulas:

$$\mathbf{L}\{f(t)[u(t - t_0)]\} = \exp(-t_0 s)\,\mathbf{L}\{f(t + t_0)\} \qquad (a)$$

$$\mathbf{L}\{f(at)\} = \frac{1}{a}\bar{f}\left(\frac{s}{a}\right) \qquad (b)$$

$$\mathbf{L}\{t(f(t))\} = -\frac{d}{ds}\bar{f}(s) \qquad (c)$$

$$\mathbf{L}\{e^{-at}f(t)\} = \bar{f}(s + a) \qquad (d)$$

(III.14)

In formulas (b) and (d) the notations $\bar{f}(s/a)$ and $\bar{f}(s+a)$ indicate a replacement of s by s/a and $s+a$, respectively, in $\mathbf{L}\{f(t)\}$. We now consider two simple examples.

Example III.1

Using Eqs. (III.14) and Table III.1, find the Laplace transform of the function $t^2[u(t-2)]$.

From Eq. (III.14a) we have

$$\mathbf{L}\{t^2[u(t-2)]\} = e^{-2s}\,\mathbf{L}\{(t+2)^2\} = e^{-2s}[\mathbf{L}\{t^2\} + 4\,\mathbf{L}\{t\} + \mathbf{L}\{4\}]$$

Now using entry (4) of Table III.1, we can proceed further and obtain

$$\mathbf{L}\{t^2[u(t-2)]\} = e^{-2s}\left[\frac{2}{s^3} + \frac{4}{s^2} + \frac{4}{s}\right] = \frac{2(1 + 2s + 2s^2)}{s^3}\,e^{-2s}$$

Example III.2

Compute the Laplace transform of the function $e^{-at}\cos bt$.

We now use Eq. (III.14d) and entry (2) of Table III.1 for this purpose. Thus

$$\mathbf{L}\{e^{-at}\cos bt\} = \mathbf{L}\{\cos bt\}_{s\to s+a} = \frac{s+a}{(s+a)^2 + b^2}$$

The few simple formulas given in Eqs. (III.14) and Table III.1 will suffice for many of the functions encountered in solid mechanics.

III.5 TRANSFORMS OF INTEGRALS

Let us first turn to the consideration of the Laplace transform of the indefinite integral

$$f(t) = \int_a^t g(t')\,dt'$$

To get the desired transform, we will integrate by parts in the ensuing formulations. Thus

$$\mathbf{L}\left\{\int_a^t g(t')\,dt'\right\} = \int_0^\infty \left[\int_a^t g(t')\,dt'\right]e^{-st}\,dt = \int_0^\infty \left[\int_a^t g(t')\,dt'\right]\left(\frac{1}{-s}\right)\frac{de^{-st}}{dt}\,dt$$

$$= \left[\frac{e^{-st}}{-s}\int_a^t g(t')\,dt'\right]\Bigg|_0^\infty + \frac{1}{s}\int_0^\infty g(t)e^{-st}\,dt$$

$$= \frac{1}{s}\int_a^0 g(t)\,dt + \frac{1}{s}\,\bar{g}(s) \qquad\qquad (\text{III.15})$$

$$= \frac{1}{s}\,\bar{g}(s) - \frac{1}{s}\int_0^a g(t)\,dt$$

Note that the last term above drops out when the lower limit of the original integral is zero.

A very important integral encountered in the study of viscoelastic materials is the *convolution integral* $h(t)$, which is defined as

$$h(t) = \int_0^t f(t')g(t-t')\,dt' \qquad\qquad (\text{III.16})$$

where $f(t)$ and $g(t)$ are *zero* for $t < 0$. It then follows that the integrand of $h(t)$ must be zero

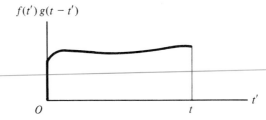

Figure III.1 Integrand in convolution integral.

for $t' < 0$ and $t' > t$, as shown schematically in Fig. III.1. Hence we may rewrite $h(t)$ alternatively as follows:

$$h(t) = \int_0^\infty f(t')g(t - t')\, dt' \qquad \text{(a)}$$

$$h(t) = \int_{-\infty}^\infty f(t')g(t - t')\, dt' \qquad \text{(b)}$$

(III.17)

Taking the Laplace transform of the equation above using form (a), we get

$$\mathbf{L}\{h(t)\} = \int_0^\infty e^{-st}\left[\int_0^\infty f(t')g(t - t')\, dt'\right] dt$$

Therefore,

$$\mathbf{L}\{h(t)\} = \int_0^\infty \left[\int_0^\infty g(t - t')\, e^{-st}\, dt\right] f(t')\, dt' \qquad \text{(III.18)}$$

Now let $t - t' = t''$ or, equivalently, $t = t' + t''$. Replace $t - t'$ and t using these relations in the integrand of the bracketed integral. In doing so, note that t' is held constant in this integral, so that $dt' = 0$. We thus get

$$\mathbf{L}\{h(t)\} = \int_0^\infty \left[\int_0^\infty g(t'')\, e^{-s(t' + t'')}\, dt''\right] f(t')\, dt'$$

Therefore,

$$\mathbf{L}\{h(t)\} = \left[\int_0^\infty g(t'')\, e^{-st''}\, dt''\right]\left[\int_0^\infty f(t')\, e^{-st'}\, dt'\right]$$

We thus reach the following important result:

$$\boxed{\mathbf{L}\{h(t)\} = \mathbf{L}\{g(t)\}\,\mathbf{L}\{f(t)\}} \qquad \text{(III.19)}$$

We have reached a simple relation between the transform of the convolution integral and the transform of the two functions in its integrand. This relationship is called the *convolution theorem*.

III.6 LIMIT THEOREMS

It is often desirable to extract the essential features of the short-time (i.e., $t \to 0^+$) and the long-time (i.e., $t \to \infty$) asymptotic behaviors from a governing differential equation. For instance, in viscoelasticity this process will enable us to distinguish between "solid" and "fluid" behavior. With the use of the Laplace transform, we shall now present two limit theorems that will enable us to determine such asymptotic behavior in a simple manner.

Our starting point will be Eq. (III.4) with the lower limit of the **L** operator and the initial condition chosen at $t = 0^+$. That is,

$$\mathbf{L}\{\dot{f}(t)\} = -f(0^+) + s\bar{f}(s) \tag{III.20}$$

You will recall that for this equation to be valid it is sufficient that $f(t)$ be of exponential order and continuous, and for the present we assume that these conditions are satisfied. We now take the limit as $s \to \infty$.

$$\lim_{s \to \infty} \mathbf{L}\{\dot{f}(t)\} = -f(0^+) + \lim_{s \to \infty} s\bar{f}(s) \tag{III.21}$$

It then follows from the definition of the Laplace transform [Eq. (III.1)] that the limit on the left side of Eq. (III.21) goes to zero. The first of our two limit theorems can then be stated from the remaining terms of the equation. That is,

$$\boxed{\lim_{s \to \infty} s\bar{f}(s) = f(0^+)} \tag{III.22}$$

This theorem enables us to determine short-time asymptotic behavior.

We have obtained Eq. (III.22) by assuming that $f(t)$ is continuous on the *open* interval $0 < t < \infty$. What happens to this result if $f(t)$ is discontinuous at $t = 0$ with $f(t) = 0$ for $t \leq 0^-$, and we choose the homogeneous initial conditions at $t = 0^-$? As demonstrated in Section III.3, we may investigate such a query by setting

$$f(t) = g(t)[u(t)] \tag{III.23}$$

where $g(t)$ is continuous everywhere on the infinite interval. We can then say on taking the derivative with respect to time,

$$\dot{f}(t) = \dot{g}(t)[u(t)] + g(t)[\delta(t)] \tag{III.24}$$

Next form the Laplace transform of the equation above with $t = 0^-$ as the lower integration limit, and then take the limit as $s \to \infty$. For the resulting expression on the left side of this equation, we proved in Section III.3 that we may employ Eq. (III.20) with the initial condition taken at $t = 0^-$ rather than at $t = 0^+$. But $f(0^-) = 0$ here, and we thus have after interchanging the sides of the equation,

$$\lim_{s \to \infty} \int_{0^-}^{\infty} \dot{g}(t)[u(t)]e^{-st}\,dt + \lim_{s \to \infty} \int_{0^-}^{\infty} g(t)[\delta(t)]e^{-st}\,dt = \lim_{s \to \infty} s\bar{f}(s) \tag{III.25}$$

The first expression in Eq. (III.25) is zero because $g(t)$ has been prescribed as continuous. As for the second expression, we use the definition of the delta function [see Eq. (II.4)] to conclude that we simply get $g(0)$, which equals $f(0^+)$. Note that this leads us to the very same equation as Eq. (III.22). Thus we find that this *same* limit theorem [i.e., with $f(0^+)$ on the right] is still valid if $f(t)$ is discontinuous at $t = 0$ in the manner prescribed by Eq. (II.23), and we employ homogeneous initial conditions at $t = 0^-$. One can also readily show that the first limit theorem is valid as stated in Eq. (III.22), if $f(t)$ has a finite number of finite discontinuities along the t axis [i.e., $f(t)$ is *piecewise continuous*] and the initial conditions are chosen at either $t = 0^-$ or $t = 0^+$.

To develop our second limit theorem, we go back to Eq. (III.20) and this time we take the limit as $s \to 0$. We thus get for continuous functions $f(t)$,

$$\lim_{s \to 0} \mathbf{L}\{\dot{f}(t)\} = -f(0^+) + \lim_{s \to 0} s\bar{f}(s) \tag{III.26}$$

Using the definition of the Laplace transform, it is seen on inspection that*

$$\lim_{s \to 0} \mathbf{L}\{\dot{f}(t)\} = \lim_{s \to 0} \int_0^\infty \frac{df(t)}{dt} e^{-st} dt = f(\infty) - f(0^+) \qquad \text{(III.27)}$$

where here $f(0) = f(0^-) = f(0^+)$. Substituting this result into Eq. (III.26), we then get our second limit theorem,

$$\boxed{\lim_{s \to 0} s\bar{f}(s) = f(\infty)} \qquad \text{(III.28)}$$

This theorem enables us to determine the long-time asymptotic behavior. By letting s approach zero (instead of infinity) in Eq. (III.25), we can easily show that Eq. (III.28) is also valid for $f(t)$ discontinuous at $t = 0$ and with homogeneous initial conditions at $t = 0^-$. Also, it can be shown that the second limit theorem is valid for functions that have discontinuities at a finite number of points along the interval $t > 0$.

III.7 CLOSURE

We have presented a brief survey of some key points concerning the Laplace transform, which will be of use to us in Chapter 6 on linear viscoelasticity and in subsequent chapters. However, there are many other important topics that we have not covered here. For example, we have only considered the process of obtaining the Laplace transform for some given function of time. The reverse process of obtaining a function of time from a given function of s is often difficult, and is called the process of *Laplace transform inversion*. Such inversions are necessary when a differential equation has been solved in the transform s-space. Extensive tables of Laplace transform pairs are available, and frequently an inversion may be accomplished with the use of these tables and basic formulas like those given in Eqs. (III.14). However, when such efforts fail it may become necessary to carry out the inversion by means of the *complex inversion integral*, which entails an extension of s into the complex domain. Excellent numerical inversion techniques are also available. The reader is referred to standard references on transform theory for the details of these important topics.

---

* In Eq. (III.27) we have assumed that we may interchange the order of integrating over t and taking the limit with respect to s. For this to be valid it is necessary that this improper integral converge *uniformly*, and this places additional restrictions on $f(t)$ and thus $\bar{f}(s)$. For further discussion on this and other aspects of the Laplace transform, see C. Ray Wylie and Louis C. Barrett, *Advanced Engineering Mathematics,* 5th ed., (New York: McGraw-Hill Book Company, 1982), Chap. 8.

Appendix IV

Note on the Flexure Formula for Beams

We have seen that the flexure formula gives exact results for *pure bending* of an isotropic, linear elastic beam (see Section 9.11 and Problem 9.21). At this time we shall prove that this exact status extends to the case where the bending moment is a *linear* function of position along the beam.

In Fig. IV.1 we have shown the coordinate axes for a prismatic linear elastic beam of *arbitrary* cross section, subjected to a bending moment $M_z(x)$ about the z axis which may vary *only with the longitudinal coordinate x*. The origin O is at the *centroid*, and *yz* are *principal* axes. We start by assuming the following stresses for the beam shown in Fig. IV.1:

$$\tau_{xx} = -\frac{M_z(x)y}{I_{zz}}, \qquad \tau_{yy} = \tau_{zz} = \tau_{yz} = 0 \tag{IV.1}$$

No assumption is made about the shear stresses τ_{xy} and τ_{xz}. For a *Hookean material* we can replace τ_{xx} by $E\varepsilon_{xx}$ and for small deformation we can further replace ε_{xx} by $\partial u_x/\partial x$, so that we can say for the flexure formula above,

$$\frac{\partial u_x}{\partial x} = -\frac{M_z(x)y}{EI_{zz}} \tag{IV.2}$$

This equation may be integrated to yield

$$u_x = -\frac{y}{EI_{zz}} \int_0^x M_z(x')\,dx' + \chi(y, z) \tag{IV.3}$$

where χ is a function of y and z. We shall set $u_x = 0$ at $x = y = z = 0$, and thus we see that $\chi(0,0) = 0$. As for the shear stresses τ_{xy} and τ_{xz}, Hooke's law and strain-displacement require that they satisfy the relations

$$\tau_{xy} = \frac{E}{1+\nu}\,\varepsilon_{xy} = \frac{E}{2(1+\nu)}\left(\frac{\partial u_x}{\partial y} + \frac{\partial u_y}{\partial x}\right) \qquad \text{(a)}$$

$$\tau_{xz} = \frac{E}{1+\nu}\,\varepsilon_{xz} = \frac{E}{2(1+\nu)}\left(\frac{\partial u_x}{\partial z} + \frac{\partial u_z}{\partial x}\right) \qquad \text{(b)} \tag{IV.4}$$

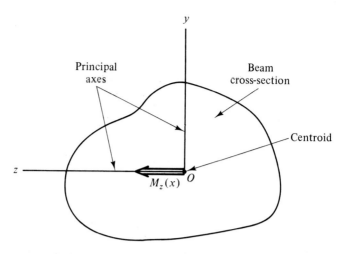

Figure IV.1 Coordinate axes for prismatic beam under discussion.

Now consider the equation of *equilibrium* in the x direction for the case of no body force. Thus

$$\frac{\partial \tau_{xx}}{\partial x} + \frac{\partial \tau_{xy}}{\partial y} + \frac{\partial \tau_{xz}}{\partial z} = 0 \tag{IV.5}$$

Substituting from Eqs. (IV.1) and (IV.4), we have for the equation above after multiplying by $2(1 + \nu)/E$,

$$-\frac{2(1+\nu)y}{EI_{zz}} \frac{dM_z(x)}{dx} + \left(\frac{\partial^2 u_x}{\partial y^2} + \frac{\partial^2 u_y}{\partial x\, \partial y} + \frac{\partial^2 u_x}{\partial z^2} + \frac{\partial^2 u_z}{\partial x\, \partial z} \right) = 0$$

Next subtract and add $\partial^2 u_x/\partial x^2$ to the equation above and rewrite it as follows:

$$-\frac{2(1+\nu)y}{EI_{zz}} \frac{dM_z(x)}{dx} + \left(-\frac{\partial^2 u_x}{\partial x^2} + \frac{\partial^2 u_x}{\partial y^2} + \frac{\partial^2 u_x}{\partial z^2} \right) + \frac{\partial}{\partial x} \left(\frac{\partial u_x}{\partial x} + \frac{\partial u_y}{\partial y} + \frac{\partial u_z}{\partial z} \right) = 0 \tag{IV.6}$$

Now, by differentiating Eq. (IV.3), we may obtain the expression

$$\left(-\frac{\partial^2 u_x}{\partial x^2} + \frac{\partial^2 u_x}{\partial y^2} + \frac{\partial^2 u_x}{\partial z^2} \right) = \frac{y}{EI_{zz}} \frac{dM_z(x)}{dx} + \frac{\partial^2 \chi(y,z)}{\partial y^2} + \frac{\partial^2 \chi(y,z)}{\partial z^2} \tag{IV.7}$$

Also, the bulk form of Hooke's law gives us [see Eqs. (5.52) and (5.53)]

$$(\varepsilon_{xx} + \varepsilon_{yy} + \varepsilon_{zz}) = \frac{1}{3K} (\tau_{xx} + \tau_{yy} + \tau_{zz}) = \frac{1 - 2\nu}{E} (\tau_{xx} + \tau_{yy} + \tau_{zz})$$

Using strain displacement and the stresses (IV.1) in this expression, we get

$$\left(\frac{\partial u_x}{\partial x} + \frac{\partial u_y}{\partial y} + \frac{\partial u_z}{\partial z} \right) = -\frac{(1 - 2\nu)y}{EI_{zz}} M_z(x) \tag{IV.8}$$

We may now insert expressions (IV.7) and (IV.8) into the second and third terms, respectively, in Eq. (IV.6). Accordingly, we finally obtain after combining terms

$$-\frac{2y}{EI_{zz}} \frac{dM_z(x)}{dx} + \frac{\partial^2 \chi(y,z)}{\partial y^2} + \frac{\partial^2 \chi(y,z)}{\partial z^2} = 0 \tag{IV.9}$$

First rearrange Eq. (IV.9) as follows:

$$\frac{dM_z(x)}{dx} = \frac{EI_{zz}}{2y}\left[\frac{\partial^2\chi(y,z)}{\partial y^2} + \frac{\partial^2\chi(y,z)}{\partial z^2}\right] \qquad \text{(IV.10)}$$

The left side of this equation is a function only of x, while the right side is only a function of y and z. Thus to satisfy this equation and thereby satisfy the basic equations of linear elasticity with the flexure formula as an integral part for prismatic beams, it is *necessary* that each side equal a separation constant. Hence, using B as this constant and integrating, we can say for the left side of Eq. (IV.10),

$$M_z(x) = A + Bx \qquad \text{(IV.11)}$$

where A is the constant of integration. Thus we have shown that for the flexure formula to be exact, the bending moment must be linear in x. The special case $B = 0$ and $A = M_0$ corresponds to *pure bending* by couple moments M_0 in the xy principal plane. If we set $A = -PL$ and $B = P$, we obtain the case of a *cantilever* beam of length L with a force P applied at the free end and parallel to the y principal axis (see Fig. IV.2). In this case we have $M_z(x) = -P(L - x)$, and thus τ_{xx} follows from Eq. (IV.1) as

$$\tau_{xx} = \frac{P(L - x)y}{I_{zz}} \qquad \text{(IV.12)}$$

To complete the solution to the cantilever beam problem above, we first go back to equilibrium equation (IV.5) and use Eq. (IV.12) to replace τ_{xx}. Thus

$$\frac{\partial\tau_{xy}}{\partial y} + \frac{\partial\tau_{xz}}{\partial z} = \frac{Py}{I_{zz}} \qquad \text{(IV.13)}$$

We also note that equilibrium in the y and z directions dictate that τ_{xy} and τ_{xz} be *independent of x*. In addition, the Beltrami–Michell stress compatibility relations [see Eq. (9.47)] yield two additional nontrivial conditions:

$$\frac{\partial^2\tau_{xy}}{\partial y^2} + \frac{\partial^2\tau_{xy}}{\partial z^2} = \frac{P}{(1 + \nu)I_{zz}} \qquad \text{(a)}$$

$$\frac{\partial^2\tau_{xz}}{\partial y^2} + \frac{\partial^2\tau_{xz}}{\partial z^2} = 0 \qquad \text{(b)}$$

$$\text{(IV.14)}$$

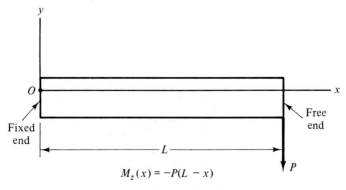

$$M_z(x) = -P(L - x)$$

Figure IV.2 The cantilever beam.

Equations (IV.13) and (IV.14) must now be solved for τ_{xy} and τ_{xz}, subject to the boundary condition that the lateral surface of the cantilever beam be *traction-free*. Finally, the strains follow from the stresses via Hooke's law, and displacements are obtained by integrating the strain-displacement equations. For details the reader is referred to the elasticity literature.[*] It is important to mention that u_x is *not* a linear function of y. Thus plane sections *do not remain plane* in this cantilever beam problem, even though τ_{xx} and ε_{xx} are linear functions in y for a fixed value of x.

---

[*] See S. Timoshenko and J. N. Goodier, *Theory of Elasticity* (New York: McGraw-Hill Book Company, 1951), Chap. 12, for a solution to Eqs. (IV.13) and (IV.14) by a stress function approach. Displacement solutions are presented in I. S. Sokolnikoff, *Mathematical Theory of Elasticity* (New York: McGraw-Hill Book Company, 1956; reprinted by R.E. Krieger Publishing Co., Melbourne, FL, 1983), pp. 209–213.

Traction Conditions in Terms of Φ for Plane Strain and Two-Dimensional Plane Stress

The following developments are based on the theory of plane strain presented in Chapter 12, but as noted in Chapter 13, it is also applicable to two-dimensional plane stress. We start with Cauchy's formula (12.20) on a boundary curve C, and Eq. (12.33) for the Airy stress function Φ in terms of the stresses. Considering these equations, we get for *zero-body forces*,

$$\tau_{\alpha\beta}(s)\nu_\beta(s) = e_{\alpha\gamma}e_{\beta\delta}\,\Phi_{,\,\gamma\delta}\,\nu_\beta(s) = T_\alpha^{(\nu)}(s) = G_\alpha(s) \qquad \text{on } C \qquad (\text{V.1})$$

where $G_\alpha(s)$ is the prescribed traction vector function* on C. We wish to express ν_β in terms of a coordinate derivative. For this purpose, observe Fig. V.1 showing a segment of a boundary curve C. Note that we have shown a unit tangent vector $\hat{\boldsymbol{\mu}}$ and a unit normal vector $\hat{\boldsymbol{\nu}}$ along the path. The position along the path is measured by the path variable s, and the position vector to point P on C is given as

$$\mathbf{r} = x_1\,\hat{\mathbf{i}}_1 + x_2\,\hat{\mathbf{i}}_2$$

Elementary differential geometry and the chain rule of calculus gives us

$$\hat{\boldsymbol{\mu}} = \frac{d\mathbf{r}}{ds} = \frac{\partial\mathbf{r}}{\partial x_1}\frac{\partial x_1}{\partial s} + \frac{\partial\mathbf{r}}{\partial x_2}\frac{\partial x_2}{\partial s}$$

and it then follows that

$$\hat{\boldsymbol{\mu}} = \frac{\partial x_1}{\partial s}\,\hat{\mathbf{i}}_1 + \frac{\partial x_2}{\partial s}\,\hat{\mathbf{i}}_2$$

The unit normal vector $\hat{\boldsymbol{\nu}}$ can meanwhile be given as a cross product between $\hat{\boldsymbol{\mu}}$ and $\hat{\mathbf{i}}_3$. Thus

$$\hat{\boldsymbol{\nu}} = \hat{\boldsymbol{\mu}} \times \hat{\mathbf{i}}_3 = \left(\frac{\partial x_1}{\partial s}\,\hat{\mathbf{i}}_1 + \frac{\partial x_2}{\partial s}\,\hat{\mathbf{i}}_2\right) \times \hat{\mathbf{i}}_3$$

$$= -\frac{\partial x_1}{\partial s}\,\hat{\mathbf{i}}_2 + \frac{\partial x_2}{\partial s}\,\hat{\mathbf{i}}_1$$

---

*For two-dimensional plane stress, simply replace $T_\alpha^{(\nu)}(s)$ in Eq. (V.1) by $\overline{T}_\alpha^{(\nu)}(s)$, which is the *average* traction over x_3 [see Eq. (13.53b)].

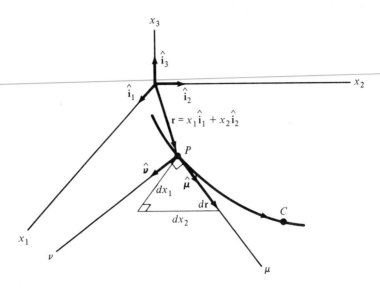

Figure V.1 Normal and tangential unit vectors on C.

In two-dimensional index notation, you may demonstrate that the formulation for $\hat{\boldsymbol{v}}$ above can be given as

$$\nu_\beta = e_{\beta\epsilon}\frac{\partial x_\epsilon}{\partial s} \tag{V.2}$$

Now returning to Eq. (V.1), we use Eq. (V.2) to replace ν_β to reach the following relation:

$$e_{\alpha\gamma}e_{\beta\delta}e_{\beta\epsilon}\Phi_{,\gamma\delta}\frac{\partial x_\epsilon}{\partial s} = G_\alpha(s) \tag{V.3}$$

Noting that $e_{\beta\delta}e_{\beta\epsilon} = \delta_{\delta\epsilon}$ [see Eq. (12.31)] we may rewrite Eq. (V.3) as

$$e_{\alpha\delta}\Phi_{,\gamma\epsilon}\frac{\partial x_\epsilon}{\partial s} = G_\alpha(s)$$

Also, $\Phi_{,\gamma\epsilon}\partial x_\epsilon/\partial s = \partial\Phi_{,\gamma}/\partial s$ via the chain rule of differentiation, so we get for the above,

$$e_{\alpha\gamma}\frac{\partial\Phi_{,\gamma}}{\partial s} = G_\alpha(s)$$

Multiply both sides by $e_{\alpha\beta}$. We then get, since $e_{\alpha\beta}e_{\alpha\gamma} = \delta_{\beta\gamma}$,

$$\delta_{\beta\gamma}\frac{\partial\Phi_{,\gamma}}{\partial s} = e_{\alpha\beta}G_\alpha(s)$$

Therefore,

$$\boxed{\frac{\partial\Phi_{,\beta}}{\partial s} = e_{\alpha\beta}G_\alpha(s) \qquad \text{on } C} \tag{V.4}$$

Since $G_\alpha(s)$ is a *prescribed* function of s, Eq. (V.4) provides *two* conditions in terms of the gradient of Φ, which must be satisfied on a boundary curve C when solving the biharmonic equation $\nabla^4\Phi = 0$. We shall now proceed to obtain from these conditions two other more convenient conditions, where one will be on Φ itself and the other will be on its normal derivative $\partial\Phi/\partial\nu$.

We begin by integrating Eq. (V.4) over s to obtain

$$\Phi_{,\beta} = \int_0^s e_{\alpha\beta} G_\alpha(s')\, ds' + a_\beta \tag{V.5}$$

where a_β is a *constant* vector of integration, since the normal coordinate is constant on C. Multiplying Eq. (V.5) by $\partial x_\beta/\partial s$, we get

$$\frac{\partial\Phi}{\partial x_\beta}\frac{\partial x_\beta}{\partial s} \equiv \frac{\partial\Phi}{\partial s} = \frac{\partial x_\beta}{\partial s}\int_0^s e_{\alpha\beta} G_\alpha(s')\, ds' + a_\beta\frac{\partial x_\beta}{\partial s} \tag{V.6}$$

Integrating once more over s, we obtain

$$\Phi(s) = \int_0^s \frac{\partial x_\beta}{\partial s''}\int_0^{s''} e_{\alpha\beta} G_\alpha(s')\, ds'\, ds'' + a_\beta x_\beta + b$$

where b is a constant scalar of integration. Finally, integrate by parts with respect to s''. We then get

$$\Phi(s) = \left[\int_0^{s''} e_{\alpha\beta} G_\alpha(s')\, ds'\right]x_\beta(s'')\Big|_0^s - \int_0^s x_\beta(s') e_{\alpha\beta} G_\alpha(s')\, ds' + a_\beta x_\beta + b$$

$$= x_\beta(s)\int_0^s e_{\alpha\beta} G_\alpha(s')\, ds' - \int_0^s x_\beta(s') e_{\alpha\beta} G_\alpha(s')\, ds' + a_\beta x_\beta + b$$

Note that $x_\beta(s)$ is a generic point, but $x_\beta(s')$ varies with s' as one goes from $s' = 0$ to $s' = s$. Since $x_\beta(s)$ is independent of the integration variable s', we may combine the two integrals above as follows:

$$\boxed{\Phi(s) = \int_0^s [x_\beta(s) - x_\beta(s')]\, e_{\alpha\beta} G_\alpha(s')\, ds' + a_\beta x_\beta + b \qquad \text{on } C} \tag{V.7}$$

Equation (V.7) is the first of the two desired conditions mentioned above. To obtain the second desired condition, we must first express ν_β in terms of a *normal* derivative. You will recall that the position vector to point P on C (see Fig. V.1) is expressed as

$$\mathbf{r} = x_1\hat{\mathbf{i}}_1 + x_2\hat{\mathbf{i}}_2$$

Now consider an increment of $\mathbf{r}$ in the direction *normal* to C at P (i.e., $d\mathbf{r} = d\nu\,\hat{\boldsymbol{\nu}}$). The chain rule now gives

$$\hat{\boldsymbol{\nu}} = \frac{d\mathbf{r}}{d\nu} = \frac{\partial\mathbf{r}}{\partial x_1}\frac{\partial x_1}{\partial\nu} + \frac{\partial\mathbf{r}}{\partial x_2}\frac{\partial x_2}{\partial\nu}$$

and therefore,

$$\hat{\boldsymbol{\nu}} = \frac{\partial x_1}{\partial\nu}\hat{\mathbf{i}}_1 + \frac{\partial x_2}{\partial\nu}\hat{\mathbf{i}}_2$$

Thus in index notation we have

$$\nu_\beta = \frac{\partial x_\beta}{\partial\nu} \tag{V.8}$$

Now go back to Eq. (V.5) and multiply the left side by $\partial x_\beta/\partial \nu$ and the right side by ν_β, in accordance with Eq. (V.8). Since $(\partial\Phi/\partial x_\beta)(\partial x_\beta/\partial \nu) \equiv \partial\Phi/\partial \nu$, we finally obtain the following condition on the normal derivative of Φ:

$$\frac{\partial\Phi}{\partial \nu}(s) = \nu_\beta \int_0^s e_{\alpha\beta}\, G_\alpha(s')\, ds' + a_\beta\, \nu_\beta \qquad \text{on } C \qquad (V.9)$$

The Airy stress function Φ is now obtained by solving the biharmonic equation $\nabla^4\Phi = 0$, with Φ and $\partial\Phi/\partial \nu$ prescribed in accordance with Eqs. (V.7) and (V.9) on the boundary curves.

Clearly, Eqs. (V.7) and (V.9) are *necessary* for the Cauchy condition (V.1) to be satisfied on a boundary curve C. To prove *sufficiency* one need only show that by inserting Eq. (V.6) [the s derivative of Eq. (V.7)] and Eq. (V.9) into the chain rule expansion

$$\frac{\partial}{\partial s}\left(\frac{\partial\Phi}{\partial x_\beta}\right) = \frac{\partial}{\partial s}\left(\frac{\partial\Phi}{\partial s}\frac{\partial s}{\partial x_\beta} + \frac{\partial\Phi}{\partial \nu}\frac{\partial \nu}{\partial x_\beta}\right)$$

we arrive back at Eq. (V.4). This is easily done, and the reader may want to verify this.

What about the constants a_β and b? Stresses depend only on the *second derivative*, $\Phi_{,\alpha\beta}$, where Φ is the solution to $\nabla^4\Phi = 0$ in the region R. One can readily see that these second derivatives are unaffected if the value of Φ in the entire closed domain is altered by the addition of a function linear in the coordinates. We may accordingly set $a_\beta = b = 0$ in setting up boundary conditions (V.7) and (V.9) for *some* boundary curve C. If the domain is *simply connected*, there is *only one* boundary curve, and thus Eqs. (V.7) and (V.9) may be simplified to read

$$\Phi(s) = \int_0^s [x_\beta(s) - x_\beta(s')]\, e_{\alpha\beta}\, G_\alpha(s')\, ds' \qquad \text{on } C$$

$$\frac{\partial\Phi}{\partial \nu}(s) = \nu_\beta \int_0^s e_{\alpha\beta}\, G_\alpha(s')\, ds' \qquad \text{on } C$$

$(V.10)$

Note that if C is *traction-free*, Eqs. (V.10) yield the *homogeneous conditions*

$$\Phi(s) = \frac{\partial\Phi}{\partial \nu}(s) = 0 \qquad \text{on } C$$

Furthermore, we note that if the domain is *multiply connected*, there is more than one boundary curve, and thus we may set $a_\beta = b = 0$ in setting up the boundary condition for *only one* of these curves. It is usually convenient to select the *outer boundary* for this purpose. The multiply connected domain is considered in Appendix VI.

If body force is present, the development above must be modified. First, the governing differential equation for the case of conservative body force (i.e., $B_\alpha = -\partial V/\partial x_\alpha$) now becomes [see Eqs. (12.42) and (13.60)]

$$\nabla^4\Phi = -(1 - \nu_1)\nabla^2 V \qquad \text{in } R \qquad \text{(for plane strain)}$$

$$\nabla^4\Phi = -(1 - \nu)\nabla^2 V \qquad \text{in } R \qquad \text{(for two-dimensional plane stress)}$$

$(V.11)$

As for the traction boundary condition, we begin by replacing Eq. (V.1) with [see Eq. (12.41)]

$$\tau_{\alpha\beta}(s)\nu_\beta(s) = [e_{\alpha\gamma}e_{\beta\delta}\,\Phi_{,\gamma\delta} + V\delta_{\alpha\beta}]\nu_\beta(s) = G_\alpha(s) \qquad \text{on } C$$

Then

$$e_{\alpha\gamma}e_{\beta\delta}\,\Phi_{,\gamma\delta}\,\nu_\beta(s) = G_\alpha(s) - V(s)\nu_\alpha(s) \qquad \text{on } C \qquad (V.12)$$

It readily follows that we again obtain conditions (V.4), (V.7), and (V.9), except that $G_\alpha(s)$ is replaced by $G_\alpha(s) - V(s)\nu_\alpha(s)$. Thus, for conservative body force we have the boundary conditions

$$\Phi(s) = \int_0^s [x_\beta(s) - x_\beta(s')] e_{\alpha\beta} [G_\alpha(s') - V(s')\nu_\alpha(s')] \, ds' + a_\beta x_\beta + b \qquad \text{on } C$$

$$\frac{\partial \Phi}{\partial \nu}(s) = \nu_\beta \int_0^s e_{\alpha\beta} [G_\alpha(s') - V(s')\nu_\alpha(s')] \, ds' + a_\beta \nu_\beta \qquad \text{on } C$$

$$(\text{V.13})$$

Cesàro Integrals in Terms of Φ for Plane Strain and Two-Dimensional Plane Stress

In Appendix I we set forth the sufficiency conditions for compatibility for multiply connected domains. We would like in this appendix to express Cesàro integrals (I.22) in terms of the Airy stress function Φ, and we repeat these $6N$ equations below:

$$\oint_{\Gamma_\alpha} (\varepsilon_{ik} - x_j e_{rij} e_{rpq} \varepsilon_{pk,q}) \, dx_k = 0 \qquad \alpha = 1, \ldots, N \qquad \text{(a)}$$

$$\text{(VI.1)}$$

$$\oint_{\Gamma_\alpha} e_{tpq} \varepsilon_{pk,q} \, dx_k = 0 \qquad \alpha = 1, \ldots, N \qquad \text{(b)}$$

An alternative form of Eq. (VI.1a) may be obtained via the following integration by parts:

$$\oint_{\Gamma_\alpha} \varepsilon_{ik} \, dx_k = 0 - \oint_{\Gamma_\alpha} x_k \varepsilon_{ik,j} \, dx_j$$

where the first term vanishes since Γ_α is a *closed* path around a cavity. Substituting this result into Eq. (VI.1a) after renaming dummy indices, we obtain

$$\oint_{\Gamma_\alpha} x_j (\varepsilon_{ij,k} + e_{rij} e_{rpq} \varepsilon_{pk,q}) \, dx_k = 0, \qquad \alpha = 1, \ldots, N \qquad \text{(VI.2)}$$

Consider now the special case of *plane strain* with *body forces absent,* for which case Hooke's law has been given earlier in two-dimensional index notation in terms of Φ as Eq. (12.34). This equation is repeated below in a more compact form:

$$\boxed{\varepsilon_{\alpha\beta} = \frac{1}{E_1} \Phi_{,\rho\rho} \delta_{\alpha\beta} - \frac{1 + \nu_1}{E_1} \Phi_{,\alpha\beta}} \qquad \text{(VI.3)}$$

Before substituting Eq. (VI.3) into Eqs. (VI.2) and (VI.1a), we must first simplify these $6N$ equations to the case of plane strain. By the definition of plane strain, $\varepsilon_{13} = \varepsilon_{23} = \varepsilon_{33} = 0$ and

$\partial/\partial x_3 \equiv 0$. Also, the cavities are now prescribed simply by n planar cross-sectional area elements in the $x_1 x_2$ plane, and thus we also may set $dx_3 \equiv 0$. Furthermore, to enable us to later introduce tractions at these cavities, we let the paths of integration conform to the *actual cavity cross-sectional boundaries*, and we designate these paths as C_i, $i = 1, \ldots, n$. Accordingly, in Eq. (VI.2) we replace Γ_α by C_i and restrict indices i, j, k, p, q to $1, 2$, which then requires that $r = 3$ for nonzero contributions. In two-dimensional index notation Eq. (VI.2) thus becomes for plane strain:

$$\oint_{C_i} x_\beta (\varepsilon_{\alpha\beta,\gamma} + e_{\alpha\beta} e_{\delta\epsilon} \varepsilon_{\delta\gamma,\epsilon}) \, dx_\gamma = 0, \qquad i = 1, \ldots, n \qquad \text{(VI.4)}$$

which is a reduced set of $2n$ conditions. Turning now to Eq. (VI.2b), we proceed in similar fashion to obtain

$$\oint_{C_i} e_{\delta\epsilon} \varepsilon_{\delta\gamma,\epsilon} \, dx_\gamma = 0, \qquad i = 1, \ldots, n \qquad \text{(VI.5)}$$

which is another reduced set of n conditions. Thus Eqs. (VI.4) and (VI.5) are a reduced set of $3n$ Cesàro integrals, where Eq. (VI.3) gives $\varepsilon_{\alpha\beta}$ in terms of Φ.

We will now proceed to express Eqs. (VI.4) and (VI.5) in terms of Φ, and will also use the development given in Appendix V to enter the tractions at the cavities into the formulation. First substitute Eq. (VI.3) into Eq. (VI.4) to obtain

$$\oint_{C_i} x_\beta (\Phi_{,\gamma\rho\rho} \delta_{\alpha\beta} + e_{\alpha\beta} e_{\gamma\epsilon} \Phi_{,\epsilon\rho\rho}) \, dx_\gamma = (1 + \nu_1) \oint_{C_i} x_\beta (\Phi_{,\alpha\beta\gamma} + e_{\alpha\beta} e_{\delta\epsilon} \Phi_{,\delta\gamma\epsilon}) \, dx_\gamma$$
$$i = 1, \ldots, n \qquad \text{(VI.6)}$$

Consider the last term in the equation above,

$$e_{\alpha\beta} e_{\delta\epsilon} \Phi_{,\delta\gamma\epsilon} \qquad \text{(VI.7)}$$

Because $e_{\delta\epsilon}$ is skew-symmetric in indices $\delta\epsilon$, whereas $\Phi_{,\delta\gamma\epsilon}$ is symmetric in $\delta\epsilon$, this term in Eq. (VI.6) clearly vanishes. Now look at the integral

$$\oint_{C_i} x_\beta \Phi_{,\alpha\beta\gamma} \, dx_\gamma$$

which stems from the first term on the right side of Eq. (VI.6). Integrating by parts, we get

$$\oint_{C_i} x_\beta \Phi_{,\alpha\beta\gamma} \, dx_\gamma = 0 - \oint_{C_i} \delta_{\beta\gamma} \Phi_{,\alpha\beta} \, dx_\gamma = -\oint_{C_i} \Phi_{,\alpha\beta} \, dx_\beta$$
$$= -\oint_{C_i} \frac{\partial}{\partial x_\beta} \left(\frac{\partial \Phi}{\partial x_\alpha} \right) \frac{\partial x_\beta}{\partial s} \, ds = -\oint_{C_i} \frac{\partial \Phi_{,\alpha}}{\partial s} \, ds \qquad \text{(VI.8)}$$

where s is a parameter along the cavity cross-sectional boundary curve C_i. Going back to Eq. (V.4) of Appendix V, we can replace $\partial \Phi_{,\alpha}/\partial s$ by $-e_{\alpha\beta} G_\beta^{(i)}(s)$, where $G_\beta^{(i)}(s)$ is the prescribed traction function on C_i. We then get, from Eq. (VI.8),

$$\oint_{C_i} x_\beta \Phi_{,\alpha\beta\gamma} \, dx_\gamma = \oint_{C_i} e_{\alpha\beta} G_\beta^{(i)}(s) \, ds \qquad \text{(VI.9)}$$

Now let us incorporate the vanishing of (VI.7) and the result from Eq. (VI.9) into the right side of Eq. (VI.6), and setting $dx_\gamma = (\partial x_\gamma / \partial s)\, ds$ on the left side, we finally obtain

$$\oint_{C_i} x_\beta \left[\Phi_{,\gamma\rho\rho}\, \delta_{\alpha\beta} \frac{\partial x_\gamma}{\partial s} + e_{\alpha\beta}\, e_{\gamma\epsilon} \Phi_{,\epsilon\rho\rho} \frac{\partial x_\gamma}{\partial s} \right] ds = (1 + \nu_1) \oint_{C_i} e_{\alpha\beta}\, G_\beta^{(i)}(s)\, ds, \qquad i = 1, \dots, n$$

(VI.10)

Equation (VI.10) may be rewritten in more convenient form by again going back to Appendix V and noting from Eqs. (V.2) and (V.8) that

$$e_{\gamma\epsilon} \frac{\partial x_\gamma}{\partial s} = -\nu_\epsilon = -\frac{\partial x_\epsilon}{\partial \nu}$$

(VI.11)

where ν_ϵ is the unit normal to C_i and $\partial/\partial \nu$ is the normal derivative. We may now make use of the following substitutions on the left side of Eq. (VI.10):

$$\Phi_{,\gamma\rho\rho} \frac{\partial x_\gamma}{\partial s} = \frac{\partial \nabla^2 \Phi}{\partial x_\gamma} \frac{\partial x_\gamma}{\partial s} = \frac{\partial \nabla^2 \Phi}{\partial s} \qquad \text{(a)}$$

$$\Phi_{,\epsilon\rho\rho}\, e_{\gamma\epsilon} \frac{\partial x_\gamma}{\partial s} = -\frac{\partial \nabla^2 \Phi}{\partial x_\epsilon} \frac{\partial x_\epsilon}{\partial s} = -\frac{\partial \nabla^2 \Phi}{\partial \nu} \qquad \text{(b)}$$

(VI.12)

where we have used Eq. (VI.11) in Eq. (VI.12b). Accordingly, we obtain the final form for *plane strain*:

$$\boxed{\oint_{C_i} x_\beta \left[\delta_{\alpha\beta} \frac{\partial \nabla^2 \Phi}{\partial s} - e_{\alpha\beta} \frac{\partial \nabla^2 \Phi}{\partial \nu} \right] ds = (1 + \nu_1) \oint_{C_i} e_{\alpha\beta}\, G_\beta^{(i)}(s)\, ds, \qquad i = 1, \dots, n}$$

(VI.13)

Returning now to Eq. (VI.5), we substitute for $\varepsilon_{\delta\gamma}$ using Eq. (VI.3) and thereby obtain

$$\oint_{C_i} e_{\delta\epsilon} \Phi_{,\rho\rho\epsilon}\, dx_\delta = (1 + \nu_1) \oint_{C_i} e_{\delta\epsilon} \Phi_{,\delta\gamma\epsilon}\, dx_\gamma$$

As explained above, the term $e_{\delta\epsilon} \Phi_{,\delta\gamma\epsilon}$ on the right side of the above vanishes, and on the left side we may use Eq. (VI.11) to write

$$e_{\delta\epsilon} \Phi_{,\rho\rho\epsilon}\, dx_\delta = \frac{\partial \nabla^2 \Phi}{\partial x_\epsilon}\, e_{\delta\epsilon} \frac{\partial x_\delta}{\partial s}\, ds = -\frac{\partial \nabla^2 \Phi}{\partial x_\epsilon} \frac{\partial x_\epsilon}{\partial \nu}\, ds = -\frac{\partial \nabla^2 \Phi}{\partial \nu}\, ds$$

Accordingly, Eq. (VI.5) assumes the final form for *plane strain*,

$$\boxed{\oint_{C_i} \frac{\partial \nabla^2 \Phi}{\partial \nu}\, ds = 0, \qquad i = 1, \dots, n}$$

(VI.14)

A conservative body force, $B_\alpha = -\partial V / \partial x_\alpha$, may be readily included in the formulation above. It is easily shown with the use of Eq. (12.41) that plane-strain constitutive law (VI.3) now becomes

$$\varepsilon_{\alpha\beta} = \frac{1}{E_1} \Phi_{,\rho\rho}\, \delta_{\alpha\beta} - \frac{1 + \nu_1}{E_1} \Phi_{,\alpha\beta} + \frac{1 - \nu_1}{E_1} V \delta_{\alpha\beta}$$

(VI.15)

Furthermore, as explained in Appendix V [see discussion after Eq. (V.12)], we must replace the prescribed traction function $G_\alpha^{(i)}(s)$ in the equations of that appendix by $G_\alpha^{(i)}(s) - V(s)\nu_\alpha(s)$. Accordingly, Eq. (VI.9) is extended to include body force as follows:

$$\oint_{C_i} x_\beta \Phi,_{\alpha\beta\gamma}\, dx_\gamma = \oint_{C_i} e_{\alpha\beta}[G_\beta^{(i)}(s) - V(s)\nu_\beta(s)]\, ds \qquad\qquad \text{(VI.16)}$$

We leave it for the reader to verify that if Eqs. (VI.3) and (VI.9) are replaced by Eqs. (VI.15) and (VI.16), respectively, the formulation above for *plane strain* generalizes to the following:

$$
\begin{aligned}
\oint_{C_i} x_\beta &\left[\delta_{\alpha\beta} \frac{\partial \nabla^2 \Phi}{\partial s} - e_{\alpha\beta} \frac{\partial \nabla^2 \Phi}{\partial \nu} \right] ds = (1 + \nu_1) \oint_{C_i} e_{\alpha\beta}[G_\beta^{(i)}(s) - V(s)\nu_\beta(s)]\, ds \\
&- (1 - \nu_1) \oint_{C_i} x_\beta \left[\delta_{\alpha\beta} \frac{\partial V}{\partial s} - e_{\alpha\beta} \frac{\partial V}{\partial \nu} \right] ds, \qquad i = 1, \ldots, n \qquad \text{(a)} \\[2mm]
&\oint_{C_i} \frac{\partial \nabla^2 \Phi}{\partial \nu}\, ds = -(1 - \nu_1) \oint_{C_i} \frac{\partial V}{\partial \nu}\, ds, \qquad i = 1, \ldots, n \qquad \text{(b)}
\end{aligned}
\qquad \text{(VI.17)}
$$

As explained in Chapter 12, the assumptions of plane strain (i.e., $\varepsilon_{13} = \varepsilon_{23} = \varepsilon_{33} = 0$ and $\partial/\partial x_3 \equiv 0$) are rigorously satisfied in the Airy stress function formulation, and thus the $3n$ integral conditions (VI.17) may be considered to be *exact*. These plane-strain assumptions are realized in long prismatic bodies loaded normal to the x_3 axis (with no variation with x_3) and constrained at the ends. We then noted in Chapter 13 that for *plane stress* we set $\tau_{13} = \tau_{23} = \tau_{33} = 0$, but it is generally *not* permissible also to set $\partial/\partial x_3 \equiv 0$. Furthermore, in plane stress the compatibility equations do not reduce to a single equation as was the case in plane strain. Similarly, for multiply connected bodies in a state of plane stress the full set of $6N$ Cesàro integrals must be considered rather than a reduced set of $3n$ integral conditions as occurred for plane strain. However, we also pointed out in Chapter 13 that if a knowledge of the *average* of the stresses over the x_3 coordinate is sufficient, one obtains a two-dimensional plane stress Airy stress function formulation identical to the plane-strain formulation, except that in the expression for $\varepsilon_{\alpha\beta}$, E_1, ν_1 are replaced by E, ν. We also noted that such an average stress distribution is often a good *approximation* to the actual stress distribution, for the case of a *thin plate* with traction-free faces and loaded symmetrically with respect to the midplane around the edge. For this *approximate* formulation of *plane stress*, Eqs. (VI.17) are modified to read as follows:

$$
\begin{aligned}
\oint_{C_i} x_\beta &\left[\delta_{\alpha\beta} \frac{\partial \nabla^2 \Phi}{\partial s} - e_{\alpha\beta} \frac{\partial \nabla^2 \Phi}{\partial \nu} \right] ds = (1 + \nu) \oint_{C_i} e_{\alpha\beta}[G_\beta^{(i)}(s) - V(s)\nu_\beta(s)]\, ds \\
&- (1 - \nu) \oint_{C_i} x_\beta \left[\delta_{\alpha\beta} \frac{\partial V}{\partial s} - e_{\alpha\beta} \frac{\partial V}{\partial r} \right] ds, \qquad i = 1, \ldots, n \qquad \text{(a)} \\[2mm]
&\oint_{C_i} \frac{\partial \nabla^2 \Phi}{\partial \nu}\, ds = -(1 - \nu) \oint_{C_i} \frac{\partial V}{\partial \nu}\, ds, \qquad i = 1, \ldots, n \qquad \text{(b)}
\end{aligned}
\qquad \text{(VI.18)}
$$

Note that Poisson's ratio ν has replaced ν_1 on the right side of Eqs. (VI.18). Also note that, if body forces are absent, Eq. (VI.18b) is unchanged. Poisson's ratio ν in the expressions $(1 + \nu)$ and $(1 - \nu)$ is not to be confused with ν in the $\partial/\partial \nu$ derivatives, which is the coordinate normal to C_i.

Appendix VII
Microscopic Considerations
of Properties of Solids

VII.1 INTRODUCTION

In simple terms, a solid is an aggregate of matter that retains its shape for a reasonable length of time, as contrasted to a liquid or gas which has no shape except that of the container. In recent years, substantial progress has been made in the field of solid-state science, wherein the properties of solids are studied from the microscopic point of view. However, atomic theories of mechanical behavior have at present resulted in quantitative results on the macroscopic level in only a relatively few cases. Nevertheless, we can gain much insight by examining the qualitative implications of a microscopic theory extrapolated to the macroscopic level. In this appendix* we first consider in Part A the atomic and molecular structure of a solid in the undeformed state. Then the various mechanisms by which this structure deforms under external influence are discussed in Part B. Whenever possible, macroscopic response is predicted and correlated with the experimental macroscopic data presented in Chapter 4.

PART A
ATOMIC AND MOLECULAR STRUCTURE

VII.2 INTRODUCTION TO INTERATOMIC ENERGIES AND FORCES

Mechanical behavior depends almost entirely on the nature of the *interatomic forces* that exist in the solid. Clearly, from the very existence of solids one may draw two general conclusions:

---

* This appendix is an abridged and updated version of Appendix X by F. A. Cozzarelli in I. H. Shames, *Mechanics of Deformable Solids* (Englewood Cliffs, NJ: Prentice-Hall, Inc., 1964; reprinted by R. E. Krieger Publishing Co., Melbourne, FL, 1979). This source contains some additional topics in materials science as well as a list of references.

1. There must exist attractive forces between the atoms or molecules which tend to resist any effort to separate them.

2. There must be repulsive forces acting between the atoms as well, since large external pressures are required to compress a solid any appreciable extent.

Let us therefore consider two atoms whose centers are separated by a distance r, and determine the conditions for a stable configuration. We will make the assumptions that the force field is conservative and that the potential energy function E_p can be formulated approximately as

$$E_p = E_R + E_A = \frac{\beta}{r^m} - \frac{\alpha}{r^n} \qquad \text{(VII.1)}$$

where E_R and E_A are the energies associated with repulsive and attractive forces, respectively; r is the interatomic distance; and m, n, α, and β are positive constants. The zero datum of potential energy is given by r approaching infinity (i.e., the atoms are completely removed from each other). Recalling the form of Coulomb's law for forces between charges, the reader may find Eq. (VII.1) physically plausible. In fact, the basic bonds that you studied in previous courses (i.e., ionic, covalent, metallic, and molecular) may be explained in terms of this equation.

From our work in mechanics we learned that the potential energy possesses a stationary value at a point of equilibrium. Hence, differentiating Eq. (VII.1), we obtain for equilibrium

$$\left(\frac{dE_p}{dr}\right)_{r=r_0} = -\frac{m\beta}{r_0^{m+1}} + \frac{n\alpha}{r_0^{n+1}} = 0 \qquad \text{(VII.2)}$$

wherein r_0 represents the equilibrium configuration. Solving for r_0, we get

$$r_0 = \left[\left(\frac{m}{n}\right)\left(\frac{\beta}{\alpha}\right)\right]^{1/(m-n)} \qquad \text{(VII.3)}$$

In order to have a *stable* equilibrium configuration, E_p must be a *minimum* at $r = r_0$. Accordingly, setting $(d^2E_p/dr^2)_{r=r_0} > 0$, we get

$$\frac{m(m+1)\beta}{r_0^{m+2}} - \frac{n(n+1)\alpha}{r_0^{n+2}} > 0$$

Multiplication by the positive factor $[r_0^{m+2}/n(n+1)\alpha]$ does not affect the direction of the inequality. Accordingly, we may obtain the following result after transposing the second term to the right:

$$\left(\frac{m}{n}\right)\left(\frac{m+1}{n+1}\right)\left(\frac{\beta}{\alpha}\right) > r_0^{m-n}$$

Using Eq. (VII.3) to replace r_0 in the preceding equation, we obtain the inequality $(m+1)/(n+1) > 1$. From this we see that the inequality

$$m > n \qquad \text{(VII.4)}$$

is necessary for stable equilibrium. Physically, this inequality requires that the *energy associated with the repulsive forces vary more rapidly with r than the energy associated with the attractive forces*.

Consider now two atoms, A and B, separated by the stable equilibrium distance r_0. By definition of equilibrium, no net force acts on atom B in this position. Let us now subject atom B to an infinitesimal positive displacement $d\mathbf{r}$ (see Fig. VII.1). By definition of *stable*

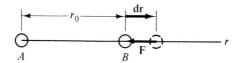

Figure VII.1 Two atoms in a stable configuration.

equilibrium, a restoring force **F** must result, as shown in the diagram. The change in potential energy is given by minus the work done by the force field on atom B during this process. Hence since **F** and $d\mathbf{r}$ are antiparallel,

$$E_p(r) - E_p(r_0) = -\int_{r_0}^{r} \mathbf{F} \cdot d\mathbf{r} = \int_{r_0}^{r} F \, dr$$

Differentiation of this equation yields

$$\frac{dE_p(r)}{dr} = F(r)$$

Accordingly, differentiating the terms in Eq. (VII.1) we can express the forces between the two atoms as follows:

$$F = F_R + F_A = -\frac{m\beta}{r^{m+1}} + \frac{n\alpha}{r^{n+1}} \qquad \text{(VII.5)}$$

Note that the positive term β/r^m for E_R in Eq. (VII.1) results in a negative term $-m\beta/r^{m+1}$ for F_R in Eq. (VII.5), and that negative term $-\alpha/r^n$ for E_A yields a positive term $n\alpha/r^{n+1}$ for F_A. Typical graphs of Eqs. (VII.1) and (VII.5) are presented in Fig. VII.2.

We now define the *bonding energy*, E_B, as that energy which must be added to achieve a dissociation of a bonded state. Also, observing Fig. VII.2, we shall denote D as the potential energy at equilibrium. This energy is less than zero for the datum we have chosen, so D will be a negative number. Parenthetically, the region of the energy curve around the equilibrium state is aptly termed an *energy well*, and D is called the depth of this well. The quantities E_B and D are seen to be simply related to each other when we realize that

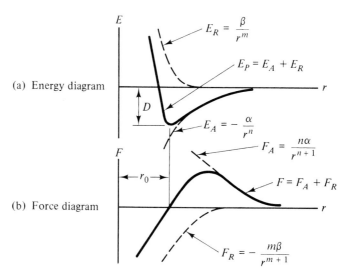

(a) Energy diagram

(b) Force diagram

Figure VII.2 Bonding diagrams.

dissociating a bond is the same, mathematically speaking, as moving the atoms from a separation distance r_0 to an infinite separation distance. This, in turn, clearly requires the addition of an amount of energy equal to D to take the potential energy from the minimum D at equilibrium to zero at complete dissociation.

To express E_B we return to Eq. (VII.1). Substituting r_0 in this equation (thereby rendering $E_p = E_B$) and eliminating β by employing Eq. (VII.3), we then have

$$E_B = -D = \frac{\alpha}{r_0^n}\left(1 - \frac{n}{m}\right) \qquad \text{(VII.6)}$$

It should be noted that the bonding energy is temperature dependent, and hence the values of α, β, m, and n will also in general depend on temperature. The results above, which apply to two atoms only, are readily extended to a system of atoms consisting of a central atom surrounded by a collection of other atoms. In so doing, the basic character of Eqs. (VII.1) and (VII.6) is retained, except that α and β are replaced by summations of constants. We shall have occasion to use the results of this section in later work.

VII.3 LATTICE GEOMETRY

The ionic, covalent, and metallic bonds are generally strong enough to produce a definite *regularity* of atomic arrangement in a solid. This regularity is characteristic of a crystalline solid, the study of which is termed *crystallography*. The fourth bond, the molecular bond, is frequently too weak to maintain this regularity, and thus results in *amorphous* solids such as cellulose and rubber. Due to the lack of structural order, the study of amorphous solids is very complex and shall not be considered here; the structure of linear polymers will, however, be discussed briefly in Section VII.12. On the other hand, crystallography is a highly developed discipline.

As an aid in studying crystals, we find it useful to examine carefully a system of points in space extending to infinity in all directions, and arranged so that each point has around it the same arrangement and spacing of neighboring points as every other point in the system. These points are called *lattice points*. It is common practice to draw a network of straight lines through *selected* lattice points, so as to divide all of space into identical parallelepipeds. The entire distribution of lines and points is called a *space lattice*, and the parallelepiped, which is the fundamental unit being repeated in the array, is termed the *unit* cell. The space lattice provides a convenient geometrical basis by which we can describe crystal structures. We shall now set forth certain important formulations and concepts pertaining to space lattices.

To describe space lattices we employ as a reference a set of three straight lines, which are concurrent at a corner of one of the unit cells and which lie along the edges of the cell. Each such line passes through lattice points that are positioned at equal intervals along the lines. These intervals, however, can be different for the different axes. Such straight lines are called *crystallographic axes*. In Fig. VII.3(a) we have shown a general crystallographic set of axes, where the position vectors **a**, **b**, and **c** have been drawn to the first lattice point on axes x, y, and z, respectively. These position vectors are called *lattice vectors*. The angles α, β, and γ orient the directions of the axes relative to each other, and the distances a, b, and c (magnitudes of **a**, **b**, and **c**) give the aforementioned intervals of spacing of lattice points along the three axes. These six quantities are called *lattice parameters*. An orthogonal set of axes ($\alpha = \beta = \gamma = 90°$) with $a \neq b \neq c$ is termed *orthorhombic*, and this important classification is illustrated in Fig. VII.3(b). The *cubic* set of axes ($a = b = c$, $\alpha = \beta = \gamma = 90°$) and the *hexagonal* set of axes ($a = b \neq c$, $\alpha = \beta = 90°$, $\gamma = 120°$) are the most important sets of axes.

Not all lattice points will lie on the edges of unit cells, and for this reason we can classify

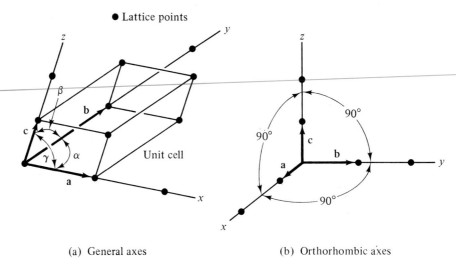

(a) General axes   (b) Orthorhombic axes

Figure VII.3 Crystallographic axes.

unit cells into various types. This classification is based on the positions of those lattice points not on the edges of the unit cells. Four such types of unit cells are:

1. *Simple unit cell*: one lattice point in each corner of the parallelepiped
2. *Base-centered unit cell*: one lattice point in each corner of the parallelepiped plus one lattice point in the center of each of one pair of opposite faces
3. *Face-centered unit cell*: one lattice point in each corner of the parallelepiped plus one lattice point in the center of each face
4. *Body-centered unit cell*: one lattice point in each corner of the parallelepiped plus one lattice point in the center of the cell

The four unit cells for orthorhombic axes have been shown in Fig. VII.4. Given a set of crystallographic axes and a unit cell, we can generate a space lattice by placing the unit cell at the origin and then performing a series of translations along the three axes.

VII.4 CRYSTALLINE STRUCTURE OF ENGINEERING MATERIALS

We can describe *crystal structures* by using as a framework a space lattice properly scaled for the crystal at hand, and by placing atoms at the lattice points and/or at positions specified relative to lattice points in the unit cells. Clearly, an unlimited number of arrangements may be so generated. Since a space lattice is by definition periodic to infinity in all directions, the crystal being considered will consist of periodic arrangements of atoms extending to infinity. This hypothetical extension can be appreciated when we realize that it is quite common for a bar of commercial metal to be composed of many nearly perfect crystals (the origin of these crystals will be explained in Section VII.5) roughly 0.01 in. in size, and although these crystals are very small, they contain a very great number of atoms–in the neighborhood of 10^{18} atoms per crystal. Clearly, this means that the interatomic distances are very small compared to the dimensions of the crystal, and this permits us to assume that the crystal extends to infinity for many calculations. Imperfections do exist in crystals and although these flaws

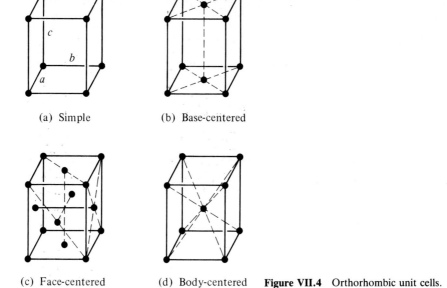

(a) Simple   (b) Base-centered

(c) Face-centered   (d) Body-centered   **Figure VII.4**   Orthorhombic unit cells.

may be few in number, they have a critical effect on some types of mechanical deformation. We shall later introduce such considerations, but for now we assume that no imperfections are present.

Just as we identified certain basic configurations of points in space to be used in the buildup of space lattices by translation, so can we identify certain basic configurations of atoms to be used in the buildup of crystals by translation. The basic configuration of points for space lattices was called the unit cell, and we shall call the basic configuration of atoms for crystals the *unit crystal*. Fortunately, we need only three unit crystals to discuss most elements. The simple cubic crystal (one atom at each simple cubic lattice site) will not be one of these three unit crystals, since practically no elements crystallize into this structure. However, we will occasionally use this simple crystal to illustrate a point. We shall now present these three unit crystals.

The *body-centered cubic unit crystal*, denoted by BCC, consists of one atom at each lattice point of a body-centered cubic unit cell. In Fig. VII.5 the atoms in the unit crystal have been depicted by small spheres so as to expose the crystal's interior. The diameters of the spheres may be enlarged to the maximum value permitted, that is, without penetration of any of the spheres into each other and without shifting of the centers of the spheres. This maximum diameter we have denoted as D. Such a technique serves to emphasize the directions of *closest packing* for the atoms–directions that will soon be seen to be of great importance in the mechanical behavior of the crystal. In the case at hand, the directions of closest packing are along the main diagonals, where the spheres just touch. From this we can deduce that $a = (2\sqrt{3}/3)D$. Using Fig. VII.5, it is also evident that each atom has eight equidistant nearest neighbors [i.e., the body-centered cubic crystal has a *coordination number* (CN) of eight]. Since each corner atom is shared by eight unit crystals and the body-centered atom is unshared, the unit crystal has a net of $n = 8/8 + 1/1 = 2$ atoms. Many metals including iron at room temperature are BCC.

Next, placing one atom at each face-centered cubic lattice point results in the so-called *face-centered cubic unit crystal*, denoted as FCC and shown in Fig. VII.6. By using the

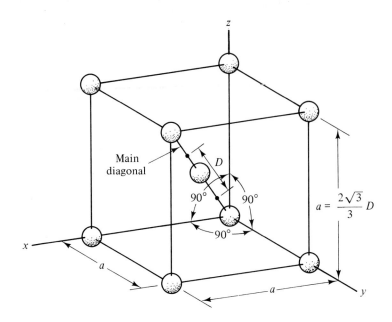

Figure VII.5 Body-centered cubic unit crystal.

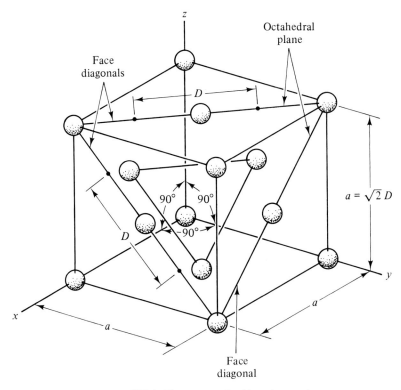

Figure VII.6 Face-centered cubic unit crystal.

technique of enlarging the diameters (as described in the preceding paragraph) we find that every sphere touches each of its six nearest neighbors in the diagonal (octahedral) planes. This is the most efficient way of packing spheres, and consequently, the octahedral planes are called *close-packed* planes (BCC has no close-packed planes). Within each octahedral plane, spheres touch along the diagonal directions parallel to the faces of the unit crystal. Parallel close-packed planes or layers are stacked so that spheres in one layer rest in the interstices (interstices refer here to the spaces between the spheres in a layer) of adjacent layers resulting in a maximum CN of 12. Also, it is to be noted that the fourth layer lies directly over the first. This stacking sequence can be expressed symbolically by $ABCAB\ldots$. For example, we see from Fig. VII.6 that the atom at (a, a, a) in the fourth close-packed layer is over $(0, 0, 0)$ in the first close-packed layer. It is easily shown that $a = \sqrt{2}D$ and that $n = 8/8 + 6/2 = 4$ atoms per crystal. Many important metals, including aluminum, are FCC.

We now examine the third of the unit crystals, called the *hexagonal close-packed unit crystal* (HCP), which as we shall soon see has an arrangement very similar to that of FCC. If we select $c/a = 2\sqrt{6}/3 = 1.633$ in the simple hexagonal unit cell (see Fig. VII.7) and associate *two* atoms with each lattice point — one at the point and one displaced by $a/3$, $2a/3, c/2$, the HCP unit crystal results. The basal planes are close-packed and have been stacked so as to minimize interstitial volume (CN = 12). This structure is identical with FCC, except that the third rather than the fourth close-packed plane lies over the first (i.e., an $ABAB\ldots$) stacking sequence. When three of these unit crystals are fitted together around

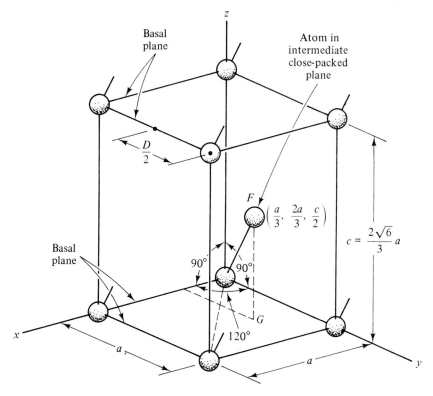

Figure VII.7 Hexagonal close-packed unit crystal. Point G is vertical projection of F onto xy plane.

the z axis, we obtain a hexagonal prism with seven atoms in the top and bottom basal planes and three atoms in the intermediate interior plane. Simple calculations show that $a = D$ and $n = 2$ per unit crystal. Magnesium and zinc form in the HCP structure.

VII.5 POLYCRYSTALLINE STRUCTURE OF ENGINEERING MATERIALS

Our discussion of the structure of single crystals will be of help in analyzing the mechanisms of deformation. However, the development is incomplete since engineering materials are generally made up of very many small crystals and are thus called *polycrystalline*. An understanding of polycrystalline structure rests on a knowledge of the process by which solidification from the liquid state occurs. As has been our practice, we will work with a simple model and concentrate on the solidification of pure metal.

When liquid metal is cooled to the freezing point, orderly atomic arrangements, called *nuclei*, begin to form in small domains [see Fig. VII.8(a)]. This process is called *nucleation*. Nuclei often occur at minute bits of solid impurities, which are always present under normal conditions in the laboratory or foundry. As heat is withdrawn, the nuclei begin growing into crystals. The growth tends to proceed more rapidly along certain preferred directions, and in an irregular manner. A needle-like structure which we call a *dendritic* structure evolves [see Fig. VII.8(b)]. Eventually, the dendrites from adjacent nuclei meet and the liquid between the branches solidifies completely, obliterating the dendritic pattern. However, a complicated polycrystalline structure results, consisting of differently oriented crystals (one per nucleus) called *grains*, with irregular *grain boundaries* between them [see Fig. VII.8(c)].

The size and shape of a grain depend on the rate of nucleation and grain growth during solidification, and on any subsequent plastic deformation and heat treatment to which the metal may be subjected. In a region of uniform distribution of nuclei (e.g., the central region of a mold) the crystallized grains tend to be roughly *equiaxed* (regular polyhedra), as in Fig. VII.9(a) showing a sketch of a photomicrograph of an aluminum alloy as cast. Elongated grains occur in regions of nonuniform distribution of nuclei, for example, adjacent to the walls of a mold, or may be formed by cold-working, as in the sketch of the photomicrograph of Fig. VII.9(b). Grain size and shape control is an important metalurgical problem, since it has a significant effect on a polycrystalline material's mechanical properties (e.g., tensile strength and hardness). We will discuss these considerations briefly in Part B. In addition to metals, many other materials of engineering interest (e.g., rock, ice, some plastics) form into polycrystals.

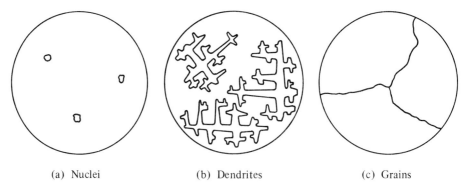

(a) Nuclei   (b) Dendrites   (c) Grains

Figure VII.8   Formation of polycrystalline structure.

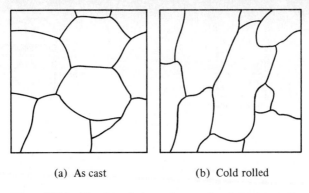

(a) As cast   (b) Cold rolled

Figure VII.9   Sketches of photomicrographs of aluminum alloy.

PART B
MECHANISMS OF MECHANICAL DEFORMATION

In this part of the chapter we examine the microscopic mechanisms associated with elastic, plastic, and creep deformations.

VII.6 NATURE OF ELASTIC DEFORMATION IN CRYSTALS

The physical basis of elastic strain in a crystalline solid may be revealed by an examination of its atomic structure and the associated bonding diagrams. Consider, for example, a single crystal of zinc (HCP), and assume for simplicity that a tensile stress τ_{xx} acts on the crystal in a direction along the x crystallographic axis in the close-packed basal plane [see Fig. VII.10(a)]. If the applied load is less than the elastic limit of zinc in this direction, the bonding force is sufficient to prevent the atoms from moving completely out of their original lattice sites. However, as shown in Fig. VII.10(b), a small local extension $\Delta x = (x - a)$ does occur along with a restoring force $F(x)$ between atoms, which results in an elastic return of the specimen to its original configuration upon removal of τ_{xx}.

We will now derive some quantitative results from the bonding diagram. Assuming that the bonding function is given by Eq. (VII.5) (with r replaced by x) and performing binomial expansions, we obtain for the deformed geometry

$$F = -\frac{m\beta}{(a + \Delta x)^{m+1}} + \frac{n\alpha}{(a + \Delta x)^{n+1}}$$

$$= \left[-\frac{m\beta}{a^{m+1}} + \frac{n\alpha}{a^{n+1}} \right] + \left[\frac{m(m+1)\beta}{a^{m+2}} - \frac{n(n+1)\alpha}{a^{n+2}} \right] \Delta x + \cdots$$

(VII.7)

Now, by means of Eq. (VII.2), we may drop the first bracketed expression on the right of Eq. (VII.7) and eliminate β from the second bracketed expression. Further, assuming that deflections are small, we may neglect higher-order terms in Δx, whereupon Eq. (VII.7) reduces to

$$F = \frac{n(m - n)\alpha}{a^{n+2}} \Delta x$$

(VII.8)

which gives $F = 0$ for $\Delta x = 0$, as required.

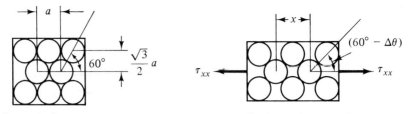

Before and after application of load   During application of load

(a) Crystal structure

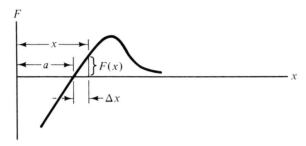

(b) Bonding diagram

Figure VII.10   Zinc in close-packed plane.

Clearly, Eq. (VII.8) enables us to relate Young's modulus E of linear elasticity to microscopic data. We will first express F (which, as noted above, is the force between atoms in a row along the x direction in a close-packed plane) in terms of the stress τ_{xx} acting on the crystal element–thus we shift from microscopic to macroscopic variables. The perpendicular distance between rows in the close-packed plane equals $a\sqrt{3}/2$, as shown in Fig. VII.10(a), and the perpendicular distance between close-packed planes is given by $c/2 = a\sqrt{6}/3$, as indicated in Fig. VII.7. Accordingly, the projected area per row of atoms in the x direction is given by $A = (a\sqrt{3}/2)(a\sqrt{6}/3) = a^2\sqrt{2}/2$. We can then express F as

$$F = \tau_{xx}\frac{\sqrt{2}}{2}a^2$$

Substituting this result into Eq. (VII.8) and using the axial strain $\varepsilon_{xx} = \Delta x/a$ to eliminate Δx from the result, we get

$$\tau_{xx} = \frac{\sqrt{2}\,n(m-n)\alpha}{a^{n+3}}\,\varepsilon_{xx}$$

from which

$$E = \frac{\sqrt{2}\,n(m-n)\alpha}{a^{n+3}} \tag{VII.9}$$

It is well known that a will increase with temperature as a result of increased thermal agitation (i.e., the crystal will experience *thermal expansion*). It then follows immediately from Eq. (VII.9) that E will decrease with temperature increase.

Due to the approximate nature of the bonding function, Eq. (VII.9) is applicable only as an order of magnitude, but its derivation does illustrate the method of approach. One refinement involves the inclusion of long-range forces in addition to the "nearest-neighbor forces." Also, since the bonding diagram and atomic spacing vary for different crystallographic directions, it is clear that a single crystal of zinc is not isotropic (i.e., it is anisotropic). Equation (VII.9) gives Young's modulus only for the case of an HCP crystal whose x crystallographic axis is collinear with the axis of a one-dimensional load. If the inclination of the crystal relative to the loading axis is varied, E can be expressed as a function of crystal orientation. Then the average value of E can be computed by appropriate integration over all possible orientations. Now if the grains in a polycrystalline sample are randomly oriented, the material will be macroscopically isotropic and E in any direction is approximated by this average value. Of course, the formation of a preferred orientation by means of cold working will introduce anisotropy macroscopically.

Figure VII.10(a) also clearly demonstrates the elastic Poisson effect, and some simple geometry will enable us to derive Poisson's ration, ν. Using ε_{lat} to designate the lateral strain, we have

$$\varepsilon_{xx} = \frac{a \, \cos(60° - \Delta\theta) - a \, \cos 60°}{a \, \cos 60°} \approx \Delta\theta \tan 60°$$

$$\varepsilon_{\text{lat}} = \frac{a \, \sin(60° - \Delta\theta) - a \, \sin 60°}{a \, \sin 60°} \approx -\Delta\theta \cot 60°$$

where $\cos \Delta\theta$ and $\sin \Delta\theta$ have been approximated by 1 and $\Delta\theta$, respectively, in the double-angle expansions. Then

$$\nu = -\frac{\varepsilon_{\text{lat}}}{\varepsilon_{xx}} = \frac{1}{3} \qquad (\text{VII.10})$$

This compares well with experimental values for most metals (e.g., $0.32 \le \nu \le 0.34$ for aluminum).

VII.7 INTRODUCTION TO PLASTIC DEFORMATION IN CRYSTALS

If a single crystal is subjected to a tensile load surpassing its yield strength, it will deform in a manner that is quite different from the simple interatomic extension characteristic of elastic deformation. For instance, it is observed that elliptical curves form on the lateral surface of a cylindrical specimen [see Fig. VII.11(a)]. As plastic flow proceeds, the material appears to "glide" or "slip" along the planes of these ellipses, as indicated in the diagram. Note that these planes have been designated as *slip planes*, and the direction of motion on each plane has been denoted as the *slip direction*. The intersections of slip planes with a specimen's surface are called *slip lines*, and in this case they are the aforementioned ellipses. Clearly, the slip planes tend to rotate during plastic flow so as to approach an orientation parallel to the loading axis, and this has been indicated in the figure. A detailed study shows that this behavior is governed by a shearing process in which layers of atoms *slip* or *glide* in relation to adjacent layers. In Fig. VII.11(b) we have illustrated slip schematically in terms of a simple cubic crystal structure. Since stable equilibrium is reestablished after deformation (permanent set takes place), the amount of slip equals an integral number of interatomic distances nr_0.

Since bonding forces are strongest in planes of densest atomic population, slip planes are most likely to be oriented *parallel* to these planes. Furthermore, slip directions are usually parallel to directions corresponding to the least interatomic spacing. Therefore, by examining a crystal's structure, we can determine along which planes and directions slip is most likely to occur. For example, in the FCC crystal (refer to Fig. VII.6) the close-packed

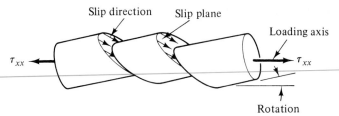

(a) Slip in a cylindrical crystal

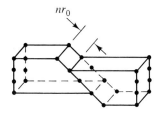

(b) Deformation of the lattice

Figure VII.11 Plastic deformation by slip.

octahedral planes are most likely to be the slip planes and the face diagonal directions are most likely to be the slip directions. We will define the number of *slip systems* in a unit crystal as the product of the number of distinct (nonparallel) planes most likely to be slip planes times the number of distinct directions most likely to be slip lines, per slip plane. One can easily show that there are 12 slip systems in FCC, but only three slip systems in HCP. The question naturally arises, along which one (if any) of the slip systems will glide first occur when a crystal is subjected to a gradually increasing tensile force P? Consider the crystal and potential slip plane shown in Fig. VII.12, where ϕ and λ are angles measured from the loading axis x to the slip plane normal ν and to a potential slip direction μ, respectively. From simple equilibrium

$$\tau_{\nu\mu} = \frac{P \cos \lambda}{A/\cos \phi} = \tau_{xx} \cos \lambda \, \cos \phi \qquad (VII.11)$$

where $\tau_{\nu\mu}$ is the shear stress in the slip direction, A the cross-sectional area, and τ_{xx} the applied tensile stress. Now, if slip is to occur along the slip system defined by $\lambda = \lambda_0$ and $\phi = \phi_0$, $\tau_{\nu\mu}$ in this direction must attain a value called the critical shear stress τ_{crit} and simultaneously τ_{xx} will reach the yield stress Y, i.e.,

$$\tau_{crit} = Y \cos \lambda_0 \cos \phi_0 \qquad (VII.12)$$

Clearly, τ_{crit} is a material property depending on the bonding forces between slip planes, and it is independent of the loading. Assuming that the atomic arrangements about all slip systems are identical, it is clear that τ_{crit} is the same for all such systems. Now, to determine along which slip system glide will first occur, we compute Y from Eq. (VII.12) corresponding to λ_0 and ϕ_0 for the various possible cases. The system yielding the smallest Y is the one desired.

The most "favorable" orientation for slip is defined by $\lambda_0 = \phi_0 = 45°$, since it can be shown that the factor $\cos \lambda_0 \cos \phi_0$ in Eq. (VII.12) attains its maximum possible value (i.e.,

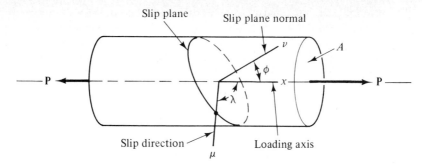

Figure VII.12 Relation between yield stress and critical shear stress.

$\frac{1}{2}$) in this case. Referring to Fig. VII.12, we note that in this case the loading axis, slip plane normal, and slip direction must be coplanar, and that the slip direction is at 45° to the loading axis. Equation (VII.12) then reduces to

$$\tau_{\text{crit}} = \frac{Y}{2} \qquad (VII.13)$$

This interesting result indicates that if a crystal is oriented so that it contains a favorably oriented slip system (i.e., one close to $\lambda_0 = \phi_0 = 45°$), the critical shear stress (a microscopic property) is approximately one-half of the yield stress (a macroscopic property). From our previous remarks, it should be clear that there is a much greater probability that a slip system will be favorably oriented in an FCC crystal than in an HCP crystal. We should add that slip may occur along a direction other than that of a slip system if all slip systems are unfavorably oriented. For example, a single HCP crystal loaded almost normally to the basal plane could slip along some other plane which is closer to 45° with the loading axis.

As we have already noted, slip planes tend to rotate during plastic flow. This can cause a transfer of slip to planes that were originally unfavorably oriented. Furthermore, it has been observed that as slip proceeds, the resistance to slip increases (strain hardening), which may also result in a transfer of slip to other slip systems. We shall soon learn that strain hardening is due to the presence of imperfections in the crystal. In polycrystalline materials (polycrystals) the strain hardening is increased by the presence of grain boundaries. Not only do the grain boundaries act as barriers to slip, but they also restrain adjacent grains from rotating and pulling apart and thereby tend to induce complex modes of deformation in the individual grains. As we show in Section VII.10, deformation occurs with greater difficulty by such complex modes than it does by slip along parallel planes. Consequently, materials with fine grains are somewhat harder and stronger than coarse grain materials, which in turn are much stronger than single crystals. It should also be clear that since HCP polycrystals contain fewer slip systems than FCC polycrystals the former are accordingly less ductile.

It is possible to employ simple calculations to estimate the critical shear stress for a slip system in a single crystal. For example, for a magnesium crystal (which is HCP) one obtains a value for τ_{crit} in the neighborhood of 700,000 psi. This result approaches the experimental value of the critical shear stress when we test very fine filaments called *whiskers* (about 10^{-4} cm in diameter). However, for the usual specimens we find that the computed critical shear stress is about 7000 times the experimental value. The explanation for this disconcerting situation is based on the fact that these whiskers are almost perfect crystals. Normal specimens, however, have imperfections and it is the presence of these imperfections that causes the lower critical shear stress.

It should now be clear that although many properties can be studied in terms of a perfect crystal structure, other properties depend on departures of the structure from perfection. Properties in the former category are termed *structure insensitive*, while those in the latter category are terms *structure sensitive*. In Section VII.6 we studied the structure-insensitive properties of Young's modulus and Poisson's ratio. In succeeding sections we study structure-sensitive properties relating to plasticity and creep in metals.

VII.8 DISLOCATIONS IN CRYSTALS

We pointed out in Section VII.7 that imperfections in a crystal can have a vital effect on the deformation characteristics of the crystal. Fortunately, there are a limited number of ways in which a crystal may be imperfect. For example, an atom may simply be missing from a possible site and thus cause a vacancy or *Schottky defect*. Analogously, an extra atom may be present in a nonlattice site and thus produce a *Frenkel defect*. These are called *point* defects, and they may drift under the action of thermal and electrical gradients. Conceivably, then, they could affect the fundamental diffusion processes, such as thermal and electrical conductivity. However, since point defects move more or less independently, it is highly unlikely that they in themselves can account for the process of slip along an entire crystallographic plane. A more likely type of defect for such considerations is one that will move readily along a definite plane when stress is applied. Of this type are the so-called *line defects* characterized by having defects extend along a direction.

Particularly important in this class is the *edge dislocation* (see Fig. VII.13), which may be produced hypothetically as follows: A perfect crystal is assumed to be "cut" along a plane [bounded by dashed lines in Fig. VII.13(a)] parallel to the x axis; the upper surface of the cut ($ABCD$) is now assumed to be compressed in the x direction, while the lower surface of the cut ($A'BCD'$) is assumed stretched in the x direction; under these conditions the cut is "resealed" by interatomic forces of a new equilibrium configuration. The resultant distortion of the crystal is shown in Fig. VII.13(b), and the corresponding lattice distortion is shown in Fig. VII.13(c) for a simple cubic structure. The line within the material that marks the terminus of the cut (i.e., line BC) is the aforementioned edge dislocation. Note that the same imperfection could have been produced by cutting the crystal vertically along plane $BCEF$ [see Figs. VII.13(b) and (c)], and inserting an extra half sheet of material from above. Consequently, the symbol $\perp$ is often used to indicate an edge dislocation of this type, and it is referred to as a *positive* dislocation. A *negative* edge dislocation is, on the other hand, designated by $\top$ since it may be produced by inserting a half sheet from below.

The magnitude (in multiples of the lattice constant a) and direction of the relative displacement of the surfaces at the *beginning* of the cut is indicated by the displacement vector **b** [see Fig. VII.13(b)]. The vector **b** is called the *Burgers vector*,* whereas the magnitude b is referred to as the strength of the dislocation. We can get the Burgers vector formally, by first considering a closed circuit in a perfect crystal. If a dislocation is now formed within the circuit, the circuit, now called a Burgers circuit, will no longer close. The Burgers vector is the vector required to close the Burgers circuit, while moving around the circuit in a clockwise sense. We have illustrated how **b** closed such a circuit in Fig. VII.13(c). If, as in the figure, the components of **b** along the crystallographic axes are in integral numbers of lattice units, the dislocation is *complete* and crystal perfection is lost only in the neighborhood of the dislocation. Otherwise, the dislocation is *partial* and lattice misalignment exists over an entire plane. If, for example, an octahedral plane in an FCC crystal is

---

* Unfortunately, **b** is also commonly used for the lattice vector in the y crystallographic direction, as we have done in Section VII.3. Of course, the Burgers vector does not have to be in this direction.

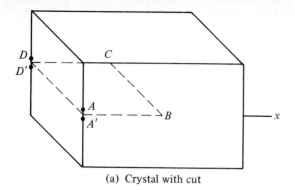

(a) Crystal with cut

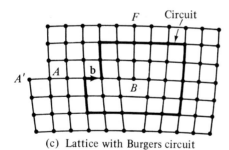

(b) Producing an edge dislocation

(c) Lattice with Burgers circuit

Figure VII.13 Positive edge dislocation.

displaced relative to the next parallel, close-packed plane so that the Burgers vector has components $b_x = -\frac{1}{2}, b_y = \frac{1}{2}, b_z = 0$ (see Fig. VII.6), a *stacking fault* results since the $ABCA \ldots$ sequence discussed in Section VII.4 is lost.

As can be seen in Fig. VII.13, the Burgers vector for an edge dislocation is *perpendicular* to the dislocation. If the Burgers vector is *parallel* to the dislocation [i.e., if this time the crystal is sheared laterally at the cut as shown in Fig. VII.14(a)], a line defect called a *screw dislocation* (line BC) results. The resultant crystal distortion and a Burgers circuit are shown in Fig. VII.14(b). Now look at the front surface of the body (this surface does not include surface EFB). Then consider a clockwise circuit on this front surface, starting at point E and going around the screw dislocation line CB and terminating at point F. Since point F is *closer* to us than point E, we see that there has been a direction of advance of the point E to F that

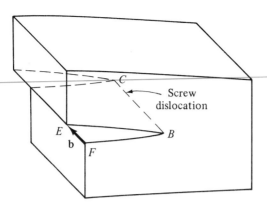

(a) Producing a screw dislocation

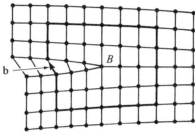

(b) Lattice with Burgers circuit

Figure VII.14 Left-handed screw dislocation.

is *opposite* to the direction of the Burgers vector **b.** Note next that a *left-handed* mechanical screw under a clockwise rotation looking toward the front surface gives the *same* direction of advance as the screw dislocation depicted in Fig. VII.14. We say then that this screw dislocation is *left-handed*. It also follows that a *right-handed* screw dislocation would have a direction of advance that is the same as the direction of the Burgers vector, for the clockwise circuit described previously. (Figure VII.16 in the next section shows a right-handed screw dislocation where the clockwise circuit should start from a point on line *CD*.) Finally, the edge and screw components of a dislocation of mixed type are obtained by resolving **b** into components perpendicular and parallel to the dislocation. Note that these components need not be integers, even if the dislocation is complete.

Conclusive evidence for the existence of dislocations in actual crystals has been produced by various experimental techniques. For example, etching produces pits at the points where these line defects pierce the crystal's surface, which may be observed with the use of optical and electron microscopes. In carefully grown metal crystals the dislocation density in a plane is of the order of 10^4 to 10^6 dislocations/cm^2. Plastically deformed crystals have dislocation densities as high as 10^{12} dislocations/cm^2.

VII.9 STRESS FIELD OF DISLOCATIONS

Even though a crystal may be free of external load and constraint, the presence of a dislocation causes the interatomic distances in the vicinity of the dislocation to differ from those which are far from the dislocation. This results in a system of net attractive and/or net repulsive bonding forces acting in equilibrium at each atom near the dislocation. Macroscopically speaking, we say that a dislocation causes *internal stresses*, in much the same way that thermal gradients produce such stresses. We can estimate these internal stresses by approximating the crystal with an isotropic elastic continuum–as we do throughout this book. In Section VII.10 we will demonstrate how these internal stresses can be used to describe the manner in which dislocations may move and interact.

Consider first a positive *edge* dislocation of strength b in an initially stress-free continuum, as shown generated in Fig. VII.15 by the "cut and displace" method described in the preceding section. Cylindrical coordinates r, θ have been used for convenience, and a small core of material has been removed to circumvent the problem of dealing with infinite stresses at $r = 0$. This difficulty of infinite stresses is a consequence of our continuum assumption, and it does not occur in the actual crystal. In Chapter 12, where we study plane strain, we show that the stress field for this problem is given by [see Eqs. (12.83)]

$$\tau_{rr} = \tau_{\theta\theta} = -\frac{bG}{2\pi(1-\nu)}\frac{\sin\theta}{4}, \qquad \tau_{r\theta} = \frac{bG}{2\pi(1-\nu)}\frac{\cos\theta}{r} \qquad \text{(VII.14)}$$

where G is the shear modulus of elasticity and ν is Poisson's ratio. Note that the stresses given by Eq. (VII.14) are equal at $\theta = 0$ and $\theta = 2\pi$, resulting in continuity across the cut. It can be shown that these equations indicate a state of compression above the $y = 0$ plane and tension below it. Also, the shear stress is greatest along this plane. Finally, all stresses become zero at infinity. These results are consistent with the state of strain shown in Fig. VII.13(b).

The stress field around a *screw* dislocation can be estimated from elementary considerations. Consider the right-handed screw dislocation illustrated in Fig. VII.16(a). Since b has been taken as independent of r and the relative displacement of the faces of the cut is a constant in the z direction, we can logically assume that $u_r = u_\theta = 0$ and $u_z = u_z(\theta)$. It follows from Hooke's law and strain displacement that all stresses vanish except the shear stresses

$$\tau_{z\theta} = \tau_{\theta z} = G\gamma_{\theta z} = \frac{G}{r}\frac{du_z}{d\theta} \qquad \text{(VII.15)}$$

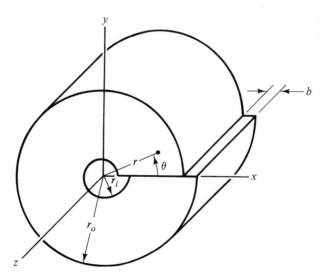

Figure VII.15   Positive edge dislocation in hollow cylinder.

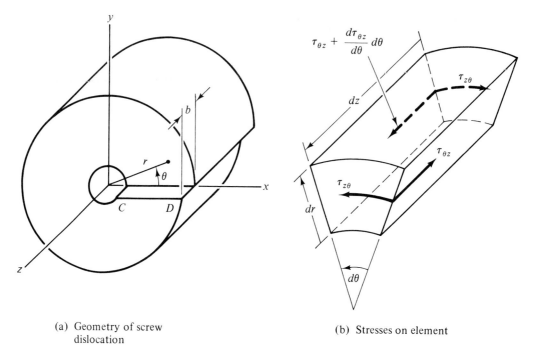

(a) Geometry of screw dislocation

(b) Stresses on element

Figure VII.16 Right-handed screw dislocation in hollow cylinder.

This stress state is independent of z and is shown on an element in Fig. VII.16(b). It is clear from the figure that equilibrium is identically satisfied in the r and θ directions, while for equilibrium in the z direction we must set $d\tau_{\theta z}/d\theta = 0$. Consequently, we obtain from Eq. (VII.15)

$$\frac{d^2 u_z}{d\theta^2} = 0 \tag{VII.16}$$

which has the general solution

$$u_z = A\theta + B \tag{VII.17}$$

Setting $u_z = 0$ at $\theta = 0$ and $u_z = b$ at $\theta = 2\pi$, in accordance with Fig. VII.16(a), yields $u_z = (b/2\pi)\theta$, which reduces Eq. (VII.15) to

$$\tau_{\theta z} = \frac{Gb}{2\pi}\frac{1}{r} \tag{VII.18}$$

The fact that $\tau_{\theta z}$ is independent of θ is closely related to the observation that a screw dislocation, as opposed to an edge dislocation, cannot be formed by the insertion of an extra half sheet of material. Also note that $\tau_{\theta z} \to 0$ for $r \to \infty$.

In this section we have presented approximate stress distributions around edge and screw dislocations. In the following section we make good use of these approximate formulations in discussing the mobility of these dislocations.

VII.10 DISLOCATIONS AND PLASTIC DEFORMATION

It is to be pointed out that the dislocations described in preceding sections may become mobile under the application of stress. We study the motion of dislocations in this section and make some general remarks concerning the effect of this motion on plastic properties. By using the results of Section VII.9 we will be able to appreciate why dislocations are mobile, and furthermore, we will indicate how the direction of motion of a dislocation can be predicted when stress is applied.

Accordingly, consider a crystal that is free of external load but which contains a positive *edge* dislocation, as shown schematically in Fig. VII.17(a). Note that the dislocation lies along the z axis (perpendicular to the page), and that the Burgers vector is in the x direction. Also note that we have selected a simple cubic structure as a convenient model. (While the general behavior of dislocations can be developed in terms of such a model, a full understanding of the particular behaviors in the important structures discussed in Section VII.4 requires further study.) According to the results of the preceding section, internal stresses exist in the crystal, with the dislocation acting as a center of stress concentration. As we have pointed out, this means that a system of net attractive and net repulsive bonding forces act in equilibrium at each atom and that these forces are greatest around atoms near the dislocation.

Let us examine the shear stresses which tend to "rupture" the bonds between the various atoms. (As employed here, a bond between two atoms is ruptured when either atom moves into a new equilibrium position.) First, we convert Eqs. (VII.14) into rectangular coordinates, giving for the shear stress

$$\tau_{zy} = \frac{bG}{2\pi(1-\nu)} \frac{x(x^2-y^2)}{(x^2+y^2)^2} \tag{VII.19}$$

An examination of Eq. (VII.19) shows that the shear stress attains its greatest magnitudes across bonds that cross the x axis in Fig. VII.17(a), and in particular it is maximum positive

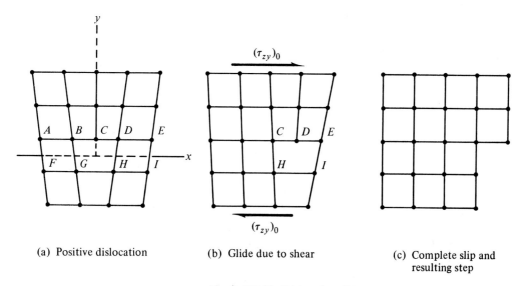

(a) Positive dislocation (b) Glide due to shear (c) Complete slip and resulting step

Figure VII.17 Dislocation glide.

across bond *D–H*, and maximum negative across bond *B–G*. This is consistent with the existence of the maximum net attractive force (tension) in bond *G–H* and the maximum net repulsive force (compression) in bonds *B–C* and *C–D*.

Now, let us superpose a positive shear stress field $(\tau_{zy})_0$ on the given dislocation stress field. The combined shear stress field attains its maximum magnitude (positive) across bond *D–H*, and assuming that the total stress is large enough, a rupture of this bond results. Since this shear stress is positive, atom *H* moves to the left relative to atom *D*, into a new equilibrium position, and the dislocation moves to the *right* as shown in Fig. VII.17(b). This process is called dislocation *slip* or *glide*. If $(\tau_{zy})_0$ is maintained, bond *E–I* will be ruptured next and the dislocation will have crossed the entire crystal, producing a step at its surface [see Fig. VII.17(c)]. This step produces the slip line discussed in Section VII.7, and accordingly the crystal now shows external evidence of having been plastically deformed. Plastic flow has occurred across the slip plane, *zx*, in the slip direction, *x*, by a process of *consecutive* slip. Recall that the critical shear stress is that stress which must be *added* to produce slip along a slip direction. Thus it is clear that the presence of dislocations in a crystal decreases the critical stress for yielding, and it is in this way that we can explain the lack of correlation between theory and experiment pointed out in Section VII.7. It is to be pointed out that in a theoretically perfect crystal, where internal stresses are absent, slip would involve a simultaneous glide of atoms along an entire slip plane and is accordingly denoted as *simultaneous* slip.

Note that a negative edge dislocation [replace b by $-b$ in Eq. (VII.19)] glides to the left under the action of a positive $(\tau_{xy})_0$, since the shear stresses add for $x < 0$. Similarly, a negative $(\tau_{xy})_0$ causes a positive edge dislocation to move to the left and a negative dislocation to move to the right. Identifying the *x* axis with the slip direction, as used above and as shown in Fig. VII.17(a), we conclude that *an applied shear stress field $(\tau_{xy})_0$ moves an edge dislocation of the same sign in the $+x$ direction and one of opposite sign in the $-x$ direction*. If the applied shear stress is directed at an angle with the *x* axis, the edge dislocation is still most likely to move in the *x* direction, since the internal shear stresses from the dislocation vanish across bonds which cut the *y* axis [see Eq. (VII.19)]. However, a larger applied stress is required. We can also show that *like* edge dislocations on the same slip plane tend to repel each other, whereas *unlike* dislocations tend to attract each other.

The motion of a *screw* dislocation is less restricted than that of an edge dislocation. Referring back to Fig. VII.14(a), we can see that shear stress applied parallel to **b** will move the dislocation in a direction perpendicular to **b**. However, it need not move in the "cut" plane since any other plane through **b** contains the same internal shear stress field [see Eq. (VII.18)]. In other words, *a screw dislocation is not identified with a preferred slip plane and it is therefore free to move in a translatory manner from BC to any new position parallel to BC*. We can easily show that *unlike* screw dislocations always attract each other and *like* screw dislocations always repel each other, even if they are moving on different slip planes.

In general, there are three types of "obstacles" that a dislocation may encounter as it glides across a crystal:

1. The stress fields of other parallel dislocations
2. The stress fields of dislocation lines that the moving dislocation line must cut
3. Impurities

In this section we have briefly mentioned item 1 only, and that only for the simple cubic structure. Detailed discussions of items 1, 2, and 3, and of dislocations in the important BCC, FCC, and HCP crystal structures may be found in works on dislocation theory. Slip along the densely packed planes in such crystals may be explained in terms of various full and partial dislocations in the different crystallographic planes. In polycrystalline materials, the grain boundaries also act as obstacles, since the grain boundaries themselves are composed of arrays of dislocations. Also, we noted in Section VII.7 that grains in a polycrystal deform plastically by complex modes which may involve slip on intersecting planes. This has the effect of increasing the number of obstacles to glide. It should be clear to the reader that a theoretical estimate of the yield strength in a commercial metal is extremely difficult to obtain, since it must take into account these various obstacles to glide. We will confine ourselves to some qualitative remarks concerning the variation of the yield stress with plastic deformation.

As we have learned, strain hardening is characterized by an increase in yield strength with plastic deformation. It has also been noted that the number of dislocations, and accordingly the number of obstacles just described, increases with plastic deformation. Hence an understanding of strain hardening requires first the development of a mechanism to generate new dislocations in a crystal as existing dislocations move to the surface and disappear. Discussions of such a mechanism, called the *Frank–Read* source, can be found in the literature. This mechanism is activated by an applied stress, but becomes immobilized when dislocations "pile up" behind obstacles and produce a "back stress" which opposes the applied stress. Thus strain hardening is explained by the fact that dislocations pile up behind obstacles, which increase in number with deformation, and this terminates slip by cutting off the supply of new dislocations. It has been found that if a Frank–Read source were to send about 1000 dislocations over a slip plane before being immobilized, a step of the same order of magnitude as is experimentally observed (around 10^{-5} to 10^{-4} cm) would occur at the surface. Direct experimental evidence for the existence of Frank–Read sources in a crystal has been found. Thus we see that the *addition of a few mobile dislocations to a perfect crystal causes the yield stress to drop considerably, while the addition of still more dislocations causes it to increase somewhat above this low value.*

Many of the inelastic properties of metals and other polycrystalline materials of engineering interest can be explained to some extent in terms of dislocation theory. In the next section we examine creep in polycrystalline materials.

VII.11 CREEP IN POLYCRYSTALLINE MATERIALS

As pointed out in Chapter 4, the time-dependent strain of a solid occurring at constant stress and temperature is defined as *thermally induced creep*. In Fig. 4.11 a "typical" creep curve was drawn for a material at an elevated temperature, showing the characteristic primary, secondary, and tertiary creep regions. Recall that an "elevated" temperature was defined as roughly greater than $T_m/3$, where T_m is the melting point of the material and where both temperatures are measured on the absolute scale. In this section we consider thermally induced creep in polycrystals, and seek an understanding of the microscopic process active during the three characteristic regions of the creep curve. We also make a few remarks about the phenomenon called irradiation-induced creep. We shall briefly discuss creep in amorphous materials in Section VII.12.

We find that creep in polycrystalline materials is significant at elevated temperatures. The most significant mechanism for such thermally activated creep is called *dislocation creep* and involves an interaction between work hardening due to dislocation pile-up and a process of thermal recovery due to *dislocation climb*. This process of dislocation climb is controlled by the diffusion of point defects. When the temperature is elevated in a polycrystal, thermal agitation can cause a vacancy (Schottky defect) to diffuse and interact with a piled-up dislocation. (A vacancy diffuses in one direction when a series of atomic jumps into the vacancy occurs in the opposite direction.) For example, when a vacancy displaces atom C in Fig. VII.17(a), one point on the dislocation [CB in Fig. VII.13(a)] moves up one interatomic distance in the direction perpendicular to the slip plane. This is the process of dislocation climb and it forms a local *jog* in the dislocation. A Frenkel defect can cause this point to move down (negative climb). The dislocation can now glide past the obstacle, and in effect the amount of work hardening has been reduced. This process has been shown schematically in Fig. VII.18. In part (a) of this figure we show the pile-up and a nearby vacancy, while directly below in part (d) of this figure we show view AA of this dislocation pile-up behind an obstacle. In parts (b) and (e) of Fig. VII.18 we see the aforementioned jog in the dislocation, while finally in parts (c) and (f) of Fig. VII.18 we see the dislocation after it has glided by the obstacle. Note that the dislocation line has a new shape. This sequence is the process of thermal recovery due to dislocation climb.

If the temperature is then reduced back to room temperature after thermal recovery as described above, we say that the polycrystal has been *annealed* and its plastic yield strength has been reduced. Creep will not occur in this material if room temperature is well below $T_m/3$, since the thermal recovery process will cease. However, if the elevated temperature is maintained the dislocations will continue to experience the climb and glide process under an applied stress, and the resulting time-dependent strain is the above-mentioned dislocation creep. The nature of the obstacles present in the lattice and the rate at which point defects diffuse control the motion of the dislocations and hence the creep rate $\dot{\varepsilon}$. The decrease in $\dot{\varepsilon}$ in the *primary period* is due to the exhaustion of the more mobile dislocations and the pile-up of dislocations behind the stronger obstacles at a rate faster than the recovery rate. Apparently, during the sustained creep of the *secondary stage* dislocations are able to climb out of the pile-ups as fast as the pile-ups form. Creep is also accompanied by the nucleation and growth of cavities, and this phenomenon is called *creep damage*. The effective area resisting an applied load is reduced by creep damage causing $\dot{\varepsilon}$ to increase, and this eventually brings on *tertiary creep* and *creep rupture*.

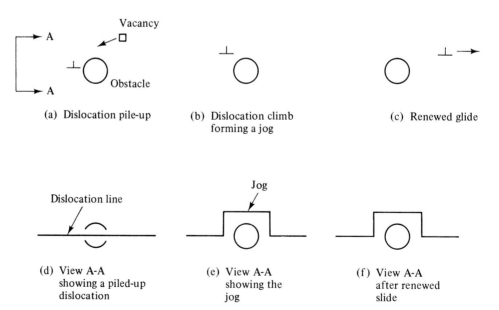

(a) Dislocation pile-up

(b) Dislocation climb forming a jog

(c) Renewed glide

(d) View A-A showing a piled-up dislocation

(e) View A-A showing the jog

(f) View A-A after renewed slide

Figure VII.18   Thermal recovery due to dislocation climb.

Dislocation creep is governed by constitutive laws which are nonlinear in the stress terms. For example, for a one-dimensional axial stress τ_{zz}, one can derive* with the use of dislocation theory the following cubic expression for the strain rate in the secondary period of dislocation creep:

$$\dot{\varepsilon}_{zz} = A_0 e^{-B/T} \tau_{zz}^3 \qquad \text{(VII.20)}$$

In this equation $A_0 e^{-B/T}$ is the so-called reciprocal viscosity, where T is the absolute temperature, and A_0 and B are material creep constants. This negative *exponential* dependence on the inverse absolute temperature is a direct consequence of the fact that dislocation creep is controlled by thermally activated diffusion, and explains why creep is *extremely sensitive* to temperature variation. The stress power is more generally designated by n, and in actual crystalline materials it may differ somewhat from the cubic law (i.e., $n = 3$) as given by Eq. (VII.20). This equation may be represented by the non-Newtonian, rheological model introduced in Section 4.7. This topic is developed extensively in Chapter 7.

At low stress levels, dislocation creep may be insignificant, but at such stress levels creep may occur by another mechanism called *diffusion creep*. This mode of creep is the direct result of the mass flux associated with the migration of individual atoms by the diffusion of point defects in the presence of a stress field. It can occur at the interior of the grains or at the grain boundaries. In the latter case it is called *Coble creep*. Since diffusion creep involves the migration of point defects rather than line defects, it rarely generates strains of the magnitude associated with dislocation creep. From the computational point of view diffusion creep is simpler than dislocation creep, in that microscopic considerations show that it is essentially governed by *linear* viscoelastic constitutive laws (see Chapter 6). However, since both creep mechanisms are controlled by thermally activated diffusion, the associated creep rates exhibit the same extremely nonlinear negative exponential dependence on the inverse absolute temperature. Thus the strain rate at low stress levels in the *secondary period* of diffusion creep is given by an expression with the same form as Eq. (VII.20), except that the stress power is now close to one.

In Chapter 4 we mentioned the phenomenon called *irradiation-induced creep*. This type of creep is not thermally activated, but rather is mechanically activated by the enhancement of the mobility of point defects due to the direct collision of bombarding neutrons with lattice atoms. This increased mobility can result in mechanically activated dislocation climb, and as previously described, dislocation glide may then resume and result in creep strain. It can be shown that irradiation-induced creep in polycrystals is also governed by viscoelastic constitutive laws which are essentially *linear* in the stress.

Although some reasonable microscopic mechanisms for the deformation processes governing creep have evolved in recent years, no completely satisfactory general theory has yet been developed. This is due primarily to the great difficulty of predicting the behavior of aggregates of dislocations from the known properties of individual dislocations.

VII.12 DEFORMATION OF AMORPHOUS POLYMERS

Although we have thus far limited ourselves to the study of deformation in crystalline materials, we should not completely ignore those solid material that lack structural order (i.e., amorphous materials). Some amorphous materials of structural importance, such as plastics and synthetic rubbers, are composed of molecules of very high molecular weight called *high*

---

*See A. J. Kennedy, *Processes of Creep and Fatigue in Metals* (New York: John Wiley & Sons, Inc., 1963), Chap. 4. This reference presents theories of dislocation creep.

polymers. We will concentrate our attention on the linear high polymer, which consists of a long "chain" of carbon atoms with side branches of hydrogen atoms. (The more complicated cross-linked polymers form three-dimensional networks.) The plastic polyethylene is composed of linear polymers that are formed by stringing together many ethylene molecules called *monomers*. These molecules are shown in Fig. VII.19, where each line drawn between two atoms represents two electrons being shared in a covalent bond. Because of the relative ease with which carbon atoms can rotate about the single bonds in a polymer chain and because of the weak molecular bonds between individual polymers, linear polymers are more or less flexible and take up various partially curled configurations. This accounts for the amorphous nature of most linear polymers. Under tensile load, the polymers tend to straighten out, and if these loads are large enough, a certain amount of permanent regularity occurs. This is called *crystallization*, although the order obtained is never as perfect as in a metal.

The deformation of linear polymers is highly temperature sensitive, and many linear polymers behave viscoelastically under low stresses at temperatures as low as 100°C. Since a liquid, like an amorphous solid, is characterized by a lack of structural order, an understanding of the mechanism of viscous flow in a liquid will help us understand the flow mechanism in an amorphous solid. We find that at any instant, liquids do exhibit a certain amount of local or *short-range* order, even though they lack *long-range* order. This means that local crystal-like structures* exist, but these local structures are arranged in a disorderly manner so that gaps or "holes" exist between them. It is important to note that in a liquid these crystal-like structures are unstable (i.e., they continually break up and reform at other positions) so that the holes are in a continual state of random motion. Now, it is well known that when a shear stress is applied to a liquid, a net transfer of momentum occurs by the relative motion of one layer of molecules past an adjacent layer. In Fig. VII.20 we see a molecular arrangement where two molecules can jump at the same time into new positions. When a shear stress τ is applied, momentum transfer is accomplished by the *rotational jump* mechanism illustrated in the figure. This diffusion mechanism appears to be the dominant one in viscous flow.

Now a linear polymer differs from a liquid in that the interlocking of the polymer chains enables it to withstand tensile loads (i.e., the material is a solid). However, when a shear stress is applied, linear polymers will flow by essentially the same mechanism that operates in a liquid. Because of the great length of the polymers, the process of rotational jump occurs for "chain segments" and not for entire molecules. Two fundamentally different effects occur simultaneously as a result of this mechanism. They are:

1. Individual molecules wander as a whole relative to adjacent molecules. This process is truly viscous since there is no recovery, that is, upon unloading there is no tendency for the molecules to migrate back to their original locations.

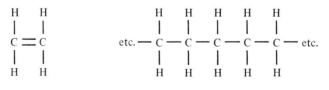

    (a) Ethylene monomer   (b) Polyethylene polymer

Figure VII.19   Basic element of a linear high polymer.

---

* These structures are the origins of the nuclei that form when liquids begin to freeze. We discussed this in Section VII.5 in connection with the formation of polycrystalline structures.

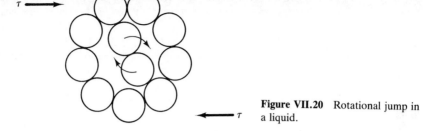

Figure VII.20 Rotational jump in a liquid.

2. Also, molecules change their shape. Assuming that crystallization does not occur, this process is anelastic since upon unloading the average configuration tends to return to the average configuration that existed prior to deformation.

It thus follows that the total response of an amorphous polymer to a tensile load consists of a purely elastic deformation due to an increase of the interatomic distances in the chains, plus creep by means of the nonrecoverable viscous and recoverable anelastic flows just described. These flows result from rotational jumps which are induced by shear stresses acting at angles to the loading axis. We find that this viscoelastic behavior may usually be represented nicely by linear viscoelastic models such as those discussed in detail in Chapter 6. We also find that the steady creep rate again varies with the temperature in accordance with the form $A_0 e^{-B/T}$ [as in Eq. (VII.20)], although it is frequently necessary to replace the constant A_0 by another function of temperature.

It should be clear that the study of creep in metals is computationally more difficult than the study of creep in polymers, since the former usually cannot be described in terms of linear viscoelastic models. Furthermore, since the use of very complicated nonlinear mechanical models is mathematically impractical, the mechanical model representation for a metal will frequently be less accurate than the mechanical model representation for a polymer. Of course, the study of crystallized polymers as well as polymers that form three-dimensional networks is more complicated than the study of linear polymers.

VII.13 CLOSURE

In this appendix we have attempted to integrate some of the microscopic fundamentals of materials science with the macroscopic study of the mechanics of deformable solids. The authors included only those topics in materials science that were of immediate value in attaining this goal. Of necessity, only a limited amount of material has been included in the treatment of these topics. Readers who are interested in extending their knowledge should consult one or more of the excellent works now available in materials science.[*]

---

[*] For example, see Z. D. Jastrzebski, *The Nature and Properties of Engineering Materials*, 2nd ed. (New York: John Wiley & Sons, Inc., 1976). This book lists many useful references in materials science.

Author Index

Subject Index

The letter n following a page number indicates a footnote. Problems and tables are referenced in parentheses.

Hardening (creep):
  strain-hardening hypothesis, 212–213
  time-hardening hypothesis, 221
Hardening (plastic):
  one-dimensional:
    kinematic, 250n
    strain, 106–108, 248–249, 252, 256
    strain-rate, 122, 256
  three-dimensional:
    in Drucker's postulate, 286
    equivalence of plastic work, 300, 307–309
    isotropic, 299–307
    linear kinematic, 311–313
    parameter K, 299, 310
    strain-rate, 315
    universal stress-strain curve, 300–301
Harmonic operator (see Laplacian operator)
Hencky-Mises or Huber-Mises yield criterion (see Mises yield criterion)
Hereditary integrals:
  for beam deflection, 414, 450 (Prob. 10.8)
  for nonlinear viscoelastic material, 217–218, 220
  for nonlinear viscoelastic material with aging, 223
  for one-dimensional Maxwell material, 178
  over one-dimensional strain history, 174
  over one-dimensional stress history, 174
  for pressure, 180
  for shear, 180
  for twist in a shaft, 468, 489, 510
Hollow:
  circular shafts, 467, 477, 518 (Prob. 11.24)
  cylinder (see Thick-walled cylinder)
  sphere (see Thick-walled sphere)
Homogeneous:
  boundary conditions for beams, 415, 416
  boundary conditions for plane strain, 672
  boundary conditions for shafts, 494, 500
  deformation (see Affine deformation)
  differential equation, 500
  initial conditions, 164, 174, 175, 347, 612, 658, 663
  material, 108, 131, 331, 460, 486

Hookean model (see Mechanical models)
Hooke's law:
  as formulated by Hooke for tension, 102
  generalized:
    matrix form, 140
    tensor form, 139
    in terms of elastic moduli, 140
  isotropic three-dimensional:
    bulk and deviatoric components, 148–149, 183, 336
    strain versus stress with engineering constants, 139, 183, 335
    strain versus stress with Lamé constants, 147
    stress versus strain with engineering constants, 139
    stress versus strain with Lamé constants, 146, 183, 336
  for plane strain:
    bulk and deviatoric components, 548–549
    strain versus stress with engineering constants, 526
    strain versus Φ, 531, 674, 676
    stress versus strain with Lamé constants, 527
  for plane stress (general):
    strain versus stress with engineering constants, 577
  for plane stress (two-dimensional):
    bulk and deviatoric components, 608
    strain versus stress with engineering constants, 587, 608
    stress versus strain with engineering constants, 608
Hydrostatic:
  line, 264–265, 277, 339
  stress, 263, 264, 268n
Hyperelastic material, 141, 143
Hysterisis, 107, 262

Ice:
  nonlinear creep in, 111, 202, 229n
Idealized stress-strain curves, 113–115
Incompressible:
  creep deformation, 229, 237
  elastic deformation, 148, 149–150, 621
  nonlinear viscous deformation, 241, 337, 505, 554
  plastic deformation, 291, 339, 621
  viscoelastic deformation, 184–186, 188–189

Incremental deformation theory of plasticity, 294n
Index notation:
  for biharmonic operator ∇^4, 22
  for curl $\mathbf{V}$, 21
  for div $\mathbf{V}$, 21
  dummy index, 2–4
  forbidden indices, 2
  free index, 1–2
  for grad ϕ, 20
  for Laplacian operator ∇^2, 21
  order, 2
  summation convention, 4
  two-dimensional, 2, 525, 530, 549, 555
Inertia:
  in equations of motion, 48–49
  in moment of momentum, 49–50
Infinite:
  elastic plate with small hole, 596–598
  extended beam, 402
  plastic disk with pressurized hole, 637–638 (Prob. 13.30)
Inhomogeneous:
  boundary condition for a beam, 418–419
  material, 430, 431n
Initial conditions in viscoelasticity, 347
Initially stress-free medium, 139n, 540
Integration of Beltrami-Michell equations:
  for general plane stress, 580–582
Integration of biharmonic equation:
  for axial symmetry, 536
  for axial symmetry with body force, 603–604
  for edge dislocation, 541
Integration of equilibrium equations:
  for plastic flow, 624
Integration of strain-displacement:
  for edge dislocation, 543
  for elastic bar under own weight, 361–363
  for elastic beam under pure bending, 367–369
  for nonlinear viscous bar under axial force, 379–380
Interatomic:
  bonds, 681
  distance, 679
  energy, 679
  force, 680, 687
Internal stress:
  due to dislocations, 695
  due to nonuniform temperature, 151